PETROLEUM PRODUCTION HANDBOOK

PETROLEUM PRODUCTION HANDBOOK

IN TWO VOLUMES

THOMAS C. FRICK, Editor-in-Chief

*Regional Manager, Eastern Gulf Coast Region
The Atlantic Refining Company*

R. WILLIAM TAYLOR, Associate Editor

Editor, Journal of Petroleum Technology

VOLUME I

MATHEMATICS AND PRODUCTION EQUIPMENT

Society of Petroleum Engineers of AIME

Dallas, Texas

PETROLEUM PRODUCTION HANDBOOK

Library of Congress Catalog Card Number: 60-10601

Second Printing

MILLET THE PRINTER, INC., DALLAS, TEX.

ISBN 0-89520-206-9

CONTRIBUTORS

JAMES W. AMYX, B.S., and M.E., Professor of Petroleum Engineering, A & M College of Texas. (*Chapter 23. Properties of Reservoir Rocks*)

JOHN F. ARMSTRONG, B.S., E.E., Senior Petroleum Engineer, Core Laboratories, Inc. (*Chapter 41. Water-injection Pressure Maintenance and Water-flood Processes*)

JAN J. ARPS, M.S., Vice President, Economics and Evaluation Department, The British-American Oil Producing Company. (*Chapter 37. Estimation of Primary Oil and Gas Reserves. Chapter 38. Valuation of Oil and Gas Reserves*)

DANIEL M. BASS, Jr., B.S., and M.S., Associate Professor of Petroleum Engineering, A & M College of Texas. (*Chapter 23. Properties of Reservoir Rocks*)

A. F. BERTUZZI, B.S. and M.S., Ch.E., Petroleum Engineer, Production Department, Phillips Petroleum Company. (*Chapter 31. Wellbore Hydraulics*)

W. B. BLEAKLEY, B.S. and M.S., P.E., Production Editor, *The Oil and Gas Journal.* (*Chapter 4. Production Packers*)

DON R. BOLING, B.S., P.E., Division Engineer, National Tank Company. (*Chapter 10. Oil Storage*)

HOWARD B. BRADLEY, B.S. and M. S., P. E., Supervisor, Technical Training, Field Research Laboratory, Socony Mobil Oil Co., Inc. (*Chapter 36. Gas-condensate Reservoirs*)

F. BARTON BROWN, A.B., M.E., M.Sc., Chief Mechanical Engineer, Product Research and Development Division, Kobe, Inc. (*Chapter 6. Hydraulic Pumps*)

PAUL BUTHOD, B.S., M.S., Head of the Department of Chemical and Petroleum Refining Engineering, The University of Tulsa. (*Chapter 18. Properties of Crude Oils and Liquid Condensate*)

JOHN L. P. CAMPBELL, A.B., Geology, Head Office Sales Engineer–Geologist, Lane-Wells Company. (*Chapter 44. Radioactivity Well Logging*)

JOHN M. CAMPBELL, B.S.C.E., Ph.D., Chairman, School of Petroleum Engineering, University of Oklahoma, and Industrial Consultant. (*Chapter 12. Gas Measurement and Regulation*)

ROY L. CHENAULT, B.S., Physics, Chief Research Engineer, Oil Well Supply Division, U.S. Steel Corporation. (*Chapter 7. Subsurface Sucker-rod Pumps*)

JOE B. CLARKE, Jr., B.S., Ch.E., District Landman, The Atlantic Refining Company. (*Chapter 49. Oil and Gas Leases*)

WILLIAM O. CLINEDINST, B.S., M.E., Manager Scientific Research, National Tube Division, United States Steel Corporation. (*Chapter 2. Casing, Tubing, and Line Pipe*)

C. J. COBERLY, A.B., M.E., President, Kobe, Inc. (*Chapter 6. Hydraulic Pumps*)

LEON L. CRAIN, B.S., Senior Petroleum Engineer, Core Laboratories, Inc. (*Chapter 41. Water-injection Pressure Maintenance and Waterflood Processes*)

RUPERT C. CRAZE, B.S., Ch.E., Research Associate, Humble Oil & Refining Company. (*Chapter 33. Development Plan for Oil Reservoirs*)

SAM CURTIS, B.S., Agriculture Engineering, Engineer, Lufkin Foundry & Machine Company. (*Chapter 9. Pumping Units and Prime Movers for Pumping Units*)

JOHN H. DAY, Jr., B.S.E., Sales Engineer, General Electric Company. (*Chapter 9. Pumping Units and Prime Movers for Pumping Units*)

H. G. DOLL, B.S., Eng. Degree, Chairman of the Board and Technical Advisor, Schlumberger Well Surveying Corporation. (*Chapter 43. Electrical Logging*)

F. BEN ELLIOTT, Jr., B.S., Experimental Engineer, Lufkin Foundry & Machine Company. (*Chapter 9. Pumping Units and Prime Movers for Pumping Units*)

W. F. ELLISON, B. S., Civil Engineering Section Chief, Mobil Oil Company. (*Chapter 14. Surface Facilities for Waterflooding and Salt-water Disposal*)

P. E. FITZGERALD (deceased),B.A., former Public Relations Manager, Dowell Division of The Dow Chemical Company. (*Chapter 46. Acidizing. Chapter 47. Formation Fracturing. Chapter 48. Remedial Clean-up and Other Stimulation Treatments*)

JAMES H. FOSTER, B.S.M.E., Western Regional Manager, McEvoy Company. (*Chapter 3. Wellhead Equipment and Flow-control Devices*)

KENNETH M. GARMS, B.S., Project Reservoir Engineer, Core Laboratories, Inc. (*Chapter 40. Gas-injection Pressure Maintenance and Miscible-phase Displacement in Oil Reservoirs*)

MURRAY F. HAWKINS, Jr., M.S., Professor of Petroleum Engineering, Louisiana State University. (*Chapter 20. Phase Diagrams*)

RICHARD F. HINDS, B.S., Project Reservoir Engineer, Core Laboratories, Inc. (*Chapter 40. Gas-injection Pressure Maintenance and Miscible-phase Displacement in Oil Reservoirs*)

J. TAYLOR HOOD, B.S.M.E., Manager, Gas Engine Department, Lufkin Foundry & Machine Company. (*Chapter 9. Pumping Units and Prime Movers for Pumping Units*)

W. L. HORNER, B.S., Petroleum Geology, Jett Drilling Company, Mobile, Alabama. (*Chapter 39. Injection Operations*)

FRANK C. KELTON, B.S., Ph.D., Chemistry, Senior Programming Engineer, Core Laboratories, Inc. (*Chapter 41. Water-injection Pressure Maintenance and Waterflood Processes*)

J. D. KIMMEL, B.S.M.E., Project Development Engineer, Texsteam Corp. (*Chapter 29. Potential Tests for Oil Wells*)

C. V. KIRKPATRICK, B.S., M.L., Chairman, Division of Chemical and Petroleum Engineering, University of Houston. (*Chapter 5. Gas Lift*)

E. H. KOEPF, B.S., M.S., Ph.D., Manager, Research and Technical Services. Core Laboratories, Inc. (*Chapter 24. Typical Core Analysis of Different Formations*)

BILL LAFAYETTE, B.S., Reservoir Engineer, Core Laboratories, Inc. (*Chapter 41. Water-injection Pressure Maintenance and Waterflood Processes*)

R. H. LASATER, B.S., Senior Production Engineer, Socony Mobil Oil Company, Inc. (*Chapter 14. Surface Facilities for Waterflooding and Salt-water Disposal*)

L. A. LITTLE, B.S.M.E., Vice President, Lufkin Foundry & Machine Company. (*Chapter 9. Pumping Units and Prime Movers for Pumping Units*)

CARROLL F. MAHONEY, B.S., M.S., Senior Petroleum Engineer, Core Laboratories, Inc. (*Chapter 41. Water-injection Pressure Maintenance and Waterflood Processes*)

M. MARTIN, B.S., Executive Vice President, Géopétrole. (*Chapter 43. Electrical Logging*)

S. J. MARTINEZ, B.S., M.S., Assistant Professor, Department of Information Services, University of Tulsa. (*Chapter 46. Acidizing. Chapter 47. Formation Fracturing. Chapter 48. Remedial Clean-up and Other Stimulation Treatments*)

JOHN J. McKETTA, B.S., M.S., Ph.D., Chairman and Graduate Professor, Department of Chemical Engineering, University of Texas. (*Chapter 22. Hydrocarbon-water and Formation Water Correlations*)

C. V. MILLIKAN, B.S., M.S., formerly Chief Engineer, Amerada Petroleum Corporation. (*Chapter 27. Bottom-hole Pressures. Chapter 28. Temperatures in Wells*)

JAMES L. MOORE, B.S., Supervising Petroleum Engineer, Core Laboratories, Inc. (*Chapter 40. Gas-injection Pressure Maintenance and Miscible-phase Displacement in Oil Reservoirs*)

RALPH F. NEILSEN, B.Sc., M.Sc., Ph.D., Professor of Petroleum and Natural Gas, The Pennsylvania State University. (*Chapter 32. Reservoir Performance Equations*)

FRED L. OLIVER, B.S., Physics, B.S., Geology, Partner, Oliver & West, Inc. (*Chapter 26. Reservoir Traps*)

HOMER C. OSBORNE, B.S., Supervising Petroleum Engineer, Core Laboratories, Inc. (*Chapter 41. Water-injection Pressure Maintenance and Waterflood Processes*)

DON R. PATTERSON, B.S., M.S., Production Engineer, The Atlantic Refining Company. (*Chapter 15. Automation of Lease Equipment*)

A. J. PEARSON, B.S.M.E., Petroleum Engineer, Continental Illinois National Bank and Trust Company of Chicago. (*Chapter 45. Miscellaneous Well Logs*)

FRED H. POETTMANN, B.S., M.S., Ph.D., Supervisor of the Engineering Department, The Ohio Oil Company. (*Chapter 31. Wellbore Hydraulics*)

T. A. POLLARD, B.A., B.S., M.S., Assistant to the Manager, Field Research Laboratory, Socony Mobil Oil Company, Inc. (*Chapter 36. Gas-condensate Reservoirs*)

WALTER H. RITTERBUSCH, Jr., B.S., Northern Division Sales Manager, The S. M. Jones Company. (*Chapter 8. Sucker Rods*)

I. F. ROEBUCK, Jr., B.S., M.S., Supervising Petroleum Engineer, Core Laboratories, Inc. (*Chapter 40. Gas-injection Pressure Maintenance and Miscible-phase Displacement in Oil Reservoirs*)

W. P. SCHULTZ, B.S., Manager, Foreign Operations, Core Laboratories, Inc. (*Chapter 39. Injection Operations*)

F. SEGESMAN, M.S., Physics, Publication and Interpretation Department, Schlumberger Well Surveying Corporation. (*Chapter 43. Electrical Logging*)

H. M. SHEARIN, B.S., Manager, Domestic Operations, Core Laboratories, Inc. (*Chapter 39. Injection Operations*)

VINCENT J. SIKORA, B.E.E., M.S.E.E., Group Leader, The Atlantic Refining Company. (*Chapter 34. Solution-gas-drive Oil Reservoirs. Chapter 35. Water-drive Oil Reservoirs*)

H. VERNON SMITH, B.S., President and General Manager, Oil Metering and Processing Equipment Corporation. (*Chapter 11. Oil and Gas Separators*)

JOE ED SMITH, B.S., Reservoir Engineer, Core Laboratories, Inc. (*Chapter 41. Water-injection Pressure Maintenance and Waterflood Processes*)

R. V. SMITH, A.B., A.M., Chief Production Engineer, Natural Gas Department, Phillips Petroleum Company. (*Chapter 30. Open Flow of Gas Wells*)

HAROLD E. STAADT, B.S., Development Engineer, Dowell Division of The Dow Chemical Company. (*Chapter 46. Acidizing.*)

MARSHALL B. STANDING, B.S., M.S., Ph.D., Research Coordinator, California Research Corporation. (*Chapter 19. Oil-system Correlations*)

C. E. THOMAS, B.S., Supervising Petroleum Engineer, Core Laboratories, Inc. (*Chapter 41. Water-injection Pressure Maintenance and Waterflood Processes*)

M. P. TIXIER, M.E., E.E., Manager of Field Interpretation, Schlumberger Well Surveying Corporation. (*Chapter 43. Electrical Logging*)

J. WADE WATKINS, A.B., Project Coordinator, Applied Production Research, Bureau of Mines, U.S. Department of the Interior. (*Chapter 21. Properties of Produced Waters*)

ALBERT H. WEHE, B.S., M.S., Research Engineer, Esso Research and Engineering. (*Chapter 22. Hydrocarbon-water and Formation Water Correlations*)

CHARLES F. WEINAUG, B.S., M.S., Ph.D., Professor and Chairman, Department of Petroleum Engineering, University of Kansas. (*Chapter 17. Gas Properties and Correlations*)

J. K. WELCHON, B.S., Analytical Engineer, Production Department, Phillips Petroleum Company. (*Chapter 31. Wellbore Hydraulics*)

M. R. J. WYLLIE, B.Sc., D.Phil., D.Sc., Director, Reservoir Mechanics Division, Gulf Research & Development Company. (*Chapter 25. Relative Permeability*)

EDWIN C. YOUNG, B.E., M.S., Ph.D., Director, Product Planning, Black, Sivalls & Bryson, Inc. (*Chapter 13. Lease-operated Hydrocarbon-recovery Systems and Gas-treating Systems*)

PREFACE

The *Petroleum Production Handbook* fills a long-time need for a comprehensive volume presenting practical information and data concerning the recovery of oil and gas from the underground reservoirs in which they occur. Petroleum production has progressed from the haphazard methods employed during the days of the "gusher" to a complex science requiring wide knowledge of available downhole and lease equipment and of the established engineering methods for controlling reservoir mechanics. Because the Handbook brings the important equipment and methods into perspective, it should prove to be the most important book in the library of the person engaged in this field of work.

The book is divided into two volumes and three sections. Volume I contains Section 1—Mathematics and Section 2—Production Equipment. In Volume II is Section 3—Reservoir Engineering. Within these sections are 47 chapters, each written by top experts in the particular field covered. Also included is the list of "Letter Symbols for Petroleum Engineering and Electric Logging" sponsored by the Society of Petroleum Engineers of AIME and accepted as a Standard by the American Standard Association.

The Mathematics Section presents the basic tables and calculation procedures required by the person engaged in petroleum production. The Production Equipment Section covers basic types of materials and tools available for use, including their capabilities and proper applications. Within the Reservoir Engineering Section are chapters treating formation rocks, fluids and gases, correlation methods, primary and secondary recovery data, and well treating.

Acknowledgement for exceptional cooperation is given to the Society of Petroleum Engineers of AIME, the American Petroleum Institute, the U.S. Bureau of Mines and the individual authors who are responsible for the excellent material presented within these pages. Also, appreciation is expressed to the following experts who reviewed material published in this Handbook:

Kenneth W. Robbins, Otis Engineering
J. B. Thompson, Guiberson Corp.
C. M. Beeson, University of Southern California
W. L. Ducker, Texas Technological College
Bruce G. Ramage, Bethlehem Steel Company

R. M. Willis, Atlantic Refining Company
R. J. Bethancourt, Sun Oil Company
R. L. Parsons, Parkersburg Rig & Reel Co.
B. E. Eakin, Illinois Institute of Technology
W. C. Goodson, Republic Natural Gas Company
George V. Ricks, Atlantic Refining Company
Ralph W. Hill, Majors Engineering Company
A. S. Trube, Tidewater Oil Company
Carl A. Connally, Socony Mobil Field Research Lab.
T. A. Pollard, Socony Mobil Field Research Lab.
H. A. Stiff, Jr., Atlantic Refining Company
R. C. LeRoy, Atlantic Refining Company
C. A. Hutchinson, Atlantic Refining Company
Roland Smith, William Ross Cabeen & Associates
John D. Rice, Sun Oil Company
G. P. Cokinos, Railroad Commission of Texas
Howard Koch, Jr., Atlantic Refining Company
A. F. Van Everdingen, Shell Oil Company
J. J. Arps, British-American Oil Producing Company
G. W. Tracy, Pan American Petroleum Corp.
W. C. Hardy, Sun Oil Company
Jack A. Crichton, Nafco Oil & Gas, Inc.
Norman J. Clark, Norman J. Clark Engineering
A. B. Dyes, Atlantic Refining Company
M. R. J. Wyllie, Gulf Research & Development Company
J. E. Grady, Welex Division, Halliburton Company
W. O. Winsauer, Humble Oil & Refining Company
Frank West, Oliver & West, Inc.
W. E. Hinchliffe, Halliburton Company
George P. Nathman, Atlantic Refining Company
Harry N. Stansbury, Atlantic Refining Company

The rapid progress of petroleum technology has been due to the willingness of its leaders to freely publish important data for use by the entire industry. It is our hope that this *Petroleum Production Handbook* will contribute to this fund of knowledge and, in doing so, will lead to further progress in the economic recovery of oil and gas.

Thomas C. Frick

CONTENTS

VOLUME I

MATHEMATICS AND PRODUCTION EQUIPMENT

Section 1

MATHEMATICS

Chapter 1

MATHEMATICAL TABLES AND
WEIGHTS AND MEASURES*

By Philip Franklin

Professor of Mathematics
Massachusetts Institute of Technology

and

Lewis V. Judson

Chief, Length Section
National Bureau of Standards

CONTENTS

REFERENCES FOR MATHEMATICAL TABLES: Allen, "Six-place Tables," McGraw-Hill. Comrie, "Chambers Shorter Six-figure Mathematical Tables," Chemical Publishing. Dwight, "Mathematical Tables of Elementary and Some Higher Mathematical Functions," McGraw-Hill. Dwight, "Tables of Integrals and Other Mathematical Data," Macmillan. Jahnke and Emde, "Tables of Functions," B. G. Teubner, Leipzig, or Dover. Peirce-Foster, "A Short Table of Integrals," Ginn. "Handbook of Chemistry and Physics," Chemical Rubber Co.

* From Marks' *Mechanical Engineers' Handbook*, Theodore Baumeister (ed.), 6th ed., McGraw-Hill, 1958.

MATHEMATICS

Squares of Numbers

N	0	1	2	3	4	5	6	7	8	9	Avg diff
1.00	1.000	1.002	1.004	1.006	1.008	1.010	1.012	1.014	1.016	1.018	2
1	1.020	1.022	1.024	1.026	1.028	1.030	1.032	1.034	1.036	1.038	
2	1.040	1.042	1.044	1.047	1.049	1.051	1.053	1.055	1.057	1.059	
3	1.061	1.063	1.065	1.067	1.069	1.071	1.073	1.075	1.077	1.080	
4	1.082	1.084	1.086	1.088	1.090	1.092	1.094	1.096	1.098	1.100	
1.05	1.102	1.105	1.107	1.109	1.111	1.113	1.115	1.117	1.119	1.121	
6	1.124	1.126	1.128	1.130	1.132	1.134	1.136	1.138	1.141	1.143	
7	1.145	1.147	1.149	1.151	1.153	1.156	1.158	1.160	1.162	1.164	
8	1.166	1.169	1.171	1.173	1.175	1.177	1.179	1.182	1.184	1.186	
9	1.188	1.190	1.192	1.195	1.197	1.199	1.201	1.203	1.206	1.208	
1.10	1.210	1.212	1.214	1.217	1.219	1.221	1.223	1.225	1.228	1.230	
1	1.232	1.234	1.237	1.239	1.241	1.243	1.245	1.248	1.250	1.252	
2	1.254	1.257	1.259	1.261	1.263	1.266	1.268	1.270	1.272	1.275	
3	1.277	1.279	1.281	1.284	1.286	1.288	1.290	1.293	1.295	1.297	
4	1.300	1.302	1.304	1.306	1.309	1.311	1.313	1.316	1.318	1.320	
1.15	1.322	1.325	1.327	1.329	1.332	1.334	1.336	1.339	1.341	1.343	
6	1.346	1.348	1.350	1.353	1.355	1.357	1.360	1.362	1.364	1.367	
7	1.369	1.371	1.374	1.376	1.378	1.381	1.383	1.385	1.388	1.390	
8	1.392	1.395	1.397	1.399	1.402	1.404	1.407	1.409	1.411	1.414	
9	1.416	1.418	1.421	1.423	1.426	1.428	1.430	1.433	1.435	1.438	
1.20	1.440	1.442	1.445	1.447	1.450	1.452	1.454	1.457	1.459	1.462	
1	1.464	1.467	1.469	1.471	1.474	1.476	1.479	1.481	1.484	1.486	
2	1.488	1.491	1.493	1.496	1.498	1.501	1.503	1.506	1.508	1.510	
3	1.513	1.515	1.518	1.520	1.523	1.525	1.528	1.530	1.533	1.535	
4	1.538	1.540	1.543	1.545	1.548	1.550	1.553	1.555	1.558	1.560	
1.25	1.562	1.565	1.568	1.570	1.573	1.575	1.578	1.580	1.583	1.585	3
6	1.588	1.590	1.593	1.595	1.598	1.600	1.603	1.605	1.608	1.610	
7	1.613	1.615	1.618	1.621	1.623	1.626	1.628	1.631	1.633	1.636	
8	1.638	1.641	1.644	1.646	1.649	1.651	1.654	1.656	1.659	1.662	
9	1.664	1.667	1.669	1.672	1.674	1.677	1.680	1.682	1.685	1.687	
1.30	1.690	1.693	1.695	1.698	1.700	1.703	1.706	1.708	1.711	1.713	
1	1.716	1.719	1.721	1.724	1.727	1.729	1.732	1.734	1.737	1.740	
2	1.742	1.745	1.748	1.750	1.753	1.756	1.758	1.761	1.764	1.766	
3	1.769	1.772	1.774	1.777	1.780	1.782	1.785	1.788	1.790	1.793	
4	1.796	1.798	1.801	1.804	1.806	1.809	1.812	1.814	1.817	1.820	
1.35	1.822	1.825	1.828	1.831	1.833	1.836	1.839	1.841	1.844	1.847	
6	1.850	1.852	1.855	1.858	1.860	1.863	1.866	1.869	1.871	1.874	
7	1.877	1.880	1.882	1.885	1.888	1.891	1.893	1.896	1.899	1.902	
8	1.904	1.907	1.910	1.913	1.915	1.918	1.921	1.924	1.927	1.929	
9	1.932	1.935	1.938	1.940	1.943	1.946	1.949	1.952	1.954	1.957	
1.40	1.960	1.963	1.966	1.968	1.971	1.974	1.977	1.980	1.982	1.985	
1	1.988	1.991	1.994	1.997	1.999	2.002	2.005	2.008	2.011	2.014	
2	2.016	2.019	2.022	2.025	2.028	2.031	2.033	2.036	2.039	2.042	
3	2.045	2.048	2.051	2.053	2.056	2.059	2.062	2.065	2.068	2.071	
4	2.074	2.076	2.079	2.082	2.085	2.088	2.091	2.094	2.097	2.100	
1.45	2.102	2.105	2.108	2.111	2.114	2.117	2.120	2.123	2.126	2.129	
6	2.132	2.135	2.137	2.140	2.143	2.146	2.149	2.152	2.155	2.158	
7	2.161	2.164	2.167	2.170	2.173	2.176	2.179	2.182	2.184	2.187	
8	2.190	2.193	2.196	2.199	2.202	2.205	2.208	2.211	2.214	2.217	
9	2.220	2.223	2.226	2.229	2.232	2.235	2.238	2.241	2.244	2.247	

Moving the decimal point ONE place in N requires moving it TWO places in body of table (see p. 1–8).

Squares (*continued*)

N	0	1	2	3	4	5	6	7	8	9	Avg diff
1.50	2.250	2.253	2.256	2.259	2.262	2.265	2.268	2.271	2.274	2.277	3
1	2.280	2.283	2.286	2.289	2.292	2.295	2.298	2.301	2.304	2.307	
2	2.310	2.313	2.316	2.320	2.323	2.326	2.329	2.332	2.335	2.338	
3	2.341	2.344	2.347	2.350	2.353	2.356	2.359	2.362	2.365	2.369	
4	2.372	2.375	2.378	2.381	2.384	2.387	2.390	2.393	2.396	2.399	
1.55	2.402	2.406	2.409	2.412	2.415	2.418	2.421	2.424	2.427	2.430	
6	2.434	2.437	2.440	2.443	2.446	2.449	2.452	2.455	2.459	2.462	
7	2.465	2.468	2.471	2.474	2.477	2.481	2.484	2.487	2.490	2.493	
8	2.496	2.500	2.503	2.506	2.509	2.512	2.515	2.519	2.522	2.525	
9	2.528	2.531	2.534	2.538	2.541	2.544	2.547	2.550	2.554	2.557	
1.60	2.560	2.563	2.566	2.570	2.573	2.576	2.579	2.582	2.586	2.589	
1	2.592	2.595	2.599	2.602	2.605	2.608	2.611	2.615	2.618	2.621	
2	2.624	2.628	2.631	2.634	2.637	2.641	2.644	2.647	2.650	2.654	
3	2.657	2.660	2.663	2.667	2.670	2.673	2.676	2.680	2.683	2.686	
4	2.690	2.693	2.696	2.699	2.703	2.706	2.709	2.713	2.716	2.719	
1.65	2.722	2.726	2.729	2.732	2.736	2.739	2.742	2.746	2.749	2.752	
6	2.756	2.759	2.762	2.766	2.769	2.772	2.776	2.779	2.782	2.786	
7	2.789	2.792	2.796	2.799	2.802	2.806	2.809	2.812	2.816	2.819	
8	2.822	2.826	2.829	2.832	2.836	2.839	2.843	2.846	2.849	2.853	
9	2.856	2.859	2.863	2.866	2.870	2.873	2.876	2.880	2.883	2.887	
1.70	2.890	2.893	2.897	2.900	2.904	2.907	2.910	2.914	2.917	2.921	
1	2.924	2.928	2.931	2.934	2.938	2.941	2.945	2.948	2.952	2.955	
2	2.958	2.962	2.965	2.969	2.972	2.976	2.979	2.983	2.986	2.989	
3	2.993	2.996	3.000	3.003	3.007	3.010	3.014	3.017	3.021	3.024	
4	3.028	3.031	3.035	3.038	3.042	3.045	3.049	3.052	3.056	3.059	
1.75	3.062	3.066	3.070	3.073	3.077	3.080	3.084	3.087	3.091	3.094	4
6	3.098	3.101	3.105	3.108	3.112	3.115	3.119	3.122	3.126	3.129	
7	3.133	3.136	3.140	3.144	3.147	3.151	3.154	3.158	3.161	3.165	
8	3.168	3.172	3.176	3.179	3.183	3.186	3.190	3.193	3.197	3.201	
9	3.204	3.208	3.211	3.215	3.218	3.222	3.226	3.229	3.233	3.236	
1.80	3.240	3.244	3.247	3.251	3.254	3.258	3.262	3.265	3.269	3.272	
1	3.276	3.280	3.283	3.287	3.291	3.294	3.298	3.301	3.305	3.309	
2	3.312	3.316	3.320	3.323	3.327	3.331	3.334	3.338	3.342	3.345	
3	3.349	3.353	3.356	3.360	3.364	3.367	3.371	3.375	3.378	3.382	
4	3.386	3.389	3.393	3.397	3.400	3.404	3.408	3.411	3.415	3.419	
1.85	3.422	3.426	3.430	3.434	3.437	3.441	3.445	3.448	3.452	3.456	
6	3.460	3.463	3.467	3.471	3.474	3.478	3.482	3.486	3.489	3.493	
7	3.497	3.501	3.504	3.508	3.512	3.516	3.519	3.523	3.527	3.531	
8	3.534	3.538	3.542	3.546	3.549	3.553	3.557	3.561	3.565	3.568	
9	3.572	3.576	3.580	3.583	3.587	3.591	3.595	3.599	3.602	3.606	
1.90	3.610	3.614	3.618	3.621	3.625	3.629	3.633	3.637	3.640	3.644	
1	3.648	3.652	3.656	3.660	3.663	3.667	3.671	3.675	3.679	3.683	
2	3.686	3.690	3.694	3.698	3.702	3.706	3.709	3.713	3.717	3.721	
3	3.725	3.729	3.733	3.736	3.740	3.744	3.748	3.752	3.756	3.760	
4	3.764	3.767	3.771	3.775	3.779	3.783	3.787	3.791	3.795	3.799	
1.95	3.802	3.806	3.810	3.814	3.818	3.822	3.826	3.830	3.834	3.838	
6	3.842	3.846	3.849	3.853	3.857	3.861	3.865	3.869	3.873	3.877	
7	3.881	3.885	3.889	3.893	3.897	3.901	3.905	3.909	3.912	3.916	
8	3.920	3.924	3.928	3.932	3.936	3.940	3.944	3.948	3.952	3.956	
9	3.960	3.964	3.968	3.972	3.976	3.980	3.984	3.988	3.992	3.996	

$$\pi^2 = 9.86960 \qquad 1/\pi^2 = 0.101321 \qquad e^2 = 7.38906$$

MATHEMATICS

Squares (continued)

N	0	1	2	3	4	5	6	7	8	9	Diff Avg
2.00	4.000	4.004	4.008	4.012	4.016	4.020	4.024	4.028	4.032	4.036	4
1	4.040	4.044	4.048	4.052	4.056	4.060	4.064	4.068	4.072	4.076	
2	4.080	4.084	4.088	4.093	4.097	4.101	4.105	4.109	4.113	4.117	
3	4.121	4.125	4.129	4.133	4.137	4.141	4.145	4.149	4.153	4.158	
4	4.162	4.166	4.170	4.174	4.178	4.182	4.186	4.190	4.194	4.198	
2.05	4.202	4.207	4.211	4.215	4.219	4.223	4.227	4.231	4.235	4.239	
6	4.244	4.248	4.252	4.256	4.260	4.264	4.268	4.272	4.277	4.281	
7	4.285	4.289	4.293	4.297	4.301	4.306	4.310	4.314	4.318	4.322	
8	4.326	4.331	4.335	4.339	4.343	4.347	4.351	4.356	4.360	4.364	
9	4.368	4.372	4.376	4.381	4.385	4.389	4.393	4.397	4.402	4.406	
2.10	4.410	4.414	4.418	4.423	4.427	4.431	4.435	4.439	4.444	4.448	
1	4.452	4.456	4.461	4.465	4.469	4.473	4.477	4.482	4.486	4.490	
2	4.494	4.499	4.503	4.507	4.511	4.516	4.520	4.524	4.528	4.533	
3	4.537	4.541	4.545	4.550	4.554	4.558	4.562	4.567	4.571	4.575	
4	4.580	4.584	4.588	4.592	4.597	4.601	4.605	4.610	4.614	4.618	
2.15	4.622	4.627	4.631	4.635	4.640	4.644	4.648	4.653	4.657	4.661	
6	4.666	4.670	4.674	4.679	4.683	4.687	4.692	4.696	4.700	4.705	
7	4.709	4.713	4.718	4.722	4.726	4.731	4.735	4.739	4.744	4.748	
8	4.752	4.757	4.761	4.765	4.770	4.774	4.779	4.783	4.787	4.792	
9	4.796	4.800	4.805	4.809	4.814	4.818	4.822	4.827	4.831	4.836	
2.20	4.840	4.844	4.849	4.853	4.858	4.862	4.866	4.871	4.875	4.880	
1	4.884	4.889	4.893	4.897	4.902	4.906	4.911	4.915	4.920	4.924	
2	4.928	4.933	4.937	4.942	4.946	4.951	4.955	4.960	4.964	4.968	
3	4.973	4.977	4.982	4.986	4.991	4.995	5.000	5.004	5.009	5.013	
4	5.018	5.022	5.027	5.031	5.036	5.040	5.045	5.049	5.054	5.058	
2.25	5.062	5.067	5.072	5.076	5.081	5.085	5.090	5.094	5.099	5.103	5
6	5.108	5.112	5.117	5.121	5.126	5.130	5.135	5.139	5.144	5.148	
7	5.153	5.157	5.162	5.167	5.171	5.176	5.180	5.185	5.189	5.194	
8	5.198	5.203	5.208	5.212	5.217	5.221	5.226	5.230	5.235	5.240	
9	5.244	5.249	5.253	5.258	5.262	5.267	5.272	5.276	5.281	5.285	
2.30	5.290	5.295	5.299	5.304	5.308	5.313	5.318	5.322	5.327	5.331	
1	5.336	5.341	5.345	5.350	5.355	5.359	5.364	5.368	5.373	5.378	
2	5.382	5.387	5.392	5.396	5.401	5.406	5.410	5.415	5.420	5.424	
3	5.429	5.434	5.438	5.443	5.448	5.452	5.457	5.462	5.466	5.471	
4	5.476	5.480	5.485	5.490	5.494	5.499	5.504	5.508	5.513	5.518	
2.35	5.522	5.527	5.532	5.537	5.541	5.546	5.551	5.555	5.560	5.565	
6	5.570	5.574	5.579	5.584	5.588	5.593	5.598	5.603	5.607	5.612	
7	5.617	5.622	5.626	5.631	5.636	5.641	5.645	5.650	5.655	5.660	
8	5.664	5.669	5.674	5.679	5.683	5.688	5.693	5.698	5.703	5.707	
9	5.712	5.717	5.722	5.726	5.731	5.736	5.741	5.746	5.750	5.755	
2.40	5.760	5.765	5.770	5.774	5.779	5.784	5.789	5.794	5.798	5.803	
1	5.808	5.813	5.818	5.823	5.827	5.832	5.837	5.842	5.847	5.852	
2	5.856	5.861	5.866	5.871	5.876	5.881	5.885	5.890	5.895	5.900	
3	5.905	5.910	5.915	5.919	5.924	5.929	5.934	5.939	5.944	5.949	
4	5.954	5.958	5.963	5.968	5.973	5.978	5.983	5.988	5.993	5.998	
2.45	6.002	6.007	6.012	6.017	6.022	6.027	6.032	6.037	6.042	6.047	
6	6.052	6.057	6.061	6.066	6.071	6.076	6.081	6.086	6.091	6.096	
7	6.101	6.106	6.111	6.116	6.121	6.126	6.131	6.136	6.140	6.145	
8	6.150	6.155	6.160	6.165	6.170	6.175	6.180	6.185	6.190	6.195	
9	6.200	6.205	6.210	6.215	6.220	6.225	6.230	6.235	6.240	6.245	

Moving the decimal point ONE place in N requires moving it TWO places in body of table (see p. 1-8).

Squares (continued)

N	0	1	2	3	4	5	6	7	8	9	Avg diff
2.50	6.250	6.255	6.260	6.265	6.270	6.275	6.280	6.285	6.290	6.295	5
1	6.300	6.305	6.310	6.315	6.320	6.325	6.330	6.335	6.340	6.345	
2	6.350	6.355	6.360	6.366	6.371	6.376	6.381	6.386	6.391	6.396	
3	6.401	6.406	6.411	6.416	6.421	6.426	6.431	6.436	6.441	6.447	
4	6.452	6.457	6.462	6.467	6.472	6.477	6.482	6.487	6.492	6.497	
2.55	6.502	6.508	6.513	6.518	6.523	6.528	6.533	6.538	6.543	6.548	
6	6.554	6.559	6.564	6.569	6.574	6.579	6.584	6.589	6.595	6.600	
7	6.605	6.610	6.615	6.620	6.625	6.631	6.636	6.641	6.646	6.651	
8	6.656	6.662	6.667	6.672	6.677	6.682	6.687	6.693	6.698	6.703	
9	6.708	6.713	6.718	6.724	6.729	6.734	6.739	6.744	6.750	6.755	
2.60	6.760	6.765	6.770	6.776	6.781	6.786	6.791	6.796	6.802	6.807	
1	6.812	6.817	6.823	6.828	6.833	6.838	6.843	6.849	6.854	6.859	
2	6.864	6.870	6.875	6.880	6.885	6.891	6.896	6.901	6.906	6.912	
3	6.917	6.922	6.927	6.933	6.938	6.943	6.948	6.954	6.959	6.964	
4	6.970	6.975	6.980	6.985	6.991	6.996	7.001	7.007	7.012	7.017	
2.65	7.022	7.028	7.033	7.038	7.044	7.049	7.054	7.060	7.065	7.070	
6	7.076	7.081	7.086	7.092	7.097	7.102	7.108	7.113	7.118	7.124	
7	7.129	7.134	7.140	7.145	7.150	7.156	7.161	7.166	7.172	7.177	
8	7.182	7.188	7.193	7.198	7.204	7.209	7.215	7.220	7.225	7.231	
9	7.236	7.241	7.247	7.252	7.258	7.263	7.268	7.274	7.279	7.285	
2.70	7.290	7.295	7.301	7.306	7.312	7.317	7.322	7.328	7.333	7.339	
1	7.344	7.350	7.355	7.360	7.366	7.371	7.377	7.382	7.388	7.393	
2	7.398	7.404	7.409	7.415	7.420	7.426	7.431	7.437	7.442	7.447	
3	7.453	7.458	7.464	7.469	7.475	7.480	7.486	7.491	7.497	7.502	
4	7.508	7.513	7.519	7.524	7.530	7.535	7.541	7.546	7.552	7.557	
2.75	7.562	7.568	7.574	7.579	7.585	7.590	7.596	7.601	7.607	7.612	6
6	7.618	7.623	7.629	7.634	7.640	7.645	7.651	7.656	7.662	7.667	
7	7.673	7.678	7.684	7.690	7.695	7.701	7.706	7.712	7.717	7.723	
8	7.728	7.734	7.740	7.745	7.751	7.756	7.762	7.767	7.773	7.779	
9	7.784	7.790	7.795	7.801	7.806	7.812	7.818	7.823	7.829	7.834	
2.80	7.840	7.846	7.851	7.857	7.862	7.868	7.874	7.879	7.885	7.890	
1	7.896	7.902	7.907	7.913	7.919	7.924	7.930	7.935	7.941	7.947	
2	7.952	7.958	7.964	7.969	7.975	7.981	7.986	7.992	7.998	8.003	
3	8.009	8.015	8.020	8.026	8.032	8.037	8.043	8.049	8.054	8.060	
4	8.066	8.071	8.077	8.083	8.088	8.094	8.100	8.105	8.111	8.117	
2.85	8.122	8.128	8.134	8.140	8.145	8.151	8.157	8.162	8.168	8.174	
6	8.180	8.185	8.191	8.197	8.202	8.208	8.214	8.220	8.225	8.231	
7	8.237	8.243	8.248	8.254	8.260	8.266	8.271	8.277	8.283	8.289	
8	8.294	8.300	8.306	8.312	8.317	8.323	8.329	8.335	8.341	8.346	
9	8.352	8.358	8.364	8.369	8.375	8.381	8.387	8.393	8.398	8.404	
2.90	8.410	8.416	8.422	8.427	8.433	8.439	8.445	8.451	8.456	8.462	
1	8.468	8.474	8.480	8.486	8.491	8.497	8.503	8.509	8.515	8.521	
2	8.526	8.532	8.538	8.544	8.550	8.556	8.561	8.567	8.573	8.579	
3	8.585	8.591	8.597	8.602	8.608	8.614	8.620	8.626	8.632	8.638	
4	8.644	8.649	8.655	8.661	8.667	8.673	8.679	8.685	8.691	8.697	
2.95	8.702	8.708	8.714	8.720	8.726	8.732	8.738	8.744	8.750	8.756	
6	8.762	8.768	8.773	8.779	8.785	8.791	8.797	8.803	8.809	8.815	
7	8.821	8.827	8.833	8.839	8.845	8.851	8.857	8.863	8.868	8.874	
8	8.880	8.886	8.892	8.898	8.904	8.910	8.916	8.922	8.928	8.934	
9	8.940	8.946	8.952	8.958	8.964	8.970	8.976	8.982	8.988	8.994	

$$\pi^2 = 9.86960 \qquad 1/\pi^2 = 0.101321 \qquad e^2 = 7.38906$$

MATHEMATICS

Squares (continued)

N	0	1	2	3	4	5	6	7	8	9	Avg diff
3.00	9.000	9.006	9.012	9.018	9.024	9.030	9.036	9.042	9.048	9.054	6
1	9.060	9.066	9.072	9.078	9.084	9.090	9.096	9.102	9.108	9.114	
2	9.120	9.126	9.132	9.139	9.145	9.151	9.157	9.163	9.169	9.175	
3	9.181	9.187	9.193	9.199	9.205	9.211	9.217	9.223	9.229	9.236	
4	9.242	9.248	9.254	9.260	9.266	9.272	9.278	9.284	9.290	9.296	
3.05	9.302	9.309	9.315	9.321	9.327	9.333	9.339	9.345	9.351	9.357	
6	9.364	9.370	9.376	9.382	9.388	9.394	9.400	9.406	9.413	9.419	
7	9.425	9.431	9.437	9.443	9.449	9.456	9.462	9.468	9.474	9.480	
8	9.486	9.493	9.499	9.505	9.511	9.517	9.523	9.530	9.536	9.542	
9	9.548	9.554	9.560	9.567	9.573	9.579	9.585	9.591	9.598	9.604	
3.10	9.610	9.616	9.622	9.629	9.635	9.641	9.647	9.653	9.660	9.666	
1	9.672	9.678	9.685	9.691	9.697	9.703	9.709	9.716	9.722	9.728	
2	9.734	9.741	9.747	9.753	9.759	9.766	9.772	9.778	9.784	9.791	
3	9.797	9.803	9.809	9.816	9.822	9.828	9.834	9.841	9.847	9.853	
4	9.860	9.866	9.872	9.878	9.885	9.891	9.897	9.904	9.910	9.916	
3.15	9.922	9.929	9.935	9.941	9.948	9.954	9.960	9.967	9.973	9.979	
6	9.986	9.992	9.998	10.005							6
3.1							9.99	10.05	10.11	10.18	6
2	10.24	10.30	10.37	10.43	10.50	10.56	10.63	10.69	10.76	10.82	
3	10.89	10.96	11.02	11.09	11.16	11.22	11.29	11.36	11.42	11.49	7
4	11.56	11.63	11.70	11.76	11.83	11.90	11.97	12.04	12.11	12.18	
3.5	12.25	12.32	12.39	12.46	12.53	12.60	12.67	12.74	12.82	12.89	
6	12.96	13.03	13.10	13.18	13.25	13.32	13.40	13.47	13.54	13.62	
7	13.69	13.76	13.84	13.91	13.99	14.06	14.14	14.21	14.29	14.36	8
8	14.44	14.52	14.59	14.67	14.75	14.82	14.90	14.98	15.05	15.13	
9	15.21	15.29	15.37	15.44	15.52	15.60	15.68	15.76	15.84	15.92	
4.0	16.00	16.08	16.16	16.24	16.32	16.40	16.48	16.56	16.65	16.73	
1	16.81	16.89	16.97	17.06	17.14	17.22	17.31	17.39	17.47	17.56	
2	17.64	17.72	17.81	17.89	17.98	18.06	18.15	18.23	18.32	18.40	
3	18.49	18.58	18.66	18.75	18.84	18.92	19.01	19.10	19.18	19.27	9
4	19.36	19.45	19.54	19.62	19.71	19.80	19.89	19.98	20.07	20.16	
4.5	20.25	20.34	20.43	20.52	20.61	20.70	20.79	20.88	20.98	21.07	
6	21.16	21.25	21.34	21.44	21.53	21.62	21.72	21.81	21.90	22.00	
7	22.09	22.18	22.28	22.37	22.47	22.56	22.66	22.75	22.85	22.94	10
8	23.04	23.14	23.23	23.33	23.43	23.52	23.62	23.72	23.81	23.91	
9	24.01	24.11	24.21	24.30	24.40	24.50	24.60	24.70	24.80	24.90	

$$\pi^2 = 9.86960 \qquad (\pi/2)^2 = 2.46740 \qquad 1/\pi^2 = 0.101321$$

Explanation of Table of Squares (pp. 1–4 to 1–9).

This table gives the value of N^2 for values of N from 1 to 10, correct to four figures. (Interpolated values may be in error by 1 in the fourth figure.)

To find the square of a number N outside the range from 1 to 10, note that moving the decimal point ONE place in column N is equivalent to moving it TWO places in the body of the table. For example:
$$(3.217)^2 = 10.35 \qquad (0.03217)^2 = 0.001035 \qquad (3217)^2 = 10350000$$
This table can also be used inversely, to give square roots.

Squares (continued)

N	0	1	2	3	4	5	6	7	8	9	Avg diff
5.0	25.00	25.10	25.20	25.30	25.40	25.50	25.60	25.70	25.81	25.91	10
1	26.01	26.11	26.21	26.32	26.42	26.52	26.63	26.73	26.83	26.94	
2	27.04	27.14	27.25	27.35	27.46	27.56	27.67	27.77	27.88	27.98	
3	28.09	28.20	28.30	28.41	28.52	28.62	28.73	28.84	28.94	29.05	11
4	29.16	29.27	29.38	29.48	29.59	29.70	29.81	29.92	30.03	30.14	
5.5	30.25	30.36	30.47	30.58	30.69	30.80	30.91	31.02	31.14	31.25	
6	31.36	31.47	31.58	31.70	31.81	31.92	32.04	32.15	32.26	32.38	
7	32.49	32.60	32.72	32.83	32.95	33.06	33.18	33.29	33.41	33.52	
8	33.64	33.76	33.87	33.99	34.11	34.22	34.34	34.46	34.57	34.69	12
9	34.81	34.93	35.05	35.16	35.28	35.40	35.52	35.64	35.76	35.88	
6.0	36.00	36.12	36.24	36.36	36.48	36.60	36.72	36.84	36.97	37.09	
1	37.21	37.33	37.45	37.58	37.70	37.82	37.95	38.07	38.19	38.32	
2	38.44	38.56	38.69	38.81	38.94	39.06	39.19	39.31	39.44	39.56	
3	39.69	39.82	39.94	40.07	40.20	40.32	40.45	40.58	40.70	40.83	13
4	40.96	41.09	41.22	41.34	41.47	41.60	41.73	41.86	41.99	42.12	
6.5	42.25	42.38	42.51	42.64	42.77	42.90	43.03	43.16	43.30	43.43	
6	43.56	43.69	43.82	43.96	44.09	44.22	44.36	44.49	44.62	44.76	
7	44.89	45.02	45.16	45.29	45.43	45.56	45.70	45.83	45.97	46.10	
8	46.24	46.38	46.51	46.65	46.79	46.92	47.06	47.20	47.33	47.47	14
9	47.61	47.75	47.89	48.02	48.16	48.30	48.44	48.58	48.72	48.86	
7.0	49.00	49.14	49.28	49.42	49.56	49.70	49.84	49.98	50.13	50.27	
1	50.41	50.55	50.69	50.84	50.98	51.12	51.27	51.41	51.55	51.70	
2	51.84	51.98	52.13	52.27	52.42	52.56	52.71	52.85	53.00	53.14	
3	53.29	53.44	53.58	53.73	53.88	54.02	54.17	54.32	54.46	54.61	15
4	54.76	54.91	55.06	55.20	55.35	55.50	55.65	55.80	55.95	56.10	
7.5	56.25	56.40	56.55	56.70	56.85	57.00	57.15	57.30	57.46	57.61	
6	57.76	57.91	58.06	58.22	58.37	58.52	58.68	58.83	58.98	59.14	
7	59.29	59.44	59.60	59.75	59.91	60.06	60.22	60.37	60.53	60.68	
8	60.84	61.00	61.15	61.31	61.47	61.62	61.78	61.94	62.09	62.25	16
9	62.41	62.57	62.73	62.88	63.04	63.20	63.36	63.52	63.68	63.84	
8.0	64.00	64.16	64.32	64.48	64.64	64.80	64.96	65.12	65.29	65.45	
1	65.61	65.77	65.93	66.10	66.26	66.42	66.59	66.75	66.91	67.08	
2	67.24	67.40	67.57	67.73	67.90	68.06	68.23	68.39	68.56	68.72	
3	68.89	69.06	69.22	69.39	69.56	69.72	69.89	70.06	70.22	70.39	17
4	70.56	70.73	70.90	71.06	71.23	71.40	71.57	71.74	71.91	72.08	
8.5	72.25	72.42	72.59	72.76	72.93	73.10	73.27	73.44	73.62	73.79	
6	73.96	74.13	74.30	74.48	74.65	74.82	75.00	75.17	75.34	75.52	
7	75.69	75.86	76.04	76.21	76.39	76.56	76.74	76.91	77.09	77.26	
8	77.44	77.62	77.79	77.97	78.15	78.32	78.50	78.68	78.85	79.03	18
9	79.21	79.39	79.57	79.74	79.92	80.10	80.28	80.46	80.64	80.82	
9.0	81.00	81.18	81.36	81.54	81.72	81.90	82.08	82.26	82.45	82.63	
1	82.81	82.99	83.17	83.36	83.54	83.72	83.91	84.09	84.27	84.46	
2	84.64	84.82	85.01	85.19	85.38	85.56	85.75	85.93	86.12	86.30	
3	86.49	86.68	86.86	87.05	87.24	87.42	87.61	87.80	87.98	88.17	19
4	88.36	88.55	88.74	88.92	89.11	89.30	89.49	89.68	89.87	90.06	
9.5	90.25	90.44	90.63	90.82	91.01	91.20	91.39	91.58	91.78	91.97	
6	92.16	92.35	92.54	92.74	92.93	93.12	93.32	93.51	93.70	93.90	
7	94.09	94.28	94.48	94.67	94.87	95.06	95.26	95.45	95.65	95.84	
8	96.04	96.24	96.43	96.63	96.83	97.02	97.22	97.42	97.61	97.81	20
9	98.01	98.21	98.41	98.60	98.80	99.00	99.20	99.40	99.60	99.80	
10.0	100.0										

Moving the decimal point ONE place in N requires moving it TWO places in body of table (see p. 1–8).

MATHEMATICS

Cubes of Numbers

N	0	1	2	3	4	5	6	7	8	9	Avg diff
1.00	1.000	1.003	1.006	1.009	1.012	1.015	1.018	1.021	1.024	1.027	3
1	1.030	1.033	1.036	1.040	1.043	1.046	1.049	1.052	1.055	1.058	
2	1.061	1.064	1.067	1.071	1.074	1.077	1.080	1.083	1.086	1.090	
3	1.093	1.096	1.099	1.102	1.106	1.109	1.112	1.115	1.118	1.122	
4	1.125	1.128	1.131	1.135	1.138	1.141	1.144	1.148	1.151	1.154	
1.05	1.158	1.161	1.164	1.168	1.171	1.174	1.178	1.181	1.184	1.188	
6	1.191	1.194	1.198	1.201	1.205	1.208	1.211	1.215	1.218	1.222	
7	1.225	1.228	1.232	1.235	1.239	1.242	1.246	1.249	1.253	1.256	
8	1.260	1.263	1.267	1.270	1.274	1.277	1.281	1.284	1.288	1.291	4
9	1.295	1.299	1.302	1.306	1.309	1.313	1.317	1.320	1.324	1.327	
1.10	1.331	1.335	1.338	1.342	1.346	1.349	1.353	1.357	1.360	1.364	
1	1.368	1.371	1.375	1.379	1.382	1.386	1.390	1.394	1.397	1.401	
2	1.405	1.409	1.412	1.416	1.420	1.424	1.428	1.431	1.435	1.439	
3	1.443	1.447	1.451	1.454	1.458	1.462	1.466	1.470	1.474	1.478	
4	1.482	1.485	1.489	1.493	1.497	1.501	1.505	1.509	1.513	1.517	
1.15	1.521	1.525	1.529	1.533	1.537	1.541	1.545	1.549	1.553	1.557	
6	1.561	1.565	1.569	1.573	1.577	1.581	1.585	1.589	1.593	1.598	
7	1.602	1.606	1.610	1.614	1.618	1.622	1.626	1.631	1.635	1.639	
8	1.643	1.647	1.651	1.656	1.660	1.664	1.668	1.672	1.677	1.681	
9	1.685	1.689	1.694	1.698	1.702	1.706	1.711	1.715	1.719	1.724	
1.20	1.728	1.732	1.737	1.741	1.745	1.750	1.754	1.758	1.763	1.767	
1	1.772	1.776	1.780	1.785	1.789	1.794	1.798	1.802	1.807	1.811	
2	1.816	1.820	1.825	1.829	1.834	1.838	1.843	1.847	1.852	1.856	
3	1.861	1.865	1.870	1.875	1.879	1.884	1.888	1.893	1.897	1.902	
4	1.907	1.911	1.916	1.920	1.925	1.930	1.934	1.939	1.944	1.948	5
1.25	1.953	1.958	1.963	1.967	1.972	1.977	1.981	1.986	1.991	1.996	
6	2.000	2.005	2.010	2.015	2.019	2.024	2.029	2.034	2.039	2.044	
7	2.048	2.053	2.058	2.063	2.068	2.073	2.078	2.082	2.087	2.092	
8	2.097	2.102	2.107	2.112	2.117	2.122	2.127	2.132	2.137	2.142	
9	2.147	2.152	2.157	2.162	2.167	2.172	2.177	2.182	2.187	2.192	
1.30	2.197	2.202	2.207	2.212	2.217	2.222	2.228	2.233	2.238	2.243	
1	2.248	2.253	2.258	2.264	2.269	2.274	2.279	2.284	2.290	2.295	
2	2.300	2.305	2.310	2.316	2.321	2.326	2.331	2.337	2.342	2.347	
3	2.353	2.358	2.363	2.369	2.374	2.379	2.385	2.390	2.395	2.401	
4	2.406	2.411	2.417	2.422	2.428	2.433	2.439	2.444	2.449	2.455	
1.35	2.460	2.466	2.471	2.477	2.482	2.488	2.493	2.499	2.504	2.510	6
6	2.515	2.521	2.527	2.532	2.538	2.543	2.549	2.554	2.560	2.566	
7	2.571	2.577	2.583	2.588	2.594	2.600	2.605	2.611	2.617	2.622	
8	2.628	2.634	2.640	2.645	2.651	2.657	2.663	2.668	2.674	2.680	
9	2.686	2.691	2.697	2.703	2.709	2.715	2.721	2.726	2.732	2.738	
1.40	2.744	2.750	2.756	2.762	2.768	2.774	2.779	2.785	2.791	2.797	
1	2.803	2.809	2.815	2.821	2.827	2.833	2.839	2.845	2.851	2.857	
2	2.863	2.869	2.875	2.881	2.888	2.894	2.900	2.906	2.912	2.918	
3	2.924	2.930	2.936	2.943	2.949	2.955	2.961	2.967	2.974	2.980	
4	2.986	2.992	2.998	3.005	3.011	3.017	3.023	3.030	3.036	3.042	
1.45	3.049	3.055	3.061	3.068	3.074	3.080	3.087	3.093	3.099	3.106	
6	3.112	3.119	3.125	3.131	3.138	3.144	3.151	3.157	3.164	3.170	
7	3.177	3.183	3.190	3.196	3.203	3.209	3.216	3.222	3.229	3.235	
8	3.242	3.248	3.255	3.262	3.268	3.275	3.281	3.288	3.295	3.301	7
9	3.308	3.315	3.321	3.328	3.335	3.341	3.348	3.355	3.362	3.368	

Moving the decimal point ONE place in N requires moving it THREE places in body of table (see p. 1–12).

Cubes (continued)

N	0	1	2	3	4	5	6	7	8	9	Avg diff
1.50	3.375	3.382	3.389	3.395	3.402	3.409	3.416	3.422	3.429	3.436	7
1	3.443	3.450	3.457	3.464	3.470	3.477	3.484	3.491	3.498	3.505	
2	3.512	3.519	3.526	3.533	3.540	3.547	3.554	3.561	3.568	3.575	
3	3.582	3.589	3.596	3.603	3.610	3.617	3.624	3.631	3.638	3.645	
4	3.652	3.659	3.667	3.674	3.681	3.688	3.695	3.702	3.709	3.717	
1.55	3.724	3.731	3.738	3.746	3.753	3.760	3.767	3.775	3.782	3.789	
6	3.796	3.804	3.811	3.818	3.826	3.833	3.840	3.848	3.855	3.863	
7	3.870	3.877	3.885	3.892	3.900	3.907	3.914	3.922	3.929	3.937	
8	3.944	3.952	3.959	3.967	3.974	3.982	3.989	3.997	4.005	4.012	8
9	4.020	4.027	4.035	4.042	4.050	4.058	4.065	4.073	4.081	4.088	
1.60	4.096	4.104	4.111	4.119	4.127	4.135	4.142	4.150	4.158	4.166	
1	4.173	4.181	4.189	4.197	4.204	4.212	4.220	4.228	4.236	4.244	
2	4.252	4.259	4.267	4.275	4.283	4.291	4.299	4.307	4.315	4.323	
3	4.331	4.339	4.347	4.355	4.363	4.371	4.379	4.387	4.395	4.403	
4	4.411	4.419	4.427	4.435	4.443	4.451	4.460	4.468	4.476	4.484	
1.65	4.492	4.500	4.508	4.517	4.525	4.533	4.541	4.550	4.558	4.566	
6	4.574	4.583	4.591	4.599	4.607	4.616	4.624	4.632	4.641	4.649	
7	4.657	4.666	4.674	4.683	4.691	4.699	4.708	4.716	4.725	4.733	
8	4.742	4.750	4.759	4.767	4.776	4.784	4.793	4.801	4.810	4.818	
9	4.827	4.835	4.844	4.853	4.861	4.870	4.878	4.887	4.896	4.904	9
1.70	4.913	4.922	4.930	4.939	4.948	4.956	4.965	4.974	4.983	4.991	
1	5.000	5.009	5.018	5.027	5.035	5.044	5.053	5.062	5.071	5.080	
2	5.088	5.097	5.106	5.115	5.124	5.133	5.142	5.151	5.160	5.169	
3	5.178	5.187	5.196	5.205	5.214	5.223	5.232	5.241	5.250	5.259	
4	5.268	5.277	5.286	5.295	5.304	5.314	5.323	5.332	5.341	5.350	
1.75	5.359	5.369	5.378	5.387	5.396	5.405	5.415	5.424	5.433	5.442	
6	5.452	5.461	5.470	5.480	5.489	5.498	5.508	5.517	5.526	5.536	
7	5.545	5.555	5.564	5.573	5.583	5.592	5.602	5.611	5.621	5.630	10
8	5.640	5.649	5.659	5.668	5.678	5.687	5.697	5.707	5.716	5.726	
9	5.735	5.745	5.755	5.764	5.774	5.784	5.793	5.803	5.813	5.822	
1.80	5.832	5.842	5.851	5.861	5.871	5.881	5.891	5.900	5.910	5.920	
1	5.930	5.940	5.949	5.959	5.969	5.979	5.989	5.999	6.009	6.019	
2	6.029	6.039	6.048	6.058	6.068	6.078	6.088	6.098	6.108	6.118	
3	6.128	6.139	6.149	6.159	6.169	6.179	6.189	6.199	6.209	6.219	
4	6.230	6.240	6.250	6.260	6.270	6.280	6.291	6.301	6.311	6.321	
1.85	6.332	6.342	6.352	6.362	6.373	6.383	6.393	6.404	6.414	6.424	
6	6.435	6.445	6.456	6.466	6.476	6.487	6.497	6.508	6.518	6.529	
7	6.539	6.550	6.560	6.571	6.581	6.592	6.602	6.613	6.623	6.634	11
8	6.645	6.655	6.666	6.677	6.687	6.698	6.708	6.719	6.730	6.741	
9	6.751	6.762	6.773	6.783	6.794	6.805	6.816	6.827	6.837	6.848	
1.90	6.859	6.870	6.881	6.892	6.902	6.913	6.924	6.935	6.946	6.957	
1	6.968	6.979	6.990	7.001	7.012	7.023	7.034	7.045	7.056	7.067	
2	7.078	7.089	7.100	7.111	7.122	7.133	7.144	7.156	7.167	7.178	
3	7.189	7.200	7.211	7.223	7.234	7.245	7.256	7.268	7.279	7.290	
4	7.301	7.313	7.324	7.335	7.347	7.358	7.369	7.381	7.392	7.403	
1.95	7.415	7.426	7.438	7.449	7.461	7.472	7.484	7.495	7.507	7.518	12
6	7.530	7.541	7.553	7.564	7.576	7.587	7.599	7.610	7.622	7.634	
7	7.645	7.657	7.669	7.680	7.692	7.704	7.715	7.727	7.739	7.751	
8	7.762	7.774	7.786	7.798	7.810	7.821	7.833	7.845	7.857	7.869	
9	7.881	7.892	7.904	7.916	7.928	7.940	7.952	7.964	7.976	7.988	

$$\pi^3 = 31.0063 \qquad 1/\pi^3 = 0.0322515+$$

MATHEMATICS

Cubes (continued)

N	0	1	2	3	4	5	6	7	8	9	Avg diff
2.00	8.000	8.012	8.024	8.036	8.048	8.060	8.072	8.084	8.096	8.108	12
1	8.121	8.133	8.145	8.157	8.169	8.181	8.194	8.206	8.218	8.230	
2	8.242	8.255	8.267	8.279	8.291	8.304	8.316	8.328	8.341	8.353	
3	8.365	8.378	8.390	8.403	8.415	8.427	8.440	8.452	8.465	8.477	
4	8.490	8.502	8.515	8.527	8.540	8.552	8.565	8.577	8.590	8.603	
2.05	8.615	8.628	8.640	8.653	8.666	8.678	8.691	8.704	8.716	8.729	13
6	8.742	8.755	8.767	8.780	8.793	8.806	8.818	8.831	8.844	8.857	
7	8.870	8.883	8.895	8.908	8.921	8.934	8.947	8.960	8.973	8.986	
8	8.999	9.012	9.025	9.038	9.051	9.064	9.077	9.090	9.103	9.116	
9	9.129	9.142	9.156	9.169	9.182	9.195	9.208	9.221	9.235	9.248	
2.10	9.261	9.274	9.287	9.301	9.314	9.327	9.341	9.354	9.367	9.381	
1	9.394	9.407	9.421	9.434	9.447	9.461	9.474	9.488	9.501	9.515	
2	9.528	9.542	9.555	9.569	9.582	9.596	9.609	9.623	9.636	9.650	14
3	9.664	9.677	9.691	9.704	9.718	9.732	9.745	9.759	9.773	9.787	
4	9.800	9.814	9.828	9.842	9.855	9.869	9.883	9.897	9.911	9.925	
2.15	9.938	9.952	9.966	9.980	9.994	10.008					14
2.1						9.94	10.08	10.22	10.36	10.50	14
2	10.65	10.79	10.94	11.09	11.24	11.39	11.54	11.70	11.85	12.01	15
3	12.17	12.33	12.49	12.65	12.81	12.98	13.14	13.31	13.48	13.65	16
4	13.82	14.00	14.17	14.35	14.53	14.71	14.89	15.07	15.25	15.44	18
2.5	15.62	15.81	16.00	16.19	16.39	16.58	16.78	16.97	17.17	17.37	20
6	17.58	17.78	17.98	18.19	18.40	18.61	18.82	19.03	19.25	19.47	21
7	19.68	19.90	20.12	20.35	20.57	20.80	21.02	21.25	21.48	21.72	23
8	21.95	22.19	22.43	22.67	22.91	23.15	23.39	23.64	23.89	24.14	24
9	24.39	24.64	24.90	25.15	25.41	25.67	25.93	26.20	26.46	26.73	26
3.0	27.00	27.27	27.54	27.82	28.09	28.37	28.65	28.93	29.22	29.50	28
1	29.79	30.08	30.37	30.66	30.96	31.26	31.55	31.86	32.16	32.46	30
2	32.77	33.08	33.39	33.70	34.01	34.33	34.65	34.97	35.29	35.61	32
3	35.94	36.26	36.59	36.93	37.26	37.60	37.93	38.27	38.61	38.96	34
4	39.30	39.65	40.00	40.35	40.71	41.06	41.42	41.78	42.14	42.51	36
3.5	42.88	43.24	43.61	43.99	44.36	44.74	45.12	45.50	45.88	46.27	39
6	46.66	47.05	47.44	47.83	48.23	48.63	49.03	49.43	49.84	50.24	40
7	50.65	51.06	51.48	51.90	52.31	52.73	53.16	53.58	54.01	54.44	42
8	54.87	55.31	55.74	56.18	56.62	57.07	57.51	57.96	58.41	58.86	44
9	59.32	59.78	60.24	60.70	61.16	61.63	62.10	62.57	63.04	63.52	47
4.0	64.00	64.48	64.96	65.45	65.94	66.43	66.92	67.42	67.92	68.42	49
1	68.92	69.43	69.93	70.44	70.96	71.47	71.99	72.51	73.03	73.56	52
2	74.09	74.62	75.15	75.69	76.23	76.77	77.31	77.85	78.40	78.95	54
3	79.51	80.06	80.62	81.18	81.75	82.31	82.88	83.45	84.03	84.60	58
4	85.18	85.77	86.35	86.94	87.53	88.12	88.72	89.31	89.92	90.52	59
4.5	91.12	91.73	92.35	92.96	93.58	94.20	94.82	95.44	96.07	96.70	62
6	97.34	97.97	98.61	99.25	99.90	100.54					64
6						100.5	101.2	101.8	102.5	103.2	7
7	103.8	104.5	105.2	105.8	106.5	107.2	107.9	108.5	109.2	109.9	7
8	110.6	111.3	112.0	112.7	113.4	114.1	114.8	115.5	116.2	116.9	7
9	117.6	118.4	119.1	119.8	120.6	121.3	122.0	122.8	123.5	124.3	7

Explanation of Table of Cubes (pp. 1–10 to 1–13).

This table gives the value of N^3 for values of N from 1 to 10, correct to four figures. (Interpolated values may be in error by 1 in the fourth figure.)

To find the cube of a number N outside the range from 1 to 10, note that moving the decimal point ONE place in column N is equivalent to moving it THREE places in the body of the table. For example:

$$(4.852)^3 = 114.2 \qquad (0.4852)^3 = 0.1142 \qquad (485.2)^3 = 114200000$$

This table may also be used inversely, to give cube roots.

Cubes (*continued*)

N	0	1	2	3	4	5	6	7	8	9	Avg diff
5.0	125.0	125.8	126.5	127.3	128.0	128.8	129.6	130.3	131.1	131.9	8
1	132.7	133.4	134.2	135.0	135.8	136.6	137.4	138.2	139.0	139.8	
2	140.6	141.4	142.2	143.1	143.9	144.7	145.5	146.4	147.2	148.0	
3	148.9	149.7	150.6	151.4	152.3	153.1	154.0	154.9	155.7	156.6	9
4	157.5	158.3	159.2	160.1	161.0	161.9	162.8	163.7	164.6	165.5	
5.5	166.4	167.3	168.2	169.1	170.0	171.0	171.9	172.8	173.7	174.7	
6	175.6	176.6	177.5	178.5	179.4	180.4	181.3	182.3	183.3	184.2	10
7	185.2	186.2	187.1	188.1	189.1	190.1	191.1	192.1	193.1	194.1	
8	195.1	196.1	197.1	198.2	199.2	200.2	201.2	202.3	203.3	204.3	
9	205.4	206.4	207.5	208.5	209.6	210.6	211.7	212.8	213.8	214.9	
6.0	216.0	217.1	218.2	219.3	220.3	221.4	222.5	223.6	224.8	225.9	11
1	227.0	228.1	229.2	230.3	231.5	232.6	233.7	234.9	236.0	237.2	
2	238.3	239.5	240.6	241.8	243.0	244.1	245.3	246.5	247.7	248.9	12
3	250.0	251.2	252.4	253.6	254.8	256.0	257.3	258.5	259.7	260.9	
4	262.1	263.4	264.6	265.8	267.1	268.3	269.6	270.8	272.1	273.4	
6.5	274.6	275.9	277.2	278.4	279.7	281.0	282.3	283.6	284.9	286.2	13
6	287.5	288.8	290.1	291.4	292.8	294.1	295.4	296.7	298.1	299.4	
7	300.8	302.1	303.5	304.8	306.2	307.5	308.9	310.3	311.7	313.0	14
8	314.4	315.8	317.2	318.6	320.0	321.4	322.8	324.2	325.7	327.1	
9	328.5	329.9	331.4	332.8	334.3	335.7	337.2	338.6	340.1	341.5	
7.0	343.0	344.5	345.9	347.4	348.9	350.4	351.9	353.4	354.9	356.4	15
1	357.9	359.4	360.9	362.5	364.0	365.5	367.1	368.6	370.1	371.7	
2	373.2	374.8	376.4	377.9	379.5	381.1	382.7	384.2	385.8	387.4	16
3	389.0	390.6	392.2	393.8	395.4	397.1	398.7	400.3	401.9	403.6	
4	405.2	406.9	408.5	410.2	411.8	413.5	415.2	416.8	418.5	420.2	17
7.5	421.9	423.6	425.3	427.0	428.7	430.4	432.1	433.8	435.5	437.2	
6	439.0	440.7	442.5	444.2	445.9	447.7	449.5	451.2	453.0	454.8	18
7	456.5	458.3	460.1	461.9	463.7	465.5	467.3	469.1	470.9	472.7	
8	474.6	476.4	478.2	480.0	481.9	483.7	485.6	487.4	489.3	491.2	
9	493.0	494.9	496.8	498.7	500.6	502.5	504.4	506.3	508.2	510.1	19
8.0	512.0	513.9	515.8	517.8	519.7	521.7	523.6	525.6	527.5	529.5	
1	531.4	533.4	535.4	537.4	539.4	541.3	543.3	545.3	547.3	549.4	20
2	551.4	553.4	555.4	557.4	559.5	561.5	563.6	565.6	567.7	569.7	
3	571.8	573.9	575.9	578.0	580.1	582.2	584.3	586.4	588.5	590.6	21
4	592.7	594.8	596.9	599.1	601.2	603.4	605.5	607.6	609.8	612.0	
8.5	614.1	616.3	618.5	620.7	622.8	625.0	627.2	629.4	631.6	633.8	22
6	636.1	638.3	640.5	642.7	645.0	647.2	649.5	651.7	654.0	656.2	
7	658.5	660.8	663.1	665.3	667.6	669.9	672.2	674.5	676.8	679.2	23
8	681.5	683.8	686.1	688.5	690.8	693.2	695.5	697.9	700.2	702.6	24
9	705.0	707.3	709.7	712.1	714.5	716.9	719.3	721.7	724.2	726.6	
9.0	729.0	731.4	733.9	736.3	738.8	741.2	743.7	746.1	748.6	751.1	25
1	753.6	756.1	758.6	761.0	763.6	766.1	768.6	771.1	773.6	776.2	
2	778.7	781.2	783.8	786.3	788.9	791.5	794.0	796.6	799.2	801.8	26
3	804.4	807.0	809.6	812.2	814.8	817.4	820.0	822.7	825.3	827.9	
4	830.6	833.2	835.9	838.6	841.2	843.9	846.6	849.3	852.0	854.7	27
9.5	857.4	860.1	862.8	865.5	868.3	871.0	873.7	876.5	879.2	882.0	
6	884.7	887.5	890.3	893.1	895.8	898.6	901.4	904.2	907.0	909.9	28
7	912.7	915.5	918.3	921.2	924.0	926.9	929.7	932.6	935.4	938.3	
8	941.2	944.1	947.0	949.9	952.8	955.7	958.6	961.5	964.4	967.4	29
9	970.3	973.2	976.2	979.1	982.1	985.1	988.0	991.0	994.0	997.0	
10.0	1000.0										

$$\pi^3 = 31.0063 \qquad 1/\pi^3 = 0.0322515+$$

Moving the decimal point ONE place in N requires moving it THREE places in body of table (see p. 1–12).

MATHEMATICS

Square Roots of Numbers

N	0	1	2	3	4	5	6	7	8	9	Avg diff
1.0	1.000	1.005	1.010	1.015	1.020	1.025	1.030	1.034	1.039	1.044	5
1	1.049	1.054	1.058	1.063	1.068	1.072	1.077	1.082	1.086	1.091	
2	1.095	1.100	1.105	1.109	1.114	1.118	1.122	1.127	1.131	1.136	4
3	1.140	1.145	1.149	1.153	1.158	1.162	1.166	1.170	1.175	1.179	
4	1.183	1.187	1.192	1.196	1.200	1.204	1.208	1.212	1.217	1.221	
1.5	1.225	1.229	1.233	1.237	1.241	1.245	1.249	1.253	1.257	1.261	
6	1.265	1.269	1.273	1.277	1.281	1.285	1.288	1.292	1.296	1.300	
7	1.304	1.308	1.311	1.315	1.319	1.323	1.327	1.330	1.334	1.338	
8	1.342	1.345	1.349	1.353	1.356	1.360	1.364	1.367	1.371	1.375	
9	1.378	1.382	1.386	1.389	1.393	1.396	1.400	1.404	1.407	1.411	
2.0	1.414	1.418	1.421	1.425	1.428	1.432	1.435	1.439	1.442	1.446	
1	1.449	1.453	1.456	1.459	1.463	1.466	1.470	1.473	1.476	1.480	3
2	1.483	1.487	1.490	1.493	1.497	1.500	1.503	1.507	1.510	1.513	
3	1.517	1.520	1.523	1.526	1.530	1.533	1.536	1.539	1.543	1.546	
4	1.549	1.552	1.556	1.559	1.562	1.565	1.568	1.572	1.575	1.578	
2.5	1.581	1.584	1.587	1.591	1.594	1.597	1.600	1.603	1.606	1.609	
6	1.612	1.616	1.619	1.622	1.625	1.628	1.631	1.634	1.637	1.640	
7	1.643	1.646	1.649	1.652	1.655	1.658	1.661	1.664	1.667	1.670	
8	1.673	1.676	1.679	1.682	1.685	1.688	1.691	1.694	1.697	1.700	
9	1.703	1.706	1.709	1.712	1.715	1.718	1.720	1.723	1.726	1.729	
3.0	1.732	1.735	1.738	1.741	1.744	1.746	1.749	1.752	1.755	1.758	
1	1.761	1.764	1.766	1.769	1.772	1.775	1.778	1.780	1.783	1.786	
2	1.789	1.792	1.794	1.797	1.800	1.803	1.806	1.808	1.811	1.814	
3	1.817	1.819	1.822	1.825	1.828	1.830	1.833	1.836	1.838	1.841	
4	1.844	1.847	1.849	1.852	1.855	1.857	1.860	1.863	1.865	1.868	
3.5	1.871	1.873	1.876	1.879	1.881	1.884	1.887	1.889	1.892	1.895	
6	1.897	1.900	1.903	1.905	1.908	1.910	1.913	1.916	1.918	1.921	
7	1.924	1.926	1.929	1.931	1.934	1.936	1.939	1.942	1.944	1.947	
8	1.949	1.952	1.954	1.957	1.960	1.962	1.965	1.967	1.970	1.972	
9	1.975	1.977	1.980	1.982	1.985	1.987	1.990	1.992	1.995	1.997	
4.0	2.000	2.002	2.005	2.007	2.010	2.012	2.015	2.017	2.020	2.022	
1	2.025	2.027	2.030	2.032	2.035	2.037	2.040	2.042	2.045	2.047	2
2	2.049	2.052	2.054	2.057	2.059	2.062	2.064	2.066	2.069	2.071	
3	2.074	2.076	2.078	2.081	2.083	2.086	2.088	2.090	2.093	2.095	
4	2.098	2.100	2.102	2.105	2.107	2.110	2.112	2.114	2.117	2.119	
4.5	2.121	2.124	2.126	2.128	2.131	2.133	2.135	2.138	2.140	2.142	
6	2.145	2.147	2.149	2.152	2.154	2.156	2.159	2.161	2.163	2.166	
7	2.168	2.170	2.173	2.175	2.177	2.179	2.182	2.184	2.186	2.189	
8	2.191	2.193	2.195	2.198	2.200	2.202	2.205	2.207	2.209	2.211	
9	2.214	2.216	2.218	2.220	2.223	2.225	2.227	2.229	2.232	2.234	

$$\sqrt{\pi} = 1.77245 + \qquad 1/\sqrt{\pi} = 0.56419 \qquad \sqrt{\pi/2} = 1.25331 \qquad \sqrt{e} = 1.64872$$

Explanation of Table of Square Roots (pp. 1-14 to 1-17).

This table gives the values of $\sqrt{N}$ for values of N from 1 to 100, correct to four figures. (Interpolated values may be in error by 1 in the fourth figure.)

To find the square root of a number N outside the range from 1 to 100, divide the digits of the number into blocks of two (beginning with the decimal point), and note that moving the decimal point TWO places in N is equivalent to moving it ONE place in the square root of N. For example:

$$\sqrt{2.718} = 1.648 \qquad \sqrt{271.8} = 16.48 \qquad \sqrt{0.0002718} = 0.01648$$

$$\sqrt{27.18} = 5.213 \qquad \sqrt{2718} = 52.13 \qquad \sqrt{0.002718} = 0.05213$$

Square Roots (*continued*)

N	0	1	2	3	4	5	6	7	8	9	Avg diff
5.0	2.236	2.238	2.241	2.243	2.245	2.247	2.249	2.252	2.254	2.256	2
1	2.258	2.261	2.263	2.265	2.267	2.269	2.272	2.274	2.276	2.278	
2	2.280	2.283	2.285	2.287	2.289	2.291	2.293	2.296	2.298	2.300	
3	2.302	2.304	2.307	2.309	2.311	2.313	2.315	2.317	2.319	2.322	
4	2.324	2.326	2.328	2.330	2.332	2.335	2.337	2.339	2.341	2.343	
5.5	2.345	2.347	2.349	2.352	2.354	2.356	2.358	2.360	2.362	2.364	
6	2.366	2.369	2.371	2.373	2.375	2.377	2.379	2.381	2.383	2.385	
7	2.387	2.390	2.392	2.394	2.396	2.398	2.400	2.402	2.404	2.406	
8	2.408	2.410	2.412	2.415	2.417	2.419	2.421	2.423	2.425	2.427	
9	2.429	2.431	2.433	2.435	2.437	2.439	2.441	2.443	2.445	2.447	
6.0	2.449	2.452	2.454	2.456	2.458	2.460	2.462	2.464	2.466	2.468	
1	2.470	2.472	2.474	2.476	2.478	2.480	2.482	2.484	2.486	2.488	
2	2.490	2.492	2.494	2.496	2.498	2.500	2.502	2.504	2.506	2.508	
3	2.510	2.512	2.514	2.516	2.518	2.520	2.522	2.524	2.526	2.528	
4	2.530	2.532	2.534	2.536	2.538	2.540	2.542	2.544	2.546	2.548	
6.5	2.550	2.551	2.553	2.555	2.557	2.559	2.561	2.563	2.565	2.567	
6	2.569	2.571	2.573	2.575	2.577	2.579	2.581	2.583	2.585	2.587	
7	2.588	2.590	2.592	2.594	2.596	2.598	2.600	2.602	2.604	2.606	
8	2.608	2.610	2.612	2.613	2.615	2.617	2.619	2.621	2.623	2.625	
9	2.627	2.629	2.631	2.632	2.634	2.636	2.638	2.640	2.642	2.644	
7.0	2.646	2.648	2.650	2.651	2.653	2.655	2.657	2.659	2.661	2.663	
1	2.665	2.666	2.668	2.670	2.672	2.674	2.676	2.678	2.680	2.681	
2	2.683	2.685	2.687	2.689	2.691	2.693	2.694	2.696	2.698	2.700	
3	2.702	2.704	2.706	2.707	2.709	2.711	2.713	2.715	2.717	2.718	
4	2.720	2.722	2.724	2.726	2.728	2.729	2.731	2.733	2.735	2.737	
7.5	2.739	2.740	2.742	2.744	2.746	2.748	2.750	2.751	2.753	2.755	
6	2.757	2.759	2.760	2.762	2.764	2.766	2.768	2.769	2.771	2.773	
7	2.775	2.777	2.778	2.780	2.782	2.784	2.786	2.787	2.789	2.791	
8	2.793	2.795	2.796	2.798	2.800	2.802	2.804	2.805	2.807	2.809	
9	2.811	2.812	2.814	2.816	2.818	2.820	2.821	2.823	2.825	2.827	
8.0	2.828	2.830	2.832	2.834	2.835	2.837	2.839	2.841	2.843	2.844	
1	2.846	2.848	2.850	2.851	2.853	2.855	2.857	2.858	2.860	2.862	
2	2.864	2.865	2.867	2.869	2.871	2.872	2.874	2.876	2.877	2.879	
3	2.881	2.883	2.884	2.886	2.888	2.890	2.891	2.893	2.895	2.897	
4	2.898	2.900	2.902	2.903	2.905	2.907	2.909	2.910	2.912	2.914	
8.5	2.915	2.917	2.919	2.921	2.922	2.924	2.926	2.927	2.929	2.931	
6	2.933	2.934	2.936	2.938	2.939	2.941	2.943	2.944	2.946	2.948	
7	2.950	2.951	2.953	2.955	2.956	2.958	2.960	2.961	2.963	2.965	
8	2.966	2.968	2.970	2.972	2.973	2.975	2.977	2.978	2.980	2.982	
9	2.983	2.985	2.987	2.988	2.990	2.992	2.993	2.995	2.997	2.998	
9.0	3.000	3.002	3.003	3.005	3.007	3.008	3.010	3.012	3.013	3.015	
1	3.017	3.018	3.020	3.022	3.023	3.025	3.027	3.028	3.030	3.032	
2	3.033	3.035	3.036	3.038	3.040	3.041	3.043	3.045	3.046	3.048	
3	3.050	3.051	3.053	3.055	3.056	3.058	3.059	3.061	3.063	3.064	
4	3.066	3.068	3.069	3.071	3.072	3.074	3.076	3.077	3.079	3.081	
9.5	3.082	3.084	3.085	3.087	3.089	3.090	3.092	3.094	3.095	3.097	
6	3.098	3.100	3.102	3.103	3.105	3.106	3.108	3.110	3.111	3.113	
7	3.114	3.116	3.118	3.119	3.121	3.122	3.124	3.126	3.127	3.129	
8	3.130	3.132	3.134	3.135	3.137	3.138	3.140	3.142	3.143	3.145	
9	3.146	3.148	3.150	3.151	3.153	3.154	3.156	3.158	3.159	3.161	

Moving the decimal point TWO places in *N* requires moving it ONE place in body of table (see p. 1–14).

MATHEMATICS

Square Roots (continued)

N	0	1	2	3	4	5	6	7	8	9	Avg diff
10.	3.162	3.178	3.194	3.209	3.225	3.240	3.256	3.271	3.286	3.302	16
1.	3.317	3.332	3.347	3.362	3.376	3.391	3.406	3.421	3.435	3.450	15
2.	3.464	3.479	3.493	3.507	3.521	3.536	3.550	3.564	3.578	3.592	14
3.	3.606	3.619	3.633	3.647	3.661	3.674	3.688	3.701	3.715	3.728	
4.	3.742	3.755	3.768	3.782	3.795	3.808	3.821	3.834	3.847	3.860	13
15.	3.873	3.886	3.899	3.912	3.924	3.937	3.950	3.962	3.975	3.987	
6.	4.000	4.012	4.025	4.037	4.050	4.062	4.074	4.087	4.099	4.111	12
7.	4.123	4.135	4.147	4.159	4.171	4.183	4.195	4.207	4.219	4.231	
8.	4.243	4.254	4.266	4.278	4.290	4.301	4.313	4.324	4.336	4.347	
9.	4.359	4.370	4.382	4.393	4.405	4.416	4.427	4.438	4.450	4.461	11
20.	4.472	4.483	4.494	4.506	4.517	4.528	4.539	4.550	4.561	4.572	
1.	4.583	4.593	4.604	4.615	4.626	4.637	4.648	4.658	4.669	4.680	
2.	4.690	4.701	4.712	4.722	4.733	4.743	4.754	4.764	4.775	4.785	
3.	4.796	4.806	4.817	4.827	4.837	4.848	4.858	4.868	4.879	4.889	10
4.	4.899	4.909	4.919	4.930	4.940	4.950	4.960	4.970	4.980	4.990	
25.	5.000	5.010	5.020	5.030	5.040	5.050	5.060	5.070	5.079	5.089	
6.	5.099	5.109	5.119	5.128	5.138	5.148	5.158	5.167	5.177	5.187	
7.	5.196	5.206	5.215	5.225	5.235	5.244	5.254	5.263	5.273	5.282	
8.	5.292	5.301	5.310	5.320	5.329	5.339	5.348	5.357	5.367	5.376	9
9.	5.385	5.394	5.404	5.413	5.422	5.431	5.441	5.450	5.459	5.468	
30.	5.477	5.486	5.495	5.505	5.514	5.523	5.532	5.541	5.550	5.559	
1.	5.568	5.577	5.586	5.595	5.604	5.612	5.621	5.630	5.639	5.648	
2.	5.657	5.666	5.675	5.683	5.692	5.701	5.710	5.718	5.727	5.736	
3.	5.745	5.753	5.762	5.771	5.779	5.788	5.797	5.805	5.814	5.822	
4.	5.831	5.840	5.848	5.857	5.865	5.874	5.882	5.891	5.899	5.908	8
35.	5.916	5.925	5.933	5.941	5.950	5.958	5.967	5.975	5.983	5.992	
6.	6.000	6.008	6.017	6.025	6.033	6.042	6.050	6.058	6.066	6.075	
7.	6.083	6.091	6.099	6.107	6.116	6.124	6.132	6.140	6.148	6.156	
8.	6.164	6.173	6.181	6.189	6.197	6.205	6.213	6.221	6.229	6.237	
9.	6.245	6.253	6.261	6.269	6.277	6.285	6.293	6.301	6.309	6.317	
40.	6.325	6.332	6.340	6.348	6.356	6.364	6.372	6.380	6.387	6.395	
1.	6.403	6.411	6.419	6.427	6.434	6.442	6.450	6.458	6.465	6.473	
2.	6.481	6.488	6.496	6.504	6.512	6.519	6.527	6.535	6.542	6.550	
3.	6.557	6.565	6.573	6.580	6.588	6.595	6.603	6.611	6.618	6.626	
4.	6.633	6.641	6.648	6.656	6.663	6.671	6.678	6.686	6.693	6.701	
45.	6.708	6.716	6.723	6.731	6.738	6.745	6.753	6.760	6.768	6.775	7
6.	6.782	6.790	6.797	6.804	6.812	6.819	6.826	6.834	6.841	6.848	
7.	6.856	6.863	6.870	6.877	6.885	6.892	6.899	6.907	6.914	6.921	
8.	6.928	6.935	6.943	6.950	6.957	6.964	6.971	6.979	6.986	6.993	
9.	7.000	7.007	7.014	7.021	7.029	7.036	7.043	7.050	7.057	7.064	

Square Roots of Certain Fractions

N	$\sqrt{N}$	N	$\sqrt{N}$	N	$\sqrt{N}$	N	$\sqrt{N}$	N	$\sqrt{N}$	N	$\sqrt{N}$
$\frac{1}{2}$	0.7071	$\frac{3}{5}$	0.7746	$\frac{4}{7}$	0.7559	$\frac{1}{9}$	0.3333	$\frac{5}{12}$	0.6455	$\frac{9}{16}$	0.7500
$\frac{1}{3}$	0.5774	$\frac{4}{5}$	0.8944	$\frac{5}{7}$	0.8452	$\frac{2}{9}$	0.4714	$\frac{7}{12}$	0.7638	$\frac{11}{16}$	0.8292
$\frac{2}{3}$	0.8165	$\frac{1}{6}$	0.4082	$\frac{6}{7}$	0.9258	$\frac{4}{9}$	0.6667	$\frac{11}{12}$	0.9574	$\frac{13}{16}$	0.9014
$\frac{1}{4}$	0.5000	$\frac{5}{6}$	0.9129	$\frac{1}{8}$	0.3536	$\frac{5}{9}$	0.7454	$\frac{1}{16}$	0.2500	$\frac{15}{16}$	0.9682
$\frac{3}{4}$	0.8660	$\frac{1}{7}$	0.3780	$\frac{3}{8}$	0.6124	$\frac{7}{9}$	0.8819	$\frac{3}{16}$	0.4330	$\frac{1}{32}$	0.1768
$\frac{1}{5}$	0.4472	$\frac{2}{7}$	0.5345	$\frac{5}{8}$	0.7906	$\frac{8}{9}$	0.9428	$\frac{5}{16}$	0.5590	$\frac{1}{64}$	0.1250
$\frac{2}{5}$	0.6325	$\frac{3}{7}$	0.6547	$\frac{7}{8}$	0.9354	$\frac{1}{12}$	0.2887	$\frac{7}{16}$	0.6614	$\frac{1}{50}$	0.1414

Square Roots (*continued*)

N	0	1	2	3	4	5	6	7	8	9	Avg diff
50.	7.071	7.078	7.085	7.092	7.099	7.106	7.113	7.120	7.127	7.134	7
1.	7.141	7.148	7.155	7.162	7.169	7.176	7.183	7.190	7.197	7.204	
2.	7.211	7.218	7.225	7.232	7.239	7.246	7.253	7.259	7.266	7.273	
3.	7.280	7.287	7.294	7.301	7.308	7.314	7.321	7.328	7.335	7.342	
4.	7.348	7.355	7.362	7.369	7.376	7.382	7.389	7.396	7.403	7.409	
55.	7.416	7.423	7.430	7.436	7.443	7.450	7.457	7.463	7.470	7.477	
6.	7.483	7.490	7.497	7.503	7.510	7.517	7.523	7.530	7.537	7.543	
7.	7.550	7.556	7.563	7.570	7.576	7.583	7.589	7.596	7.603	7.609	
8.	7.616	7.622	7.629	7.635	7.642	7.649	7.655	7.662	7.668	7.675	
9.	7.681	7.688	7.694	7.701	7.707	7.714	7.720	7.727	7.733	7.740	6
60.	7.746	7.752	7.759	7.765	7.772	7.778	7.785	7.791	7.797	7.804	
1.	7.810	7.817	7.823	7.829	7.836	7.842	7.849	7.855	7.861	7.868	
2.	7.874	7.880	7.887	7.893	7.899	7.906	7.912	7.918	7.925	7.931	
3.	7.937	7.944	7.950	7.956	7.962	7.969	7.975	7.981	7.987	7.994	
4.	8.000	8.006	8.012	8.019	8.025	8.031	8.037	8.044	8.050	8.056	
65.	8.062	8.068	8.075	8.081	8.087	8.093	8.099	8.106	8.112	8.118	
6.	8.124	8.130	8.136	8.142	8.149	8.155	8.161	8.167	8.173	8.179	
7.	8.185	8.191	8.198	8.204	8.210	8.216	8.222	8.228	8.234	8.240	
8.	8.246	8.252	8.258	8.264	8.270	8.276	8.283	8.289	8.295	8.301	
9.	8.307	8.313	8.319	8.325	8.331	8.337	8.343	8.349	8.355	8.361	
70.	8.367	8.373	8.379	8.385	8.390	8.396	8.402	8.408	8.414	8.420	
1.	8.426	8.432	8.438	8.444	8.450	8.456	8.462	8.468	8.473	8.479	
2.	8.485	8.491	8.497	8.503	8.509	8.515	8.521	8.526	8.532	8.538	
3.	8.544	8.550	8.556	8.562	8.567	8.573	8.579	8.585	8.591	8.597	
4.	8.602	8.608	8.614	8.620	8.626	8.631	8.637	8.643	8.649	8.654	
75.	8.660	8.666	8.672	8.678	8.683	8.689	8.695	8.701	8.706	8.712	
6.	8.718	8.724	8.729	8.735	8.741	8.746	8.752	8.758	8.764	8.769	
7.	8.775	8.781	8.786	8.792	8.798	8.803	8.809	8.815	8.820	8.826	
8.	8.832	8.837	8.843	8.849	8.854	8.860	8.866	8.871	8.877	8.883	
9.	8.888	8.894	8.899	8.905	8.911	8.916	8.922	8.927	8.933	8.939	
80.	8.944	8.950	8.955	8.961	8.967	8.972	8.978	8.983	8.989	8.994	
1.	9.000	9.006	9.011	9.017	9.022	9.028	9.033	9.039	9.044	9.050	
2.	9.055	9.061	9.066	9.072	9.077	9.083	9.088	9.094	9.099	9.105	5
3.	9.110	9.116	9.121	9.127	9.132	9.138	9.143	9.149	9.154	9.160	
4.	9.165	9.171	9.176	9.182	9.187	9.192	9.198	9.203	9.209	9.214	
85.	9.220	9.225	9.230	9.236	9.241	9.247	9.252	9.257	9.263	9.268	
6.	9.274	9.279	9.284	9.290	9.295	9.301	9.306	9.311	9.317	9.322	
7.	9.327	9.333	9.338	9.343	9.349	9.354	9.359	9.365	9.370	9.375	
8.	9.381	9.386	9.391	9.397	9.402	9.407	9.413	9.418	9.423	9.429	
9.	9.434	9.439	9.445	9.450	9.455	9.460	9.466	9.471	9.476	9.482	
90.	9.487	9.492	9.497	9.503	9.508	9.513	9.518	9.524	9.529	9.534	
1.	9.539	9.545	9.550	9.555	9.560	9.566	9.571	9.576	9.581	9.586	
2.	9.592	9.597	9.602	9.607	9.612	9.618	9.623	9.628	9.633	9.638	
3.	9.644	9.649	9.654	9.659	9.664	9.670	9.675	9.680	9.685	9.690	
4.	9.695	9.701	9.706	9.711	9.716	9.721	9.726	9.731	9.737	9.742	
95.	9.747	9.752	9.757	9.762	9.767	9.772	9.778	9.783	9.788	9.793	
6.	9.798	9.803	9.808	9.813	9.818	9.823	9.829	9.834	9.839	9.844	
7.	9.849	9.854	9.859	9.864	9.869	9.874	9.879	9.884	9.889	9.894	
8.	9.899	9.905	9.910	9.915	9.920	9.925	9.930	9.935	9.940	9.945	
9.	9.950	9.955	9.960	9.965	9.970	9.975	9.980	9.985	9.990	9.995	

$\sqrt{\pi} = 1.77245+$ $1/\sqrt{\pi} = 0.56419$ $\sqrt{\pi/2} = 1.25331$ $\sqrt{e} = 1.64872$

Moving the decimal point TWO places in N requires moving it ONE place in body of table (see p. 1–14).

MATHEMATICS

Cube Roots of Numbers

N	0	1	2	3	4	5	6	7	8	9	Avg diff
1.0	1.000	1.003	1.007	1.010	1.013	1.016	1.020	1.023	1.026	1.029	3
1	1.032	1.035	1.038	1.042	1.045	1.048	1.051	1.054	1.057	1.060	
2	1.063	1.066	1.069	1.071	1.074	1.077	1.080	1.083	1.086	1.089	
3	1.091	1.094	1.097	1.100	1.102	1.105	1.108	1.111	1.113	1.116	
4	1.119	1.121	1.124	1.127	1.129	1.132	1.134	1.137	1.140	1.142	
1.5	1.145	1.147	1.150	1.152	1.155	1.157	1.160	1.162	1.165	1.167	2
6	1.170	1.172	1.174	1.177	1.179	1.182	1.184	1.186	1.189	1.191	
7	1.193	1.196	1.198	1.200	1.203	1.205	1.207	1.210	1.212	1.214	
8	1.216	1.219	1.221	1.223	1.225	1.228	1.230	1.232	1.234	1.236	
9	1.239	1.241	1.243	1.245	1.247	1.249	1.251	1.254	1.256	1.258	
2.0	1.260	1.262	1.264	1.266	1.268	1.270	1.272	1.274	1.277	1.279	
1	1.281	1.283	1.285	1.287	1.289	1.291	1.293	1.295	1.297	1.299	
2	1.301	1.303	1.305	1.306	1.308	1.310	1.312	1.314	1.316	1.318	
3	1.320	1.322	1.324	1.326	1.328	1.330	1.331	1.333	1.335	1.337	
4	1.339	1.341	1.343	1.344	1.346	1.348	1.350	1.352	1.354	1.355	
2.5	1.357	1.359	1.361	1.363	1.364	1.366	1.368	1.370	1.372	1.373	
6	1.375	1.377	1.379	1.380	1.382	1.384	1.386	1.387	1.389	1.391	
7	1.392	1.394	1.396	1.398	1.399	1.401	1.403	1.404	1.406	1.408	
8	1.409	1.411	1.413	1.414	1.416	1.418	1.419	1.421	1.423	1.424	
9	1.426	1.428	1.429	1.431	1.433	1.434	1.436	1.437	1.439	1.441	
3.0	1.442	1.444	1.445	1.447	1.449	1.450	1.452	1.453	1.455	1.457	
1	1.458	1.460	1.461	1.463	1.464	1.466	1.467	1.469	1.471	1.472	
2	1.474	1.475	1.477	1.478	1.480	1.481	1.483	1.484	1.486	1.487	
3	1.489	1.490	1.492	1.493	1.495	1.496	1.498	1.499	1.501	1.502	
4	1.504	1.505	1.507	1.508	1.510	1.511	1.512	1.514	1.515	1.517	
3.5	1.518	1.520	1.521	1.523	1.524	1.525	1.527	1.528	1.530	1.531	1
6	1.533	1.534	1.535	1.537	1.538	1.540	1.541	1.542	1.544	1.545	
7	1.547	1.548	1.549	1.551	1.552	1.554	1.555	1.556	1.558	1.559	
8	1.560	1.562	1.563	1.565	1.566	1.567	1.569	1.570	1.571	1.573	
9	1.574	1.575	1.577	1.578	1.579	1.581	1.582	1.583	1.585	1.586	
4.0	1.587	1.589	1.590	1.591	1.593	1.594	1.595	1.597	1.598	1.599	
1	1.601	1.602	1.603	1.604	1.606	1.607	1.608	1.610	1.611	1.612	
2	1.613	1.615	1.616	1.617	1.619	1.620	1.621	1.622	1.624	1.625	
3	1.626	1.627	1.629	1.630	1.631	1.632	1.634	1.635	1.636	1.637	
4	1.639	1.640	1.641	1.642	1.644	1.645	1.646	1.647	1.649	1.650	
4.5	1.651	1.652	1.653	1.655	1.656	1.657	1.658	1.659	1.661	1.662	
6	1.663	1.664	1.666	1.667	1.668	1.669	1.670	1.671	1.673	1.674	
7	1.675	1.676	1.677	1.679	1.680	1.681	1.682	1.683	1.685	1.686	
8	1.687	1.688	1.689	1.690	1.692	1.693	1.694	1.695	1.696	1.697	
9	1.698	1.700	1.701	1.702	1.703	1.704	1.705	1.707	1.708	1.709	

$$\sqrt[3]{\pi} = 1.46459 \qquad 1/\sqrt[3]{\pi} = 0.682784$$

Explanation of Table of Cube Roots (pp. 1–18 to 1–23).

This table gives the values of $\sqrt[3]{N}$ for all values of N from 1 to 1000, correct to four figures. (Interpolated values may be in error by 1 in the fourth figure.)

To find the cube root of a number N outside the range from 1 to 1000, divide the digits of the number into blocks of three (beginning with the decimal point), and note that moving the decimal point THREE places in column N is equivalent to moving it ONE place in the cube root of N. For example:

$$\sqrt[3]{2.718} = 1.396 \qquad \sqrt[3]{2718} = 13.96 \qquad \sqrt[3]{0.000002718} = 0.01396$$
$$\sqrt[3]{27.18} = 3.007 \qquad \sqrt[3]{27180} = 30.07 \qquad \sqrt[3]{0.00002718} = 0.03007$$
$$\sqrt[3]{271.8} = 6.477 \qquad \sqrt[3]{271800} = 64.77 \qquad \sqrt[3]{0.0002718} = 0.06477$$

Cube Roots (*continued*)

N	0	1	2	3	4	5	6	7	8	9	Avg diff
5.0	1.710	1.711	1.712	1.713	1.715	1.716	1.717	1.718	1.719	1.720	1
1	1.721	1.722	1.724	1.725	1.726	1.727	1.728	1.729	1.730	1.731	
2	1.732	1.734	1.735	1.736	1.737	1.738	1.739	1.740	1.741	1.742	
3	1.744	1.745	1.746	1.747	1.748	1.749	1.750	1.751	1.752	1.753	
4	1.754	1.755	1.757	1.758	1.759	1.760	1.761	1.762	1.763	1.764	
5.5	1.765	1.766	1.767	1.768	1.769	1.771	1.772	1.773	1.774	1.775	
6	1.776	1.777	1.778	1.779	1.780	1.781	1.782	1.783	1.784	1.785	
7	1.786	1.787	1.788	1.789	1.790	1.792	1.793	1.794	1.795	1.796	
8	1.797	1.798	1.799	1.800	1.801	1.802	1.803	1.804	1.805	1.806	
9	1.807	1.808	1.809	1.810	1.811	1.812	1.813	1.814	1.815	1.816	
6.0	1.817	1.818	1.819	1.820	1.821	1.822	1.823	1.824	1.825	1.826	
1	1.827	1.828	1.829	1.830	1.831	1.832	1.833	1.834	1.835	1.836	
2	1.837	1.838	1.839	1.840	1.841	1.842	1.843	1.844	1.845	1.846	
3	1.847	1.848	1.849	1.850	1.851	1.852	1.853	1.854	1.855	1.856	
4	1.857	1.858	1.859	1.860	1.860	1.861	1.862	1.863	1.864	1.865	
6.5	1.866	1.867	1.868	1.869	1.870	1.871	1.872	1.873	1.874	1.875	
6	1.876	1.877	1.878	1.879	1.880	1.881	1.881	1.882	1.883	1.884	
7	1.885	1.886	1.887	1.888	1.889	1.890	1.891	1.892	1.893	1.894	
8	1.895	1.895	1.896	1.897	1.898	1.899	1.900	1.901	1.902	1.903	
9	1.904	1.905	1.906	1.907	1.907	1.908	1.909	1.910	1.911	1.912	
7.0	1.913	1.914	1.915	1.916	1.917	1.917	1.918	1.919	1.920	1.921	
1	1.922	1.923	1.924	1.925	1.926	1.926	1.927	1.928	1.929	1.930	
2	1.931	1.932	1.933	1.934	1.935	1.935	1.936	1.937	1.938	1.939	
3	1.940	1.941	1.942	1.943	1.943	1.944	1.945	1.946	1.947	1.948	
4	1.949	1.950	1.950	1.951	1.952	1.953	1.954	1.955	1.956	1.957	
7.5	1.957	1.958	1.959	1.960	1.961	1.962	1.963	1.964	1.964	1.965	
6	1.966	1.967	1.968	1.969	1.970	1.970	1.971	1.972	1.973	1.974	
7	1.975	1.976	1.976	1.977	1.978	1.979	1.980	1.981	1.981	1.982	
8	1.983	1.984	1.985	1.986	1.987	1.987	1.988	1.989	1.990	1.991	
9	1.992	1.992	1.993	1.994	1.995	1.996	1.997	1.997	1.998	1.999	
8.0	2.000	2.001	2.002	2.002	2.003	2.004	2.005	2.006	2.007	2.007	
1	2.008	2.009	2.010	2.011	2.012	2.012	2.013	2.014	2.015	2.016	
2	2.017	2.017	2.018	2.019	2.020	2.021	2.021	2.022	2.023	2.024	
3	2.025	2.026	2.026	2.027	2.028	2.029	2.030	2.030	2.031	2.032	
4	2.033	2.034	2.034	2.035	2.036	2.037	2.038	2.038	2.039	2.040	
8.5	2.041	2.042	2.042	2.043	2.044	2.045	2.046	2.046	2.047	2.048	
6	2.049	2.050	2.050	2.051	2.052	2.053	2.054	2.054	2.055	2.056	
7	2.057	2.057	2.058	2.059	2.060	2.061	2.061	2.062	2.063	2.064	
8	2.065	2.065	2.066	2.067	2.068	2.068	2.069	2.070	2.071	2.072	
9	2.072	2.073	2.074	2.075	2.075	2.076	2.077	2.078	2.079	2.079	
9.0	2.080	2.081	2.082	2.082	2.083	2.084	2.085	2.085	2.086	2.087	
1	2.088	2.089	2.089	2.090	2.091	2.092	2.092	2.093	2.094	2.095	
2	2.095	2.096	2.097	2.098	2.098	2.099	2.100	2.101	2.101	2.102	
3	2.103	2.104	2.104	2.105	2.106	2.107	2.107	2.108	2.109	2.110	
4	2.110	2.111	2.112	2.113	2.113	2.114	2.115	2.116	2.116	2.117	
9.5	2.118	2.119	2.119	2.120	2.121	2.122	2.122	2.123	2.124	2.125	
6	2.125	2.126	2.127	2.128	2.128	2.129	2.130	2.130	2.131	2.132	
7	2.133	2.133	2.134	2.135	2.136	2.136	2.137	2.138	2.139	2.139	
8	2.140	2.141	2.141	2.142	2.143	2.144	2.144	2.145	2.146	2.147	
9	2.147	2.148	2.149	2.149	2.150	2.151	2.152	2.152	2.153	2.154	

Moving the decimal point THREE places in N requires moving it ONE place in body of table (see p. 1–18).

Cube Roots (continued)

N	0	1	2	3	4	5	6	7	8	9	Avg diff
10.	2.154	2.162	2.169	2.176	2.183	2.190	2.197	2.204	2.210	2.217	7
1.	2.224	2.231	2.237	2.244	2.251	2.257	2.264	2.270	2.277	2.283	6
2.	2.289	2.296	2.302	2.308	2.315	2.321	2.327	2.333	2.339	2.345	
3.	2.351	2.357	2.363	2.369	2.375	2.381	2.387	2.393	2.399	2.404	
4.	2.410	2.416	2.422	2.427	2.433	2.438	2.444	2.450	2.455	2.461	
15.	2.466	2.472	2.477	2.483	2.488	2.493	2.499	2.504	2.509	2.515	5
6.	2.520	2.525	2.530	2.535	2.541	2.546	2.551	2.556	2.561	2.566	
7.	2.571	2.576	2.581	2.586	2.591	2.596	2.601	2.606	2.611	2.616	
8.	2.621	2.626	2.630	2.635	2.640	2.645	2.650	2.654	2.659	2.664	
9.	2.668	2.673	2.678	2.682	2.687	2.692	2.696	2.701	2.705	2.710	
20.	2.714	2.719	2.723	2.728	2.732	2.737	2.741	2.746	2.750	2.755	4
1.	2.759	2.763	2.768	2.772	2.776	2.781	2.785	2.789	2.794	2.798	
2.	2.802	2.806	2.811	2.815	2.819	2.823	2.827	2.831	2.836	2.840	
3.	2.844	2.848	2.852	2.856	2.860	2.864	2.868	2.872	2.876	2.880	
4.	2.884	2.888	2.892	2.896	2.900	2.904	2.908	2.912	2.916	2.920	
25.	2.924	2.928	2.932	2.936	2.940	2.943	2.947	2.951	2.955	2.959	
6.	2.962	2.966	2.970	2.974	2.978	2.981	2.985	2.989	2.993	2.996	
7.	3.000	3.004	3.007	3.011	3.015	3.018	3.022	3.026	3.029	3.033	
8.	3.037	3.040	3.044	3.047	3.051	3.055	3.058	3.062	3.065	3.069	
9.	3.072	3.076	3.079	3.083	3.086	3.090	3.093	3.097	3.100	3.104	
30.	3.107	3.111	3.114	3.118	3.121	3.124	3.128	3.131	3.135	3.138	3
1.	3.141	3.145	3.148	3.151	3.155	3.158	3.162	3.165	3.168	3.171	
2.	3.175	3.178	3.181	3.185	3.188	3.191	3.195	3.198	3.201	3.204	
3.	3.208	3.211	3.214	3.217	3.220	3.224	3.227	3.230	3.233	3.236	
4.	3.240	3.243	3.246	3.249	3.252	3.255	3.259	3.262	3.265	3.268	
35.	3.271	3.274	3.277	3.280	3.283	3.287	3.290	3.293	3.296	3.299	
6.	3.302	3.305	3.308	3.311	3.314	3.317	3.320	3.323	3.326	3.329	
7.	3.332	3.335	3.338	3.341	3.344	3.347	3.350	3.353	3.356	3.359	
8.	3.362	3.365	3.368	3.371	3.374	3.377	3.380	3.382	3.385	3.388	
9.	3.391	3.394	3.397	3.400	3.403	3.406	3.409	3.411	3.414	3.417	
40.	3.420	3.423	3.426	3.428	3.431	3.434	3.437	3.440	3.443	3.445	
1.	3.448	3.451	3.454	3.457	3.459	3.462	3.465	3.468	3.471	3.473	
2.	3.476	3.479	3.482	3.484	3.487	3.490	3.493	3.495	3.498	3.501	
3.	3.503	3.506	3.509	3.512	3.514	3.517	3.520	3.522	3.525	3.528	
4.	3.530	3.533	3.536	3.538	3.541	3.544	3.546	3.549	3.552	3.554	
45.	3.557	3.560	3.562	3.565	3.567	3.570	3.573	3.575	3.578	3.580	
6.	3.583	3.586	3.588	3.591	3.593	3.596	3.599	3.601	3.604	3.606	
7.	3.609	3.611	3.614	3.616	3.619	3.622	3.624	3.627	3.629	3.632	
8.	3.634	3.637	3.639	3.642	3.644	3.647	3.649	3.652	3.654	3.657	2
9.	3.659	3.662	3.664	3.667	3.669	3.672	3.674	3.677	3.679	3.682	

Cube Roots of Certain Fractions

N	$\sqrt[3]{N}$	N	$\sqrt[3]{N}$	N	$\sqrt[3]{N}$	N	$\sqrt[3]{N}$	N	$\sqrt[3]{N}$	N	$\sqrt[3]{N}$
1/2	.7937	3/5	.8434	4/7	.8298	1/9	.4807	5/12	.7469	9/16	.8255
1/3	.6934	4/5	.9283	5/7	.8939	2/9	.6057	7/12	.8355	11/16	.8826
2/3	.8736	1/6	.5503	6/7	.9499	4/9	.7631	11/12	.9714	13/16	.9331
1/4	.6300	5/6	.9410	1/8	.5000	5/9	.8221	1/16	.3969	15/16	.9787
3/4	.9086	1/7	.5228	3/8	.7211	7/9	.9196	3/16	.5724	1/32	.3150
1/5	.5848	2/7	.6586	5/8	.8550	8/9	.9615	5/16	.6786	1/64	.2500
2/5	.7368	3/7	.7539	7/8	.9565	1/12	.4368	7/16	.7591	1/60	.2714

Cube Roots (*continued*)

N	0	1	2	3	4	5	6	7	8	9	Avg diff
50.	3.684	3.686	3.689	3.691	3.694	3.696	3.699	3.701	3.704	3.706	2
1.	3.708	3.711	3.713	3.716	3.718	3.721	3.723	3.725	3.728	3.730	
2.	3.733	3.735	3.737	3.740	3.742	3.744	3.747	3.749	3.752	3.754	
3.	3.756	3.759	3.761	3.763	3.766	3.768	3.770	3.773	3.775	3.777	
4.	3.780	3.782	3.784	3.787	3.789	3.791	3.794	3.796	3.798	3.801	
55.	3.803	3.805	3.808	3.810	3.812	3.814	3.817	3.819	3.821	3.824	
6.	3.826	3.828	3.830	3.833	3.835	3.837	3.839	3.842	3.844	3.846	
7.	3.849	3.851	3.853	3.855	3.857	3.860	3.862	3.864	3.866	3.869	
8.	3.871	3.873	3.875	3.878	3.880	3.882	3.884	3.886	3.889	3.891	
9.	3.893	3.895	3.897	3.900	3.902	3.904	3.906	3.908	3.911	3.913	
60.	3.915	3.917	3.919	3.921	3.924	3.926	3.928	3.930	3.932	3.934	
1.	3.936	3.939	3.941	3.943	3.945	3.947	3.949	3.951	3.954	3.956	
2.	3.958	3.960	3.962	3.964	3.966	3.968	3.971	3.973	3.975	3.977	
3.	3.979	3.981	3.983	3.985	3.987	3.990	3.992	3.994	3.996	3.998	
4.	4.000	4.002	4.004	4.006	4.008	4.010	4.012	4.015	4.017	4.019	
65.	4.021	4.023	4.025	4.027	4.029	4.031	4.033	4.035	4.037	4.039	
6.	4.041	4.043	4.045	4.047	4.049	4.051	4.053	4.055	4.058	4.060	
7.	4.062	4.064	4.066	4.068	4.070	4.072	4.074	4.076	4.078	4.080	
8.	4.082	4.084	4.086	4.088	4.090	4.092	4.094	4.096	4.098	4.100	
9.	4.102	4.104	4.106	4.108	4.109	4.111	4.113	4.115	4.117	4.119	
70.	4.121	4.123	4.125	4.127	4.129	4.131	4.133	4.135	4.137	4.139	
1.	4.141	4.143	4.145	4.147	4.149	4.151	4.152	4.154	4.156	4.158	
2.	4.160	4.162	4.164	4.166	4.168	4.170	4.172	4.174	4.176	4.177	
3.	4.179	4.181	4.183	4.185	4.187	4.189	4.191	4.193	4.195	4.196	
4.	4.198	4.200	4.202	4.204	4.206	4.208	4.210	4.212	4.213	4.215	
75.	4.217	4.219	4.221	4.223	4.225	4.227	4.228	4.230	4.232	4.234	
6.	4.236	4.238	4.240	4.241	4.243	4.245	4.247	4.249	4.251	4.252	
7.	4.254	4.256	4.258	4.260	4.262	4.264	4.265	4.267	4.269	4.271	
8.	4.273	4.274	4.276	4.278	4.280	4.282	4.284	4.285	4.287	4.289	
9.	4.291	4.293	4.294	4.296	4.298	4.300	4.302	4.303	4.305	4.307	
80.	4.309	4.311	4.312	4.314	4.316	4.318	4.320	4.321	4.323	4.325	
1.	4.327	4.329	4.330	4.332	4.334	4.336	4.337	4.339	4.341	4.343	
2.	4.344	4.346	4.348	4.350	4.352	4.353	4.355	4.357	4.359	4.360	
3.	4.362	4.364	4.366	4.367	4.369	4.371	4.373	4.374	4.376	4.378	
4.	4.380	4.381	4.383	4.385	4.386	4.388	4.390	4.392	4.393	4.395	
85.	4.397	4.399	4.400	4.402	4.404	4.405	4.407	4.409	4.411	4.412	
6.	4.414	4.416	4.417	4.419	4.421	4.423	4.424	4.426	4.428	4.429	
7.	4.431	4.433	4.434	4.436	4.438	4.440	4.441	4.443	4.445	4.446	
8.	4.448	4.450	4.451	4.453	4.455	4.456	4.458	4.460	4.461	4.463	
9.	4.465	4.466	4.468	4.470	4.471	4.473	4.475	4.476	4.478	4.480	
90.	4.481	4.483	4.485	4.486	4.488	4.490	4.491	4.493	4.495	4.496	
1.	4.498	4.500	4.501	4.503	4.505	4.506	4.508	4.509	4.511	4.513	
2.	4.514	4.516	4.518	4.519	4.521	4.523	4.524	4.526	4.527	4.529	
3.	4.531	4.532	4.534	4.536	4.537	4.539	4.540	4.542	4.544	4.545	
4.	4.547	4.548	4.550	4.552	4.553	4.555	4.556	4.558	4.560	4.561	
95.	4.563	4.565	4.566	4.568	4.569	4.571	4.572	4.574	4.576	4.577	
6.	4.579	4.580	4.582	4.584	4.585	4.587	4.588	4.590	4.592	4.593	
7.	4.595	4.596	4.598	4.599	4.601	4.603	4.604	4.606	4.607	4.609	
8.	4.610	4.612	4.614	4.615	4.617	4.618	4.620	4.621	4.623	4.625	
9.	4.626	4.628	4.629	4.631	4.632	4.634	4.635	4.637	4.638	4.640	

Moving the decimal point THREE places in *N* requires moving it ONE place in body of table (see p. 1–18).

Cube Roots (*continued*)

Cube roots of numbers from 100. to 499.

N	0.	1.	2.	3.	4.	5.	6.	7.	8.	9.	Avg diff
10	4.642	4.657	4.672	4.688	4.703	4.718	4.733	4.747	4.762	4.777	15
1	4.791	4.806	4.820	4.835	4.849	4.863	4.877	4.891	4.905	4.919	14
2	4.932	4.946	4.960	4.973	4.987	5.000	5.013	5.027	5.040	5.053	13
3	5.066	5.079	5.092	5.104	5.117	5.130	5.143	5.155	5.168	5.180	
4	5.192	5.205	5.217	5.229	5.241	5.254	5.266	5.278	5.290	5.301	12
15	5.313	5.325	5.337	5.348	5.360	5.372	5.383	5.395	5.406	5.418	
6	5.429	5.440	5.451	5.463	5.474	5.485	5.496	5.507	5.518	5.529	11
7	5.540	5.550	5.561	5.572	5.583	5.593	5.604	5.615	5.625	5.636	
8	5.646	5.657	5.667	5.677	5.688	5.698	5.708	5.718	5.729	5.739	10
9	5.749	5.759	5.769	5.779	5.789	5.799	5.809	5.819	5.828	5.838	
20	5.848	5.858	5.867	5.877	5.887	5.896	5.906	5.915	5.925	5.934	
1	5.944	5.953	5.963	5.972	5.981	5.991	6.000	6.009	6.018	6.028	9
2	6.037	6.046	6.055	6.064	6.073	6.082	6.091	6.100	6.109	6.118	
3	6.127	6.136	6.145	6.153	6.162	6.171	6.180	6.188	6.197	6.206	
4	6.214	6.223	6.232	6.240	6.249	6.257	6.266	6.274	6.283	6.291	
25	6.300	6.308	6.316	6.325	6.333	6.341	6.350	6.358	6.366	6.374	8
6	6.383	6.391	6.399	6.407	6.415	6.423	6.431	6.439	6.447	6.455	
7	6.463	6.471	6.479	6.487	6.495	6.503	6.511	6.519	6.527	6.534	
8	6.542	6.550	6.558	6.565	6.573	6.581	6.589	6.596	6.604	6.611	
9	6.619	6.627	6.634	6.642	6.649	6.657	6.664	6.672	6.679	6.687	
30	6.694	6.702	6.709	6.717	6.724	6.731	6.739	6.746	6.753	6.761	7
1	6.768	6.775	6.782	6.790	6.797	6.804	6.811	6.818	6.826	6.833	
2	6.840	6.847	6.854	6.861	6.868	6.875	6.882	6.889	6.896	6.903	
3	6.910	6.917	6.924	6.931	6.938	6.945	6.952	6.959	6.966	6.973	
4	6.980	6.986	6.993	7.000	7.007	7.014	7.020	7.027	7.034	7.041	
35	7.047	7.054	7.061	7.067	7.074	7.081	7.087	7.094	7.101	7.107	
6	7.114	7.120	7.127	7.133	7.140	7.147	7.153	7.160	7.166	7.173	6
7	7.179	7.186	7.192	7.198	7.205	7.211	7.218	7.224	7.230	7.237	
8	7.243	7.250	7.256	7.262	7.268	7.275	7.281	7.287	7.294	7.300	
9	7.306	7.312	7.319	7.325	7.331	7.337	7.343	7.350	7.356	7.362	
40	7.368	7.374	7.380	7.386	7.393	7.399	7.405	7.411	7.417	7.423	
1	7.429	7.435	7.441	7.447	7.453	7.459	7.465	7.471	7.477	7.483	
2	7.489	7.495	7.501	7.507	7.513	7.518	7.524	7.530	7.536	7.542	
3	7.548	7.554	7.560	7.565	7.571	7.577	7.583	7.589	7.594	7.600	
4	7.606	7.612	7.617	7.623	7.629	7.635	7.640	7.646	7.652	7.657	
45	7.663	7.669	7.674	7.680	7.686	7.691	7.697	7.703	7.708	7.714	5
6	7.719	7.725	7.731	7.736	7.742	7.747	7.753	7.758	7.764	7.769	
7	7.775	7.780	7.786	7.791	7.797	7.802	7.808	7.813	7.819	7.824	
8	7.830	7.835	7.841	7.846	7.851	7.857	7.862	7.868	7.873	7.878	
9	7.884	7.889	7.894	7.900	7.905	7.910	7.916	7.921	7.926	7.932	

Auxiliary Table of Two-thirds Powers and Three-halves Powers (see pp. 1–24 to 1–25)
(To assist in locating the decimal point)

N	$N^{2/3}(=\sqrt[3]{N^2})$	$N^{3/2}(=\sqrt{N^3})$	
.0001	.002154	.000001	For complete table of three-halves powers, see pp. 1–24 to 1–25. That table, used inversely, provides a complete table of two-thirds powers.
.001	.01	.00003162	
.01	.0464	.001	
.1	.2154	.03162278	
.1	1.	1.	
10.	4.64	31.62278	
100.	21.54	1000.	
1000.	100.	31622.78	
10000.	464.16	1000000.	

Cube Roots (*continued*)

Cube roots of numbers from 500. to 1000.

N	0.	1.	2.	3.	4.	5.	6.	7.	8.	9.	Avg diff
50	7.937	7.942	7.948	7.953	7.958	7.963	7.969	7.974	7.979	7.984	5
1	7.990	7.995	8.000	8.005	8.010	8.016	8.021	8.026	8.031	8.036	
2	8.041	8.047	8.052	8.057	8.062	8.067	8.072	8.077	8.082	8.088	
3	8.093	8.098	8.103	8.108	8.113	8.118	8.123	8.128	8.133	8.138	
4	8.143	8.148	8.153	8.158	8.163	8.168	8.173	8.178	8.183	8.188	
55	8.193	8.198	8.203	8.208	8.213	8.218	8.223	8.228	8.233	8.238	
6	8.243	8.247	8.252	8.257	8.262	8.267	8.272	8.277	8.282	8.286	
7	8.291	8.296	8.301	8.306	8.311	8.316	8.320	8.325	8.330	8.335	
8	8.340	8.344	8.349	8.354	8.359	8.363	8.368	8.373	8.378	8.382	
9	8.387	8.392	8.397	8.401	8.406	8.411	8.416	8.420	8.425	8.430	
60	8.434	8.439	8.444	8.448	8.453	8.458	8.462	8.467	8.472	8.476	
1	8.481	8.486	8.490	8.495	8.499	8.504	8.509	8.513	8.518	8.522	
2	8.527	8.532	8.536	8.541	8.545	8.550	8.554	8.559	8.564	8.568	
3	8.573	8.577	8.582	8.586	8.591	8.595	8.600	8.604	8.609	8.613	4
4	8.618	8.622	8.627	8.631	8.636	8.640	8.645	8.649	8.653	8.658	
65	8.662	8.667	8.671	8.676	8.680	8.685	8.689	8.693	8.698	8.702	
6	8.707	8.711	8.715	8.720	8.724	8.729	8.733	8.737	8.742	8.746	
7	8.750	8.755	8.759	8.763	8.768	8.772	8.776	8.781	8.785	8.789	
8	8.794	8.798	8.802	8.807	8.811	8.815	8.819	8.824	8.828	8.832	
9	8.837	8.841	8.845	8.849	8.854	8.858	8.862	8.866	8.871	8.875	
70	8.879	8.883	8.887	8.892	8.896	8.900	8.904	8.909	8.913	8.917	
1	8.921	8.925	8.929	8.934	8.938	8.942	8.946	8.950	8.955	8.959	
2	8.963	8.967	8.971	8.975	8.979	8.984	8.988	8.992	8.996	9.000	
3	9.004	9.008	9.012	9.016	9.021	9.025	9.029	9.033	9.037	9.041	
4	9.045	9.049	9.053	9.057	9.061	9.065	9.069	9.073	9.078	9.082	
75	9.086	9.090	9.094	9.098	9.102	9.106	9.110	9.114	9.118	9.122	
6	9.126	9.130	9.134	9.138	9.142	9.146	9.150	9.154	9.158	9.162	
7	9.166	9.170	9.174	9.178	9.182	9.185	9.189	9.193	9.197	9.201	
8	9.205	9.209	9.213	9.217	9.221	9.225	9.229	9.233	9.237	9.240	
9	9.244	9.248	9.252	9.256	9.260	9.264	9.268	9.272	9.275	9.279	
80	9.283	9.287	9.291	9.295	9.299	9.302	9.306	9.310	9.314	9.318	
1	9.322	9.326	9.329	9.333	9.337	9.341	9.345	9.348	9.352	9.356	
2	9.360	9.364	9.368	9.371	9.375	9.379	9.383	9.386	9.390	9.394	
3	9.398	9.402	9.405	9.409	9.413	9.417	9.420	9.424	9.428	9.432	
4	9.435	9.439	9.443	9.447	9.450	9.454	9.458	9.462	9.465	9.469	
85	9.473	9.476	9.480	9.484	9.488	9.491	9.495	9.499	9.502	9.506	
6	9.510	9.513	9.517	9.521	9.524	9.528	9.532	9.535	9.539	9.543	
7	9.546	9.550	9.554	9.557	9.561	9.565	9.568	9.572	9.576	9.579	
8	9.583	9.586	9.590	9.594	9.597	9.601	9.605	9.608	9.612	9.615	
9	9.619	9.623	9.626	9.630	9.633	9.637	9.641	9.644	9.648	9.651	
90	9.655	9.658	9.662	9.666	9.669	9.673	9.676	9.680	9.683	9.687	
1	9.691	9.694	9.698	9.701	9.705	9.708	9.712	9.715	9.719	9.722	
2	9.726	9.729	9.733	9.736	9.740	9.743	9.747	9.750	9.754	9.758	
3	9.761	9.764	9.768	9.771	9.775	9.778	9.782	9.785	9.789	9.792	
4	9.796	9.799	9.803	9.806	9.810	9.813	9.817	9.820	9.824	9.827	
95	9.830	9.834	9.837	9.841	9.844	9.848	9.851	9.855	9.858	9.861	
6	9.865	9.868	9.872	9.875	9.879	9.882	9.885	9.889	9.892	9.896	
7	9.899	9.902	9.906	9.909	9.913	9.916	9.919	9.923	9.926	9.930	
8	9.933	9.936	9.940	9.943	9.946	9.950	9.953	9.956	9.960	9.963	
9	9.967	9.970	9.973	9.977	9.980	9.983	9.987	9.990	9.993	9.997	
100	10.00										

Moving the decimal point THREE places in N requires moving it ONE place in body of table (see p. 1–18).

MATHEMATICS

Three-halves Powers of Numbers (see also p. 1-22)

N	0	1	2	3	4	5	6	7	8	9	Avg diff
1.	1.000	1.154	1.315	1.482	1.657	1.837	2.024	2.217	2.415	2.619	183
2.	2.828	3.043	3.263	3.488	3.718	3.953	4.192	4.437	4.685	4.939	237
3.	5.196	5.458	5.724	5.995	6.269	6.548	6.831	7.117	7.408	7.702	280
4.	8.000	8.302	8.607	8.917	9.230	9.546	9.866	10.190			313
4.								10.19	10.52	10.85	33
5.	11.18	11.52	11.86	12.20	12.55	12.90	13.25	13.61	13.97	14.33	35
6.	14.70	15.07	15.44	15.81	16.19	16.57	16.96	17.34	17.73	18.12	38
7.	18.52	18.92	19.32	19.72	20.13	20.54	20.95	21.37	21.78	22.20	41
8.	22.63	23.05	23.48	23.91	24.35	24.78	25.22	25.66	26.11	26.55	44
9.	27.00	27.45	27.90	28.36	28.82	29.28	29.74	30.21	30.68	31.15	46
10.	31.62	32.10	32.58	33.06	33.54	34.02	34.51	35.00	35.49	35.99	49
1.	36.48	36.98	37.48	37.99	38.49	39.00	39.51	40.02	40.53	41.05	51
2.	41.57	42.09	42.61	43.14	43.66	44.19	44.73	45.26	45.79	46.33	53
3.	46.87	47.41	47.96	48.50	49.05	49.60	50.15	50.71	51.26	51.82	55
4.	52.38	52.95	53.51	54.08	54.64	55.21	55.79	56.36	56.94	57.51	57
15.	58.09	58.68	59.26	59.85	60.43	61.02	61.62	62.21	62.80	63.40	59
6.	64.00	64.60	65.20	65.81	66.41	67.02	67.63	68.25	68.86	69.48	61
7.	70.09	70.71	71.33	71.96	72.58	73.21	73.84	74.47	75.10	75.73	63
8.	76.37	77.00	77.64	78.28	78.93	79.57	80.22	80.87	81.51	82.17	65
9.	82.82	83.47	84.13	84.79	85.45	86.11	86.77	87.44	88.10	88.77	66
20.	89.44	90.11	90.79	91.46	92.14	92.82	93.50	94.18	94.86	95.55	68
1.	96.23	96.92	97.61	98.30	99.00	99.69	100.38				69
1.							100.4	101.1	101.8	102.5	7
2.	103.2	103.9	104.6	105.3	106.0	106.7	107.4	108.2	108.9	109.6	7
3.	110.3	111.0	111.7	112.5	113.2	113.9	114.6	115.4	116.1	116.8	7
4.	117.6	118.3	119.0	119.8	120.5	121.3	122.0	122.8	123.5	124.3	7
25.	125.0	125.8	126.5	127.3	128.0	128.8	129.5	130.3	131.0	131.8	8
6.	132.6	133.3	134.1	134.9	135.6	136.4	137.2	138.0	138.7	139.5	8
7.	140.3	141.1	141.9	142.6	143.4	144.2	145.0	145.8	146.6	147.4	8
8.	148.2	149.0	149.8	150.5	151.3	152.1	153.0	153.8	154.6	155.4	8
9.	156.2	157.0	157.8	158.6	159.4	160.2	161.9	161.9	162.7	163.5	8
30.	164.3	165.1	166.0	166.8	167.6	168.4	169.3	170.1	170.9	171.8	8
1.	172.6	173.4	174.3	175.1	176.0	176.8	177.6	178.5	179.3	180.2	8
2.	181.0	181.9	182.7	183.6	184.4	185.3	186.1	187.0	187.9	188.7	9
3.	189.6	190.4	191.3	192.2	193.0	193.9	194.8	195.6	196.5	197.4	9
4.	198.3	199.1	200.0	200.9	201.8	202.6	203.5	204.4	205.3	206.2	9
35.	207.1	208.0	208.8	209.7	210.6	211.5	212.4	213.3	214.2	215.1	9
6.	216.0	216.9	217.8	218.7	219.6	220.5	221.4	222.3	223.2	224.2	9
7.	225.1	226.0	226.9	227.8	228.7	229.6	230.6	231.5	232.4	233.3	9
8.	234.2	235.2	236.1	237.0	238.0	238.9	239.8	240.8	241.7	242.6	9
9.	243.6	244.5	245.4	246.4	247.3	248.3	249.2	250.1	251.1	252.0	9
40.	253.0	253.9	254.9	255.8	256.8	257.7	258.7	259.7	260.6	261.6	10
1.	262.5	263.5	264.5	265.4	266.4	267.3	268.3	269.3	270.2	271.2	10
2.	272.2	273.2	274.1	275.1	276.1	277.1	278.0	279.0	280.0	281.0	10
3.	282.0	283.0	283.9	284.9	285.9	286.9	287.9	288.9	289.9	290.9	10
4.	291.9	292.9	293.9	294.9	295.9	296.9	297.9	298.9	299.9	300.9	10
45.	301.9	302.9	303.9	304.9	305.9	306.9	307.9	308.9	310.0	311.0	10
6.	312.0	313.0	314.0	315.0	316.1	317.1	318.1	319.1	320.2	321.2	10
7.	322.2	323.2	324.3	325.3	326.3	327.4	328.4	329.4	330.5	331.5	10
8.	332.6	333.6	334.6	335.7	336.7	337.8	338.8	339.9	340.9	342.0	10
9.	343.0	344.0	345.1	346.2	347.2	348.3	349.3	350.4	351.4	352.5	11

This table gives $N^{3/2}$ from $N = 1$ to $N = 100$. Moving the decimal point TWO places in N requires moving it THREE places in body of table. Thus:

$(7.23)^{3/2} = 19.44$ $(723.)^{3/2} = 19440$ $(0.0723)^{3/2} = 0.01944$

$(72.3)^{3/2} = 614.8$ $(7230.)^{3/2} = 614800$ $(0.723)^{3/2} = 0.6148$

Used inversely, table gives $M^{2/3}$ from $M = 1$ to $M = 1000$. Thus: $(0.6148)^{2/3} = 0.7230$.

Three-halves Powers (*continued*) (see also p. 1–22)

N	0	1	2	3	4	5	6	7	8	9	Avg diff
50.	353.6	354.6	355.7	356.7	357.8	358.9	359.9	361.0	362.1	363.1	11
1.	364.2	365.3	366.4	367.4	368.5	369.6	370.7	371.7	372.8	373.9	11
2.	375.0	376.1	377.1	378.2	379.3	380.4	381.5	382.6	383.7	384.8	11
3.	385.8	386.9	388.0	389.1	390.2	391.3	392.4	393.5	394.6	395.7	11
4.	396.8	397.9	399.0	400.1	401.2	402.3	403.4	404.6	405.7	406.8	11
55.	407.9	409.0	410.1	411.2	412.3	413.5	414.6	415.7	416.8	418.0	11
6.	419.1	420.2	421.3	422.4	423.6	424.7	425.8	426.9	428.1	429.2	11
7.	430.3	431.5	432.6	433.7	434.9	436.0	437.1	438.3	439.4	440.6	11
8.	441.7	442.9	444.0	445.1	446.3	447.4	448.6	449.7	450.9	452.0	11
9.	453.2	454.3	455.5	456.6	457.8	459.0	460.1	461.3	462.4	463.6	12
60.	464.8	465.9	467.1	468.2	469.4	470.6	471.7	472.9	474.1	475.3	12
1.	476.4	477.6	478.7	479.9	481.1	482.3	483.5	484.6	485.8	487.0	12
2.	488.2	489.4	490.6	491.7	492.9	494.1	495.3	496.5	497.7	498.9	12
3.	500.0	501.2	502.4	503.6	504.8	506.0	507.2	508.4	509.6	510.8	12
4.	512.0	513.2	514.4	515.6	516.8	518.0	519.2	520.4	521.6	522.8	12
65.	524.0	525.3	526.5	527.7	528.9	530.1	531.3	532.5	533.8	535.0	12
6.	536.2	537.4	538.6	539.8	541.1	542.3	543.5	544.7	546.0	547.2	12
7.	548.4	549.6	550.9	552.1	553.3	554.6	555.8	557.0	558.3	559.5	12
8.	560.7	562.0	563.2	564.5	565.7	566.9	568.2	569.4	570.7	571.9	12
9.	573.2	574.4	575.7	576.9	578.1	579.4	580.6	581.9	583.2	584.4	13
70.	585.7	586.9	588.2	589.4	590.7	591.9	593.2	594.5	595.7	597.0	13
1.	598.3	599.5	600.8	602.1	603.3	604.6	605.9	607.1	608.4	609.7	13
2.	610.9	612.2	613.5	614.8	616.0	617.3	618.6	619.9	621.2	622.4	13
3.	623.7	625.0	626.3	627.6	628.8	630.1	631.4	632.7	634.0	635.3	13
4.	636.6	637.9	639.2	640.4	641.7	643.0	644.3	645.6	646.9	648.2	13
75.	649.5	650.8	652.1	653.4	654.7	656.0	657.3	658.6	659.9	661.2	13
6.	662.6	663.9	665.2	666.5	667.8	669.1	670.4	671.7	673.0	674.4	13
7.	675.7	677.0	678.3	679.6	680.9	682.3	683.6	684.9	686.2	687.6	13
8.	688.9	690.2	691.5	692.9	694.2	695.5	696.8	698.2	699.5	700.8	13
9.	702.2	703.5	704.8	706.2	707.5	708.8	710.2	711.5	712.9	714.2	13
80.	715.5	716.9	718.2	719.6	720.9	722.3	723.6	725.0	726.3	727.7	13
1.	729.0	730.4	731.7	733.1	734.4	735.8	737.1	738.5	739.8	741.2	14
2.	742.5	743.9	745.3	746.6	748.0	749.3	750.7	752.1	753.4	754.8	14
3.	756.2	757.5	758.9	760.3	761.6	763.0	764.4	765.8	767.1	768.5	14
4.	769.9	771.2	772.6	774.0	775.4	776.8	778.1	779.5	780.9	782.3	14
85.	783.7	785.0	786.4	787.8	789.2	790.6	792.0	793.4	794.8	796.1	14
6.	797.5	798.9	800.3	801.7	803.1	804.5	805.9	807.3	808.7	810.1	14
7.	811.5	812.9	814.3	815.7	817.1	818.5	819.9	821.3	822.7	824.1	14
8.	825.5	826.9	828.3	829.7	831.1	832.6	834.0	835.4	836.8	838.2	14
9.	839.6	841.0	842.5	843.9	845.3	846.7	848.1	849.5	851.0	852.4	14
90.	853.8	855.2	856.7	858.1	859.5	860.9	862.4	863.8	865.2	866.7	14
1.	868.1	869.5	870.9	872.4	873.8	875.2	876.7	878.1	879.6	881.0	14
2.	882.4	883.9	885.3	886.8	888.2	889.6	891.1	892.5	894.0	895.4	14
3.	896.9	898.3	899.8	901.2	902.7	904.1	905.6	907.0	908.5	909.9	15
4.	911.4	912.8	914.3	915.7	917.2	918.6	920.1	921.6	923.0	924.5	15
95.	925.9	927.4	928.9	930.3	931.8	933.3	934.7	936.2	937.7	939.1	15
6.	940.6	942.1	943.5	945.0	946.5	948.0	949.4	950.9	952.4	953.9	15
7.	955.3	956.8	958.3	959.8	961.3	962.7	964.2	965.7	967.2	968.7	15
8.	970.2	971.6	973.1	974.6	976.1	977.6	979.1	980.6	982.1	983.5	15
9.	985.0	986.5	988.0	989.5	991.0	992.5	994.0	995.5	997.0	998.5	15
100.	1000.0										

Moving the decimal point TWO places in *N* requires moving it THREE places in body of table (see also auxiliary table on p. 1–22).

MATHEMATICS

Reciprocals of Numbers

N	0	1	2	3	4	5	6	7	8	9	Avg diff
1.00		.9990	.9980	.9970	.9960	.9950	.9940	.9930	.9921	.9911	−10
1	.9901	.9891	.9881	.9872	.9862	.9852	.9843	.9833	.9823	.9814	
2	.9804	.9794	.9785	.9775	.9766	.9756	.9747	.9737	.9728	.9718	
3	.9709	.9699	.9690	.9681	.9671	.9662	.9653	.9643	.9634	.9625	−9
4	.9615	.9606	.9597	.9588	.9579	.9569	.9560	.9551	.9542	.9533	
1.05	.9524	.9515	.9506	.9497	.9488	.9479	.9470	.9461	.9452	.9443	
6	.9434	.9425	.9416	.9407	.9398	.9390	.9381	.9372	.9363	.9355	
7	.9346	.9337	.9328	.9320	.9311	.9302	.9294	.9285	.9276	.9268	
8	.9259	.9251	.9242	.9234	.9225	.9217	.9208	.9200	.9191	.9183	−8
9	.9174	.9166	.9158	.9149	.9141	.9132	.9124	.9116	.9107	.9099	
1.10	.9091	.9083	.9074	.9066	.9058	.9050	.9042	.9033	.9025	.9017	
1	.9009	.9001	.8993	.8985	.8977	.8969	.8961	.8953	.8945	.8937	
2	.8929	.8921	.8913	.8905	.8897	.8889	.8881	.8873	.8865	.8857	
3	.8850	.8842	.8834	.8826	.8818	.8811	.8803	.8795	.8787	.8780	
4	.8772	.8764	.8757	.8749	.8741	.8734	.8726	.8718	.8711	.8703	
1.15	.8696	.8688	.8681	.8673	.8666	.8658	.8651	.8643	.8636	.8628	
6	.8621	.8613	.8606	.8598	.8591	.8584	.8576	.8569	.8562	.8554	−7
7	.8547	.8540	.8532	.8525	.8518	.8511	.8503	.8496	.8489	.8482	
8	.8475	.8467	.8460	.8453	.8446	.8439	.8432	.8425	.8418	.8410	
9	.8403	.8396	.8389	.8382	.8375	.8368	.8361	.8354	.8347	.8340	
1.20	.8333	.8326	.8319	.8313	.8306	.8299	.8292	.8285	.8278	.8271	
1	.8264	.8258	.8251	.8244	.8237	.8230	.8224	.8217	.8210	.8203	
2	.8197	.8190	.8183	.8177	.8170	.8163	.8157	.8150	.8143	.8137	
3	.8130	.8123	.8117	.8110	.8104	.8097	.8091	.8084	.8078	.8071	−6
4	.8065	.8058	.8052	.8045	.8039	.8032	.8026	.8019	.8013	.8006	
1.25	.8000	.7994	.7987	.7981	.7974	.7968	.7962	.7955	.7949	.7943	
6	.7937	.7930	.7924	.7918	.7911	.7905	.7899	.7893	.7886	.7880	
7	.7874	.7868	.7862	.7855	.7849	.7843	.7837	.7831	.7825	.7819	
8	.7812	.7806	.7800	.7794	.7788	.7782	.7776	.7770	.7764	.7758	
9	.7752	.7746	.7740	.7734	.7728	.7722	.7716	.7710	.7704	.7698	
1.30	.7692	.7686	.7680	.7675	.7669	.7663	.7657	.7651	.7645	.7639	
1	.7634	.7628	.7622	.7616	.7610	.7605	.7599	.7593	.7587	.7582	
2	.7576	.7570	.7564	.7559	.7553	.7547	.7541	.7536	.7530	.7524	
3	.7519	.7513	.7508	.7502	.7496	.7491	.7485	.7479	.7474	.7468	
4	.7463	.7457	.7452	.7446	.7440	.7435	.7429	.7424	.7418	.7413	
1.35	.7407	.7402	.7396	.7391	.7386	.7380	.7375	.7369	.7364	.7358	−5
6	.7353	.7348	.7342	.7337	.7331	.7326	.7321	.7315	.7310	.7305	
7	.7299	.7294	.7289	.7283	.7278	.7273	.7267	.7262	.7257	.7252	
8	.7246	.7241	.7236	.7231	.7225	.7220	.7215	.7210	.7205	.7199	
9	.7194	.7189	.7184	.7179	.7174	.7168	.7163	.7158	.7153	.7148	
1.40	.7143	.7138	.7133	.7128	.7123	.7117	.7112	.7107	.7102	.7097	
1	.7092	.7087	.7082	.7077	.7072	.7067	.7062	.7057	.7052	.7047	
2	.7042	.7037	.7032	.7027	.7022	.7018	.7013	.7008	.7003	.6998	
3	.6993	.6988	.6983	.6978	.6974	.6969	.6964	.6959	.6954	.6949	
4	.6944	.6940	.6935	.6930	.6925	.6920	.6916	.6911	.6906	.6901	
1.45	.6897	.6892	.6887	.6882	.6878	.6873	.6868	.6863	.6859	.6854	
6	.6849	.6845	.6840	.6835	.6831	.6826	.6821	.6817	.6812	.6807	
7	.6803	.6798	.6793	.6789	.6784	.6780	.6775	.6770	.6766	.6761	
8	.6757	.6752	.6748	.6743	.6739	.6734	.6729	.6725	.6720	.6716	
9	.6711	.6707	.6702	.6698	.6693	.6689	.6684	.6680	.6676	.6671	

$1/\pi = 0.318310$ $1/e = 0.367879$

Moving the decimal point in either direction in N requires moving it in the OPPOSITE direction in body of table (see p. 1–28).

Reciprocals (continued)

N	0	1	2	3	4	5	6	7	8	9	Avg diff
1.50	.6667	.6662	.6658	.6653	.6649	.6645	.6640	.6636	.6631	.6627	−4
1	.6623	.6618	.6614	.6609	.6605	.6601	.6596	.6592	.6588	.6583	
2	.6579	.6575	.6570	.6566	.6562	.6557	.6553	.6549	.6545	.6540	
3	.6536	.6532	.6527	.6523	.6519	.6515	.6510	.6506	.6502	.6498	
4	.6494	.6489	.6485	.6481	.6477	.6472	.6468	.6464	.6460	.6456	
1.55	.6452	.6447	.6443	.6439	.6435	.6431	.6427	.6423	.6418	.6414	
6	.6410	.6406	.6402	.6398	.6394	.6390	.6386	.6382	.6378	.6373	
7	.6369	.6365	.6361	.6357	.6353	.6349	.6345	.6341	.6337	.6333	
8	.6329	.6325	.6321	.6317	.6313	.6309	.6305	.6301	.6297	.6293	
9	.6289	.6285	.6281	.6277	.6274	.6270	.6266	.6262	.6258	.6254	
1.60	.6250	.6246	.6242	.6238	.6234	.6231	.6227	.6223	.6219	.6215	
1	.6211	.6207	.6203	.6200	.6196	.6192	.6188	.6184	.6180	.6177	
2	.6173	.6169	.6165	.6161	.6158	.6154	.6150	.6146	.6143	.6139	
3	.6135	.6131	.6127	.6124	.6120	.6116	.6112	.6109	.6105	.6101	
4	.6098	.6094	.6090	.6086	.6083	.6079	.6075	.6072	.6068	.6064	
1.65	.6061	.6057	.6053	.6050	.6046	.6042	.6039	.6035	.6031	.6028	
6	.6024	.6020	.6017	.6013	.6010	.6006	.6002	.5999	.5995	.5992	
7	.5988	.5984	.5981	.5977	.5974	.5970	.5967	.5963	.5959	.5956	
8	.5952	.5949	.5945	.5942	.5938	.5935	.5931	.5928	.5924	.5921	
9	.5917	.5914	.5910	.5907	.5903	.5900	.5896	.5893	.5889	.5886	
1.70	.5882	.5879	.5875	.5872	.5869	.5865	.5862	.5858	.5855	.5851	−3
1	.5848	.5845	.5841	.5838	.5834	.5831	.5828	.5824	.5821	.5817	
2	.5814	.5811	.5807	.5804	.5800	.5797	.5794	.5790	.5787	.5784	
3	.5780	.5777	.5774	.5770	.5767	.5764	.5760	.5757	.5754	.5750	
4	.5747	.5744	.5741	.5737	.5734	.5731	.5727	.5724	.5721	.5718	
1.75	.5714	.5711	.5708	.5705	.5701	.5698	.5695	.5692	.5688	.5685	
6	.5682	.5679	.5675	.5672	.5669	.5666	.5663	.5659	.5656	.5653	
7	.5650	.5647	.5643	.5640	.5637	.5634	.5631	.5627	.5624	.5621	
8	.5618	.5615	.5612	.5609	.5605	.5602	.5599	.5596	.5593	.5590	
9	.5587	.5583	.5580	.5577	.5574	.5571	.5568	.5565	.5562	.5559	
1.80	.5556	.5552	.5549	.5546	.5543	.5540	.5537	.5534	.5531	.5528	
1	.5525	.5522	.5519	.5516	.5513	.5510	.5507	.5504	.5501	.5498	
2	.5495	.5491	.5488	.5485	.5482	.5479	.5476	.5473	.5470	.5467	
3	.5464	.5461	.5459	.5456	.5453	.5450	.5447	.5444	.5441	.5438	
4	.5435	.5432	.5429	.5426	.5423	.5420	.5417	.5414	.5411	.5408	
1.85	.5405	.5402	.5400	.5397	.5394	.5391	.5388	.5385	.5382	.5379	
6	.5376	.5373	.5371	.5368	.5365	.5362	.5359	.5356	.5353	.5350	
7	.5348	.5345	.5342	.5339	.5336	.5333	.5330	.5328	.5325	.5322	
8	.5319	.5316	.5313	.5311	.5308	.5305	.5302	.5299	.5297	.5294	
9	.5291	.5288	.5285	.5283	.5280	.5277	.5274	.5271	.5269	.5266	
1.90	.5263	.5260	.5258	.5255	.5252	.5249	.5247	.5244	.5241	.5238	
1	.5236	.5233	.5230	.5227	.5225	.5222	.5219	.5216	.5214	.5211	
2	.5208	.5206	.5203	.5200	.5198	.5195	.5192	.5189	.5187	.5184	
3	.5181	.5179	.5176	.5173	.5171	.5168	.5165	.5163	.5160	.5157	
4	.5155	.5152	.5149	.5147	.5144	.5141	.5139	.5136	.5133	.5131	
1.95	.5128	.5126	.5123	.5120	.5118	.5115	.5112	.5110	.5107	.5105	
6	.5102	.5099	.5097	.5094	.5092	.5089	.5086	.5084	.5081	.5079	
7	.5076	.5074	.5071	.5068	.5066	.5063	.5061	.5058	.5056	.5053	−2
8	.5051	.5048	.5045	.5043	.5040	.5038	.5035	.5033	.5030	.5028	
9	.5025	.5023	.5020	.5018	.5015	.5013	.5010	.5008	.5005	.5003	

Moving the decimal point in either direction in N requires moving it in the OPPOSITE direction in body of table (see p. 1–28).

MATHEMATICS

Reciprocals (continued)

N	0	1	2	3	4	5	6	7	8	9	Avg diff
2.0	.5000	.4975	.4950	.4926	.4902	.4878	.4854	.4831	.4808	.4785	−24
1	.4762	.4739	.4717	.4695	.4673	.4651	.4630	.4608	.4587	.4566	−21
2	.4545	.4525	.4505	.4484	.4464	.4444	.4425	.4405	.4386	.4367	−20
3	.4348	.4329	.4310	.4292	.4274	.4255	.4237	.4219	.4202	.4184	−18
4	.4167	.4149	.4132	.4115	.4098	.4082	.4065	.4049	.4032	.4016	−17
2.5	.4000	.3984	.3968	.3953	.3937	.3922	.3906	.3891	.3876	.3861	−15
6	.3846	.3831	.3817	.3802	.3788	.3774	.3759	.3745	.3731	.3717	−14
7	.3704	.3690	.3676	.3663	.3650	.3636	.3623	.3610	.3597	.3584	−13
8	.3571	.3559	.3546	.3534	.3521	.3509	.3497	.3484	.3472	.3460	−12
9	.3448	.3436	.3425	.3413	.3401	.3390	.3378	.3367	.3356	.3344	−12
3.0	.3333	.3322	.3311	.3300	.3289	.3279	.3268	.3257	.3247	.3236	−11
1	.3226	.3215	.3205	.3195	.3185	.3175	.3165	.3155	.3145	.3135	−10
2	.3125	.3115	.3106	.3096	.3086	.3077	.3067	.3058	.3049	.3040	−10
3	.3030	.3021	.3012	.3003	.2994	.2985	.2976	.2967	.2959	.2950	−9
4	.2941	.2933	.2924	.2915	.2907	.2899	.2890	.2882	.2874	.2865	−8
3.5	.2857	.2849	.2841	.2833	.2825	.2817	.2809	.2801	.2793	.2786	−8
6	.2778	.2770	.2762	.2755	.2747	.2740	.2732	.2725	.2717	.2710	−8
7	.2703	.2695	.2688	.2681	.2674	.2667	.2660	.2653	.2646	.2639	−7
8	.2632	.2625	.2618	.2611	.2604	.2597	.2591	.2584	.2577	.2571	−7
9	.2564	.2558	.2551	.2545	.2538	.2532	.2525	.2519	.2513	.2506	−6
4.0	.2500	.2494	.2488	.2481	.2475	.2469	.2463	.2457	.2451	.2445	−6
1	.2439	.2433	.2427	.2421	.2415	.2410	.2404	.2398	.2392	.2387	−6
2	.2381	.2375	.2370	.2364	.2358	.2353	.2347	.2342	.2336	.2331	−6
3	.2326	.2320	.2315	.2309	.2304	.2299	.2294	.2288	.2283	.2278	−5
4	.2273	.2268	.2262	.2257	.2252	.2247	.2242	.2237	.2232	.2227	−5
4.5	.2222	.2217	.2212	.2208	.2203	.2198	.2193	.2188	.2183	.2179	−5
6	.2174	.2169	.2165	.2160	.2155	.2151	.2146	.2141	.2137	.2132	−5
7	.2128	.2123	.2119	.2114	.2110	.2105	.2101	.2096	.2092	.2088	−4
8	.2083	.2079	.2075	.2070	.2066	.2062	.2058	.2053	.2049	.2045	−4
9	.2041	.2037	.2033	.2028	.2024	.2020	.2016	.2012	.2008	.2004	−4

$$1/\pi = 0.318310 \qquad 1/e = 0.367879$$

Explanation of Table of Reciprocals (pp. 1–26 to 1–29).

This table gives the values of $1/N$ for values of N from 1 to 10, correct to four figures. (Interpolated values may be in error by 1 in the fourth figure.)

To find the reciprocal of a number N outside the range from 1 to 10, note that moving the decimal point any number of places in either direction in column N is equivalent to moving it the same number of places in the OPPOSITE direction in the body of the table. For example:

$$\frac{1}{3.217} = 0.3109 \qquad \frac{1}{3217.} = 0.000\ 3109 \qquad \frac{1}{0.003217} = 310.9$$

Reciprocals (*continued*)

N	0	1	2	3	4	5	6	7	8	9	Avg diff
5.0	.2000	.1996	.1992	.1988	.1984	.1980	.1976	.1972	.1969	.1965	−4
.1	.1961	.1957	.1953	.1949	.1946	.1942	.1938	.1934	.1931	.1927	
.2	.1923	.1919	.1916	.1912	.1908	.1905	.1901	.1898	.1894	.1890	
.3	.1887	.1883	.1880	.1876	.1873	.1869	.1866	.1862	.1859	.1855	
.4	.1852	.1848	.1845	.1842	.1838	.1835	.1832	.1828	.1825	.1821	−3
5.5	.1818	.1815	.1812	.1808	.1805	.1802	.1799	.1795	.1792	.1789	
.6	.1786	.1783	.1779	.1776	.1773	.1770	.1767	.1764	.1761	.1757	
.7	.1754	.1751	.1748	.1745	.1742	.1739	.1736	.1733	.1730	.1727	
.8	.1724	.1721	.1718	.1715	.1712	.1709	.1706	.1704	.1701	.1698	
.9	.1695	.1692	.1689	.1686	.1684	.1681	.1678	.1675	.1672	.1669	
6.0	.1667	.1664	.1661	.1658	.1656	.1653	1650	.1647	.1645	.1642	
.1	.1639	.1637	.1634	.1631	.1629	.1626	.1623	.1621	.1618	.1616	
.2	.1613	.1610	.1608	.1605	.1603	.1600	.1597	.1595	.1592	.1590	
.3	.1587	.1585	.1582	.1580	.1577	.1575	.1572	.1570	.1567	.1565	−2
.4	.1563	.1560	.1558	.1555	.1553	.1550	.1548	.1546	.1543	.1541	
6.5	.1538	.1536	.1534	.1531	.1529	.1527	.1524	.1522	.1520	.1517	
.6	.1515	.1513	.1511	.1508	.1506	.1504	.1502	.1499	.1497	.1495	
.7	.1493	.1490	.1488	.1486	.1484	.1481	.1479	.1477	.1475	.1473	
.8	.1471	.1468	.1466	.1464	.1462	.1460	.1458	.1456	.1453	.1451	
.9	.1449	.1447	.1445	.1443	.1441	.1439	.1437	.1435	.1433	.1431	
7.0	.1429	.1427	.1425	.1422	.1420	.1418	.1416	.1414	.1412	.1410	
.1	.1408	.1406	.1404	.1403	.1401	.1399	.1397	.1395	.1393	.1391	
.2	.1389	.1387	.1385	.1383	.1381	.1379	.1377	.1376	.1374	.1372	
.3	.1370	.1368	.1366	.1364	.1362	.1361	.1359	.1357	.1355	.1353	
.4	.1351	.1350	.1348	.1346	.1344	.1342	.1340	.1339	.1337	.1335	
7.5	.1333	.1332	.1330	.1328	.1326	.1325	.1323	.1321	.1319	.1318	
.6	.1316	.1314	.1312	.1311	.1309	.1307	.1305	.1304	.1302	.1300	
.7	.1299	.1297	.1295	.1294	.1292	.1290	.1289	.1287	.1285	.1284	
.8	.1282	.1280	.1279	.1277	.1276	.1274	.1272	.1271	.1269	.1267	
.9	.1266	.1264	.1263	.1261	.1259	.1258	.1256	.1255	.1253	.1252	
8.0	.1250	.1248	.1247	.1245	.1244	.1242	.1241	.1239	.1238	.1236	
.1	.1235	.1233	.1232	.1230	.1229	.1227	.1225	.1224	.1222	.1221	
.2	.1220	.1218	.1217	.1215	.1214	.1212	.1211	.1209	.1208	.1206	
.3	.1205	.1203	.1202	.1200	.1199	.1198	.1196	.1195	.1193	.1192	
.4	.1190	.1189	.1188	.1186	.1185	.1183	.1182	.1181	.1179	.1178	−1
8.5	.1176	.1175	.1174	.1172	.1171	.1170	.1168	.1167	.1166	.1164	
.6	.1163	.1161	.1160	.1159	.1157	.1156	.1155	.1153	.1152	.1151	
.7	.1149	.1148	.1147	.1145	.1144	.1143	.1142	.1140	.1139	.1138	
.8	.1136	.1135	.1134	.1133	.1131	.1130	.1129	.1127	.1126	.1125	
.9	.1124	.1122	.1121	.1120	.1119	.1117	.1116	.1115	.1114	.1112	
9.0	.1111	.1110	.1109	.1107	.1106	.1105	.1104	.1103	.1101	.1100	
.1	.1099	.1098	.1096	.1095	.1094	.1093	.1092	.1091	.1089	.1088	
.2	.1087	.1086	.1085	.1083	.1082	.1081	.1080	.1079	.1078	.1076	
.3	.1075	.1074	.1073	.1072	.1071	.1070	.1068	.1067	.1066	.1065	
.4	.1064	.1063	.1062	.1060	.1059	.1058	.1057	.1056	.1055	.1054	
9.5	.1053	.1052	.1050	.1049	.1048	.1047	.1046	.1045	.1044	.1043	
.6	.1042	.1041	.1040	.1038	.1037	.1036	.1035	.1034	.1033	.1032	
.7	.1031	.1030	.1029	.1028	.1027	.1026	.1025	.1024	.1022	.1021	
.8	.1020	.1019	.1018	.1017	.1016	.1015	.1014	.1013	.1012	.1011	
.9	.1010	.1009	.1008	.1007	.1006	.1005	.1004	.1003	.1002	.1001	

Moving the decimal point in either direction in *N* requires moving it in the OPPOSITE direction in body of table (see p. 1–28).

MATHEMATICS

Circumferences of Circles by Hundredths
(For circumferences by eighths, see p. 1–32)

D	0	1	2	3	4	5	6	7	8	9	Avg diff
1.0	3.142	3.173	3.204	3.236	3.267	3.299	3.330	3.362	3.393	3.424	31
.1	3.456	3.487	3.519	3.550	3.581	3.613	3.644	3.676	3.707	3.738	
.2	3.770	3.801	3.833	3.864	3.896	3.927	3.958	3.990	4.021	4.053	
.3	4.084	4.115	4.147	4.178	4.210	4.241	4.273	4.304	4.335	4.367	
.4	4.398	4.430	4.461	4.492	4.524	4.555	4.587	4.618	4.650	4.681	
1.5	4.712	4.744	4.775	4.807	4.838	4.869	4.901	4.932	4.964	4.995	
.6	5.027	5.058	5.089	5.121	5.152	5.184	5.215	5.246	5.278	5.309	
.7	5.341	5.372	5.404	5.435	5.466	5.498	5.529	5.561	5.592	5.623	
.8	5.655	5.686	5.718	5.749	5.781	5.812	5.843	5.875	5.906	5.938	
.9	5.969	6.000	6.032	6.063	6.095	6.126	6.158	6.189	6.220	6.252	
2.0	6.283	6.315	6.346	6.377	6.409	6.440	6.472	6.503	6.535	6.566	
.1	6.597	6.629	6.660	6.692	6.723	6.754	6.786	6.817	6.849	6.880	
.2	6.912	6.943	6.974	7.006	7.037	7.069	7.100	7.131	7.163	7.194	
.3	7.226	7.257	7.288	7.320	7.351	7.383	7.414	7.446	7.477	7.508	
.4	7.540	7.571	7.603	7.634	7.665	7.697	7.728	7.760	7.791	7.823	
2.5	7.854	7.885	7.917	7.948	7.980	8.011	8.042	8.074	8.105	8.137	
.6	8.168	8.200	8.231	8.262	8.294	8.325	8.357	8.388	8.419	8.451	
.7	8.482	8.514	8.545	8.577	8.608	8.639	8.671	8.702	8.734	8.765	
.8	8.796	8.828	8.859	8.891	8.922	8.954	8.985	9.016	9.048	9.079	
.9	9.111	9.142	9.173	9.205	9.236	9.268	9.299	9.331	9.362	9.393	
3.0	9.425	9.456	9.488	9.519	9.550	9.582	9.613	9.645	9.676	9.708	
.1	9.739	9.770	9.802	9.833	9.865	9.896	9.927	9.959	9.990	10.022	31
.1										10.02	3
.2	10.05	10.08	10.12	10.15	10.18	10.21	10.24	10.27	10.30	10.34	
.3	10.37	10.40	10.43	10.46	10.49	10.52	10.56	10.59	10.62	10.65	
.4	10.68	10.71	10.74	10.78	10.81	10.84	10.87	10.90	10.93	10.96	
3.5	11.00	11.03	11.06	11.09	11.12	11.15	11.18	11.22	11.25	11.28	
.6	11.31	11.34	11.37	11.40	11.44	11.47	11.50	11.53	11.56	11.59	
.7	11.62	11.66	11.69	11.72	11.75	11.78	11.81	11.84	11.88	11.91	
.8	11.94	11.97	12.00	12.03	12.06	12.10	12.13	12.16	12.19	12.22	
.9	12.25	12.28	12.32	12.35	12.38	12.41	12.44	12.47	12.50	12.53	
4.0	12.57	12.60	12.63	12.66	12.69	12.72	12.75	12.79	12.82	12.85	
.1	12.88	12.91	12.94	12.97	13.01	13.04	13.07	13.10	13.13	13.16	
.2	13.19	13.23	13.26	13.29	13.32	13.35	13.38	13.41	13.45	13.48	
.3	13.51	13.54	13.57	13.60	13.63	13.67	13.70	13.73	13.76	13.79	
.4	13.82	13.85	13.89	13.92	13.95	13.98	14.01	14.04	14.07	14.11	
4.5	14.14	14.17	14.20	14.23	14.26	14.29	14.33	14.36	14.39	14.42	
.6	14.45	14.48	14.51	14.55	14.58	14.61	14.64	14.67	14.70	14.73	
.7	14.77	14.80	14.83	14.86	14.89	14.92	14.95	14.99	15.02	15.05	
.8	15.08	15.11	15.14	15.17	15.21	15.24	15.27	15.30	15.33	15.36	
.9	15.39	15.43	15.46	15.49	15.52	15.55	15.58	15.61	15.65	15.68	

Explanation of Table of Circumferences (pp. 1–30 to 1–31).

This table gives the product of π times any number D from 1 to 10; that is, it is a table of multiples of π. (D = diameter.)

Moving the decimal point ONE place in column D is equivalent to moving it ONE place in the body of the table.

$$\text{Circumference} = \pi \times \text{diam} = 3.141593 \times \text{diam}$$

Conversely,

$$\text{Diameter} = \frac{1}{\pi} \times \text{circum} = 0.31831 \times \text{circum}$$

Circumferences by Hundredths (*continued*)

D	0	1	2	3	4	5	6	7	8	9	Avg diff
5.0	15.71	15.74	15.77	15.80	15.83	15.87	15.90	15.93	15.96	15.99	3
.1	16.02	16.05	16.08	16.12	16.15	16.18	16.21	16.24	16.27	16.30	
.2	16.34	16.37	16.40	16.43	16.46	16.49	16.52	16.56	16.59	16.62	
.3	16.65	16.68	16.71	16.74	16.78	16.81	16.84	16.87	16.90	16.93	
.4	16.96	17.00	17.03	17.06	17.09	17.12	17.15	17.18	17.22	17.25	
5.5	17.28	17.31	17.34	17.37	17.40	17.44	17.47	17.50	17.53	17.56	
.6	17.59	17.62	17.66	17.69	17.72	17.75	17.78	17.81	17.84	17.88	
.7	17.91	17.94	17.97	18.00	18.03	18.06	18.10	18.13	18.16	18.19	
.8	18.22	18.25	18.28	18.32	18.35	18.38	18.41	18.44	18.47	18.50	
.9	18.54	18.57	18.60	18.63	18.66	18.69	18.72	18.76	18.79	18.82	
6.0	18.85	18.88	18.91	18.94	18.98	19.01	19.04	19.07	19.10	19.13	
.1	19.16	19.20	19.23	19.26	19.29	19.32	19.35	19.38	19.42	19.45	
.2	19.48	19.51	19.54	19.57	19.60	19.63	19.67	19.70	19.73	19.76	
.3	19.79	19.82	19.85	19.89	19.92	19.95	19.98	20.01	20.04	20.07	
.4	20.11	20.14	20.17	20.20	20.23	20.26	20.29	20.33	20.36	20.39	
6.5	20.42	20.45	20.48	20.51	20.55	20.58	20.61	20.64	20.67	20.70	
.6	20.73	20.77	20.80	20.83	20.86	20.89	20.92	20.95	20.99	21.02	
.7	21.05	21.08	21.11	21.14	21.17	21.21	21.24	21.27	21.30	21.33	
.8	21.36	21.39	21.43	21.46	21.49	21.52	21.55	21.58	21.61	21.65	
.9	21.68	21.71	21.74	21.77	21.80	21.83	21.87	21.90	21.93	21.96	
7.0	21.99	22.02	22.05	22.09	22.12	22.15	22.18	22.21	22.24	22.27	
.1	22.31	22.34	22.37	22.40	22.43	22.46	22.49	22.53	22.56	22.59	
.2	22.62	22.65	22.68	22.71	22.75	22.78	22.81	22.84	22.87	22.90	
.3	22.93	22.97	23.00	23.03	23.06	23.09	23.12	23.15	23.18	23.22	
.4	23.25	23.28	23.31	23.34	23.37	23.40	23.44	23.47	23.50	23.53	
7.5	23.56	23.59	23.62	23.66	23.69	23.72	23.75	23.78	23.81	23.84	
.6	23.88	23.91	23.94	23.97	24.00	24.03	24.06	24.10	24.13	24.16	
.7	24.19	24.22	24.25	24.28	24.32	24.35	24.38	24.41	24.44	24.47	
.8	24.50	24.54	24.57	24.60	24.63	24.66	24.69	24.72	24.76	24.79	
.9	24.82	24.85	24.88	24.91	24.94	24.98	25.01	25.04	25.07	25.10	
8.0	25.13	25.16	25.20	25.23	25.26	25.29	25.32	25.35	25.38	25.42	
.1	25.45	25.48	25.51	25.54	25.57	25.60	25.64	25.67	25.70	25.73	
.2	25.76	25.79	25.82	25.86	25.89	25.92	25.95	25.98	26.01	26.04	
.3	26.08	26.11	26.14	26.17	26.20	26.23	26.26	26.30	26.33	26.36	
.4	26.39	26.42	26.45	26.48	26.52	26.55	26.58	26.61	26.64	26.67	
8.5	26.70	26.73	26.77	26.80	26.83	26.86	26.89	26.92	26.95	26.99	
.6	27.02	27.05	27.08	27.11	27.14	27.17	27.21	27.24	27.27	27.30	
.7	27.33	27.36	27.39	27.43	27.46	27.49	27.52	27.55	27.58	27.61	
.8	27.65	27.68	27.71	27.74	27.77	27.80	27.83	27.87	27.90	27.93	
.9	27.96	27.99	28.02	28.05	28.09	28.12	28.15	28.18	28.21	28.24	
9.0	28.27	28.31	28.34	28.37	28.40	28.43	28.46	28.49	28.53	28.56	
.1	28.59	28.62	28.65	28.68	28.71	28.75	28.78	28.81	28.84	28.87	
.2	28.90	28.93	28.97	29.00	29.03	29.06	29.09	29.12	29.15	29.19	
.3	29.22	29.25	29.28	29.31	29.34	29.37	29.41	29.44	29.47	29.50	
.4	29.53	29.56	29.59	29.63	29.66	29.69	29.72	29.75	29.78	29.81	
9.5	29.85	29.88	29.91	29.94	29.97	30.00	30.03	30.07	30.10	30.13	
.6	30.16	30.19	30.22	30.25	30.28	30.32	30.35	30.38	30.41	30.44	
.7	30.47	30.50	30.54	30.57	30.60	30.63	30.66	30.69	30.72	30.76	
.8	30.79	30.82	30.85	30.88	30.91	30.94	30.98	31.01	31.04	31.07	
.9	31.10	31.13	31.16	31.20	31.23	31.26	31.29	31.32	31.35	31.38	
10.0	31.42										

Moving the decimal point ONE place in *D* requires moving it ONE place in body of table (see p. 1–30).

Areas of Circles by Hundredths
(For areas by eighths, see p. 1–34)

D	0	1	2	3	4	5	6	7	8	9	Avg diff
1.0	0.785	0.801	0.817	0.833	0.849	0.866	0.882	0.899	0.916	0.933	16
.1	0.950	0.968	0.985	1.003	1.021	1.039	1.057	1.075	1.094	1.112	18
.2	1.131	1.150	1.169	1.188	1.208	1.227	1.247	1.267	1.287	1.307	20
.3	1.327	1.348	1.368	1.389	1.410	1.431	1.453	1.474	1.496	1.517	21
.4	1.539	1.561	1.584	1.606	1.629	1.651	1.674	1.697	1.720	1.744	23
1.5	1.767	1.791	1.815	1.839	1.863	1.887	1.911	1.936	1.961	1.986	24
.6	2.011	2.036	2.061	2.087	2.112	2.138	2.164	2.190	2.217	2.243	26
.7	2.270	2.297	2.324	2.351	2.378	2.405	2.433	2.461	2.488	2.516	27
.8	2.545	2.573	2.602	2.630	2.659	2.688	2.717	2.746	2.776	2.806	29
.9	2.835	2.865	2.895	2.926	2.956	2.986	3.017	3.048	3.079	3.110	31
2.0	3.142	3.173	3.205	3.237	3.269	3.301	3.333	3.365	3.398	3.431	32
.1	3.464	3.497	3.530	3.563	3.597	3.631	3.664	3.698	3.733	3.767	34
.2	3.801	3.836	3.871	3.906	3.941	3.976	4.011	4.047	4.083	4.119	35
.3	4.155	4.191	4.227	4.264	4.301	4.337	4.374	4.412	4.449	4.486	37
.4	4.524	4.562	4.600	4.638	4.676	4.714	4.753	4.792	4.831	4.870	38
2.5	4.909	4.948	4.988	5.027	5.067	5.107	5.147	5.187	5.228	5.269	40
.6	5.309	5.350	5.391	5.433	5.474	5.515	5.557	5.599	5.641	5.683	42
.7	5.726	5.768	5.811	5.853	5.896	5.940	5.983	6.026	6.070	6.114	43
.8	6.158	6.202	6.246	6.290	6.335	6.379	6.424	6.469	6.514	6.560	45
.9	6.605	6.651	6.697	6.743	6.789	6.835	6.881	6.928	6.975	7.022	46
3.0	7.069	7.116	7.163	7.211	7.258	7.306	7.354	7.402	7.451	7.499	48
.1	7.548	7.596	7.645	7.694	7.744	7.793	7.843	7.892	7.942	7.992	49
.2	8.042	8.093	8.143	8.194	8.245	8.296	8.347	8.398	8.450	8.501	51
.3	8.553	8.605	8.657	8.709	8.762	8.814	8.867	8.920	8.973	9.026	53
.4	9.079	9.133	9.186	9.240	9.294	9.348	9.402	9.457	9.511	9.566	54
3.5	9.621	9.676	9.731	9.787	9.842	9.898	9.954	10.010			56
								10.01	10.07	10.12	6
.6	10.18	10.24	10.29	10.35	10.41	10.46	10.52	10.58	10.64	10.69	6
.7	10.75	10.81	10.87	10.93	10.99	11.04	11.10	11.16	11.22	11.28	
.8	11.34	11.40	11.46	11.52	11.58	11.64	11.70	11.76	11.82	11.88	
.9	11.95	12.01	12.07	12.13	12.19	12.25	12.32	12.38	12.44	12.50	
4.0	12.57	12.63	12.69	12.76	12.82	12.88	12.95	13.01	13.07	13.14	7
.1	13.20	13.27	13.33	13.40	13.46	13.53	13.59	13.66	13.72	13.79	
.2	13.85	13.92	13.99	14.05	14.12	14.19	14.25	14.32	14.39	14.45	
.3	14.52	14.59	14.66	14.73	14.79	14.86	14.93	15.00	15.07	15.14	
.4	15.21	15.27	15.34	15.41	15.48	15.55	15.62	15.69	15.76	15.83	
4.5	15.90	15.98	16.05	16.12	16.19	16.26	16.33	16.40	16.47	16.55	
.6	16.62	16.69	16.76	16.84	16.91	16.98	17.06	17.13	17.20	17.28	
.7	17.35	17.42	17.50	17.57	17.65	17.72	17.80	17.87	17.95	18.02	
.8	18.10	18.17	18.25	18.32	18.40	18.47	18.55	18.63	18.70	18.78	8
.9	18.86	18.93	19.01	19.09	19.17	19.24	19.32	19.40	19.48	19.56	

Explanation of Table of Areas of Circles (pp. 1–32 to 1–33).

Moving the decimal point ONE place in column D is equivalent to moving it TWO places in the body of the table. (D = diameter.)

$$\text{Area of circle} = \frac{\pi}{4} \times (\text{diam}^2) = 0.785398 \times (\text{diam}^2)$$

Conversely,

$$\text{Diam} = \sqrt{\frac{4}{\pi}} \times \sqrt{\text{area}} = 1.128379 \times \sqrt{\text{area}}$$

Areas of Circles by Hundredths (continued)

D	0	1	2	3	4	5	6	7	8	9	Avg diff
5.0	19.63	19.71	19.79	19.87	19.95	20.03	20.11	20.19	20.27	20.35	8
.1	20.43	20.51	20.59	20.67	20.75	20.83	20.91	20.99	21.07	21.16	
.2	21.24	21.32	21.40	21.48	21.57	21.65	21.73	21.81	21.90	21.98	
.3	22.06	22.15	22.23	22.31	22.40	22.48	22.56	22.65	22.73	22.82	
.4	22.90	22.99	23.07	23.16	23.24	23.33	23.41	23.50	23.59	23.67	9
5.5	23.76	23.84	23.93	24.02	24.11	24.19	24.28	24.37	24.45	24.54	
.6	24.63	24.72	24.81	24.89	24.98	25.07	25.16	25.25	25.34	25.43	
.7	25.52	25.61	25.70	25.79	25.88	25.97	26.06	26.15	26.24	26.33	
.8	26.42	26.51	26.60	26.69	26.79	26.88	26.97	27.06	27.15	27.25	
.9	27.34	27.43	27.53	27.62	27.71	27.81	27.90	27.99	28.09	28.18	
6.0	28.27	28.37	28.46	28.56	28.65	28.75	28.84	28.94	29.03	29.13	10
.1	29.22	29.32	29.42	29.51	29.61	29.71	29.80	29.90	30.00	30.09	
.2	30.19	30.29	30.39	30.48	30.58	30.68	30.78	30.88	30.97	31.07	
.3	31.17	31.27	31.37	31.47	31.57	31.67	31.77	31.87	31.97	32.07	
.4	32.17	32.27	32.37	32.47	32.57	32.67	32.78	32.88	32.98	33.08	
6.5	33.18	33.29	33.39	33.49	33.59	33.70	33.80	33.90	34.00	34.11	
.6	34.21	34.32	34.42	34.52	34.63	34.73	34.84	34.94	35.05	35.15	
.7	35.26	35.36	35.47	35.57	35.68	35.78	35.89	36.00	36.10	36.21	11
.8	36.32	36.42	36.53	36.64	36.75	36.85	36.96	37.07	37.18	37.28	
.9	37.39	37.50	37.61	37.72	37.83	37.94	38.05	38.16	38.26	38.37	
7.0	38.48	38.59	38.70	38.82	38.93	39.04	39.15	39.26	39.37	39.48	
.1	39.59	39.70	39.82	39.93	40.04	40.15	40.26	40.38	40.49	40.60	
.2	40.72	40.83	40.94	41.06	41.17	41.28	41.40	41.51	41.62	41.74	
.3	41.85	41.97	42.08	42.20	42.31	42.43	42.54	42.66	42.78	42.89	12
.4	43.01	43.12	43.24	43.36	43.47	43.59	43.71	43.83	43.94	44.06	
7.5	44.18	44.30	44.41	44.53	44.65	44.77	44.89	45.01	45.13	45.25	
.6	45.36	45.48	45.60	45.72	45.84	45.96	46.08	46.20	46.32	46.45	
.7	46.57	46.69	46.81	46.93	47.05	47.17	47.29	47.42	47.54	47.66	
.8	47.78	47.91	48.03	48.15	48.27	48.40	48.52	48.65	48.77	48.89	
.9	49.02	49.14	49.27	49.39	49.51	49.64	49.76	49.89	50.01	50.14	
8.0	50.27	50.39	50.52	50.64	50.77	50.90	51.02	51.15	51.28	51.40	13
.1	51.53	51.66	51.78	51.91	52.04	52.17	52.30	52.42	52.55	52.68	
.2	52.81	52.94	53.07	53.20	53.33	53.46	53.59	53.72	53.85	53.98	
.3	54.11	54.24	54.37	54.50	54.63	54.76	54.89	55.02	55.15	55.29	
.4	55.42	55.55	55.68	55.81	55.95	56.08	56.21	56.35	56.48	56.61	
8.5	56.75	56.88	57.01	57.15	57.28	57.41	57.55	57.68	57.82	57.95	
.6	58.09	58.22	58.36	58.49	58.63	58.77	58.90	59.04	59.17	59.31	14
.7	59.45	59.58	59.72	59.86	59.99	60.13	60.27	60.41	60.55	60.68	
.8	60.82	60.96	61.10	61.24	61.38	61.51	61.65	61.79	61.93	62.07	
.9	62.21	62.35	62.49	62.63	62.77	62.91	63.05	63.19	63.33	63.48	
9.0	63.62	63.76	63.90	64.04	64.18	64.33	64.47	64.61	64.75	64.90	15
.1	65.04	65.18	65.33	65.47	65.61	65.76	65.90	66.04	66.19	66.33	
.2	66.48	66.62	66.77	66.91	67.06	67.20	67.35	67.49	67.64	67.78	
.3	67.93	68.08	68.22	68.37	68.51	68.66	68.81	68.96	69.10	69.25	
.4	69.40	69.55	69.69	69.84	69.99	70.14	70.29	70.44	70.58	70.73	
9.5	70.88	71.03	71.18	71.33	71.48	71.63	71.78	71.93	72.08	72.23	
.6	72.38	72.53	72.68	72.84	72.99	73.14	73.29	73.44	73.59	73.75	
.7	73.90	74.05	74.20	74.36	74.51	74.66	74.82	74.97	75.12	75.28	
.8	75.43	75.58	75.74	75.89	76.05	76.20	76.36	76.51	76.67	76.82	
.9	76.98	77.13	77.29	77.44	77.60	77.76	77.91	78.07	78.23	78.38	16

Moving the decimal point ONE place in D requires moving it TWO places in body of table (see p. 1–32).

MATHEMATICS

Circumferences and Areas of Circles by Eighths, etc.

(For tenths, see p. 1–30)

Diam	Circum	Area	Diam	Circum	Area	Diam	Circum	Area	Diam	Circum	Area
1/64	.04909	.00019	7/8	2.749	.6013	4	12.57	12.57	9	28.27	63.62
1/32	.09817	.00077	57/64	2.798	.6230	1/16	12.76	12.96	1/8	28.67	65.40
3/64	.1473	.00173	29/32	2.847	.6450	1/8	12.96	13.36	1/4	29.06	67.20
1/16	.1963	.00307	59/64	2.896	.6675	3/16	13.16	13.77	3/8	29.45	69.03
5/64	.2454	.00479	15/16	2.945	.6903	1/4	13.35	14.19	1/2	29.85	70.88
3/32	.2945	.00690	61/64	2.994	.7135	5/16	13.55	14.61	5/8	30.24	72.76
7/64	.3436	.00940	31/32	3.043	.7371	3/8	13.74	15.03	3/4	30.63	74.66
1/8	.3927	.01227	63/64	3.093	.7610	7/16	13.94	15.47	7/8	31.02	76.59
9/64	.4418	.01553	1	3.142	.7854	1/2	14.14	15.90	10	31.42	78.54
5/32	.4909	.01917	1 1/16	3.338	.8866	9/16	14.33	16.35	1/8	31.81	80.52
11/64	.5400	.02320	1 1/8	3.534	.9940	5/8	14.53	16.80	1/4	32.20	82.52
3/16	.5890	.02761	1 3/16	3.731	1.108	11/16	14.73	17.26	3/8	32.59	84.54
13/64	.6381	.03241	1/4	3.927	1.227	3/4	14.92	17.72	1/2	32.99	86.59
7/32	.6872	.03758	5/16	4.123	1.353	13/16	15.12	18.19	5/8	33.38	88.66
15/64	.7363	.04314	3/8	4.320	1.485	7/8	15.32	18.67	3/4	33.77	90.76
1/4	.7854	.04909	7/16	4.516	1.623	15/16	15.51	19.15	7/8	34.16	92.89
17/64	.8345	.05542	1/2	4.712	1.767	5	15.71	19.63	11	34.56	95.03
9/32	.8836	.06213	9/16	4.909	1.917	1/16	15.90	20.13	1/8	34.95	97.21
19/64	.9327	.06922	5/8	5.105	2.074	1/8	16.10	20.63	1/4	35.34	99.40
5/16	.9817	.07670	11/16	5.301	2.237	3/16	16.30	21.14	3/8	35.74	101.6
21/64	1.031	.08456	3/4	5.498	2.405	1/4	16.49	21.65	1/2	36.13	103.9
11/32	1.080	.09281	13/16	5.694	2.580	5/16	16.69	22.17	5/8	36.52	106.1
23/64	1.129	.1014	7/8	5.890	2.761	3/8	16.89	22.69	3/4	36.91	108.4
3/8	1.178	.1104	15/16	6.087	2.948	7/16	17.08	23.22	7/8	37.31	110.8
25/64	1.227	.1198	2	6.283	3.142	1/2	17.28	23.76	12	37.70	113.1
13/32	1.276	.1296	1/16	6.480	3.341	9/16	17.48	24.30	1/8	38.09	115.5
27/64	1.325	.1398	1/8	6.676	3.547	5/8	17.67	24.85	1/4	38.48	117.9
7/16	1.374	.1503	3/16	6.872	3.758	11/16	17.87	25.41	3/8	38.88	120.3
29/64	1.424	.1613	1/4	7.069	3.976	3/4	18.06	25.97	1/2	39.27	122.7
15/32	1.473	.1726	5/16	7.265	4.200	13/16	18.26	26.53	5/8	39.66	125.2
31/64	1.522	.1843	3/8	7.461	4.430	7/8	18.46	27.11	3/4	40.06	127.7
1/2	1.571	.1963	7/16	7.658	4.666	15/16	18.65	27.69	7/8	40.45	130.2
33/64	1.620	.2088	1/2	7.854	4.909	6	18.85	28.27	13	40.84	132.7
17/32	1.669	.2217	9/16	8.050	5.157	1/8	19.24	29.46	1/8	41.23	135.3
35/64	1.718	.2349	5/8	8.247	5.412	1/4	19.63	30.68	1/4	41.63	137.9
9/16	1.767	.2485	11/16	8.443	5.673	3/8	20.03	31.92	3/8	42.02	140.5
37/64	1.816	.2625	3/4	8.639	5.940	1/2	20.42	33.18	1/2	42.41	143.1
19/32	1.865	.2769	13/16	8.836	6.213	5/8	20.81	34.47	5/8	42.80	145.8
39/64	1.914	.2916	7/8	9.032	6.492	3/4	21.21	35.78	3/4	43.20	148.5
5/8	1.963	.3068	15/16	9.228	6.777	7/8	21.60	37.12	7/8	43.59	151.2
41/64	2.013	.3223	3	9.425	7.069	7	21.99	38.48	14	43.98	153.9
21/32	2.062	.3382	1/16	9.621	7.366	1/8	22.38	39.87	1/8	44.37	156.7
43/64	2.111	.3545	1/8	9.817	7.670	1/4	22.78	41.28	1/4	44.77	159.5
11/16	2.160	.3712	3/16	10.01	7.980	3/8	23.17	42.72	3/8	45.16	162.3
45/64	2.209	.3883	1/4	10.21	8.296	1/2	23.56	44.18	1/2	45.55	165.1
23/32	2.258	.4057	5/16	10.41	8.618	5/8	23.95	45.66	5/8	45.95	168.0
47/64	2.307	.4236	3/8	10.60	8.946	3/4	24.35	47.17	3/4	46.34	170.9
3/4	2.356	.4418	7/16	10.80	9.281	7/8	24.74	48.71	7/8	46.73	173.8
49/64	2.405	.4604	1/2	11.00	9.621	8	25.13	50.27	15	47.12	176.7
25/32	2.454	.4794	9/16	11.19	9.968	1/8	25.53	51.85	1/8	47.52	179.7
51/64	2.503	.4987	5/8	11.39	10.32	1/4	25.92	53.46	1/4	47.91	182.7
13/16	2.553	.5185	11/16	11.58	10.68	3/8	26.31	55.09	3/8	48.30	185.7
53/64	2.602	.5386	3/4	11.78	11.04	1/2	26.70	56.75	1/2	48.69	188.7
27/32	2.651	.5591	13/16	11.98	11.42	5/8	27.10	58.43	5/8	49.09	191.7
55/64	2.700	.5800	7/8	12.17	11.79	3/4	27.49	60.13	3/4	49.48	194.8
			15/16	12.37	12.18	7/8	27.88	61.86	7/8	49.87	197.9

Circumferences and Areas by Eighths (continued)

Diam	Circum	Area	Diam	Circum	Area	Diam	Circum	Area	Diam	Circum	Area
16	50.27	201.1	19½	61.26	298.6	23	72.26	415.5	29	91.11	660.5
⅛	50.66	204.2	⅝	61.65	302.5	⅛	72.65	420.0	¼	91.89	672.0
¼	51.05	207.4	¾	62.05	306.4	¼	73.04	424.6	½	92.68	683.5
⅜	51.44	210.6	⅞	62.44	310.2	⅜	73.43	429.1	¾	93.46	695.1
½	51.84	213.8	20	62.83	314.2	½	73.83	433.7	30	94.25	706.9
⅝	52.23	217.1	⅛	63.22	318.1	⅝	74.22	438.4	¼	95.03	718.7
¾	52.62	220.4	¼	63.62	322.1	¾	74.61	443.0	½	95.82	730.6
⅞	53.01	223.7	⅜	64.01	326.1	⅞	75.01	447.7	¾	96.60	742.6
17	53.41	227.0	½	64.40	330.1	24	75.40	452.4	31	97.39	754.8
⅛	53.80	230.3	⅝	64.80	334.1	¼	76.18	461.9	¼	98.17	767.0
¼	54.19	233.7	¾	65.19	338.2	½	76.97	471.4	½	98.96	779.3
⅜	54.59	237.1	⅞	65.58	342.2	¾	77.75	481.1	¾	99.75	791.7
½	54.98	240.5	21	65.97	346.4	25	78.54	490.9	32	100.5	804.2
⅝	55.37	244.0	⅛	66.37	350.5	¼	79.33	500.7	¼	101.3	816.9
¾	55.76	247.4	¼	66.76	354.7	½	80.11	510.7	½	102.1	829.6
⅞	56.16	250.9	⅜	67.15	358.8	¾	80.90	520.8	¾	102.9	842.4
18	56.55	254.5	½	67.54	363.1	26	81.68	530.9	33	103.7	855.3
⅛	56.94	258.0	⅝	67.94	367.3	¼	82.47	541.2	¼	104.5	868.3
¼	57.33	261.6	¾	68.33	371.5	½	83.25	551.5	½	105.2	881.4
⅜	57.73	265.2	⅞	68.72	375.8	¾	84.04	562.0	¾	106.0	894.6
½	58.12	268.8	22	69.12	380.1	27	84.82	572.6	34	106.8	907.9
⅝	58.51	272.4	⅛	69.51	384.5	¼	85.61	583.2	¼	107.6	921.3
¾	58.90	276.1	¼	69.90	388.8	½	86.39	594.0	½	108.4	934.8
⅞	59.30	279.8	⅜	70.29	393.2	¾	87.18	604.8	¾	109.2	948.4
19	59.69	283.5	½	70.69	397.6	28	87.96	615.8	35	110.0	962.1
⅛	60.08	287.3	⅝	71.08	402.0	¼	88.75	626.8	¼	110.7	975.9
¼	60.48	291.0	¾	71.47	406.5	½	89.54	637.9	½	111.5	989.8
⅜	60.87	294.8	⅞	71.86	411.0	¾	90.32	649.2	¾	112.3	1003.8

Areas of Circles. Diameters in Feet and Inches, Areas in Square Feet

Feet	Inches											
	0	1	2	3	4	5	6	7	8	9	10	11
0	.0000	.0055	.0218	.0491	.0873	.1364	.1963	.2673	.3491	.4418	.5454	.6600
1	.7854	.9218	1.069	1.227	1.396	1.576	1.767	1.969	2.182	2.405	2.640	2.885
2	3.142	3.409	3.687	3.976	4.276	4.587	4.909	5.241	5.585	5.940	6.305	6.681
3	7.069	7.467	7.876	8.296	8.727	9.168	9.621	10.08	10.56	11.04	11.54	12.05
4	12.57	13.10	13.64	14.19	14.75	15.32	15.90	16.50	17.10	17.72	18.35	18.99
5	19.63	20.29	20.97	21.65	22.34	23.04	23.76	24.48	25.22	25.97	26.73	27.49
6	28.27	29.07	29.87	30.68	31.50	32.34	33.18	34.04	34.91	35.78	36.67	37.57
7	38.48	39.41	40.34	41.28	42.24	43.20	44.18	45.17	46.16	47.17	48.19	49.22
8	50.27	51.32	52.38	53.46	54.54	55.64	56.75	57.86	58.99	60.13	61.28	62.44
9	63.62	64.80	66.00	67.20	68.42	69.64	70.88	72.13	73.39	74.66	75.94	77.24
10	78.54	79.85	81.18	82.52	83.86	85.22	86.59	87.97	89.36	90.76	92.18	93.60
11	95.03	96.48	97.93	99.40	100.9	102.4	103.9	105.4	106.9	108.4	110.0	111.5
12	113.1	114.7	116.3	117.9	119.5	121.1	122.7	124.4	126.0	127.7	129.4	131.0
13	132.7	134.4	136.2	137.9	139.6	141.4	143.1	144.9	146.7	148.5	150.3	152.1
14	153.9	155.8	157.6	159.5	161.4	163.2	165.1	167.0	168.9	170.9	172.8	174.8

If given diameter is not found in this table, reduce diameter to feet and decimals of a foot by aid of the following auxiliary table, and then find area from pp. 1–32 to 1–33.

From Inches and Fractions of an Inch to Decimals of a Foot

Inches	1	2	3	4	5	6	7	8	9	10	11
Feet	.0833	.1667	.2500	.3333	.4167	.5000	.5833	.6667	.7500	.8333	.9167

Inches	⅛	¼	⅜	½	⅝	¾	⅞
Feet	.0104	.0208	.0313	.0417	.0521	.0625	.0729

Example. 5 ft. 7⅜ in. = 5.0 + 0.5833 + 0.0313 = 5.6146 ft.

MATHEMATICS

Segments of Circles, Given h/c

Given: h = height; c = chord. (For explanation of this table, see p. 1–40)

$\dfrac{h}{c}$	Diam c	Diff	Arc c	Diff	Area $h \times c$	Diff	Central angle, v	Diff	$\dfrac{h}{\text{Diam}}$	Diff
.00			1.000	0	.6667	0	0.00°	458	.0000	4
1	25.010	12490	1.000	1	.6667	2	4.58	458	.0004	12
2	12.520	*4157	1.001	1	.6669	2	9.16	457	.0016	20
3	8.363	*2073	1.002	2	.6671	4	13.73	457	.0036	28
4	6.290	*1240	1.004	3	.6675	5	18.30	454	.0064	35
.05	5.050	*823	1.007	3	.6680	6	22.84°	453	.0099	43
6	4.227	*586	1.010	3	.6686	7	27.37	451	.0142	50
7	3.641	*436	1.013	4	.6693	8	31.88	448	.0192	58
8	3.205	*337	1.017	4	.6701	9	36.36	446	.0250	64
9	2.868	*268	1.021	5	.6710	10	40.82	442	.0314	71
.10	2.600	*217	1.026	6	.6720	11	45.24°	439	.0385	77
1	2.383	*180	1.032	6	.6731	12	49.63	435	.0462	83
2	2.203	*150	1.038	6	.6743	13	53.98	432	.0545	88
3	2.053	*127	1.044	7	.6756	14	58.30	427	.0633	94
4	1.926	*109	1.051	8	.6770	15	62.57	423	.0727	99
.15	1.817	*94	1.059	8	.6785	16	66.80°	418	.0826	103
6	1.723	*82	1.067	8	.6801	17	70.98	413	.0929	107
7	1.641	*72	1.075	9	.6818	18	75.11	409	.1036	111
8	1.569	*63	1.084	10	.6836	19	79.20	403	.1147	116
9	1.506	56	1.094	9	.6855	20	83.23	399	.1263	116
.20	1.450	50	1.103	11	.6875	21	87.21°	392	.1379	120
1	1.400	44	1.114	10	.6896	22	91.13	387	.1499	123
2	1.356	39	1.124	12	.6918	23	95.00	381	.1622	124
3	1.317	35	1.136	11	.6941	24	98.81	375	.1746	127
4	1.282	32	1.147	12	.6965	24	102.56	370	.1873	127
.25	1.250	28	1.159	12	.6989	25	106.26°	364	.2000	128
6	1.222	26	1.171	13	.7014	27	109.90	358	.2128	130
7	1.196	23	1.184	13	.7041	27	113.48	352	.2258	129
8	1.173	21	1.197	14	.7068	28	117.00	345	.2387	130
9	1.152	19	1.211	14	.7096	29	120.45	341	.2517	130
.30	1.133	17	1.225	14	.7125	29	123.86°	334	.2647	130
1	1.116	15	1.239	15	.7154	31	127.20	328	.2777	129
2	1.101	13	1.254	15	.7185	31	130.48	322	.2906	128
3	1.088	13	1.269	15	.7216	32	133.70	316	.3034	128
4	1.075	11	1.284	16	.7248	32	136.86	311	.3162	127
.35	1.064	10	1.300	16	.7280	34	139.97°	305	.3289	125
6	1.054	8	1.316	16	.7314	34	143.02	299	.3414	124
7	1.046	8	1.332	17	.7348	35	146.01	293	.3538	123
8	1.038	7	1.349	17	.7383	36	148.94	288	.3661	122
9	1.031	6	1.366	17	.7419	36	151.82	282	.3783	119
.40	1.025	5	1.383	18	.7455	37	154.64°	277	.3902	119
1	1.020	5	1.401	18	.7492	38	157.41	271	.4021	116
2	1.015	4	1.419	18	.7530	38	160.12	266	.4137	115
3	1.011	3	1.437	18	.7568	39	162.78	261	.4252	112
4	1.008	2	1.455	19	.7607	40	165.39	256	.4364	111
.45	1.006	3	1.474	19	.7647	40	167.95°	251	.4475	109
6	1.003	1	1.493	19	.7687	41	170.46	245	.4584	107
7	1.002	1	1.512	19	.7728	41	172.91	241	.4691	105
8	1.001	1	1.531	20	.7769	42	175.32	237	.4796	103
9	1.000	0	1.551	20	.7811	43	177.69	231	.4899	101
.50	1.000		1.571		.7854		180.00°		.5000	

* Interpolation may be inaccurate at these points.

Segments of Circles, Given h/D

Given: h = height; D = diameter of circle. (For explanation of this table, see p. 1–40)

$\dfrac{h}{D}$	$\dfrac{Arc}{D}$	Diff	$\dfrac{Area}{D^2}$	Diff	Central angle, v	Diff	$\dfrac{Chord}{D}$	Diff	$\dfrac{Arc}{Circum}$	Diff	$\dfrac{Area}{Circle}$	Diff
.00	0.000		.0000		0.00°		.0000		.0000		.0000	
		2003		13		2296		*1990		*638		17
1	.2003		.0013		22.96		.1990		.0638		.0017	
		*835		24		*956		*810		*265		31
2	.2838		.0037		32.52		.2800		.0903		.0048	
		*644		32		*738		*612		*205		39
3	.3482		.0069		39.90		.3412		.1108		.0087	
		*545		36		*625		*507		*174		47
4	.4027		.0105		46.15		.3919		.1282		.0134	
		*483		42		*553		*440		*154		53
.05	.4510		.0147		51.68°		.4359		.1436		.0187	
		*439		45		*504		*391		*139		58
6	.4949		.0192		56.72		.4750		.1575		.0245	
		*406		50		*465		*353		*130		63
7	.5355		.0242		61.37		.5103		.1705		.0308	
		*380		52		*435		*323		121		67
8	.5735		.0294		65.72		.5426		.1826		.0375	
		*359		56		*411		*298		114		71
9	.6094		.0350		69.83		.5724		.1940		.0446	
		*341		59		*391		*276		108		74
.10	.6435		.0409		73.74°		.6000		.2048		.0520	
		*326		61		*374		*258		104		78
1	.6761		.0470		77.48		.6258		.2152		.0598	
		*314		64		*359		*241		100		82
2	.7075		.0534		81.07		.6499		.2252		.0680	
		*302		66		*347		*227		96		84
3	.7377		.0600		84.54		.6726		.2348		.0764	
		*293		68		*335		*214		93		87
4	.7670		.0668		87.89		.6940		.2441		.0851	
		*284		71		*326		*201		91		90
.15	.7954		.0739		91.15°		.7141		.2532		.0941	
		276		72		316		*191		88		92
6	.8230		.0811		94.31		.7332		.2620		.1033	
		270		74		309		*181		86		94
7	.8500		.0885		97.40		.7513		.2706		.1127	
		263		76		302		*171		83		97
8	.8763		.0961		100.42		.7684		.2789		.1224	
		258		78		295		162		82		99
9	.9021		.1039		103.37		.7846		.2871		.1323	
		252		79		289		154		81		101
.20	0.9273		.1118		106.26°		.8000		.2952		.1424	
		248		81		284		146		79		103
1	0.9521		.1199		109.10		.8146		.3031		.1527	
		243		82		279		139		77		104
2	0.9764		.1281		111.89		.8285		.3108		.1631	
		240		84		274		132		76		107
3	1.0004		.1365		114.63		.8417		.3184		.1738	
		235		84		271		125		75		108
4	1.0239		.1449		117.34		.8542		.3259		.1846	
		233		86		266		118		74		109
.25	1.0472		.1535		120.00°		.8660		.3333		.1955	
		229		88		263		113		73		111
6	1.0701		.1623		122.63		.8773		.3406		.2066	
		227		88		260		106		72		112
7	1.0928		.1711		125.23		.8879		.3478		.2178	
		224		89		256		101		72		114
8	1.1152		.1800		127.79		.8980		.3550		.2292	
		222		90		254		95		70		115
9	1.1374		.1890		130.33		.9075		.3620		.2407	
		219		92		251		90		70		116
.30	1.1593		.1982		132.84°		.9165		.3690		.2523	
		217		92		249		85		69		117
1	1.1810		.2074		135.33		.9250		.3759		.2640	
		215		93		247		80		69		119
2	1.2025		.2167		137.80		.9330		.3828		.2759	
		214		93		245		74		68		119
3	1.2239		.2260		140.25		.9404		.3896		.2878	
		212		95		242		70		67		120
4	1.2451		.2355		142.67		.9474		.3963		.2998	
		210		95		241		65		67		121
.35	1.2661		.2450		145.08°		.9539		.4030		.3119	
		209		96		240		61		67		122
6	1.2870		.2546		147.48		.9600		.4097		.3241	
		208		96		238		56		66		123
7	1.3078		.2642		149.86		.9656		.4163		.3364	
		206		97		237		52		66		123
8	1.3284		.2739		152.23		.9708		.4229		.3487	
		206		97		235		47		65		124
9	1.3490		.2836		154.58		.9755		.4294		.3611	
		204		98		235		43		65		124
.40	1.3694		.2934		156.93°		.9798		.4359		.3735	
		204		98		233		39		65		125
1	1.3898		.3032		159.26		.9837		.4424		.3860	
		203		98		233		34		65		126
2	1.4101		.3130		161.59		.9871		.4489		.3986	
		202		99		231		31		64		126
3	1.4303		.3229		163.90		.9902		.4553		.4112	
		202		99		232		26		64		126
4	1.4505		.3328		166.22		.9928		.4617		.4238	
		201		100		230		22		64		126
.45	1.4706		.3428		168.52°		.9950		.4681		.4364	
		201		99		230		18		64		127
6	1.4907		.3527		170.82		.9968		.4745		.4491	
		201		100		230		14		64		127
7	1.5108		.3627		173.12		.9982		.4809		.4618	
		200		100		229		10		64		127
8	1.5308		.3727		175.41		.9992		.4873		.4745	
		200		100		230		6		63		128
9	1.5508		.3827		177.71		.9998		.4936		.4873	
		200		100		229		2		64		127
.50	1.5708		.3927		180.00°		1.0000		.5000		.5000	

*Interpolation may be inaccurate at these points.

Volumes of Spheres by Hundredths

D	0	1	2	3	4	5	6	7	8	9	Avg diff
1.0	.5236	.5395	.5556	.5722	.5890	.6061	.6236	.6414	.6596	.6781	173
.1	.6969	.7161	.7356	.7555	.7757	.7963	.8173	.8386	.8603	.8823	208
.2	.9048	.9276	.9508	.9743	.9983	1.0227					236
.2						1.023	1.047	1.073	1.098	1.124	25
.3	1.150	1.177	1.204	1.232	1.260	1.288	1.317	1.346	1.376	1.406	29
.4	1.437	1.468	1.499	1.531	1.563	1.596	1.630	1.663	1.697	1.732	33
1.5	1.767	1.803	1.839	1.875	1.912	1.950	1.988	2.026	2.065	2.105	38
.6	2.145	2.185	2.226	2.268	2.310	2.352	2.395	2.439	2.483	2.527	43
.7	2.572	2.618	2.664	2.711	2.758	2.806	2.855	2.903	2.953	3.003	48
.8	3.054	3.105	3.157	3.209	3.262	3.315	3.369	3.424	3.479	3.535	54
.9	3.591	3.648	3.706	3.764	3.823	3.882	3.942	4.003	4.064	4.126	60
2.0	4.189	4.252	4.316	4.380	4.445	4.511	4.577	4.644	4.712	4.780	66
.1	4.849	4.919	4.989	5.060	5.131	5.204	5.277	5.350	5.425	5.500	73
.2	5.575	5.652	5.729	5.806	5.885	5.964	6.044	6.125	6.206	6.288	80
.3	6.371	6.454	6.538	6.623	6.709	6.795	6.882	6.970	7.059	7.148	87
.4	7.238	7.329	7.421	7.513	7.606	7.700	7.795	7.890	7.986	8.083	94
2.5	8.181	8.280	8.379	8.478	8.580	8.682	8.785	8.888	8.992	9.097	102
.6	9.203	9.309	9.417	9.525	9.634	9.744	9.855	9.966	10.079		110
.6									10.08	10.19	11
.7	10.31	10.42	10.54	10.65	10.77	10.89	11.01	11.13	11.25	11.37	12
.8	11.49	11.62	11.74	11.87	11.99	12.12	12.25	12.38	12.51	12.64	13
.9	12.77	12.90	13.04	13.17	13.31	13.44	13.58	13.72	13.86	14.00	14
3.0	14.14	14.28	14.42	14.57	14.71	14.86	15.00	15.15	15.30	15.45	15
.1	15.60	15.75	15.90	16.06	16.21	16.37	16.52	16.68	16.84	17.00	16
.2	17.16	17.32	17.48	17.64	17.81	17.97	18.14	18.31	18.48	18.65	17
.3	18.82	18.99	19.16	19.33	19.51	19.68	19.86	20.04	20.22	20.40	18
.4	20.58	20.76	20.94	21.13	21.31	21.50	21.69	21.88	22.07	22.26	19
3.5	22.45	22.64	22.84	23.03	23.23	23.43	23.62	23.82	24.02	24.23	20
.6	24.43	24.63	24.84	25.04	25.25	25.46	25.67	25.88	26.09	26.31	21
.7	26.52	26.74	26.95	27.17	27.39	27.61	27.83	28.06	28.28	28.50	22
.8	28.73	28.96	29.19	29.42	29.65	29.88	30.11	30.35	30.58	30.82	23
.9	31.06	31.30	31.54	31.78	32.02	32.27	32.52	32,76	33.01	33.26	25
4.0	33.51	33.76	34.02	34.27	34.53	34.78	35.04	35.30	35.56	35.82	26
.1	36.09	36.35	36.62	36.88	37.15	37.42	37.69	37.97	38.24	38.52	27
.2	38.79	39.07	39.35	39.63	39.91	40.19	40.48	40.76	41.05	41.34	28
.3	41.63	41.92	42.21	42.51	42.80	43.10	43.40	43.70	44.00	44.30	30
.4	44.60	44.91	45.21	45.52	45.83	46.14	46.45	46.77	47.08	47.40	31
4.5	47.71	48.03	48.35	48.67	49.00	49.32	49.65	49.97	50.30	50.63	33
.6	50.97	51.30	51.63	51.97	52.31	52.65	52.99	53.33	53.67	54.02	34
.7	54.36	54.71	55.06	55.41	55.76	56.12	56.47	56.83	57.19	57.54	35
.8	57.91	58.27	58.63	59.00	59.37	59.73	60.10	60.48	60.85	61.22	37
.9	61.60	61.98	62.36	62.74	63.12	63.51	63.89	64.28	64.67	65.06	38

Explanation of Table of Volumes of Spheres (pp. 1–38 to 1–39).

Moving the decimal point ONE place in column D is equivalent to moving it THREE places in the body of the table. (D = diameter.)

$$\text{Volume of sphere} = \frac{\pi}{6} \times (\text{diam}^3) = 0.523599 \times (\text{diam}^3)$$

Conversely,

$$\text{Diam} = \sqrt[3]{\frac{6}{\pi}} \times \sqrt[3]{\text{volume}} = 1.240701 \times \sqrt[3]{\text{volume}}$$

Volumes of Spheres (continued)

D	0	1	2	3	4	5	6	7	8	9	Avg diff
5.0	65.45	65.84	66.24	66.64	67.03	67.43	67.83	68.24	68.64	69.05	40
.1	69.46	69.87	70.28	70.69	71.10	71.52	71.94	72.36	72.78	73.20	42
.2	73.62	74.05	74.47	74.90	75.33	75.77	76.20	76.64	77.07	77.51	43
.3	77.95	78.39	78.84	79.28	79.73	80.18	80.63	81.08	81.54	81.99	45
.4	82.45	82.91	83.37	83.83	84.29	84.76	85.23	85.70	86.17	86.64	47
5.5	87.11	87.59	88.07	88.55	89.03	89.51	90.00	90.48	90.97	91.49	48
.6	91.95	92.45	92.94	93.44	93.94	94.44	94.94	95.44	95.95	96.46	50
.7	96.97	97.48	97.99	98.51	99.02	99.54	100.06				52
.7							100.1	100.6	101.1	101.6	5
.8	102.2	102.7	103.2	103.8	104.3	104.8	105.4	105.9	106.4	107.0	5
.9	107.5	108.1	108.6	109.2	109.7	110.3	110.9	111.4	112.0	112.5	6
6.0	113.1	113.7	114.2	114.8	115.4	115.9	116.5	117.7	117.1	118.3	6
.1	118.8	119.4	120.0	120.6	121.2	121.8	122.4	123.6	123.0	124.2	
.2	124.8	125.4	126.0	126.6	127.2	127.8	128.4	129.1	129.7	130.3	
.3	130.9	131.5	132.2	132.8	133.4	134.1	134.7	135.3	136.0	136.6	
.4	137.3	137.9	138.5	139.2	139.8	140.5	141.2	141.8	142.5	143.1	7
6.5	143.8	144.5	145.1	145.8	146.5	147.1	147.8	148.5	149.2	149.8	
.6	150.5	151.2	151.9	152.6	153.3	154.0	154.7	155.4	156.1	156.8	
.7	157.5	158.2	158.9	159.6	160.3	161.0	161.7	162.5	163.2	163.9	
.8	164.6	165.4	166.1	166.8	167.6	168.3	169.0	169.8	170.5	171.3	
.9	172.0	172.8	173.5	174.3	175.0	175.8	176.5	177.3	178.1	178.8	8
7.0	179.6	180.4	181.1	181.9	182.7	183.5	184.3	185.0	185.8	186.6	
.1	187.4	188.2	189.0	189.8	190.6	191.4	192.2	193.0	193.8	194.6	
.2	195.4	196.2	197.1	197.9	198.7	199.5	200.4	201.2	202.0	202.9	
.3	203.7	204.5	205.4	206.2	207.1	207.9	208.8	209.6	210.5	211.3	
.4	212.2	213.0	213.9	214.8	215.6	216.5	217.4	218.3	219.1	220.0	9
7.5	220.9	221.8	222.7	223.6	224.4	225.3	226.2	227.1	228.0	228.9	
.6	229.8	230.8	231.7	232.6	233.5	234.4	235.3	236.3	237.2	238.1	
.7	239.0	240.0	240.9	241.8	242.8	243.7	244.7	245.6	246.6	247.5	
.8	248.5	249.4	250.4	251.4	252.3	253.3	254.3	255.2	256.2	257.2	10
.9	258.2	259.1	260.1	261.1	262.1	263.1	264.1	265.1	266.1	267.1	
8.0	268.1	269.1	270.1	271.1	272.1	273.1	274.2	275.2	276.2	277.2	
.1	278.3	279.3	280.3	281.4	282.4	283.4	284.5	285.5	286.6	287.6	11
.2	288.7	289.8	290.8	291.9	292.9	294.0	295.1	296.2	297.2	298.3	
.3	299.4	300.5	301.6	302.6	303.7	304.8	305.9	307.0	308.1	309.2	
.4	310.3	311.4	312.6	313.7	314.8	315.9	317.0	318.2	319.3	320.4	
8.5	321.6	322.7	323.8	325.0	326.1	327.3	328.4	329.6	330.7	331.9	
.6	333.0	334.2	335.4	336.5	337.7	338.9	340.1	341.2	342.4	343.6	12
.7	344.8	346.0	347.2	348.4	349.6	350.8	352.0	353.2	354.4	355.6	
.8	356.8	358.0	359.3	360.5	361.7	362.9	364.2	365.4	366.6	367.9	
.9	369.1	370.4	371.6	372.9	374.1	375.4	376.6	377.9	379.2	380.4	13
9.0	381.7	383.0	384.3	385.5	386.8	388.1	389.4	390.7	392.0	393.3	
.1	394.6	395.9	397.2	398.5	399.8	401.1	402.4	403.7	405.1	406.4	
.2	407.7	409.1	410.4	411.7	413.1	414.4	415.7	417.1	418.4	419.8	14
.3	421.2	422.5	423.9	425.2	426.6	428.0	429.4	430.7	432.1	433.5	
.4	434.9	436.3	437.7	439.1	440.5	441.9	443.3	444.7	446.1	447.5	
9.5	448.9	450.3	451.8	453.2	454.6	456.0	457.5	458.9	460.4	461.8	
.6	463.2	464.7	466.1	467.6	469.1	470.5	472.0	473.5	474.9	476.4	15
.7	477.9	479.4	480.8	482.3	483.8	485.3	486.8	488.3	489.8	491.3	
.8	492.8	494.3	495.8	497.3	498.9	500.4	501.9	503.4	505.0	506.5	16
.9	508.0	509.6	511.1	512.7	514.2	515.8	517.3	518.9	520.5	522.0	
10.0	523.6										

Moving the decimal point ONE place in *D* requires moving it THREE places in body of table (see p. 1–38).

Segments of Spheres

(h = height of segment; D = diam of sphere)

$\dfrac{h}{D}$	$\dfrac{\text{Vol segm}}{D^3}$	Diff	$\dfrac{\text{Vol segm}}{\text{Vol sphere}}$	Diff
0.00	0.0000		0.0000	
		2		3
1	0.0002		0.0003	
		4		9
2	0.0006		0.0012	
		8		14
3	0.0014		0.0026	
		10		21
4	0.0024		0.0047	
		14		26
0.05	0.0038		0.0073	
		16		31
6	0.0054		0.0104	
		19		36
7	0.0073		0.0140	
		22		42
8	0.0095		0.0182	
		25		46
9	0.0120		0.0228	
		27		52
0.10	0.0147		0.0280	
		29		56
1	0.0176		0.0336	
		32		61
2	0.0208		0.0397	
		34		66
3	0.0242		0.0463	
		37		70
4	0.0279		0.0533	
		39		74
0.15	0.0318		0.0607	
		41		79
6	0.0359		0.0686	
		44		83
7	0.0403		0.0769	
		45		86
8	0.0448		0.0855	
		47		91
9	0.0495		0.0946	
		50		94
0.20	0.0545		0.1040	
		51		98
1	0.0596		0.1138	
		53		101
2	0.0649		0.1239	
		55		105
3	0.0704		0.1344	
		56		108
4	0.0760		0.1452	
		58		110
0.25	0.0818		0.1562	
		60		114
6	0.0878		0.1676	
		61		117
7	0.0939		0.1793	
		63		120
8	0.1002		0.1913	
		64		122
9	0.1066		0.2035	
		65		125
0.30	0.1131		0.2160	
		67		127
1	0.1198		0.2287	
		67		130
2	0.1265		0.2417	
		69		131
3	0.1334		0.2548	
		70		134
4	0.1404		0.2682	
		71		135
0.35	0.1475		0.2817	
		72		138
6	0.1547		0.2955	
		73		139
7	0.1620		0.3094	
		74		141
8	0.1694		0.3235	
		74		142
9	0.1768		0.3377	
		75		143
0.40	0.1843		0.3520	
		76		145
1	0.1919		0.3665	
		76		145
2	0.1995		0.3810	
		77		147
3	0.2072		0.3957	
		77		147
4	0.2149		0.4104	
		78		148
0.45	0.2227		0.4252	
		78		149
6	0.2305		0.4401	
		78		150
7	0.2383		0.4551	
		78		149
8	0.2461		0.4700	
		78		150
9	0.2539		0.4850	
		79		150
0.50	0.2618		0.5000	

Explanation of Table on this page

Given, h = height of segment,

D = diameter of sphere.

To find the volume of the segment, form the ratio h/D and find from the table the value of (vol/D^3): then, by a simple multiplication,

$$\text{volume segment} = D^3 \times (\text{vol}/D^3)$$

The table gives also the ratio of the volume of the segment to the entire volume of the sphere.

NOTE. Area of zone = $\pi \times h \times D$.

(Use Table of Multiples of π, p. 1–30)

Explanation of Table on p. 1–36

Given, h = height of segment,

c = chord.

To find the diameter of the circle, the length of arc, or the area of the segment, form the ratio h/c, and find from the table the value of (diam/c), (arc/c), or (area/hc); then, by a simple multiplication,

diam = $c \times (\text{diam}/c)$,

arc = $c \times (\text{arc}/c)$,

area = $h \times c \times (\text{area}/hc)$.

The table gives also the angle subtended at the center, and the ratio of h to D. See p. 2–19.

Explanation of Table on p. 1–37

Given, h = height of segment,

D = diameter of circle.

To find the chord, the length of arc, or the area of the segment, form the ratio h/D, and find from the table the value of (chord/D), (arc/D), or (area/D^2); then, by a simple multiplication,

chord = $D \times (\text{chord}/D)$,

arc   = $D \times (\text{arc}/D)$,

area = $D^2 \times (\text{area}/D^2)$.

The table gives also the angle subtended at the center, the ratio of the arc of the segment to the whole circumference, and the ratio of the area of the segment to the area of the whole circle. See p. 2–19.

NOTE. Vol segm = $\tfrac{1}{6}\,\pi\,h^2\,(3D - 2h)$.

Regular Polygons

n = number of sides;
$v = 360°/n$ = angle subtended at the center by one side;

a = length of one side = $R\left(2\sin\dfrac{v}{2}\right) = r\left(2\tan\dfrac{v}{2}\right)$;

R = radius of circumscribed circle = $a\left(\tfrac{1}{2}\csc\dfrac{v}{2}\right) = r\left(\sec\dfrac{v}{2}\right)$;

r = radius of inscribed circle = $R\left(\cos\dfrac{v}{2}\right) = a\left(\tfrac{1}{2}\cot\dfrac{v}{2}\right)$;

Area = $a^2\left(\tfrac{1}{4}n\cot\dfrac{v}{2}\right) = R^2(\tfrac{1}{2}n\sin v) = r^2\left(n\tan\dfrac{v}{2}\right)$.

n	v	$\dfrac{\text{Area}}{a^2}$	$\dfrac{\text{Area}}{R^2}$	$\dfrac{\text{Area}}{r^2}$	$\dfrac{R}{a}$	$\dfrac{R}{r}$	$\dfrac{a}{R}$	$\dfrac{a}{r}$	$\dfrac{r}{R}$	$\dfrac{r}{a}$
3	120°	0.4330	1.299	5.196	0.5774	2.000	1.732	3.464	0.5000	0.2887
4	90°	1.000	2.000	4.000	0.7071	1.414	1.414	2.000	0.7071	0.5000
5	72°	1.721	2.378	3.633	0.8507	1.236	1.176	1.453	0.8090	0.6882
6	60°	2.598	2.598	3.464	1.0000	1.155	1.000	1.155	0.8660	0.8660
7	51°.43	3.634	2.736	3.371	1.152	1.110	0.8678	0.9631	0.9010	1.038
8	45°	4.828	2.828	3.314	1.307	1.082	0.7654	0.8284	0.9239	1.207
9	40°	6.182	2.893	3.276	1.462	1.064	0.6840	0.7279	0.9397	1.374
10	36°	7.694	2.939	3.249	1.618	1.052	0.6180	0.6498	0.9511	1.539
12	30°	11.20	3.000	3.215	1.932	1.035	0.5176	0.5359	0.9659	1.866
15	24°	17.64	3.051	3.188	2.405	1.022	0.4158	0.4251	0.9781	2.352
16	22°.50	20.11	3.062	3.183	2.563	1.020	0.3902	0.3978	0.9808	2.514
20	18°	31.57	3.090	3.168	3.196	1.013	0.3129	0.3168	0.9877	3.157
24	15°	45.58	3.106	3.160	3.831	1.009	0.2611	0.2633	0.9914	3.798
32	11°.25	81.23	3.121	3.152	5.101	1.005	0.1960	0.1970	0.9952	5.077
48	7°.50	183.1	3.133	3.146	7.645	1.002	0.1308	0.1311	0.9979	7.629
64	5°.625	325.7	3.137	3.144	10.19	1.001	0.0981	0.0983	0.9968	10.18

Binomial Coefficients

$(n)_0 = 1$; $(n)_1 = n$; $(n)_2 = \dfrac{n(n-1)}{1\times 2}$; $(n)_3 = \dfrac{n(n-1)(n-2)}{1\times 2\times 3}$; etc.; in general,

$(n)_r = \dfrac{n(n-1)(n-2)\ldots(n-[r-1])}{1\times 2\times 3\ldots\times r}$. Other notations: $_nC_r = \begin{pmatrix} n \\ r \end{pmatrix} = (n)_r$.

n	$(n)_0$	$(n)_1$	$(n)_2$	$(n)_3$	$(n)_4$	$(n)_5$	$(n)_6$	$(n)_7$	$(n)_8$	$(n)_9$	$(n)_{10}$	$(n)_{11}$	$(n)_{12}$	$(n)_{13}$
1	1	1												
2	1	2	1											
3	1	3	3	1										
4	1	4	6	4	1									
5	1	5	10	10	5	1								
6	1	6	15	20	15	6	1							
7	1	7	21	35	35	21	7	1						
8	1	8	28	56	70	56	28	8	1					
9	1	9	36	84	126	126	84	36	9	1				
10	1	10	45	120	210	252	210	120	45	10	1			
11	1	11	55	165	330	462	462	330	165	55	11	1		
12	1	12	66	220	495	792	924	792	495	220	66	12	1	
13	1	13	78	286	715	1287	1716	1716	1287	715	286	78	13	1
14	1	14	91	364	1001	2002	3003	3432	3003	2002	1001	364	91	14
15	1	15	105	455	1365	3003	5005	6435	6435	5005	3003	1365	455	105

For $n = 14$, $(n)_{14} = 1$; for $n = 15$, $(n)_{14} = 15$, and $(n)_{15} = 1$.

MATHEMATICS

Common Logarithms (1.00 to 2.00)

Num-ber	0	1	2	3	4	5	6	7	8	9	Avg diff
1.00	0.0000	0004	0009	0013	0017	0022	0026	0030	0035	0039	4
1.01	0043	0048	0052	0056	0060	0065	0069	0073	0077	0082	
1.02	0086	0090	0095	0099	0103	0107	0111	0116	0120	0124	
1.03	0128	0133	0137	0141	0145	0149	0154	0158	0162	0166	
1.04	0170	0175	0179	0183	0187	0191	0195	0199	0204	0208	
1.05	0212	0216	0220	0224	0228	0233	0237	0241	0245	0249	
1.06	0253	0257	0261	0265	0269	0273	0278	0282	0286	0290	
1.07	0294	0298	0302	0306	0310	0314	0318	0322	0326	0330	
1.08	0334	0338	0342	0346	0350	0354	0358	0362	0366	0370	
1.09	0374	0378	0382	0386	0390	0394	0398	0402	0406	0410	
1.10	0.0414	0418	0422	0426	0430	0434	0438	0441	0445	0449	
1.11	0453	0457	0461	0465	0469	0473	0477	0481	0484	0488	
1.12	0492	0496	0500	0504	0508	0512	0515	0519	0523	0527	
1.13	0531	0535	0538	0542	0546	0550	0554	0558	0561	0565	
1.14	0569	0573	0577	0580	0584	0588	0592	0596	0599	0603	
1.15	0607	0611	0615	0618	0622	0626	0630	0633	0637	0641	
1.16	0645	0648	0652	0656	0660	0663	0667	0671	0674	0678	
1.17	0682	0686	0689	0693	0697	0700	0704	0708	0711	0715	
1.18	0719	0722	0726	0730	0734	0737	0741	0745	0748	0752	
1.19	0755	0759	0763	0766	0770	0774	0777	0781	0785	0788	
1.20	0.0792	0795	0799	0803	0806	0810	0813	0817	0821	0824	
1.21	0828	0831	0835	0839	0842	0846	0849	0853	0856	0860	
1.22	0864	0867	0871	0874	0878	0881	0885	0888	0892	0896	
1.23	0899	0903	0906	0910	0913	0917	0920	0924	0927	0931	
1.24	0934	0938	0941	0945	0948	0952	0955	0959	0962	0966	
1.25	0969	0973	0976	0980	0983	0986	0990	0993	0997	1000	3
1.26	1004	1007	1011	1014	1017	1021	1024	1028	1031	1035	
1.27	1038	1041	1045	1048	1052	1055	1059	1062	1065	1069	
1.28	1072	1075	1079	1082	1086	1089	1092	1096	1099	1103	
1.29	1106	1109	1113	1116	1119	1123	1126	1129	1133	1136	
1.30	0.1139	1143	1146	1149	1153	1156	1159	1163	1166	1169	
1.31	1173	1176	1179	1183	1186	1189	1193	1196	1199	1202	
1.32	1206	1209	1212	1216	1219	1222	1225	1229	1232	1235	
1.33	1239	1242	1245	1248	1252	1255	1258	1261	1265	1268	
1.34	1271	1274	1278	1281	1284	1287	1290	1294	1297	1300	
1.35	1303	1307	1310	1313	1316	1319	1323	1326	1329	1332	
1.36	1335	1339	1342	1345	1348	1351	1355	1358	1361	1364	
1.37	1367	1370	1374	1377	1380	1383	1386	1389	1392	1396	
1.38	1399	1402	1405	1408	1411	1414	1418	1421	1424	1427	
1.39	1430	1433	1436	1440	1443	1446	1449	1452	1455	1458	
1.40	0.1461	1464	1467	1471	1474	1477	1480	1483	1486	1489	
1.41	1492	1495	1498	1501	1504	1508	1511	1514	1517	1520	
1.42	1523	1526	1529	1532	1535	1538	1541	1544	1547	1550	
1.43	1553	1556	1559	1562	1565	1569	1572	1575	1578	1581	
1.44	1584	1587	1590	1593	1596	1599	1602	1605	1608	1611	
1.45	1614	1617	1620	1623	1626	1629	1632	1635	1638	1641	
1.46	1644	1647	1649	1652	1655	1658	1661	1664	1667	1670	
1.47	1673	1676	1679	1682	1685	1688	1691	1694	1697	1700	
1.48	1703	1706	1708	1711	1714	1717	1720	1723	1726	1729	
1.49	1732	1735	1738	1741	1744	1746	1749	1752	1755	1758	

Moving the decimal point n places to the right [or left] in the number requires adding $+ n$ [or $- n$] in the body of the table (see p. 1–44).

Common Logarithms (1.00 to 2.00) (*continued*)

Number	0	1	2	3	4	5	6	7	8	9	Avg diff
1.50	0.1761	1764	1767	1770	1772	1775	1778	1781	1784	1787	3
1.51	1790	1793	1796	1798	1801	1804	1807	1810	1813	1816	
1.52	1818	1821	1824	1827	1830	1833	1836	1838	1841	1844	
1.53	1847	1850	1853	1855	1858	1861	1864	1867	1870	1872	
1.54	1875	1878	1881	1884	1886	1889	1892	1895	1898	1901	
1.55	1903	1906	1909	1912	1915	1917	1920	1923	1926	1928	
1.56	1931	1934	1937	1940	1942	1945	1948	1951	1953	1956	
1.57	1959	1962	1965	1967	1970	1973	1976	1978	1981	1984	
1.58	1987	1989	1992	1995	1998	2000	2003	2006	2009	2011	
1.59	2014	2017	2019	2022	2025	2028	2030	2033	2036	2038	
1.60	0.2041	2044	2047	2049	2052	2055	2057	2060	2063	2066	
1.61	2068	2071	2074	2076	2079	2082	2084	2087	2090	2092	
1.62	2095	2098	2101	2103	2106	2109	2111	2114	2117	2119	
1.63	2122	2125	2127	2130	2133	2135	2138	2140	2143	2146	
1.64	2148	2151	2154	2156	2159	2162	2164	2167	2170	2172	
1.65	2175	2177	2180	2183	2185	2188	2191	2193	2196	2198	
1.66	2201	2204	2206	2209	2212	2214	2217	2219	2222	2225	
1.67	2227	2230	2232	2235	2238	2240	2243	2245	2248	2251	
1.68	2253	2256	2258	2261	2263	2266	2269	2271	2274	2276	
1.69	2279	2281	2284	2287	2289	2292	2294	2297	2299	2302	
1.70	0.2304	2307	2310	2312	2315	2317	2320	2322	2325	2327	
1.71	2330	2333	2335	2338	2340	2343	2345	2348	2350	2353	
1.72	2355	2358	2360	2363	2365	2368	2370	2373	2375	2378	
1.73	2380	2383	2385	2388	2390	2393	2395	2398	2400	2403	
1.74	2405	2408	2410	2413	2415	2418	2420	2423	2425	2428	2
1.75	2430	2433	2435	2438	2440	2443	2445	2448	2450	2453	
1.76	2455	2458	2460	2463	2465	2467	2470	2472	2475	2477	
1.77	2480	2482	2485	2487	2490	2492	2494	2497	2499	2502	
1.78	2504	2507	2509	2512	2514	2516	2519	2521	2524	2526	
1.79	2529	2531	2533	2536	2538	2541	2543	2545	2548	2550	
1.80	0.2553	2555	2558	2560	2562	2565	2567	2570	2572	2574	
1.81	2577	2579	2582	2584	2586	2589	2591	2594	2596	2598	
1.82	2601	2603	2605	2608	2610	2613	2615	2617	2620	2622	
1.83	2625	2627	2629	2632	2634	2636	2639	2641	2643	2646	
1.84	2648	2651	2653	2655	2658	2660	2662	2665	2667	2669	
1.85	2672	2674	2676	2679	2681	2683	2686	2688	2690	2693	
1.86	2695	2697	2700	2702	2704	2707	2709	2711	2714	2716	
1.87	2718	2721	2723	2725	2728	2730	2732	2735	2737	2739	
1.88	2742	2744	2746	2749	2751	2753	2755	2758	2760	2762	
1.89	2765	2767	2769	2772	2774	2776	2778	2781	2783	2785	
1.90	0.2788	2790	2792	2794	2797	2799	2801	2804	2806	2808	
1.91	2810	2813	2815	2817	2819	2822	2824	2826	2828	2831	
1.92	2833	2835	2838	2840	2842	2844	2847	2849	2851	2853	
1.93	2856	2858	2860	2862	2865	2867	2869	2871	2874	2876	
1.94	2878	2880	2882	2885	2887	2889	2891	2894	2896	2898	
1.95	2900	2903	2905	2907	2909	2911	2914	2916	2918	2920	
1.96	2923	2925	2927	2929	2931	2934	2936	2938	2940	2942	
1.97	2945	2947	2949	2951	2953	2956	2958	2960	2962	2964	
1.98	2967	2969	2971	2973	2975	2978	2980	2982	2984	2986	
1.99	2989	2991	2993	2995	2997	2999	3002	3004	3006	3008	

MATHEMATICS

Common Logarithms

Number	0	1	2	3	4	5	6	7	8	9	Avg diff
1.0	0.0000	0043	0086	0128	0170	0212	0253	0294	0334	0374	
1.1	0414	0453	0492	0531	0569	0607	0645	0682	0719	0755	
1.2	0792	0828	0864	0899	0934	0969	1004	1038	1072	1106	
1.3	1139	1173	1206	1239	1271	1303	1335	1367	1399	1430	
1.4	1461	1492	1523	1553	1584	1614	1644	1673	1703	1732	
1.5	1761	1790	1818	1847	1875	1903	1931	1959	1987	2014	See pages 1–42 to 1–44
1.6	2041	2068	2095	2122	2148	2175	2201	2227	2253	2279	
1.7	2304	2330	2355	2380	2405	2430	2455	2480	2504	2529	
1.8	2553	2577	2601	2625	2648	2672	2695	2718	2742	2765	
1.9	2788	2810	2833	2856	2878	2900	2923	2945	2967	2989	
2.0	0.3010	3032	3054	3075	3096	3118	3139	3160	3181	3201	21
2.1	3222	3243	3263	3284	3304	3324	3345	3365	3385	3404	20
2.2	3424	3444	3464	3483	3502	3522	3541	3560	3579	3598	19
2.3	3617	3636	3655	3674	3692	3711	3729	3747	3766	3784	18
2.4	3802	3820	3838	3856	3874	3892	3909	3927	3945	3962	17
2.5	3979	3997	4014	4031	4048	4065	4082	4099	4116	4133	17
2.6	4150	4166	4183	4200	4216	4232	4249	4265	4281	4298	16
2.7	4314	4330	4346	4362	4378	4393	4409	4425	4440	4456	16
2.8	4472	4487	4502	4518	4533	4548	4564	4579	4594	4609	15
2.9	4624	4639	4654	4669	4683	4698	4713	4728	4742	4757	15
3.0	0.4771	4786	4800	4814	4829	4843	4857	4871	4886	4900	14
3.1	4914	4928	4942	4955	4969	4983	4997	5011	5024	5038	14
3.2	5051	5065	5079	5092	5105	5119	5132	5145	5159	5172	13
3.3	5185	5198	5211	5224	5237	5250	5263	5276	5289	5302	13
3.4	5315	5328	5340	5353	5366	5378	5391	5403	5416	5428	13
3.5	5441	5453	5465	5478	5490	5502	5514	5527	5539	5551	12
3.6	5563	5575	5587	5599	5611	5623	5635	5647	5658	5670	12
3.7	5682	5694	5705	5717	5729	5740	5752	5763	5775	5786	12
3.8	5798	5809	5821	5832	5843	5855	5866	5877	5888	5899	11
3.9	5911	5922	5933	5944	5955	5966	5977	5988	5999	6010	11
4.0	0.6021	6031	6042	6053	6064	6075	6085	6096	6107	6117	11
4.1	6128	6138	6149	6160	6170	6180	6191	6201	6212	6222	10
4.2	6232	6243	6253	6263	6274	6284	6294	6304	6314	6325	10
4.3	6335	6345	6355	6365	6375	6385	6395	6405	6415	6425	10
4.4	6435	6444	6454	6464	6474	6484	6493	6503	6513	6522	10
4.5	6532	6542	6551	6561	6571	6580	6590	6599	6609	6618	10
4.6	6628	6637	6646	6656	6665	6675	6684	6693	6702	6712	10
4.7	6721	6730	6739	6749	6758	6767	6776	6785	6794	6803	9
4.8	6812	6821	6830	6839	6848	6857	6866	6875	6884	6893	9
4.9	6902	6911	6920	6928	6937	6946	6955	6964	6972	6981	9

$$\log \pi = 0.4971 \qquad \log \pi/2 = 0.1961 \qquad \log \pi^2 = 0.9943 \qquad \log \sqrt{\pi} = 0.2486$$
$$\log e = 0.4343 \qquad \log (0.4343) = 0.6378 - 1$$

These two pages give the common logarithms of numbers between 1 and 10, correct to four places. Moving the decimal point n places to the right [or left] in the number is equivalent to adding n [or $-n$] to the logarithm. Thus, log 0.017453 = 0.2419 − 2, which may also be written $\bar{2}$.2419 or 8.2419 − 10.

$$\log (ab) = \log a + \log b \qquad \log (a^N) = N \log a$$
$$\log \left(\frac{a}{b}\right) = \log a - \log b \qquad \log \left(\sqrt[N]{a}\right) = \frac{1}{N} \log a$$

Common Logarithms (continued)

Number	0	1	2	3	4	5	6	7	8	9	Avg diff
5.0	0.6990	6998	7007	7016	7024	7033	7042	7050	7059	7067	9
5.1	7076	7084	7093	7101	7110	7118	7126	7135	7143	7152	8
5.2	7160	7168	7177	7185	7193	7202	7210	7218	7226	7235	8
5.3	7243	7251	7259	7267	7275	7284	7292	7300	7308	7316	8
5.4	7324	7332	7340	7348	7356	7364	7372	7380	7388	7396	8
5.5	7404	7412	7419	7427	7435	7443	7451	7459	7466	7474	8
5.6	7482	7490	7497	7505	7513	7520	7528	7536	7543	7551	8
5.7	7559	7566	7574	7582	7589	7597	7604	7612	7619	7627	8
5.8	7634	7642	7649	7657	7664	7672	7679	7686	7694	7701	7
5.9	7709	7716	7723	7731	7738	7745	7752	7760	7767	7774	7
6.0	0.7782	7789	7796	7803	7810	7818	7825	7832	7839	7846	7
6.1	7853	7860	7868	7875	7882	7889	7896	7903	7910	7917	7
6.2	7924	7931	7938	7945	7952	7959	7966	7973	7980	7987	7
6.3	7993	8000	8007	8014	8021	8028	8035	8041	8048	8055	7
6.4	8062	8069	8075	8082	8089	8096	8102	8109	8116	8122	7
6.5	8129	8136	8142	8149	8156	8162	8169	8176	8182	8189	7
6.6	8195	8202	8209	8215	8222	8228	8235	8241	8248	8254	7
6.7	8261	8267	8274	8280	8287	8293	8299	8306	8312	8319	6
6.8	8325	8331	8338	8344	8351	8357	8363	8370	8376	8382	6
6.9	8388	8395	8401	8407	8414	8420	8426	8432	8439	8445	6
7.0	0.8451	8457	8463	8470	8476	8482	8488	8494	8500	8506	6
7.1	8513	8519	8525	8531	8537	8543	8549	8555	8561	8567	6
7.2	8573	8579	8585	8591	8597	8603	8609	8615	8621	8627	6
7.3	8633	8639	8645	8651	8657	8663	8669	8675	8681	8686	6
7.4	8692	8698	8704	8710	8716	8722	8727	8733	8739	8745	6
7.5	8751	8756	8762	8768	8774	8779	8785	8791	8797	8802	6
7.6	8808	8814	8820	8825	8831	8837	8842	8848	8854	8859	6
7.7	8865	8871	8876	8882	8887	8893	8899	8904	8910	8915	6
7.8	8921	8927	8932	8938	8943	8949	8954	8960	8965	8971	6
7.9	8976	8982	8987	8993	8998	9004	9009	9015	9020	9025	5
8.0	0.9031	9036	9042	9047	9053	9058	9063	9069	9074	9079	5
8.1	9085	9090	9096	9101	9106	9112	9117	9122	9128	9133	5
8.2	9138	9143	9149	9154	9159	9165	9170	9175	9180	9186	5
8.3	9191	9196	9201	9206	9212	9217	9222	9227	9232	9238	5
8.4	9243	9248	9253	9258	9263	9269	9274	9279	9284	9289	5
8.5	9294	9299	9304	9309	9315	9320	9325	9330	9335	9340	5
8.6	9345	9350	9355	9360	9365	9370	9375	9380	9385	9390	5
8.7	9395	9400	9405	9410	9415	9420	9425	9430	9435	9440	5
8.8	9445	9450	9455	9460	9465	9469	9474	9479	9484	9489	5
8.9	9494	9499	9504	9509	9513	9518	9523	9528	9533	9538	5
9.0	0.9542	9547	9552	9557	9562	9566	9571	9576	9581	9586	5
9.1	9590	9595	9600	9605	9609	9614	9619	9624	9628	9633	5
9.2	9638	9643	9647	9652	9657	9661	9666	9671	9675	9680	5
9.3	9685	9689	9694	9699	9703	9708	9713	9717	9722	9727	5
9.4	9731	9736	9741	9745	9750	9754	9759	9763	9768	9773	5
9.5	9777	9782	9786	9791	9795	9800	9805	9809	9814	9818	5
9.6	9823	9827	9832	9836	9841	9845	9850	9854	9859	9863	4
9.7	9868	9872	9877	9881	9886	9890	9894	9899	9903	9908	4
9.8	9912	9917	9921	9926	9930	9934	9939	9943	9948	9952	4
9.9	9956	9961	9965	9969	9974	9978	9983	9987	9991	9996	4

Degrees and Minutes Expressed in Radians (see also p. 1–71)

Degrees						Hundredths				Minutes	
1°	.0175	61°	1.0647	121°	2.1118	0°.01	.0002	0°.51	.0089	1′	.0003
2	.0349	2	1.0821	2	2.1293	2	.0003	2	.0091	2′	.0006
3	.0524	3	1.0996	3	2.1468	3	.0005	3	.0093	3′	.0009
4	.0698	4	1.1170	4	2.1642	4	.0007	4	.0094	4′	.0012
5°	.0873	65°	1.1345	125°	2.1817	.05	.0009	.55	.0096	5′	.0015
6	.1047	6	1.1519	6	2.1991	6	.0010	6	.0098	6′	.0017
7	.1222	7	1.1694	7	2.2166	7	.0012	7	.0099	7′	.0020
8	.1396	8	1.1868	8	2.2340	8	.0014	8	.0101	8′	.0023
9	.1571	9	1.2043	9	2.2515	9	.0016	9	.0103	9′	.0026
10°	.1745	70°	1.2217	130°	2.2689	0°.10	.0017	0°.60	.0105	10′	.0029
1	.1920	1	1.2392	1	2.2864	1	.0019	1	.0106	11′	.0032
2	.2094	2	1.2566	2	2.3038	2	.0021	2	.0108	12′	.0035
3	.2269	3	1.2741	3	2.3213	3	.0023	3	.0110	13′	.0038
4	.2443	4	1.2915	4	2.3387	4	.0024	4	.0112	14′	.0041
15°	.2618	75°	1.3090	135°	2.3562	.15	.0026	.65	.0113	15′	.0044
6	.2793	6	1.3265	6	2.3736	6	.0028	6	.0115	16′	.0047
7	.2967	7	1.3439	7	2.3911	7	.0030	7	.0117	17′	.0049
8	.3142	8	1.3614	8	2.4086	8	.0031	8	.0119	18′	.0052
9	.3316	9	1.3788	9	2.4260	9	.0033	9	.0120	19′	.0055
20°	.3491	80°	1.3963	140°	2.4435	0°.20	.0035	0°.70	.0122	20′	.0058
1	.3665	1	1.4137	1	2.4609	1	.0037	1	.0124	21′	.0061
2	.3840	2	1.4312	2	2.4784	2	.0038	2	.0126	22′	.0064
3	.4014	3	1.4486	3	2.4958	3	.0040	3	.0127	23′	.0067
4	.4189	4	1.4661	4	2.5133	4	.0042	4	.0129	24′	.0070
25°	.4363	85°	1.4835	145°	2.5307	.25	.0044	.75	.0131	25′	.0073
6	.4538	6	1.5010	6	2.5482	6	.0045	6	.0133	26′	.0076
7	.4712	7	1.5184	7	2.5656	7	.0047	7	.0134	27′	.0079
8	.4887	8	1.5359	8	2.5831	8	.0049	8	.0136	28′	.0081
9	.5061	9	1.5533	9	2.6005	9	.0051	9	.0138	29′	.0084
30°	.5236	90°	1.5708	150°	2.6180	0°.30	.0052	0°.80	.0140	30′	.0087
1	.5411	1	1.5882	1	2.6354	1	.0054	1	.0141	31′	.0090
2	.5585	2	1.6057	2	2.6529	2	.0056	2	.0143	32′	.0093
3	.5760	3	1.6232	3	2.6704	3	.0058	3	.0145	33′	.0096
4	.5934	4	1.6406	4	2.6878	4	.0059	4	.0147	34′	.0099
35°	.6109	95°	1.6581	155°	2.7053	.35	.0061	.85	.0148	35′	.0102
6	.6283	6	1.6755	6	2.7227	6	.0063	6	.0150	36′	.0105
7	.6458	7	1.6930	7	2.7402	7	.0065	7	.0152	37′	.0108
8	.6632	8	1.7104	8	2.7576	8	.0066	8	.0154	38′	.0111
9	.6807	9	1.7279	9	2.7751	9	.0068	9	.0155	39′	.0113
40°	.6981	100°	1.7453	160°	2.7925	0°.40	.0070	0°.90	.0157	40′	.0116
1	.7156	1	1.7628	1	2.8100	1	.0072	1	.0159	41′	.0119
2	.7330	2	1.7802	2	2.8274	2	.0073	2	.0161	42′	.0122
3	.7505	3	1.7977	3	2.8449	3	.0075	3	.0162	43′	.0125
4	.7679	4	1.8151	4	2.8623	4	.0077	4	.0164	44′	.0128
45°	.7854	105°	1.8326	165°	2.8798	.45	.0079	.95	.0166	45′	.0131
6	.8029	6	1.8500	6	2.8972	6	.0080	6	.0168	46′	.0134
7	.8203	7	1.8675	7	2.9147	7	.0082	7	.0169	47′	.0137
8	.8378	8	1.8850	8	2.9322	8	.0084	8	.0171	48′	.0140
9	.8552	9	1.9024	9	2.9496	9	.0086	9	.0173	49′	.0143
50°	.8727	110°	1.9199	170°	2.9671	0°.50	.0087	1°.00	.0175	50′	.0145
1	.8901	1	1.9373	1	2.9845					51′	.0148
2	.9076	2	1.9548	2	3.0020					52′	.0151
3	.9250	3	1.9722	3	3.0194					53′	.0154
4	.9425	4	1.9897	4	3.0369					54′	.0157
55°	.9599	115°	2.0071	175°	3.0543					55′	.0160
6	.9774	6	2.0246	6	3.0718					56′	.0163
7	.9948	7	2.0420	7	3.0892					57′	.0166
8	1.0123	8	2.0595	8	3.1067					58′	.0169
9	1.0297	9	2.0769	9	3.1241					59′	.0172
60°	1.0472	120°	2.0944	180°	3.1416					60′	.0175

Arc 1° = 0.0174533   Arc 1′ = 0.000290888   Arc 1″ = 0.00000484814
1 radian = 57°.295780 = 57° 17′.7468 = 57° 17′ 44″.806

Radians Expressed in Degrees

rad	deg	rad	deg	rad	deg	rad	deg	rad	deg
0.01	0°.57	.64	36°.67	1.27	72°.77	1.90	108°.86	2.53	144°.96
2	1°.15	.65	37°.24	8	73°.34	1	109°.43	4	145°.53
3	1°.72	6	37°.82	9	73°.91	2	110°.01	2.55	146°.10
4	2°.29	7	38°.39	1.30	74°.48	3	110°.58	6	146°.68
.05	2°.86	8	38°.96	1	75°.06	4	111°.15	7	147°.25
6	3°.44	9	39°.53	2	75°.63	1.95	111°.73	8	147°.82
7	4°.01	.70	40°.11	3	76°.20	6	112°.30	9	148°.40
8	4°.58	1	40°.68	4	76°.78	7	112°.87	2.60	148°.97
9	5°.16	2	41°.25	1.35	77°.35	8	113°.45	1	149°.54
.10	5°.73	3	41°.83	6	77°.92	9	114°.02	2	150°.11
1	6°.30	4	42°.40	7	78°.50	2.00	114°.59	3	150°.69
2	6°.88	.75	42°.97	8	79°.07	1	115°.16	4	151°.26
3	7°.45	6	43°.54	9	79°.64	2	115°.74	2.65	151°.83
4	8°.02	7	44°.12	1.40	80°.21	3	116°.31	6	152°.41
.15	8°.59	8	44°.69	1	80°.79	4	116°.88	7	152°.98
6	9°.17	9	45°.26	2	81°.36	2.05	117°.46	8	153°.55
7	9°.74	.80	45°.84	3	81°.93	6	118°.03	9	154°.13
8	10°.31	1	46°.41	4	82°.51	7	118°.60	2.70	154°.70
9	10°.89	2	46°.98	1.45	83°.08	8	119°.18	1	155°.27
.20	11°.46	3	47°.56	6	83°.65	9	119°.75	2	155°.84
1	12°.03	4	48°.13	7	84°.22	2.10	120°.32	3	156°.42
2	12°.61	.85	48°.70	8	84°.80	1	120°.89	4	156°.99
3	13°.18	6	49°.27	9	85°.37	2	121°.47	2.75	157°.56
4	13°.75	7	49°.85	1.50	85°.94	3	122°.04	6	158°.14
.25	14°.32	8	50°.42	1	86°.52	4	122°.61	7	158°.71
6	14°.90	9	50°.99	2	87°.09	2.15	123°.19	8	159°.28
7	15°.47	.90	51°.57	3	87°.66	6	123°.76	9	159°.86
8	16°.04	1	52°.14	4	88°.24	7	124°.33	2.80	160°.43
9	16°.62	2	52°.71	1.55	88°.81	8	124°.90	1	161°.00
.30	17°.19	3	53°.29	6	89°.38	9	125°.48	2	161°.57
1	17°.76	4	53°.86	7	89°.95	2.20	126°.05	3	162°.15
2	18°.33	.95	54°.43	8	90°.53	1	126°.62	4	162°.72
3	18°.91	6	55°.00	9	91°.10	2	127°.20	2.85	163°.29
4	19°.48	7	55°.58	1.60	91°.67	3	127°.77	6	163°.87
.35	20°.05	8	56°.15	1	92°.25	4	128°.34	7	164°.44
6	20°.63	9	56°.72	2	92°.82	2.25	128°.92	8	165°.01
7	21°.20	1.00	57°.30	3	93°.39	6	129°.49	9	165°.58
8	21°.77	1	57°.87	4	93°.97	7	130°.06	2.90	166°.16
9	22°.35	2	58°.44	1.65	94°.54	8	130°.63	1	166°.73
.40	22°.92	3	59°.01	6	95°.11	9	131°.21	2	167°.30
1	23°.49	4	59°.59	7	95°.68	2.30	131°.78	3	167°.88
2	24°.06	1.05	60°.16	8	96°.26	1	132°.35	4	168°.45
3	24°.64	6	60°.73	9	96°.83	2	132°.93	2.95	169°.02
4	25°.21	7	61°.31	1.70	97°.40	3	133°.50	6	169°.60
.45	25°.78	8	61°.88	1	97°.98	4	134°.07	7	170°.17
6	26°.36	9	62°.45	2	98°.55	2.35	134°.65	8	170°.74
7	26°.93	1.10	63°.03	3	99°.12	6	135°.22	9	171°.31
8	27°.50	1	63°.60	4	99°.69	7	135°.79	3.00	171°.89
9	28°.07	2	64°.17	1.75	100°.27	8	136°.36	1	172°.46
.50	28°.65	3	64°.74	6	100°.84	9	136°.94	2	173°.03
1	29°.22	4	65°.32	7	101°.41	2.40	137°.51	3	173°.61
2	29°.79	1.15	65°.89	8	101°.99	1	138°.08	4	174°.18
3	30°.37	6	66°.46	9	102°.56	2	138°.66	3.05	174°.75
4	30°.94	7	67°.04	1.80	103°.13	3	139°.23	6	175°.33
.55	31°.51	8	67°.61	1	103°.71	4	139°.80	7	175°.90
6	32°.09	9	68°.18	2	104°.28	2.45	140°.37	8	176°.47
7	32°.66	1.20	68°.75	3	104°.85	6	140°.95	9	177°.04
8	33°.23	1	69°.33	4	105°.42	7	141°.52	3.10	177°.62
9	33°.80	2	69°.90	1.85	106°.00	8	142°.09	1	178°.19
.60	34°.38	3	70°.47	6	106°.57	9	142°.67	2	178°.76
1	34°.95	4	71°.05	7	107°.14	2.50	143°.24	3	179°.34
2	35°.52	1.25	71°.62	8	107°.72	1	143°.81	4	179°.91
3	36°.10	6	72°.19	9	108°.29	2	144°.39	3.15	180°.48

Interpolation

.0002	0°.01	.0050	0°.29
04	.02	52	.30
06	.03	54	.31
08	.05	56	.32
.0010	0°.06	58	.33
12	.07	.0060	0°.34
14	.08	62	.36
16	.09	64	.37
18	.10	66	.38
.0020	0°.11	68	.39
22	.13	.0070	0°.40
24	.14	72	.41
26	.15	74	.42
28	.16	76	.44
.0030	0°.17	78	.45
32	.18	.0080	0°.46
34	.19	82	.47
36	.21	84	.48
38	.22	86	.49
.0040	0°.23	88	.50
42	.24	.0090	0°.52
44	.25	92	.53
46	.26	94	.54
48	.28	96	.55
		98	.56

Multiples of π

1	3.1416	180°
2	6.2832	360°
3	9.4248	540°
4	12.5664	720°
5	15.7080	900°
6	18.8496	1080°
7	21.9911	1260°
8	25.1327	1440°
9	28.2743	1620°
10	31.4159	1800°

Natural Sines and Cosines

Natural Sines at intervals of 0°.1, or 6′.　　　(For 10′ intervals, see pp. 1–54 to 1–58)

Deg	°.0 =(0′)	°.1 (6′)	°.2 (12′)	°.3 (18′)	°.4 (24′)	°.5 (30′)	°.6 (36′)	°.7 (42′)	°.8 (48′)	°.9 (54′)			Avg diff
											0.0000	90°	
0°	0.0000	0017	0035	0052	0070	0087	0105	0122	0140	0157	0175	89	17
1	0175	0192	0209	0227	0244	0262	0279	0297	0314	0332	0349	88	17
2	0349	0366	0384	0401	0419	0436	0454	0471	0488	0506	0523	87	17
3	0523	0541	0558	0576	0593	0610	0628	0645	0663	0680	0698	86	17
4	0698	0715	0732	0750	0767	0785	0802	0819	0837	0854	0.0872	85	17
5	0.0872	0889	0906	0924	0941	0958	0976	0993	1011	1028	1045	84	17
6	1045	1063	1080	1097	1115	1132	1149	1167	1184	1201	1219	83	17
7	1219	1236	1253	1271	1288	1305	1323	1340	1357	1374	1392	82	17
8	1392	1409	1426	1444	1461	1478	1495	1513	1530	1547	1564	81	17
9	1564	1582	1599	1616	1633	1650	1668	1685	1702	1719	0.1736	80°	17
10°	0.1736	1754	1771	1788	1805	1822	1840	1857	1874	1891	1908	79	17
11	1908	1925	1942	1959	1977	1994	2011	2028	2045	2062	2079	78	17
12	2079	2096	2113	2130	2147	2164	2181	2198	2215	2233	2250	77	17
13	2250	2267	2284	2300	2317	2334	2351	2368	2385	2402	2419	76	17
14	2419	2436	2453	2470	2487	2504	2521	2538	2554	2571	0.2588	75	17
15	0.2588	2605	2622	2639	2656	2672	2689	2706	2723	2740	2756	74	17
16	2756	2773	2790	2807	2823	2840	2857	2874	2890	2907	2924	73	17
17	2924	2940	2957	2974	2990	3007	3024	3040	3057	3074	3090	72	17
18	3090	3107	3123	3140	3156	3173	3190	3206	3223	3239	3256	71	17
19	3256	3272	3289	3305	3322	3338	3355	3371	3387	3404	0.3420	70°	16
20°	0.3420	3437	3453	3469	3486	3502	3518	3535	3551	3567	3584	69	16
21	3584	3600	3616	3633	3649	3665	3681	3697	3714	3730	3746	68	16
22	3746	3762	3778	3795	3811	3827	3843	3859	3875	3891	3907	67	16
23	3907	3923	3939	3955	3971	3987	4003	4019	4035	4051	4067	66	16
24	4067	4083	4099	4115	4131	4147	4163	4179	4195	4210	0.4226	65	16
25	0.4226	4242	4258	4274	4289	4305	4321	4337	4352	4368	4384	64	16
26	4384	4399	4415	4431	4446	4462	4478	4493	4509	4524	4540	63	16
27	4540	4555	4571	4586	4602	4617	4633	4648	4664	4679	4695	62	16
28	4695	4710	4726	4741	4756	4772	4787	4802	4818	4833	4848	61	15
29	4848	4863	4879	4894	4909	4924	4939	4955	4970	4985	0.5000	60°	15
30°	0.5000	5015	5030	5045	5060	5075	5090	5105	5120	5135	5150	59	15
31	5150	5165	5180	5195	5210	5225	5240	5255	5270	5284	5299	58	15
32	5299	5314	5329	5344	5358	5373	5388	5402	5417	5432	5446	57	15
33	5446	5461	5476	5490	5505	5519	5534	5548	5563	5577	5592	56	15
34	5592	5606	5621	5635	5650	5664	5678	5693	5707	5721	0.5736	55	14
35	0.5736	5750	5764	5779	5793	5807	5821	5835	5850	5864	5878	54	14
36	5878	5892	5906	5920	5934	5948	5962	5976	5990	6004	6018	53	14
37	6018	6032	6046	6060	6074	6088	6101	6115	6129	6143	6157	52	14
38	6157	6170	6184	6198	6211	6225	6239	6252	6266	6280	6293	51	14
39	6293	6307	6320	6334	6347	6361	6374	6388	6401	6414	0.6428	50°	13
40°	0.6428	6441	6455	6468	6481	6494	6508	6521	6534	6547	6561	49	13
41	6561	6574	6587	6600	6613	6626	6639	6652	6665	6678	6691	48	13
42	6691	6704	6717	6730	6743	6756	6769	6782	6794	6807	6820	47	13
43	6820	6833	6845	6858	6871	6884	6896	6909	6921	6934	6947	46	13
44	6947	6959	6972	6984	6997	7009	7022	7034	7046	7059	0.7071	45°	12
45°	0.7071												

	°.9 =(54′)	°.8 (48′)	°.7 (42′)	°.6 (36′)	°.5 (30′)	°.4 (24′)	°.3 (18′)	°.2 (12′)	°.1 (6′)	°.0 (0′)	Deg

Natural Cosines

Natural Sines and Cosines (*continued*)

Natural Sines at intervals of 0°.1, or 6'. (For 10' intervals, see pp. 1-54 to 1-58)

Deg	°.0 = (0')	°.1 (6')	°.2 (12')	°.3 (18')	°.4 (24')	°.5 (30')	°.6 (36')	°.7 (42')	°.8 (48')	°.9 (54')			Avg diff
											0.7071	45°	
45°	0.7071	7083	7096	7108	7120	7133	7145	7157	7169	7181	7193	44	12
46	7193	7206	7218	7230	7242	7254	7266	7278	7290	7302	7314	43	12
47	7314	7325	7337	7349	7361	7373	7385	7396	7408	7420	7431	42	12
48	7431	7443	7455	7466	7478	7490	7501	7513	7524	7536	7547	41	12
49	7547	7559	7570	7581	7593	7604	7615	7627	7638	7649	0.7660	40°	11
50°	0.7660	7672	7683	7694	7705	7716	7727	7738	7749	7760	7771	39	11
51	7771	7782	7793	7804	7815	7826	7837	7848	7859	7869	7880	38	11
52	7880	7891	7902	7912	7923	7934	7944	7955	7965	7976	7986	37	11
53	7986	7997	8007	8018	8028	8039	8049	8059	8070	8080	8090	36	10
54	8090	8100	8111	8121	8131	8141	8151	8161	8171	8181	0.8192	35	10
55	0.8192	8202	8211	8221	8231	8241	8251	8261	8271	8281	8290	34	10
56	8290	8300	8310	8320	8329	8339	8348	8358	8368	8377	8387	33	10
57	8387	8396	8406	8415	8425	8434	8443	8453	8462	8471	8480	32	9
58	8480	8490	8499	8508	8517	8526	8536	8545	8554	8563	8572	31	9
59	8572	8581	8590	8599	8607	8616	8625	8634	8643	8652	0.8660	30°	9
60°	0.8660	8669	8678	8686	8695	8704	8712	8721	8729	8738	8746	29	9
61	8746	8755	8763	8771	8780	8788	8796	8805	8813	8821	8829	28	8
62	8829	8838	8846	8854	8862	8870	8878	8886	8894	8902	8910	27	8
63	8910	8918	8926	8934	8942	8949	8957	8965	8973	8980	8988	26	8
64	8988	8996	9003	9011	9018	9026	9033	9041	9048	9056	0.9063	25	7
65	0.9063	9070	9078	9085	9092	9100	9107	9114	9121	9128	9135	24	7
66	9135	9143	9150	9157	9164	9171	9178	9184	9191	9198	9205	23	7
67	9205	9212	9219	9225	9232	9239	9245	9252	9259	9265	9272	22	7
68	9272	9278	9285	9291	9298	9304	9311	9317	9323	9330	9336	21	6
69	9336	9342	9348	9354	9361	9367	9373	9379	9385	9391	0.9397	20°	6
70°	0.9397	9403	9409	9415	9421	9426	9432	9438	9444	9449	9455	19	6
71	9455	9461	9466	9472	9478	9483	9489	9494	9500	9505	9511	18	6
72	9511	9516	9521	9527	9532	9537	9542	9548	9553	9558	9563	17	5
73	9563	9568	9573	9578	9583	9588	9593	9598	9603	9608	9613	16	5
74	9613	9617	9622	9627	9632	9636	9641	9646	9650	9655	0.9659	15	5
75	0.9659	9664	9668	9673	9677	9681	9686	9690	9694	9699	9703	14	4
76	9703	9707	9711	9715	9720	9724	9728	9732	9736	9740	9744	13	4
77	9744	9748	9751	9755	9759	9763	9767	9770	9774	9778	9781	12	4
78	9781	9785	9789	9792	9796	9799	9803	9806	9810	9813	9816	11	3
79	9816	9820	9823	9826	9829	9833	9836	9839	9842	9845	0.9848	10°	3
80°	0.9848	9851	9854	9857	9860	9863	9866	9869	9871	9874	9877	9	3
81	9877	9880	9882	9885	9888	9890	9893	9895	9898	9900	9903	8	3
82	9903	9905	9907	9910	9912	9914	9917	9919	9921	9923	9925	7	2
83	9925	9928	9930	9932	9934	9936	9938	9940	9942	9943	9945	6	2
84	9945	9947	9949	9951	9952	9954	9956	9957	9959	9960	0.9962	5	2
85	0.9962	9963	9965	9966	9968	9969	9971	9972	9973	9974	9976	4	1
86	9976	9977	9978	9979	9980	9981	9982	9983	9984	9985	9986	3	1
87	9986	9987	9988	9989	9990	9990	9991	9992	9993	9993	9994	2	1
88	9994	9995	9995	9996	9996	9997	9997	9997	9998	9998	0.9998	1	0
89	0.9998	9999	9999	9999	9999	0000	0000	0000	0000	0000	1.0000	0°	0
90°	1.0000												

	°.9 = (54')	°.8 (48')	°.7 (42')	°.6 (36')	°.5 (30')	°.4 (24')	°.3 (18')	°.2 (12')	°.1 (6')	°.0 (0')	Deg

Natural Cosines

Natural Tangents and Cotangents

Natural Tangents at intervals of 0°.1, or 6'.   (For 10' intervals, see pp. 1–54 to 1–58)

Deg	°.0 ⇒(0')	°.1 (6')	°.2 (12')	°,3 (18')	°.4 (24')	°.5 (30')	°.6 (36')	°.7 (42')	°.8 (48')	°.9 (54')			Avg diff
											0.0000	90°	
0°	0.0000	0017	0035	0052	0070	0087	0105	0122	0140	0157	0175	89	17
1	0175	0192	0209	0227	0244	0262	0279	0297	0314	0332	0349	88	17
2	0349	0367	0384	0402	0419	0437	0454	0472	0489	0507	0524	87	17
3	0524	0542	0559	0577	0594	0612	0629	0647	0664	0682	0699	86	18
4	0699	0717	0734	0752	0769	0787	0805	0822	0840	0857	0.0875	85	18
5	0.0875	0892	0910	0928	0945	0963	0981	0998	1016	1033	1051	84	18
6	1051	1069	1086	1104	1122	1139	1157	1175	1192	1210	1228	83	18
7	1228	1246	1263	1281	1299	1317	1334	1352	1370	1388	1405	82	18
8	1405	1423	1441	1459	1477	1495	1512	1530	1548	1566	1584	81	18
9	1584	1602	1620	1638	1655	1673	1691	1709	1727	1745	0.1763	80°	18
10°	0.1763	1781	1799	1817	1835	1853	1871	1890	1908	1926	1944	79	18
11	1944	1962	1980	1998	2016	2035	2053	2071	2089	2107	2126	78	18
12	2126	2144	2162	2180	2199	2217	2235	2254	2272	2290	2309	77	18
13	2309	2327	2345	2364	2382	2401	2419	2438	2456	2475	2493	76	18
14	2493	2512	2530	2549	2568	2586	2605	2623	2642	2661	0.2679	75	19
15	0.2679	2698	2717	2736	2754	2773	2792	2811	2830	2849	2867	74	19
16	2867	2886	2905	2924	2943	2962	2981	3000	3019	3038	3057	73	19
17	3057	3076	3096	3115	3134	3153	3172	3191	3211	3230	3249	72	19
18	3249	3269	3288	3307	3327	3346	3365	3385	3404	3424	3443	71	19
19	3443	3463	3482	3502	3522	3541	3561	3581	3600	3620	0.3640	70°	20
20°	0.3640	3659	3679	3699	3719	3739	3759	3779	3799	3819	3839	69	20
21	3839	3859	3879	3899	3919	3939	3959	3979	4000	4020	4040	68	20
22	4040	4061	4081	4101	4122	4142	4163	4183	4204	4224	4245	67	21
23	4245	4265	4286	4307	4327	4348	4369	4390	4411	4431	4452	66	21
24	4452	4473	4494	4515	4536	4557	4578	4599	4621	4642	0.4663	65	21
25	0.4663	4684	4706	4727	4748	4770	4791	4813	4834	4856	4877	64	21
26	4877	4899	4921	4942	4964	4986	5008	5029	5051	5073	5095	63	22
27	5095	5117	5139	5161	5184	5206	5228	5250	5272	5295	5317	62	22
28	5317	5340	5362	5384	5407	5430	5452	5475	5498	5520	5543	61	23
29	5543	5566	5589	5612	5635	5658	5681	5704	5727	5750	0.5774	60°	23
30°	0.5774	5797	5820	5844	5867	5890	5914	5938	5961	5985	6009	59	24
31	6009	6032	6056	6080	6104	6128	6152	6176	6200	6224	6249	58	24
32	6249	6273	6297	6322	6346	6371	6395	6420	6445	6469	6494	57	25
33	6494	6519	6544	6569	6594	6619	6644	6669	6694	6720	6745	56	25
34	6745	6771	6796	6822	6847	6873	6899	6924	6950	6976	0.7002	55	26
35	0.7002	7028	7054	7080	7107	7133	7159	7186	7212	7239	7265	54	26
36	7265	7292	7319	7346	7373	7400	7427	7454	7481	7508	7536	53	27
37	7536	7563	7590	7618	7646	7673	7701	7729	7757	7785	7813	52	28
38	7813	7841	7869	7898	7926	7954	7983	8012	8040	8069	8098	51	28
39	8098	8127	8156	8185	8214	8243	8273	8302	8332	8361	0.8391	50°	29
40°	0.8391	8421	8451	8481	8511	8541	8571	8601	8632	8662	8693	49	30
41	8693	8724	8754	8785	8816	8847	8878	8910	8941	8972	9004	48	31
42	9004	9036	9067	9099	9131	9163	9195	9228	9260	9293	9325	47	32
43	9325	9358	9391	9424	9457	9490	9523	9556	9590	9623	0.9657	46	33
44	0.9657	9691	9725	9759	9793	9827	9861	9896	9930	9965	1.0000	45°	34
45°	1.0000												

	°.9 =(54')	°.8 (48')	°.7 (42')	°.6 (36')	°.5 (30')	°.4 (24')	°.3 (18')	°.2 (12')	°.1 (6')	°.0 (0')	Deg

Natural Cotangents

Natural Tangents and Cotangents (*continued*)

Natural Tangents at intervals of 0°.1, or 6′. (For 10′ intervals, see pp. 1–54 to 1–58)

Deg	°.0 =(0′)	°.1 (6′)	°.2 (12′)	°.3 (18′)	°.4 (24′)	°.5 (30′)	°.6 (36′)	°.7 (42′)	°.8 (48′)	°.9 (54′)			Avg diff
											1.0000	45°	
45°	1.0000	0035	0070	0105	0141	0176	0212	0247	0283	0319	0355	44	35
46	0355	0392	0428	0464	0501	0538	0575	0612	0649	0686	0724	43	37
47	0724	0761	0799	0837	0875	0913	0951	0990	1028	1067	1106	42	38
48	1106	1145	1184	1224	1263	1303	1343	1383	1423	1463	1504	41	40
49	1504	1544	1585	1626	1667	1708	1750	1792	1833	1875	1.1918	40°	41
50°	1.1918	1960	2002	2045	2088	2131	2174	2218	2261	2305	2349	39	43
51	2349	2393	2437	2482	2527	2572	2617	2662	2708	2753	2799	38	45
52	2799	2846	2892	2938	2985	3032	3079	3127	3175	3222	3270	37	47
53	3270	3319	3367	3416	3465	3514	3564	3613	3663	3713	3764	36	49
54	3764	3814	3865	3916	3968	4019	4071	4124	4176	4229	1.4281	35	52
55	1.4281	4335	4388	4442	4496	4550	4605	4659	4715	4770	4826	34	55
56	4826	4882	4938	4994	5051	5108	5166	5224	5282	5340	5399	33	57
57	5399	5458	5517	5577	5637	5697	5757	5818	5880	5941	6003	32	60
58	6003	6066	6128	6191	6255	6319	6383	6447	6512	6577	6643	31	64
59	1.6643	6709	6775	6842	6909	6977	7045	7113	7182	7251	1.7321	30°	67
60°	1.732	1.739	1.746	1.753	1.760	1.767	1.775	1.782	1.789	1.797	1.804	29	7
61	1.804	1.811	1.819	1.827	1.834	1.842	1.849	1.857	1.865	1.873	1.881	28	8
62	1.881	1.889	1.897	1.905	1.913	1.921	1.929	1.937	1.946	1.954	1.963	27	8
63	1.963	1.971	1.980	1.988	1.997	2.006	2.014	2.023	2.032	2.041	2.050	26	9
64	2.050	2.059	2.069	2.078	2.087	2.097	2.106	2.116	2.125	2.135	2.145	25	9
65	2.145	2.154	2.164	2.174	2.184	2.194	2.204	2.215	2.225	2.236	2.246	24	10
66	2.246	2.257	2.267	2.278	2.289	2.300	2.311	2.322	2.333	2.344	2.356	23	11
67	2.356	2.367	2.379	2.391	2.402	2.414	2.426	2.438	2.450	2.463	2.475	22	12
68	2.475	2.488	2.500	2.513	2.526	2.539	2.552	2.565	2.578	2.592	2.605	21	13
69	2.605	2.619	2.633	2.646	2.660	2.675	2.689	2.703	2.718	2.733	2.747	20°	14
70°	2.747	2.762	2.778	2.793	2.808	2.824	2.840	2.856	2.872	2.888	2.904	19	16
71	2.904	2.921	2.937	2.954	2.971	2.989	3.006	3.024	3.042	3.060	3.078	18	17
72	3.078	3.096	3.115	3.133	3.152	3.172	3.191	3.211	3.230	3.251	3.271	17	19
73	3.271	3.291	3.312	3.333	3.354	3.376	3.398	3.420	3.442	3.465	3.487	16	22
74	3.487	3.511	3.534	3.558	3.582	3.606	3.630	3.655	3.681	3.706	3.732	15	24
75	3.732	3.758	3.785	3.812	3.839	3.867	3.895	3.923	3.952	3.981	4.011	14	28
76	4.011	4.041	4.071	4.102	4.134	4.165	4.198	4.230	4.264	4.297	4.331	13	32
77	4.331	4.366	4.402	4.437	4.474	4.511	4.548	4.586	4.625	4.665	4.705	12	37
78	4.705	4.745	4.787	4.829	4.872	4.915	4.959	5.005	5.050	5.097	5.145	11	44
79	5.145	5.193	5.242	5.292	5.343	5.396	5.449	5.503	5.558	5.614	5.671	10°	53
80°	5.671	5.730	5.789	5.850	5.912	5.976	6.041	6.107	6.174	6.243	6.314	9	
81	6.314	6.386	6.460	6.535	6.612	6.691	6.772	6.855	6.940	7.026	7.115	8	
82	7.115	7.207	7.300	7.396	7.495	7.596	7.700	7.806	7.916	8.028	8.144	7	
83	8.144	8.264	8.386	8.513	8.643	8.777	8.915	9.058	9.205	9.357	9.514	6	
84	9.514	9.677	9.845	10.02	10.20	10.39	10.58	10.78	10.99	11.20	11.43	5	
85	11.43	11.66	11.91	12.16	12.43	12.71	13.00	13.30	13.62	13.95	14.30	4	
86	14.30	14.67	15.06	15.46	15.90	16.35	16.83	17.34	17.89	18.46	19.08	3	
87	19.08	19.74	20.45	21.20	22.02	22.90	23.86	24.90	26.03	27.27	28.64	2	
88	28.64	30.14	31.82	33.69	35.80	38.19	40.92	44.07	47.74	52.08	57.29	1	
89	57.29	63.66	71.62	81.85	95.49	114.6	143.2	191.0	286.5	573.0	∞	0°	
90°	∞												

	°.9 =(54′)	°.8 (48′)	°.7 (42′)	°.6 (36′)	°.5 (30′)	°.4 (24′)	°.3 (18′)	°.2 (12′)	°.1 (6′)	°.0 (0′)	Deg

Natural Cotangents

Natural Secants and Cosecants
Natural Secants at intervals of 0°.1, or 6'.

Deg	°.0 =(0')	°.1 (6')	°.2 (12')	°.3 (18')	°.4 (24')	°.5 (30')	°.6 (36')	°.7 (42')	°.8 (48')	°.9 (54')			Avg diff
											1.0000	90°	
0°	1.0000	0000	0000	0000	0000	0000	0001	0001	0001	0001	0002	89	0
1	0002	0002	0002	0003	0003	0003	0004	0004	0005	0006	0006	88	0
2	0006	0007	0007	0008	0009	0010	0010	0011	0012	0013	0014	87	1
3	0014	0015	0016	0017	0018	0019	0020	0021	0022	0023	0024	86	1
4	0024	0026	0027	0028	0030	0031	0032	0034	0035	0037	1.0038	85	1
5	1.0038	0040	0041	0043	0045	0046	0048	0050	0051	0053	0055	84	2
6	0055	0057	0059	0061	0063	0065	0067	0069	0071	0073	0075	83	2
7	0075	0077	0079	0082	0084	0086	0089	0091	0093	0096	0098	82	2
8	0098	0101	0103	0106	0108	0111	0114	0116	0119	0122	0125	81	3
9	0125	0127	0130	0133	0136	0139	0142	0145	0148	0151	1.0154	80°	3
10°	1.0154	0157	0161	0164	0167	0170	0174	0177	0180	0184	0187	79	3
11	0187	0191	0194	0198	0201	0205	0209	0212	0216	0220	0223	78	4
12	0223	0227	0231	0235	0239	0243	0247	0251	0255	0259	0263	77	4
13	0263	0267	0271	0276	0280	0284	0288	0293	0297	0302	0306	76	4
14	0306	0311	0315	0320	0324	0329	0334	0338	0343	0348	1.0353	75	5
15	1.0353	0358	0363	0367	0372	0377	0382	0388	0393	0398	0403	74	5
16	0403	0408	0413	0419	0424	0429	0435	0440	0446	0451	0457	73	5
17	0457	0463	0468	0474	0480	0485	0491	0497	0503	0509	0515	72	6
18	0515	0521	0527	0533	0539	0545	0551	0557	0564	0570	0576	71	6
19	0576	0583	0589	0595	0602	0608	0615	0622	0628	0635	1.0642	70°	7
20°	1.0642	0649	0655	0662	0669	0676	0683	0690	0697	0704	0711	69	7
21	0711	0719	0726	0733	0740	0748	0755	0763	0770	0778	0785	68	7
22	0785	0793	0801	0808	0816	0824	0832	0840	0848	0856	0864	67	8
23	0864	0872	0880	0888	0896	0904	0913	0921	0929	0938	0946	66	8
24	0946	0955	0963	0972	0981	0989	0998	1007	1016	1025	1.1034	65	9
25	1.1034	1043	1052	1061	1070	1079	1089	1098	1107	1117	1126	64	9
26	1126	1136	1145	1155	1164	1174	1184	1194	1203	1213	1223	63	10
27	1223	1233	1243	1253	1264	1274	1284	1294	1305	1315	1326	62	10
28	1326	1336	1347	1357	1368	1379	1390	1401	1412	1423	1434	61	11
29	1434	1445	1456	1467	1478	1490	1501	1512	1524	1535	1.1547	60°	11
30°	1.1547	1559	1570	1582	1594	1606	1618	1630	1642	1654	1666	59	12
31	1666	1679	1691	1703	1716	1728	1741	1753	1766	1779	1792	58	13
32	1792	1805	1818	1831	1844	1857	1870	1883	1897	1910	1924	57	13
33	1924	1937	1951	1964	1978	1992	2006	2020	2034	2048	2062	56	14
34	2062	2076	2091	2105	2120	2134	2149	2163	2178	2193	1.2208	55	15
35	1.2208	2223	2238	2253	2268	2283	2299	2314	2329	2345	2361	54	15
36	2361	2376	2392	2408	2424	2440	2456	2472	2489	2505	2521	53	16
37	2521	2538	2554	2571	2588	2605	2622	2639	2656	2673	2690	52	17
38	2690	2708	2725	2742	2760	2778	2796	2813	2831	2849	2868	51	18
39	2868	2886	2904	2923	2941	2960	2978	2997	3016	3035	1.3054	50°	19
40°	1.3054	3073	3093	3112	3131	3151	3171	3190	3210	3230	3250	49	20
41	3250	3270	3291	3311	3331	3352	3373	3393	3414	3435	3456	48	21
42	3456	3478	3499	3520	3542	3563	3585	3607	3629	3651	3673	47	22
43	3673	3696	3718	3741	3763	3786	3809	3832	3855	3878	3902	46	23
44	3902	3925	3949	3972	3996	4020	4044	4069	4093	4118	1.4142	45°	24
45°	1.4142												

	°.9 =(54')	°.8 (48')	°.7 (42')	°.6 (36')	°.5 (30')	°.4 (24')	°.3 (18')	°.2 (12')	°.1 (6')	°.0 (0')	Deg

Natural Cosecants

Natural Secants and Cosecants (*continued*)
Natural Secants at intervals of 0°.1, or 6′.

Deg	°.0 = (0′)	°.1 (6′)	°.2 (12′)	°.3 (18′)	°.4 (24′)	°.5 (30′)	°.6 (36′)	°.7 (42′)	°.8 (48′)	°.9 (54′)			Avg diff
											1.4142	45°	
45°	1.4142	4167	4192	4217	4242	4267	4293	4318	4344	4370	4396	44	25
46	4396	4422	4448	4474	4501	4527	4554	4581	4608	4635	4663	43	27
47	4663	4690	4718	4746	4774	4802	4830	4859	4887	4916	4945	42	28
48	4945	4974	5003	5032	5062	5092	5121	5151	5182	5212	5243	41	30
49	5243	5273	5304	5335	5366	5398	5429	5461	5493	5525	1.5557	40°	31
50°	1.5557	5590	5622	5655	5688	5721	5755	5788	5822	5856	5890	39	33
51	5890	5925	5959	5994	6029	6064	6099	6135	6171	6207	6243	38	35
52	6243	6279	6316	6353	6390	6427	6464	6502	6540	6578	6616	37	37
53	6616	6655	6694	6733	6772	6812	6852	6892	6932	6972	7013	36	40
54	7013	7054	7095	7137	7179	7221	7263	7305	7348	7391	1.7434	35	42
55	1.7434	7478	7522	7566	7610	7655	7700	7745	7791	7837	7883	34	45
56	7883	7929	7976	8023	8070	8118	8166	8214	8263	8312	8361	33	48
57	8361	8410	8460	8510	8561	8612	8663	8714	8766	8818	8871	32	51
58	8871	8924	8977	9031	9084	9139	9194	9249	9304	9360	1.9416	31	54
59	1.9416	9473	9530	9587	9645	9703	9762	9821	9880	9940	2.0000	30°	58
60°	2.000	2.006	2.012	2.018	2.025	2.031	2.037	2.043	2.050	2.056	2.063	29	6
61	2.063	2.069	2.076	2.082	2.089	2.096	2.103	2.109	2.116	2.123	2.130	28	7
62	2.130	2.137	2.144	2.151	2.158	2.166	2.173	2.180	2.188	2.195	2.203	27	7
63	2.203	2.210	2.218	2.226	2.233	2.241	2.249	2.257	2.265	2.273	2.281	26	8
64	2.281	2.289	2.298	2.306	2.314	2.323	2.331	2.340	2.349	2.357	2.366	25	8
65	2.366	2.375	2.384	2.393	2.402	2.411	2.421	2.430	2.439	2.449	2.459	24	9
66	2.459	2.468	2.478	2.488	2.498	2.508	2.518	2.528	2.538	2.549	2.559	23	10
67	2.559	2.570	2.581	2.591	2.602	2.613	2.624	2.635	2.647	2.658	2.669	22	11
68	2.669	2.681	2.693	2.705	2.716	2.729	2.741	2.753	2.765	2.778	2.790	21	12
69	2.790	2.803	2.816	2.829	2.842	2.855	2.869	2.882	2.896	2.910	2.924	20°	13
70°	2.924	2.938	2.952	2.967	2.981	2.996	3.011	3.026	3.041	3.056	3.072	19	15
71	3.072	3.087	3.103	3.119	3.135	3.152	3.168	3.185	3.202	3.219	3.236	18	16
72	3.236	3.254	3.271	3.289	3.307	3.326	3.344	3.363	3.382	3.401	3.420	17	18
73	3.420	3.440	3.460	3.480	3.500	3.521	3.542	3.563	3.584	3.606	3.628	16	21
74	3.628	3.650	3.673	3.695	3.719	3.742	3.766	3.790	3.814	3.839	3.864	15	24
75	3.864	3.889	3.915	3.941	3.967	3.994	4.021	4.049	4.077	4.105	4.134	14	27
76	4.134	4.163	4.192	4.222	4.253	4.284	4.315	4.347	4.379	4.412	4.445	13	31
77	4.445	4.479	4.514	4.549	4.584	4.620	4.657	4.694	4.732	4.771	4.810	12	36
78	4.810	4.850	4.890	4.931	4.973	5.016	5.059	5.103	5.148	5.194	5.241	11	43
79	5.241	5.288	5.337	5.386	5.436	5.487	5.540	5.593	5.647	5.702	5.759	10°	52
80°	5.759	5.816	5.875	5.935	5.996	6.059	6.123	6.188	6.255	6.323	6.392	9	
81	6.392	6.464	6.537	6.611	6.687	6.765	6.845	6.927	7.011	7.097	7.185	8	
82	7.185	7.276	7.368	7.463	7.561	7.661	7.764	7.870	7.979	8.091	8.206	7	
83	8.206	8.324	8.446	8.571	8.700	8.834	8.971	9.113	9.259	9.411	9.567	6	
84	9.567	9.728	9.895	10.07	10.25	10.43	10.63	10.83	11.03	11.25	11.47	5	
85	11.47	11.71	11.95	12.20	12.47	12.75	13.03	13.34	13.65	13.99	14.34	4	
86	14.34	14.70	15.09	15.50	15.93	16.38	16.86	17.37	17.91	18.49	19.11	3	
87	19.11	19.77	20.47	21.23	22.04	22.93	23.88	24.92	26.05	27.29	28.65	2	
88	28.65	30.16	31.84	33.71	35.81	38.20	40.93	44.08	47.75	52.09	57.30	1	
89	57.30	63.66	71.62	81.85	95.49	114.6	143.2	191.0	286.5	573.0	∞	0°	
90°	∞												
	°.9 = (54′)	°.8 (48′)	°.7 (42′)	°.6 (36′)	°.5 (30′)	°.4 (24′)	°.3 (18′)	°.2 (12′)	°.1 (6′)	°.0 (0′)		Deg	

Natural Cosecants

Trigonometric Functions (at intervals of 10′)

Annex—10 in columns marked *.   (For 0°.1 intervals, see pp. 1–48 to 1–53)

De-grees	Ra-dians	Sines Nat.	Sines Log *	Cosines Nat.	Cosines Log *	Tangents Nat.	Tangents Log *	Cotangents Nat.	Cotangents Log		
0° 00′	0.0000	.0000	∞	1.0000	0.0000	.0000	∞	∞	∞	1.5708	90° 00′
10	0.0029	.0029	7.4637	1.0000	.0000	.0029	7.4637	343.77	2.5363	1.5679	50
20	0.0058	.0058	.7648	1.0000	.0000	.0058	.7648	171.89	.2352	1.5650	40
30	0.0087	.0087	.9408	1.0000	.0000	.0087	.9409	114.59	.0591	1.5621	30
40	0.0116	.0116	8.0658	.9999	.0000	.0116	8.0658	85.940	1.9342	1.5592	20
50	0.0145	.0145	.1627	.9999	.0000	.0145	.1627	68.750	.8373	1.5563	10
1° 00′	0.0175	.0175	8.2419	.9998	9.9999	.0175	8.2419	57.290	1.7581	1.5533	89° 00′
10	0.0204	.0204	.3088	.9998	.9999	.0204	.3089	49.104	.6911	1.5504	50
20	0.0233	.0233	.3668	.9997	.9999	.0233	.3669	42.964	.6331	1.5475	40
30	0.0262	.0262	.4179	.9997	.9999	.0262	.4181	38.188	.5819	1.5446	30
40	0.0291	.0291	.4637	.9996	.9998	.0291	.4638	34.368	.5362	1.5417	20
50	0.0320	.0320	.5050	.9995	.9998	.0320	.5053	31.242	.4947	1.5388	10
2° 00′	0.0349	.0349	8.5428	.9994	9.9997	.0349	8.5431	28.636	1.4569	1.5359	88° 00′
10	0.0378	.0378	.5776	.9993	.9997	.0378	.5779	26.432	.4221	1.5330	50
20	0.0407	.0407	.6097	.9992	.9996	.0407	.6101	24.542	.3899	1.5301	40
30	0.0436	.0436	.6397	.9990	.9996	.0437	.6401	22.904	.3599	1.5272	30
40	0.0465	.0465	.6677	.9989	.9995	.0466	.6682	21.470	.3318	1.5243	20
50	0.0495	.0494	.6940	.9988	.9995	.0495	.6945	20.206	.3055	1.5213	10
3° 00′	0.0524	.0523	8.7188	.9986	9.9994	.0524	8.7194	19.081	1.2806	1.5184	87° 00′
10	0.0553	.0552	.7423	.9985	.9993	.0553	.7429	18.075	.2571	1.5155	50
20	0.0582	.0581	.7645	.9983	.9993	.0582	.7652	17.169	.2348	1.5126	40
30	0.0611	.0610	.7857	.9981	.9992	.0612	.7865	16.350	.2135	1.5097	30
40	0.0640	.0640	.8059	.9980	.9991	.0641	.8067	15.605	.1933	1.5068	20
50	0.0669	.0669	.8251	.9978	.9990	.0670	.8261	14.924	.1739	1.5039	10
4° 00′	0.0698	.0698	8.8436	.9976	9.9989	.0699	8.8446	14.301	1.1554	1.5010	86° 00′
10	0.0727	.0727	.8613	.9974	.9989	.0729	.8624	13.727	.1376	1.4981	50
20	0.0756	.0756	.8783	.9971	.9988	.0758	.8795	13.197	.1205	1.4952	40
30	0.0785	.0785	.8946	.9969	.9987	.0787	.8960	12.706	.1040	1.4923	30
40	0.0814	.0814	.9104	.9967	.9986	.0816	.9118	12.251	.0882	1.4893	20
50	0.0844	.0843	.9256	.9964	.9985	.0846	.9272	11.826	.0728	1.4864	10
5° 00′	0.0873	.0872	8.9403	.9962	9.9983	.0875	8.9420	11.430	1.0580	1.4835	85° 00′
10	0.0902	.0901	.9545	.9959	.9982	.0904	.9563	11.059	.0437	1.4306	50
20	0.0931	.0929	.9682	.9957	.9981	.0934	.9701	10.712	.0299	1.4777	40
30	0.0960	.0958	.9816	.9954	.9980	.0963	.9836	10.385	.0164	1.4748	30
40	0.0989	.0987	.9945	.9951	.9979	.0992	.9966	10.078	.0034	1.4719	20
50	0.1018	.1016	9.0070	.9948	.9977	.1022	9.0093	9.7882	0.9907	1.4690	10
6° 00′	0.1047	.1045	9.0192	.9945	9.9976	.1051	9.0216	9.5144	0.9784	1.4661	84° 00′
10	0.1076	.1074	.0311	.9942	.9975	.1080	.0336	9.2553	.9664	1.4632	50
20	0.1105	.1103	.0426	.9939	.9973	.1110	.0453	9.0098	.9547	1.4603	40
30	0.1134	.1132	.0539	.9936	.9972	.1139	.0567	8.7769	.9433	1.4574	30
40	0.1164	.1161	.0648	.9932	.9971	.1169	.0678	8.5555	.9322	1.4544	20
50	0.1193	.1190	.0755	.9929	.9969	.1198	.0786	8.3450	.9214	1.4515	10
7° 00′	0.1222	.1219	9.0859	.9925	9.9968	.1228	9.0891	8.1443	0.9109	1.4486	83° 00′
10	0.1251	.1248	.0961	.9922	.9966	.1257	.0995	7.9530	.9005	1.4457	50
20	0.1280	.1276	.1060	.9918	.9964	.1287	.1096	7.7704	.8904	1.4428	40
30	0.1309	.1305	.1157	.9914	.9963	.1317	.1194	7.5958	.8806	1.4399	30
40	0.1338	.1334	.1252	.9911	.9961	.1346	.1291	7.4287	.8709	1.4370	20
50	0.1367	.1363	.1345	.9907	.9959	.1376	.1385	7.2687	.8615	1.4341	10
8° 00′	0.1396	.1392	9.1436	.9903	9.9958	.1405	9.1478	7.1154	0.8522	1.4312	82° 00′
10	0.1425	.1421	.1525	.9899	.9956	.1435	.1569	6.9682	.8431	1.4283	50
20	0.1454	.1449	.1612	.9894	.9954	.1465	.1658	6.8269	.8342	1.4254	40
30	0.1484	.1478	.1697	.9890	.9952	.1495	.1745	6.6912	.8255	1.4224	30
40	0.1513	.1507	.1781	.9886	.9950	.1524	.1831	6.5606	.8169	1.4195	20
50	0.1542	.1536	.1863	.9881	.9948	.1554	.1915	6.4348	.8085	1.4166	10
9° 00′	0.1571	.1564	9.1943	.9877	9.9946	.1584	9.1997	6.3138	0.8003	1.4137	81° 00′
		Nat.	Log *	Nat.	Log *	Nat.	Log *	Nat.	Log		
		Cosines		Sines		Cotangents		Tangents		Ra-dians	De-grees

Trigonometric Functions (continued)

Annex—10 in columns marked *. (For 0°.1 intervals, see pp. 1–48 to 1–53)

De-grees	Ra-dians	Sines		Cosines		Tangents		Cotangents			
		Nat.	Log *	Nat.	Log *	Nat.	Log *	Nat.	Log		
9° 00′	0.1571	.1564	9.1943	.9877	9.9946	.1584	9.1997	6.3138	0.8003	1.4137	81° 00′
10	0.1600	.1593	.2022	.9872	.9944	.1614	.2078	6.1970	.7922	1.4108	50
20	0.1629	.1622	.2100	.9868	.9942	.1644	.2158	6.0844	.7842	1.4079	40
30	0.1658	.1650	.2176	.9863	.9940	.1673	.2236	5.9758	.7764	1.4050	30
40	0.1687	.1679	.2251	.9858	.9938	.1703	.2313	5.8708	.7687	1.4021	20
50	0.1716	.1708	.2324	.9853	.9936	.1733	.2389	5.7694	.7611	1.3992	10
10° 00′	0.1745	.1736	9.2397	.9848	9.9934	.1763	9.2463	5.6713	0.7537	1.3963	80° 00′
10	0.1774	.1765	.2468	.9843	.9931	.1793	.2536	5.5764	.7464	1.3934	50
20	0.1804	.1794	.2538	.9838	.9929	.1823	.2609	5.4845	.7391	1.3904	40
30	0.1833	.1822	.2606	.9833	.9927	.1853	.2680	5.3955	.7320	1.3875	30
40	0.1862	.1851	.2674	.9827	.9924	.1883	.2750	5.3093	.7250	1.3846	20
50	0.1891	.1880	.2740	.9822	.9922	.1914	.2819	5.2257	.7181	1.3817	10
11° 00′	0.1920	.1908	9.2806	.9816	9.9919	.1944	9.2887	5.1446	0.7113	1.3788	79° 00′
10	0.1949	.1937	.2870	.9811	.9917	.1974	.2953	5.0658	.7047	1.3759	50
20	0.1978	.1965	.2934	.9805	.9914	.2004	.3020	4.9894	.6980	1.3730	40
30	0.2007	.1994	.2997	.9799	.9912	.2035	.3085	4.9152	.6915	1.3701	30
40	0.2036	.2022	.3058	.9793	.9909	.2065	.3149	4.8430	.6851	1.3672	20
50	0.2065	.2051	.3119	.9787	.9907	.2095	.3212	4.7729	.6788	1.3643	10
12° 00′	0.2094	.2079	9.3179	.9781	9.9904	.2126	9.3275	4.7046	0.6725	1.3614	78° 00′
10	0.2123	.2108	.3238	.9775	.9901	.2156	.3336	4.6382	.6664	1.3584	50
20	0.2153	.2136	.3296	.9769	.9899	.2186	.3397	4.5736	.6603	1.3555	40
30	0.2182	.2164	.3353	.9763	.9896	.2217	.3458	4.5107	.6542	1.3526	30
40	0.2211	.2193	.3410	.9757	.9893	.2247	.3517	4.4494	.6483	1.3497	20
50	0.2240	.2221	.3466	.9750	.9890	.2278	.3576	4.3897	.6424	1.3468	10
13° 00′	0.2269	.2250	9.3521	.9744	9.9887	.2309	9.3634	4.3315	0.6366	1.3439	77° 00′
10	0.2298	.2278	.3575	.9737	.9884	.2339	.3691	4.2747	.6309	1.3410	50
20	0.2327	.2306	.3629	.9730	.9881	.2370	.3748	4.2193	.6252	1.3381	40
30	0.2356	.2334	.3682	.9724	.9878	.2401	.3804	4.1653	.6196	1.3352	30
40	0.2385	.2363	.3734	.9717	.9875	.2432	.3859	4.1126	.6141	1.3323	20
50	0.2414	.2391	.3786	.9710	.9872	.2462	.3914	4.0611	.6086	1.3294	10
14° 00′	0.2443	.2419	9.3837	.9703	9.9869	.2493	9.3968	4.0108	0.6032	1.3265	76° 00′
10	0.2473	.2447	.3887	.9696	.9866	.2524	.4021	3.9617	.5979	1.3235	50
20	0.2502	.2476	.3937	.9689	.9863	.2555	.4074	3.9136	.5926	1.3206	40
30	0.2531	.2504	.3986	.9681	.9859	.2586	.4127	3.8667	.5873	1.3177	30
40	0.2560	.2532	.4035	.9674	.9856	.2617	.4178	3.8208	.5822	1.3148	20
50	0.2589	.2560	.4083	.9667	.9853	.2648	.4230	3.7760	.5770	1.3119	10
15° 00′	0.2618	.2588	9.4130	.9659	9.9849	.2679	9.4281	3.7321	0.5719	1.3090	75° 00′
10	0.2647	.2616	.4177	.9652	.9846	.2711	.4331	3.6891	.5669	1.3061	50
20	0.2676	.2644	.4223	.9644	.9843	.2742	.4381	3.6470	.5619	1.3032	40
30	0.2705	.2672	.4269	.9636	.9839	.2773	.4430	3.6059	.5570	1.3003	30
40	0.2734	.2700	.4314	.9628	.9836	.2805	.4479	3.5656	.5521	1.2974	20
50	0.2763	.2728	.4359	.9621	.9832	.2836	.4527	3.5261	.5473	1.2945	10
16° 00′	0.2793	.2756	9.4403	.9613	9.9828	.2867	9.4575	3.4874	0.5425	1.2915	74° 00′
10	0.2822	.2784	.4447	.9605	.9825	.2899	.4622	3.4495	.5378	1.2886	50
20	0.2851	.2812	.4491	.9596	.9821	.2931	.4669	3.4124	.5331	1.2857	40
30	0.2880	.2840	.4533	.9588	.9817	.2962	.4716	3.3759	.5284	1.2828	30
40	0.2909	.2868	.4576	.9580	.9814	.2994	.4762	3.3402	.5238	1.2799	20
50	0.2938	.2896	.4618	.9572	.9810	.3026	.4808	3.3052	.5192	1.2770	10
17° 00′	0.2967	.2924	9.4659	.9563	9.9806	.3057	9.4853	3.2709	0.5147	1.2741	73° 00′
10	0.2996	.2952	.4700	.9555	.9802	.3089	.4898	3.2371	.5102	1.2712	50
20	0.3025	.2979	.4741	.9546	.9798	.3121	.4943	3.2041	.5057	1.2683	40
30	0.3054	.3007	.4781	.9537	.9794	.3153	.4987	3.1716	.5013	1.2654	30
40	0.3083	.3035	.4821	.9528	.9790	.3185	.5031	3.1397	.4969	1.2625	20
50	0.3113	.3062	.4861	.9520	.9786	.3217	.5075	3.1084	.4925	1.2595	10
18° 00′	0.3142	.3090	9.4900	.9511	9.9782	.3249	9.5118	3.0777	0.4882	1.2566	72° 00′
		Nat.	Log *	Nat.	Log *	Nat.	Log *	Nat.	Log		
		Cosines		Sines		Cotangents		Tangents		Ra-dians	De-grees

Trigonometric Functions (continued)

Annex—10 in columns marked *.   (For 0°.1 intervals, see pp. 1–48 to 1–53)

De-grees	Ra-dians	Sines Nat.	Sines Log *	Cosines Nat.	Cosines Log *	Tangents Nat.	Tangents Log *	Cotangents Nat.	Cotangents Log		
18° 00′	0.3142	.3090	9.4900	.9511	9.9782	.3249	9.5118	3.0777	0.4882	1.2566	72° 00′
10	0.3171	.3118	.4939	.9502	.9778	.3281	.5161	3.0475	.4839	1.2537	50
20	0.3200	.3145	.4977	.9492	.9774	.3314	.5203	3.0178	.4797	1.2508	40
30	0.3229	.3173	.5015	.9483	.9770	.3346	.5245	2.9887	.4755	1.2479	30
40	0.3258	.3201	.5052	.9474	.9765	.3378	.5287	2.9600	.4713	1.2450	20
50	0.3287	.3228	.5090	.9465	.9761	.3411	.5329	2.9319	.4671	1.2421	10
19° 00′	0.3316	.3256	9.5126	.9455	9.9757	.3443	9.5370	2.9042	0.4630	1.2392	71° 00′
10	0.3345	.3283	.5163	.9446	.9752	.3476	.5411	2.8770	.4589	1.2363	50
20	0.3374	.3311	.5199	.9436	.9748	.3508	.5451	2.8502	.4549	1.2334	40
30	0.3403	.3338	.5235	.9426	.9743	.3541	.5491	2.8239	.4509	1.2305	30
40	0.3432	.3365	.5270	.9417	.9739	.3574	.5531	2.7980	.4469	1.2275	20
50	0.3462	.3393	.5306	.9407	.9734	.3607	.5571	2.7725	.4429	1.2246	10
20° 00′	0.3491	.3420	9.5341	.9397	9.9730	.3640	9.5611	2.7475	0.4389	1.2217	70° 00′
10	0.3520	.3448	.5375	.9387	.9725	.3673	.5650	2.7228	.4350	1.2188	50
20	0.3549	.3475	.5409	.9377	.9721	.3706	.5689	2.6985	.4311	1.2159	40
30	0.3578	.3502	.5443	.9367	.9716	.3739	.5727	2.6746	.4273	1.2130	30
40	0.3607	.3529	.5477	.9356	.9711	.3772	.5766	2.6511	.4234	1.2101	20
50	0.3636	.3557	.5510	.9346	.9706	.3805	.5804	2.6279	.4196	1.2072	10
21° 00′	0.3665	.3584	9.5543	.9336	9.9702	.3839	9.5842	2.6051	0.4158	1.2043	69° 00′
10	0.3694	.3611	.5576	.9325	.9697	.3872	.5879	2.5826	.4121	1.2014	50
20	0.3723	.3638	.5609	.9315	.9692	.3906	.5917	2.5605	.4083	1.1985	40
30	0.3752	.3665	.5641	.9304	.9687	.3939	.5954	2.5386	.4046	1.1956	30
40	0.3782	.3692	.5673	.9293	.9682	.3973	.5991	2.5172	.4009	1.1926	20
50	0.3811	.3719	.5704	.9283	.9677	.4006	.6028	2.4960	.3972	1.1897	10
22° 00′	0.3840	.3746	9.5736	.9272	9.9672	.4040	9.6064	2.4751	0.3936	1.1868	68° 00′
10	0.3869	.3773	.5767	.9261	.9667	.4074	.6100	2.4545	.3900	1.1839	50
20	0.3898	.3800	.5798	.9250	.9661	.4108	.6136	2.4342	.3864	1.1810	40
30	0.3927	.3827	.5828	.9239	.9656	.4142	.6172	2.4142	.3828	1.1781	30
40	0.3956	.3854	.5859	.9228	.9651	.4176	.6208	2.3945	.3792	1.1752	20
50	0.3985	.3881	.5889	.9216	.9646	.4210	.6243	2.3750	.3757	1.1723	10
23° 00′	0.4014	.3907	9.5919	.9205	9.9640	.4245	9.6279	2.3559	0.3721	1.1694	67° 00′
10	0.4043	.3934	.5948	.9194	.9635	.4279	.6314	2.3369	.3686	1.1665	50
20	0.4072	.3961	.5978	.9182	.9629	.4314	.6348	2.3183	.3652	1.1636	40
30	0.4102	.3987	.6007	.9171	.9624	.4348	.6383	2.2998	.3617	1.1606	30
40	0.4131	.4014	.6036	.9159	.9618	.4383	.6417	2.2817	.3583	1.1577	20
50	0.4160	.4041	.6065	.9147	.9613	.4417	.6452	2.2637	.3548	1.1548	10
24° 00′	0.4189	.4067	9.6093	.9135	9.9607	.4452	9.6486	2.2460	0.3514	1.1519	66° 00′
10	0.4218	.4094	.6121	.9124	.9602	.4487	.6520	2.2286	.3480	1.1490	50
20	0.4247	.4120	.6149	.9112	.9596	.4522	.6553	2.2113	.3447	1.1461	40
30	0.4276	.4147	.6177	.9100	.9590	.4557	.6587	2.1943	.3413	1.1432	30
40	0.4305	.4173	.6205	.9088	.9584	.4592	.6620	2.1775	.3380	1.1403	20
50	0.4334	.4200	.6232	.9075	.9579	.4628	.6654	2.1609	.3346	1.1374	10
25° 00′	0.4363	.4226	9.6259	.9063	9.9573	.4663	9.6687	2.1445	0.3313	1.1345	65° 00′
10	0.4392	.4253	.6286	.9051	.9567	.4699	.6720	2.1283	.3280	1.1316	50
20	0.4422	.4279	.6313	.9038	.9561	.4734	.6752	2.1123	.3248	1.1286	40
30	0.4451	.4305	.6340	.9026	.9555	.4770	.6785	2.0965	.3215	1.1257	30
40	0.4480	.4331	.6366	.9013	.9549	.4806	.6817	2.0809	.3183	1.1228	20
50	0.4509	.4358	.6392	.9001	.9543	.4841	.6850	2.0655	.3150	1.1199	10
26° 00′	0.4538	.4384	9.6418	.8988	9.9537	.4877	9.6882	2.0503	0.3118	1.1170	64° 00′
10	0.4567	.4410	.6444	.8975	.9530	.4913	.6914	2.0353	.3086	1.1141	50
20	0.4596	.4436	.6470	.8962	.9524	.4950	.6946	2.0204	.3054	1.1112	40
30	0.4625	.4462	.6495	.8949	.9518	.4986	.6977	2.0057	.3023	1.1083	30
40	0.4654	.4488	.6521	.8936	.9512	.5022	.7009	1.9912	.2991	1.1054	20
50	0.4683	.4514	.6546	.8923	.9505	.5059	.7040	1.9768	.2960	1.1025	10
27° 00′	0.4712	.4540	9.6570	.8910	9.9499	.5095	9.7072	1.9626	0.2928	1.0996	63° 00′
		Nat.	Log *	Nat.	Log *	Nat.	Log *	Nat.	Log		
		Cosines		Sines		Cotangents		Tangents		Ra-dians	De-grees

Trigonometric Functions (continued)
Annex—10 in columns marked *. (For 0°.1 intervals, see pp. 1–48 to 1–53)

De-grees	Ra-dians	Sines Nat.	Sines Log *	Cosines Nat.	Cosines Log *	Tangents Nat.	Tangents Log *	Cotangents Nat.	Cotangents Log		
27° 00′	0.4712	.4540	9.6570	.8910	9.9499	.5095	9.7072	1.9626	0.2928	1.0996	63° 00′
10	0.4741	.4566	.6595	.8897	.9492	.5132	.7103	1.9486	.2897	1.0966	50
20	0.4771	.4592	.6620	.8884	.9486	.5169	.7134	1.9347	.2866	1.0937	40
30	0.4800	.4617	.6644	.8870	.9479	.5206	.7165	1.9210	.2835	1.0908	30
40	0.4829	.4643	.6668	.8857	.9473	.5243	.7196	1.9074	.2804	1.0879	20
50	0.4858	.4669	.6692	.8843	.9466	.5280	.7226	1.8940	.2774	1.0850	10
28° 00′	0.4887	.4695	9.6716	.8829	9.9459	.5317	9.7257	1.8807	0.2743	1.0821	62° 00′
10	0.4916	.4720	.6740	.8816	.9453	.5354	.7287	1.8676	.2713	1.0792	50
20	0.4945	.4746	.6763	.8802	.9446	.5392	.7317	1.8546	.2683	1.0763	40
30	0.4974	.4772	.6787	.8788	.9439	.5430	.7348	1.8418	.2652	1.0734	30
40	0.5003	.4797	.6810	.8774	.9432	.5467	.7378	1.8291	.2622	1.0705	20
50	0.5032	.4823	.6833	.8760	.9425	.5505	.7408	1.8165	.2592	1.0676	10
29° 00′	0.5061	.4848	9.6856	.8746	9.9418	.5543	9.7438	1.8040	0.2562	1.0647	61° 00′
10	0.5091	.4874	.6878	.8732	.9411	.5581	.7467	1.7917	.2533	1.0617	50
20	0.5120	.4899	.6901	.8718	.9404	.5619	.7497	1.7796	.2503	1.0588	40
30	0.5149	.4924	.6923	.8704	.9397	.5658	.7526	1.7675	.2474	1.0559	30
40	0.5178	.4950	.6946	.8689	.9390	.5696	.7556	1.7556	.2444	1.0530	20
50	0.5207	.4975	.6968	.8675	.9383	.5735	.7585	1.7437	.2415	1.0501	10
30° 00′	0.5236	.5000	9.6990	.8660	9.9375	.5774	9.7614	1.7321	0.2386	1.0472	60° 00′
10	0.5265	.5025	.7012	.8646	.9368	.5812	.7644	1.7205	.2356	1.0443	50
20	0.5294	.5050	.7033	.8631	.9361	.5851	.7673	1.7090	.2327	1.0414	40
30	0.5323	.5075	.7055	.8616	.9353	.5890	.7701	1.6977	.2299	1.0385	30
40	0.5352	.5100	.7076	.8601	.9346	.5930	.7730	1.6864	.2270	1.0356	20
50	0.5381	.5125	.7097	.8587	.9338	.5969	.7759	1.6753	.2241	1.0327	10
31° 00′	0.5411	.5150	9.7118	.8572	9.9331	.6009	9.7788	1.6643	0.2212	1.0297	59° 00′
10	0.5440	.5175	.7139	.8557	.9323	.6048	.7816	1.6534	.2184	1.0268	50
20	0.5469	.5200	.7160	.8542	.9315	.6088	.7845	1.6426	.2155	1.0239	40
30	0.5498	.5225	.7181	.8526	.9308	.6128	.7873	1.6319	.2127	1.0210	30
40	0.5527	.5250	.7201	.8511	.9300	.6168	.7902	1.6212	.2098	1.0181	20
50	0.5556	.5275	.7222	.8496	.9292	.6208	.7930	1.6107	.2070	1.0152	10
32° 00′	0.5585	.5299	9.7242	.8480	9.9284	.6249	9.7958	1.6003	0.2042	1.0123	58° 00′
10	0.5614	.5324	.7262	.8465	.9276	.6289	.7986	1.5900	.2014	1.0094	50
20	0.5643	.5348	.7282	.8450	.9268	.6330	.8014	1.5798	.1986	1.0065	40
30	0.5672	.5373	.7302	.8434	.9260	.6371	.8042	1.5697	.1958	1.0036	30
40	0.5701	.5398	.7322	.8418	.9252	.6412	.8070	1.5597	.1930	1.0007	20
50	0.5730	.5422	.7342	.8403	.9244	.6453	.8097	1.5497	.1903	0.9977	10
33° 00′	0.5760	.5446	9.7361	.8387	9.9236	.6494	9.8125	1.5399	0.1875	0.9948	57° 00′
10	0.5789	.5471	.7380	.8371	.9228	.6536	.8153	1.5301	.1847	0.9919	50
20	0.5818	.5495	.7400	.8355	.9219	.6577	.8180	1.5204	.1820	0.9890	40
30	0.5847	.5519	.7419	.8339	.9211	.6619	.8208	1.5108	.1792	0.9861	30
40	0.5876	.5544	.7438	.8323	.9203	.6661	.8235	1.5013	.1765	0.9832	20
50	0.5905	.5568	.7457	.8307	.9194	.6703	.8263	1.4919	.1737	0.9803	10
34° 00′	0.5934	.5592	9.7476	.8290	9.9186	.6745	9.8290	1.4826	0.1710	0.9774	56° 00′
10	0.5963	.5616	.7494	.8274	.9177	.6787	.8317	1.4733	.1683	0.9745	50
20	0.5992	.5640	.7513	.8258	.9169	.6830	.8344	1.4641	.1656	0.9716	40
30	0.6021	.5664	.7531	.8241	.9160	.6873	.8371	1.4550	.1629	0.9687	30
40	0.6050	.5688	.7550	.8225	.9151	.6916	.8398	1.4460	.1602	0.9657	20
50	0.6080	.5712	.7568	.8208	.9142	.6959	.8425	1.4370	.1575	0.9628	10
35° 00′	0.6109	.5736	9.7586	.8192	9.9134	.7002	9.8452	1.4281	0.1548	0.9599	55° 00′
10	0.6138	.5760	.7604	.8175	.9125	.7046	.8479	1.4193	.1521	0.9570	50
20	0.6167	.5783	.7622	.8158	.9116	.7089	.8506	1.4106	.1494	0.9541	40
30	0.6196	.5807	.7640	.8141	.9107	.7133	.8533	1.4019	.1467	0.9512	30
40	0.6225	.5831	.7657	.8124	.9098	.7177	.8559	1.3934	.1441	0.9483	20
50	0.6254	.5854	.7675	.8107	.9089	.7221	.8586	1.3848	.1414	0.9454	10
36° 00′	0.6283	.5878	9.7692	.8090	9.9080	.7265	9.8613	1.3764	0.1387	0.9425	54° 00′
		Nat.	Log *	Nat.	Log *	Nat.	Log *	Nat.	Log		
		Cosines		Sines		Cotangents		Tangents		Ra-dians	De-grees

Trigonometric Functions (*continued*)

Annex—10 in columns marked *.　(For 0°.1 intervals, see pp. 1-48 to 1-53)

De-grees	Ra-dians	Sines Nat.	Sines Log *	Cosines Nat.	Cosines Log *	Tangents Nat.	Tangents Log *	Cotangents Nat.	Cotangents Log		
36° 00'	0.6283	.5878	9.7692	.8090	9.9080	.7265	9.8613	1.3764	0.1387	0.9425	54° 00'
10	0.6312	.5901	.7710	.8073	.9070	.7310	.8639	1.3680	.1361	0.9396	50
20	0.6341	.5925	.7727	.8056	.9061	.7355	.8666	1.3597	.1334	0.9367	40
30	0.6370	.5948	.7744	.8039	.9052	.7400	.8692	1.3514	.1308	0.9338	30
40	0.6400	.5972	.7761	.8021	.9042	.7445	.8718	1.3432	.1282	0.9308	20
50	0.6429	.5995	.7778	.8004	.9033	.7490	.8745	1.3351	.1255	0.9279	10
37° 00'	0.6458	.6018	9.7795	.7986	9.9023	.7536	9.8771	1.3270	0.1229	0.9250	53° 00'
10	0.6487	.6041	.7811	.7969	.9014	.7581	.8797	1.3190	.1203	0.9221	50
20	0.6516	.6065	.7828	.7951	.9004	.7627	.8824	1.3111	.1176	0.9192	40
30	0.6545	.6088	.7844	.7934	.8995	.7673	.8850	1.3032	.1150	0.9163	30
40	0.6574	.6111	.7861	.7916	.8985	.7720	.8876	1.2954	.1124	0.9134	20
50	0.6603	.6134	.7877	.7898	.8975	.7766	.8902	1.2876	.1098	0.9105	10
38° 00'	0.6632	.6157	9.7893	.7880	9.8965	.7813	9.8928	1.2799	0.1072	0.9076	52° 00'
10	0.6661	.6180	.7910	.7862	.8955	.7860	.8954	1.2723	.1046	0.9047	50
20	0.6690	.6202	.7926	.7844	.8945	.7907	.8980	1.2647	.1020	0.9018	40
30	0.6720	.6225	.7941	.7826	.8935	.7954	.9006	1.2572	.0994	0.8988	30
40	0.6749	.6248	.7957	.7808	.8925	.8002	.9032	1.2497	.0968	0.8959	20
50	0.6778	.6271	.7973	.7790	.8915	.8050	.9058	1.2423	.0942	0.8930	10
39° 00'	0.6807	.6293	9.7989	.7771	9.8905	.8098	9.9084	1.2349	0.0916	0.8901	51° 00'
10	0.6836	.6316	.8004	.7753	.8895	.8146	.9110	1.2276	.0890	0.8872	50
20	0.6865	.6338	.8020	.7735	.8884	.8195	.9135	1.2203	.0865	0.8843	40
30	0.6894	.6361	.8035	.7716	.8874	.8243	.9161	1.2131	.0839	0.8814	30
40	0.6923	.6383	.8050	.7698	.8864	.8292	.9187	1.2059	.0813	0.8785	20
50	0.6952	.6406	.8066	.7679	.8853	.8342	.9212	1.1988	.0788	0.8756	10
40° 00'	0.6981	.6428	9.8081	.7660	9.8843	.8391	9.9238	1.1918	0.0762	0.8727	50° 00'
10	0.7010	.6450	.8096	.7642	.8832	.8441	.9264	1.1847	.0736	0.8698	50
20	0.7039	.6472	.8111	.7623	.8821	.8491	.9289	1.1778	.0711	0.8668	40
30	0.7069	.6494	.8125	.7604	.8810	.8541	.9315	1.1708	.0685	0.8639	30
40	0.7098	.6517	.8140	.7585	.8800	.8591	.9341	1.1640	.0659	0.8610	20
50	0.7127	.6539	.8155	.7566	.8789	.8642	.9366	1.1571	.0634	0.8581	10
41° 00'	0.7156	.6561	9.8169	.7547	9.8778	.8693	9.9392	1.1504	0.0608	0.8552	49° 00'
10	0.7185	.6583	.8184	.7528	.8767	.8744	.9417	1.1436	.0583	0.8523	50
20	0.7214	.6604	.8198	.7509	.8756	.8796	.9443	1.1369	.0557	0.8494	40
30	0.7243	.6626	.8213	.7490	.8745	.8847	.9468	1.1303	.0532	0.8465	30
40	0.7272	.6648	.8227	.7470	.8733	.8899	.9494	1.1237	.0506	0.8436	20
50	0.7301	.6670	.8241	.7451	.8722	.8952	.9519	1.1171	.0481	0.8407	10
42° 00'	0.7330	.6691	9.8255	.7431	9.8711	.9004	9.9544	1.1106	0.0456	0.8378	48° 00'
10	0.7359	.6713	.8269	.7412	.8699	.9057	.9570	1.1041	.0430	0.8348	50
20	0.7389	.6734	.8283	.7392	.8688	.9110	.9595	1.0977	.0405	0.8319	40
30	0.7418	.6756	.8297	.7373	.8676	.9163	.9621	1.0913	.0379	0.8290	30
40	0.7447	.6777	.8311	.7353	.8665	.9217	.9646	1.0850	.0354	0.8261	20
50	0.7476	.6799	.8324	.7333	.8653	.9271	.9671	1.0786	.0329	0.8232	10
43° 00'	0.7505	.6820	9.8338	.7314	9.8641	.9325	9.9697	1.0724	0.0303	0.8203	47° 00'
10	0.7534	.6841	.8351	.7294	.8629	.9380	.9722	1.0661	.0278	0.8174	50
20	0.7563	.6862	.8365	.7274	.8618	.9435	.9747	1.0599	.0253	0.8145	40
30	0.7592	.6884	.8378	.7254	.8606	.9490	.9772	1.0538	.0228	0.8116	30
40	0.7621	.6905	.8391	.7234	.8594	.9545	.9798	1.0477	.0202	0.8087	20
50	0.7650	.6926	.8405	.7214	.8582	.9601	.9823	1.0416	.0177	0.8058	10
44° 00'	0.7679	.6947	9.8418	.7193	9.8569	.9657	9.9848	1.0355	0.0152	0.8029	46° 00'
10	0.7709	.6967	.8431	.7173	.8557	.9713	.9874	1.0295	.0126	0.7999	50
20	0.7738	.6988	.8444	.7153	.8545	.9770	.9899	1.0235	.0101	0.7970	40
30	0.7767	.7009	.8457	.7133	.8532	.9827	.9924	1.0176	.0076	0.7941	30
40	0.7796	.7030	.8469	.7112	.8520	.9884	.9949	1.0117	.0051	0.7912	20
50	0.7825	.7050	.8482	.7092	.8507	.9942	.9975	1.0058	.0025	0.7883	10
45° 00'	0.7854	.7071	9.8495	.7071	9.8495	1.0000	0.0000	1.0000	0.0000	0.7854	45° 00'
		Nat.	Log *	Nat.	Log *	Nat.	Log *	Nat.	Log		
		Cosines		Sines		Cotangents		Tangents		Ra-dians	De-grees

Exponentials [e^n and e^{-n}]

n	e^n	Diff	n	e^n	Diff	n	e^n	n	e^{-n}	Diff	n	e^{-n}	n	e^{-n}
0.00	1.000	10	0.50	1.649	16	1.0	2.718*	0.00	1.000	−10	0.50	.607	1.0	.368*
.01	1.010	10	.51	1.665	17	.1	3.004	.01	0.990	−10	.51	.600	.1	.333
.02	1.020	10	.52	1.682	17	.2	3.320	.02	.980	−10	.52	.595	.2	.301
.03	1.030	11	.53	1.699	17	.3	3.669	.03	.970	−9	.53	.589	.3	.273
.04	1.041	10	.54	1.716	17	.4	4.055	.04	.961	−10	.54	.583	.4	.247
0.05	1.051	11	0.55	1.733	18	1.5	4.482	0.05	.951	−9	0.55	.577	1.5	.223
.06	1.062	11	.56	1.751	17	.6	4.953	.06	.942	−10	.56	.571	.6	.202
.07	1.073	10	.57	1.768	18	.7	5.474	.07	.932	−9	.57	.566	.7	.183
.08	1.083	11	.58	1.786	18	.8	6.050	.08	.923	−9	.58	.560	.8	.165
.09	1.094	11	.59	1.804	18	.9	6.686	.09	.914	−9	.59	.554	.9	.150
0.10	1.105	11	0.60	1.822	18	2.0	7.389	0.10	.905	−9	0.60	.549	2.0	.135
.11	1.116	11	.61	1.840	19	.1	8.166	.11	.896	−9	.61	.543	.1	.122
.12	1.127	12	.62	1.859	19	.2	9.025	.12	.887	−9	.62	.538	.2	.111
.13	1.139	11	.63	1.878	18	.3	9.974	.13	.878	−9	.63	.533	.3	.100
.14	1.150	12	.64	1.896	20	.4	11.02	.14	.869	−8	.64	.527	.4	.0907
0.15	1.162	12	0.65	1.916	19	2.5	12.18	0.15	.861	−9	0.65	.522	2.5	.0821
.16	1.174	11	.66	1.935	19	.6	13.46	.16	.852	−8	.66	.517	.6	.0743
.17	1.185	12	.67	1.954	20	.7	14.88	.17	.844	−9	.67	.512	.7	.0672
.18	1.197	12	.68	1.974	20	.8	16.44	.18	.835	−8	.68	.507	.8	.0608
.19	1.209	12	.69	1.994	20	.9	18.17	.19	.827	−8	.69	.502	.9	.0550
0.20	1.221	13	0.70	2.014	20	3.0	20.09	0.20	.819	−8	0.70	.497	3.0	.0498
.21	1.234	12	.71	2.034	20	.1	22.20	.21	.811	−8	.71	.492	.1	.0450
.22	1.246	13	.72	2.054	21	.2	24.53	.22	.803	−8	.72	.487	.2	.0408
.23	1.259	12	.73	2.075	21	.3	27.11	.23	.795	−8	.73	.482	.3	.0369
.24	1.271	13	.74	2.096	21	.4	29.96	.24	.787	−8	.74	.477	.4	.0334
0.25	1.284	13	0.75	2.117	21	3.5	33.12	0.25	.779	−8	0.75	.472	3.5	.0302
.26	1.297	13	.76	2.138	22	.6	36.60	.26	.771	−8	.76	.468	.6	.0273
.27	1.310	13	.77	2.160	21	.7	40.45	.27	.763	−7	.77	.463	.7	.0247
.28	1.323	13	.78	2.181	22	.8	44.70	.28	.756	−8	.78	.458	.8	.0224
.29	1.336	14	.79	2.203	23	.9	49.40	.29	.748	−7	.79	.454	.9	.0202
0.30	1.350	13	0.80	2.226	22	4.0	54.60	0.30	.741	−8	0.80	.449	4.0	.0183
.31	1.363	14	.81	2.248	22	.1	60.34	.31	.733	−7	.81	.445	.1	.0166
.32	1.377	14	.82	2.270	23	.2	66.69	.32	.726	−7	.82	.440	.2	.0150
.33	1.391	14	.83	2.293	23	.3	73.70	.33	.719	−7	.83	.436	.3	.0136
.34	1.405	14	.84	2.316	24	.4	81.45	.34	.712	−7	.84	.432	.4	.0123
0.35	1.419	14	0.85	2.340	23	4.5	90.02	0.35	.705	−7	0.85	.427	4.5	.0111
.36	1.433	15	.86	2.363	24			.36	.698	−7	.86	.423		
.37	1.448	14	.87	2.387	24	5.0	148.4	.37	.691	−7	.87	.419	5.0	.00674
.38	1.462	15	.88	2.411	24	6.0	403.4	.38	.684	−7	.88	.415	6.0	.00248
.39	1.477	15	.89	2.435	25	7.0	1097.	.39	.677	−7	.89	.411	7.0	.000912
0.40	1.492	15	0.90	2.460	24	8.0	2981.	0.40	.670	−6	0.90	.407	8.0	.000335
.41	1.507	15	.91	2.484	25	9.0	8103.	.41	.664	−7	.91	.403	9.0	.000123
.42	1.522	15	.92	2.509	26	10.0	22026.	.42	.657	−6	.92	.399	10.0	.000045
.43	1.537	16	.93	2.535	25			.43	.651	−7	.93	.395		
.44	1.553	15	.94	2.560	26	$\pi/2$	4.810	.44	.644	−6	.94	.391	$\pi/2$	.208
						$2\pi/2$	23.14						$2\pi/2$	.0432
0.45	1.568	16	0.95	2.586	26	$3\pi/2$	111.3	0.45	.638	−7	0.95	.387	$3\pi/2$	.00898
.46	1.584	16	.96	2.612	26	$4\pi/2$	535.5	.46	.631	−6	.96	.383	$4\pi/2$	.00187
.47	1.600	16	.97	2.638	26	$5\pi/2$	2576.	.47	.625	−6	.97	.379	$5\pi/2$	.000388
.48	1.616	16	.98	2.664	27	$6\pi/2$	12392.	.48	.619	−6	.98	.375	$6\pi/2$	.000081
.49	1.632	17	.99	2.691	27	$7\pi/2$	59610.	.49	.613	−6	.99	.372	$7\pi/2$	.000017
						$8\pi/2$	286751.						$8\pi/2$	.000003
0.50	1.649		1.00	2.718				0.50	0.607		1.00	.368		

* Note: Do not interpolate in this column.
$e = 2.71828$ $1/e = 0.367879$ $\log_{10} e = 0.4343$ $1/(0.4343) = 2.3026$
$\log_{10}(0.4343) = \overline{1}.6378$ $\log_{10}(e^n) = n(0.4343)$
For table of multiples of 0.4343, see p. 1–64.

Natural Logarithms

	n	n (2.3026)	n (0.6974−3)
These two pages give the natural or Napierian logarithms (ln) of numbers between 1 and 10, correct to four places. Moving the decimal point n places to the right [or left] in the number is equivalent to adding n times 2.3026 [or n times $\bar{3}$.6974] to the logarithm. Base $e = 2.71828 +$	1	2.3026	0.6974−3
	2	4.6052	0.3948−5
	3	6.9078	0.0922−7
	4	9.2103	0.7897−10
	5	11.5129	0.4871−12
	6	13.8155	0.1845−14
	7	16.1181	0.8819−17
	8	18.4207	0.5793−19
	9	20.7233	0.2767−21

Number	0	1	2	3	4	5	6	7	8	9	Avg diff
1.0	0.0000	0100	0198	0296	0392	0488	0583	0677	0770	0862	95
1.1	0953	1044	1133	1222	1310	1398	1484	1570	1655	1740	87
1.2	1823	1906	1989	2070	2151	2231	2311	2390	2469	2546	80
1.3	2624	2700	2776	2852	2927	3001	3075	3148	3221	3293	74
1.4	3365	3436	3507	3577	3646	3716	3784	3853	3920	3988	69
1.5	0.4055	4121	4187	4253	4318	4383	4447	4511	4574	4637	65
1.6	4700	4762	4824	4886	4947	5008	5068	5128	5188	5247	61
1.7	5306	5365	5423	5481	5539	5596	5653	5710	5766	5822	57
1.8	5878	5933	5988	6043	6098	6152	6206	6259	6313	6366	54
1.9	6419	6471	6523	6575	6627	6678	6729	6780	6831	6881	51
2.0	0.6931	6981	7031	7080	7129	7178	7227	7275	7324	7372	49
2.1	7419	7467	7514	7561	7608	7655	7701	7747	7793	7839	47
2.2	7885	7930	7975	8020	8065	8109	8154	8198	8242	8286	44
2.3	8329	8372	8416	8459	8502	8544	8587	8629	8671	8713	43
2.4	8755	8796	8838	8879	8920	8961	9002	9042	9083	9123	41
2.5	0.9163	9203	9243	9282	9322	9361	9400	9439	9478	9517	39
2.6	9555	9594	9632	9670	9708	9746	9783	9821	9858	9895	38
2.7	0.9933	9969	*0006	*0043	*0080	*0116	*0152	*0188	*0225	*0260	36
2.8	1.0296	0332	0367	0403	0438	0473	0508	0543	0578	0613	35
2.9	0647	0682	0716	0750	0784	0818	0852	0886	0919	0953	34
3.0	1.0986	1019	1053	1086	1119	1151	1184	1217	1249	1282	33
3.1	1314	1346	1378	1410	1442	1474	1506	1537	1569	1600	32
3.2	1632	1663	1694	1725	1756	1787	1817	1848	1878	1909	31
3.3	1939	1969	2000	2030	2060	2090	2119	2149	2179	2208	30
3.4	2238	2267	2296	2326	2355	2384	2413	2442	2470	2499	29
3.5	1.2528	2556	2585	2613	2641	2669	2698	2726	2754	2782	28
3.6	2809	2837	2865	2892	2920	2947	2975	3002	3029	3056	27
3.7	3083	3110	3137	3164	3191	3218	3244	3271	3297	3324	27
3.8	3350	3376	3403	3429	3455	3481	3507	3533	3558	3584	26
3.9	3610	3635	3661	3686	3712	3737	3762	3788	3813	3838	25
4.0	1.3863	3888	3913	3938	3962	3987	4012	4036	4061	4085	25
4.1	4110	4134	4159	4183	4207	4231	4255	4279	4303	4327	24
4.2	4351	4375	4398	4422	4446	4469	4493	4516	4540	4563	23
4.3	4586	4609	4633	4656	4679	4702	4725	4748	4770	4793	23
4.4	4816	4839	4861	4884	4907	4929	4951	4974	4996	5019	22
4.5	1.5041	5063	5085	5107	5129	5151	5173	5195	5217	5239	22
4.6	5261	5282	5304	5326	5347	5369	5390	5412	5433	5454	21
4.7	5476	5497	5518	5539	5560	5581	5602	5623	5644	5665	21
4.8	5686	5707	5728	5748	5769	5790	5810	5831	5851	5872	20
4.9	5892	5913	5933	5953	5974	5994	6014	6034	6054	6074	20

$$\ln x = (2.3026) \log_{10} x \qquad \log_{10} x = (0.4343) \ln x$$
where $2.3026 = \ln 10$ and $0.4343 = \log_{10} e$ (see p. 1-64).

Natural Logarithms (*continued*)

Number	0	1	2	3	4	5	6	7	8	9	Avg diff
5.0	1.6094	6114	6134	6154	6174	6194	6214	6233	6253	6273	20
5.1	6292	6312	6332	6351	6371	6390	6409	6429	6448	6467	19
5.2	6487	6506	6525	6544	6563	6582	6601	6620	6639	6658	19
5.3	6677	6696	6715	6734	6752	6771	6790	6808	6827	6845	18
5.4	6864	6882	6901	6919	6938	6956	6974	6993	7011	7029	18
5.5	1.7047	7066	7084	7102	7120	7138	7156	7174	7192	7210	18
5.6	7228	7246	7263	7281	7299	7317	7334	7352	7370	7387	18
5.7	7405	7422	7440	7457	7475	7492	7509	7527	7544	7561	17
5.8	7579	7596	7613	7630	7647	7664	7681	7699	7716	7733	17
5.9	7750	7766	7783	7800	7817	7834	7851	7867	7884	7901	17
6.0	1.7918	7934	7951	7967	7984	8001	8017	8034	8050	8066	16
6.1	8083	8099	8116	8132	8148	8165	8181	8197	8213	8229	16
6.2	8245	8262	8278	8294	8310	8326	8342	8358	8374	8390	16
6.3	8405	8421	8437	8453	8469	8485	8500	8516	8532	8547	16
6.4	8563	8579	8594	8610	8625	8641	8656	8672	8687	8703	15
6.5	1.8718	8733	8749	8764	8779	8795	8810	8825	8840	8856	15
6.6	8871	8886	8901	8916	8931	8946	8961	8976	8991	9006	15
6.7	9021	9036	9051	9066	9081	9095	9110	9125	9140	9155	15
6.8	9169	9184	9199	9213	9228	9242	9257	9272	9286	9301	15
6.9	9315	9330	9344	9359	9373	9387	9402	9416	9430	9445	14
7.0	1.9459	9473	9488	9502	9516	9530	9544	9559	9573	9587	14
7.1	9601	9615	9629	9643	9657	9671	9685	9699	9713	9727	14
7.2	9741	9755	9769	9782	9796	9810	9824	9838	9851	9865	14
7.3	1.9879	9892	9906	9920	9933	9947	9961	9974	9988	*0001	13
7.4	2.0015	0028	0042	0055	0069	0082	0096	0109	0122	0136	13
7.5	2.0149	0162	0176	0189	0202	0215	0229	0242	0255	0268	13
7.6	0281	0295	0308	0321	0334	0347	0360	0373	0386	0399	13
7.7	0412	0425	0438	0451	0464	0477	0490	0503	0516	0528	13
7.8	0541	0554	0567	0580	0592	0605	0618	0631	0643	0656	13
7.9	0669	0681	0694	0707	0719	0732	0744	0757	0769	0782	12
8.0	2.0794	0807	0819	0832	0844	0857	0869	0882	0894	0906	12
8.1	0919	0931	0943	0956	0968	0980	0992	1005	1017	1029	12
8.2	1041	1054	1066	1078	1090	1102	1114	1126	1138	1150	12
8.3	1163	1175	1187	1199	1211	1223	1235	1247	1258	1270	12
8.4	1282	1294	1306	1318	1330	1342	1353	1365	1377	1389	12
8.5	2.1401	1412	1424	1436	1448	1459	1471	1483	1494	1506	12
8.6	1518	1529	1541	1552	1564	1576	1587	1599	1610	1622	12
8.7	1633	1645	1656	1668	1679	1691	1702	1713	1725	1736	11
8.8	1748	1759	1770	1782	1793	1804	1815	1827	1838	1849	11
8.9	1861	1872	1883	1894	1905	1917	1928	1939	1950	1961	11
9.0	2.1972	1983	1994	2006	2017	2028	2039	2050	2061	2072	11
9.1	2083	2094	2105	2116	2127	2138	2148	2159	2170	2181	11
9.2	2192	2203	2214	2225	2235	2246	2257	2268	2279	2289	11
9.3	2300	2311	2322	2332	2343	2354	2364	2375	2386	2396	11
9.4	2407	2418	2428	2439	2450	2460	2471	2481	2492	2502	11
9.5	2.2513	2523	2534	2544	2555	2565	2576	2586	2597	2607	10
9.6	2618	2628	2638	2649	2659	2670	2680	2690	2701	2711	10
9.7	2721	2732	2742	2752	2762	2773	2783	2793	2803	2814	10
9.8	2824	2834	2844	2854	2865	2875	2885	2895	2905	2915	10
9.9	2925	2935	2946	2956	2966	2976	2986	2996	3006	3016	10
10.0	2.3026										

Moving the decimal point n places to the right [or left] in the number requires adding n times 2.3026 [or n times (0.6974–3)] in the body of the table. See auxiliary table of multiples on top of the preceding page.

Hyperbolic Sines [sinh $x = \frac{1}{2}(e^x - e^{-x})$]

x	0	1	2	3	4	5	6	7	8	9	Avg diff
0.0	.0000	.0100	.0200	.0300	.0400	.0500	.0600	.0701	.0801	.0901	100
1	.1002	.1102	.1203	.1304	.1405	.1506	.1607	.1708	.1810	.1911	101
2	.2013	.2115	.2218	,.2320	.2423	.2526	.2629	.2733	.2837	.2941	103
3	.3045	.3150	.3255	.3360	.3466	.3572	.3678	.3785	.3892	.4000	106
4	.4108	.4216	.4325	.4434	.4543	.4653	.4764	.4875	.4986	.5098	110
0.5	.5211	.5324	.5438	.5552	.5666	.5782	.5897	.6014	.6131	.6248	116
6	.6367	.6485	.6605	.6725	.6846	.6967	.7090	.7213	.7336	.7461	122
7	.7586	.7712	.7838	.7966	.8094	.8223	.8353	.8484	.8615	.8748	130
8	.8881	.9015	.9150	.9286	.9423	.9561	.9700	.9840	.9981	1.012	138
9	1.027	1.041	1.055	1.070	1.085	1.099	1.114	1.129	1.145	1.160	15
1.0	1.175	1.191	1.206	1.222	1.238	1.254	1.270	1.286	1.303	1.319	16
1	1.336	1.352	1.369	1.386	1.403	1.421	1.438	1.456	1.474	1.491	17
2	1.509	1.528	1.546	1.564	1.583	1.602	1.621	1.640	1.659	1.679	19
3	1.698	1.718	1.738	1.758	1.779	1.799	1.820	1.841	1.862	1.883	21
4	1.904	1.926	1.948	1.970	1.992	2.014	2.037	2.060	2.083	2.106	22
1.5	2.129	2.153	2.177	2.201	2.225	2.250	2.274	2.299	2.324	2.350	25
6	2.376	2.401	2.428	2.454	2.481	2.507	2.535	2.562	2.590	2.617	27
7	2.646	2.674	2.703	2.732	2.761	2.790	2.820	2.850	2.881	2.911	30
8	2.942	2.973	3.005	3.037	3.069	3.101	3.134	3.167	3.200	3.234	33
9	3.268	3.303	3.337	3.372	3.408	3.443	3.479	3.516	3.552	3.589	36
2.0	3.627	3.665	3.703	3.741	3.780	3.820	3.859	3.899	3.940	3.981	39
1	4.022	4.064	4.106	4.148	4.191	4.234	4.278	4.322	4.367	4.412	44
2	4.457	4.503	4.549	4.596	4.643	4.691	4.739	4.788	4.837	4.887	48
3	4.937	4.988	5.039	5.090	5.142	5.195	5.248	5.302	5.356	5.411	53
4	5.466	5.522	5.578	5.635	5.693	5.751	5.810	5.869	5.929	5.989	58
2.5	6.050	6.112	6.174	6.237	6.300	6.365	6.429	6.495	6.561	6.627	64
6	6.695	6.763	6.831	6.901	6.971	7.042	7.113	7.185	7.258	7.332	71
7	7.406	7.481	7.557	7.634	7.711	7.789	7.868	7.948	8.028	8.110	79
8	8.192	8.275	8.359	8.443	8.529	8.615	8.702	8.790	8.879	8.969	87
9	9.060	9.151	9.244	9.337	9.431	9.527	9.623	9.720	9.819	9.918	96
3.0	10.02	10.12	10.22	10.32	10.43	10.53	10.64	10.75	10.86	10.97	11
1	11.08	11.19	11.30	11.42	11.53	11.65	11.76	11.88	12.00	12.12	12
2	12.25	12.37	12.49	12.62	12.75	12.88	13.01	13.14	13.27	13.40	13
3	13.54	13.67	13.81	13.95	14.09	14.23	14.38	14.52	14.67	14.82	14
4	14.97	15.12	15.27	15.42	15.58	15.73	15.89	16.05	16.21	16.38	16
3.5	16.54	16.71	16.88	17.05	17.22	17.39	17.57	17.74	17.92	18.10	17
6	18.29	18.47	18.66	18.84	19.03	19.22	19.42	19.61	19.81	20.01	19
7	20.21	20.41	20.62	20.83	21.04	21.25	21.46	21.68	21.90	22.12	21
8	22.34	22.56	22.79	23.02	23.25	23.49	23.72	23.96	24.20	24.45	24
9	24.69	24.94	25.19	25.44	25.70	25.96	26.22	26.48	26.75	27.02	26
4.0	27.29	27.56	27.84	28.12	28.40	28.69	28.98	29.27	29.56	29.86	29
1	30.16	30.47	30.77	31.08	31.39	31.71	32.03	32.35	32.68	33.00	32
2	33.34	33.67	34.01	34.35	34.70	35.05	35.40	35.75	36.11	36.48	35
3	36.84	37.21	37.59	37.97	38.35	38.73	39.12	39.52	39.91	40.31	39
4	40.72	41.13	41.54	41.96	42.38	42.81	43.24	43.67	44.11	44.56	43
4.5	45.00	45.46	45.91	46.37	46.84	47.31	47.79	48.27	48.75	49.24	47
6	49.74	50.24	50.74	51.25	51.77	52.29	52.81	53.34	53.88	54.42	52
7	54.97	55.52	56.08	56.64	57.21	57.79	58.37	58.96	59.55	60.15	58
8	60.75	61.36	61.98	62.60	63.23	63.87	64.51	65.16	65.81	67.47	64
9	67.14	67.82	68.50	69.19	69.88	70.58	71.29	72.01	72.73	73.46	71
5.0	74.20										

If $x > 5$, sinh $x = \frac{1}{2}(e^x)$ and $\log_{10}$ sinh $x = (0.4343)x + 0.6990 - 1$, correct to four significant figures. For table of multiples of 0.4343, see p. 1–64.

Hyperbolic Cosines $[\cosh x = \tfrac{1}{2}(e^x + e^{-x})]$

x	0	1	2	3	4	5	6	7	8	9	Avg diff
0.0	1.000	1.000	1.000	1.000	1.001	1.001	1.002	1.002	1.003	1.004	1
1	1.005	1.006	1.007	1.008	1.010	1.011	1.013	1.014	1.016	1.018	2
2	1.020	1.022	1.024	1.027	1.029	1.031	1.034	1.037	1.039	1.042	3
3	1.045	1.048	1.052	1.055	1.058	1.062	1.066	1.069	1.073	1.077	4
4	1.081	1.085	1.090	1.094	1.098	1.103	1.108	1.112	1.117	1.122	5
0.5	1.128	1.133	1.138	1.144	1.149	1.155	1.161	1.167	1.173	1.179	6
6	1.185	1.192	1.198	1.205	1.212	1.219	1.226	1.233	1.240	1.248	7
7	1.255	1.263	1.271	1.278	1.287	1.295	1.303	1.311	1.320	1.329	8
8	1.337	1.346	1.355	1.365	1.374	1.384	1.393	1.403	1.413	1.423	10
9	1.433	1.443	1.454	1.465	1.475	1.486	1.497	1.509	1.520	1.531	11
1.0	1.543	1.555	1.567	1.579	1.591	1.604	1.616	1.629	1.642	1.655	13
1	1.669	1.682	1.696	1.709	1.723	1.737	1.752	1.766	1.781	1.796	14
2	1.811	1.826	1.841	1.857	1.872	1.888	1.905	1.921	1.937	1.954	16
3	1.971	1.988	2.005	2.023	2.040	2.058	2.076	2.095	2.113	2.132	18
4	2.151	2.170	2.189	2.209	2.229	2.249	2.269	2.290	2.310	2.331	20
1.5	2.352	2.374	2.395	2.417	2.439	2.462	2.484	2.507	2.530	2.554	23
6	2.577	2.601	2.625	2.650	2.675	2.700	2.725	2.750	2.776	2.802	25
7	2.828	2.855	2.882	2.909	2.936	2.964	2.992	3.021	3.049	3.078	28
8	3.107	3.137	3.167	3.197	3.228	3.259	3.290	3.321	3.353	3.385	31
9	3.418	3.451	3.484	3.517	3.551	3.585	3.620	3.655	3.690	3.726	34
2.0	3.762	3.799	3.835	3.873	3.910	3.948	3.987	4.026	4.065	4.104	38
1	4.144	4.185	4.226	4.267	4.309	4.351	4.393	4.436	4.480	4.524	42
2	4.568	4.613	4.658	4.704	4.750	4.797	4.844	4.891	4.939	4.988	47
3	5.037	5.087	5.137	5.188	5.239	5.290	5.343	5.395	5.449	5.503	52
4	5.557	5.612	5.667	5.723	5.780	5.837	5.895	5.954	6.013	6.072	58
2.5	6.132	6.193	6.255	6.317	6.379	6.443	6.507	6.571	6.636	6.702	64
6	6.769	6.836	6.904	6.973	7.042	7.112	7.183	7.255	7.327	7.400	70
7	7.473	7.548	7.623	7.699	7.776	7.853	7.932	8.011	8.091	8.171	78
8	8.253	8.335	8.418	8.502	8.587	8.673	8.759	8.847	8.935	9.024	86
9	9.115	9.206	9.298	9.391	9.484	9.579	9.675	9.772	9.869	9.968	95
3.0	10.07	10.17	10.27	10.37	10.48	10.58	10.69	10.79	10.90	11.01	11
1	11.12	11.23	11.35	11.46	11.57	11.69	11.81	11.92	12.04	12.16	12
2	12.29	12.41	12.53	12.66	12.79	12.91	13.04	13.17	13.31	13.44	13
3	13.57	13.71	13.85	13.99	14.13	14.27	14.41	14.56	14.70	14.85	14
4	15.00	15.15	15.30	15.45	15.61	15.77	15.92	16.08	16.25	16.41	16
3.5	16.57	16.74	16.91	17.08	17.25	17.42	17.60	17.77	17.95	18.13	17
6	18.31	18.50	18.68	18.87	19.06	19.25	19.44	19.64	19.84	20.03	19
7	20.24	20.44	20.64	20.85	21.06	21.27	21.49	21.70	21.92	22.14	21
8	22.36	22.59	22.81	23.04	23.27	23.51	23.74	23.98	24.22	24.47	23
9	24.71	24.96	25.21	25.46	25.72	25.98	26.24	26.50	26.77	27.04	26
4.0	27.31	27.58	27.86	28.14	28.42	28.71	29.00	29.29	29.58	29.88	29
1	30.18	30.48	30.79	31.10	31.41	31.72	32.04	32.37	32.69	33.02	32
2	33.35	33.69	34.02	34.37	34.71	35.06	35.41	35.77	36.13	36.49	35
3	36.86	37.23	37.60	37.98	38.36	38.75	39.13	39.53	39.93	40.33	39
4	40.73	41.14	41.55	41.97	42.39	42.82	43.25	43.68	44.12	44.57	43
4.5	45.01	45.47	45.92	46.38	46.85	47.32	47.80	48.28	48.76	49.25	47
6	49.75	50.25	50.75	51.26	51.78	52.30	52.82	53.35	53.89	54.43	52
7	54.98	55.53	56.09	56.65	57.22	57.80	58.38	58.96	59.56	60.15	58
8	60.76	61.37	61.99	62.61	63.24	63.87	64.52	65.16	65.82	66.48	64
9	67.15	67.82	68.50	69.19	69.89	70.59	71.30	72.02	72.74	73.47	71
5.0	74.21										

If $x > 5$, $\cosh x = \tfrac{1}{2}(e^x)$ and $\log_{10} \cosh x = (0.4343)x + 0.6990 - 1$, correct to four significant figures. For table of multiples of 0.4343, see p. 1–64.

Hyperbolic Tangents [tanh $x = (e^x - e^{-x})/(e^x + e^{-x}) = \sinh x/\cosh x$]

x	0	1	2	3	4	5	6	7	8	9	Avg diff
0.0	.0000	.0100	.0200	.0300	.0400	.0500	.0599	.0699	.0798	.0898	100
1	.0997	.1096	.1194	.1293	.1391	.1489	.1587	.1684	.1781	.1878	98
2	.1974	.2070	.2165	.2260	.2355	.2449	.2543	.2636	.2729	.2821	94
3	.2913	.3004	.3095	.3185	.3275	.3364	.3452	.3540	.3627	.3714	89
4	.3800	.3885	.3969	.4053	.4137	.4219	.4301	.4382	.4462	.4542	82
0.5	.4621	.4700	.4777	.4854	.4930	.5005	.5080	.5154	.5227	.5299	75
6	.5370	.5441	.5511	.5581	.5649	.5717	.5784	.5850	.5915	.5980	67
7	.6044	.6107	.6169	.6231	.6291	.6352	.6411	.6469	.6527	.6584	60
8	.6640	.6696	.6751	.6805	.6858	.6911	.6963	.7014	.7064	.7114	52
9	.7163	.7211	.7259	.7306	.7352	.7398	.7443	.7487	.7531	.7574	45
1.0	.7616	.7658	.7699	.7739	.7779	.7818	.7857	.7895	.7932	.7969	39
1	.8005	.8041	.8076	.8110	.8144	.8178	.8210	.8243	.8275	.8306	33
2	.8337	.8367	.8397	.8426	.8455	.8483	.8511	.8538	.8565	.8591	28
3	.8617	.8643	.8668	.8693	.8717	.8741	.8764	.8787	.8810	.8832	24
4	.8854	.8875	.8896	.8917	.8937	.8957	.8977	.8996	.9015	.9033	20
1.5	.9052	.9069	.9087	.9104	.9121	.9138	.9154	.9170	.9186	.9202	17
6	.9217	.9232	.9246	.9261	.9275	.9289	.9302	.9316	.9329	.9342	14
7	.9354	.9367	.9379	.9391	.9402	.9414	.9425	.9436	.9447	.9458	11
8	.9468	.9478	.9488	.9498	.9508	.9518	.9527	.9536	.9545	.9554	9
9	.9562	.9571	.9579	.9587	.9595	.9603	.9611	.9619	.9626	.9633	8
2.0	.9640	.9647	.9654	.9661	.9668	.9674	.9680	.9687	.9693	.9699	6
1	.9705	.9710	.9716	.9722	.9727	.9732	.9738	.9743	.9748	.9753	5
2	.9757	.9762	.9767	.9771	.9776	.9780	.9785	.9789	.9793	.9797	4
3	.9801	.9805	.9809	.9812	.9816	.9820	.9823	.9827	.9830	.9834	4
4	.9837	.9840	.9843	.9846	.9849	.9852	.9855	.9858	.9861	.9863	3
2.5	.9866	.9869	.9871	.9874	.9876	.9879	.9881	.9884	.9886	.9888	2
6	.9890	.9892	.9895	.9897	.9899	.9901	.9903	.9905	.9906	.9908	2
7	.9910	.9912	.9914	.9915	.9917	.9919	.9920	.9922	.9923	.9925	2
8	.9926	.9928	.9929	.9931	.9932	.9933	.9935	.9936	.9937	.9938	1
2.9	.9940	.9941	.9942	.9943	.9944	.9945	.9946	.9947	.9949	.9950	1
3.	.9951	.9959	.9967	.9973	.9978	.9982	.9985	.9988	.9990	.9992	4
4.	.9993	.9995	.9996	.9996	.9997	.9998	.9998	.9998	.9999	.9999	1
5.	.9999	If $x > 5$, tanh $x = 1.0000$ to four decimal places.									

Multiples of 0.4343 $(0.43429448 = \log_{10} e)$

x	0	1	2	3	4	5	6	7	8	9
0.	0.0000	0.0434	0.0869	0.1303	0.1737	0.2171	0.2606	0.3040	0.3474	0.3909
1.	0.4343	0.4777	0.5212	0.5646	0.6080	0.6514	0.6949	0.7383	0.7817	0.8252
2.	0.8686	0.9120	0.9554	0.9989	1.0423	1.0857	1.1292	1.1726	1.2160	1.2595
3.	1.3029	1.3463	1.3897	1.4332	1.4766	1.5200	1.5635	1.6069	1.6503	1.6937
4.	1.7372	1.7806	1.8240	1.8675	1.9109	1.9543	1.9978	2.0412	2.0846	2.1280
5.	2.1715	2.2149	2.2583	2.3018	2.3452	2.3886	2.4320	2.4755	2.5189	2.5623
6.	2.6058	2.6492	2.6926	2.7361	2.7795	2.8229	2.8663	2.9098	2.9532	2.9966
7.	3.0401	3.0835	3.1269	3.1703	3.2138	3.2572	3.3006	3.3441	3.3875	3.4309
8.	3.4744	3.5178	3.5612	3.6046	3.6481	3.6915	3.7349	3.7784	3.8218	3.8652
9.	3.9087	3.9521	3.9955	4.0389	4.0824	4.1258	4.1692	4.2127	4.2561	4.2995

Multiples of 2.3026 $(2.3025851 = \ln 10 = 1/0.4343)$

x	0	1	2	3	4	5	6	7	8	9
0.	0.0000	0.2303	0.4605	0.6908	0.9210	1.1513	1.3816	1.6118	1.8421	2.0723
1.	2.3026	2.5328	2.7631	2.9934	3.2236	3.4539	3.6841	3.9144	4.1447	4.3749
2.	4.6052	4.8354	5.0657	5.2959	5.5262	5.7565	5.9867	6.2170	6.4472	6.6775
3.	6.9078	7.1380	7.3683	7.5985	7.8288	8.0590	8.2893	8.5196	8.7498	8.9801
4.	9.2103	9.4406	9.6709	9.9011	10.131	10.362	10.592	10.822	11.052	11.283
5.	11.513	11.743	11.973	12.204	12.434	12.664	12.894	13.125	13.355	13.585
6.	13.816	14.046	14.276	14.506	14.737	14.967	15.197	15.427	15.658	15.888
7.	16.118	16.348	16.579	16.809	17.039	17.269	17.500	17.730	17.960	18.190
8.	18.421	18.651	18.881	19.111	19.342	19.572	19.802	20.032	20.263	20.493
9.	20.723	20.954	21.184	21.414	21.644	21.875	22.105	22.335	22.565	22.796

Standard Distribution of Residuals

a = any positive quantity;
y = the number of residuals which are numerically $< a$;
r = the probable error of a single observation;
n = number of observations.

$\dfrac{a}{r}$	$\dfrac{y}{n}$	Diff
0.0	.000	54
1	.054	53
2	.107	53
3	.160	53
4	.213	51
0.5	.264	50
6	.314	49
7	.363	48
8	.411	45
9	.456	44
1.0	.500	42
1	.542	40
2	.582	37
3	.619	36
4	.655	33
1.5	.688	31
6	.719	29
7	.748	27
8	.775	25
9	.800	23
2.0	.823	20
1	.843	19
2	.862	17
3	.879	16
4	.895	13
2.5	.908	13
6	.921	10
7	.931	10
8	.941	9
9	.950	7
3.0	.957	6
1	.963	6
2	.969	5
3	.974	4
4	.978	4
3.5	.982	3
6	.985	2
7	.987	3
8	.990	1
9	.991	2
4.0	.993	6
5.0	.999	

Factors for Computing Probable Error

n	Bessel		Peters	
	$\dfrac{0.6745}{\sqrt{(n-1)}}$	$\dfrac{0.6745}{\sqrt{n(n-1)}}$	$\dfrac{0.8453}{\sqrt{n(n-1)}}$	$\dfrac{0.8453}{n\sqrt{n-1}}$
2	.6745	.4769	.5978	.4227
3	.4769	.2754	.3451	.1993
4	.3894	.1947	.2440	.1220
5	.3372	.1508	.1890	.0845
6	.3016	.1231	.1543	.0630
7	.2754	.1041	.1304	.0493
8	.2549	.0901	.1130	.0399
9	.2385	.0795	.0996	.0332
10	.2248	.0711	.0891	.0282
11	.2133	.0643	.0806	.0243
12	.2034	.0587	.0736	.0212
13	.1947	.0540	.0677	.0188
14	.1871	.0500	.0627	.0167
15	.1803	.0465	.0583	.0151
16	.1742	.0435	.0546	.0136
17	.1686	.0409	.0513	.0124
18	.1636	.0386	.0483	.0114
19	.1590	.0365	.0457	.0105
20	.1547	.0346	.0434	.0097
21	.1508	.0329	.0412	.0090
22	.1472	.0314	.0393	.0084
23	.1438	.0300	.0376	.0078
24	.1406	.0287	.0360	.0073
25	.1377	.0275	.0345	.0069
26	.1349	.0265	.0332	.0065
27	.1323	.0255	.0319	.0061
28	.1298	.0245	.0307	.0058
29	.1275	.0237	.0297	.0055
30	.1252	.0229	.0287	.0052
31	.1231	.0221	.0277	.0050
32	.1211	.0214	.0268	.0047
33	.1192	.0208	.0260	.0045
34	.1174	.0201	.0252	.0043
35	.1157	.0196	.0245	.0041
36	.1140	.0190	.0238	.0040
37	.1124	.0185	.0232	.0038
38	.1109	.0180	.0225	.0037
39	.1094	.0175	.0220	.0035
40	.1080	.0171	.0214	.0034
45	.1017	.0152	.0190	.0028
50	.0964	.0136	.0171	.0024
55	.0918	.0124	.0155	.0021
60	.0878	.0113	.0142	.0018
65	.0843	.0105	.0131	.0016
70	.0812	.0097	.0122	.0015
75	.0784	.0091	.0113	.0013
80	.0759	.0085	.0106	.0012
85	.0736	.0080	.0100	.0011
90	.0715	.0075	.0094	.0010
95	.0696	.0071	.0089	.0009
100	.0678	.0068	.0085	.0008

MATHEMATICS

Compound Interest. Amount of a Given Principal

The amount A at the end of n years of a given principal P placed at compound interest to-day is $A = P \times x$ or $A = P \times y$ or $A = P \times z$, according as the interest (at the rate of r percent per annum) is compounded annually, semi-annually, or quarterly; the factor x or y or z being taken from the following tables.

Values of x.   (Interest compounded annually; $A = P \times x$)

Years	$r = 2$	2½	3	3½	4	4½	5	6	7	
1	1.0200	1.0250	1.0300	1.0350	1.0400	1.0450	1.0500	1.0600	1.0700	
2	1.0404	1.0506	1.0609	1.0712	1.0816	1.0920	1.1025	1.1236	1.1449	
3	1.0612	1.0769	1.0927	1.1087	1.1249	1.1412	1.1576	1.1910	1.2250	
4	1.0824	1.1038	1.1255	1.1475	1.1699	1.1925	1.2155	1.2625	1.3108	
5	1.1041	1.1314	1.1593	1.1877	1.2167	1.2462	1.2763	1.3382	1.4026	
6	1.1262	1.1597	1.1941	1.2293	1.2653	1.3023	1.3401	1.4185	1.5007	
7	1.1487	1.1887	1.2299	1.2723	1.3159	1.3609	1.4071	1.5036	1.6058	
8	1.1717	1.2184	1.2668	1.3168	1.3686	1.4221	1.4775	1.5938	1.7182	
9	1.1951	1.2489	1.3048	1.3629	1.4233	1.4861	1.5513	1.6895	1.8385	
10	1.2190	1.2801	1.3439	1.4106	1.4802	1.5530	1.6289	1.7908	1.9672	
11	1.2434	1.3121	1.3842	1.4600	1.5395	1.6229	1.7103	1.8983	2.1049	
12	1.2682	1.3449	1.4258	1.5111	1.6010	1.6959	1.7959	2.0122	2.2522	
13	1.2936	1.3785	1.4685	1.5640	1.6651	1.7722	1.8856	2.1329	2.4098	
14	1.3195	1.4130	1.5126	1.6187	1.7317	1.8519	1.9799	2.2609	2.5785	
15	1.3459	1.4483	1.5580	1.6753	1.8009	1.9353	2.0789	2.3966	2.7590	
16	1.3728	1.4845	1.6047	1.7340	1.8730	2.0224	2.1829	2.5404	2.9522	
17	1.4002	1.5216	1.6528	1.7947	1.9479	2.1134	2.2920	2.6928	3.1588	
18	1.4282	1.5597	1.7024	1.8575	2.0258	2.2085	2.4066	2.8543	3.3799	
19	1.4568	1.5987	1.7535	1.9225	2.1068	2.3079	2.5270	3.0256	3.6165	
20	1.4859	1.6386	1.8061	1.9898	2.1911	2.4117	2.6533	3.2071	3.8697	
25	1.6406	1.8539	2.0938	2.3632	2.6658	3.0054	3.3864	4.2919	5.4274	
30	1.8114	2.0976	2.4273	2.8068	3.2434	3.7453	4.3219	5.7435	7.6123	
40	2.2080	2.6851	3.2620	3.9593	4.8010	5.8164	7.0400	10.286	14.974	
50	2.6916	3.4371	4.3839	5.5849	7.1067	9.0326	11.467	18.420	29.457	
60	3.2810	4.3998	5.8916	7.8781	10.520	14.027	18.679	32.988	57.946	

This table is computed from the formula $x = [1 + (r/100)]^n$

Values of y.   (Interest compounded semi-annually; $A = P \times y$)

Years	$r = 2$	2½	3	3½	4	4½	5	6	7	
1	1.0201	1.0252	1.0302	1.0353	1.0404	1.0455	1.0506	1.0609	1.0712	
2	1.0406	1.0509	1.0614	1.0719	1.0824	1.0931	1.1038	1.1255	1.1475	
3	1.0615	1.0774	1.0934	1.1097	1.1262	1.1428	1.1597	1.1941	1.2293	
4	1.0829	1.1045	1.1265	1.1489	1.1717	1.1948	1.2184	1.2668	1.3168	
5	1.1046	1.1323	1.1605	1.1894	1.2190	1.2492	1.2801	1.3439	1.4106	
6	1.1268	1.1608	1.1956	1.2314	1.2682	1.3060	1.3449	1.4258	1.5111	
7	1.1495	1.1900	1.2318	1.2749	1.3195	1.3655	1.4130	1.5126	1.6187	
8	1.1726	1.2199	1.2690	1.3199	1.3728	1.4276	1.4845	1.6047	1.7340	
9	1.1961	1.2506	1.3073	1.3665	1.4282	1.4926	1.5597	1.7024	1.8575	
10	1.2202	1.2820	1.3469	1.4148	1.4859	1.5605	1.6386	1.8061	1.9898	
11	1.2447	1.3143	1.3876	1.4647	1.5460	1.6315	1.7216	1.9161	2.1315	
12	1.2697	1.3474	1.4295	1.5164	1.6084	1.7058	1.8087	2.0328	2.2833	
13	1.2953	1.3812	1.4727	1.5700	1.6734	1.7834	1.9003	2.1566	2.4460	
14	1.3213	1.4160	1.5172	1.6254	1.7410	1.8645	1.9965	2.2879	2.6202	
15	1.3478	1.4516	1.5631	1.6828	1.8114	1.9494	2.0976	2.4273	2.8068	
16	1.3749	1.4881	1.6103	1.7422	1.8845	2.0381	2.2038	2.5751	3.0067	
17	1.4026	1.5256	1.6590	1.8037	1.9607	2.1308	2.3153	2.7319	3.2209	
18	1.4308	1.5639	1.7091	1.8674	2.0399	2.2278	2.4325	2.8983	3.4503	
19	1.4595	1.6033	1.7608	1.9333	2.1223	2.3292	2.5557	3.0748	3.6960	
20	1.4889	1.6436	1.8140	2.0016	2.2080	2.4352	2.6851	3.2620	3.9593	
25	1.6446	1.8610	2.1052	2.3808	2.6916	3.0420	3.4371	4.3839	5.5849	
30	1.8167	2.1072	2.4432	2.8318	3.2810	3.8001	4.3998	5.8916	7.8781	
40	2.2167	2.7015	3.2907	4.0064	4.8754	5.9301	7.2096	10.641	15.676	
50	2.7048	3.4634	4.4320	5.6682	7.2446	9.2540	11.814	19.219	31.191	
60	3.3004	4.4402	5.9693	8.0192	10.765	14.441	19.358	34.711	62.064	

Formula: $y = [1 + (r/200)]^{2n}$

Values of z. (Interest compounded quarterly; $A = P \times z$; see opposite page)

Years	r = 2	2½	3	3½	4	4½	5	6	7	
1	1.0202	1.0252	1.0303	1.0355	1.0406	1.0458	1.0509	1.0614	1.0719	
2	1.0407	1.0511	1.0616	1.0722	1.0829	1.0936	1.1045	1.1265	1.1489	
3	1.0617	1.0776	1.0938	1.1102	1.1268	1.1437	1.1608	1.1956	1.2314	
4	1.0831	1.1048	1.1270	1.1496	1.1726	1.1960	1.2199	1.2690	1.3199	
5	1.1049	1.1327	1.1612	1.1903	1.2202	1.2508	1.2820	1.3469	1.4148	
6	1.1272	1.1613	1.1964	1.2326	1.2697	1.3080	1.3474	1.4295	1.5164	
7	1.1499	1.1906	1.2327	1.2763	1.3213	1.3679	1.4160	1.5172	1.6254	
8	1.1730	1.2206	1.2701	1.3215	1.3749	1.4305	1.4881	1.6103	1.7422	
9	1.1967	1.2514	1.3086	1.3684	1.4308	1.4959	1.5639	1.7091	1.8674	
10	1.2208	1.2830	1.3483	1.4169	1.4889	1.5644	1.6436	1.8140	2.0016	
11	1.2454	1.3154	1.3893	1.4672	1.5493	1.6360	1.7274	1.9253	2.1454	
12	1.2705	1.3486	1.4314	1.5192	1.6122	1.7108	1.8154	2.0435	2.2996	
13	1.2961	1.3826	1.4748	1.5731	1.6777	1.7891	1.9078	2.1689	2.4648	
14	1.3222	1.4175	1.5196	1.6288	1.7458	1.8710	2.0050	2.3020	2.6420	
15	1.3489	1.4533	1.5657	1.6866	1.8167	1.9566	2.1072	2.4432	2.8318	
16	1.3760	1.4900	1.6132	1.7464	1.8905	2.0462	2.2145	2.5931	3.0353	
17	1.4038	1.5276	1.6621	1.8083	1.9672	2.1398	2.3274	2.7523	3.2534	
18	1.4320	1.5661	1.7126	1.8725	2.0471	2.2378	2.4459	2.9212	3.4872	
19	1.4609	1.6056	1.7645	1.9389	2.1302	2.3402	2.5705	3.1004	3.7378	
20	1.4903	1.6462	1.8180	2.0076	2.2167	2.4473	2.7015	3.2907	4.0064	
25	1.6467	1.8646	2.1111	2.3898	2.7048	3.0609	3.4634	4.4320	5.6682	
30	1.8194	2.1121	2.4514	2.8446	3.3004	3.8285	4.4402	5.9693	8.0192	
40	2.2211	2.7098	3.3053	4.0306	4.9138	5.9892	7.2980	10.828	16.051	
50	2.7115	3.4768	4.4567	5.7110	7.3160	9.3693	11.995	19.643	32.128	
60	3.3102	4.4608	6.0092	8.0919	10.893	14.657	19.715	35.633	64.307	Formula: $z = [1 + (r/400)]^{4n}$

Amount of an Annuity

The amount S accumulated at the end of n years by a given annual payment Y set aside at the end of each year is $S = Y \times v$, where the factor v is to be taken from the following table. (Interest at r percent per annum, compounded annually.)

Values of v

Years	r = 2	2½	3	3½	4	4½	5	6	7	
1	1.0000	1.0000	1.0000	1.0000	1.0000	1.0000	1.0000	1.0000	1.0000	
2	2.0200	2.0250	2.0300	2.0350	2.0400	2.0450	2.0500	2.0600	2.0700	
3	3.0604	3.0756	3.0909	3.1062	3.1216	3.1370	3.1525	3.1836	3.2149	
4	4.1216	4.1525	4.1836	4.2149	4.2465	4.2782	4.3101	4.3746	4.4399	
5	5.2040	5.2563	5.3091	5.3625	5.4163	5.4707	5.5256	5.6371	5.7507	
6	6.3081	6.3877	6.4684	6.5502	6.6330	6.7169	6.8019	6.9753	7.1533	
7	7.4343	7.5474	7.6625	7.7794	7.8983	8.0192	8.1420	8.3938	8.6540	
8	8.5830	8.7361	8.8923	9.0517	9.2142	9.3800	9.5491	9.8975	10.260	
9	9.7546	9.9545	10.159	10.368	10.583	10.802	11.027	11.491	11.978	
10	10.950	11.203	11.464	11.731	12.006	12.288	12.578	13.181	13.816	
11	12.169	12.483	12.808	13.142	13.486	13.841	14.207	14.972	15.784	
12	13.412	13.796	14.192	14.602	15.026	15.464	15.917	16.870	17.888	
13	14.680	15.140	15.618	16.113	16.627	17.160	17.713	18.882	20.141	
14	15.974	16.519	17.086	17.677	18.292	18.932	19.599	21.015	22.550	
15	17.293	17.932	18.599	19.296	20.024	20.784	21.579	23.276	25.129	
16	18.639	19.380	20.157	20.971	21.825	22.719	23.657	25.673	27.888	
17	20.012	20.865	21.762	22.705	23.698	24.742	25.840	28.213	30.840	
18	21.412	22.386	23.414	24.500	25.645	26.855	28.132	30.906	33.999	
19	22.841	23.946	25.117	26.357	27.671	29.064	30.539	33.760	37.379	
20	24.297	25.545	26.870	28.280	29.778	31.371	33.066	36.786	40.995	
25	32.030	34.158	36.459	38.950	41.646	44.565	47.727	54.865	63.249	
30	40.568	43.903	47.575	51.623	56.085	61.007	66.439	79.058	94.461	
40	60.402	67.403	75.401	84.550	95.026	107.03	120.80	154.76	199.64	
50	84.579	97.484	112.80	131.00	152.67	178.50	209.35	290.34	406.53	
60	114.05	135.99	163.05	196.52	237.99	289.50	353.58	533.13	813.52	Formula: $v = \dfrac{[1 + (r/100)]^n - 1}{(r/100)} = \dfrac{(x^n - 1)}{(x - 1)}$; $x = 1 + (r/100)$

MATHEMATICS

Principal Which Will Amount to a Given Sum

The principal P, which, if placed at compound interest to-day, will amount to a given sum A at the end of n years is $P = A \times x'$ or $P = A \times y'$ or $P = A \times z'$, according as the interest (at the rate of r percent per annum) is compounded annually, semi-annually, or quarterly; the factor x' or y' or z' being taken from the following tables.

Values of x'.   (Interest compounded annually; $P = A \times x'$)

Years	$r = 2$	2½	3	3½	4	4½	5	6	7
1	.98039	.97561	.97087	.96618	.96154	.95694	.95238	.94340	.93458
2	.96117	.95181	.94260	.93351	.92456	.91573	.90703	.89000	.87344
3	.94232	.92860	.91514	.90194	.88900	.87630	.86384	.83962	.81630
4	.92385	.90595	.88849	.87144	.85480	.83856	.82270	.79209	.76290
5	.90573	.88385	.86261	.84197	.82193	.80245	.78353	.74726	.71299
6	.88797	.86230	.83748	.81350	.79031	.76790	.74622	.70496	.66634
7	.87056	.84127	.81309	.78599	.75992	.73483	.71068	.66506	.62275
8	.85349	.82075	.78941	.75941	.73069	.70319	.67684	.62741	.58201
9	.83676	.80073	.76642	.73373	.70259	.67290	.64461	.59190	.54393
10	.82035	.78120	.74409	.70892	.67556	.64393	.61391	.55839	.50835
11	.80426	.76214	.72242	.68495	.64958	.61620	.58468	.52679	.47509
12	.78849	.74356	.70138	.66178	.62460	.58966	.55684	.49697	.44401
13	.77303	.72542	.68095	.63940	.60057	.56427	.53032	.46884	.41496
14	.75788	.70773	.66112	.61778	.57748	.53997	.50507	.44230	.38783
15	.74301	.69047	.64186	.59689	.55526	.51672	.48102	.41727	.36245
16	.72845	.67362	.62317	.57671	.53391	.49447	.45811	.39365	.33873
17	.71416	.65720	.60502	.55720	.51337	.47318	.43630	.37136	.31657
18	.70016	.64117	.58739	.53836	.49363	.45280	.41552	.35034	.29586
19	.68643	.62553	.57029	.52016	.47464	.43330	.39573	.33051	.27651
20	.67297	.61027	.55368	.50257	.45639	.41464	.37689	.31180	.25842
25	.60953	.53939	.47761	.42315	.37512	.33273	.29530	.23300	.18425
30	.55207	.47674	.41199	.35628	.30832	.26700	.23138	.17411	.13137
40	.45289	.37243	.30656	.25257	.20829	.17193	.14205	.09722	.06678
50	.37153	.29094	.22811	.17905	.14071	.11071	.08720	.05429	.03395
60	.30478	.22728	.16973	.12693	.09506	.07129	.05354	.03031	.01726

Formula: $x' = [1 + (r/100)]^{-n} = 1/x$

Values of y'.   (Interest compounded semi-annually; $P = A \times y'$)

Years	$r = 2$	2½	3	3½	4	4½	5	6	7
1	.98030	.97546	.97066	.96590	.96117	.95647	.95181	.94260	.93351
2	.96098	.95152	.94218	.93296	.92385	.91484	.90595	.88849	.87144
3	.94205	.92817	.91454	.90114	.88797	.87502	.86230	.83748	.81350
4	.92348	.90540	.88771	.87041	.85349	.83694	.82075	.78941	.75941
5	.90529	.88318	.86167	.84073	.82035	.80051	.78120	.74409	.70892
6	.88745	.86151	.83639	.81206	.78849	.76567	.74356	.70138	.66178
7	.86996	.84037	.81185	.78436	.75788	.73234	.70773	.66112	.61778
8	.85282	.81975	.78803	.75762	.72845	.70047	.67362	.62317	.57671
9	.83602	.79963	.76491	.73178	.70016	.66996	.64117	.58739	.53836
10	.81954	.78001	.74247	.70682	.67297	.64082	.61027	.55368	.50257
11	.80340	.76087	.72069	.68272	.64684	.61292	.58086	.52189	.46915
12	.78757	.74220	.69954	.65944	.62172	.58625	.55288	.49193	.43796
13	.77205	.72398	.67902	.63695	.59758	.56073	.52623	.46369	.40884
14	.75684	.70622	.65910	.61523	.57437	.53632	.50088	.43708	.38165
15	.74192	.68889	.63976	.59425	.55207	.51298	.47674	.41199	.35628
16	.72730	.67198	.62099	.57398	.53063	.49065	.45377	.38834	.33259
17	.71297	.65549	.60277	.55441	.51003	.46930	.43191	.36604	.31048
18	.69892	.63941	.58509	.53550	.49022	.44887	.41109	.34503	.28983
19	.68515	.62372	.56792	.51724	.47119	.42933	.39128	.32523	.27056
20	.67165	.60841	.55126	.49960	.45289	.41065	.37243	.30656	.25257
25	.60804	.53734	.47500	.42003	.37153	.32873	.29094	.22811	.17905
30	.55045	.47457	.40930	.35313	.30478	.26315	.22728	.16973	.12693
40	.45112	.37017	.30389	.24960	.20511	.16863	.13870	.09398	.06379
50	.36971	.28873	.22563	.17642	.13803	.10806	.08465	.05203	.03206
60	.30299	.22521	.16752	.12470	.09289	.06925	.05166	.02881	.01611

Formula: $y' = [1 + (r/200)]^{-2n} = 1/y$

Values of z'. (Interest compounded quarterly; $P = A \times z'$; see opposite page)

Years	r = 2	2½	3	3½	4	4½	5	6	7
1	.98025	.97539	.97055	.96575	.96098	.95624	.95152	.94218	.93296
2	.96089	.95138	.94198	.93268	.92348	.91439	.90540	.88771	.87041
3	.94191	.92796	.91424	.90074	.88745	.87437	.86151	.83639	.81206
4	.92330	.90512	.88732	.86989	.85282	.83611	.81975	.78803	.75762
5	.90506	.88284	.86119	.84010	.81954	.79952	.78001	.74247	.70682
6	.88719	.86111	.83583	.81132	.78757	.76453	.74220	.69954	.65944
7	.86966	.83991	.81122	.78354	.75684	.73107	.70622	.65910	.61523
8	.85248	.81924	.78733	.75670	.72730	.69908	.67198	.62099	.57390
9	.83564	.79908	.76415	.73079	.69892	.66849	.63941	.58509	.53550
10	.81914	.77941	.74165	.70576	.67165	.63923	.60841	.55126	.49960
11	.80296	.76022	.71981	.68159	.64545	.61126	.57892	.51939	.46611
12	.78710	.74151	.69861	.65825	.62026	.58451	.55086	.48936	.43486
13	.77155	.72326	.67804	.63570	.59606	.55893	.52415	.46107	.40570
14	.75631	.70546	.65808	.61393	.57280	.53447	.49874	.43441	.37851
15	.74137	.68809	.63870	.59291	.55045	.51108	.47457	.40930	.35313
16	.72673	.67115	.61989	.57260	.52897	.48871	.45156	.38563	.32946
17	.71237	.65464	.60164	.55299	.50833	.46733	.42967	.36334	.30737
18	.69830	.63852	.58392	.53405	.48850	.44687	.40884	.34233	.28676
19	.68451	.62281	.56673	.51576	.46944	.42732	.38903	.32254	.26754
20	.67099	.60748	.55004	.49810	.45112	.40862	.37017	.30389	.24960
25	.60729	.53630	.47369	.41845	.36921	.32670	.28873	.22563	.17642
30	.54963	.47347	.40794	.35154	.30299	.26120	.22521	.16752	.12470
40	.45023	.36903	.30255	.24810	.20351	.16697	.13702	.09235	.06230
50	.36880	.28762	.22438	.17510	.13669	.10673	.08337	.05091	.03113
60	.30210	.22417	.16641	.12358	.09181	.06823	.05072	.02806	.01555

Formula: $z' = [1 + (r/400)]^{-4n} = 1/z$

Annuity Which Will Amount to a Given Sum (Sinking Fund)

The annual payment, Y, which, if set aside at the end of each year, will amount with accumulated interest to a given sum S at the end of n years is $Y = S \times v'$, where the factor v' is given below. (Interest at r percent per annum, compounded annually.)

Values of v'

Years	r = 2	2½	3	3½	4	4½	5	6	7
2	.49505	.49383	.49261	.49140	.49020	.48900	.48780	.48544	.48309
3	.32675	.32514	.32353	.32193	.32035	.31877	.31721	.31411	.31105
4	.24262	.24082	.23903	.23725	.23549	.23374	.23201	.22859	.22523
5	.19216	.19025	.18835	.18648	.18463	.18279	.18097	.17740	.17389
6	.15853	.15655	.15460	.15267	.15076	.14888	.14702	.14336	.13980
7	.13451	.13250	.13051	.12854	.12661	.12470	.12282	.11914	.11555
8	.11651	.11447	.11246	.11048	.10853	.10661	.10472	.10104	.09747
9	.10252	.10046	.09843	.09645	.09449	.09257	.09069	.08702	.08349
10	.09133	.08926	.08723	.08524	.08329	.08138	.07950	.07587	.07238
11	.08218	.08011	.07808	.07609	.07415	.07225	.07039	.06679	.06336
12	.07456	.07249	.07046	.06848	.06655	.06467	.06283	.05928	.05590
13	.06812	.06605	.06403	.06206	.06014	.05828	.05646	.05296	.04965
14	.06260	.06054	.05853	.05657	.05467	.05282	.05102	.04758	.04434
15	.05783	.05577	.05377	.05183	.04994	.04811	.04634	.04296	.03979
16	.05365	.05160	.04961	.04768	.04582	.04402	.04227	.03895	.03586
17	.04997	.04793	.04595	.04404	.04220	.04042	.03870	.03544	.03243
18	.04670	.04467	.04271	.04082	.03899	.03724	.03555	.03236	.02941
19	.04378	.04176	.03981	.03794	.03614	.03441	.03275	.02962	.02675
20	.04116	.03915	.03722	.03536	.03358	.03188	.03024	.02718	.02439
25	.03122	.02928	.02743	.02567	.02401	.02244	.02095	.01823	.01581
30	.02465	.02278	.02102	.01937	.01783	.01639	.01505	.01265	.01059
40	.01656	.01484	.01326	.01183	.01052	.00934	.00828	.00646	.00467
50	.01182	.01026	.00887	.00763	.00655	.00560	.00478	.00344	.00238
60	.00877	.00735	.00613	.00509	.00420	.00345	.00283	.00188	.00121

Formula: $v' = (r/100) \div [[1 + (r/100)]^n - 1] = 1/v$

MATHEMATICS

Present Worth of an Annuity

The capital C, which, if placed at interest today, will provide for a given annual payment Y for a term of n years before it is exhausted is $C = Y \times w$, where the factor w is given below. (Interest at r percent per annum, compounded annually.)

Values of w

Years	$r = 2$	2½	3	3½	4	4½	5	6	7
1	0.9804	0.9756	0.9709	0.9662	0.9615	0.9569	0.9524	0.9434	0.9346
2	1.9416	1.9274	1.9135	1.8997	1.8861	1.8727	1.8594	1.8334	1.8080
3	2.8839	2.8560	2.8286	2.8016	2.7751	2.7490	2.7232	2.6730	2.6243
4	3.8077	3.7620	3.7171	3.6731	3.6299	3.5875	3.5460	3.4651	3.3872
5	4.7135	4.6458	4.5797	4.5151	4.4518	4.3900	4.3295	4.2124	4.1002
6	5.6014	5.5081	5.4172	5.3286	5.2421	5.1579	5.0757	4.9173	4.7665
7	6.4720	6.3494	6.2303	6.1145	6.0021	5.8927	5.7864	5.5824	5.3893
8	7.3255	7.1701	7.0197	6.8740	6.7327	6.5959	6.4632	6.2098	5.9713
9	8.1622	7.9709	7.7861	7.6077	7.4353	7.2688	7.1078	6.8017	6.5152
10	8.9826	8.7521	8.5302	8.3166	8.1109	7.9127	7.7217	7.3601	7.0236
11	9.7868	9.5142	9.2526	9.0016	8.7605	8.5289	8.3064	7.8869	7.4987
12	10.575	10.258	9.9540	9.6633	9.3851	9.1186	8.8633	8.3838	7.9427
13	11.348	10.983	10.635	10.303	9.9856	9.6829	9.3936	8.8527	8.3577
14	12.106	11.691	11.296	10.921	10.563	10.223	9.8986	9.2950	8.7455
15	12.849	12.381	11.938	11.517	11.118	10.740	10.380	9.7122	9.1079
16	13.578	13.055	12.561	12.094	11.652	11.234	10.838	10.106	9.4466
17	14.292	13.712	13.166	12.651	12.166	11.707	11.274	10.477	9.7632
18	14.992	14.353	13.754	13.190	12.659	12.160	11.690	10.828	10.059
19	15.678	14.979	14.324	13.710	13.134	12.593	12.085	11.158	10.336
20	16.351	15.589	14.877	14.212	13.590	13.008	12.462	11.470	10.594
25	19.523	18.424	17.413	16.482	15.622	14.828	14.094	12.783	11.654
30	22.396	20.930	19.600	18.392	17.292	16.289	15.372	13.765	12.409
40	27.355	25.103	23.115	21.355	19.793	18.402	17.159	15.046	13.332
50	31.424	28.362	25.730	23.456	21.482	19.762	18.256	15.762	13.801
60	34.761	30.909	27.676	24.945	22.623	20.638	18.929	16.161	14.039

Formula: $w = [1 - [1 + (r/100)]^{-n}] \div [r/100] = v/z$

Annuity Provided for by a Given Capital

The annual payment Y provided for for a term of n years by a given capital C placed at interest today is $Y = C \times w'$. (Interest at r percent per annum, compounded annually; the fund supposed to be exhausted at the end of the term.)

Values of w'

Years	$r = 2$	2½	3	3½	4	4½	5	6	7
2	.51505	.51883	.52261	.52640	.53020	.53400	.53780	.54544	.55309
3	.34675	.35014	.35353	.35693	.36035	.36377	.36721	.37411	.38105
4	.26262	.26582	.26903	.27225	.27549	.27874	.28201	.28859	.29523
5	.21216	.21525	.21835	.22148	.22463	.22779	.23097	.23740	.24389
6	.17853	.18155	.18460	.18767	.19076	.19388	.19702	.20336	.20980
7	.15451	.15750	.16051	.16354	.16661	.16970	.17282	.17914	.18555
8	.13651	.13947	.14246	.14548	.14853	.15161	.15472	.16104	.16747
9	.12252	.12546	.12843	.13145	.13449	.13757	.14069	.14702	.15349
10	.11133	.11426	.11723	.12024	.12329	.12638	.12950	.13587	.14238
11	.10218	.10511	.10808	.11109	.11415	.11725	.12039	.12679	.13336
12	.09456	.09749	.10046	.10348	.10655	.10967	.11283	.11928	.12590
13	.08812	.09105	.09403	.09706	.10014	.10328	.10646	.11296	.11965
14	.08260	.08554	.08853	.09157	.09467	.09782	.10102	.10758	.11434
15	.07783	.08077	.08377	.08683	.08994	.09311	.09634	.10296	.10979
16	.07365	.07660	.07961	.08268	.08582	.08902	.09227	.09895	.10586
17	.06997	.07293	.07595	.07904	.08220	.08542	.08870	.09544	.10243
18	.06670	.06967	.07271	.07582	.07899	.08224	.08555	.09236	.09941
19	.06378	.06676	.06981	.07294	.07614	.07941	.08275	.08962	.09675
20	.06116	.06415	.06722	.07036	.07358	.07688	.08024	.08718	.09439
25	.05122	.05428	.05743	.06067	.06401	.06744	.07095	.07823	.08581
30	.04465	.04778	.05102	.05437	.05783	.06139	.06505	.07265	.08059
40	.03656	.03984	.04326	.04683	.05052	.05434	.05828	.06646	.07467
50	.03182	.03526	.03887	.04263	.04655	.05060	.05478	.06344	.07238
60	.02877	.03235	.03613	.04009	.04420	.04845	.05283	.06188	.07121

Formula: $w' = [r/100] \div [1 - [1 + (r/100)]^{-n}] = 1/w = v' + (r/100)$

Decimal Equivalents

From minutes and seconds into decimal parts of a degree

min	decimal	sec	decimal
0'	0°.0000	0''	0°.0000
1	.0167	1	.0003
2	.0333	2	.0006
3	.05	3	.0008
4	.0667	4	.0011
5'	.0833	5''	.0014
6	.10	6	.0017
7	.1167	7	.0019
8	.1333	8	.0022
9	.15	9	.0025
10'	0°.1667	10''	0°.0028
1	.1833	1	.0031
2	.20	2	.0033
3	.2167	3	.0036
4	.2333	4	.0039
15'	.25	15''	.0042
6	.2667	6	.0044
7	.2833	7	.0047
8	.30	8	.005
9	.3167	9	.0053
20'	0°.3333	20''	0°.0056
1	.35	1	.0058
2	.3667	2	.0061
3	.3833	3	.0064
4	.40	4	.0067
25'	.4167	25''	.0069
6	.4333	6	.0072
7	.45	7	.0075
8	.4667	8	.0078
9	.4833	9	.0081
30'	0°.50	30''	0°.0083
1	.5167	1	.0086
2	.5333	2	.0089
3	.55	3	.0092
4	.5667	4	.0094
35'	.5833	35''	.0097
6	.60	6	.01
7	.6167	7	.0103
8	.6333	8	.0106
9	.65	9	.0108
40'	0°.6667	40''	0°.0111
1	.6833	1	.0114
2	.70	2	.0117
3	.7167	3	.0119
4	.7333	4	.0122
45'	.75	45''	.0125
6	.7667	6	.0128
7	.7833	7	.0131
8	.80	8	.0133
9	.8167	9	.0136
50'	0°.8333	50''	0°.0139
1	.85	1	.0142
2	.8667	2	.0144
3	.8833	3	.0147
4	.90	4	.015
55'	.9167	55''	.0153
6	.9333	6	.0156
7	.95	7	.0158
8	.9667	8	.0161
9	.9833	9	.0164
60'	1.00	60''	0°.0167

From decimal parts of a degree into minutes and seconds (exact values)

decimal	min/sec	decimal	min/sec
0°.00	0'	0°.50	30'
1	0' 36''	1	30' 36''
2	1' 12''	2	31' 12''
3	1' 48''	3	31' 48''
4	2' 24''	4	32' 24''
0°.05	3'	0°.55	33'
6	3' 36''	6	33' 36''
7	4' 12''	7	34' 12''
8	4' 48''	8	34' 48''
9	5' 24''	9	35' 24''
0°.10	6'	0°.60	36'
1	6' 36''	1	36' 36''
2	7' 12''	2	37' 12''
3	7' 48''	3	37' 48''
4	8' 24''	4	38' 24''
0°.15	9'	0°.65	39'
6	9' 36''	6	39' 36''
7	10' 12''	7	40' 12''
8	10' 48''	8	40' 48''
9	11' 24''	9	41' 24''
0°.20	12'	0°.70	42'
1	12' 36''	1	42' 36''
2	13' 12''	2	43' 12''
3	13' 48''	3	43' 48''
4	14' 24''	4	44' 24''
0°.25	15'	0°.75	45'
6	15' 36''	6	45' 36''
7	16' 12''	7	46' 12''
8	16' 48''	8	46' 48''
9	17' 24''	9	47' 24''
0°.30	18'	0°.80	48'
1	18' 36''	1	48' 36''
2	19' 12''	2	49' 12''
3	19' 48''	3	49' 48''
4	20' 24''	4	50' 24''
0°.35	21'	0°.85	51'
6	21' 36''	6	51' 36''
7	22' 12''	7	52' 12''
8	22' 48''	8	52' 48''
9	23' 24''	9	53' 24''
0°.40	24'	0°.90	54'
1	24' 36''	1	54' 36''
2	25' 12''	2	55' 12''
3	25' 48''	3	55' 48''
4	26' 24''	4	56' 24''
0°.45	27'	0°.95	57'
6	27' 36''	6	57' 36''
7	28' 12''	7	58' 12''
8	28' 48''	8	58' 48''
9	29' 24''	9	59' 24''
0°.50	30'	1°.00	60'

decimal	sec
0°.000	0''.0
1	3''.6
2	7''.2
3	10''.8
4	14''.4
0°.005	18''
6	21''.6
7	25''.2
8	28''.8
9	32''.4
0°.010	36''

Common fractions

8 ths	16 ths	32 nds	64 ths	Exact decimal values
			1	.01 5625
		1	2	.03 125
			3	.04 6875
	1	2	4	.06 25
			5	.07 8125
		3	6	.09 375
			7	.10 9375
1	2	4	8	.12 5
			9	.14 0625
		5	10	.15 625
			11	.17 1875
	3	6	12	.18 75
			13	.20 3125
		7	14	.21 875
			15	.23 4375
2	4	8	16	.25
			17	.26 5625
		9	18	.28 125
			19	.29 6875
	5	10	20	.31 25
			21	.32 8125
		11	22	.34 375
			23	.35 9375
3	6	12	24	.37 5
			25	.39 0625
		13	26	.40 625
			27	.42 1875
	7	14	28	.43 75
			29	.45 3125
		15	30	.46 875
			31	.48 4375
4	8	16	32	.50
			33	.51 5625
		17	34	.53 125
			35	.54 6875
	9	18	36	.56 25
			37	.57 8125
		19	38	.59 375
			39	.60 9375
5	10	20	40	.62 5
			41	.64 0625
		21	42	.65 625
			43	.67 1875
	11	22	44	.68 75
			45	.70 3125
		23	46	.71 875
			47	.73 4375
6	12	24	48	.75
			49	.76 5625
		25	50	.78 125
			51	.79 6875
	13	26	52	.81 25
			53	.82 8125
		27	54	.84 375
			55	.85 9375
7	14	28	56	.87 5
			57	.89 0625
		29	58	.90 625
			59	.92 1875
	15	30	60	.93 75
			61	.95 3125
		31	62	.96 875
			63	.98 4375

WEIGHTS AND MEASURES

BY

Lewis V. Judson

REFERENCES: "International Critical Tables," McGraw-Hill. "Smithsonian Physical Tables," Smithsonian Institution. Landolt, "Landolt-Börnstein Zahlenwerte und Funktionen aus Physik, Chemie, Astronomie, Geophysik und Technik," Springer. "Handbook of Chemistry and Physics," Chemical Rubber Co. "Units of Weight and Measure; Definitions and Tables of Equivalents," Misc. Pub. 214, NBS. "Units and Systems of Weights and Measures; Their Origin, Development, and Present Status," Circ. 570, NBS.

In the United States the measures of weight and length commonly employed are identical for practical purposes with the corresponding English units, but the capacity measures differ from those now in use in the British Empire, the U.S. gallon being defined as 231 cu in. and the bushel as 2,150.42 cu in., whereas the corresponding British Imperial units are, respectively, 277.42 cu in., and 2,219.36 cu in. (1 Imp gal = 1.2 U.S. gal, approx; 1 Imp bu = 1.03 U.S. bu, approx).

The metric system of weights and measures was legalized and its use made permissive in the United States by an Act of Congress, passed in 1866. In 1872, by the concurrent action of the principal governments of the world, it was agreed to establish an International Bureau of Weights and Measures near Paris. The convention was held, and the treaty signed in 1875. It was ratified by the United States in 1878.

Prior to 1893, the British Imperial yard was regarded as the real standard of the United States. In 1893, the Office of Weights and Measures (now National Bureau of Standards) by executive order fixed the value of the United States yard in terms of the international meter, according to the ratio: one yard = 3,600/3,937 meters. At the same time, the pound was fixed in terms of the international kilogram, according to the relation: one pound = 453.5924277 grams.

U.S. Customary Weights and Measures

Measures of Length		Measures of Area	
Measures of Length		**Measures of Area**	
12 inches	= 1 foot	144 square inches	= 1 square foot
3 feet	= 1 yard	9 square feet	= 1 square yard
5½ yards = 16½ feet	= 1 rod, pole, or perch	30¼ square yards	= 1 square rod, pole, or perch
40 poles = 220 yards	= 1 furlong	160 square rods	
8 furlongs = 1,760 yards = 5,280 feet	= 1 mile	= 10 square chains = 43,560 square feet = 5,645 sq varas (Texas)	= 1 acre
3 miles	= 1 league		
4 inches	= 1 hand	640 acres = 1 square mile =	1 "section" of U.S. Govt. surveyed land
9 inches	= 1 span		
		1 circular inch	
Nautical Units		= area of circle 1 inch in diameter	= 0.7854 sq in.
6,076.10333 feet	= 1 international nautical mile	1 square inch	= 1.2732 circular inches
6 feet	= 1 fathom	1 circular mil	= area of circle 0.001 in. in diam
120 fathoms	= 1 cable length	1,000,000 cir mils	= 1 circular inch
1 nautical mile per hr	= 1 knot		
		Measures of Volume	
Surveyor's or Gunter's Measure			
7.92 inches	= 1 link	1,728 cubic inches	= 1 cubic foot
100 links = 66 ft = 4 rods	= 1 chain	27 cubic feet	= 1 cubic yard
80 chains	= 1 mile	1 cord of wood	= 128 cubic feet
33⅓ inches	= 1 vara (Texas)	1 perch of masonry	= 16½ to 25 cu ft

U.S. Customary Weights and Measures (*continued*)

Measures of Volume

Liquid or Fluid Measure

4 gills	= 1 pint
2 pints	= 1 quart
4 quarts	= 1 gallon
7.4805 gallons	= 1 cubic foot

(There is no standard liquid barrel; by trade custom, 1 bbl of petroleum oil, unrefined = 42 gal)

Apothecaries' Liquid Measure

60 minims	= 1 liquid dram or drachm
8 drams	= 1 liquid ounce
16 ounces	= 1 pint

Water Measure

The **miner's inch** is the quantity of water that will pass through an orifice 1 sq in. in cross section under a head of 4 to 6½ in., as fixed by statutes, and varies from $\frac{1}{40}$ to $\frac{1}{50}$ cu ft per sec. The units now most in use are 1 cu ft per sec and 1 gal per sec, the U.S. Reclamation Service employing the former.

Dry Measure

2 pints	= 1 quart
8 quarts	= 1 peck
4 pecks	= 1 bushel

1 std bbl for fruits and vegetables = 7056 cu in. or 105 dry qt, struck measure

Shipping Measure

1 Register ton	= 100 cu ft
1 U.S. shipping ton	= 40 cu ft
	= 32.14 U.S. bu or 31.14 Imp bu
1 British shipping ton	= 42 cu ft
	= 32.70 Imp bu or 33.75 U.S. bu

Board Measure

1 board foot = $\begin{cases} 144 \text{ cu in.} = \text{volume of board} \\ 1 \text{ ft sq and 1 in. thick} \end{cases}$

The international log rule, based upon ¼ in. kerf, is expressed by the formula

$$X = 0.904762(0.22D^2 - 0.71D)$$

where X is the number of board feet in a 4 ft section of a log and D is the top diam in in. In computing the number of board feet in a log the taper is taken at ½ in. per 4 ft linear, and separate computation is made for each 4 ft section.

Weights
(The grain is the same in all systems)

Avoirdupois Weight

16 drams = 437.5 grains	= 1 ounce
16 ounces = 7,000 grains	= 1 pound
100 pounds	= 1 cental
2,000 pounds	= 1 short ton
2,240 pounds	= 1 long ton
1 std lime bbl, small	= 180 lb net
1 std lime bbl, large	= 280 lb net

Also (in Great Britain):

14 pounds	= 1 stone
2 stone = 28 pounds	= 1 quarter
4 quarters = 112 pounds	= 1 hundredweight (cwt)
20 hundredweight	= 1 long ton

Troy Weight

24 grains	= 1 pennyweight (dwt)
20 pennyweights = 480 grains	= 1 ounce
12 ounces = 5,760 grains	= 1 pound

1 assay ton = 29,167 milligrams, or as many milligrams as there are troy ounces in a ton of 2,000 lb avoirdupois. Consequently, the number of milligrams of precious metal yielded by an assay ton of ore gives directly the number of troy ounces that would be obtained from a ton of 2,000 lb avoirdupois.

Apothecaries' Weight

20 grains	= 1 scruple ℈
3 scruples = 60 grains	= 1 dram ʒ
8 drams	= 1 ounce ℥
12 ounces = 5,760 grains	= 1 pound

Weight for Precious Stones

1 carat = 200 milligrams
(Used by almost all important nations)

Circular Measure

60 seconds	= 1 minute
60 minutes	= 1 degree
90 degrees	= 1 quadrant
360 degrees	= circumference
57.2957795 degrees ($= 57°17'44.806''$)	= 1 radian (or angle having arc of length equal to radius)

METRIC SYSTEM

The fundamental units of the metric system are the meter (the unit of length) and the kilogram (the unit of mass). The unit of volume, the cubic decimeter (which was also designated the liter), and the unit of mass, the kilogram, were originally derived from the meter. The kilogram and the meter are now defined independently, and the liter is defined as the volume of a kilogram of water at the temperature of its maximum density, 4 C, and under a pressure of 76 cm of mercury. The liter is slightly greater than the cubic decimeter, and according to the best information, 1 liter = 1.000028 cubic decimeters.

The U.S. customary lengths, areas, and cubic measures derived from the international meter are based on the relation 1 meter = 39.37 inches (exactly), or 1 yard = 0.9144018 meter.

The U.S. customary weights derived from the international kilogram are based on the value 1 avoirdupois pound = 453.5924277 grams. The value of the troy pound is based on the same relation and also the equivalent 5,760/7,000 avoirdupois pound = 1 troy pound.

Metric Measures

Length			Area		
Unit	Symbol	Value in meters	Unit	Symbol	Value in sq meters
Micron................	μ	0.000001	....	.....	....
Millimeter.............	mm	0.001	Sq millimeter.........	mm²	0.000001
Centimeter............	cm	0.01	Sq centimeter........	cm²	0.0001
Decimeter.............	dm	0.1	Sq decimeter.........	dm²	0.01
Meter (unit)...........	m	1.0	Sq meter (centiare)....	m²	1.0
Dekameter............	dkm	10.0	Sq dekameter (are).....	a	100.0
Hectometer............	hm	100.0	Hectare..............	ha	10,000.0
Kilometer.............	km	1,000.0	Sq kilometer..........	km²	1,000,000.0
Myriameter............	Mm	10,000.0	....	.....	....
Megameter............	......	1,000,000.0	....	.....	....

Volume			Cubic measure		
Unit	Symbol	Value in liters	Unit	Symbol	Value in cubic meters
Milliliter.................	ml	0.001	Cubic kilometer............	km³	10^9
Liter (unit)...............	l	1.0	Cubic hectometer.........	hm³	10^6
Kiloliter..................	kl	1,000.0	Cubic dekameter..........	dkm³	10^3
Also			Cubic meter..............	m³	1
Centiliter................	cl	0.01	Cubic decimeter..........	dm³	10^{-3}
Deciliter.................	dl	0.1	Cubic centimeter.........	cm³	10^{-6}
Dekaliter.................	dkl	10.0	Cubic millimeter..........	mm³	10^{-9}
Hectoliter................	hl	100.0	Cubic micron.............	μ^3	10^{-18}
....	.....	....			

Mass					
Unit	Symbol	Value in grams	Unit	Symbol	Value in grams
Microgram...............	γ	0.000001	Dekagram.................	dkg	10.0
Milligram................	mg	0.001	Hectogram................	hg	100.0
Centigram................	cg	0.01	Kilogram.................	kg	1,000.0
Decigram................	dg	0.1	Myriagram................	Mg	10,000.0
Gram (unit)..............	g	1.0	Quintal...................	q	100,000.0
....	.....	....	Ton.....................	t	1,000,000.0

The prefixes used to designate multiples and submultiples of metric units have also been used in recent years in connection with other units. Examples are microinch and kilowatt. Other prefixes besides those originally used with metric units have come into use. In the case of the prefixes for 10^{12} and 10^9 caution should be used, as these have been interchanged in some instances from those given in the following list:

Tera	10^{12}	Deci	10^{-1}
Giga	10^9	Centi	10^{-2}
Mega	10^6	Milli	10^{-3}
Myria	10^4	Micro	10^{-6}
Kilo	10^3	Nano	10^{-9}
Hecto	10^2	Pico	10^{-12}
Deca	10^1		

SYSTEMS OF UNITS

The principal units of interest to mechanical engineers can all be derived from the three units of **force, length,** and **time.** These three units may be chosen at pleasure; each such choice gives rise to a "system" of units. The following table gives the units of the four "systems" most often met with in the literature.

In these systems the "standard pound body" and the "standard kilogram body" refer to two material standards of mass, carefully preserved at London and Paris, respectively (the U.S. pound is derived from the kilogram); the "standard locality" means sea level, 45 deg latitude, or, more strictly any locality in which the acceleration due to gravity has the value 980.665 cm per sec per sec = 32.1740 ft per sec per sec, which may be called the **standard acceleration.**

The **pound force** is the force required to support the standard pound body against gravity, *in vacuo*, in the standard locality; or, it is the force which, if applied to the standard pound body, supposed free to move, would give that body the "standard acceleration." The word "pound" is used for the unit of both force and mass and consequently is ambiguous. To avoid uncertainty it is desirable to call the units "pound force" and "pound mass," respectively.

The **kilogram force** is the force required to support the standard kilogram against gravity, *in vacuo*, in the standard locality; or, it is the force which, if applied to the standard kilogram body, supposed free to move, would give that body the "standard acceleration." The word "kilogram" is used for the unit of both force and mass and consequently is ambiguous. To avoid uncertainty it is desirable to call the units "kilogram force" and "kilogram mass," respectively.

The **poundal** is the force which, if applied to the standard pound body, would give that body an acceleration of 1 ft per sec per sec; *i.e.*, 1 poundal = 1/32.1740 lb force.

The **dyne** is the force which, if applied to the standard gram body, would give that body an acceleration of 1 cm per sec per sec; *i.e.*, 1 dyne = 1/980.665 of a gram force.

Systems of Units

Name of unit	Dimensions of units in terms of F, L, T	British "gravitational" system, or "foot-pound-second" system	Metric "gravitational" system, or "kilogram-meter-second" system	Metric "absolute" system, or "C. G. S." system	British "absolute" system (little used)
Force....................	F	1 lb	1 kg	1 dyne	1 poundal
Length..................	L	1 ft	1 m	1 cm	1 ft
Time....................	T	1 sec	1 sec	1 sec	1 sec
Velocity................	L/T	1 ft per sec	1 m per sec	1 cm per sec	1 ft per sec
Acceleration............	L/T^2	1 ft per sec²	1 m per sec²	1 cm per sec²	1 ft per sec²
Pressure................	F/L^2	1 lb per ft²	1 kg per m²	1 dyne per cm²	1 pdl per ft²
Impulse or momentum.....	FT	1 lb-sec	1 kg-sec	1 dyne-sec	1 pdl-sec
Work or energy..........	FL	1 ft-lb	1 kg-m	1 dyne-cm = 1 "erg"	1 ft-pdl
Power...................	FL/T	1 ft-lb per sec	1 kg-m per sec	1 dyne-cm per sec	1 ft-pdl per sec
Mass....................	$F/(L/T^2)$	1 lb per (ft per sec²) = 1 "slug."	1 kg per (m per sec²) = 1 "metric slug."	1 dyne per (cm per sec²) = 1 gram mass.	1 pdl per (ft per sec²) = 1 pound

NOTE. The "slug" (also called the "geepound," or the "engineer's unit of mass"), the "metric slug," and the "poundal" are rarely used in practice.

Other common units are as follows:

Work: 1 joule (absolute) = 10^7 ergs = 10,000,000 dyne-cm.
1 kilowatt-hour (absolute) = 3,600,000 joules (absolute) = $3,600 \times 10^{10}$ dyne-cm.

Power: 1 horsepower = 550 ft-lb per sec.
1 poncelet = 100 kg-m per sec.
1 cheval-vapeur = 75 kg-m per sec = 1 metric horsepower = 1 pferde starke.
1 watt (absolute) = 1 joule (absolute) per sec = 1×10^7 dyne-cm per sec.
1 kilowatt = 1,000 watts = 10^{10} dyne-cm per sec.

A new horsepower of 550.220 ft-lb per sec, or 746 watts, has been proposed, but has not been accepted by mechanical engineers.

Prior to Jan. 1, 1948, the international system of electrical units was in general use instead of the absolute system.

$$1 \text{ international watt} = 1.000165 \text{ absolute watts}$$

The *weight* of a body (in a given locality) means a *force*, namely, the force required to support the body against gravity (in that locality). When no particular locality is specified, the standard locality may be assumed. Thus, the "standard weight" of the pound body is 1 lb force; the "standard weight" of the kilogram body is 1 kg force.

Force Equivalents

Dynes $\times 10^6$	Kilograms	Pounds	Poundals
1	1.020	2.248	72.33
	0.00848	0.3518	1.85933
0.9807	1	2.205	70.93
1.99149		0.34334	1.85084
0.4448	0.4536	1	32.17
1.64819	1.65667		1.50750
0.01383	0.01410	0.03108	1
2.14067	2.14916	2.49249	

Heat Units. The units of heat commonly used are (1) the quantity of heat required to raise the temperature of 1 gram of water 1 C and (2) the quantity of heat required to raise the temperature of 1 pound of water 1 F. These units are (1) the **calorie** and (2) the **British thermal unit** or Btu. Work done in recent years on the International Steam Tables has led to the definition of the **IT calorie** and of the Btu in terms of other units. These definitions are

$$1 \text{ IT calorie} = {}^1\!/_{860} \text{ international watt-hour}$$
$$1 \text{ Btu} = 251.996 \text{ IT calories}$$

These units have been used on the following pages. The **kilocalorie,** sometimes called the kilogram calorie or large calorie, is equal to 1,000 calories and is used in engineering work in metric countries. The calorie is sometimes called the small calorie or gram calorie.

The mean calorie (0 to 100 C) is about 1.001 IT calorie, and the corresponding mean Btu is approximately 779 ft-lb.

Mechanical Equivalent of Heat. The values now accepted as the work equivalents of the heat units are 778.2 ft-lb for the Btu and 4.187 absolute joules for the IT calorie.

CONVERSION TABLES
Length Equivalents

Centimeters	Inches	Feet	Yards	Meters	Chains	Kilometers	Miles
1	0.3937	0.03281	0.01094	0.01	0.0$_3$4971	10^{-5}	0.0$_6$6214
	1.59517	2.51598	2.03886	2.00000	4.69644	5.00000	6.79335
2.540	1	0.08333	0.02778	0.0254	0.001263	0.0$_4$254	0.0$_4$1578
0.40483		2.92082	2.44370	2.40483	3.10127	5.40483	5.19818
30.48	12	1	0.3333	0.3048	0.01515	0.0$_3$3048	0.0$_3$1894
1.48402	1.07918		1.52288	1.48402	2.18046	4.48402	4.27736
91.44	36	3	1	0.9144	0.04545	0.0$_3$9144	0.0$_3$5682
1.96114	1.55630	0.47712		1.96114	2.65758	4.96114	4.75449
100	39.37	3.281	1.0936	1	0.04971	0.001	0.0$_3$6214
2.00000	1.59517	0.51598	0.03886		2.69644	3.00000	4.79335
2012	792	66	22	20.12	1	0.02012	0.0125
3.30356	2.89873	1.81954	1.34242	1.30356		2.30356	2.09691
100000	39370	3281	1093.6	1000	49.71	1	0.6214
5.00000	4.59517	3.51598	3.03886	3.00000	1.69644		1.79335
160935	63360	5280	1760	1609	80	1.609	1
5.20665	4.80182	3.72263	3.24551	3.20665	1.90309	0.20665	

The equivalents are given in the heavier type. Logarithms of the equivalents are given immediately below. In some cases the equivalents have been rounded off, while the logarithm corresponds to the equivalent carried to a greater number of decimal places.

Subscripts after any figure, 0$_3$, 9$_4$, etc., mean that that figure is to be repeated the indicated number of times.

Conversion of Lengths *

	Inches to milli-meters	Milli-meters to inches	Feet to meters	Meters to feet	Yards to meters	Meters to yards	Miles to kilo-meters	Kilo-meters to miles
1	25.40	0.03937	0.3048	3.281	0.9144	1.094	1.609	0.6214
2	50.80	0.07874	0.6096	6.562	1.829	2.187	3.219	1.243
3	76.20	0.1181	0.9144	9.842	2.743	3.281	4.828	1.864
4	101.60	0.1575	1.219	13.12	3.658	4.374	6.437	2.485
5	127.00	0.1968	1.524	16.40	4.572	5.468	8.047	3.107
6	152.40	0.2362	1.829	19.68	5.486	6.562	9.656	3.728
7	177.80	0.2756	2.134	22.97	6.401	7.655	11.27	4.350
8	203.20	0.3150	2.438	26.25	7.315	8.749	12.87	4.971
9	228.60	0.3543	2.743	29.53	8.230	9.842	14.48	5.592

* EXAMPLE: 1 in. = 25.40 mm.

COMMON FRACTIONS OF AN INCH TO MILLIMETERS (FROM $\frac{1}{64}$ TO 1 IN.)

64ths	Milli-meters	64ths	Milli-meters	64ths	Milli-meters	64ths	Milli-meters	64ths	Milli-meters	64ths	Milli-meters
1	0.397	13	5.159	25	9.922	37	14.684	49	19.447	57	22.622
2	0.794	14	5.556	26	10.319	38	15.081	50	19.844	58	23.019
3	1.191	15	5.953	27	10.716	39	15.478	51	20.241	59	23.416
4	1.588	16	6.350	28	11.113	40	15.875	52	20.638	60	23.813
5	1.984	17	6.747	29	11.509	41	16.272	53	21.034	61	24.209
6	2.381	18	7.144	30	11.906	42	16.669	54	21.431	62	24.606
7	2.778	19	7.541	31	12.303	43	17.066	55	21.828	63	25.003
8	3.175	20	7.938	32	12.700	44	17.463	56	22.225	64	25.400
9	3.572	21	8.334	33	13.097	45	17.859				
10	3.969	22	8.731	34	13.494	46	18.256				
11	4.366	23	9.128	35	13.891	47	18.653				
12	4.763	24	9.525	36	14.288	48	19.050				

DECIMALS OF AN INCH TO MILLIMETERS (FROM 0.01 IN. TO 0.99 IN.)

	0	1	2	3	4	5	6	7	8	9
.0		0.254	0.508	0.762	1.016	1.270	1.524	1.778	2.032	2.286
.1	2.540	2.794	3.048	3.302	3.556	3.810	4.064	4.318	4.572	4.826
.2	5.080	5.334	5.588	5.842	6.096	6.350	6.604	6.858	7.112	7.366
.3	7.620	7.874	8.128	8.382	8.636	8.890	9.144	9.398	9.652	9.906
.4	10.160	10.414	10.668	10.922	11.176	11.430	11.684	11.938	12.192	12.446
.5	12.700	12.954	13.208	13.462	13.716	13.970	14.224	14.478	14.732	14.986
.6	15.240	15.494	15.748	16.002	16.256	16.510	16.764	17.018	17.272	17.526
.7	17.780	18.034	18.288	18.542	18.796	19.050	19.304	19.558	19.812	20.066
.8	20.320	20.574	20.828	21.082	21.336	21.590	21.844	22.098	22.352	22.606
.9	22.860	23.114	23.368	23.622	23.876	24.130	24.384	24.638	24.892	25.146

MILLIMETERS TO DECIMALS OF AN INCH (FROM 1 TO 99 MM)

	0.	1.	2.	3.	4.	5.	6.	7.	8.	9.
0		0.0394	0.0787	0.1181	0.1575	0.1968	0.2362	0.2756	0.3150	0.3543
1	0.3937	0.4331	0.4724	0.5118	0.5512	0.5906	0.6299	0.6693	0.7087	0.7480
2	0.7874	0.8268	0.8661	0.9055	0.9449	0.9842	1.0236	1.0630	1.1024	1.1417
3	1.1811	1.2205	1.2598	1.2992	1.3386	1.3780	1.4173	1.4567	1.4961	1.5354
4	1.5748	1.6142	1.6535	1.6929	1.7323	1.7716	1.8110	1.8504	1.8898	1.9291
5	1.9685	2.0079	2.0472	2.0866	2.1260	2.1654	2.2047	2.2441	2.2835	2.3228
6	2.3622	2.4016	2.4409	2.4803	2.5197	2.5590	2.5984	2.6378	2.6772	2.7165
7	2.7559	2.7953	2.8346	2.8740	2.9134	2.9528	2.9921	3.0315	3.0709	3.1102
8	3.1496	3.1890	3.2283	3.2677	3.3071	3.3464	3.3858	3.4252	3.4646	3.5039
9	3.5433	3.5827	3.6220	3.6614	3.7008	3.7402	3.7795	3.8189	3.8583	3.8976

Area Equivalents

(1 hectare = 100 ares = 10,000 centiares or square meters)

Square meters	Square inches	Square feet	Square yards	Square rods	Square chains	Roods	Acres	Square miles or sections
1	1550	10.76	1.196	0.0395	0.002471	$0.0_3 9884$	$0.0_2 2471$	$0.0_6 3861$
	3.19033	1.03197	0.07773	$\bar{2}.59699$	$\bar{3}.39288$	$\bar{3}.99494$	$\bar{4}.39288$	$\bar{7}.58670$
$0.0_3 6452$	1	0.006944	$0.0_3 7716$	$0.0_4 2551$	$0.0_5 1594$	$0.0_6 6377$	$0.0_6 1594$	$0.0_9 2491$
$\bar{4}.80967$		$\bar{3}.84164$	$\bar{4}.88740$	$\bar{5}.40667$	$\bar{6}.20255$	$\bar{7}.80461$	$\bar{7}.20255$	$\bar{10}.39637$
0.09290	144	1	0.1111	0.003673	$0.0_3 2296$	$0.0_4 9184$	$0.0_4 2296$	$0.0_7 3587$
$\bar{2}.96803$	2.15836		$\bar{1}.04576$	$\bar{3}.56503$	$\bar{4}.36091$	$\bar{5}.96297$	$\bar{4}.36091$	$\bar{8}.55473$
0.8361	1296	9	1	0.03306	0.002066	$0.0_3 8264$	0.0002066	$0.0_6 3228$
$\bar{1}.92227$	3.11260	0.95424		$\bar{2}.51927$	$\bar{3}.31515$	$\bar{4}.91721$	$\bar{4}.31515$	$\bar{7}.50898$
25.29	39204	272.25	30.25	1	0.0625	0.02500	0.00625	$0.0_6 9766$
1.40300	4.59333	2.43497	1.48072		$\bar{2}.79588$	$\bar{2}.39794$	$\bar{3}.79588$	$\bar{6}.98970$
404.7	627264	4356	484	16	1	0.4	0.1	0.0001562
2.60712	5.79745	3.63909	2.68484	1.20412		$\bar{1}.60206$	$\bar{1}.00000$	$\bar{4}.19382$
1012	1568160	10890	1210	40	2.5	1	0.25	$0.0_3 3906$
3.00506	6.19539	4.03703	3.08278	1.60206	0.39794		$\bar{1}.39794$	$\bar{4}.59176$
4047	6272640	43560	4840	160	10	4	1	0.001562
3.60712	6.79745	4.63909	3.68484	2.20412	1.00000	0.60206		$\bar{3}.19382$
2589998		27878400	3097600	102400	6400	2560	640	1
6.41330		7.44527	6.49102	5.01030	3.80618	3.40824	2.80618	

Volume and Capacity Equivalents

Cubic inches	Cubic feet	Cubic yards	U.S. Apothecary fluid ounces	U.S. quarts Liquid	U.S. quarts Dry	U.S. gallons	Bushels U.S.	Liters
1	$0.0_3 5787$	$0.0_4 2143$	0.5541	0.01732	0.01488	$0.0_2 4329$	$0.0_3 4650$	0.01639
	$\bar{4}.76246$	$\bar{5}.33109$	$\bar{1}.74360$	$\bar{2}.23845$	$\bar{2}.17263$	$\bar{3}.63639$	$\bar{4}.66748$	$\bar{2}.21450$
1728	1	0.03704	957.5	29.92	25.71	7.481	0.8036	28.32
3.23754		$\bar{2}.56864$	2.98114	1.47599	1.41017	0.87393	$\bar{1}.90502$	1.45205
46656	27	1	25853	807.9	694.3	202.2	21.70	764.5
4.66891	1.43136		4.41251	2.90736	2.84153	2.30530	1.33638	2.88340
1.805	0.001044	$0.0_3 3868$	1	0.03125	0.02686	0.007812	$0.0_8 8392$	0.02957
0.25640	$\bar{3}.01886$	$\bar{5}.58749$		$\bar{2}.49485$	$\bar{2}.42903$	$\bar{3}.89279$	$\bar{4}.92388$	$\bar{2}.47091$
57.75	0.03342	0.001238	32	1	0.8594	0.25	0.02686	0.9463
1.76155	$\bar{2}.52401$	$\bar{3}.09264$	1.50515		$\bar{1}.93418$	$\bar{1}.39794$	$\bar{2}.42903$	$\bar{1}.97604$
67.20	0.03889	0.001441	37.24	1.164	1	0.2909	0.03125	1.101
1.82737	$\bar{2}.58983$	$\bar{3}.15847$	1.57097	0.06582		$\bar{1}.46376$	$\bar{2}.49485$	0.04188
231	0.1337	0.004951	128	4	3.437	1	0.1074	3.785
2.36361	$\bar{1}.12607$	$\bar{3}.69470$	2.10721	0.60206	0.53624		$\bar{1}.03109$	0.57812
2150	1.244	0.04609	1192	37.24	32	9.309	1	35.24
3.33252	0.09498	$\bar{2}.66362$	3.07612	1.57097	1.50515	0.96891		1.54703
61.03	0.03532	0.001308	33.81	1.057	0.9081	0.2642	0.02838	1
1.78551	$\bar{2}.54796$	$\bar{3}.11659$	1.52909	0.02394	$\bar{1}.95812$	$\bar{1}.42188$	$\bar{2}.45297$	

Conversion of Areas *

	Sq in. to sq cm	Sq cm to sq in.	Sq ft to sq m	Sq m to sq ft	Sq yd to sq m	Sq m to sq yd	Acres to hectares	Hectares to acres	Sq mi to sq km	Sq km to sq mi
1	6.452	0.1550	0.0929	10.76	0.8361	1.196	0.4047	2.471	2.590	0.3861
2	12.90	0.3100	0.1858	21.53	1.672	2.392	0.8094	4.942	5.180	0.7722
3	19.35	0.4650	0.2787	32.29	2.508	3.588	1.214	7.413	7.770	1.158
4	25.81	0.6200	0.3716	43.06	3.345	4.784	1.619	9.884	10.360	1.544
5	32.26	0.7750	0.4645	53.82	4.181	5.980	2.023	12.355	12.950	1.931
6	38.71	0.9300	0.5574	64.58	5.017	7.176	2.428	14.826	15.540	2.317
7	45.16	1.085	0.6503	75.35	5.853	8.372	2.833	17.297	18.130	2.703
8	51.61	1.240	0.7432	86.11	6.689	9.568	3.237	19.768	20.720	3.089
9	58.06	1.395	0.8361	96.87	7.525	10.764	3.642	22.239	23.310	3.475

* EXAMPLE: 1 sq in. = 6.452 sq cm.

Conversion of Volumes or Cubic Measure

	Cu in. to cu cm	Cu cm to cu in.	Cu ft to cu m	Cu m to cu ft	Cu yd to cu m	Cu m to cu yd	Gallons to cu ft	Cu ft to gallons
1	16.39	0.06102	0.02832	35.31	0.7646	1.308	0.1337	7.481
2	32.77	0.1220	0.05663	70.63	1.529	2.616	0.2674	14.96
3	49.16	0.1831	0.08495	105.9	2.294	3.924	0.4010	22.44
4	65.55	0.2441	0.1133	141.3	3.058	5.232	0.5347	29.92
5	81.94	0.3051	0.1416	176.6	3.823	6.540	0.6684	37.40
6	98.32	0.3661	0.1699	211.9	4.587	7.848	0.8021	44.88
7	114.7	0.4272	0.1982	247.2	5.352	9.156	0.9358	52.36
8	131.1	0.4882	0.2265	282.5	6.116	10.46	1.069	59.84
9	147.5	0.5492	0.2549	317.8	6.881	11.77	1.203	67.32

Conversion of Volumes or Capacities

	Fluid ounces to cu cm	Cu cm to fluid ounces	Liquid pints to liters	Liters to liquid pints	Liquid quarts to liters	Liters to liquid quarts	Gallons to liters	Liters to gallons	Bushels to hectoliters	Hectoliters to bushels
1	29.57	0.03381	0.4732	2.113	0.9463	1.057	3.785	0.2642	0.3524	2.838
2	59.15	0.06763	0.9463	4.227	1.893	2.113	7.571	0.5284	0.7048	5.676
3	88.72	0.1014	1.420	6.340	2.839	3.170	11.36	0.7925	1.057	8.513
4	118.3	0.1353	1.893	8.454	3.785	4.227	15.14	1.057	1.410	11.35
5	147.9	0.1691	2.366	10.57	4.732	5.284	18.93	1.321	1.762	14.19
6	177.4	0.2092	2.839	12.68	5.678	6.340	22.71	1.585	2.114	17.03
7	207.0	0.2367	3.312	14.79	6.624	7.397	26.50	1.849	2.467	19.86
8	236.6	0.2705	3.785	16.91	7.571	8.454	30.28	2.113	2.819	22.70
9	266.2	2.3043	4.259	19.02	8.517	9.510	34.07	2.378	3.171	25.54

Mass Equivalents

Kilograms	Grains	Ounces Troy and apoth	Ounces Avoirdupois	Pounds Troy and apoth	Pounds Avoirdupois	Tons Short	Tons Long	Tons Metric
1 	**15432** 4.18843	**32.15** 1.50719	**35.27** 1.54745	**2.6792** 0.42801	**2.205** 0.34333	**0.0_21102** $\bar{3}.04230$	**0.0_39842** $\bar{4}.99309$	**0.001** $\bar{3}.00000$
0.0_6480 $\bar{5}.81157$	**1** 	**0.0_22083** $\bar{3}.31876$	**0.0_22286** $\bar{3}.35902$	**0.0_31736** $\bar{4}.23958$	**0.0_31429** $\bar{4}.15490$	**0.0_77143** $\bar{8}.85387$	**0.0_66378** $\bar{8}.80465$	**0.0_6480** $\bar{8}.81157$
0.03110 $\bar{2}.49281$	**480** 2.68124	**1** 	**1.09714** 0.04026	**0.08333** $\bar{2}.92082$	**0.06857** $\bar{2}.83614$	**0.0_43429** $\bar{5}.53511$	**0.0_43061** $\bar{5}.48590$	**0.0_43110** $\bar{5}.49281$
0.02835 $\bar{2}.45255$	**437.5** 2.64098	**0.9115** $\bar{1}.95974$	**1** 	**0.07595** $\bar{2}.88056$	**0.0625** $\bar{2}.79588$	**0.0_43125** $\bar{5}.49485$	**0.0_42790** $\bar{5}.44563$	**0.0_42835** $\bar{5}.45255$
0.3732 $\bar{1}.57199$	**5760** 3.76042	**12** 1.07918	**13.17** 1.11944	**1** 	**0.8229** $\bar{1}.91532$	**0.0_34114** $\bar{4}.61429$	**0.0_33673** $\bar{4}.56508$	**0.0_33732** $\bar{4}.57199$
0.4536 $\bar{1}.65667$	**7000** 3.84510	**14.58** 1.16386	**16** 1.20412	**1.215** 0.08468	**1** 	**0.0005** $\bar{4}.69897$	**0.0_34464** $\bar{4}.64975$	**0.0_34536** $\bar{4}.65667$
907.2 2.95770	**140_6** 7.14613	**29167** 4.46489	**320_3** 4.50515	**2431** 3.38571	**2000** 3.30103	**1** 	**0.8929** $\bar{1}.95078$	**0.9072** $\bar{1}.95770$
1016 3.00691	**15680_4** 7.19535	**32667** 4.51411	**35840** 4.55437	**2722** 3.43492	**2240** 3.35025	**1.12** 0.04922	**1** 	**1.016** 0.00691
1000 3.00000	**15432356** 7.18843	**32151** 4.50719	**35274** 4.54745	**2679** 3.42801	**2205** 3.34333	**1.102** 0.04230	**0.9842** $\bar{1}.99309$	**1**

The equivalents are given in the heavier type. Logarithms of the equivalents are given immediately below. In some cases the equivalents have been rounded off, while the logarithm corresponds to the equivalent carried to a greater number of decimal places.

Subscripts after any figure, 0_3, 9_4, etc., mean that that figure is to be repeated the indicated number of times.

Conversion of Masses

	Grains to grams	Grams to grains	Ounces (avdp) to grams	Grams to ounces (avdp)	Pounds (avdp) to kilo-grams	Kilo-grams to pounds (avdp)	Short tons (2000 lb) to metric tons	Metric tons (1000 kg) to short tons	Long tons (2240 lb) to metric tons	Metric tons to long tons
1	0.06480	15.43	28.35	0.03527	0.4536	2.205	0.907	1.102	1.016	0.984
2	0.1296	30.86	56.70	0.07055	0.9072	4.409	1.814	2.205	2.032	1.968
3	0.1944	46.30	85.05	0.1058	1.361	6.614	2.722	3.307	3.048	2.953
4	0.2592	61.73	113.40	0.1411	1.814	8.818	3.629	4.409	4.064	3.937
5	0.3240	77.16	141.75	0.1764	2.268	11.02	4.536	5.512	5.080	4.921
6	0.3888	92.59	170.10	0.2116	2.722	13.23	5.443	6.614	6.096	5.905
7	0.4536	108.03	198.45	0.2469	3.175	15.43	6.350	7.716	7.112	6.889
8	0.5184	123.46	226.80	0.2822	3.629	17.64	7.257	8.818	8.128	7.874
9	0.5832	138.89	255.15	0.3175	4.082	19.84	8.165	9.921	9.144	8.858

Velocity Equivalents

Centimeters per sec	Meters per sec	Meters per min	Kilo-meters per hour	Feet per sec	Feet per min	Miles per hour	Knots
1	0.01	0.6 $\bar{1}$.77815	0.036 $\bar{2}$.55630	0.03281 $\bar{2}$.51598	1.9685 0.29414	0.02237 $\bar{2}$.34965	0.01943 $\bar{2}$.28836
100 2.00000	1	60 1.77815	3.6 0.55630	3.281 0.51598	196.85 2.29414	2.237 0.34965	1.943 0.28836
1.667 0.22184	0.01667 $\bar{2}$.22184	1	0.06 $\bar{2}$.77815	0.05468 $\bar{2}$.73783	3.281 0.51598	0.03728 $\bar{2}$.57150	0.03238 $\bar{2}$.51022
27.78 1.44370	0.2778 $\bar{1}$.44370	16.67 1.22184	1	0.9113 $\bar{1}$.95968	54.68 1.73783	0.6214 $\bar{1}$.79335	0.53959 $\bar{1}$.73205
30.48 1.48402	0.3048 $\bar{1}$.48402	18.29 1.26217	1.097 0.04032	1	60 1.77815	0.6818 $\bar{1}$.83367	0.59209 $\bar{1}$.77238
0.5080 1.70586	0.005080 $\bar{3}$.70586	0.3048 $\bar{1}$.48402	0.01829 $\bar{2}$.26217	0.01667 $\bar{2}$.22185	1	0.01136 $\bar{2}$.05553	0.00987 $\bar{3}$.99423
44.70 1.65035	0.4470 $\bar{1}$.65035	26.82 1.42850	1.609 0.20670	1.467 0.16633	88 1.94448	1	0.86839 $\bar{1}$.93871
51.479 1.71163	0.51479 $\bar{1}$.71163	30.887 1.48978	1.8532 0.26793	1.68894 0.22761	101.337 2.00577	1.15155 0.06128	1

Conversion of Linear and Angular Velocities

	Cm per sec to feet per min	Feet per min to cm per sec	Cm per sec to miles per hour	Miles per hour to cm per sec	Feet per sec to miles per hour	Miles per hour to feet per sec	Radians per sec to rev per min	Rev per min to radians per sec
1	1.97	0.508	0.0224	44.70	0.682	1.47	9.55	0.1047
2	3.94	1.016	0.0447	89.41	1.364	2.93	19.10	0.2094
3	5.91	1.524	0.0671	134.1	2.045	4.40	28.65	0.3142
4	7.87	2.032	0.0895	178.8	2.727	5.87	38.20	0.4189
5	9.84	2.540	0.1118	223.5	3.409	7.33	47.75	0.5236
6	11.81	3.048	0.1342	268.2	4.091	8.80	57.30	0.6283
7	13.78	3.556	0.1566	312.9	4.773	10.27	66.84	0.7330
8	15.75	4.064	0.1790	357.6	5.455	11.73	76.39	0.8378
9	17.72	4.572	0.2013	402.3	6.136	13.20	85.94	0.9425

Conversion of Pressures *

	Pounds per sq in. to kilograms per sq cm	Kilograms per sq cm to pounds per sq in.	Atmospheres to pounds per sq in.	Pounds per sq in. to atmospheres	Atmospheres to kilograms per sq cm	Kilograms per sq cm to atmospheres
1	0.0703	14.22	14.70	0.0680	1.033	0.9678
2	0.1406	28.45	29.39	0.1361	2.066	1.936
3	0.2109	42.67	44.09	0.2041	3.100	2.904
4	0.2812	56.89	58.78	0.2722	4.133	3.871
5	0.3515	71.12	73.48	0.3402	5.166	4.839
6	0.4218	85.34	88.18	0.4083	6.199	5.807
7	0.4921	99.56	102.9	0.4763	7.233	6.775
8	0.5625	113.8	117.6	0.5444	8.266	7.743
9	0.6328	128.0	132.3	0.6124	9.299	8.711

* EXAMPLE: 1 lb per sq in. = 0.0703 kg per sq cm.

Pressure Equivalents
(For conversion table see immediately above)

Megabars or megadynes per sq cm	Kilograms per sq cm (metric atmospheres)	Pounds per sq in.	Short tons per sq ft	Atmospheres	Columns of mercury at temperature 0 C and $g = 980.665$ cm per sec^2		Columns of water at temperature 15 C and $g = 980.665$ cm per sec^2		
					Meters	Inches	Meters	Inches	Feet
1	1.0197	14.50	1.044	0.9869	0.7501	29.53	10.21	401.8	33.49
	0.00848	1.16148	0.01882	$\bar{1}$.99427	$\bar{1}$.87510	1.47025	1.00886	2.60402	1.52485
0.9807	1	14.22	1.024	0.9678	0.7356	28.96	10.01	394.1	32.84
$\bar{1}$.99152		1.15300	0.01034	$\bar{1}$.98579	$\bar{1}$.86662	1.46177	1.00038	2.59556	1.51636
0.06895	0.07031	1	0.072	0.06805	0.05171	2.036	0.7037	27.70	2.309
$\bar{2}$.83852	$\bar{2}$.84700		$\bar{2}$.85733	$\bar{2}$.83280	$\bar{2}$.71360	0.30876	$\bar{1}$.84738	1.44254	0.36336
0.9576	0.9765	13.89	1	0.9451	0.7183	28.28	9.774	384.8	32.07
$\bar{1}$.98119	$\bar{1}$.98966	1.14267		$\bar{1}$.97547	$\bar{1}$.85628	1.45143	0.99006	2.58521	1.50604
1.0133	1.0332	14.70	1.058	1	0.76	29.92	10.34	407.1	33.93
0.00573	0.01420	1.16722	0.02453		$\bar{1}$.88081	1.47598	1.01459	2.60975	1.53058
1.3332	1.3595	19.34	1.392	1.316	1	39.37	13.61	535.7	44.64
0.12490	0.13338	1.28640	0.14373	0.11919		1.59517	1.13378	2.72894	1.64976
0.03386	0.03453	0.4912	0.03536	0.03342	0.02540	1	0.3456	13.61	1.134
$\bar{2}$.52975	$\bar{2}$.53823	$\bar{1}$.69124	$\bar{2}$.54857	$\bar{2}$.52402	$\bar{2}$.40484		$\bar{1}$.53861	1.13378	0.05460
0.09798	0.09991	1.421	0.1023	0.09670	0.07349	2.893	1	39.37	3.281
$\bar{2}$.99114	$\bar{2}$.99962	0.15262	$\bar{1}$.00996	$\bar{2}$.98541	$\bar{2}$.86622	0.46139		1.59517	0.51598
0.002489	0.002538	0.03609	0.002599	0.002456	0.001867	0.07349	0.02540	1	0.08333
$\bar{3}$.39598	$\bar{3}$.40446	$\bar{2}$.55745	$\bar{3}$.41479	$\bar{3}$.39024	$\bar{3}$.27106	$\bar{2}$.86622	$\bar{2}$.40484		$\bar{2}$.92082
0.02986	0.03045	0.4331	0.03119	0.02947	0.02240	0.8819	0.3048	12	1
$\bar{2}$.47516	$\bar{2}$.48364	$\bar{1}$.63663	$\bar{2}$.49397	$\bar{2}$.46942	$\bar{2}$.35024	$\bar{1}$.94540	$\bar{1}$.48402	1.07918	

MATHEMATICS

Energy or Work Equivalents

Joules	Kilogram-meters	Foot-pounds	Kilowatt-hours	Metric horse-power-hours	Horse-power-hours	Liter-atmospheres	Kilocalories	British thermal units
1	0.10197 $\bar{1}$.00848	0.7376 $\bar{1}$.86780	0.0$_2$2778 $\bar{7}$.44370	0.0$_3$3777 $\bar{7}$.57711	0.0$_3$3725 $\bar{7}$.57113	0.009869 $\bar{3}$.99427	0.0$_2$2388 $\bar{4}$.37809	0.0$_3$9478 $\bar{4}$.97670
9.80665 0.9915207	1	7.233 0.85932	0.0$_2$2724 $\bar{6}$.43521	0.0$_3$37037 $\bar{6}$.56863	0.0$_3$3653 $\bar{7}$.56265	0.09678 $\bar{2}$.98579	0.002342 $\bar{3}$.36961	0.009295 $\bar{3}$.96825
1.356 0.13220	0.1383 $\bar{1}$.14068	1	0.0$_3$3766 $\bar{7}$.57590	0.0$_5$1206 $\bar{7}$.70932	0.0$_5$0505 $\bar{6}$.70333	0.01338 $\bar{2}$.12647	0.0$_3$3238 $\bar{4}$.51029	0.001285 $\bar{3}$.10890
3.600 × 10⁶ 6.55630	3.671 × 10⁵ 5.56478	2.655 × 10⁶ 6.42410	1	1.3596 0.13342	1.341 0.12743	35528 4.55057	859.9 2.93443	3412 3.53303
2.648 × 10⁶ 6.42288	270000 5.43136	1.9529 × 10⁶ 6.29068	0.7355 $\bar{1}$.86658	1	0.9863 $\bar{1}$.99401	26131 4.41715	632.4 2.80098	2510 3.39961
2.6845 × 10⁶ 6.42887	2.7375 × 10⁵ 5.43735	1.98 × 10⁶ 6.29667	0.7457 $\bar{1}$.87356	1.0139 0.00598	1	26493 4.42314	641.2 2.80699	2544 3.40557
101.33 2.00573	10.333 1.01421	74.74 1.87353	0.0$_4$2815 $\bar{5}$.44952	0.0$_3$3827 $\bar{5}$.58284	0.0$_4$3775 $\bar{5}$.57686	1	0.02420 $\bar{2}$.38382	0.09604 $\bar{2}$.98246
4187 3.62191	426.9 2.63036	3088 3.48971	0.001163 $\bar{3}$.06558	0.001581 $\bar{3}$.19902	0.001560 $\bar{3}$.19304	41.32 1.61618	1	3.968 0.59861
1055 3.02300	107.6 2.03178	778.2 2.89110	0.0$_3$2931 $\bar{4}$.46697	0.0$_3$3985 $\bar{4}$.60042	0.0$_3$3930 $\bar{4}$.59444	10.41 1.01757	0.25200 $\bar{1}$.40139	1

The equivalents are given in the heavier type. Logarithms of the equivalents are given immediately below. In some cases the equivalents have been rounded off, although the logarithm corresponds to the equivalent carried to a greater number of decimal places.

Subscripts after any figure, 0₃, 9₄, etc., mean that that figure is to be repeated the indicated number of times.

Conversion of Energy, Work, Heat

	Ft-lb to kilogrammeters	Kilogrammeters to ft-lb	Ft-lb to Btu	Btu to ft-lb	Kilogrammeters to kilocalories	Kilocalories to kilogrammeters	Joules to calories	Calories to joules
1	0.1383	7.233	0.001285	778.2	0.002342	426.9	0.2388	4.187
2	0.2765	14.47	0.002570	1,556.	0.004685	853.9	0.4777	8.374
3	0.4148	21.70	0.003855	2,334.	0.007027	1,281.	0.7165	12.56
4	0.5530	28.93	0.005140	3,113.	0.009369	1,708.	0.9554	16.75
5	0.6913	36.16	0.006425	3,891.	0.01172	2,135.	1.194	20.93
6	0.8295	43.40	0.007710	4,669.	0.01405	2,562.	1.433	25.12
7	0.9678	50.63	0.008995	5,447.	0.01640	2,989.	1.672	29.31
8	1.106	57.86	0.01028	6,225.	0.01874	3,415.	1.911	33.49
9	1.244	65.10	0.01156	7,003.	0.02108	3,842.	2.150	37.68

Power Equivalents *

Horse-power	Kilo-watts	Metric horse-power	Ponce-lets	Kg-m per sec	Ft-lb per sec	Kilo-calories per sec	Btu per sec
1	0.7457 $\bar{1}$.87256	1.014 0.00599	0.7604 $\bar{1}$.88105	76.04 1.88105	550 2.74036	0.1781 $\bar{1}$.25066	0.7068 $\bar{1}$.84936
1.341 0.12743	1	1.360 0.13343	1.020 0.00848	102.0 2.00848	737.6 2.86780	0.2388 $\bar{1}$.37813	0.9478 $\bar{1}$.97673
0.9863 $\bar{1}$.99402	0.7355 $\bar{1}$.86658	1	0.75 $\bar{1}$.87506	75 1.87506	542.5 2.73438	0.1757 $\bar{1}$.24467	0.6971 $\bar{1}$.84328
1.315 0.11896	0.9807 $\bar{1}$.99152	1.333 0.12493	1	100 2.00000	723.3 2.85932	0.2342 $\bar{1}$.36961	0.9295 $\bar{1}$.96825
0.01315 $\bar{2}$.11896	0.009807 $\bar{3}$.99152	0.01333 $\bar{2}$.12493	0.01 $\bar{2}$.00000	1	7.233 0.85932	0.002342 $\bar{3}$.36961	0.009295 $\bar{3}$.96825
0.00182 $\bar{3}$.25946	0.001356 $\bar{3}$.13220	0.00184 $\bar{3}$.26562	0.00138 $\bar{3}$.14067	0.1383 $\bar{1}$.14067	1	$0.0_3 3238$ $\bar{4}$.51029	0.001285 $\bar{3}$.10890
5.615 0.74934	4.187 0.62187	5.692 0.75530	4.269 0.63036	426.9 2.63036	3088 3.48971	1	3.968 0.59861
1.415 0.15074	1.055 0.02320	1.434 0.15668	1.076 0.03178	107.6 2.03178	778.2 2.89110	0.2520 $\bar{1}$.40138	1

* EXAMPLE: 1 horsepower = 0.7457 kilowatts.

Conversion of Power

	Horsepower to kilowatts	Kilowatts to horsepower	Metric horsepower to kilowatts	Kilowatts to metric horsepower	Horsepower to metric horsepower	Metric horsepower to horsepower
1	0.7457	1.341	0.7355	1.360	1.014	0.9863
2	1.491	2.682	1.471	2.719	2.028	1.973
3	2.237	4.023	2.206	4.079	3.042	2.959
4	2.983	5.364	2.942	5.438	4.055	3.945
5	3.729	6.705	3.677	6.798	5.069	4.932
6	4.474	8.046	4.412	8.158	6.083	5.918
7	5.220	9.387	5.147	9.520	7.097	6.904
8	5.966	10.73	5.883	10.88	8.111	7.891
9	6.711	12.07	6.618	12.24	9.125	8.877

MATHEMATICS

Density Equivalents and Conversion Factors *

Equivalents					Conversion factors				
Grams per cu cm	Lb per cu in.	Lb per cu ft	Short tons (2,000 lb) per cu yd	Lb per U.S. gal		Grams per cu cm to lb per cu ft	Lb per cu ft to grams per cu cm	Grams per cu cm to short tons per cu yd	Short tons per cu yd to grams per cu cm
1	0.03613	62.43	0.8428	8.345	1	62.43	0.01602	0.8428	1.187
	$\bar{2}$.55787	1.79539	$\bar{1}$.92572	0.92143	2	124.86	0.03204	1.6856	2.373
27.68	1	1728	23.33	231	3	187.28	0.04805	2.5283	3.560
1.44217		3.23754	1.36792	2.36361	4	249.71	0.06407	3.3711	4.746
0.01602	0.0$_3$5787	1	0.0135	0.1337	5	312.14	0.08009	4.2139	5.933
$\bar{2}$.20466	$\bar{4}$.76245		$\bar{2}$.13033	$\bar{1}$.12613	6	374.57	0.09611	5.0567	7.119
1.187	0.04287	74.07	1	9.902	7	437.00	0.11213	5.8995	8.306
0.07428	$\bar{2}$.63212	1.86964		0.99572	8	499.43	0.12814	6.7423	9.492
0.1198	0.004329	7.481	0.1010	1	9	561.85	0.14416	7.5850	10.679
$\bar{1}$.07855	$\bar{3}$.63639	0.87396	$\bar{1}$.00432		10	624.28	0.16018	8.4278	11.865

* EXAMPLE: 1 gm per cu cm = 62.43 lb per cu ft.

Thermal Conductivity

Calories per sec per sq cm per cm per deg C	Watts per sq cm per cm per deg C	Calories per hr per sq cm per cm per deg C	Btu per hr per sq ft per ft per deg F	Btu per day per sq ft per in. per deg F
1	4.187	3,600	241.9	69,670
0.2388	1	860	57.79	16,641
0.0002778	0.001163	1	0.0672	19.35
0.004134	0.01731	14.88	1	288
0.00001435	0.00006009	0.05167	0.00347	1

Thermal Conductance

Calories per sec per sq cm per deg C	Watts per sq cm per deg C	Calories per hr per sq cm per deg C	Btu per hr per sq ft per deg F	Btu per day per sq ft per deg F
1	4.187	3,600	7,373	176,962
0.2388	1	860	1,761	42,267
0.0002778	0.001163	1	2.048	49.16
0.0001356	0.0005678	0.4882	1	24
0.000005651	0.00002366	0.02034	0.04167	1

Heat Flow

Calories per sec per sq cm	Watts per sq cm	Calories per hr per sq cm	Btu per hr per sq ft	Btu per day per sq ft
1	4.187	3,600	13,272	318,531
0.2388	1	860	3,170	76,081
0.0002778	0.001163	1	3.687	88.48
0.00007535	0.0003154	0.2712	1	24
0.000003139	0.00001314	0.01130	0.04167	1

Time

Kinds of Time. Three kinds of time are recognized by astronomers: sidereal, apparent solar, and mean solar time. The **sidereal day** is the interval between two consecutive transits of some fixed celestial object across any given meridian, or it is the interval required by the earth to make one complete revolution on its axis. This interval is constant, but it is inconvenient as a time unit because the noon of the sidereal day occurs at all hours of the day and night. The **apparent solar day** is the interval between two consecutive transits of the sun across any given meridian. On account of the variable distance between the sun and earth, the variable speed of the earth in its orbit, the effect of the moon, etc., this interval is not constant and consequently cannot be kept by any simple mechanism, such as clocks or watches. To overcome the objection noted above, the **mean solar day** was devised. The mean solar day is the length of the average apparent solar day. Like the sidereal day it is constant, and like the apparent solar day its noon always occurs at approximately the same time of day. By international agreement, beginning Jan. 1, 1925, the astronomical day, like the civil day, is from midnight to midnight. The hours of the astronomical day run from 0 to 24, and the hours of the civil day usually run from 0 to 12 A.M. and 0 to 12 P.M. In some countries the hours of the civil day also run from 0 to 24.

The Year. There are three different kinds of year used: the sidereal, the tropical, and the anomalistic. The **sidereal year** is the time taken by the earth to complete one revolution around the sun from a given star to the same star again. Its length is 365 days, 6 hours, 9 minutes, and 9 seconds. The **tropical year** is the time included between two successive passages of the vernal equinox by the sun, and since the equinox moves westward 50.2 seconds of arc a year, the tropical year is shorter by 20 minutes 23 seconds in time than the sidereal year. As the seasons depend upon the earth's position with respect to the equinox, the tropical year is the year of civil reckoning. The **anomalistic year** is the interval between two successive passages of the perihelion, *viz.*, the time of the earth's nearest approach to the sun. The anomalistic year is only used in special calculations in astronomy.

The Calendar. The month depended originally upon the changes of the moon. The Mohammedan nations still use a lunar calendar with years of 12 lunar months, which contain 354 or 355 days in a specified cycle. According to their method of reckoning, the same month falls in different seasons and their calendars gain 1 year on ours about every 33 years. The **Julian calendar** (established 45 B.C. and now seldom used except in astronomy) discards all consideration of the moon and adopts 365¼ days as the true length of the year. The **Gregorian calendar,** now used in most of the civilized world, was adopted in Catholic countries of Europe in 1582 and in Great Britain and her colonies Jan. 1, 1752. For several years prior to the adoption of the Gregorian calendar the calendar year had begun on Mar. 25. When the change was made in Great Britain and her colonies, the year 1751 contained no January or February and no Mar. 1 to 24 inclusive. The calendar year 1751 was, therefore, short of a full year by 83 days. The calendar year 1752 was also 11 days short of a full year as the dates Sept. 3 to 13 inclusive, in that year, were dropped to correct the 11 day error that had accumulated during the use of the Julian calendar. The average length of the Gregorian calendar year is 365¼ − ¾₀₀ days, or 365.2425 days. This is equivalent to 365 days, 5 hours, 49 minutes, 12 seconds. The length of the tropical year is 365.2422 days, or 365 days, 5 hours, 48 minutes, 46 seconds. Thus the Gregorian calendar year is longer than the tropical year by 0.0003 day, or 26 seconds. This difference amounts to 1 day in slightly more than 3,300 years and can properly be neglected.

Standard Time. Prior to 1883, each city of the United States had its own time, which was determined by the time of passage of the sun across the local meridian. A system of standard time has been used since its first adoption by the railroads in 1883 but was first legalized on Mar. 19, 1918, when Congress directed the Interstate Commerce Commission to establish limits of the standard time zones. The United States, which extends from 65 to 125 deg west longitude, is divided into four zones each of approximately 15 deg of longitude. The first or **Eastern zone** includes all territory between the Atlantic coast and an irregular line drawn from the United States–Canadian boundary just south of Drummond Island, through the Straits of Mackinac and the center of Lake Michigan, along the southern border of Michigan and the western border of Ohio, through the eastern part of Tennessee and Kentucky, and along the western boundary of Georgia and the Apalachicola River to the Gulf of Mexico at Apalachicola Bay, Fla. The time of this zone is that of the 75 deg meridian, which is 5 hr slower than Greenwich time. The second or **Central zone** includes all territory between the line mentioned and an irregular line drawn from the United States–Canadian boundary at the boundary line between North Dakota and Montana, along the western and southern borders of North Dakota to the Missouri River, through Phillipsburg, Kans., along the western boundary of Oklahoma and Texas to the Rio Grande River, and to the Mexican border. The time is that of the 90 deg meridian. The third or **Mountain zone** includes all territory between the last-named line and an irregular line drawn from the United States–Canadian boundary at the northwest corner of Montana along the boundary between Montana and Idaho, the Salmon River, the western and southern borders of Idaho, through Utah and Arizona to the United States–Mexican boundary on the Colorado River. The time is that of the 105 deg meridian. The fourth or **Pacific zone** includes all territory west of the last-named line to the Pacific coast except Alaska. The time is that of the 120 deg meridian. A fifth or **Alaska zone** includes Alaska only, the time being that of the 150 deg meridian. Standard time is uniform in each of these zones, and the time in one zone (except Alaska) differs by exactly 1 hr from the zone next to it. However, four different times are actually used in Alaska: Pacific, 120°; Yukon, 135°; Alaska, 150°; and Western Alaska, 165°. In cities situated on the border line of two zones, the standard time of the easterly zone is commonly used; in such cities when the time is given, it should be specified as Eastern, Central, etc. The system of standard time has been adopted in almost all civilized countries and now is used by ships on the high seas.

Terrestrial Gravity

Standard acceleration of gravity is g^0 = 980.665 cm per sec per sec, or 32.1740 ft per sec per sec. This value g^0 is assumed to be the value of g at sea level and latitude 45 deg.

Acceleration of Gravity
(U.S. Coast and Geodetic Survey, 1912)

Latitude, deg	g		g/g^0	Latitude, deg	g		g/g^0
	Cm/sec²	Ft/sec²			Cm/sec²	Ft/sec²	
0	978.0	32.088	0.9973	50	981.1	32.187	1.0004
10	978.2	32.093	0.9975	60	981.9	32.215	1.0013
20	978.6	32.108	0.9979	70	982.6	32.238	1.0020
30	979.3	32.130	0.9986	80	983.1	32.253	1.0024
40	980.2	32.158	0.9995	90	983.2	32.258	1.0026

Correction for altitude above sea level: −0.3 cm per sec² for each 1,000 meters; −0.003 ft per sec² for each 1,000 ft.

Specific Gravity and Density

The **specific gravity of a solid or liquid** is the ratio of the mass of the body to the mass of an equal volume of water at some standard temperature. At the present time a temperature of 4 C (39 F) is commonly used by physicists, but the engineer uses 60 F. The specific gravity **of gases** is usually expressed in terms of hydrogen or air.

The **density** of a body is its mass per unit volume. If the gram is used as the unit of mass and the milliliter as the unit of volume, the figures representing the density are the same as the specific gravity of the body referred to water at 4 C as unity. The customary unit is pounds per cubic foot.

The specific gravity of liquids is usually measured by means of an hydrometer, and different special arbitrary hydrometer scales are used in various trades and industries. The most common of these are the API and Baumé. The API (American Petroleum Institute) scale is approved by the American Petroleum Institute, the ASTM, the U.S. Bureau of Mines, and the National Bureau of Standards and is recommended for exclusive use in the United States petroleum industry, superseding the Baumé scale for liquids lighter than water. The relation between API degrees and specific gravity is expressed by the following equation:

$$\text{Degrees API} = \frac{141.5}{\text{sp gr 60/60 F}} - 131.5$$

The specific gravities corresponding to the indications of the Baumé hydrometer are given in the following tables.

Specific Gravities at $\frac{60}{60}$ F Corresponding to Degrees API

and Weights per U.S. Gallon at 60 F

$$\left(\text{Calculated from the formula, specific gravity} = \frac{141.5}{131.5 + \text{deg API}}\right)$$

Degrees API	Specific gravity	Lb per U.S. gallon	Degrees API	Specific gravity	Lb per U.S. gallon	Degrees API	Specific gravity	Lb per U.S. gallon	Degrees API	Specific gravity	Lb per U.S. gallon
10	1.0000	8.328	33	0.8602	7.163	56	0.7547	6.283	79	0.6722	5.595
11	0.9930	8.270	34	0.8550	7.119	57	0.7507	6.249	80	0.6690	5.568
12	0.9861	8.212	35	0.8498	7.076	58	0.7467	6.216	81	0.6659	5.542
13	0.9792	8.155	36	0.8448	7.034	59	0.7428	6.184	82	0.6628	5.516
14	0.9725	8.099	37	0.8398	6.993	60	0.7389	6.151	83	0.6597	5.491
15	0.9659	8.044	38	0.8348	6.951	61	0.7351	6.119	84	0.6566	5.465
16	0.9593	7.989	39	0.8299	6.910	62	0.7313	6.087	85	0.6536	5.440
17	0.9529	7.935	40	0.8251	6.870	63	0.7275	6.056	86	0.6506	5.415
18	0.9465	7.882	41	0.8203	6.830	64	0.7238	6.025	87	0.6476	5.390
19	0.9402	7.830	42	0.8155	6.790	65	0.7201	5.994	88	0.6446	5.365
20	0.9340	7.778	43	0.8109	6.752	66	0.7165	5.964	89	0.6417	5.341
21	0.9279	7.727	44	0.8063	6.713	67	0.7128	5.934	90	0.6388	5.316
22	0.9218	7.676	45	0.8017	6.675	68	0.7093	5.904	91	0.6360	5.293
23	0.9159	7.627	46	0.7972	6.637	69	0.7057	5.874	92	0.6331	5.269
24	0.9100	7.578	47	0.7927	6.600	70	0.7022	5.845	93	0.6303	5.246
25	0.9042	7.529	48	0.7883	6.563	71	0.6988	5.817	94	0.6275	5.222
26	0.8984	7.481	49	0.7839	6.526	72	0.6953	5.788	95	0.6247	5.199
27	0.8927	7.434	50	0.7796	6.490	73	0.6919	5.759	96	0.6220	5.176
28	0.8871	7.387	51	0.7753	6.455	74	0.6886	5.731	97	0.6193	5.154
29	0.8816	7.341	52	0.7711	6.420	75	0.6852	5.703	98	0.6166	5.131
30	0.8762	7.296	53	0.7669	6.385	76	0.6819	5.676	99	0.6139	5.109
31	0.8708	7.251	54	0.7628	6.350	77	0.6787	5.649	100	0.6112	5.086
32	0.8654	7.206	55	0.7587	6.316	78	0.6754	5.622			

The weights in this table are weights in air at 60 F with humidity 50 percent and pressure 760 mm.

Specific Gravities at $\frac{60}{60}$ F Corresponding to Degrees Baumé

for Liquids Lighter than Water and Weights per U.S. Gallon at 60 F

$$\left(\text{Calculated from the formula, specific gravity } \frac{60}{60} \text{ F} = \frac{140}{130 + \text{deg Baumé}} \right)$$

Degrees Baumé	Specific gravity	Lb per gallon	Degrees Baumé	Specific gravity	Lb per gallon	Degrees Baumé	Specific gravity	Lb per gallon	Degrees Baumé	Specific gravity	Lb per gallon
10.0	1.0000	8.328	33.0	0.8589	7.152	55.0	0.7568	6.300	78.0	0.6731	5.602
11.0	0.9929	8.269	34.0	0.8537	7.108	56.0	0.7527	6.266	79.0	0.6699	5.576
12.0	0.9859	8.211	35.0	0.8485	7.065	57.0	0.7487	6.233	80.0	0.6667	5.549
13.0	0.9790	8.153	36.0	0.8434	7.022	58.0	0.7447	6.199	81.0	0.6635	5.522
14.0	0.9722	8.096	37.0	0.8383	6.980	59.0	0.7407	6.166	82.0	0.6604	5.497
15.0	0.9655	8.041	38.0	0.8333	6.939	60.0	0.7368	6.134	83.0	0.6573	5.471
16.0	0.9589	7.986	39.0	0.8284	6.898	61.0	0.7330	6.102	84.0	0.6542	5.445
17.0	0.9524	7.931	40.0	0.8235	6.857	62.0	0.7292	6.070	85.0	0.6512	5.420
18.0	0.9459	7.877	41.0	0.8187	6.817	63.0	0.7254	6.038	86.0	0.6482	5.395
19.0	0.9396	7.825	42.0	0.8140	6.777	64.0	0.7216	6.007	87.0	0.6452	5.370
20.0	0.9333	7.772	43.0	0.8092	6.738	65.0	0.7179	5.976	88.0	0.6422	5.345
21.0	0.9272	7.721	44.0	0.8046	6.699	66.0	0.7143	5.946	89.0	0.6393	5.320
22.0	0.9211	7.670	45.0	0.8000	6.661	67.0	0.7107	5.916	90.0	0.6364	5.296
23.0	0.9150	7.620	46.0	0.7955	6.623	68.0	0.7071	5.886	91.0	0.6335	5.272
24.0	0.9091	7.570	47.0	0.7910	6.586	69.0	0.7035	5.856	92.0	0.6306	5.248
25.0	0.9032	7.522	48.0	0.7865	6.548	70.0	0.7000	5.827	93.0	0.6278	5.225
26.0	0.8974	7.473	49.0	0.7821	6.511	71.0	0.6965	5.798	94.0	0.6250	5.201
27.0	0.8917	7.425	50.0	0.7778	6.476	72.0	0.6931	5.769	95.0	0.6222	5.178
28.0	0.8861	7.378	51.0	0.7735	6.440	73.0	0.6897	5.741	96.0	0.6195	5.155
29.0	0.8805	7.332	52.0	0.7692	6.404	74.0	0.6863	5.712	97.0	0.6167	5.132
30.0	0.8750	7.286	53.0	0.7650	6.369	75.0	0.6829	5.685	98.0	0.6140	5.110
31.0	0.8696	7.241	54.0	0.7609	6.334	76.0	0.6796	5.657	99.0	0.6114	5.088
32.0	0.8642	7.196				77.0	0.6763	5.629	100.0	0.6087	5.066

Specific Gravities at $\frac{60}{60}$ F Corresponding to Degrees Baumé

for Liquids Heavier than Water

$$\left(\text{Calculated from the formula, specific gravity } \frac{60}{60} \text{ F} = \frac{145}{145 - \text{deg Baumé}} \right)$$

Degrees Baumé	Specific gravity	Degrees Baumé	Specific gravity	Degrees Baumé	Specific gravity	Degrees Baumé	Specific gravity	Degrees Baumé	Specific gravity	Degrees Baumé	Specific gravity
0	1.0000	12	1.0902	24	1.1983	36	1.3303	48	1.4948	60	1.7059
1	1.0069	13	1.0985	25	1.2083	37	1.3426	49	1.5104	61	1.7262
2	1.0140	14	1.1069	26	1.2185	38	1.3551	50	1.5263	62	1.7470
3	1.0211	15	1.1154	27	1.2288	39	1.3679	51	1.5426	63	1.7683
4	1.0284	16	1.1240	28	1.2393	40	1.3810	52	1.5591	64	1.7901
5	1.0357	17	1.1328	29	1.2500	41	1.3942	53	1.5761	65	1.8125
6	1.0432	18	1.1417	30	1.2609	42	1.4078	54	1.5934	66	1.8354
7	1.0507	19	1.1508	31	1.2719	43	1.4216	55	1.6111	67	1.8590
8	1.0584	20	1.1600	32	1.2832	44	1.4356	56	1.6292	68	1.8831
9	1.0662	21	1.1694	33	1.2946	45	1.4500	57	1.6477	69	1.9079
10	1.0741	22	1.1789	34	1.3063	46	1.4646	58	1.6667	70	1.9333
11	1.0821	23	1.1885	35	1.3182	47	1.4796	59	1.6860	.....	....

Mohs Scale of Hardness

1. Talc.	5. Apatite.	8. Topaz.
2. Gypsum.	6. Feldspar.	9. Sapphire.
3. Calc-spar.	7. Quartz.	10. Diamond.
4. Fluorspar.		

Section 2

PRODUCTION EQUIPMENT

Chapter 2

CASING, TUBING, AND LINE PIPE

By WILLIAM O. CLINEDINST

Manager, Scientific Research
National Tube Division
United States Steel Corporation

CONTENTS

PART 1: CASING

PART 1: CASING

REFERENCES FOR CASING AND TUBING: API Standard 5A, American Petroleum Institute. Bulletins and handbooks of the following companies: National Tube Division, United States Steel Corporation; The Youngstown Sheet and Tube Company; Jones & Laughlin Steel Corporation; The National Supply Company, Subsidiary of Armco Steel Corporation; Republic Steel Corporation; Bethlehem Steel Company; Hydril Company; Gray Tool Company; Hardy-Griffin Engineering Corporation, A Division of Atlas Pipe Incorporated; Naylor Pipe Company.

The successful production of oil and gas is dependent upon the proper performance of casing, which serves as a structural retainer in the well, excludes undesirable fluids, and acts to confine and conduct oil or gas from subsurface strata to ground level. Casing must be capable of withstanding external collapsing pressure from fluid surrounding the casing, the internal pressures encountered in conducting oil or gas from the producing formation, and the tension loads resulting from its own suspended weight. In addition, it must be equipped also with threaded joints that can be made up easily and provide leakproof connections.

API CASING

The American Petroleum Institute has developed specifications for casing meeting the major needs of the oil and gas industry and has published these in API Standard 5A. This API standard provides standard dimensions, strengths, and performance properties and the required thread-gauging practice to ensure complete interchangeability.

In addition to the API strength grades, the following tables include information on higher-strength casing developed to meet the needs of unusually deep wells.

API Casing—Short and Long Thread—Weights, Dimensions, Collapse and Tension Properties, and Internal Pressures

Size, OD, in.	Wt./ft, lb		Dimensions, in.							Steel grade	Min properties						Internal pressures, psi			Plain-end yield strength,[a] (min), 1,000 lb
			Casing			Coupling					Tension				Collapse		Test		Yield[e] (min)	
						OD		Length			API short		API long							
	Nom., threads and coupling	Plain end	Wall thick-ness	ID	Drift diam	API	Spec. clear-ance[a,c]	API short	API long		Equiv. length, ft sf = 2	Ult. joint strength,[d] 1,000 lb	Equiv. length, ft sf = 2	Ult. joint strength,[d] 1,000 lb	Set-ting depth,[b] ft sf = 1⅛	Pres-sure, psi	Mill[c]	At fiber stress equal to 80% of min yield strength		
	9.50	9.40	0.205	4.090	3.965	5.000	......	6¼	....	F	3,740	71	......	.....	3,410	1,920	1,800	1,800	1,990	
	9.50	9.40	0.205	4.090	3.965	5.000	4.875	6¼	....	H	5,050	96	......	.....	4,530	2,550	2,900	2,900	3,190	
	9.50	9.40	0.205	4.099	3.965	5.000	4.875	6¼	....	J	6,740	128	......	.....	5,900	3,320	3,000	4,000	4,380	
	10.50	10.23	0.224	4.052	3.927	5.000	4.875	6¼	....	J	6,710	141	......	.....	6,810	3,830	3,000	4,400	4,790	166
	11.60	11.35	0.250	4.000	3.875	5.000	4.875	6¼	7	J	6,850	159	8,150	189	8,070	4,540	3,000	4,900	5,350	184
4½	11.60	11.35	0.250	4.000	3.875	5.000	4.875	...	7	N	......	.....	9,480	220	10,540	5,930	7,100	7,100	7,780	267
	13.50	13.04	0.290	3.920	3.795	5.000	4.875	...	7	N	......	.....	9,560	258	13,070	7,350	8,200	8,200	9,020	307
	11.60	11.35	0.250	4.000	3.875	5.000	4.875	...	7	P	......	.....	12,410	288	15,270	8,590	9,800	9,800	10,690	367
	13.50	13.04	0.290	3.920	3.795	5.000	4.875	...	7	P	......	.....	12,480	337	18,920	10,640	10,000	11,300	12,410	422
	15.10	14.98	0.337	3.826	3.701	5.000	4.875	...	7	P	......	.....	13,050	394	22,720	12,780	10,000	13,200	14,420	485
	11.50	11.23	0.220	4.560	4.435	5.563	......	6½	....	F	3,650	84	......	.....	3,240	1,820	1,800	1,800	1,930	
	11.50	11.23	0.220	4.560	4.435	5.563	5.375	6½	....	J	6,610	152	......	.....	5,560	3,130	3,000	3,900	4,240	
	13.00	12.83	0.253	4.494	4.369	5.563	5.375	6½	7¾	J	6,850	178	8,080	210	6,990	3,930	3,000	4,500	4,870	208
	15.00	14.87	0.296	4.408	4.283	5.563	5.375	6½	7¾	J	7,000	210	8,230	247	8,850	4,980	3,000	5,200	5,700	241
	15.00	14.87	0.296	4.408	4.283	5.563	5.375	...	7¾	N	......	.....	9,600	288	11,590	6,520	7,600	7,600	8,290	350
5	18.00	17.93	0.362	4.276	4.151	5.563	5.375	...	7¾	N	......	.....	9,830	354	15,200	8,550	9,300	9,300	10,140	422
	15.00	14.87	0.296	4.408	4.283	5.563	5.375	...	7¾	P	......	.....	12,570	377	16,760	9,430	10,000	10,400	11,390	481
	18.00	17.93	0.362	4.276	4.151	5.563	5.375	...	7¾	P	......	.....	12,860	463	22,030	12,390	10,000	12,700	13,940	580
	15.00	14.87	0.296	4.408	4.283	5.563	5.375	...	7¾	V	......	.....	14,930	448	19,570	11,010	10,000	14,200	15,540	658
	18.00	17.93	0.362	4.276	4.151	5.563	5.375	...	7¾	V	......	.....	15,310	551	29,190	16,420	10,000	17,400	19,000	791

	13.00	12.84	0.228	5.044	4.919	6.050	......	6¾	....	F	3,650	95	......	.....	2,950	1,660	1,700	1,700	1,810	
	14.00	13.70	0.244	5.012	4.887	6.050	5.875	6¾	....	H	4,960	139	......	.....	4,340	2,440	2,800	2,800	3,110	
	14.00	13.70	0.244	5.012	4.887	6.050	5.875	6¾	....	J	6,640	186	......	.....	5,640	3,170	3,000	3,900	4,270	
	15.50	15.35	0.275	4.950	4.825	6.050	5.875	6¾	8	J	6,810	211	7,970	247	6,860	3,860	3,000	4,400	4,810	248
	17.00	16.87	0.304	4.892	4.767	6.050	5.875	6¾	8	J	6,880	234	8,090	275	8,000	4,500	3,000	4,900	5,320	273
	17.00	16.87	0.304	4.892	4.767	6.050	5.875	...	8	N	......	.....	9,410	320	10,470	5,890	7,100	7,100	7,740	397
5½	20.00	19.81	0.381	4.778	4.653	6.050	5.875	...	8	N	......	.....	9,550	382	13,400	7,540	8,400	8,400	9,190	466
	23.00	22.54	0.415	4.670	4.545	6.050	5.875	...	8	N	......	.....	9,570	440	15,820	8,900	9,700	9,700	10,560	530
	17.00	16.87	0.304	4.892	4.767	6.050	5.875	...	8	P	......	.....	12,290	418	15,150	8,520	9,700	9,700	10,640	546
	20.00	19.81	0.361	4.778	4.653	6.050	5.875	...	8	P	......	.....	12,500	500	19,400	10,910	10,000	11,600	12,640	641
	23.00	22.54	0.415	4.670	4.545	6.050	5.875	...	8	P	......	.....	12,520	576	22,880	12,870	10,000	13,300	14,520	729
	20.00	19.81	0.361	4.778	4.653	6.050	5.875	...	8	V	......	.....	14,880	595	25,710	14,460	10,000	15,800	17,230	874
	23.00	22.54	0.415	4.670	4.545	6.050	5.875	...	8	V	......	.....	14,910	686	30,330	17,060	10,000	18,100	19,810	994
	17.00	16.69	0.245	6.135	6.010	7.390	......	7¼	....	F	3,560	121	......	.....	2,440	1,370	1,500	1,500	1,620	
	20.00	19.49	0.288	6.049	5.924	7.390	7.000	7¼	....	H	4,800	195	......	.....	4,200	2,360	2,800	2,800	3,040	
	20.00	19.49	0.288	6.049	5.924	7.390	7.000	7¼	8¾	J	6,480	259	7,480	299	5,440	3,060	3,000	3,800	4,180	315
	24.00	23.58	0.352	5.921	5.796	7.390	7.000	7¼	8¾	J	6,670	320	7,710	370	7,560	4,250	3,000	4,700	5,110	382
	24.00	23.58	0.352	5.921	5.796	7.390	7.000	...	8¾	N	......	.....	8,960	430	9,870	5,550	6,800	6,800	7,440	555
6⅝	28.00	27.65	0.417	5.791	5.666	7.390	7.000	...	8¾	N	......	.....	9,120	511	12,640	7,110	8,100	8,100	8,810	651
	32.00	31.20	0.475	5.675	5.550	7.390	7.000	...	8¾	N	......	.....	9,090	582	15,090	8,490	9,200	9,200	10,040	734
	24.00	23.58	0.352	5.921	5.796	7.390	7.000	...	8¾	P	......	.....	11,710	562	13,960	7,850	9,400	9,400	10,230	763
	28.00	27.65	0.417	5.791	5.660	7.390	7.000	...	8¾	P	......	.....	11,950	669	18,290	10,290	10,000	11,100	12,120	895
	32.00	31.20	0.475	5.675	5.550	7.390	7.000	...	8¾	P	......	.....	11,910	762	21,830	12,280	10,000	12,600	13,800	1,009
	17.00	16.70	0.231	6.538	6.413	7.656	......	7¼	....	F	3,470	118	......	.....	1,960	11,00	1,300	1,300	1,440	
	17.00	16.70	0.231	6.538	6.413	7.656	7.375	7¼	....	H	4,710	160	......	.....	2,440	1,370	2,100	2,100	2,310	
	20.00	19.54	0.272	6.456	6.331	7.656	7.375	7¼	....	H	4,780	191	......	.....	3,410	1,920	2,500	2,500	2,720	
	20.00	19.54	0.272	6.456	6.331	7.656	7.375	7¼	....	J	6,350	254	......	.....	4,440	2,500	3,000	3,400	3,740	
	23.00	22.63	0.317	6.366	6.241	7.656	7.375	7¼	9	J	6,520	300	7,480	344	5,850	3,290	3,000	4,000	4,360	366
7	26.00	25.66	0.362	6.276	6.151	7.656	7.375	7¼	9	J	6,630	345	7,600	395	7,220	4,060	3,000	4,600	4,980	415
	23.00	22.63	0.317	6.366	6.241	7.656	7.375	...	9	N	......	.....	8,700	400	7,640	4,300	5,800	5,800	6,340	532
	26.00	25.66	0.362	6.276	6.151	7.656	7.375	...	9	N	......	.....	8,850	460	9,460	5,320	6,600	6,600	7,240	604
	29.00	28.72	0.408	6.184	6.059	7.656	7.375	...	9	N	......	.....	8,970	520	11,320	6,370	7,500	7,500	8,160	676
	32.00	31.68	0.453	6.094	5.969	7.656	7.375	...	9	N	......	.....	9,030	578	13,160	7,400	8,300	8,300	9,060	745
	35.00	34.58	0.498	6.004	5.879	7.656	7.375	...	9	N	......	.....	9,070	635	14,970	8,420	9,100	9,100	9,960	814
	38.00	37.26	0.540	5.920	5.795	7.656	7.375	...	9	N	......	.....	9,050	688	16,140	9,080	9,900	9,900	10,800	877

API Casing—Short and Long Thread—Weights, Dimensions, Collapse and Tension Properties, and Internal Pressures *(Continued)*

Size, OD, in.	Wt./ft, lb: Nom., threads and coupling	Wt./ft, lb: Plain end	Dimensions, in.: Casing: Wall thick-ness	Dimensions, in.: Casing: ID	Dimensions, in.: Casing: Drift diam	Dimensions, in.: Coupling: OD: API	Dimensions, in.: Coupling: OD: Spec. clear-ance[a,c]	Dimensions, in.: Coupling: Length: API short	Dimensions, in.: Coupling: Length: API long	Steel grade	Min properties: Tension: API short: Equiv. length, ft sf = 2	Min properties: Tension: API short: Ult. joint strength,[d] 1,000 lb	Min properties: Tension: API long: Equiv. length, ft sf = 2	Min properties: Tension: API long: Ult. joint strength,[d] 1,000 lb	Min properties: Collapse: Setting depth,[b] ft sf = 1⅛	Min properties: Collapse: Pressure, psi	Internal pressures, psi: Test: Mill[c]	Internal pressures, psi: Test: At fiber stress equal to 80% of min yield strength	Internal pressures, psi: Yield[e] (min)	Plain-end yield strength,[a] (min), 1,000 lb
7	26.00	25.66	0.362	6.276	6.151	7.656	7.375	...	9	P	......	.....	11,580	602	12,840	7,220	9,100	9,100	9,960	831
	29.00	28.72	0.408	6.184	6.059	7.656	7.375	...	9	P	......	.....	11,740	681	16,390	9,220	10,000	10,300	11,220	930
	32.00	31.68	0.453	6.094	5.969	7.656	7.375	...	9	P	......	.....	11,810	756	19.020	10,700	10,000	11,400	12,460	1,024
	35.00	34.58	0.498	6.004	5.879	7.656	7.375	...	9	P	......	.....	11,870	831	21,650	12,180	10,000	12,500	13,690	1,119
	38.00	37.26	0.540	5.920	5.795	7.656	7.375	...	9	P	......	.....	11,840	900	23,340	13,130	10,000	13,600	14,850	1,206
	29.00	28.72	0.408	6.184	6.059	7.656	7.375	...	9	V	......	.....	13,970	810	18,630	10,480	10,000	14,000	15,300	1,267
	32.00	31.68	0.453	6.094	5.969	7.656	7.375	...	9	V	......	.....	14,060	900	25,210	14,180	10,000	15,500	16,980	1,398
	35.00	34.58	0.498	6.004	5.879	7.656	7.375	...	9	V	......	.....	14,130	989	28,710	16,150	10,000	17,100	18,670	1,526
	38.00	37.26	0.540	5.920	5.795	7.656	7.375	...	9	V	......	.....	14,080	1,070	30,950	17,410	10,000	18,500	20,250	1,644
7⅝	20.00	19.69	0.250	7.125	7.000	8.500	......	7½	....	F	3,450	138	......	.....	1,960	1,100	1,300	1,300	1,430	
	24.00	23.47	0.300	7.025	6.900	8.500	8.125	7½	....	H	4,730	227	......	.....	3,500	1,970	2,500	2,500	2,750	
	26.40	25.56	0.328	6.969	6.844	8.500	8.125	7½	9¼	J	6,310	333	7,160	378	5,350	3,010	3,000	3,800	4,140	414
	26.40	25.56	0.328	6.969	6.844	8.500	8.125	...	9¼	N	......	.....	8,310	439	6,990	3,930	5,500	5,500	6,020	602
	29.70	29.04	0.375	6.875	6.750	8.500	8.125	...	9¼	N	......	.....	8,500	505	8,730	4,910	6,300	6,300	6,890	683
	33.70	33.04	0.430	6.765	6.640	8.500	8.125	...	9¼	N	......	.....	8,620	581	10,790	6,070	7,200	7,200	7,890	778
	39.00	38.05	0.500	6.625	6.500	8.500	8.125	...	9¼	N	......	.....	8,670	676	13,390	7,530	8,400	8,400	9,180	895
	29.70	29.04	0.375	6.875	6.750	8.500	8.125	...	9¼	P	......	.....	11,130	661	10,990	6,180	8,700	8,700	9,470	939
	33.70	33.04	0.430	6.765	6.640	8.500	8.125	...	9¼	P	......	.....	11,280	760	15,610	8,780	9,900	9,900	10,860	1,070
	39.00	38.05	0.500	6.625	6.500	8.500	8.125	...	9¼	P	......	.....	11,350	885	19,380	10,900	10,000	11,500	12,630	1,231
	33.70	33.04	0.430	6.765	6.640	8.500	8.125	...	9¼	V	......	.....	13,430	905	16,820	9,460	10,000	13,500	14,800	1,458
	39.00	38.05	0.500	6.625	6.500	8.500	8.125	...	9¼	V	......	.....	13,500	1,053	25,670	14,440	10,000	15,700	17,210	1,679
	45.30[a]	44.67	0.595	6.435	6.310	8.500	8.125	...	9¼	V	......	.....	13,790	1,249	31,270	17,590	10,000	18,700	20,480	1,971

8⅝	24.00	23.57	0.264	8.097	7.972	9.625	......	7¾	....	F	3,350	161	......	.....	1,690	950	1,200	1,200	1,340	
	28.00	27.02	0.304	8.107	7.892	9.625	9.125	7¾	....	H	4,500	252	......	.....	2,810	1,580	2,300	2,300	2,470	
	32.00	31.10	0.352	7.921	7.796	9.625	9.125	7¾	....	H	4,610	295	......	.....	3,750	2,110	2,600	2,600	2,860	
	24.00	23.57	0.264	8.097	7.972	9.625	9.125	7¾	....	J	6,000	288	......	.....	2,540	1,430	2,700	2,700	2,950	
	32.00	31.10	0.352	7.921	7.796	9.625	9.125	7¾	10	J	6,140	393	6,830	437	4,870	2,740	3,000	3,600	3,930	503
	36.00	35.14	0.400	7.825	7.700	9.625	9.125	7¾	10	J	6,220	448	6,930	499	6,080	3,420	3,000	4,100	4,460	568
	36.00	35.14	0.400	7.825	7.700	9.625	9.125	...	10	N	......	.....	8,070	581	7,950	4,470	5,900	5,900	6,490	827
	40.00	39.29	0.450	7.725	7.600	9.625	9.125	...	10	N	......	.....	8,190	655	9,580	5,390	6,700	6,700	7,300	925
	44.00	43.39	0.500	7.625	7.500	9.625	9.125	...	10	N	......	.....	8,280	729	11,240	6,320	7,400	7,400	8,120	1,021
	49.00	48.00	0.557	7.511	7.386	9.625	9.125	...	10	N	......	.....	8,290	812	13,100	7,370	8,300	8,300	9,040	1,129
	40.00	39.29	0.450	7.725	7.600	9.625	9.125	...	10	P	......	.....	10,720	858	13,190	7,420	9,200	9,200	10,040	1,272
	44.00	43.39	0.500	7.625	7.500	9.625	9.125	...	10	P	......	.....	10,840	954	16,250	9,140	10,000	10,200	11,160	1,404
	49.00	48.00	0.557	7.511	7.386	9.625	9.125	...	10	P	......	.....	10,840	1,062	18,950	10,660	10,000	11,400	12,430	1,552
	44.00	43.39	0.500	7.625	7.500	9.625	9.125	...	10	V	......	.....	12,900	1,135	18,310	10,300	10,000	13,900	15,220	1,914
	49.00	48.00	0.557	7.511	7.386	9.625	9.125	...	10	V	......	.....	12,900	1,264	25,140	14,140	10,000	15,500	16,950	2,118
9⅝	29.30	28.04	0.281	9.063	8.907	10.625	......	7¾	....	F	3,160	185	......	.....	1,530	860	1,200	1,200	1,280	
	32.30	31.03	0.312	9.001	8.845	10.625	10.125	7¾	....	H	4,320	279	......	.....	2,350	1,320	2,100	2,100	2,270	
	36.00	34.86	0.352	8.921	8.765	10.625	10.125	7¾	....	H	4,420	318	......	.....	3,040	1,710	2,300	2,300	2,560	
	36.00	34.86	0.352	8.921	8.765	10.625	10.125	7¾	10½	J	5,860	422	6,420	462	3,950	2,220	3,000	3,200	3,520	564
	40.00	38.94	0.395	8.835	8.679	10.625	10.125	7¾	10½	J	5,960	477	6,510	521	4,920	2,770	3,000	3,600	3,950	630
	40.00	38.94	0.395	8.835	8.679	10.625	10.125	...	10½	N	......	.....	7,580	606	6,280	3,530	5,300	5,300	5,750	916
	43.50	42.70	0.435	8.755	8.599	10.625	10.125	...	10½	N	......	.....	7,700	670	7,610	4,280	5,800	5,800	6,330	1,005
	47.00	46.14	0.472	8.681	8.525	10.625	10.125	...	10½	N	......	.....	7,730	727	8,710	4,900	6,300	6,300	6,870	1,086
	53.50	52.85	0.545	8.535	8.379	10.625	10.125	...	10½	N	......	.....	7,860	841	10,860	6,110	7,200	7,200	7,930	1,244
	43.50	42.70	0.435	8.755	8.599	10.625	10.125	...	10½	P	......	.....	10,060	875	8,460	4,760	8,000	8,000	8,700	1,381
	47.00	46.14	0.472	8.681	8.525	10.625	10.125	...	10½	P	......	.....	10,130	952	10,880	6,120	8,600	8,600	9,440	1,493
	53.50	52.85	0.545	8.535	8.379	10.625	10.125	...	10½	P	......	.....	10,280	1,100	15,700	8,830	10,000	10,000	10,900	1,711
	53.50	52.85	0.545	8.535	8.379	10.625	10.125	...	10½	V	......	.....	12,230	1,309	17,030	9,580	10,000	13,600	14,870	2,332
	58.40[a]	57.38	0.595	8.435	8.279	10.625	10.125	...	10½	V	......	.....	12,230	1,428	22,400	12,600	10,000	14,800	16,230	2,532
	61.10[a]	60.08	0.625	8.375	8.219	10.625	10.125	...	10½	V	......	.....	12,270	1,499	25,320	14,240	10,000	15,600	17,040	2,651
10¾	32.75	31.20	0.279	10.192	10.036	11.750	......	8	....	F	2,990	196	......	.....	1,160	650	800	1,000	1,140	
	32.75	31.20	0.279	10.192	10.036	11.750	11.250	8	....	H	4,050	265	......	.....	1,480	830	1,200	1,700	1,820	
	40.50	38.88	0.350	10.050	9.894	11.750	11.250	8	....	H	4,170	338	......	.....	2,380	1,340	1,600	2,100	2,280	

API Casing—Short and Long Thread—Weights, Dimensions, Collapse and Tension Properties, and Internal Pressures (*Continued*)

Size, OD, in.	Wt./ft, lb Nom., threads and coupling	Wt./ft, lb Plain end	Casing Wall thickness	Casing ID	Casing Drift diam	Coupling OD API	Coupling OD Spec. clearance[c]	Coupling Length API short	Coupling Length API long	Steel grade	Tension API short Equiv. length, ft sf = 2	Tension API short Ult. joint strength,[d] 1,000 lb	Tension API long Equiv. length, ft sf = 2	Tension API long Ult. joint strength,[d] 1,000 lb	Collapse Setting depth,[b] ft sf = 1⅛	Collapse Pressure, psi	Test Mille	Test At fiber stress equal to 80% of min yield strength	Yield[e] (min)	Plain-end yield strength,[a] (min), 1,000 lb
10¾	40.50	38.88	0.350	10.050	9.894	11.750	11.250	8	.....	J	5,560	450	.....	.....	3,080	1,730	2,100	2,900	3,130	629
	45.50	44.22	0.400	9.950	9.794	11.750	11.250	8	.....	J	5,690	518	.....	.....	4,090	2,300	2,500	3,300	3,580	715
	51.00	49.50	0.450	9.850	9.694	11.750	11.250	8	.....	J	5,740	585	.....	.....	5,100	2,870	2,800	3,700	4,030	801
	51.00	49.50	0.450	9.850	9.694	11.750	11.250	8	.....	N	6,670	680	.....	.....	6,670	3,750	5,400	5,400	5,860	1,165
	55.50	54.21	0.495	9.760	9.604	11.750	11.250	8	.....	N	6,760	750	.....	.....	7,860	4,420	5,900	5,900	6,450	1,276
	51.00	49.50	0.450	9.850	9.694	11.750	11.250	8	.....	P	8,730	890	.....	.....	6,670	3,750	7,400	7,400	8,060	1,602
	55.50	54.21	0.495	9.760	9.604	11.750	11.250	8	.....	P	8,840	981	.....	.....	8,960	5,040	8,100	8,100	8,860	1,754
	60.70	59.40	0.545	9.660	9.504	11.750	11.250	8	.....	P	8,900	1,081	.....	.....	12,070	6,790	8,900	8,900	9,760	1,922
	65.70	64.53	0.595	9.560	9.404	11.750	11.250	8	.....	P	8,980	1,180	.....	.....	15,180	8,540	9,700	9,700	10,660	2,088
	71.10a	70.12	0.650	9.450	9.294	11.750	11.250	8	.....	P	9,060	1,288	.....	.....	17,280	9,720	10,000	10,600	11,640	2,269
	76.00a	75.13	0.700	9.350	9.194	11.750	11.250	8	.....	P	9,110	1,385	.....	.....	19,180	10,790	10,000	11,500	12,540	2,431
	81.00a	80.10	0.750	9.250	9.094	11.750	11.250	8	.....	P	9,140	1,481	.....	.....	21,100	11,870	10,000	12,100	13,430	2,592
	65.70	64.53	0.595	9.560	9.404	11.750	11.250	8	.....	V	10,690	1,405	.....	.....	15,860	8,920	10,000	13,300	14,520	2,847
	71.10a	70.12	0.650	9.450	9.294	11.750	11.250	8	.....	V	10,790	1,534	.....	.....	20,910	11,760	10,000	14,500	15,870	3,094
	76.00a	75.13	0.700	9.350	9.194	11.750	11.250	8	.....	V	10,850	1,649	.....	.....	25,420	14,300	10,000	15,600	17,090	3,315
	81.00a	80.10	0.750	9.250	9.094	11.750	11.250	8	.....	V	10,850	1,763	.....	.....	27,960	15,730	10,000	16,700	18,310	3,534
11¾	38.00	36.69	0.300	11.150	10.994	12.750	.....	8	.....	F	2,920	222	.....	.....	1,100	620	750	1,000	1,120	
	42.00	40.60	0.333	11.084	10.928	12.750	.....	8	.....	H	4,000	336	.....	.....	1,670	940	1,400	1,800	1,980	
	47.00	45.56	0.375	11.000	10.844	12.750	.....	8	.....	J	5,390	507	.....	.....	2,900	1,630	2,100	2,800	3,070	737
	54.00	52.57	0.435	10.880	10.724	12.750	.....	8	.....	J	5,490	593	.....	.....	4,040	2,270	2,400	3,300	3,560	850
	60.00	58.81	0.489	10.772	10.616	12.750	.....	8	.....	J	5,570	668	.....	.....	5,050	2,840	2,700	3,700	4,010	952
	60.00	58.81	0.489	10.772	10.616	12.750	.....	8	.....	N	6,480	778	.....	.....	6,540	3,680	5,300	5,300	5,830	1,384

Size	Weight T&C	Plain-end wt	Wall thickness	ID	Drift	Coupling OD		No.	Grade									
13⅜	48.00	45.98	0.330	12.715	12.559	14.375		8	F	2,710	260		1,000	560	750	1,000	1,080	
	48.00	45.98	0.330	12.715	12.559	14.375		8	H	3,670	352		1,320	740	1,200	1,600	1,730	
	54.50	52.74	0.380	12.615	12.459	14.375		8	J	5,000	545		2,030	1,140	1,900	2,500	2,730	853
	61.00	59.45	0.430	12.515	12.359	14.375		8	J	5,020	613		2,970	1,670	2,100	2,800	3,090	962
	68.00	66.11	0.480	12.415	12.259	14.375		8	J	5,110	695		3,800	2,140	2,400	3,200	3,450	1,069
	72.00	70.60	0.514	12.347	12.191	14.375		8	N	6,030	868		5,120	2,880	4,900	4,900	5,380	1,661
	77.00[a]	75.34	0.550	12.275	12.119	14.375		8	N	6,040	930		6,310	3,550	5,300	5,300	5,760	1,773
	85.00[a]	82.90	0.608	12.159	12.003	14.375		8	N	6,050	1,029		7,680	4,320	5,800	5,800	6,360	1,951
16	55.00	52.36	0.312	15.376	15.188	17.000		9	F	2,350	258		520	290	600		850	
	65.00	62.58	0.375	15.250	15.062	17.000		9	H	3,250	423		1,140	640	1,100	1,500	1,640	
	75.00	72.72	0.438	15.124	14.938	17.000		9	J	4,410	662		1,800	1,010	1,800	2,400	2,630	1,178
	84.00	81.97	0.495	15.010	14.822	17.000		9	J	4,480	753		2,630	1,480	2,000	2,700	2,980	1,326
	109.00[a]	107.50	0.656	14.688	14.500	17.000		9	J	4,610	1,003		4,910	2,760	2,700	3,600	3,950	1,739
	118.00[a]	116.72	0.715	14.570	14.382	17.000		9	N	5,390	1,273		7,470	4,200	5,700	5,700	6,260	2,747
20	94.00	91.41	0.438	19.124	18.936	21.000		9	F	1,910	359		730	410	650		960	
	94.00	91.41	0.438	19.124	18.936	21.000		9	H	2,590	487		920	520	1,100	1,400	1,530	
	133.00[a]	131.33	0.635	18.730	18.542	21.000		9	J	3,560	948		2,840	1,600	2,100	2,800	3,050	2,125

The permissible variation in weight for any length of casing is 6½ per cent above and 3½ per cent below; but the carload weight shall not be more than 1¾ per cent under the calculated weight.

For coupling weights, see p. 2-15.

Wall-thickness tolerance; minus 12½ per cent.

Values for grade P are tentative API. Values for grade V are non-API and are furnished in range 3 lengths.

Furnished with threads and coupling unless otherwise ordered.

For tables of tensile requirements and range lengths, see p. 2-45.

The weight per foot of casing with threads and coupling is based on a length of 20 ft, including the coupling.

Field conditions vary so widely that definite safety factors for collapse or tension cannot be recommended.

All joints; 8 threads per inch; taper ¾ in./ft measured on the diameter; for illustration of joints and threading data see pp. 2-16 and 2-17.

[a] Sizes or values indicated are non-API.

[b] Since salt water is practically always encountered in drilling, the length of string is based upon 2 ft of water column to each pound of collapsing pressure. To obtain setting depths in collapse in fluids of other densities use chart on p. 2-47. Collapsing pressure in the fundamental units (psi) adjusted for axial tension stress can be found on pp. 2-40 to 2-44.

[c] High test pressures for casing furnished with special clearance couplings are approximately 85 per cent of the listed pressures.

[d] Tension strengths for casing furnished with special clearance couplings are approximately 90 per cent of the listed strengths.

[e] Based on 87½ per cent for internal pressure at minimum yield strength.

[f] 20 in. OD T & C casing is tested plain ends only.

PRODUCTION EQUIPMENT

API Plain-end Liner Casing (Tentative)

Size, OD, in.	Wt./ft, lb	Wall thickness, in.	ID, in.	Mill test pressure, psi, standard	alternative*
$3\frac{1}{2}$	9.91	0.289	2.922	3,000	7,300
4	11.34	0.286	3.428	3,000	6,300
$4\frac{1}{2}$	13.04	0.290	3.920	3,000	5,700
5	17.93	0.362	4.276	3,000	6,400
$5\frac{1}{2}$	19.81	0.361	4.778	3,000	5,800
$6\frac{5}{8}$	27.65	0.417	5.791	3,000	5,500

Furnished in J-55 grade steel and ranges 2 and 3.
Liners are to be manufactured and drifted to API Standard 5A Specification.
 * Alternative test pressures are applicable when so agreed upon between the purchaser and manufacturer.

Casing Ranges

	Range		
	1	2	3
Total range length (incl.)................	16–25	25–34	34 or more
Range length for 95% or more of carload:			
Permissible variation (max)...........	6	5	6
Min permissible length................	18	28	36
Jointers:* min length of shortest piece.....	5	5	5

 * Jointers are two lengths connected by coupling and may be shipped to a maximum of 5 per cent of the order.

Gross Lineal Footage from Net Footage—Multiplication Factor
API Seamless Casing
Short Coupling

Size, OD, in.	Wt./ft threads and coupling (nominal), lb	No. of threads per in.	Make-up loss per joint, in.	Multiplication factor*		
				Avg length of joint		
				20 ft	30 ft	40 ft
$4\frac{1}{2}$	9.50	8	2.000	1.0084	1.0056	1.0042
$4\frac{1}{2}$	Others	8	2.625	1.0111	1.0073	1.0055
5	11.50	8	2.500	1.0105	1.0070	1.0052
5	Others	8	2.750	1.0116	1.0077	1.0058
$5\frac{1}{2}$	13.00	8	2.625	1.0111	1.0073	1.0055
$5\frac{1}{2}$	Others	8	2.875	1.0121	1.0081	1.0060
$6\frac{5}{8}$	Others	8	3.125	1.0132	1.0088	1.0066
7	17.00	8	2.375	1.0100	1.0066	1.0050
7	Others	8	3.125	1.0132	1.0088	1.0066
$7\frac{5}{8}$	20.00	8	2.875	1.0121	1.0081	1.0060
$7\frac{5}{8}$	Others	8	3.250	1.0137	1.0091	1.0068
$8\frac{5}{8}$	24.00	8	3.000	1.0127	1.0084	1.0063
$8\frac{5}{8}$	Others	8	3.375	1.0143	1.0095	1.0071
$9\frac{5}{8}$	29.30	8	3.250	1.0137	1.0091	1.0068
$9\frac{5}{8}$	Others	8	3.275	1.0134	1.0095	1.0071
$10\frac{3}{4}$	32.75	8	2.750	1.0116	1.0077	1.0058
$10\frac{3}{4}$	Others	8	3.500	1.0148	1.0098	1.0073
$11\frac{3}{4}$	38.00	8	3.250	1.0137	1.0091	1.0068
$11\frac{3}{4}$	Others	8	3.500	1.1348	1.0098	1.0073
$13\frac{3}{8}$	All	8	3.500	1.0148	1.0098	1.0073
16	All	8	3.875	1.0164	1.0109	1.0081
20	94.00	8	3.875	1.0164	1.0109	1.0081

Long Coupling

4½	All	8	3.000	1.0127	1.0084	1.0063
5	All	8	3.375	1.0143	1.0095	1.0071
5½	All	8	3.500	1.0148	1.0098	1.0073
6⅝	All	8	3.875	1.0164	1.0109	1.0081
7	All	8	4.000	1.0169	1.0112	1.0084
7⅝	All	8	4.125	1.0175	1.0116	1.0087
8⅝	All	8	4.500	1.0191	1.0127	1.0095
9⅝	All	8	4.750	1.0202	1.0134	1.0100

* To obtain the gross or shipping length, multiply net length in feet by multiplication factor.

Coupling Weights
API Casing—Short and Long Coupling

Size, OD, in.	Coupling OD, in.	Short		Long	
		Length, in.	Wt., lb	Length, in.	Wt., lb
4½	5.000	6¼	8.05	7	9.07
5	5.563	6½	10.18	7¾	12.56
5½	6.050	6¾	11.44	8	14.03
6⅝	7.390	7¼	19.97	8¾	24.82
7	7.656	7¼	18.34	9	23.67
7⅝	8.500	7½	26.93	9¼	34.23
8⅝	9.625	7¾	35.58	10	47.48
9⅝	10.625	7¾	39.51	10½	55.77
10¾	11.750	8	45.53		
11¾	12.750	8	49.61		
13⅜	14.375	8	56.23		
16	17.000	9	78.98		
20	21.000	9	98.25		

Special Clearance—Short and Long Coupling

Size, OD, in.	Coupling OD, in.	Short		Long	
		Length, in.	Wt., lb	Length, in.	Wt., lb
4½	4.875	6¼	6.33	7	7.24
5	5.375	6½	7.32	7¾	9.12
5½	5.875	6¾	8.42	8	10.43
6⅝	7.000	7¼	11.06	8¾	14.04
7	7.375	7¼	11.67	9	15.36
7⅝	8.125	7½	16.70	9¼	21.58
8⅝	9.125	7¾	19.61	10	26.82
9⅝	10.125	7¾	21.84	10½	31.75
10¾	11.250	8	25.31		

Special clearance coupling OD values are non-API.

API Casing Joints (Short or Long Threads)
Section of Joints—Shown Handtight

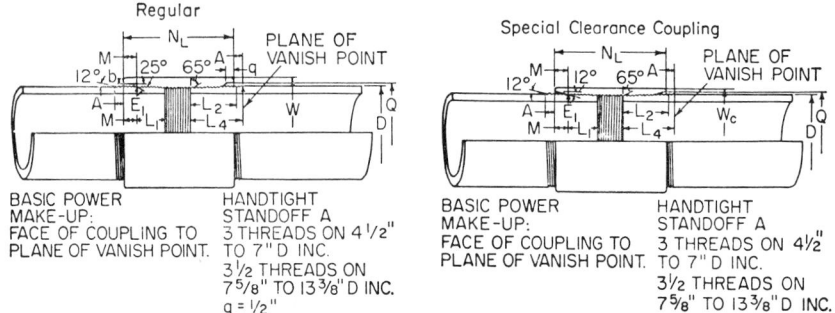

Regular

BASIC POWER MAKE-UP:
FACE OF COUPLING TO PLANE OF VANISH POINT.

HANDTIGHT STANDOFF A
3 THREADS ON 4 1/2" TO 7" D INC.
3 1/2 THREADS ON 7 5/8" TO 13 3/8" D INC.
q = 1/2"

Special Clearance Coupling

BASIC POWER MAKE-UP:
FACE OF COUPLING TO PLANE OF VANISH POINT.

HANDTIGHT STANDOFF A
3 THREADS ON 4 1/2" TO 7" D INC.
3 1/2 THREADS ON 7 5/8" TO 13 3/8" D INC.

Pipe-thread Dimensions

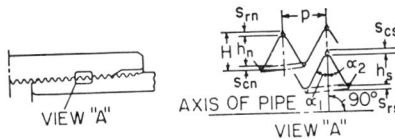

VIEW "A"

AXIS OF PIPE

VIEW "A"

API Standard Round Thread
(8 threads per inch)

Thread element	Inches
$p =$	0.1250
$H = 0.866p$	0.1082
$h_n = h_s = 0.626p = 0.007$	0.0712
$S_{rn} = S_{rs} = 0.120p + 0.002$	0.0170
$S_{cn} = S_{cs} = 0.120p + 0.005$	0.0200
$\alpha_1 - \alpha_2 = 30°.$	

Threading Data for API Casing—Short and Long Threads

Pipe size, OD, D, in.	Nom wt./ft threads and coupling, lb	Threads: Length, in., end of pipe to hand-tight plane L_1 Short	Length, in., end of pipe to hand-tight plane L_1 Long	Effective length, in. L_2 Short	Effective length, in. L_2 Long	Total length, in., end of pipe to vanish point L_4 Short	Total length, in., end of pipe to vanish point L_4 Long	Pitch diam at hand-tight plane E_1 Short or long	Coupling short or long: Recess diam, in. Q API*	Recess diam, in. Q Spec. clearance	Bearing face width, in., API b	Length, in., face of coupling to hand-tight plane, API or spec. clearance M
$4\frac{1}{2}$	9.50	0.921	.....	1.715	.....	2.000	.....	4.40337	$4\frac{19}{32}$	4.703	$\frac{5}{32}$	0.704
$4\frac{1}{2}$	All	1.546	1.921	2.340	2.175	2.625	3.000	4.40337	$4\frac{19}{32}$	4.703	$\frac{5}{32}$	0.704
5	11.50	1.421	.....	2.215	.....	2.500	.....	4.90337	$5\frac{3}{32}$	5.203	$\frac{3}{16}$	0.704
5	All	1.671	2.296	2.465	3.090	2.750	3.375	4.90337	$5\frac{3}{32}$	5.203	$\frac{3}{16}$	0.704
$5\frac{1}{2}$	13.00	1.546	.....	2.340	.....	2.625	.....	5.40337	$5\frac{19}{32}$	5.703	$\frac{1}{8}$	0.704
$5\frac{1}{2}$	All	1.796	2.421	2.590	3.215	2.875	3.500	5.40337	$5\frac{19}{32}$	5.703	$\frac{1}{8}$	0.704
$6\frac{5}{8}$	All	2.046	2.796	2.840	3.590	3.125	3.875	6.52837	$6\frac{23}{32}$	6.828	$\frac{1}{4}$	0.704
7	17.00	1.296	.....	2.090	.....	2.375	.....	6.90337	$7\frac{3}{32}$	7.203	$\frac{3}{16}$	0.704
7	All	2.046	2.921	2.840	3.715	3.125	4.000	6.90337	$7\frac{3}{32}$	7.203	$\frac{3}{16}$	0.704
$7\frac{5}{8}$	20.00	1.729	.....	2.590	.....	2.875	.....	7.52418	$7\frac{23}{32}$	7.826	$\frac{1}{4}$	0.709
$7\frac{5}{8}$	All	2.104	2.979	2.965	3.840	3.250	4.125	7.52418	$7\frac{23}{32}$	7.826	$\frac{1}{4}$	0.709
$8\frac{5}{8}$	24.00	1.854	.....	2.715	.....	3.000	.....	8.52418	$8\frac{23}{32}$	8.826	$\frac{9}{32}$	0.709
$8\frac{5}{8}$	All	2.229	3.354	3.090	4.215	3.375	4.500	8.52418	$8\frac{23}{32}$	8.826	$\frac{9}{32}$	0.709
$9\frac{5}{8}$	29.30	2.104	.....	2.965	.....	3.250	.....	9.52418	$9\frac{23}{32}$	9.826	$\frac{9}{32}$	0.709
$9\frac{5}{8}$	All	2.229	3.604	3.090	4.465	3.375	4.750	9.52418	$9\frac{23}{32}$	9.826	$\frac{9}{32}$	0.709
$10\frac{3}{4}$	32.75	1.604	.....	2.465	.....	2.750	.....	10.64918	$10\frac{27}{32}$	10.951	$\frac{9}{32}$	0.709
$10\frac{3}{4}$	All	2.354	.....	3.215	.....	3.500	.....	10.64918	$10\frac{27}{32}$	10.951	$\frac{9}{32}$	0.709
$11\frac{3}{4}$	38.00	2.104	.....	2.965	.....	3.250	.....	11.64918	$11\frac{27}{32}$	......	$\frac{9}{32}$	0.709
$11\frac{3}{4}$	All	2.354	.....	3.215	.....	3.500	.....	11.64918	$11\frac{27}{32}$	......	$\frac{9}{32}$	0.709
$13\frac{3}{8}$	All	2.354	.....	3.215	.....	3.500	.....	13.27418	$13\frac{15}{32}$	......	$\frac{5}{16}$	0.709
16	All	2.854	.....	3.715	.....	4.000	.....	15.89918	$16\frac{3}{32}$	......	$\frac{5}{16}$	0.709
20	94.00	2.854	.....	3.715	.....	4.000	.....	19.89918	$20\frac{3}{32}$	......	$\frac{5}{16}$	0.709

All joints; 8 threads per inch; taper $\frac{3}{4}$ in./ft measured on the diameter.
For thread dimensions see view p. 2–16.
For weights and dimensions see pp. 2–8 to 2–13.
* Depth of recess q is $\frac{1}{2}$ in. for all sizes.

CEMENT-LINED CASING

Cement-lined casing was developed to meet the needs of the oil- and gas-producing industry requiring protection of the inside surface of steel pipe against unusual corrosive conditions.

Cement-lined Casing
Weights, Dimensions, and Tension Properties

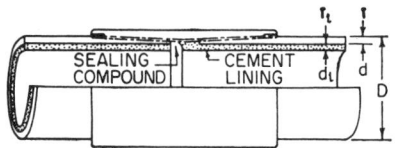

Size, OD D, in.	Unlined				Cement-lined				Grade	Short couplings		Long couplings	
	Nom. wt./ft, lb	P.E. wt./ft, lb	Wall thickness t, in.	ID d, in.	Nom. wt./ft, lb	P.E. wt./ft, lb	Wall thickness t_i, in.	ID d_i, in.		Joint strength min, 1,000 lb	Equiv. length, ft sf = 2	Joint strength min, 1,000 lb	Equiv. length, ft sf = 2
4½	9.50	9.40	0.205	4.090	12.01	11.91	0.2030	3.684	H	96	4,000		
									J	128	5,330		
	11.60	11.35	0.250	4.000	14.05	13.80	0.2030	3.594	J	159	5,660	189	6,730
									N	185	6,580	220	7,830
5	11.50	11.23	0.220	4.560	14.72	14.45	0.2340	4.092	J	152	5,160		
	13.00	12.83	0.253	4.494	16.17	16.00	0.2340	4.026	J	178	5,500	210	6,490
	15.00	14.87	0.296	4.408	18.11	17.98	0.2340	3.940	J	210	5,800	247	6,820
									N	244	6,740	288	7,950
5½	14.00	13.70	0.244	5.012	17.79	17.49	0.2500	4.512	H	139	3,910		
									J	186	5,230		
	15.50	15.35	0.275	4.950	19.24	19.09	0.2500	4.450	J	211	5,480	247	6,420
	17.00	16.87	0.304	4.892	20.70	20.57	0.2500	4.392	J	234	5,650	275	6,640
									N	273	6,590	320	7,730
6⅝	20.00	19.49	0.288	6.049	25.72	25.21	0.3125	5.424	H	195	3,790		
									J	259	5,030	299	5,810
	24.00	23.58	0.352	5.921	29.58	29.16	0.3125	5.296	J	320	5,410	370	6,250
									N	373	6,300	430	7,270
7	17.00	16.70	0.231	6.538	23.20	22.90	0.3125	5.913	H	160	3,450		
	20.00	19.54	0.272	6.456	26.13	25.67	0.3125	5.831	H	191	3,650		
									J	254	4,860		
	23.00	22.63	0.317	6.366	29.03	28.66	0.3125	5.741	J	300	5,170	344	5,920
									N	350	6,030	400	6,890

Cement-lined casing is supplied only in range 1 lengths.
Unlined casing joints conform in all details to API casing; see pp. 2-16 and 2-17.
Cement-lined casing is lined integrally with coupling made up power-tight on mill end.
An adequate supply of sealing compound is supplied with each shipment to provide for making up field end.
For mill test pressures, collapsing pressures, and minimum internal yield pressures see API casing tables, pp. 2-8 to 2-13.
For method of calculating strengths and pressures see performance section, p. 2-36.
The gross or shipping-length determination is identical with API casing of the same size and weight; see p. 2-14.

SPECIAL CASING JOINTS

Extreme conditions at times arise in the production of oil and gas wells which result in the need for casing joints with greater clearance, strength, or leak resistance than provided with standard API casing joints. The following tables give dimensional and strength data on the special casing joints designed to provide for these special conditions.

Buttress-thread Casing
Weights, Dimensions, and Tension Properties

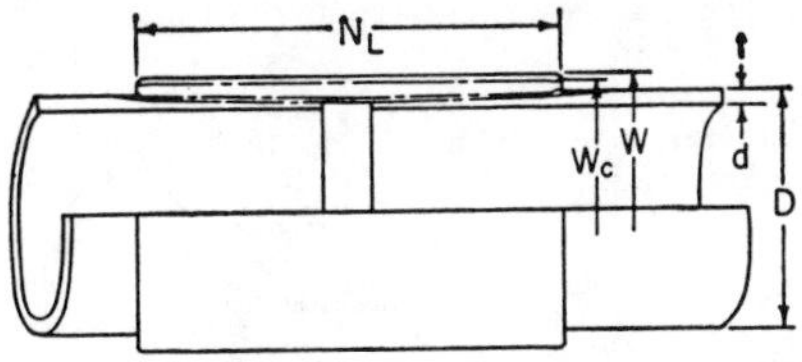

Size, OD D, in.	Nom. wt./ft, in.	Wall thickness t, in.	ID d, in.	Drift diam, in.	Coupling OD, in. Regular W	Coupling OD, in. Spec. clearance W_c	Coupling Length, in., regular or spec. clearance N_L	Steel grade	Regular coupling Joint strength min, 1,000 lb	Regular coupling Equiv. length, ft sf = 2	Spec. clearance coupling Joint strength min, 1,000 lb	Spec. clearance coupling Equiv. length, ft sf = 2
4½	9.50	0.205	4.090	3.965	5.000	4.875	8⅞	J	274	14,420	247	13,000
	10.50	0.224	4.052	3.927	5.000	4.875	8⅞	J	298	14,190	268	12,760
	11.60	0.250	4.000	3.875	5.000	4.875	8⅞	J	331	14,270	298	12,840
	11.60	0.250	4.000	3.875	5.000	4.875	8⅞	N	355	15,300	320	19,790
	13.50	0.290	3.920	3.795	5.000	4.875	8⅞	N	408	15,110	367	13,590
	11.60	0.250	4.000	3.875	5.000	4.875	8⅞	P	430	18,530	387	16,680
	13.50	0.290	3.920	3.795	5.000	4.875	8⅞	P	494	18,300	445	16,480
	15.10	0.337	3.826	3.701	5.000	4.875	8⅞	P	567	18,770	472	15,630
5	11.50	0.220	4.560	4.435	5.563	5.375	9⅛	J	326	14,170	293	12,740
	13.00	0.253	4.494	4.369	5.563	5.375	9⅛	J	372	14,310	335	12,880
	15.00	0.296	4.408	4.283	5.563	5.375	9⅛	J	431	14,370	356	11,870
	15.00	0.296	4.408	4.283	5.563	5.375	9⅛	N	463	15,430	417	13,900
	18.00	0.362	4.276	4.151	5.563	5.375	9⅛	N	559	15,530	429	11,920
	15.00	0.296	4.408	4.283	5.563	5.375	9⅛	P	560	18,670	504	16,800
	18.00	0.362	4.276	4.151	5.563	5.375	9⅛	P	675	18,750	528	14,670
	15.00	0.296	4.408	4.283	5.563	5.375	9⅛	V	689	22,970	528	17,600
	18.00	0.362	4.276	4.151	5.563	5.375	9⅛	V	831	23,080	528	14,670
5½	14.00	0.244	5.012	4.887	6.050	5.875	9¼	J	395	14,110	356	12,710
	15.50	0.275	4.950	4.825	6.050	5.875	9¼	J	443	14,290	392	12,650
	17.00	0.304	4.892	4.767	6.050	5.875	9¼	J	487	14,320	392	11,530
	17.00	0.304	4.892	4.767	6.050	5.875	9¼	N	523	15,380	471	13,850
	20.00	0.361	4.778	4.653	6.050	5.875	9¼	N	614	15,350	472	11,800
	23.00	0.415	4.670	4.545	6.050	5.875	9¼	N	699	15,200	472	10,260
	17.00	0.304	4.892	4.767	6.050	5.875	9¼	P	632	18,590	569	16,740
	20.00	0.361	4.778	4.653	6.050	5.875	9¼	P	742	18,550	581	14,520
	23.00	0.415	4.670	4.545	6.050	5.875	9¼	P	845	18,370	581	12,630
	20.00	0.361	4.778	4.653	6.050	5.875	9¼	V	903	22,580	581	14,520
	23.00	0.415	4.670	4.545	6.050	5.875	9¼	V	903	19,630	581	12,630
6⅝	20.00	0.288	6.049	5.924	7.390	7.000	9⅝	J	556	13,900	475	11,880
	24.00	0.352	5.921	5.796	7.390	7.000	9⅝	J	672	14,000	475	9,900
	24.00	0.352	5.921	5.796	7.390	7.000	9⅝	N	723	15,060	574	11,960
	28.00	0.417	5.791	5.666	7.390	7.000	9⅝	N	847	15,120	574	10,250
	32.00	0.475	5.675	5.550	7.390	7.000	9⅝	N	956	14,940	574	8,970
	24.00	0.352	5.921	5.796	7.390	7.000	9⅝	P	874	18,210	706	14,710
	28.00	0.417	5.791	5.666	7.390	7.000	9⅝	P	1,024	18,290	706	12,610
	32.00	0.475	5.675	5.550	7.390	7.000	9⅝	P	1,156	18,060	706	11,030

Buttress-thread Casing *(Continued)*

Size, OD *D*, in.	Nom. wt./ft, in.	Wall thick-ness *t*, in.	ID *d*, in.	Drift diam, in.	Coupling OD, in. Regular *W*	Coupling OD, in. Spec. clearance W_c	Coupling Length, in., regular or spec. clearance N_L	Steel grade	Regular coupling Joint strength min, 1,000 lb	Regular coupling Equiv. length, ft sf = 2	Spec. clearance coupling Joint strength min, 1,000 lb	Spec. clearance coupling Equiv. length, ft sf = 2
7	20.00	0.272	6.456	6.331	7.656	7.375	10	J	555	13,880	500	12,500
	23.00	0.317	6.366	6.241	7.656	7.375	10	J	643	13,980	511	11,110
	26.00	0.362	6.276	6.151	7.656	7.375	10	J	729	14,020	511	9,830
	23.00	0.317	6.366	6.241	7.656	7.375	10	N	691	15,020	618	13,430
	26.00	0.362	6.276	6.151	7.656	7.375	10	N	783	15,060	618	11,880
	29.00	0.408	6.184	6.059	7.656	7.375	10	N	877	15,120	618	10,660
	32.00	0.453	6.094	5.969	7.655	7.375	10	N	967	15,110	618	9,660
	35.00	0.498	6.004	5.879	7.656	7.375	10	N	1,056	15,090	618	8,830
	38.00	0.540	5.920	5.795	7.656	7.375	10	N	1,103	14,510	618	8,130
	26.00	0.362	6.276	6.151	7.656	7.375	10	P	947	18,210	760	14,620
	29.00	0.408	6.184	6.059	7.656	7.375	10	P	1,060	18,280	760	13,100
	32.00	0.453	6.094	5.969	7.656	7.375	10	P	1,169	18,270	760	11,880
	35.00	0.498	6.004	5.879	7.656	7.375	10	P	1,276	18,230	760	10,860
	38.00	0.540	5.920	5.795	7.656	7.375	10	P	1,357	17,860	760	10,000
	29.00	0.408	6.184	6.059	7.656	7.375	10	V	1,304	22,480	760	13,100
	32.00	0.453	6.094	5.969	7.656	7.375	10	V	1,357	21,200	760	11,880
	35.00	0.498	6.004	5.879	7.656	7.375	10	V	1,357	19,390	760	10,860
	38.00	0.540	5.920	5.795	7.656	7.375	10	V	1,357	17,860	760	10,000
7⅝	26.40	0.328	6.969	6.844	8.500	8.125	10⅜	J	721	13,660	649	12,290
	26.40	0.328	6.969	6.844	8.500	8.125	10⅜	N	775	14,680	698	13,220
	29.70	0.375	6.875	6.750	8.500	8.125	10⅜	N	881	14,830	793	13,350
	33.70	0.430	6.765	6.640	8.500	8.125	10⅜	N	1,002	14,870	860	12,760
	39.00	0.500	6.625	6.500	8.500	8.125	10⅜	N	1,154	14,790	860	10,030
	29.70	0.375	6.875	6.750	8.500	8.125	10⅜	P	1,064	17,910	958	16,130
	33.70	0.430	6.765	6.640	8.500	8.125	10⅜	P	1,211	17,970	1,059	15,710
	39.00	0.500	6.625	6.500	8.500	8.125	10⅜	P	1,395	17,880	1,059	13,580
	33.70	0.430	6.765	6.640	8.500	8.125	10⅜	V	1,490	22,110	1,059	15,710
	39.00	0.500	6.625	6.500	8.500	8.125	10⅜	V	1,716	22,000	1,059	13,580
	45.30	0.595	6.435	6.310	8.500	8.125	10⅜	V	1,927	21,270	1,059	11,690
8⅝	24.00	0.264	8.097	7.972	9.625	9.125	10⅝	J	658	13,710	593	12,350
	32.00	0.352	7.921	7.796	9.625	9.125	10⅝	J	869	13,580	782	12,220
	36.00	0.400	7.825	8.700	9.625	9.125	10⅝	J	981	13,620	805	11,180
	36.00	0.400	7.825	7.700	9.625	9.125	10⅝	N	1,055	14,650	950	13,190
	40.00	0.450	7.725	7.600	9.625	9.125	10⅝	N	1,179	14,740	972	12,150
	44.00	0.500	7.625	7.500	9.625	9.125	10⅝	N	1,302	14,800	972	11,050
	49.00	0.557	7.511	7.386	9.625	9.125	10⅝	N	1,441	14,700	972	9,920
	40.00	0.450	7.725	7.600	9.625	9.125	10⅝	P	1,425	17,810	1,196	14,950
	44.00	0.500	7.625	7.500	9.625	9.125	10⅝	P	1,574	17,890	1,196	13,590
	49.00	0.557	7.511	7.386	9.625	9.125	10⅝	P	1,741	17,700	1,196	12,200
	44.00	0.500	7.625	7.500	9.625	9.125	10⅝	V	1,937	22,010	1,196	13,590
	49.00	0.557	7.511	7.386	9.525	9.125	10⅝	V	2,142	21,860	1,196	12,200
9⅝	36.00	0.352	8.921	8.765	10.625	10.125	10⅝	J	963	13,380	867	12,040
	40.00	0.395	8.835	8.679	10.625	10.125	10⅝	J	1,076	13,450	886	11,080
	40.00	0.395	8.835	8.679	10.625	10.125	10⅝	N	1,157	14,460	1,041	13,010
	43.50	0.435	8.755	8.599	10.625	10.125	10⅝	N	1,268	14,570	1,071	12,310
	47.00	0.472	8.681	8.525	10.625	10.125	10⅝	N	1,370	14,570	1,071	11.390
	53.50	0.545	8.535	8.379	10.625	10.125	10⅝	N	1,570	14,670	1,071	10,010

Buttress-thread Casing (*Continued*)

Size, OD D, in.	Nom. wt./ft, in.	Wall thickness t, in.	ID d, in.	Drift diam, in.	Coupling OD, in. Regular W	Coupling OD, in. Spec. clearance W_c	Coupling Length, in., regular or spec. clearance N_L	Steel grade	Regular coupling Joint strength min, 1,000 lb	Regular coupling Equiv. length, ft sf = 2	Spec. clearance coupling Joint strength min, 1,000 lb	Spec. clearance coupling Equiv. length, ft sf = 2
	43.50	0.435	8.755	8.599	10.625	10.125	10⅝	P	1,533	17,620	1,318	15,150
	47.00	0.472	8.681	8.525	10.625	10.125	10⅝	P	1,656	17,620	1,318	14,020
9⅝	53.50	0.545	8.535	8.379	10.625	10.125	10⅝	P	1,897	17,730	1,318	12,320
	53.50	0.545	8.535	8.379	10.625	10.125	10⅝	V	2,334	21,810	1,318	12,320
	58.40	0.595	8.435	8.279	10.625	10.125	10⅝	V	2,534	21,700	1,318	11,280
	61.10	0.625	8.375	8.219	10.625	10.125	10⅝	V	2,653	21,710	1,318	10,790
	40.50	0.350	10.050	9.894	11.750	11.250	10⅝	J	1,061	13,100	955	11,790
	45.50	0.400	9.950	9.794	11.750	11.250	10⅝	J	1,207	13,260	976	10,730
	51.00	0.450	9.850	9.694	11.750	11.250	10⅝	J	1,352	13,250	976	9,570
	51.00	0.450	9.850	9.694	11.750	11.250	10⅝	N	1,453	14,250	1,180	11,570
	55.50	0.495	9.760	9.604	11.750	11.250	10⅝	N	1,591	14,330	1,180	10,630
	51.00	0.450	9.850	9.694	11.750	11.250	10⅝	P	1,756	17,220	1,452	14,240
	55.50	0.495	9.760	9.604	11.750	11.250	10⅝	P	1,923	17,320	1,452	13,080
10¾	60.70	0.545	9.660	9.504	11.750	11.250	10⅝	P	2,107	17,360	1,452	11,960
	65.70	0.595	9.560	9.404	11.750	11.250	10⅝	P	2,289	17,420	1,452	11,050
	71.10	0.650	9.450	9.294	11.750	11.250	10⅝	P	2,487	17,490	1,452	10,210
	76.00	0.700	9.350	9.194	11.750	11.250	10⅝	P	2,665	17,530	1,452	9,550
	65.70	0.595	9.560	9.404	11.750	11.250	10⅝	V	2,816	21,430	1,452	11,050
	71.10	0.650	9.450	9.294	11.750	11.250	10⅝	V	2,953	20,770	1,452	10,210
	76.00	0.700	9.350	9.194	11.750	11.250	10⅝	V	2,953	19,430	1,452	9,550
	81.00	0.750	9.250	9.094	11.750	11.250	10⅝	P	2,841	17,540	1,452	8,960
	81.00	0.750	9.250	9.094	11.750	11.250	10⅝	V	2,953	18,230	1,452	8,960
	47.00	0.375	11.000	10.844	12.750	......	10⅝	J	1,230	13,090	......	......
	54.00	0.435	10.880	10.724	12.750	......	10⅝	J	1,420	13,150	......	......
11¾	60.00	0.489	10.772	10.616	12.750	......	10⅝	J	1,588	13,230	......	......
	60.00	0.489	10.772	10.616	12.750	......	10⅝	N	1,707	14,220	......	......
	54.50	0.380	12.615	12.459	14.375	......	10⅝	J	1,399	12,830	......	......
	61.00	0.430	12.515	12.359	14.375	......	10⅝	J	1,577	12,930	......	......
	68.00	0.480	12.415	12.259	14.375	......	10⅝	J	1,754	12,900	......	......
13⅜	72.00	0.514	12.347	12.191	14.375	......	10⅝	N	2,013	13,980	......	......
	77.00	0.550	12.275	12.119	14.375	......	10⅝	N	2,148	13,950	......	......
	85.00	0.608	12.159	12.003	14.357	......	10⅝	N	2,364	13,910	......	......

5 buttress threads per inch: taper ¾ in./ft on the diameter. For mill test pressures, collapsing pressures, and minimum internal yield pressures, see API casing tables, pp. 2-8 to 2-13.

For method of calculating strengths and pressures see performance section, p. 2-36.

Gross Lineal Footage from Net Footage—Multiplication Factors
Buttress-thread Casing

Size, OD, in.	Wt./ft threads and coupling (nom.), lb	Make-up loss per joint, in.	Multiplication factor* Avg length of joint		
			20 ft	30 ft	40 ft
4½	All	3.9375	1.0167	1.0111	1.0083
5	All	4.0625	1.0172	1.0114	1.0085
5½	All	4.1250	1.0175	1.0116	1.0087
6⅝	All	4.3125	1.0183	1.0121	1.0091
7	All	4.5000	1.0191	1.0127	1.0095
7⅝	All	4.6875	1.0199	1.0132	1.0099
8⅝	All	4.8125	1.0205	1.0135	1.0101
9⅝	All	4.8125	1.0205	1.0135	1.0101
10¾	All	4.8125	1.0205	1.0135	1.0101
11¾	All	4.8125	1.0205	1.0135	1.0101
13⅜	All	4.8125	1.0205	1.0135	1.0101

* To obtain the gross or shipping length, multiply the net length in feet by the multiplication factor.

Extreme Line Casing
Weights, Dimensions, and Tension Properties

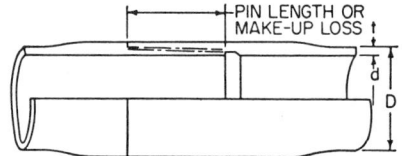

Size, OD D, in.	Nom. wt./ft, lb	Wall thickness t, in.	ID d, in.	Casing drift diam, in.	Made-up joint					Grade	Std. joint		Opt. joint	
					ID bored, in.	Drift, in.	OD machined, in.				Joint strength min, 1,000 lb	Equiv. length, ft sf = 2	Joint strength min, 1,000 lb	Equiv. length, ft sf = 2
							Std.	Opt.						
5	15.00	0.296	4.408	4.151	4.198*	4.183	5.360	......	J	374	12,470			
									N	402	13,400			
									P	503	16,770			
	18.00	0.362	4.276	4.151	4.198	4.183	5.360	......	N	432	12,000			
									P	540	15,000			
5½	15.50	0.275	4.950	4.653	4.736*	4.721	5.860	5.780	J	386	12,450	386	12,450
									J	425	12,500	425	12,500
	17.00	0.304	4.892	4.653	4.701*	4.686	5.860	5.780	N	457	13,440	457	13,440
									P	571	16,790	571	16,790
	20.00	0.361	4.778	4.653	4.701	4.686	5.860	5.780	N	480	12,000	465	11,620
									P	600	15,000	582	14,550
	23.00	0.415	4.670	4.545	4.610	4.595	5.860	5.780	N	533	11,590	465	10,110
									P	666	14,480	582	12,650
	26.00	0.476	4.548	4.423	4.378	4.363	6.045	......	N	691	13,290		
									P	864	16,620		

Extreme Line Casing (*Continued*)

Size, OD D, in.	Nom. wt./ft, lb	Wall thickness t, in.	ID d, in.	Casing drift diam, in.	Made-up joint ID bored, in.	Drift, in.	OD machined, in. Std	OD machined, in. Opt	Grade	Std. joint Joint strength min, 1,000 lb	Std. joint Equiv. length, ft sf = 2	Opt. joint Joint strength min, 1,000 lb	Opt. joint Equiv. length, ft sf = 2
6⅝	24.00	0.352	5.921	5.730	5.781*	5.766	7.000	6.930	J	541	11,270	541	11,270
									N	582	12,120	582	12,120
									P	727	15,150	727	15,150
	28.00	0.417	5.791	5.666	5.731	5.716	7.000	6.930	N	623	11,120	623	11,120
									P	779	13,910	779	13,910
	32.00	0.475	5.675	5.550	5.615	5.600	7.000	6.930	N	698	10,910	628	9,810
									P	873	13,640	785	12,270
7	23.00	0.317	6.366	6.151	6.171*	6.156	7.390	7.310	J	570	12,390	570	12,390
									N	612	13,300	612	13,300
	26.00	0.362	6.276	6.151	6.171	6.156	7.390	7.310	J	576	11,080	576	11,080
									N	619	11,900	619	11,900
									P	774	14,800	774	14,880
	29.00	0.408	6.184	6.059	6.123	6.108	7.390	7.310	N	662	11,410	654	11,280
									P	827	14,260	818	14,100
	32.00	0.453	6.094	5.969	6.032	6.017	7.390	7.310	N	739	11,550	654	10,220
									P	924	14,470	818	12,780
	35.00	0.498	6.004	5.879	5.940	5.925	7.530	7.390	N	821	11,730	739	10,560
									P	1,026	14,660	924	13,200
	38.00	0.540	5.920	5.795	5.860	5.845	7.530	7.390	N	889	11,700	739	9,720
									P	1,112	14,630	924	12,160
7⅝	26.40	0.328	6.969	6.750	6.770*	6.775	8.101	7.920	J	631	11,950	631	11,950
									N	678	12,840	678	12,840
	29.70	0.375	6.875	6.750	6.770	6.755	8.010	7.920	N	678	11,410	678	11,410
									P	848	14,280	848	14,280
	33.70	0.430	6.765	6.640	6.705	6.690	8.010	7.920	N	742	11,010	721	10,700
									P	927	13,750	901	13,370
	39.00	0.500	6.625	6.500	6.565	6.550	8.010	7.920	N	824	10,560	721	9,240
									P	1,031	13,220	901	11,550
8⅝	32.00	0.352	7.921	7.700	7.725*	7.710	9.120	9.030	J	783	12,230	783	12,230
									J	784	10,890	784	10,890
	36.00	0.400	7.825	7.770	7.725	7.710	9.120	9.030	N	842	11,690	842	11,690
									P	1,053	14,620	1,053	14,620
	40.00	0.450	7.725	7.600	7.663	7.648	9.120	9.030	N	911	11,390	859	10,740
									P	1,139	14,240	1,074	13,420
	44.00	0.500	7.625	7.500	7.565	7.550	9.120	9.030	N	977	11,100	859	9,760
									P	1,221	13,870	1,074	12,200
	49.00	0.557	7.511	7.386	7.451	7.436	9.120	9.030	N	977	9,970	859	8,770
									P	1,221	12,460	1,074	10,960
9⅝	40.00	0.395	8.835	8.599	8.665*	8.650	10.100	10.020	J	875	10,940	875	10,940
									N	940	11,750	940	11,750
	43.50	0.435	8.755	8.599	8.665	8.650	10.100	10.020	N	940	10,800	940	10,800
									P	1,176	13,520	1,176	13,520
	47.00	0.472	8.681	8.525	8.621	8.606	10.100	10.020	N	995	10,590	995	10,590
									P	1,244	13,230	1,244	13,230
	53.50	0.545	8.535	8.379	8.475	8.460	10.100	10.020	N	1,140	10,650	1,024	9,570
									P	1,425	13,320	1,180	11,030
10¾	45.50	0.400	9.950	9.794	9.819	9.804	11.460	......	J	1,113	12,230		
									J	1,246	12,220		
	51.00	0.450	9.850	9.694	9.719	9.704	11.460	......	N	1,340	13,140		
									P	1,602	15,710		
	55.50	0.495	9.760	9.604	9.629	9.614	11.460	......	N	1,467	13,220		
									P	1,754	15,800		
	60.70	0.545	9.660	9.504	9.529	9.514	11.460	......	P	1,760	14,500		

Joint strengths for the 10¾-in. size P grades are based on 105,000 psi minimum yield strength.
Sizes 5 through 7⅝-in. have 6 threads per inch and 1½-in. taper per foot on diameter.
Sizes 8⅝ through 10¾-in. have 5 threads per inch and 1¼-in. taper per foot on diameter.
For mill test pressures, collapsing pressures, and minimum internal yield pressures see API casing tables, pp. 2–8 to 2–13.
For method of calculating strengths and pressures see performance section, p. 2–36.
* Joint will not pass API casing drift for this weight.

Gross Lineal Footage from Net Footage—Multiplication Factors
Extreme Line Casing

Size, OD, in.	Nom. wt./ft, lb	Pin length or make-up loss per joint, in.	Multiplication factors*		
			Avg length of joint		
			23 ft	30 ft	40 ft
5	All	4.590	1.0169	1.0129	1.0097
5½	All	4.590	1.0169	1.0129	1.0097
6⅝	All	4.590	1.0169	1.0129	1.0097
7	All	4.590	1.0169	1.0129	1.0097
7⅝	All	4.590	1.0169	1.0129	1.0097
8⅝	All	6.0625	1.0225	1.0171	1.0128
9⅝	All	6.0625	1.0225	1.0171	1.0128
10¾	All	6.0625	1.0225	1.0171	1.0128

* To obtain the gross or shipping length, multiply net length in feet by the multiplication factor.

Hydril FJ Joint for Flush-joint Casing
Weights, Dimensions, and Tension Properties

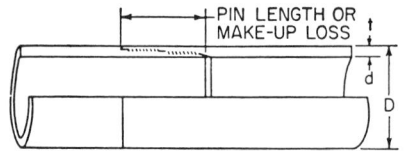

Size, OD D, in.	Nom. wt./ft, lb	Wall thickness t, in.	ID d, in.	Drift diam, in.	Grade	Joint strength min ultimate, 1,000 lb	Equiv. length, ft sf = 2
4½	12.60	0.271	3.958	3.833	J	176	7,190
					N	201	8,210
	13.50	0.290	3.920	3.795	J	176	6,740
					N	201	7,690
					P	239	9,150
	15.10	0.337	3.826	3.701	J	215	7,180
					N	245	8,190
					P	292	9,760
	18.10	0.373	3.754	3.629	J	215	6,840
					N	245	7,460
5	15.00	0.296	4.408	4.283	J	206	6,910
					N	235	7,890
					P	279	9,390
	18.00	0.362	4.276	4.151	J	261	7,270
					N	298	8,300
					P	354	9,880
5½	17.00	0.304	4.892	4.767	J	235	6,960
					N	268	7,950
					P	319	9,460
	20.00	0.361	4.778	4.653	J	289	7,310
					N	330	8,330
					P	393	9,920
	23.00	0.415	4.670	4.545	N	330	7,320
					P	393	8,720
6⅝	24.00	0.352	5.921	5.796	J	314	6,650
					N	358	7,590
					P	426	9,040
	28.00	0.417	5.791	5.666	J	400	7,240
					N	457	8,260
					P	544	9,830
	32.00	0.475	5.675	5.550	N	488	7,820
					P	581	9,310

Hydril FJ Joint for Flush-joint Casing (*Continued*)

Size, OD D, in.	Nom. wt./ft, lb	Wall thickness t, in.	ID d, in.	Drift diam, in.	Grade	Joint strength min ultimate, 1,000 lb	Equiv. length, ft sf = 2
7	23.00	0.317	6.366	6.241	J	319	7,050
					N	364	8,050
	26.00	0.362	6.276	6.151	J	372	7,250
					N	425	8,290
					P	506	9,850
	29.00	0.408	6.184	6.059	N	467	8,130
					P	556	9,680
	32.00	0.453	6.094	5.969	N	509	8,040
					P	606	9,570
	35.00	0.498	6.004	5.879	N	565	8,170
					P	673	9,730
	38.00	0.540	5.920	5.795	N	615	8,260
					P	733	9,830
7⅝	26.40	0.328	6.969	6.844	J	345	6,750
					N	394	7,710
	29.70	0.375	6.875	6.750	N	484	8,330
					P	576	9,920
	33.70	0.430	6.765	6.640	N	563	8,530
					P	671	10,150
	39.00	0.500	6.625	6.500	N	627	8,240
					P	746	9,810
8⅝	32.00	0.352	7.921	7.796	J	429	6,890
	36.00	0.400	7.825	7.700	J	505	7,180
					N	576	8,200
	40.00	0.450	7.725	7.600	N	614	7,810
					P	731	9,300
	44.00	0.500	7.625	7.500	N	717	8,270
					P	854	9,840
	49.00	0.557	7.511	7.386	N	821	8,550
					P	976	10,170
9⅝	36.00	0.352	8.921	8.765	J	479	6,870
	40.00	0.395	8.835	8.679	J	551	7,080
					N	629	8,080
	43.50	0.435	8.755	8.599	N	707	8,280
	47.00	0.472	8.681	8.525	N	776	8,410
					P	924	10,020
	53.50	0.545	8.535	8.379	N	918	8,690
					P	1,093	10,340
10¾	45.50	0.400	9.950	9.794	J	628	7,100
	51.00	0.450	9.850	9.694	J	722	7,290
					N	824	8,320
	55.50	0.495	9.760	9.604	N	918	8,470
11¾	47.00	0.375	11.000	10.844	J	610	6,690
	54.00 ⎫	0.435	10.880	10.724	J	761	7,240
	60.00 ⎭	0.489	10.772	10.616	J	872	7,410
					N	995	8,460
13⅜	54.50	0.380	12.615	12.459	J	711	6,740
	61.00	0.430	12.515	12.359	J	874	7,350
	68.00 ⎫	0.480	12.415	12.259	J	976	7,380
	72.00 ⎭	0.514	12.347	12.191	N	1,114	7,890

Hydril FJ threads are not interchangeable between different weights except where weights are shown bracketed together.

For mill test pressures, collapsing pressures, and minimum internal yield pressures see API casing tables, pp. 2–8 to 2–13.

For method of calculating strengths and pressures see performance section, p. 2–36.

Gross Lineal Footage from Net Footage—Multiplication Factors Hydril FJ Joint for Flush-joint Casing

Size, OD, in.	Nom. wt./ft, lb	Pin length or make-up loss per joint, in.	Multiplication factors* Avg length of joint 20 ft	30 ft	40 ft
4½	12.6	2⅝	1.0111	1.0073	1.0055
	13.5	2 11/16	1.0113	1.0075	1.0056
	15.1, 18.1	2¾	1.0116	1.0077	1.0058
5	15.0	2 15/16	1.0124	1.0082	1.0062
	18.0	3	1.0127	1.0084	1.0063
5½	17.0	3 5/16	1.0140	1.0093	1.0069
	20.0	3⅜	1.0143	1.0095	1.0071
	23.0	3 7/16	1.0145	1.0096	1.0072
6⅝	24.0	3⅝	1.0153	1.0102	1.0076
	28.0	3 11/16	1.0156	1.0103	1.0077
	32.0	3¾	1.0159	1.0105	1.0079
7	23.0	3 1/32	1.0128	1.0085	1.0064
	26.0	3⅝	1.0153	1.0102	1.0076
	29.0, 32.0	3 11/16	1.0156	1.0103	1.0077
	35.0, 38.0	3¾	1.0159	1.0105	1.0079
7⅝	26.4, 29.7	3⅝	1.0153	1.0102	1.0076
	33.7	3 11/16	1.0156	1.0103	1.0077
	39.0	3¾	1.0159	1.0105	1.0079
8⅝	32.0, 36.0	3⅝	1.0153	1.0102	1.0076
	40.0, 44.0	3¾	1.0159	1.0105	1.0079
	49.0	4⅛	1.0175	1.0116	1.0087
9⅝	36.0	3⅝	1.0153	1.0102	1.0076
	40.0, 43.5, 47.0	3 11/16	1.0156	1.0103	1.0077
	53.5	4⅛	1.0175	1.0116	1.0087
10¾	45.5, 51.0	3 11/16	1.0156	1.0103	1.0077
	55.5	3¾	1.0159	1.0105	1.0079
11¾	47.0	4 5/32	1.0176	1.0117	1.0087
	54.0	4 3/16	1.0178	1.0118	1.0088
	60.0	4¼	1.0180	1.0119	1.0089
13⅜	54.5	4 5/32	1.0176	1.0117	1.0087
	61.0	4 3/16	1.0178	1.0118	1.0088
	68.0, 72.0	4¼	1.0180	1.0119	1.0089

* To obtain the gross or shipping length, multiply net length in feet by the multiplication factor.

Hydril FJ-40 Joint for Flush-joint Casing or Liners
Weights, Dimensions, and Tension Properties

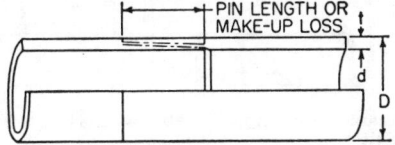

PIN LENGTH OR
MAKE-UP LOSS

d

D

Size, OD D, in.	Nom. wt./ft, lb	Wall thickness t, in.	Inside diam d, in.	Drift diam, in.	Grade	Joint strength min ultimate, 1,000 lb	Equiv. length, ft sf = 2
3½	7.70	0.216	3.068	2.943	H J N	56 73 84	3,690 4,810 5,540
4	9.50	0.226	3.548	3.423	H J N	68 90 102	3,740 4,910 5,610
4½	11.00 11.60	0.237 0.250	4.026 4.000	3.901 3.875	H J N	82 108 123	3,800 4,750 5,420
5	13.00	0.253	4.494	4.369	J	131	5,090
5½	14.00 15.50	0.244 0.275	5.012 4.950	4.887 4.825	H J J	105 138 168	3,820 5,020 5,480
6⅝	20.00	0.288	6.049	5.924	H J	163 215	4,190 5,500
7	20.00	0.272	6.456	6.331	H J	153 201	3,920 5,150
8⅝	28.00	0.304	8.017	7.892	H	229	4,240

All sizes have 6-pitch Hydril square threads.
For mill test pressures, collapsing pressures, and minimum internal yield pressures see API casing tables, pp. 2–8 to 2–13.
For method of calculating strengths and pressures see performance section, p. 2–36.

Gross Lineal Footage from Net Footage—Multiplication Factors
Hydril FJ-40 Joint for Flush-joint Casing or Liners

Size, OD, in.	Nom. wt./ft, lb	Pin length or make-up loss per joint, in.	Multiplication factors*		
			Avg length of joint		
			20 ft	30 ft	40 ft
3½	7.7	1¹³⁄₁₆	1.0076	1.0051	1.0038
4	9.5	1¹³⁄₁₆	1.0076	1.0051	1.0038
4½	11.0, 6.0	1²⁷⁄₃₂	1.0077	1.0051	1.0039
5	13.0	2¼	1.0095	1.0063	1.0047
5½	14.0, 15.5	2¼	1.0095	1.0063	1.0047
6⅝	20.0	2¼	1.0095	1.0063	1.0047
7	20.0	2¼	1.0095	1.0063	1.0047
8⅝	28.0	2¼	1.0095	1.0063	1.0047

* To obtain the gross or shipping length, multiply net length in feet by the multiplication factor.

Hydril Super FJ Casing Joint

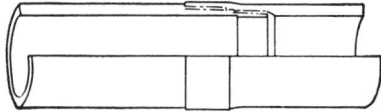

Hydril Super FJ threads are interchangeable with Hydril FJ threads, but the ends of the pipe are formed to improve the thin sections.

Hydril FJ-WP Joint for Wash Pipe

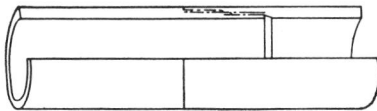

Hydril FJ-WP joints are obtainable for most sizes and weights of pipe. These special threads are always cut to meet special needs. Consult Hydril when choosing a flush-joint wash-pipe thread.

Hydril EU Joint for External-upset Casing and Speedtite Casing
Weights, Dimensions, and Tension Properties

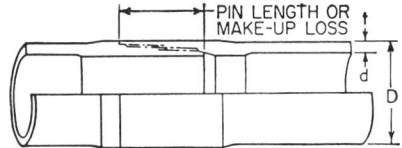

Size, OD D, in.	Nom. wt./ft, lb	Wall thick-ness t, in.	ID d, in.	Casing drift diam, in.	Joint ID bored, in.	Joint OD machined, in.	Grade	Joint strength min yield, 1,000 lb	Equiv. length, ft sf = 2
4½	11.60	0.250	4.000	3.875	3.920	4.855	J	190	8,190
							N	276	11,900
							P	379	16,340
	13.50	0.290	3.920	3.795	3.840	4.855	N	303	11,220
							P	417	15,440
5	15.00	0.296	4.408	4.283	4.328	5.370	J	229	7,630
							N	334	11,130
							P	459	15,300
	18.00	0.362	4.276	4.151	4.196	5.370	N	404	11,220
							P	556	15,440
5½	15.50	0.275	4.950	4.825	4.870	5.835	J	236	7,610
	17.00	0.304	4.892	4.767	4.812	5.835	J	260	7,650
							N	378	11,120
							P	520	15,290
	20.00	0.361	4.778	4.653	4.698	5.835	N	397	9,920
							P	546	13,650
	23.00	0.415	4.670	4.545	4.590	5.835	N	397	8,630
							P	546	11,870

Hydril EU Joint for External-upset Casing and Speedtite Casing (*Continued*)

Size, OD D, in.	Nom. wt./ft, lb	Wall thickness t, in.	ID d, in.	Casing drift diam, in.	Joint ID bored, in.	Joint OD machined, in.	Grade	Joint strength min yield, 1,000 lb	Equiv. length, ft sf = 2
6⅝	24.00	0.352	5.921	5.666	5.811	7.007	J	373	7,770
							N	542	11,290
							P	745	15,520
	28.00	0.417	5.791	5.666	5.711	7.007	N	569	10,160
							P	782	13,960
	32.00	0.475	5.675	5.550	5.595	7.007	N	569	8,890
							P	782	12,220
7	23.00	0.317	6.366	6.151	6.256	7.379	J	362	7,870
							N	526	11,430
	26.00	0.362	6.276	6.151	6.196	7.379	J	394	7,580
							N	573	11,020
							P	788	14,070
	29.00	0.408	6.184	6.059	6.104	7.379	N	592	10,210
							P	814	14,030
	32.00	0.453	6.094	5.969	6.014	7.379	N	592	9,250
							P	814	12,720
	35.00	0.498	6.004	5.879	5.924	7.379	N	592	8,460
							P	814	11,630
	38.00	0.540	5.920	5.795	5.840	7.379	N	592	7,790
							P	814	10,710
7⅝	26.40	0.328	6.969	6.750	6.859	8.027	J	409	7,750
							N	594	11,250
	29.70	0.375	6.875	6.750	6.795	8.027	N	639	10,760
							P	879	14,800
	33.70	0.430	6.765	6.640	6.685	8.027	N	639	9,480
							P	879	13,040
	39.00	0.500	6.625	6.500	6.545	8.027	N	639	8,190
							P	879	11,270
8⅝	32.00	0.352	7.921	7.700	7.811	9.070	J	493	7,700
	36.00	0.400	7.825	7.700	7.745	9.070	J	538	7,470
							N	782	10,860
	40.00	0.450	7.725	7.600	7.645	9.070	N	822	10,280
							P	1,130	14,120
	44.00	0.500	7.625	7.500	7.545	9.070	N	822	9,340
							P	1,130	12,840
	49.00	0.557	7.511	7.386	7.431	9.070	N	822	8,390
							P	1,130	11,530
9⅝	36.00	0.352	8.921	8.679	8.781	10.107	J	561	7,790
	40.00	0.395	8.835	8.679	8.725	10.107	J	603	7,540
							N	878	10,970
	43.50	0.435	8.755	8.599	8.675	10.107	N	932	10,710
							P	1,281	14,720
	47.00	0.472	8.681	8.525	8.601	10.107	N	984	10,470
							P	1,353	14,390
	53.50	0.545	8.535	8.379	8.455	10.107	N	984	9,200
							P	1,353	12,640

Hydril EU and Speedtite casing joints are interchangeable.

For mill test pressures, collapsing pressures, and minimum internal yield pressures see API casing tables, pp. 2–8 to 2–13.

For method of calculating strengths and pressures see performance section, p. 2–36.

Gross Lineal Footage from Net Footage—Multiplication Factors
Hydril EU Joint for External-upset Casing and Speedtite Casing

Size, OD, in.	Nom. wt./ft, lb	Pin length or make-up loss per joint, in.	Multiplication factors*		
			Avg length of joint		
			20 ft	30 ft	40 ft
4½	11.6	2¾	1.0116	1.0077	1.0058
	13.5	2 13/16	1.0119	1.0079	1.0059
5	15.0	3	1.0127	1.0084	1.0063
	18.0	3⅛	1.0132	1.0088	1.0066
5½	15.5, 17.0	3 7/16	1.0145	1.0096	1.0072
	20.0, 23.0	3 9/16	1.0151	1.0100	1.0075
6⅝	24.0	3 13/16	1.0161	1.0107	1.0080
	28.0	3⅞	1.0164	1.0109	1.0081
	32.0	3 15/16	1.0167	1.0111	1.0083
7	23.0	3 11/16	1.0156	1.0103	1.0077
	26.0	3¾	1.0159	1.0105	1.0079
	29.0	3 13/16	1.0161	1.0107	1.0080
	32.0, 35.0, 38.0	4	1.0169	1.0112	1.0084
7⅝	26.4	4⅛	1.0175	1.0116	1.0087
	29.7	4 3/16	1.0178	1.0118	1.0088
	33.7	4 5/16	1.0183	1.0121	1.0091
	39.0	4⅜	1.0186	1.0123	1.0092
8⅝	32.0	4⅛	1.0175	1.0116	1.0087
	36.0	4 3/16	1.0178	1.0118	1.0088
	40.0	4 5/16	1.0183	1.0121	1.0091
	44.0, 49.0	4⅜	1.0186	1.0123	1.0092
9⅝	36.0	4⅛	1.0157	1.0116	1.0087
	40.0, 43.5	4 3/16	1.0178	1.0118	1.0088
	47.0	4 5/16	1.0183	1.0121	1.0091
	53.5	4⅜	1.0186	1.0123	1.0092

* To obtain the gross or shipping length, multiply net length in feet by the multiplication factor.

Hydril Tripleseal Casing Joint
Weights, Dimensions, and Tension Properties

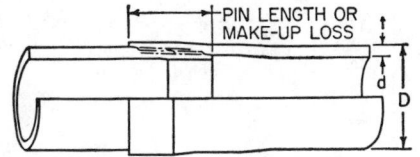

Size, OD D, in.	Nom. wt./ft, lb	Wall thickness t, in.	ID d, in.	Casing drift diam, in.	Joint ID bored, in.	Joint OD machined, in.	Grade	Joint strength min ultimate, 1,000 lb	Equiv. length, ft sf = 2
4½	11.00	0.237	4.026	3.901	3.930	$4\frac{25}{32}$	J	168	7,730
							J	204	8,970
	11.60	0.250	4.000	3.875	3.920	$4\frac{23}{32}$	N	232	10,230
							P	276	12,190
	12.60	0.271	3.958	3.833	3.878	$4\frac{23}{32}$	J	228	9,310
							N	260	10,620
	13.50	0.290	3.920	3.795	3.840	$4\frac{23}{32}$	J	249	9,570
							N	285	10,900
							P	339	13,000
	15.10	0.337	3.826	3.701	3.746	$4\frac{3}{4}$	J	302	10,080
							N	345	11,500
							P	411	13,690
5	13.00	0.253	4.494	4.369	4.414	$5\frac{7}{32}$	J	232	9,040
							J	287	9,650
	15.00	0.296	4.408	4.283	4.328	$5\frac{7}{32}$	N	328	11,020
							P	390	13,120
	18.00	0.362	4.276	4.151	4.196	$5\frac{1}{4}$	J	357	9,960
							N	408	11,370
							P	485	13,540
5½	14.00	0.244	5.012	4.887	4.932	$5\frac{3}{4}$	J	244	8,910
	15.50	0.275	4.950	4.825	4.870	$5\frac{3}{4}$	J	288	9,380
							J	330	9,790
	17.00	0.304	4.892	4.767	4.812	$5\frac{3}{4}$	N	376	11,140
							P	448	13,280
	20.00	0.361	4.778	4.653	4.698	$5\frac{3}{4}$	J	409	10,330
							N	467	11,790
							P	556	14,040
	23.00	0.415	4.670	4.545	4.590	$5\frac{25}{32}$	N	478	10,600
							P	558	12,380
6⅝	20.00	0.288	6.049	5.924	5.969	$6\frac{15}{16}$	J	360	9,230
							J	471	9,900
	24.00	0.352	5.921	5.796	5.841	$6\frac{15}{16}$	N	538	11,400
							P	640	13,570
	28.00	0.417	5.791	5.666	5.711	$6\frac{31}{32}$	J	581	11,500
							N	663	11,990
							P	789	14,270
	32.00	0.475	5.675	5.550	5.595	$6\frac{31}{32}$	N	672	10,770
							P	800	12,820
7	20.00	0.272	6.456	6.331	6.376	$7\frac{5}{16}$	J	352	9,000
							J	436	9,630
	23.00	0.317	6.366	6.241	6.286	$7\frac{5}{16}$	N	497	10,980
							P	592	13,070
	26.00	0.362	6.276	6.151	6.196	$7\frac{5}{16}$	J	518	10,090
							N	591	11,520
							P	703	13,710
	29.00	0.408	6.184	6.059	6.104	$7\frac{5}{16}$	N	685	11,920
							P	816	14,200

Hydril Tripleseal Casing Joint (Continued)

Size, OD D, in.	Nom. wt./ft, lb	Wall thickness t, in.	ID d, in.	Casing drift diam, in.	Joint ID bored, in.	Joint OD machined, in.	Grade	Joint strength min yield, 1,000 lb	Equiv. length, ft sf = 2
7	32.00	0.453	6.094	5.969	6.014	$7\frac{11}{32}$	N	734	11,590
							P	874	13,800
	35.00	.0498	6.004	5.879	5.924	$7\frac{11}{32}$	N	734	10,620
							P	874	12,640
	38.00	0.540	5.920	5.795	5.840	$7\frac{11}{32}$	N	734	9,830
							P	874	11,730
$7\frac{5}{8}$	26.40	0.328	6.969	6.844	6.889	$7\frac{15}{16}$	J	499	9,765
							N	569	11,130
	29.70	0.375	6.875	6.750	6.795	$7\frac{15}{16}$	N	677	11,600
							P	806	13,870
	33.70	0.430	6.765	6.640	6.685	8	N	779	11,790
							P	928	14,040
	39.00	0.500	6.625	6.500	6.545	8	N	833	10,950
							P	992	13,040
$8\frac{5}{8}$	32.00	0.352	7.921	7.796	7.811	$8\frac{15}{16}$	J	565	9,080
	36.00	0.400	7.825	7.700	7.745	$8\frac{15}{16}$	J	674	9,580
							N	769	10,940
	40.00	0.450	7.725	7.600	7.645	$8\frac{15}{16}$	N	897	11,410
							P	1,608	13,600
	44.00	0.500	7.625	7.500	7.545	9	N	1,004	11,570
							P	1,195	13,770
	49.00	0.557	7.511	7.386	7.431	9	N	1,004	10,460
							P	1,195	12,450
$9\frac{5}{8}$	36.00	0.352	8.921	8.765	8.781	10	J	634	9,090
	40.00	0.395	8.835	8.679	8.755	10	J	744	9,550
							N	850	10,920
	43.50	0.435	8.755	8.599	8.675	10	N	966	11,310
							P	1,150	13,460
	47.00	0.472	8.681	8.525	8.601	10	N	1,072	11,620
							P	1,276	13,830
	53.50	0.545	8.535	8.379	8.455	$10\frac{1}{16}$	N	1,223	11,560
							P	1,456	13,770
$10\frac{3}{4}$	40.50	0.350	10.050	9.894	9.910	$11\frac{3}{16}$	J	706	9,080
	45.50	0.400	9.950	9.794	9.870	$11\frac{3}{16}$	J	851	9,620
							J	994	10,040
	51.00	0.450	9.850	9.964	9.770	$11\frac{3}{16}$	N	1,134	11,460
							P	1,350	13,640
	55.50	0.495	9.760	9.604	9.680	$11\frac{3}{16}$	N	1,280	11,810
							P	1,523	14,050
	60.70	0.545	9.660	9.504	9.580	$11\frac{3}{16}$	P	1,625	13,680
$11\frac{3}{4}$	47.00	0.375	11.000	10.844	10.860	$12\frac{3}{16}$	J	854	9,380
	54.00	0.435	10.880	10.724	10.800	$12\frac{3}{16}$	J	1,044	9,940
	60.00	0.489	10.772	10.616	10.692	$12\frac{3}{16}$	J	1,213	10,310
							N	1,385	11,770
$13\frac{3}{8}$	54.50	0.380	12.615	12.459	12.535	$13\frac{13}{16}$	J	996	9,440
	61.00	0.430	12.515	12.359	12.435	$13\frac{13}{16}$	J	1,178	9,910
	68.00	0.480	12.415	12.259	12.335	$13\frac{13}{16}$	J	1,358	10,270
	72.00	0.514	12.347	12.191	12.267	$13\frac{13}{16}$	N	1,688	11,950

All Hydril Tripleseal casing threads are interchangeable.

For mill test pressures, collapsing pressures, and minimum internal yield pressures, see API casing tables, pp. 2-8 to 2-13.

For method of calculating strengths and pressures, see performance section, p. 2-36.

Gross Lineal Footage from Net Footage—Multiplication Factors
Hydril Tripleseal Casing Joint

Size, OD, in.	Nom. wt/ft, lb	Pin length or make-up loss per joint, in.	Multiplication factors* Avg length of joint		
			20 ft	30 ft	40 ft
4½	All	3 3/16	1.0135	1.0089	1.0067
5	All	3 3/16	1.0135	1.0089	1.0067
5½	All	3 3/16	1.0135	1.0089	1.0067
6⅝	All	3 3/4	1.0159	1.0105	1.0079
7	All	3 3/4	1.0159	1.0105	1.0079
7⅝	All	3 3/4	1.0159	1.0105	1.0079
8⅝	All	4 3/16	1.0178	1.0118	1.0088
9⅝	All	4 3/16	1.0178	1.0118	1.0088
10¾	All	4 3/16	1.0178	1.0118	1.0088
11¾	All	4 3/16	1.0178	1.0118	1.0088
13⅜	All	4 3/16	1.0178	1.0118	1.0088

* To obtain the gross or shipping length, multiply net length in feet by the multiplication factor.

Hydril RB Casing Joint
Weights, Dimensions, and Tension Properties

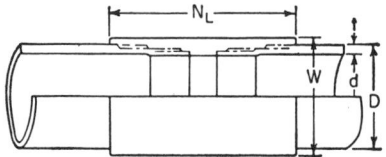

Size, OD D, in.	Nom. wt/ft, lb	Wall thickness t, in.	ID d, in.	Casing drift diam, in.	Joint ID bored, in.	Coupling OD W, in.	Coupling Length N_L, in.	Grade	Joint strength min ultimate 1,000 lb	Equiv. length sf = 2 ft
$4\frac{1}{2}$	15.10	0.337	3.826	3.701	3.746	5	$7\frac{1}{2}$	P-110	410	13,580
								P-145	508	16,820
5	18.00	0.362	4.276	4.151	4.196	$5\frac{5}{8}$	$7\frac{1}{2}$	P-110	503	13,970
								P-145	624	17,330
	26.30	0.548	3.904	3.779	3.824	$5\frac{5}{8}$	$9\frac{3}{8}$	P-110	766	14,560
$5\frac{1}{2}$	23.00	0.415	4.670	4.545	4.590	$6\frac{1}{8}$	$7\frac{1}{2}$	P-110	656	14,260
								P-145	813	17,670
	26.00	0.476	4.548	4.423	4.468	$6\frac{1}{8}$	$9\frac{3}{8}$	P-110	727	13,980
								P-145	901	17,330
	27.00	0.500	4.500	4.375	4.420	$6\frac{1}{8}$	$9\frac{3}{8}$	P-110	770	14,260
								P-145	955	17,690
7	32.00	0.435	6.094	5.969	6.014	$7\frac{11}{16}$	$8\frac{5}{8}$	P-110	924	14,440
								P-145	1,146	17,910
	35.00	0.498	6.004	5.879	5.924	$7\frac{11}{16}$	$8\frac{5}{8}$	P-110	1,031	14,730
								P-145	1,278	18,260
	38.00	0.540	5.920	5.795	5.840	$7\frac{11}{16}$	$9\frac{3}{8}$	P-110	1,079	14,200
								P-145	1,338	17,610
$7\frac{5}{8}$	39.00	0.500	6.625	6.500	6.545	$8\frac{5}{16}$	$8\frac{5}{8}$	P-110	1,137	14,580
								P-145	1,410	18,080
$8\frac{5}{8}$	44.00	0.500	7.625	7.500	7.545	$9\frac{3}{8}$	$9\frac{1}{2}$	P-110	1,219	13,850
								P-145	1,512	17,180
	49.00	0.557	7.511	7.386	7.431	$9\frac{3}{8}$	$9\frac{1}{2}$	P-110	1,389	14,170
								P-145	1,722	17,570
$9\frac{5}{8}$	53.50	0.545	8.535	8.379	8.455	$10\frac{3}{8}$	$9\frac{1}{2}$	P-110	1,523	14,230
								P-145	1,888	17,640

Hydril RB joints are generally applied to very heavy walled P grade casing.

For mill test pressures, collapsing pressures, and minimum internal yield pressures, see API casing tables, pp. 2–8 to 2–13.

For method of calculating strengths and pressures, see performance section, p. 2–36.

Integral-joint Casing
Weights, Dimensions, and Tension Properties

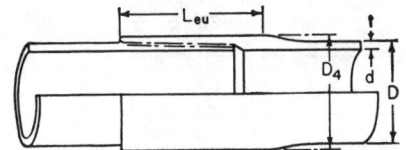

Size, OD D, in.	Nom. wt/ft, lb	Wall thickness t, in.	ID d, in.	Casing drift diam, in.	Joint OD D_4, in.	Joint Box length L_{eu}	Grade	Regular end Joint strength min, 1,000 lb	Regular end Equiv. length, ft sf = 2	Hardened end Joint strength min, 1,000 lb	Hardened end Equiv. length, ft sf = 2
5½	14.00	0.244	5.012	4.887	6.050	4.000	J-55	217	7,750		
	15.50	0.275	4.950	4.825	6.050	4.000	J-55	247	7,970	334	10,770
							J-55	275	8,090	372	10,940
	17.00	0.304	4.892	4.767	6.050	4.000	N-80	320	9,410	434	12,760
							P-105	384	11,290		
	20.00	0.361	4.778	4.653	6.050	4.000	N-80	382	9,550	518	12,950
							P-105	459	11,480		
	23.00	0.415	4.670	4.545	6.050	4.000	N-80	440	9,570	596	12,960
							P-105	528	11,480		
7	20.00	0.272	6.456	6.331	7.656	4.500	J-55	292	7,300		
	23.00	0.317	6.366	6.241	7.656	4.500	J-55	344	7,480	466	10,130
							N-08	400	8,700	542	11,780
							P-105	480	10,440		
	26.00	0.362	6.276	6.151	7.656	4.500	J-55	395	7,600	534	10,270
							N-80	460	8,850	623	11,980
							P-105	552	10,620		
	29.00	0.408	6.184	6.059	7.656	4.500	N-80	520	8,970	704	12,140
							P-105	624	10,760		
	32.00	0.453	6.094	5.969	7.656	4.500	N-80	578	9,030	783	12,240
							P-105	694	10,640		
	35.00	0.498	6.004	5.879	7.656	4.500	N-80	635	9,070	860	12,280
							P-105	762	10,890		
	38.00	0.540	5.920	5.795	7.656	4.500	N-80	688	9,050	931	12,250
							P-105	825	10,860		
8⅝	32.00	0.352	7.921	7.796	9.625	5.000	J-55	437	6,830	591	9,230
	36.00	0.400	7.825	7.700	9.625	5.000	J-55	499	6,930	675	9,370
							N-80	581	8,070	786	10,920
							P-105	697	9,680		
	40.00	0.450	7.725	7.600	9.625	5.000	N-80	655	8,190	887	11,090
							P-105	787	9,840		
	44.00	0.500	7.625	7.500	9.625	5.000	N-80	729	8,280	987	11,220
							P-105	875	9,940		
	49.00	0.557	7.511	7.386	9.625	5.000	N-80	812	8,290	1,099	11,210
							P-105	974	9,940		
9⅝	36.00	0.352	8.921	8.765	10.625	5.250	J-55	462	6,420	624	8,670
	40.00	0.395	8.835	8.679	10.625	5.250	J-55	521	6,510	704	8,800
							N-80	606	7,580	820	10,250
							P-105	727	9,090		
	43.50	0.435	8.755	8.599	10.625	5.250	N-80	670	7,700	906	10,410
							P-105	803	9,230		
	47.00	0.472	8.681	8.525	10.625	5.250	N-80	727	7,730	985	10,480
							P-105	873	9,290		
	53.50	0.545	8.535	8.379	10.625	5.250	N-80	841	7,860	1,138	10,640
							P-105	1,009	9,430		

Thread form on pin end is identical with and interchanges with API short-thread casing; see pp. 2-16 and 2-17.

For mill test pressures, collapsing pressures, and minimum internal yield pressures see API casing tables, pp. 2-8 to 2-13.

For method of calculating strengths and pressures see performance section, p. 2-36.

The gross or shipping-length determination is identical with API short-thread casing of the same size and weight; see p. 2-14.

Naylor Threaded Surface Casing
Weights, Dimensions, Test Pressures, and Properties

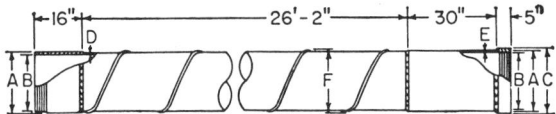

Size, OD A, in.	Wt./ft, lb	ID B, in.	Female OD C, in.	Wall thickness D, in.	Section below female end E, in.	OD spiral-weld section F, in.	Test pressure, lb	Setting depth in collapse (salt water), ft		Suspension depth in tension, ft
								sf = 2	sf = 1½	sf = 2½
10¾	25.5	10.000	11.750	0.172	¼	11.376	860	469	625	2,586
13⅜	32.4	12.715	14.375	0.172	¼	14.098	673	294	392	2,578
16	38.5	15.250	17.000	0.172	¼	16.626	564	206	275	2,580
20	48.0	19.250	21.000	0.172	⁵⁄₁₆	20.626	447	129	172	2,623

Furnished in uniform lengths of 30 ft.
Threads are interchangeable with API casing; see p. 2–17.

DESIGN FACTORS AND USE

Formulas for collapse resistance, internal yield pressures, and joint strengths for the various grades of casing are for the purpose of providing minimum performance properties on which the design of casing strings may be based, and do not include factors of safety. In the design of casing strings, factors of safety should be applied to suit the particular application.

Formulas Used in Determining Performance Properties of Casing

Values for collapse resistance, internal yield pressure, and joint strength for the various grades of casing shown in the tables are minimum values and were determined by means of the following formulas:

Collapse Pressure (Also Applicable to Tubing)

Grade F-25. * For failure in the plastic range (for D/t values less than 43.5),

$$P_c = 0.75 \left(\frac{86{,}670}{D/t} - 1{,}386 \right) \tag{1}$$

For failure in the elastic range (for D/t values greater than 43.5),

$$P_c = 0.75 \frac{50{,}210{,}000}{(D/t)^3} \tag{2}$$

Grades H-40, J-55, N-80, P-110, and V-150. For failure in the plastic range and for D/t values less than 14, approximately,

$$P_c = 0.75 \times 2Y_a \frac{(D/t) - 1}{(D/t)^2}$$

For failure in the plastic range and for D/t values of 14, approximately, and up to the point at which the curve for plastic failure intersects the elastic curve,

$$P_c = 0.75 \times Y_a \left(\frac{2.503}{D/t} - 0.046 \right)$$

* The elastic equation for grade F-25 is not related to that for the other grades.

For failure in the elastic range,

$$P_c = 0.75 \frac{62.6 \times 10^6}{(D/t)[(D/t) - 1]^2}$$

where P_c = minimum collapse pressure, psi
$\quad D$ = nominal outside diameter, in.
$\quad t$ = nominal wall thickness, in.
$\quad Y_a$ = average yield factor in collapse, psi, as follows:

Grade H-40....................	50,000
Grade J-55....................	65,000
Grade N-80...................	85,000
Grade P-105 (tubing)...........	115,000
Grade P-110..................	123,000
Grade V-150*.................	163,000

Internal Yield Pressure (Also Applicable to Tubing)

$$P_i = 0.875 \frac{2Y_m t}{D}$$

where P_i = minimum internal yield pressure, psi
$\quad D$ = nominal outside diameter, in.
$\quad t$ = nominal wall thickness, in.
$\quad Y_m$ = specified minimum yield strength, psi, as follows:

Grade F-25....................	25,000
Grade H-40....................	40,000
Grade J-55....................	55,000
Grade N-80....................	80,000
Grade P-105 (tubing)...........	105,000
Grade P-110..................	110,000
Grade V-150*.................	150,000

Joint Strength

For casing with short threads and couplings,

$$L_j = 0.80 \ C(33.71 - D) \left(\frac{1}{t - 0.07125} + 24.45 \right) A_j$$

For casing with long threads and couplings,

$$L_j = 0.80 \ C(25.58 - D) \left(\frac{1}{t - 0.07125} + 24.45 \right) A_j$$

where L_j = minimum joint strength, lb
$\quad D$ = nominal outside diameter, in.
$\quad t$ = nominal wall thickness, in.
$\quad A_j$ = cross-sectional area of the pipe wall at the thread root of the last perfect thread, sq in.
$\qquad = 0.7854 \ [(D - 0.1425)^2 - d^2]$
$\quad d$ = nominal inside diameter, in.
$\quad C$ = a constant for the grade of steel, as follows:

	Short T & C	Long T & C
Grade F-25.............	53.5	
Grade H-40.............	72.5	
Grade J-55.............	96.5	159.0
Grade N-80.............	112.3	185.0
Grade P-110........	146.9	242.0
Grade V-150*..........	174.9	288.0

* Values for grade V-150 are tentative.

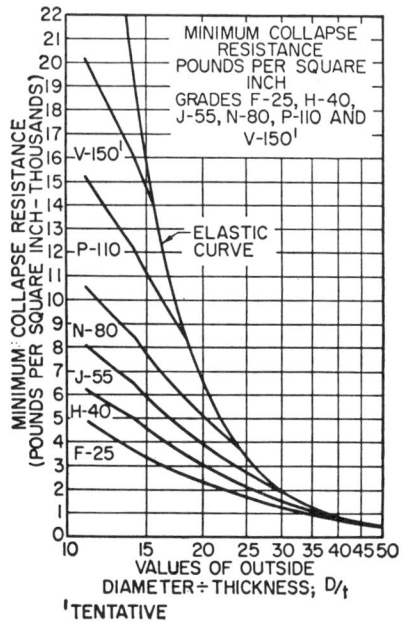

'TENTATIVE

This chart may be used to obtain collapsing pressures of grades F-25, H-40, J-55, N-80, P-110, and V-150 casing when the thickness t and outside diameter D are given. The formulas for determining resistance to collapse for the various grades shown above are to be found on pp. 2-36 and 2-37.

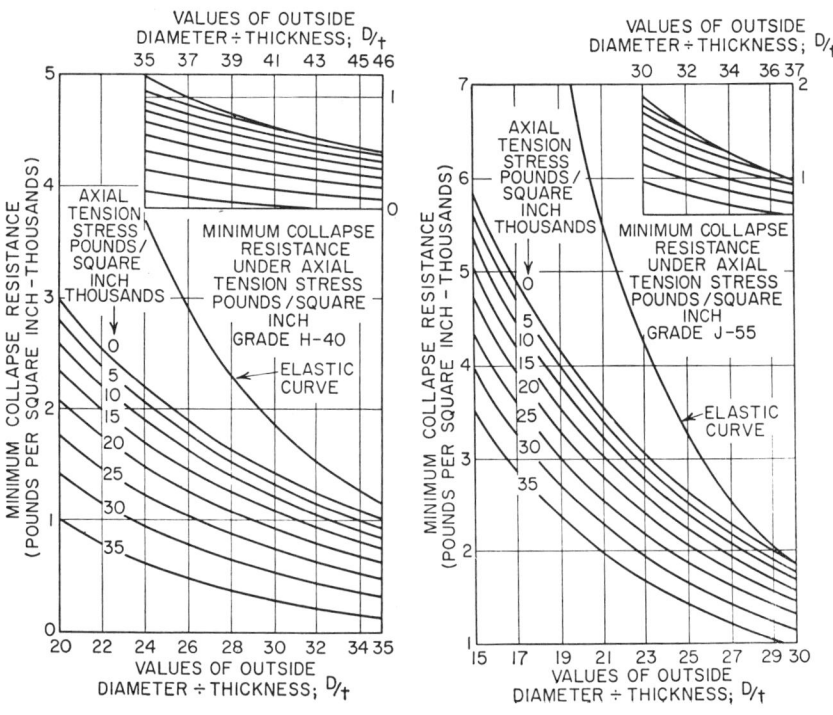

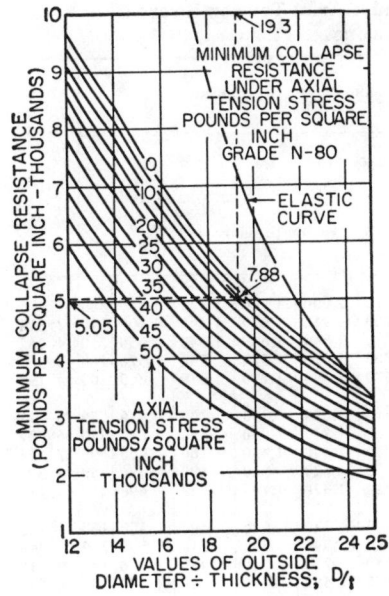

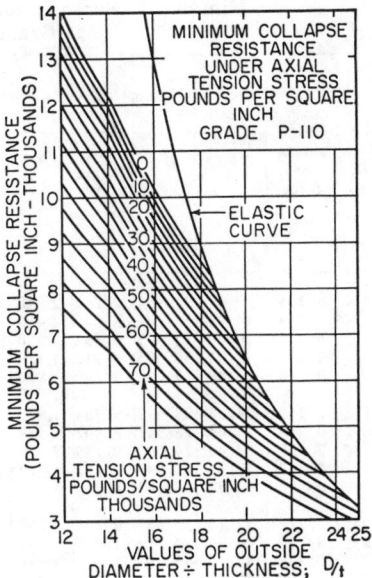

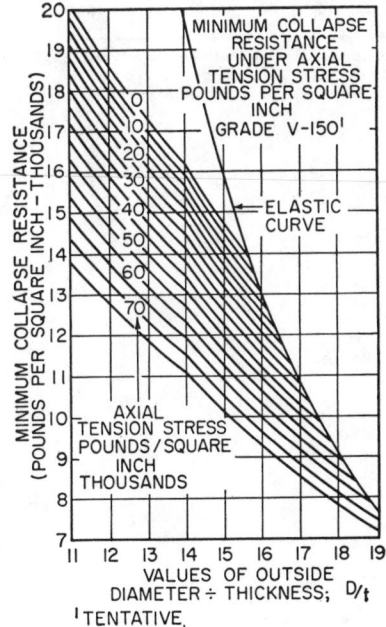

¹TENTATIVE.

Minimum Collapse Resistance under Axial Tension Stress
Grade H-40 Casing

Size, OD D, in.	Wall thickness t, in.	Wt/ft T & C, lb	D/t	Plain-end area,† sq in.	Unit tensile stress, psi, thousands								Area of pipe wall under last perfect thread (API), sq in.†
					0	5	10	15	20	25	30	35	
					Adjusted collapsing pressure, psi*								
4½	0.205	9.50	21.951	2.766	2,550	2,390	2,210	2,000	1,760	1,470	1,160	800	1.775
5½	0.244	14.00	22.541	4.029	2,440	2,300	2,120	1,910	1,670	1,400	1,100	740	2.814
6⅝	0.288	20.00	23.003	5.734	2,360	2,210	2,040	1,840	1,610	1,340	1,050	710	4.267
7	0.231	17.00	30.303	4.912	1,370	1,310	1,200	1,070	920	740	520	280	3.361
7	0.272	20.00	25.735	5.749	1,920	1,810	1,670	1,490	1,290	1,070	800	500	4.198
7⅝	0.300	24.00	25.417	6.904	1,970	1,850	1,710	1,530	1,330	1,100	830	520	5.213
8⅝	0.304	28.00	28.371	7.947	1,580	1,490	1,380	1,230	1,050	860	620	350	6.032
8⅝	0.352	32.00	24.502	9.149	2,110	1,980	1,830	1,640	1,430	1,180	900	590	7.234
9⅝	0.312	32.30	30.849	9.128	1,320	1,240	1,150	1,020	860	690	490	250	6.990
9⅝	0.352	36.00	27.343	10.254	1,710	1,610	1,480	1,320	1,140	930	690	410	8.116
10¾	0.279	32.75	38.530	9.178	830	820	800	720	620	490	350	180	6.788
10¾	0.350	40.50	30.714	11.435	1,340	1,260	1,160	1,040	890	710	500	250	9.045
11¾	0.333	42.00	35.285	11.944	940	920	840	750	620	480	320	130	9.330
13⅜	0.330	48.00	40.530	13.524	740	660	600	520	430	320	180	30	10.546
16	0.375	65.00	42.667	18.408	*640	580	520	450	360	260	130	4	14.842
20	0.438	94.00	45.662	26.918	*520	490	430	360	280	200	90	0	22.457

* Collapsing pressures in psi for listed unit tensile stress correspond to setting depths in feet with a safety factor of 2 when set in salt water—specific gravity 1.15.

† For method of determining minimum yield strength safety factor, see p. 2-37.

Minimum Collapse Resistance under Axial Tension Stress
Grade J-55 Casing

Size, OD D, in.	Wall thick-ness t, in.	Wt/ft T & C, lb	D/t	Plain-end area,† sq in.	Unit tensile stress, psi, thousands								Area of pipe wall under last perfect thread (API), sq in.†
					0	5	10	15	20	25	30	35	
					Adjusted collapsing pressure, psi*								
4½	0.205	9.50	21.951	2.766	3,320	3,170	3,020	2,820	2,610	2,380	2,120	1,830	1.775
4½	0.224	10.50	20.089	3.009	3,830	3,670	3,480	3,260	3,030	2,760	2,480	2,150	2.018
4½	0.250	11.60	18.000	3.388	4,540	4,340	4,130	3,880	3,620	3,320	2,980	2,610	2.347
5	0.220	11.50	22.727	3.304	3,130	2,990	2,840	2,660	2,460	2,240	1,990	1,710	2.200
5	0.253	13.00	19.762	3.773	3,930	3,770	3,580	3,350	3,120	2,840	2,550	2,220	2.670
5	0.296	15.00	16.891	4.374	4,980	4,770	4,530	4,270	3,980	3,650	3,300	2,910	3.721
5½	0.244	14.00	22.541	4.029	3,170	3,030	2,880	2,690	2,490	2,260	2,010	1,740	2.814
5½	0.275	15.50	20.000	4.514	3,860	3,690	3,500	3,290	3,050	2,780	2,500	2,180	3.299
5½	0.304	17.00	18.092	4.962	4,500	4,310	4,100	3,860	3,580	3,280	2,960	2,600	3.747
6⅝	0.288	20.00	23.003	5.734	3,060	2,930	2,780	2,600	2,400	2,180	1,940	1,680	4.267
6⅝	0.352	24.00	18.821	6.937	4,250	4,060	3,860	3,620	3,360	3,080	2,760	2,420	5.470
7	0.272	20.00	25.735	5.749	2,500	2,390	2,270	2,110	1,950	1,770	1,560	1,340	4.198
7	0.317	23.00	22.032	6.656	3,290	3,140	2,990	2,790	2,580	2,360	2,090	1,820	5.105
7	0.362	26.00	19.337	7.549	4,060	3,870	3,680	3,450	3,280	2,940	2,610	2,290	5.998
7⅝	0.328	26.40	23.246	7.519	3,010	2,870	2,730	2,550	2,360	2,140	1,900	1,640	5.828
8⅝	0.264	24.00	32.670	6.934	1,430	1,430	1,390	1,320	1,230	1,090	950	790	5.020
8⅝	0.352	32.00	24.502	9.149	2,740	2,620	2,490	2,320	2,140	1,950	1,720	1,480	7.234
8⅝	0.400	36.00	21.562	10.336	3,420	3,270	3,110	2,900	2,690	2,450	2,180	1,900	8.421
9⅝	0.352	36.00	27.343	10.255	2,220	2,130	2,030	1,890	1,740	1,580	1,380	1,170	8.116
9⅝	0.395	40.00	24.367	11.454	2,770	2,650	2,510	2,350	2,160	1,970	1,750	1,490	9.315
10¾	0.350	40.50	30.714	11.435	1,730	1,690	1,610	1,490	1,380	1,250	1,090	900	9.045
10¾	0.400	45.50	26.875	13.006	2,300	2,210	2,090	1,950	1,800	1,640	1,440	1,220	10.616
10¾	0.450	51.00	23.888	14.561	2,870	2,740	2,600	2,430	2,250	2,040	1,810	1,550	12.717
11¾	0.375	47.00	31.333	13.401	‡1,630	1,590	1,520	1,430	1,330	1,190	1,030	860	10.787
11¾	0.435	54.00	27.011	15.463	2,270	2,180	2,070	1,940	1,790	1,620	1,420	1,210	12.849
11¾	0.489	60.00	24.029	17.300	2,840	2,720	2,580	2,410	2,230	2,020	1,800	1,530	14.685
13⅜	0.380	54.50	35.197	15.514	‡1,140	‡1,140	‡1,140	1,110	1,020	920	800	650	12.536
13⅜	0.430	61.00	31.105	17.487	‡1,670	1,620	1,540	1,450	1,340	1,200	1,050	880	14.509
13⅜	0.480	68.00	27.865	19.445	2,140	2,050	1,950	1,820	1,680	1,530	1,330	1,120	16.467
16	0.438	75.00	36.530	21.414	‡1,010	‡1,010	‡1,010	‡1,010	950	850	740	600	17.848
16	0.495	84.00	32.323	24.112	‡1,480	‡1,480	1,420	1,340	1,240	1,110	960	800	20.546
16	0.656	109.00	24.390	31.662	2,760	2,640	2,510	2,340	2,160	1,960	1,740	1,490	28.057
20	0.635	133.00	31.496	38.632	‡1,600	1,570	1,500	1,410	1,310	1,170	1,020	850	34.171

* Collapsing pressures in psi for listed unit tensile stress correspond to setting depths in feet with a safety factor of 2 when set in salt water—specific gravity 1.15.
† For method of determining minimum yield strength safety factor, see p. 2-48.
‡ Elastic collapse.

Minimum Collapse Resistance under Axial Tension Stress
Grade N-80 Casing

Size, OD D, in.	Wall thick- ness t, in.	Wt/ft T & C, lb	D/t	Plain- end area,† sq in.	Unit tensile stress, psi, thousands											Area of pipe wall under last perfect thread (API), sq in.†
					0	5	10	15	20	25	30	35	40	45	50	
					Adjusted collapsing pressure, psi*											
4½	0.250	11.60	18.000	3.338	5,930	5,750	5,560	5,330	5,080	4,820	4,520	4,210	3,900	3,560	3,200	2.347
4½	0.290	13.50	15.517	3.836	7,350	7,160	6,930	6,640	6,340	6,020	5,670	5,310	4,900	4,500	4,090	2.844
5	0.296	15.00	16.891	4.374	6,520	6,330	6,110	5,870	5,600	5,310	4,970	4,660	4,330	3,950	3,560	3.271
5	0.362	18.00	13.812	5.275	8,550	8,320	8,020	7,720	7,360	7,000	6,610	6,210	5,850	5,380	4,910	4.171
5½	0.304	17.00	18.092	4.962	5,890	5,700	5,510	5,290	5,040	4,780	4,480	4,180	3,870	3,540	3,180	3.747
5½	0.361	20.00	15.235	5.828	7,540	7,320	7,090	6,800	6,490	6,170	5,810	5,450	5,080	4,670	4,220	4.613
5½	0.415	23.00	13.253	6.630	8,900	8,660	8,430	8,130	7,760	7,380	6,980	6,560	6,170	5,720	5,220	5.414
6⅝	0.352	24.00	18.821	6.937	5,550	5,380	5,180	4,960	4,740	4,490	4,210	3,920	3,630	3,300	3,960	5.470
6⅝	0.417	28.00	15.887	8.133	7,110	6,910	6,680	6,410	6,120	5,810	5,470	5,110	4,730	4,340	3,920	6.666
6⅝	0.475	32.00	13.947	9.177	8,490	8,210	7,920	7,620	7,280	6,920	6,530	6,140	5,780	5,310	5,810	7.710
7	0.317	23.00	22.082	6.656	4,300	4,180	4,040	3,870	3,680	3,480	3,260	3,030	2,780	2,520	2,250	5.105
7	0.362	26.00	19.337	7.549	5,320	5,160	4,980	4,770	4,540	4,300	4,040	3,760	3,490	3,180	2,850	5.998
7	0.408	29.00	17.157	8.449	6,370	6,180	5,970	5,740	5,480	5,180	4,870	4,540	4,210	3,840	3,450	6.899
7	0.453	32.00	15.453	9.317	7,400	7,210	6,970	6,680	6,380	6,040	5,700	5,340	4,980	4,570	4,120	7.766
7	0.498	35.00	14.056	10.173	8,420	8,150	7,870	7,570	7,230	6,870	6,470	6,100	5,730	5,270	4,790	8.622
7	0.540	38.00	12.962	10.969	9,080	8,840	8,600	8,340	8,000	7,590	7,170	6,740	6,340	5,890	5,400	9.408
7⅝	0.328	26.40	23.246	7.519	3,930	3,820	3,690	3,540	3,380	3,190	2,990	2,780	2,540	2,300	2,060	5.828
7⅝	0.375	29.70	20.333	8.541	4,910	4,780	4,610	4,420	4,200	3,980	3,740	3,470	3,220	2,930	2,620	6.850
7⅝	0.430	33.70	17.732	9.720	6,070	5,890	5,690	5,470	5,200	4,940	4,630	4,310	4,020	3,660	3,280	8.029
7⅝	0.500	39.00	15.250	11.192	7,530	7,340	7,090	6,790	6,490	6,160	5,800	5,440	5,080	4,680	4,310	9.501
8⅝	0.400	36.00	21.562	10.336	4,470	4,340	4,200	4,030	3,830	3,620	3,390	3,160	2,920	2,650	2,270	8.421
8⅝	0.450	40.00	19.166	11.557	5,390	5,240	5,060	4,840	4,620	4,360	4,100	3,820	3,540	3,210	2,890	9.642
8⅝	0.500	44.00	17.250	12.763	6,320	6,140	5,920	5,700	5,430	5,140	4,830	4,500	4,190	3,820	3,430	10.848
8⅝	0.557	49.00	15.458	14.118	7,370	7,180	6,940	6,650	6,360	6,030	5,680	5,320	4,970	4,560	4,110	12.203
9⅝	0.395	40.00	24.367	11.454	3,530	3,500	3,400	3,260	3,120	2,960	2,780	2,560	2,380	2,160	1,940	9.315
9⅝	0.435	43.50	22.126	12.559	4,280	4,160	4,020	3,860	3,670	3,460	3,260	3,020	2,780	2,530	2,250	10.421
9⅝	0.472	47.00	20.391	13.572	4,900	4,750	4,580	4,390	4,180	3,940	3,700	3,460	3,200	2,930	2,620	11.434
9⅝	0.545	53.50	17.660	15.547	6,110	5,920	5,730	5,550	5,240	4,960	4,650	4,340	4,040	3,690	3,310	13.408
10¾	0.450	51.00	23.888	14.561	3,750	3,640	3,520	3,380	3,220	3,040	2,860	2,640	2,430	2,200	1,980	12.171
10¾	0.495	55.50	21.717	15.947	4,420	4,290	4,150	3,980	3,780	3,570	3,350	3,120	2,860	2,600	2,320	13.557
11¾	0.489	60.00	24.029	17.300	‡3,680	3,600	3,490	3,360	3,210	3,020	2,840	2,620	2,420	2,200	1,980	14.685
13⅜	0.514	72.00	26.021	20.768	‡2,880	‡2,880	‡2,880	‡2,880	2,780	2,640	2,470	2,280	2,120	1,940	1,740	17.790
13⅜	0.550	77.00	24.318	22.160	‡3,550	3,520	3,410	3,280	3,140	2,960	2,780	2,570	2,380	2,160	1,940	19.182
13⅜	0.608	85.00	21.998	24.386	4,320	4,200	4,060	3,890	3,700	3,500	3,280	3,040	2,880	2,540	2,280	21.408
16	0.715	118.00	22.378	33.334	4,200	4,080	3,940	3,780	3,600	3,400	3,190	2,970	2,720	2,480	2,210	30.768

Example: For 26-lb 7-in. D casing under a tensile load of 7,880 psi (see step 3, p. 2–50), interpolate as follows: 5,160 − 4,980 = 180 psi × (10,000 − 7,880) ÷ 5,000 = 76 psi + 4,980 = 5,056 psi.

* Collapsing pressures in psi for listed unit tensile stress correspond to setting depths in feet with a safety factory of 2 when set in salt water—specific gravity 1.15.

† For method of determining minimum yield strength safety factor, see p. 2–48.

‡ Elastic collapse.

Minimum Collapse Resistance under Axial Tension Stress
Grade P-110 Casing

Size, OD D, in.	Wall thick-ness t, in.	Wt./ft T & C, lb	D/t	Plain-end area,† sq in.	Unit tensile stress, psi, thousands — Adjusted collapsing pressure, psi*																Area of pipe wall under last perfect thread (API),† sq in.
					0	5	10	15	20	25	30	35	40	45	50	55	60	65	70	75	
4½	0.250	11.60	18.000	3.338	8,590	8,410	8,240	8,030	7,800	7,590	7,330	7,080	6,840	6,570	6,300	5,900	5,690	5,360	5,010	4,670	2.347
4½	0.290	13.50	15.517	3.836	10,640	10,410	10,200	9,950	9,660	9,410	9,080	8,770	8,470	8,140	7,800	7,420	7,050	6,640	6,210	5,790	2.844
4½	0.337	15.10	13.353	4.407	12,780	12,510	12,250	11,950	11,600	11,300	10,910	10,540	10,180	9,780	9,370	8,910	8,470	7,970	7,460	6,950	3.416
5	0.296	15.00	16.891	4.374	9,430	9,230	9,040	8,810	8,560	8,340	8,050	7,780	7,510	7,210	6,920	6,580	6,250	5,880	5,510	5,130	3.271
5	0.362	18.00	13.812	5.275	12,390	12,130	11,880	11,580	11,250	10,950	10,570	10,220	9,870	9,480	9,090	8,640	8,210	7,730	7,230	6,740	4.171
5½	0.304	17.00	18.092	4.962	8,520	8,340	8,170	7,960	7,740	7,530	7,270	7,030	6,780	6,520	6,250	5,940	5,640	5,320	4,970	4,630	3.747
5½	0.361	20.00	15.235	5.828	10,910	10,680	10,460	10,200	9,910	9,640	9,310	9,000	8,690	8,350	8,000	7,610	7,230	6,810	6,370	5,930	4.613
5½	0.415	23.00	13.253	6.630	12,870	12,600	12,340	12,030	11,690	11,380	10,980	10,610	10,250	9,850	9,440	8,980	8,530	8,030	7,510	7,000	5.414
6⅝	0.352	24.00	18.821	6.937	7,850‡	7,850‡	7,690	7,500	7,280	7,090	6,840	6,610	6,390	6,140	5,880	5,590	5,310	5,000	4,680	4,360	5.470
6⅝	0.417	28.00	15.887	8.133	10,290	10,070	9,870	9,620	9,340	9,100	8,780	8,490	8,190	7,870	7,550	7,180	6,820	6,420	6,010	5,600	6.666
6⅝	0.475	32.00	13.947	9.177	12,280	12,020	11,770	11,480	11,150	10,860	10,480	10,130	9,780	9,390	9,000	8,570	8,140	7,660	7,170	6,680	7.710
7	0.362	26.00	19.337	7.549	7,220‡	7,220‡	7,220‡	7,200	6,990	6,810	6,570	6,350	6,130	5,890	5,650	5,370	5,100	4,800	4,500	4,190	5.998
7	0.408	29.00	17.157	8.449	9,220	9,020	8,840	8,620	8,370	8,150	7,870	7,600	7,340	7,050	6,760	6,430	6,110	5,750	5,380	5,010	6.899
7	0.453	32.00	15.453	9.317	10,700	10,470	10,260	10,000	9,720	9,460	9,130	8,820	8,520	8,190	7,850	7,460	7,090	6,680	6,250	5,820	7.766
7	0.498	35.00	14.056	10.173	12,180	11,920	11,680	11,380	11,060	10,770	10,390	10,040	9,700	9,320	8,930	8,500	8,070	7,600	7,110	6,620	8.622
7	0.540	38.00	12.962	10.959	13,130	12,850	12,590	12,270	11,920	11,610	11,200	10,830	10,460	10,040	9,630	9,160	8,700	8,190	7,670	7,140	9.408
7⅝	0.375	29.70	20.333	8.541	6,180‡	6,180‡	6,180‡	6,180‡	6,180‡	6,180‡	6,070	5,860	5,660	5,440	5,210	4,960	4,710	4,440	4,150	3,870	6.850
7⅝	0.430	33.70	17.732	9.720	8,780	8,590	8,420	8,210	7,970	7,760	7,490	7,240	6,990	6,720	6,440	6,120	5,820	5,480	5,130	4,770	8.029
7⅝	0.500	39.00	15.250	11.192	10,900	10,670	10,450	10,190	9,900	9,640	9,300	8,990	8,880	8,340	7,990	7,600	7,220	6,800	6,360	5,930	9.501
8⅝	0.450	40.00	19.166	11.557	7,420‡	7,420‡	7,420‡	7,300	7,090	6,900	6,660	6,440	6,220	5,970	5,730	5,450	5,170	4,870	4,560	4,250	9.642
8⅝	0.500	44.00	17.250	12.763	9,140	8,950	8,760	8,540	8,300	8,080	7,800	7,540	7,280	6,990	6,700	6,380	6,060	5,700	5,340	4,970	10.848
8⅝	0.557	49.00	15.485	14.118	10,660	10,430	10,220	9,960	9,680	9,420	9,100	8,790	8,490	8,150	7,820	7,440	7,060	6,650	6,220	5,800	12.203
9⅝	0.435	43.50	22.126	12.559	4,760‡	4,760‡	4,760‡	4,760‡	4,760‡	4,760‡	4,760‡	4,760‡	4,760‡	4,740	4,550	4,320	4,110	3,870	3,620	3,370	10.421
9⅝	0.472	47.00	20.391	13.572	6,120‡	6,120‡	6,120‡	6,120‡	6,120‡	6,120‡	6,040	5,840	5,640	5,420	5,190	4,940	4,690	4,420	4,130	3,850	11.434
9⅝	0.545	53.50	17.660	15.547	8,830	8,640	8,470	8,250	8,020	7,810	7,530	7,280	7,030	6,750	6,480	6,160	5,850	5,510	5,150	4,800	13.408
10¾	0.450	51.00	23.889	14.561	3,750‡	3,750‡	3,750‡	3,750‡	3,750‡	3,750‡	3,750‡	3,750‡	3,750‡	3,750‡	3,750‡	3,750‡	3,590	3,380	3,160	2,950	12.171
10¾	0.495	55.50	21.717	15.947	5,040‡	5,040‡	5,040‡	5,040‡	5,040‡	5,040‡	5,040‡	5,040‡	5,040‡	4,890	4,690	4,460	4,230	3,990	3,730	3,470	13.557
10¾	0.545	60.70	19.725	17.473	6,790‡	6,790‡	6,790‡	6,790‡	6,770	6,590	6,370	6,150	5,940	5,710	5,470	5,200	4,940	4,660	4,360	4,060	15.082
10¾	0.595	65.70	18.067	18.982	8,540	8,360	8,190	7,980	7,750	7,550	7,290	7,040	6,800	6,530	6,260	5,960	5,660	5,330	4,990	4,640	16.592
10¾	0.650	71.10	16.538	20.625	9,720	9,510	9,320	9,090	8,830	8,590	8,290	8,020	7,740	7,440	7,130	6,780	6,440	6,070	5,670	5,290	18.234
10¾	0.700	76.00	15.357	22.101	10,790	10,560	10,340	10,090	9,800	9,540	9,210	8,900	8,590	8,250	7,910	7,530	7,150	6,730	6,300	5,870	19.711
10¾	0.750	81.00	14.333	23.562	11,870	11,620	11,380	11,090	10,780	10,490	10,130	9,790	9,450	9,080	8,700	8,280	7,860	7,410	6,930	6,450	21.172

Example: For 29-lb 7-in. D casing under a tensile load of 8,650 psi, interpolate as follows: 9,020 − 8,840 = 180 psi × (10,000 − 8,650) ÷ 5,000 = 49 psi + 8,840 = 8,889 psi.
* Collapsing pressures in psi for listed unit tensile stress correspond to setting depths in feet with a safety factor of 2 when set in salt water—specific gravity 1.15.
† For method of determining minimum yield strength safety factors, see p. 2-48.
‡ Elastic collapse.

Minimum Collapse Resistance under Axial Tension Stress
Grade V-150 Casing*

Unit tensile stress, psi, thousands — Adjusted collapsing pressure, psi†

Size, OD D, in.	Wall thickness t, in.	Wt./ft T & C, lb	D/t	Plain-end area,‡ sq in.	0	5	10	15	20	25	30	35	40	45	50	55	60	65	70	75	Area of pipe wall under last perfect thread (API), sq in.‡
5	0.296	15.00	16.891	4.374	11,010§	11,010§	11,010§	11,010§	11,010§	11,010§	11,010§	10,930	10,670	10,400	10,120	9,840	9,540	9,240	8,920	8,580	3.271
5	0.362	18.00	13.812	5.275	16,420	16,160	15,890	15,600	15,310	15,000	14,690	14,350	14,010	13,660	13,300	12,920	12,530	12,130	11,720	11,270	4.171
5½	0.361	20.00	15.235	5.828	14,460	14,230	13,990	13,740	13,480	13,210	12,930	12,640	12,340	12,030	11,710	11,380	11,040	10,690	10,320	9,930	4.613
5½	0.415	23.00	13.253	6.630	17,060	16,790	16,510	16,210	15,910	15,590	15,260	14,910	14,560	14,190	13,820	13,430	13,020	12,610	12,170	11,710	5.414
7	0.408	29.00	17.157	8.449	10,480§	10,480§	10,480§	10,480§	10,480§	10,480§	10,480§	10,480§	10,420	10,160	9,890	9,610	9,320	9,020	8,710	8,380	6.899
7	0.453	32.00	14.453	9.317	14,180	13,950	13,720	13,470	13,220	12,960	12,680	12,400	12,100	11,800	11,490	11,160	10,820	10,480	10,120	9,730	7.766
7	0.498	35.00	14.056	10.173	16,150	15,890	15,630	15,340	15,060	14,760	14,450	14,120	13,780	13,440	13,080	12,710	12,330	11,930	11,520	11,090	8.622
7	0.540	38.00	12.962	10.959	17,410	17,130	16,840	16,540	16,230	15,910	15,570	15,220	14,860	14,490	14,100	13,700	13,290	12,870	12,420	11,950	9.408
7⅝	0.430	33.70	17.732	9.720	9,460§	9,460§	9,460§	9,460§	9,460§	9,460§	9,460§	9,460§	9,460§	9,460§	9,420	9,150	8,880	8,590	8,300	7,980	8.029
7⅝	0.500	39.00	15.250	11.192	14,440	14,210	13,970	13,720	13,470	13,200	12,920	12,620	12,320	12,010	11,700	11,360	11,020	10,670	10,300	9,910	9.501
7⅝	0.595	45.30	12.815	13.141	17,590	17,310	17,020	16,710	16,400	16,070	15,730	15,380	15,010	14,630	14,250	13,840	13,430	13,000	12,550	12,080	11.450
8⅝	0.500	44.00	17.250	12.763	10,300§	10,300§	10,300§	10,300§	10,300§	10,300§	10,300§	10,300§	10,300§	10,080	9,810	9,530	9,240	8,950	8,640	8,310	10.848
8⅝	0.557	49.00	15.485	14.118	14,140	13,910	13,680	13,430	13,190	12,920	12,650	12,360	12,070	11,760	11,450	11,130	10,790	10,450	10,090	9,710	12.203
9⅝	0.545	53.50	17.660	15.547	9,580§	9,580§	9,580§	9,580§	9,580§	9,580§	9,580§	9,580§	9,580§	9,580§	9,480	9,210	8,930	8,650	8,350	8,030	13.408
9⅝	0.595	58.40	16.176	16.879	12,600§	12,600§	12,600§	12,600§	12,390	12,140	11,890	11,620	11,340	11,060	10,760	10,460	10,140	9,820	9,480	9,120	14.741
9⅝	0.625	61.10	15.400	17.672	14,240	14,010	13,780	13,530	13,280	13,010	12,740	12,450	12,150	11,850	11,530§	11,210	10,870	10,520	10,160	9,780	15.533
10¾	0.595	65.70	18.067	18.982	8,920§	8,920§	8,920§	8,920§	8,920§	8,920§	8,920§	8,920§	8,920§	8,920§	8,920§	8,900	8,630	8,360	8,070	7,760	16.592
10¾	0.650	71.10	16.538	20.625	11,760§	11,760§	11,760§	11,760§	11,760§	11,760§	11,520	11,260	10,990	10,720	10,430	10,140	9,830	9,520	9,190	8,840	18.234
10¾	0.700	76.00	15.357	22.101	14,300	14,070	13,840	13,580	13,330	13,070	12,790	12,500	12,210	11,900	11,580	11,250	10,920	10,570	10,200	9,820	19.711
10¾	0.750	81.00	14.333	23.562	15,730	15,480	15,220	14,940	14,670	14,370	14,070	13,750	13,430	13,090	12,740	12,380	12,010	11,620	11,220	10,800	21.172

Example: For 32-lb 7-in. D casing under a tensile load of 14,250 psi, interpolate as follows: 13,720 − 13,470 = 250 psi × (15,000 − 14,250) ÷ 5,000 = 38 psi + 13,470 = 13,508 psi.

* Tentative.
† Collapsing pressures in psi for listed unit tensile stress correspond to setting depths in feet with a safety factor of 2 when set in salt water—specific gravity 1.15.
‡ For method of determining minimum yield strength safety factors, see p. 2-48.
§ Elastic collapse.

Tensile Requirements

Grade	Yield strength, min, psi	Tensile strength, min, psi	Elongation, min, % in 2 in.	
			Strip specimens	Full-section specimens
Casing:				
F-25	25,000	40,000	40*	45*
H-40	40,000	60,000	27	32
J-55†	55,000	75,000	20	25
N-80	80,000	100,000	16	18
P-110	110,000	125,000	15	17
V-150‡	150,000			

* The minimum elongation in 8 in. shall be 20 per cent for all grade F-25 material except wrought iron, for which the minimum elongation in 8 in. shall be 12 per cent.
† Applies also to plain-end liners.   ‡ Tentative.

Hydrostatic Tests

Test Pressures. Test pressures shall be the standard pressures listed in tables on pp. **2**–8 to **2**–13 or a higher pressure as agreed upon between the purchaser and the manufacturer.

NOTE: The hydrostatic test pressures specified herein are mill-inspection test pressures, are not intended as a basis for design, and do not necessarily have any direct relationship to working pressures.

NOTE: The hydrostatic test pressures specified herein are based on the following formulas:

1. For grades F-25, H-40, and J-55,

$$P = \frac{2St}{D}$$

or 3,000, whichever is smaller.

2. For grades N-80, P-105, P-110, and V-150,*

$$P = \frac{2St}{D}$$

or 10,000, whichever is smaller.

where P = hydrostatic test pressure, psi
S = fiber stress, as given below
t = tabulated wall thickness, in.
D = tabulated outside diameter, in.

Grade	Fiber stress, psi		
	Standard test pressures		Alternative test pressures, all sizes
	Sizes 9⅝ in. and smaller	Sizes 10¾ in. and larger	
F-25	20,000*	15,000†	20,000*
H-40	32,000*	24,000†	32,000*
J-55	44,000*	33,000†	44,000*
N-80	64,000*	64,000*	
P-110	88,000*	88,000*	
V-150‡	120,000*	120,000*	

* Based on 80 per cent of the specified minimum yield strength.
† Based on 60 per cent of the specified minimum yield strength.   ‡ Tentative.

* Tentative.

Correction Factors for Collapse in Fluids of Various Densities

The setting depths in collapse as listed in the tables are for casing and tubing, when set in salt water having the following constants:

Specific gravity...................	1.154
Density:	
Gallon........................	9.625 lb
Cubic foot....................	72.000 lb
Fluid head:	
Pressure per ft of depth.........	0.500 psi
Height per psi..................	2.000 ft

The setting depth in fluid of any other density may be obtained by multiplying the setting depth in salt water by a correction factor that may be determined in the following manner:

When density of fluid is in gallons,

$$\text{Correction factor} = \frac{\text{density of salt water per gallon}}{\text{density of fluid per gallon}}$$

When density of fluid is in cubic feet,

$$\text{Correction factor} = \frac{\text{density of salt water per cubic foot}}{\text{density of fluid per cubic foot}}$$

When specific gravity of fluid is known,

$$\text{Correction factor} = \frac{\text{specific gravity of salt water}}{\text{specific gravity of fluid}}$$

Example. What is the setting depth in collapse of 7-in. × 23.0 grade J-55 casing when set in drilling mud weighing 90 lb/cu ft?

The collapsing pressure or its equivalent setting depth with a safety factor of 2.0 is obtained from either the table on page **2–41** or the chart on page **2–38** and is equal to 3,290 psi, or 3,290 ft (sf = 2.0).

The correction factor for a drilling mud having a weight of 90 lb/cu ft will be $^{72}\!\!/_{90}$ = 0.80, and the setting depth in mud of this weight, with a safety factor of 2.0 against collapse, is therefore 3,290 × 0.80 = 2.632 ft. For any other safety factor in collapse, say 1⅛, the setting depth in the same mud would be

$$\frac{3,290 \times 2 \times 0.80}{1.125} = 4,679 \text{ ft}$$

If the casing is to be set at 4,000 ft, the safety factor will be

$$\frac{3,290 \times 2 \times 0.80}{4,000} = 1.316$$

Correction factors F_m for fluids of various densities may be read directly from the chart on page **2–47**.

Example of a Method for Designing a Typical 11,000-ft Single-weight and Grade String to Meet Preselected Safety Factors for Collapse, Tension, and Internal Yield Pressure When Based on Minimum Physical Properties

Safety factors: Collapse.......... 1.125   Yield strength.................. 1.25
Tension.......... 2.00   Internal yield pressure.......... 1.00

Tabulated Design Data

Well depth, ft	Casing							Safety factors			
	Wt/ft, lb	Steel grade	Type of joint		Amount required, ft	Wt. of string, lb		Collapse*	Tension		Internal yield pressure
			Coupling	Type of thread		Section	Total		Ultimate strength	Yield strength	
11,000	29.00	N	Long	Buttress	2,050	59,450	319,000	4.70	2.75	2.12	1.48
	29.00	N	Long	API	8,950	259,550		1.16	2.00	2.13	1.48

* Effect of axial tension included.

Example of the design steps in setting up the string shown in the table above: Make a sketch similar to the one shown below and add a detailed description of each section as it is developed, such as length, weight, type of joint, safety factors.

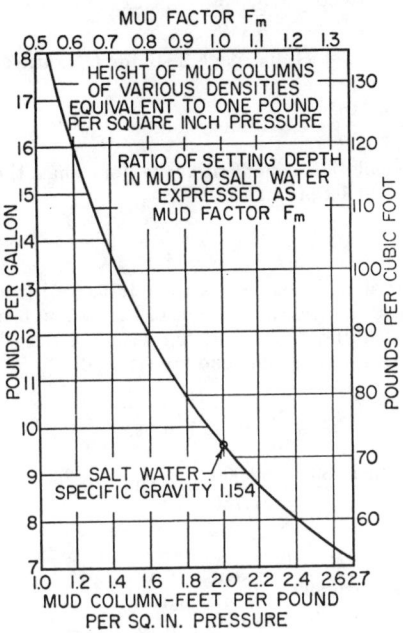

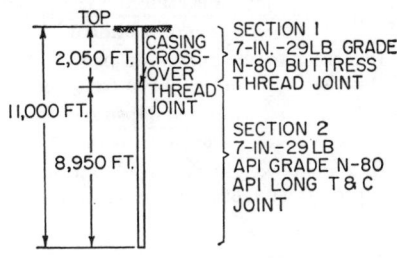

TOP

2,050 FT. CASING CROSS-OVER THREAD JOINT

11,000 FT.

8,950 FT.

SECTION 1
7-IN.–29LB GRADE
N-80 BUTTRESS
THREAD JOINT

SECTION 2
7-IN.–29 LB
API GRADE N-80
API LONG T & C
JOINT

Calculations, Collapse and Tension

Step 1. Determine lightest weight and lowest grade of casing necessary to resist collapse pressure for a setting depth of 11,000 ft. Refer to table of Collapse and Tension Properties, page **2–9**; the collapse column shows the maximum depths to which the casing may be set. Read the figure for 7 in. OD which equals or closely exceeds total depth of 11,000 ft. 29-lb N-80 casing reads 11,320 ft with a safety factor of 1⅛. Select this casing for section 2 and determine the safety factor.

$$\frac{2 \times \text{min collapse resistance}}{\text{Total depth of well}} = \frac{2 \times 6,370}{11,000} = 1.16 \text{ calculated safety factor}$$

Step 2. Determine the largest amount of 7 in. OD 29-lb N-80 API casing, long T & C, that can be set in tension with a minimum safety factor of 2.00.

Referring to the tables, the minimum ultimate joint strength is 520,000 lb. We divide this value by the desired safety factor and by the nominal weight per foot.

$$\frac{520,000}{2 \times 29.00} = 8,966$$

or in 50-ft increments equals 8,950 ft for section 2

$$\text{Safety factor} = \frac{\text{ultimate joint strength}}{\text{wt. of section 2}} = \frac{520,000}{8,950 \times 29.00} = 2.00$$

Step 3. The remainder of the string must be made up with a joint that will support the full weight of 11,000 ft of 29.00-lb casing with a minimum safety factor of 2 in tension. For this we select the 7 in. OD 29-lb N-80 casing with buttress threads. The amount required for section 1 equals 11,000 − 8,950 = 2,050 ft.

$$\text{Safety factor} = \frac{\text{ultimate joint strength}}{\text{weights of sections 1 and 2}} = \frac{877,000}{59,450 + 259,550} = 2.75$$

Step 4. Determine the safety factor in collapse for the buttress thread joint section 1.

Plain-end unit tensile stress

$$\frac{\text{Wt. of section 2}}{\text{Plain-end area of section 1}} = \frac{8{,}950 \times 29.00}{8.449} = \frac{259{,}550}{8.449} = 30{,}720 \text{ psi}$$

Referring to the curves on page **2**–39 for N-80 steel and page **2**–42 for D/t ratio of 17.16, the minimum collapse resistance is 4,820 psi.

$$\frac{2 \times \text{min collapse resistance}}{\text{Depth of section 1}} = \frac{9{,}640}{2{,}050} = 4.70 \text{ safety factor}$$

In a single-weight and grade string this calculation is not ordinarily done since the collapse safety factor is always higher in section 1 than in section 2.

Yield Strength

The minimum yield strength safety factor should not be less than 1.25. For the regular API threaded and coupled casing, the unit stress at the root of the last perfect thread should be determined, but for threaded and coupled casing with the runout thread such as the buttress thread, the unit stress at the plain end area is used.

Section 1:

$$\frac{\text{Total wt. of sections 1 and 2}}{\text{Plain-end metal area of section 1}} = \frac{319{,}000}{8.449} = 37{,}756 \text{ psi}$$

$$\text{Safety factor} = \frac{\text{min tensile yield N-80}}{37{,}756} = \frac{80{,}000}{37{,}756} = 2.12$$

Section 2:

$$\frac{\text{Wt. of section 2}}{\text{Root-thread area of section 2}} = \frac{259{,}550}{6.899} = 37{,}621 \text{ psi}$$

$$\text{Safety factor} = \frac{\text{min tensile yield N-80}}{37{,}621} = \frac{80{,}000}{37{,}621} = 2.13$$

Internal Yield Pressure

The safety factor for internal pressure based on minimum yield strength should never be less than 1.

When the proper weight has been selected for collapse calculations, it is good practice to check immediately the internal yield pressure safety factor for that weight. Internal yield pressures often govern design of deep strings. It is usual practice to estimate the pressure encountered in drilling as equivalent to 1 psi for every 2 ft of depth, or ½ psi for every foot of depth. However, if the formation pressure is known, this value should be divided into the internal yield strength to obtain the internal yield pressure safety factor.

In single-weight and grade strings the safety factors will be the same for all sections.

$$\frac{\text{Internal yield, psi}}{0.5 \times \text{total depth of well}} = \frac{8{,}160}{0.5 \times 11{,}000} = 1.48 \text{ safety factor}$$

Method of Designing Combination Strings

The term "combination casing" is generally applied to a casing string which is composed of more than one weight per foot, or more than one grade of steel, or of both.

Substantial savings can be effected by a suitable combination of weights and grades of casing, particularly when used in the deeper wells. The combinations are almost infinite and the savings are in proportion to the selection of the most effective weights or grades that can be used. There is, however, a practical limit to these combinations. Again it is well to keep in mind that there is considerable danger of weights or grades of casing becoming mixed in handling and being run in the wrong section at the well, and for this reason it is not recommended that combination casing strings be used except where the purchaser is prepared to give very close supervision to their handling around the well while the casing is being run.

Setting-depth information and the savings by the use of a combination casing string can be readily determined for any combination. For those who wish to work out their own combination strings, a typical example is offered on the following pages of the procedure to be followed in designing an 11,000-ft combination casing string. It should be recognized that there will be an additional saving in the use of combination strings in direct proportion to the cost of freight to destination.

Example of a Method for Designing a Typical 11,000-ft Casing Combination String to Meet Preselected Safety Factors for Collapse, Tension, and Internal Yield Pressure When Based on Minimum Physical Properties

Safety factors:

Collapse..........	1.125	Yield strength.................	1.25
Tension..........	2.00	Internal yield pressure..........	1.00

Tabulated Design Data

Well depth, ft	Casing							Safety factors			
	Wt./ft, lb	Steel grade	Type of joint		Amount required, ft	Wt. of string, lb		Collapse*	Tension		Internal yield pressure
			Coupling	Type of thread		Section	Total		Ultimate strength	Yield strength	
11,000	23.00	N	Long	Buttress	6,650	152,950	....	1.13	2.54	1.96	1.15
	26.00	N	Long	API	2,300	59,800	272,200	1.13	3.86	4.02	1.32
	29.00	N	Long	API	2,050	59,450	....	1.16	8.75	9.28	1.48

* Effect of axial tension included.

Example of the design steps followed in setting up the combination shown in the table above: Make a sketch similar to one shown below and add detailed description of each section as it is developed, such as length, weight, type of joint, safety factors.

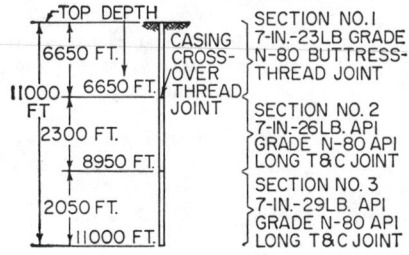

As a guide for estimating the number of sections for 7 in. OD combination casing, we arbitrarily suggest one section or a straight string up to 4,400 ft, two sections up to 7,500 ft, three sections up to 12,500 ft, etc.

Calculations, Collapse

Step 1. Determine lightest weight and grade of casing to resist collapse pressure for a setting depth of 11,000 ft. Refer to table of Collapse and Tension Properties, page **2**–29. The collapse column shows the maximum depths to which the casing may be set. Read the figure for 7 in. OD which equals or closely exceeds total depth of 11,000 ft. 29-lb N-80 casing reads 11,320 ft with a safety factor of 1⅛. Select this casing for section 3.

Step 2. Determine setting depth for next lighter weight for section 2. 7 in. OD 26-lb N-80 casing reads 9,460 ft. When there is casing hung below a section, as in all cases except the bottom section, the ability of the casing to resist collapse is reduced by the tensile load. Therefore, the 9,460 ft must be adjusted to suit the weight of casing beneath section 2. Subtract from total depth the maximum depth to which section 2 can be set

$$11{,}000 - 9{,}460 = 1{,}540 \text{ ft}$$

As an estimate of the tensile load reduction, take 30 per cent of the difference (30 per cent is not an exact value—only a guide to final design).

$1,540 \times 0.30 = 462$, or in 100-ft increments this is a 500-ft estimated reduction. Setting depth of section 2 from tables, minus estimated reduction,

$$9,460 - 500 = 8,960 \text{ ft}$$

or in 50-ft increments 8,950 ft estimated setting depth section 2:

Total setting depth minus estimated setting depth section 2,

$$11,000 - 8,950 = 2,050 \text{ ft}$$

of 29-lb N-80 casing, section 3.

Step 3. Check calculations for estimated setting depth section 2.

Plain-end unit tensile stress

D/t values and areas for all sizes of casing are listed on pages 2–40 to 2–44.

$$\frac{\text{Wt. of section 3}}{\text{Plain-end area of section 2}} = \frac{2,050 \times 29}{7.549} = \frac{59,450}{7.549} = 7,880 \text{ psi}$$

$$\frac{\text{Diameter}}{\text{Wall thickness}} = \frac{D}{t} = 19.3 \text{ for 7 in OD 26-lb casing}$$

Referring to curves for N-80 steel, page **2**–39, the minimum collapse resistance is 5,050 psi.

Tables on pages **2**–40 to **2**–44 may be used in place of curves on pages **2**–38 to **2**–39. See footnote on page **2**–42.

Since salt water is nearly always encountered in drilling, the length of the string is based on 2 ft of water column to each pound of collapsing pressure.

$$\frac{2 \times \text{min collapse resistance}}{\text{Safety factor}} = \frac{2 \times 5,050}{1.125} = 8,977 \text{ ft calculated setting depth}$$

This checks estimated setting depth of 8,950 ft.

In case the calculated setting depth is less than the estimated depth, a larger estimated reduction should be assumed and rechecked. Should the calculated setting depth be considerably greater than the estimated depth use a smaller estimated reduction and recheck.

Step 4. Determine the setting depth for the next lighter weight than section 2 from table used in steps 1 and 2. 7 in. OD 23-lb N-80 casing reads 7,640 ft. Subtract from total depth the maximum depth to which section 1 can be set,

$11,000 - 7,640 = 3,360 \text{ ft} \times 30 \text{ per cent} = 1,000 \text{ ft estimated reduction}$

$7,640 - 1,000 = 6,640$ or in 50-ft increments equals 6,650 ft estimated setting depth section 1.

Setting depth section 2 minus estimated setting depth section 1,

$$8,950 - 6,650 = 2,300 \text{ ft}$$

of 26-lb N-80 casing, section 2.

Step 5. Check calculations for estimated setting depth section 1:

Plain-end unit tensile stress

$$\frac{\text{Wt. of sections 2 and 3}}{\text{Plain-end area of section 1}} = \frac{2,300 \times 26 + 59,450}{6.656} = \frac{59,800 + 59,450}{6.656} = 17,900 \text{ psi}$$

Referring to curves on page **2**–39 for N-80 steel, and page **2**–42 for D/t ratio of 22.1, the minimum collapse resistance is 3,760 psi,

$$\frac{2 \times \text{min collapse resistance}}{\text{Safety factor}} = \frac{2 \times 3,760}{1.125} = 6,684 \text{ ft calculated setting depth}$$

This checks estimated setting depth of 6,650 ft. Place this figure at the bottom of section 1 in the sketch along with 2,300 ft of 7 in. OD 26-lb N-80 casing for section 2.

Tension

Conforming to regular design practice the safety factor in tension should be a minimum of 2.00. It is determined by dividing the minimum ultimate joint strength by the total weight beneath the top joint in each section.

Step 1. Top joint section 1. Select ultimate joint strength of 23-lb N-80 API long coupling from the table of Collapse and Tension Properties, page **2**–9, or $400 \times 1,000$.

$$\text{Safety factor} = \frac{\text{ultimate joint strength}}{\text{wt. of sections 1, 2, and 3}} = \frac{400,000}{6,650 \times 23 + 59,800 + 59,450}$$

$$= \frac{400,000}{272,200} = 1.47 \text{ safety factor}$$

Since 1.47 is less than 2.00, the long coupling must be replaced by a stronger joint. This is the advantage of the buttress-thread joint, whose performance properties are given in the table, page 2-20. As an example, select the minimum ultimate joint strength for 7 in. OD 23-lb N-80 buttress-thread casing,

$$\frac{691 \times 1,000}{272,200} = 2.54 \text{ safety factor}$$

In case the minimum ultimate joint strength of this size and grade does not give a safety factor of 2.00 when divided by the total weight below the critical joint, selection of another grade or weight or combination of both should be made.

Step 2. Top joint section 2. Try 26-lb N-80 long coupling API minimum ultimate joint strength,

$$\frac{\text{Ultimate joint strength}}{\text{Wt. of sections 2 and 3}} = \frac{460,000}{59,800 + 59,450} = 3.86 \text{ safety factor}$$

Since 3.86 is greater than the required factor of 2.00, the long coupling joint is satisfactory.

Step 3. Top joint section 3.

$$\frac{\text{Ultimate joint strength}}{\text{Wt. of section 3}} = \frac{520,000}{59,450} = 8.75 \text{ safety factor}$$

Yield Strength

The minimum yield strength safety factor should never be less than 1.25. For threaded and coupled casing, the unit stress at the root of the last perfect thread should be determined, but for threaded and coupled casing with the runout thread such as the buttress thread, the unit stress at the plain-end area is necessary.

Section 1:

$$\frac{\text{Total wt. of sections 1, 2, and 3}}{\text{Plain-end metal area of section 1}} = \frac{272,200}{6.656} = 40,865 \text{ psi}$$

$$\text{Safety factor} = \frac{\text{tensile yield N-80}}{40,865} = \frac{80,000}{40,865} = 1.96$$

Section 2:

$$\frac{\text{Wt. of sections 2 and 3}}{\text{Root-thread area of section 2}} = \frac{119,250}{5.998} = 19,882 \text{ psi}$$

$$\text{Safety factor} = \frac{\text{tensile yield N-80}}{19,882} = \frac{80,000}{19,882} = 4.02$$

Section 3:

$$\frac{\text{Wt. of section 3}}{\text{Root-thread area of section 3}} = \frac{59,450}{6.898} = 8,618 \text{ psi}$$

$$\text{Safety factor} = \frac{\text{tensile yield N-80}}{8,618} = \frac{80,000}{8,618} = 9.28$$

Internal Yield Pressure

The safety factor for internal pressure based on minimum yield strength should never be less than 1.

When the lightest weight has been selected during collapse calculations, it is good practice to check immediately the internal yield pressure safety factor for that weight. Internal yield pressure often governs design for the top sections of deep strings. It is usual practice to estimate the pressure encountered in drilling as equivalent to 1 psi for every 2 ft of depth, or $\frac{1}{2}$ psi for every foot of depth. However, if the formation pressure is known, this value should be divided into the internal yield strength of each section to obtain internal yield pressure safety factors.

$$\frac{\text{Internal yield, psi, for section 1}}{0.5 \times \text{total depth of well}} = \frac{6{,}340}{0.5 \times 11{,}000} = 1.15 \text{ safety factor}$$

$$\frac{\text{Internal yield, psi, for section 2}}{0.5 \times \text{total depth of well}} = \frac{7{,}240}{0.5 \times 11{,}000} = 1.32 \text{ safety factor}$$

$$\frac{\text{Internal yield, psi, for section 3}}{0.5 \times \text{total depth of well}} = \frac{8{,}160}{0.5 \times 11{,}000} = 1.48 \text{ safety factor}$$

Typical 15,600-ft Casing Combination String—Design A
7-in. OD Buttress Threads and API Long Threads and Coupling. API Grade
N-80 and API Grade P-110[1]

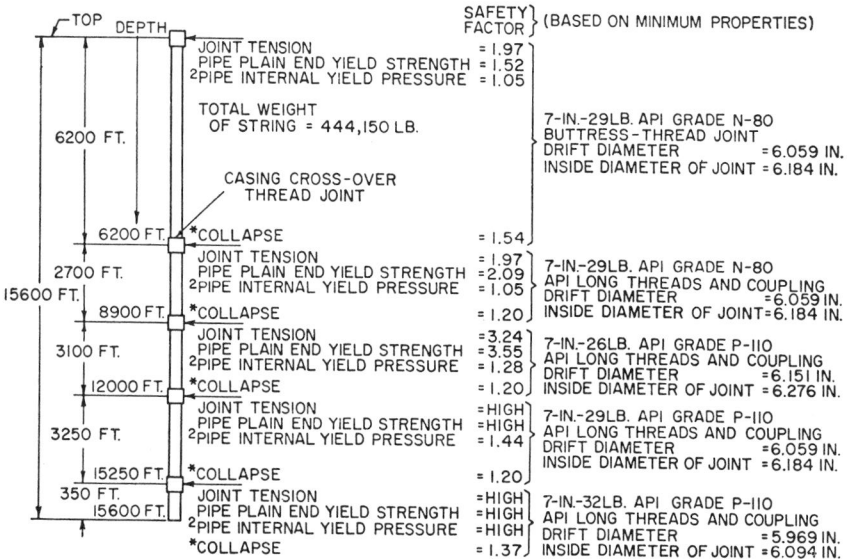

[1] Tentative.

[2] Pipe internal yield pressure safety factors are calculated using the minimum internal yield pressure strength of the casing subjected to a uniform internal pressure equal to $\frac{1}{2}$ psi/ft for the total depth.

* Based on minimum collapsing pressures, and effect of axial tension included, based on a 72-lb/cu ft drilling fluid.

Typical 22,000-ft Casing Combination String—Design B
7-in. OD Buttress Threads and API Long Threads and Coupling. API Grade
P-110[1] and Grade V-150[1]

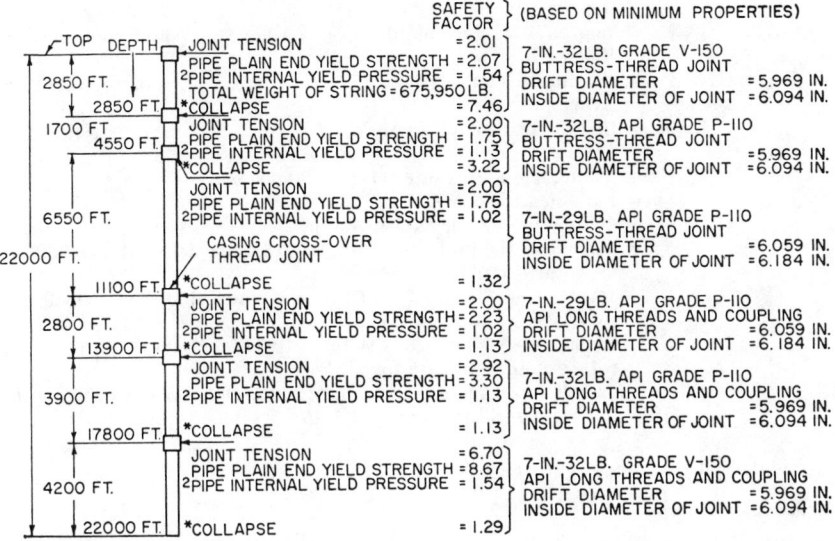

SAFETY FACTOR } (BASED ON MINIMUM PROPERTIES)

TOP DEPTH	JOINT TENSION = 2.01	7-IN.-32LB. GRADE V-150
2850 FT.	PIPE PLAIN END YIELD STRENGTH = 2.07	BUTTRESS-THREAD JOINT
	[2]PIPE INTERNAL YIELD PRESSURE = 1.54	DRIFT DIAMETER = 5.969 IN.
	TOTAL WEIGHT OF STRING = 675,950 LB.	INSIDE DIAMETER OF JOINT = 6.094 IN.
2850 FT.	*COLLAPSE = 7.46	
1700 FT.	JOINT TENSION = 2.00	7-IN.-32LB. API GRADE P-110
4550 FT.	PIPE PLAIN END YIELD STRENGTH = 1.75	BUTTRESS-THREAD JOINT
	[2]PIPE INTERNAL YIELD PRESSURE = 1.13	DRIFT DIAMETER = 5.969 IN.
	*COLLAPSE = 3.22	INSIDE DIAMETER OF JOINT = 6.094 IN.
6550 FT.	JOINT TENSION = 2.00	
	PIPE PLAIN END YIELD STRENGTH = 1.75	7-IN.-29LB. API GRADE P-110
	[2]PIPE INTERNAL YIELD PRESSURE = 1.02	BUTTRESS-THREAD JOINT
22000 FT.	CASING CROSS-OVER THREAD JOINT	DRIFT DIAMETER = 6.059 IN.
		INSIDE DIAMETER OF JOINT = 6.184 IN.
11100 FT.	*COLLAPSE = 1.32	
2800 FT.	JOINT TENSION = 2.00	7-IN.-29LB. API GRADE P-110
	PIPE PLAIN END YIELD STRENGTH = 2.23	API LONG THREADS AND COUPLING
	[2]PIPE INTERNAL YIELD PRESSURE = 1.02	DRIFT DIAMETER = 6.059 IN.
13900 FT.	*COLLAPSE = 1.13	INSIDE DIAMETER OF JOINT = 6.184 IN.
3900 FT.	JOINT TENSION = 2.92	7-IN.-32LB. API GRADE P-110
	PIPE PLAIN END YIELD STRENGTH = 3.30	API LONG THREADS AND COUPLING
	[2]PIPE INTERNAL YIELD PRESSURE = 1.13	DRIFT DIAMETER = 5.969 IN.
17800 FT.	*COLLAPSE = 1.13	INSIDE DIAMETER OF JOINT = 6.094 IN.
4200 FT.	JOINT TENSION = 6.70	7-IN.-32LB. GRADE V-150
	PIPE PLAIN END YIELD STRENGTH = 8.67	API LONG THREADS AND COUPLING
	[2]PIPE INTERNAL YIELD PRESSURE = 1.54	DRIFT DIAMETER = 5.969 IN.
		INSIDE DIAMETER OF JOINT = 6.094 IN.
22000 FT.	*COLLAPSE = 1.29	

[1] Tentative.

[2] Pipe internal yield pressure safety factors are calculated using the minimum internal yield pressure strength of the casing subjected to a uniform internal pressure equal to $\frac{1}{2}$ psi/ft for the total depth.

For method of designing a casing combination string see pp. 2-48 to 2-52.

* Based on minimum collapsing pressures, and effect of axial tension included, based on a 72-lb/cu ft drilling fluid.

Stretch in Casing When Freely Suspended in Fluid Media (Also Applicable to Tubing)

When pipe is subjected to an axial stress, either tension or compression, which does not exceed the elastic limit of the material, the stretch or contraction may be determined by use of Young's modulus of elasticity, expressed thus

$$E = \frac{S}{u} \quad \text{or} \quad E = \frac{P/A}{e/l} \tag{1}$$

when l = length of pipe, in.
S = unit stress, psi
e = total axial stretch or contraction, in.
u = unit axial stretch or contraction, in.
P = superimposed tension or compression, axial load, lb
A = cross-sectional metal area of pipe, sq in.
E = Young's modulus of elasticity = 30,000,000 psi for steel pipe

The unit tension or compression stress in pipe, when lateral deflection is prevented, is $S = P/A$, unit axial stretch or contraction being $u = e/l$.

The charts on page 2-55 give stretch in single-weight strings of pipe of one grade, or in combination strings of more than one weight or grade.

Formulas from which these charts were developed are also given and are based on a modified form of Eq. (1), with the lateral contraction of the pipe taken into consideration.

Symbols for Charts and Formulas

$$e = \text{total stretch of combination string, in.}$$

$e_1, e_2, \ldots, e_n$ = free stretch of single-weight sections 1, 2, . . . , n of combination strings, in.

$L_1, L_2, \ldots, L_n$ = lengths of single-weight sections 1, 2, . . . , n of combination strings, ft

$W_1, W_2, \ldots, W_n$ = weights of single-weight sections 1, 2, . . . , n of combination strings, lb

$b_1, b_2, \ldots, b_n$ = factor corresponding to $L_1, L_2, \ldots, L_n$ (n represents any number)

E = Young's modulus of elasticity, 30,000,000

μ = Poisson's ratio = 0.3

d = density of steel, 0.2833 lb/cu in.

f = density of floatant, lb/cu in., 0.041728 for salt water, 0.052385 for rotary mud

C_1 = constant—0.000000120177 for salt water, 0.000000150869 for rotary mud, and zero for air

C_2 = constant—0.000000200294 for salt water, 0.000000251448 for rotary mud, and zero for air

f, C_1, and C_2 are based on salt water having a specific gravity of 1.155 and rotary mud having a specific gravity of 1.45

Formulas for Charts on Page 2-55

Combination Strings

$$e = e_1 + e_2 + \cdots + e_n + b_1 \frac{W_2 + W_3 + \cdots + W_n}{W_1} + b_2 \frac{W_3 + \cdots + W_n}{W_2} +$$

$$\cdots + b_{n-1} \frac{W_n}{W_{n-1}} + C_1[L_1 \times L_2 + (L_1 + L_2)L_3 + \cdots + (L_1 + \cdots + L_{n-1})L_n]$$

$$- C_2 \left[L_2{}^2 \frac{W_1}{W_2} + L_3{}^2 \frac{W_1 + W_2}{W_3} + \cdots + L_n{}^2 \frac{W_1 + \cdots + W_{n-1}}{W_n} \right] \quad (2)$$

$$e_n = \frac{72}{E} [d - 2f(1 - \mu)]L_n{}^2 \qquad \text{for air } e_n = \frac{72d}{E} L_n{}^2 \quad (3)$$

$$b_n = \frac{144}{E} (d - f)L_n{}^2 \quad (4)$$

$$C_1 = \frac{288 \times \mu \times f}{E} \quad (5)$$

$$C_2 = \frac{144 \times f}{E} \quad (6)$$

2-weight Combination Strings

$$e = e_1 + e_2 + b_1 \frac{W_2}{W_1} + C_1 (L_1 L_2) - C_2 \left(L_2{}^2 \frac{W_1}{W_2} \right) \quad (7)$$

Single-weight Strings

$$e = \text{total free stretch, in.}$$

$$e = \frac{72}{E} [d - 2f(1 - \mu)]L^2 \qquad \text{for air } e = \frac{72d}{E} L^2 \quad (8)$$

Example

3-weight combination string freely suspended in salt water:

Wt. per ft of top section = 23 lb, 5,000 ft long (L_1) W_1 = 5,000 × 23 = 115,000 lb
Wt. per ft of middle section = 26 lb, 3,000 ft long (L_2) W_2 = 3,000 × 26 = 78,000 lb
Wt. per ft of bottom section = 29 lb, 2,000 ft long (L_3) W_3 = 2,000 × 29 = 58,000 lb

From Eq. (2),

$$e = e_1 + e_2 + e_3 + b_1 \frac{W_2 + W_3}{W_1} + b_2 \frac{W_3}{W_2} + C_1[L_1 \times L_2 + (L_1 + L_2)L_3]$$

$$- C_2 \left(L_2{}^2 \frac{W_1}{W_2} + L_3{}^2 \frac{W_1 + W_2}{W_3} \right)$$

From the charts on this page we get the values of e_1 and b_1 corresponding to length L_1; e_2, b_2 from L_2; and e_3 from L_3.

$$e = 13.5 + 4.86 + 2.16 + 29\frac{78,000 + 58,000}{115,000} + 10.4\frac{58,000}{78,000}$$

$$+ 0.000000120177[5,000 \times 3,000 + (5,000 + 3,000)2,000]$$

$$- 0.000000200294 \left[3,000^2 \frac{115,000}{78,000} + 2,000^2 \frac{115,000 + 78,000}{58,000} \right]$$

$$= 20.52 + 29 \times 1.183 + 10.4 \times 0.744 + 0.000000120177 \times 31,000,000$$
$$- 0.000000200294 \times 26,578,000$$
$$= 20.52 + 34.31 + 7.74 + 3.73 - 5.32 = 60.98 \text{ in.}$$

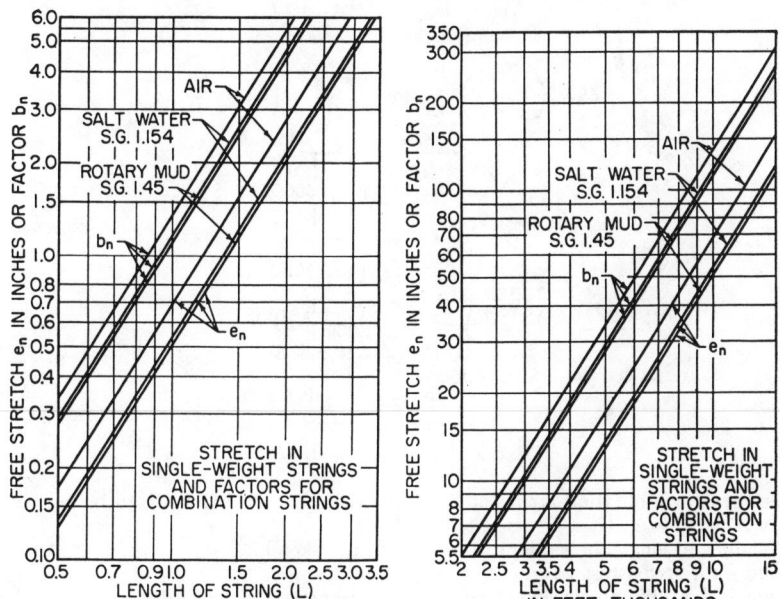

Relieving Stresses in Suspended Casing Strings

Method of determining tension stresses in strings of casing after they are set and cemented.

Combination String

Symbols

$L_1, L_2, \ldots, L_n$ = lengths of single-weight sections 1, 2, . . . , n of combination strings, ft—above top of cement
$L_1', L_2', \ldots, L_n'$ = same as above but below top of cement
$w_1, w_2, \ldots, w_n$ = weights, lb/ft, of single-weight sections 1, 2, . . . , n of combination string—above top of cement
$w_1', w_2', \ldots, w_n'$ = same as above but below top of cement

C_1 = constant—0.8527 for salt water (specific gravity = 1.155), 0.8151 for rotary mud (specific gravity = 1.45), and 1.0 for air

C_2 = constant (0.00000136)

P = total load, below top of cement, lb

k = distance, in., required to lower top of casing for zero stress at top of cement

S = tension stress desired to be left at top of cement, psi

k_s = stretch, in., corresponding to S

k_d = distance, in., to lower top of casing for a desired stress S at top of cement

C_3 = constant (0.0000004)

Other symbols are given on pages **2–53** and **2–54**.

Formulas

$$P = C_1(w_1'L_1' + w_2'L_2' + \cdots + w_n'L_n')$$
$$k = C_2P \left(\frac{L_1}{w_1} + \frac{L_2}{w_2} + \cdots + \frac{L_n}{w_n} \right)$$
$$k_s = C_3SL \text{ where } L = (L_1 + L_2 + \cdots + L_n)$$
$$k_d = k - k_s$$
$$C_1 = \left(1 - \frac{f}{d} \right) \qquad C_2 = \frac{40.8}{E} \qquad C_3 = \frac{12}{E}$$

Examples

Assume a combination string of 7 in. OD casing, 11,000 ft long, to be suspended freely in salt water, then cemented 4,000 ft up.

Weight and length of sections, as shown in the sketch.

Find k for zero stress at top of cement.

Find k_d for 5,000 lb tension stress at top of cement.

$$P = C_1(w_1'L_1' + w_2'L_2') = 0.8527(32 \times 2,000) + 38 \times 2,000)$$
$$= 0.8527(64,000 + 76,000) = 0.8527 \times 140,000 = 119,378 \text{ lb}$$
$$k = 0.00000136P \left(\frac{L_1}{w_1} + \frac{L_2}{w_2} + \frac{L_3}{w_3} \right)$$
$$= 0.00000136 \times 119,378 \left(\frac{3,500}{26} + \frac{3,000}{29} + \frac{500}{32} \right)$$
$$= 0.16235(134.62 + 103.45 + 15.63)$$
$$= 0.16235 \times 253.70 = 41.19 \text{ in.}$$
$$k_s = C_3SL = 0.0000004 \times 5,000(3,500 + 3,000 + 500) = 0.002 \times 7,000$$
$$= 14 \text{ in.}$$
$$k_d = k - k_s = 41.19 - 14 = 27.19 \text{ in.}$$

For any variation in temperature after cementing, the corresponding expansion or contraction for the part of the string above the cement must be taken into consideration.

Cementing of Casing—Capacity
Based on One Sack of Cement When Set Equaling 1.1 Cubic Feet

Size, OD, in.	ID, in.	Wt./ft, lb.	Wall thickness, in.	Lin ft inside of casing filled by 1 sack of cement	Fluid capacity of casing per 100 lin ft	
					Bbl (42 gal)	Cu ft
4½	4.090	9.50	0.205	12.1	1.6	9.12
4½	4.000	11.60	0.250	12.6	1.6	8.73
4½	3.920	13.50	0.290	13.1	1.5	8.38
5	4.560	11.50	0.220	9.7	2.0	11.34
5	4.494	13.00	0.253	10.0	2.0	11.02
5	4.408	15.00	0.296	10.4	1.9	10.60
5	4.276	18.00	0.362	11.0	1.8	9.97
5½	5.044	13.00	0.228	7.9	2.5	13.88
5½	5.012	14.00	0.244	8.0	2.4	13.70
5½	4.950	15.50	0.275	8.2	2.4	13.36
5½	4.892	17.00	0.304	8.4	2.3	13.05
5½	4.778	20.00	0.361	8.8	2.2	12.45
5½	4.670	23.00	0.415	9.2	2.1	11.89
6⅝	6.135	17.00	0.245	5.4	3.7	20.53
6⅝	6.049	20.00	0.288	5.5	3.5	19.96
6⅝	5.921	24.00	0.352	5.8	3.4	19.12
6⅝	5.791	28.00	0.417	6.0	3.3	18.29
6⅝	5.675	32.00	0.475	6.3	3.1	17.57
7	6.538	17.00	0.231	4.7	4.2	23.31
7	6.456	20.00	0.272	4.8	4.1	22.73
7	6.366	23.00	0.317	5.0	3.9	22.10
7	6.276	26.00	0.362	5.1	3.8	21.48
7	6.184	29.00	0.408	5.3	3.7	20.86
7	6.094	32.00	0.453	5.4	3.6	20.26
7	6.004	35.00	0.498	5.6	3.5	19.66
7	5.920	38.00	0.540	5.8	3.4	19.11
7⅝	7.125	20.00	0.250	4.0	4.9	27.69
7⅝	7.025	24.00	0.300	4.1	4.8	26.92
7⅝	6.969	26.40	0.328	4.2	4.7	26.49
7⅝	6.875	29.70	0.375	4.3	4.6	25.78
7⅝	6.765	33.70	0.430	4.4	4.5	24.96
7⅝	6.625	39.00	0.500	4.6	4.3	23.94
8⅝	8.097	24.00	0.264	3.1	6.4	35.76
8⅝	8.017	28.00	0.304	3.1	6.2	35.05
8⅝	7.921	32.00	0.352	3.2	6.1	34.22
8⅝	7.825	36.00	0.400	3.3	6.0	32.40
8⅝	7.725	40.00	0.450	3.4	5.8	32.55
8⅝	7.625	44.00	0.500	3.5	5.7	31.71
8⅝	7.511	49.00	0.557	3.6	5.5	30.77
9⅝	9.063	29.30	0.281	2.5	8.0	44.80
9⅝	9.001	32.30	0.312	2.5	7.9	44.19
9⅝	8.921	36.00	0.352	2.5	7.7	43.41
9⅝	8.835	40.00	0.395	2.6	7.6	42.57
9⅝	8.755	43.50	0.435	2.6	7.5	41.81
9⅝	8.681	47.00	0.472	2.7	7.3	41.10
9⅝	8.535	53.50	0.545	2.8	7.1	39.73
10¾	10.192	32.75	0.279	1.9	10.1	56.66
10¾	10.045	40.50	0.350	2.0	9.8	55.09
10¾	9.950	45.50	0.400	2.0	9.6	54.00
10¾	9.850	51.00	0.450	2.1	9.4	52.92
10¾	9.760	55.50	0.495	2.1	9.2	51.95

PRODUCTION EQUIPMENT

Cementing of Casing—Capacity (*Continued*)

Size, OD, in.	ID, in.	Wt./ft, lb.	Wall thickness, in.	Lin ft inside of casing filled by 1 sack of cement	Fluid capacity of casing per 100 lin ft	
					Bbl (42 gal)	Cu ft
11¾	11.150	38.00	0.300	1.6	12.1	67.81
11¾	11.084	42.00	0.333	1.6	11.9	67.01
11¾	11.000	47.00	0.375	1.7	11.7	65.99
11¾	10.880	54.00	0.435	1.7	11.5	64.56
11¾	10.772	60.00	0.489	1.7	11.3	63.29
13⅜	12.715	48.00	0.330	1.2	15.7	88.18
13⅜	12.615	54.50	0.380	1.3	15.5	86.79
13⅜	12.515	61.00	0.430	1.3	15.2	85.42
13⅜	12.415	68.00	0.480	1.3	15.0	84.06
13⅜	12.347	72.00	0.514	1.3	14.8	83.15
16	15.375	55.00	0.3125	0.86	23.0	128.93
16	15.250	65.00	0.375	0.87	22.6	126.84
16	15.125	75.00	0.4375	0.88	22.2	124.77
16	15.010	84.00	0.495	0.90	21.9	122.88
20	19.124	94.00	0.438	0.55	35.5	199.47

Cementing of Casing—Outside
Lineal Feet Cemented Outside of Casing per Sack of Cement

Diam of hole, in.

Size, OD, in.	6	6¼	6½	6¾	7	7⅜	7⅝	7⅞	8	8⅝	8¾	9	9⅝	9¾	9⅞	10	10½	11	11½	12	12¼	12½
4½	12.8	10.7	9.2	8.0	7.0	5.9	5.3	4.8	4.6	3.7	3.6	3.3	2.8	2.7	2.6	2.5	2.2	2.0	2.0	1.8	1.7	1.6
5	18.4	14.3	11.7	9.8	8.4	6.9	6.1	5.4	5.2	4.1	3.9	3.6	3.0	2.9	2.8	2.7	2.4	2.1	2.3	2.0	1.9	1.8
5⅝		22.9	16.8	13.2	10.8	8.4	7.2	6.3	6.0	4.6	4.4	4.0	3.2	3.1	3.0	2.9	2.5	2.6	2.4	2.1	2.0	1.9
6⅝							14.2	11.1	10.0	6.6	6.2	5.4	4.1	3.9	3.8	3.6	3.0	2.8	2.7	2.3	2.2	2.1
7									13.4	7.9	7.3	6.3	4.6	4.4	4.2	4.0	3.3	3.2	3.5	2.9	2.7	2.5
7⅝										12.4	10.9	8.8	5.8	5.5	5.1	4.8	3.9	4.3	5.1	3.9	3.5	3.2
8⅝													11.1	9.8	8.7	7.8	5.6	7.1	12.1	7.1	5.8	5.0
9⅝																	11.4					11.1
10¾																						
11¾																						

Diam of hole, in.

Size, OD, in.	13	13⅜	13¾	14	14½	14¾	15	15½	16	16½	17	17½	18	18½	19	19¾	20	21	22	24	26	28
5½	1.5	1.5	1.4	1.3	1.3	1.2	1.1	1.4	1.2	1.3	1.2	1.2	1.1	1.2	1.1	1.0	0.9	1.1	0.9	1.2	0.8	0.5
6⅝	1.6	1.6	1.4	1.4	1.3	1.3	1.2	1.6	1.4	1.5	1.3	1.6	1.4	2.3	1.9	1.5	1.4	4.9	2.4			
7	1.7	1.7	1.5	1.5	1.5	1.4	1.3	2.0	1.7	2.2	1.8	4.0	2.9									
7⅝	1.8	1.9	1.8	1.7	1.7	1.6	1.5	3.3	2.6		6.1											
8⅝	2.1	2.3	2.1	2.0	2.1	2.0	1.8															
9⅝	2.6	3.2	2.7	2.5	2.8	2.5	2.3															
10¾	3.8	4.9	4.0	3.5	6.4	5.2	4.4															
11¾	6.5																					
13⅜																						
16																						
20																						

Single-weight String Suspended in Rotary Mud

Distance k required to lower top of casing for a zero stress at top of cement.

Formula

$$k = C_4(D - L')L'$$

when $C_4 = C_1C_2 = 0.00000136C_1$

D = total depth of well or length of string, ft

L' = height to which cemented or length of casing below top of cement, ft

Example

Assume a single-weight string of any outside diameter and weight, 8,000 ft long, suspended freely in rotary mud having a specific gravity of 1.45, then cemented 2,100 ft up.

$C_1 = 0.8151$ $D = 8,000$ ft $L' = 2,100$

$k = C_4(D - L')L'$, $= 0.00000136 \times 0.8151(8,000 - 2,100)2,100$

$\quad = 0.0000011085 \times 5,900 \times 21,00$

$\quad = 13.7$ in., representing the amount the top of casing has to be lowered for a zero stress at top of cement

API RECOMMENDED PRACTICE FOR CARE AND USE OF CASING

Running and Pulling Casing

Preparation and Inspection before Running

1. All casing, whether new, used, or reconditioned, should always be handled with thread protectors in place.

2. Slip elevators are recommended for long strings. Both spider and elevator slips should be clean and sharp and should fit properly. Slips should be extra long for heavy casing strings.

3. If collar-pull elevators are used, the bearing surface should be carefully inspected for (1) uneven wear which may produce a side lift on the coupling with danger of jumping it off, and (2) uniform distribution of the load when applied over the bearing face of the coupling.

4. Spider and elevator slips should be examined and watched to see that all lower together. If they lower unevenly, there is danger of denting the pipe or badly slip-cutting it.

5. Care must be exercised, particularly when running long casing strings, to ensure that the slip bushing or bowl is in good condition.

6. The following precautions should be taken in the preparation of casing threads for make-up in the casing strings:

    a. Immediately before running, remove thread protectors from both field and coupling ends of a number of lengths of casing on the top row of the rack, and clean the threads thoroughly, repeating as additional rows become uncovered.

    b. Carefully inspect the threads. Those found damaged, even slightly, should be laid aside unless satisfactory means are available for correcting thread damage.

    c. Place a clean thread protector on the field end of the pipe so that the thread will not be damaged while rolling pipe on the rack and pulling into the derrick. Several thread protectors may be cleaned and used repeatedly for this operation.

    d. Before stabbing, apply ample thread compound over the entire threaded section of both external and internal threads.

    e. Check each coupling for make-up. If the stand-off is abnormally great, check the joint for tightness. Tighten any loose couplings after thoroughly cleaning the threads and applying fresh compound over entire thread surfaces, and before pulling the pipe into the derrick.

7. *Drifting of Casing.* It is recommended that each length of casing be drifted for its entire length just before running, with mandrels conforming to the requirements of Standard 5A. Casing which will not pass the drift test should be laid aside.

8. Lower or roll each piece of casing carefully to the walk without dropping. Use rope snubber if necessary. Avoid hitting casing against any part of derrick or other equipment. Provide a hold-back rope at window. For mixed or unmarked strings, a drift or "jack rabbit" should be run through each length of casing when it is picked up from the catwalk and pulled onto the derrick floor, to avoid running a heavier length or one with a lesser inside diameter than called for in the casing string.

Stabbing, Making Up, and Lowering

9. Do not remove thread protector from field end of casing until ready to stab.

10. If necessary, apply thread compound over entire surface of threads just before stabbing. The brush or utensil used in applying thread compound should be kept free of foreign matter and the compound should never be thinned.

11. In stabbing, lower casing carefully to avoid injuring threads. Stab vertically, preferably with assistance of a man on the stabbing board. If the casing stand tilts to one side after stabbing, lift up, clean, and correct any damaged thread with three-cornered file, then carefully remove any fillings and reapply compound over the thread surface. After stabbing, if spinning line or rotary table make-up post is used, the casing should be rotated very slowly at first to ensure that threads are engaging properly and that they are not cross-threading. The spinning line should pull close to the coupling.

Note: *The following recommendations for casing make-up apply to the use of spinning lines and the conventional casing tongs.*

12. Tighten with tongs to proper degree of tightness. The joint should be made up beyond the handtight position at least 3 turns for sizes 4½ through 7 in., and at least 3½ turns for sizes 7⅝ in. and larger. When using a spinning line it is necessary to compare handtightness with spin-up tightness. In order to do this, make up the first few joints to the handtight position, then back off and spin up joints to the spin-up tight position. Compare relative position of these two make-ups and use this information to determine when the joint is made up the recommended number of turns beyond handtight. However, the final make-up should be more than the recommended number of turns if there are sufficient indications that the joint is still not tight at the recommended number of turns make-up. A supplemental method for determining the effectiveness of make-up is to place the bare hand on the coupling at frequent intervals; when the proper method is being used, the coupling will get uniformly warm. A hot spot on the coupling is an indication of galling.

13. Joints that are questionable as to their proper tightness should be unscrewed and the casing laid down for inspection and repair, if practical. When this is done, the mating coupling should be carefully inspected for damaged threads. Parted joints should never be reused without shopping or regauging, even though the joints may have little appearance of damage.

14. If casing has a tendency to wobble unduly at its upper end when making up, indicating that the thread may not be in line with the axis of the casing, the speed of rotation should be decreased to prevent galling of threads. If wobbling should persist despite reduced rotational speed, the casing should be laid down for inspection. Serious consideration should be given before using such casing in a position in the string where a heavy tensile load is imposed.

15. In making up the field joint it is possible for the coupling to make up slightly on the mill end. This does not indicate that the coupling on the mill end is too loose, but simply that the field end has reached the tightness with which the coupling was screwed on at the mill.

16. Casing strings should be picked up and lowered carefully, and care exercised in setting slips to avoid shock loads. Dropping a string even a short distance may loosen couplings at the bottom of the string. Care should be exercised in setting casing down on bottom, or otherwise placing it in compression because of the danger of buckling, particularly in that part of the well where hole enlargement has occurred.

17. Definite instructions should be available as to the design of the casing string, including the proper location of the various grades of steel, weights of casing, and types of joint. Care should be exercised to run the string in exactly the order in which it was designed. If any length cannot be clearly identified, it should be laid aside until its grade, weight, or type of joint can be positively established.

18. Immediately after each length of casing is made up, the string lowered, and the slips set, the length should be filled with mud, using a conveniently located hose of adequate size to fill each length during the time required to raise the next length from the runway into the derrick and prepare the field thread for running. A quick-opening and -closing plug valve on the mud hose will facilitate the operation and prevent overflow. If rubber hose is used, it is recommended that the quick-closing valve be mounted where the hose is connected to the mud line, rather than at the outlet end of the hose. It is also recommended that at least one other discharge connection be left open on the mud system to prevent build-up of excessive pressure when the quick-closing valve is closed while the pump is still running. A copper nipple at the end of the mud hose may be used to prevent damaging of the coupling threads during the filling operation. (The foregoing mud fill-up practice will be unnecessary, if automatic fill-up casing shoes and collars are used.)

Casing Landing Procedure

19. Definite instructions should be available for the proper string tension, also on the proper landing procedure after the cement has set. The purpose is to avoid critical stresses or excessive and unsafe tensile stresses at any time during the life of the well. In arriving at the proper tension and landing procedure, consideration should be given to all factors such as well temperature and pressure, temperature developed due to cement hydration, mud temperature, and changes of temperature during producing operations. The adequacy of the original tension safety factor of the string as designed will influence the landing procedure and should be considered. If, however, after due consideration it is not considered necessary to develop special landing procedure instructions (and this probably applies to a very large majority of the wells drilled), then the procedure should be followed of landing the casing in the casing head at exactly the position in which it was hanging when the cement plus reached its lowest point or "as cemented."

Care of Casing in Hole

20. Drill pipe run inside of casing should be equipped with suitable drill-pipe protectors.

Recovery of Casing

21. Break-out tongs should be positioned close to the coupling. Hammering the coupling to break the joint is an injurious practice. If tapping is required, use the flat face, *never* the peen face of the hammer, and *under no circumstances* should a sledge hammer be used. Tap lightly near the center and completely around the coupling, never near the end or on opposite sides only.

22. Great care should be exercised to disengage all the thread before lifting the casing out of the coupling. Do not jump casing out of coupling.

23. Lubricate all threads, or coat with noncorrosive protective coating, and place protectors on the casing before laying down.

24. Before casing is stored or reused, pipe and thread should be inspected and defective joints marked for shopping and regauging.

Causes of Casing Troubles

25. The more common causes of casing troubles are as follows:
a. Improper selection for depth and pressures encountered.
b. Insufficient inspection of each length of casing or of field-shop threads.
c. Abuse in mill, transportation, and field handling.

d. Nonobservance of good rules in running and pulling casing.
e. Improper cutting of field-shop threads.
f. The use of poorly manufactured couplings for replacements and additions.
g. Improper care in storage.
h. Excessive tonging of casing to force it through tight places in the hole.
i. Pulling too hard on a string (to free it). This may loosen the couplings at the top of the string. They should be retightened with tongs before finally setting the string.
j. Rotary drilling inside casing after it has been cemented sometimes results in a concentration of bending stresses at the root of the last engaged pipe thread and causes failure at this point. Such failures usually occur near the top of the string above the top of the cement and are due to vibration fatigue caused by the slapping of the tool joints. Setting the casing with improper tension after cementing is probably a contributing cause of such failures.
k. Wire-line cutting, by swabbing or cable-tool drilling.
l. Buckling of casing in an enlarged, washed-out uncemented cavity if too much tension is released in landing.
m. Dropping a string, even a very short distance.
n. Leaky joints, under external or internal pressure, are a common trouble, and may be due to:
    1. Improper thread compound.
    2. Undertonging.
    3. Dirty threads.
    4. Galled threads, due to dirt, careless stabbing, damaged threads, too rapid spinning, overtonging, or wobbling during spinning or tonging operations.
    5. Improper cutting of field-shop threads.
    6. Pulling too hard on string.
    7. Dropping string.
    8. Excessive making and breaking.
    9. Tonging too high on casing, especially on breaking out. This gives a bending effect which tends to gall the threads.
    10. Improper joint make-up at mill.
    11. Casing ovality or out of roundness.
    12. Improper landing practice which produces stresses in the threaded joint in excess of the yield point.
o. *Corrosion.* Both the inside and outside of tubing can be damaged by corrosion. The damage is generally in the form of pitting, box wear, stress-corrosion cracking, and sulfide stress cracking, but localized attack like corrosion-erosion, ringworm, and caliper tracks can also occur. Pitting and wear by the sucker rod box can be determined visually by caliper surveys. Cracking may require aids, such as magnetic powder, for detection. Corrosion products may or may not adhere to the pipe walls. Corrosion is generally due to the corrosive well fluid but may be aggravated by abrasive effects of pumping equipment, by gas lifting or by high velocities. Corrosion can also be influenced by dissimilar metals in close proximity to each other (bimetallic corrosion), and by variations in grain structure, surface conditions, and deposits (concentration cell corrosion). Since corrosion can result from many causes and influences and take different forms, no simple or universal remedy can be given for control. Each problem must be treated individually, and the solution must be attempted in light of known factors and operating conditions.
    1. Where internal or external tubing corrosion is known to exist and corrosive fluids are being produced, the following measures can be employed:
        a. In flowing wells the annulus can be packed off and the corrosive fluid confined to the inside of the tubing. The inside of tubing can be protected with special liners, coatings, or inhibitors. Under severe conditions, special alloy steel or glass reinforced plastics may be used. Alloys do not always eliminate corrosion. For stress-corrosion cracking or sulfide cracking, steels with controlled mechanical properties are needed. Chemical inhibitors may be used.
        b. In pumping and gas-lift wells, inhibitors can be introduced via the casing-

tubing annulus and afford appreciable protection. In this type of completion, especially in pumping wells, better operating practices can also aid in extending the life of tubing; viz., through the use of rod protectors, rotation of tubing, and longer and slower pumping strokes.

2. To determine the value and effectiveness of the above practices and measures, cost and equipment failure records can be compared before and after application of control measures. Inhibitor effectiveness can also be checked by means of coupons, caliper surveys, and visual examinations of readily accessible pieces of equipment. Water analyses to determine the iron content before and after starting the inhibitor treatment may also serve as an indication of the comparative rates of corrosion. When lacking previous experience with any of the above measures, these should be used cautiously and on a limited scale until appraised for the particular operating conditions.

3. In general, all new areas should be considered as being potentially corrosive and investigations should be initiated early in the life of a field, and repeated periodically, to detect and localize corrosion before it has done destructive damage. These investigations should cover: (a) an analysis of produced gas for carbon dioxide and hydrogen sulfide. Also desirable is an analysis of the effluent water for pH, iron content, organic acids, total chlorides, and other substances believed to influence the individual problem; (b) corrosion rate tests by using coupons of the same materials as in the well; and (c) the use of caliper or optional instrument inspections. Where conditions favorable to corrosion exist, a qualified corrosion engineer should be consulted. Particular attention should be given to mitigation of corrosion where the probable life of subsurface equipment is less than the time expected to deplete a well.

PART 2: TUBING

The performance of tubing, which is run inside casing to conduct oil or gas to ground level, is most important.   Tubing must not only withstand the same types of stresses to which casing is subjected but must also resist corrosive action of well fluids, which in some areas is most severe.

API TUBING

The American Petroleum Institute has developed specifications for tubing meeting the major needs of the oil and gas industry and published these in API Standard 5A. This API standard provides standard dimensions, strengths, and performance properties and the required thread gauging practice to ensure complete interchangeability.

API Nonupset Tubing
Weights, Dimensions, Areas, Internal Pressures, and Collapse and Tension Properties

Size, OD, in.	Wt./ft, lb		Dimensions, in.					Calc. wt. of cou-pling, lb	Areas, sq in.		Steel grade	Internal pressures, psi			Minimum properties			
			Tubing			Coupling						Test			Tension		Collapse	
	Nominal, threads and coupling	Plain end	Wall thick-ness	ID	Drift diam	OD	Length		Plain end	Pipe wall under last perfect thread		Mill[b]	At fiber stress equal to 80% of min yield strength	Yield (min)[d]	Equiv. length, ft[c] sf = 2	Yield load, lb	Setting depth, ft[a] sf = 1⅛	Pres-sure, psi
1.900	2.75	2.72	0.145	1.610	1.516	2.200	3¾	1.23	0.800	0.477	F	3,000	3,100	3,340	2,170	11,930	6,970	3,920
											H	3,000	4,900	5,350	3,470	19,090	9,400	5,290
											J	3,000	6,700	7,350	4,470	26,250	12,210	6,870
											N	9,800	9,800	10,680	6,940	38,180	15,960	8,980
2⅜	4.00	3.94	0.167	2.041	1.947	2.875	4¼	2.82	1.158	0.753	F	2,800	2,800	3,080	2,350	18,830	6,280	3,530
											H	3,000	4,500	4,930	3,770	30,130	8,680	4,880
											J	3,000	6,200	6,770	5,180	41,430	11,270	6,340
											N	9,000	9,000	9,840	7,530	60,260	14,740	8,290
	4.60	4.43	0.190	1.995	1.901	2.875	4¼	2.82	1.304	0.899	F	3,000	3,200	3,500	2,440	22,480	7,400	4,160
											H	3,000	5,100	5,600	3,910	35,960	9,810	5,520
											J	3,000	7,000	7,700	5,370	49,440	12,760	7,180
											N	10,000	10,200	11,200	7,820	71,920	16,680	9,380
											P†	10,000	13,400	14,700	10,260	94,400	22,580	12,700
	5.80†	5.75	0.254	1.867	1.773	2.875	4¼	2.82	1.692	1.287	N†	10,000	13,700	14,970	8,880	102,980	21,650	12,180
											P†	10,000	18,000	19,650	11,650	135,170	29,300	16,480
2⅞	6.40	6.16	0.217	2.441	2.347	3.500	5⅛	5.15	1.812	1.320	F	3,000	3,000	3,300	2,580	32,990	6,880	3,870
											H	3,000	4,800	5,280	4,120	52,780	9,320	5,240
											J	3,000	6,600	7,260	5,670	72,570	12,090	6,800
											N	9,700	9,700	10,570	8,250	105,560	15,820	8,900
											P†	10,000	12,700	13,870	10,820	138,550	21,400	12,040
	8.60†	8.44	0.308	2.259	2.165	3.500	5⅛	5.15	2.484	1.991	N†	10,000	13,700	15,000	9,260	159,310	21,690	12,200
											P†	10,000	18,000	19,690	12,160	209,100	29,330	16,500

Size	Nom. wt.	Wt.	Wall	ID	Drift						Grade							
3½	7.70	7.58	0.218	3.068	2.943	4.250	5⅝	8.17	2.228	1.627	F	2,500	2,500	2,700	2,640	40,670	5,280	2,970
											H	3,000	3,900	4,320	4,230	65,070	7,220	4,060
											J	3,000	5,400	5,940	5,810	89,470	9,400	5,290
											N	7,900	7,900	8,640	8,450	130,140	12,300	6,920
	9.20	8.81	0.254	2.992	2.867	4.250	5⅝	8.17	2.590	1.988	F	2,900	2,900	3,180	2,700	49,710	6,540	3,680
											H	3,000	4,600	5,080	4,320	79,540	8,980	5,050
											J	3,000	6,400	6,980	5,940	109,370	11,660	6,560
											N	9,300	9,300	10,160	8,650	159,080	15,250	8,580
											P†	10,000	12,200	13,340	11,350	208,790	20,640	11,610
	10.20*	9.91	0.289	2.922	2.797	4.250	5⅝	8.17	2.915	2.314	F	3,000	3,300	3,610	2,840	57,840	7,700	4,330
											H	3,000	5,300	5,780	4,540	92,550	10,100	5,680
											J	3,000	7,300	7,940	6,240	127,250	13,140	7,390
											N	10,000	10,600	11,560	9,070	185,100	17,170	9,660
	12.70†	12.52	0.375	2.750	2.625	4.250	5⅝	8.17	3.682	3.080	N†	10,000	13,700	15,000	9,700	246,390	21,690	12,200
											P†	10,000	18,000	19,690	12,730	323,390	29,330	16,500
4	9.50	9.11	0.226	3.548	3.423	4.750	5¾	9.57	2.680	1.800	F	2,300	2,300	2,470	2,370	45,000	4,680	2,630
											H	3,000	3,600	3,960	3,790	72,020	6,360	3,580
											J	3,000	5,000	5,440	5,210	99,010	8,270	4,650
											N	7,200	7,200	7,910	7,580	144,010	10,810	6,080
4½	12.60	12.24	0.271	3.958	3.833	5.200	6⅛	10.76	3.600	2.609	F	2,400	2,400	2,630	2,590	65,230	5,100	2,870
											H	3,000	3,900	4,220	4,140	104,360	6,990	3,930
											J	3,000	5,300	5,790	5,690	143,500	9,080	5,110
											N	7,700	7,700	8,440	8,280	208,730	11,880	6,680

For threading data see pp. 2-71 and 2-72.
For additional notes, see p. 2-68.
* On direct mill shipments only.
† Tentative API.

API External-
Weights, Dimensions, Areas, Internal Pressures,

Size, OD, in.	Wt./ft, lb		Dimensions, in.									Calc. wt. of coupling, lb	
			Tubing					Coupling					
	Nominal, threads and coupling	Plain end	Wall thickness	ID	Drift diam	External upset		OD		Length		Regular OD	Spec. clearance*,f
						OD	Min length	Regular	Spec. clearance*,b,f				
1.050	1.20	1.13	0.113	0.824	0.730	1.315	1⅞	1.660	.....	3¼		0.84	....
1.315	1.80	1.68	0.133	1.049	0.955	1.469	2	1.900	.....	3½		1.26	....
1.660	2.40	2.27	0.140	1.380	1.286	1.812	2	2.200	.....	3¾		1.49	....
1.900	2.90	2.72	0.145	1.610	1.516	2.094	2¼	2.500	.....	3⅞		1.85	....
2⅜	4.70	4.43	0.190	1.995	1.901	2.549	3½	3.063	2.910	4⅞		3.42	2.38
	5.95†	5.75	0.254	1.867	1.773	2.594	3½	3.063	.....	4⅞		3.42	....
2⅞	6.50	6.16	0.217	2.441	2.347	3.094	3¾	3.668	3.460	5¼		5.29	3.45
	8.70†	8.44	0.308	2.259	2.165	3.094	3¾	3.668	.....	5¼		5.29	....
3½	9.30	8.81	0.254	2.992	2.867	3.750	4	4.500	.....	5¾		9.02	....
	12.95†	12.52	0.375	2.750	2.625	3.750	4	4.500	.....	5¾		9.02	....
4	11.00	10.46	0.262	3.476	3.351	4.250	4	5.000	.....	6		10.62	....
4½	12.75	12.24	0.271	3.958	3.833	4.750	4¼	5.563	.....	6¼		13.31	....

For threading data see pp. 2-71 and 2-72.
* Sizes or values indicated are non-API.
† Tentative API.

NOTES:
   The permissible variation in weight for any length of tubing is 6½ per cent above and 3½ per cent below; but the carload weight shall not be more than 1¾ per cent under the calculated weight.
   Furnished with threads and coupling unless otherwise ordered.
   For tables of tensile requirements and range lengths, see pp. 2-66, 2-67, and 2-70.
   The weight per foot of tubing with threads and coupling is based on a length of 20 feet, including the coupling.
   Field conditions vary so widely that definite safety factors for collapse or tension cannot be recommended.

upset Tubing
and Collapse and Tension Properties

Areas, sq in.			Steel grade	Internal pressures, psi			Min properties					
				Test			Tension Regular OD coupling		Collapse		Tension Spec. clearance coupling	
Plain end	Pipe wall under last perfect thread	Spec. clearance coupling[e,f]		Mill[b]	At fiber stress equal to 80% of min yield strength	Yield (min)[d]	Equiv. length, ft[c] sf = 2	Yield load, lb	Setting depth, ft[a] sf = 1⅛	Pressure, psi	Equiv. length, ft[c] sf = 2	Yield load,[f] lb
0.333	0.605	.....	F	3,000	4,300	4,710	3,470	8,320	10,600	5,960		
			H	3,000	6,900	7,530	5,540	13,300	12,800	7,200		
			J	3,000	9,500	10,360	7,620	18,290	16,640	9,360		
			N	10,000	13,800	15,070	11,090	26,610	21,780	12,250		
0.494	0.584	.....	F	3,000	4,000	4,430	3,430	12,350	9,850	5,540		
			H	3,000	6,500	7,080	5,490	19,760	12,120	6,820		
			J	3,000	8,900	9,730	7,540	27,160	15,750	8,860		
			N	10,000	12,900	14,160	10,980	39,510	20,620	11,600		
0.668	0.776	.....	F	3,000	3,400	3,690	3,480	16,710	7,890	4,440		
			H	3,000	5,400	5,910	5,570	26,740	10,290	5,790		
			J	3,000	7,400	8,120	7,660	36,770	13,390	7,530		
			N	10,000	10,800	11,800	11,400	53,480	17,510	9,850		
0.800	1.052	.....	F	3,000	3,100	3,340	3,450	19,990	6,970	3,920		
			H	3,000	4,900	5,350	5,510	31,980	9,400	5,290		
			J	3,000	6,700	7,350	7,580	43,970	12,210	6,870		
			N	9,800	9,800	10,680	11,140	63,960	15,960	8,980		
1.304	1.594	1.663	F	3,000	3,200	3,500	3,470	32,600	7,400	4,160		
			H	3,000	5,100	5,600	5,550	52,170	9,810	5,520	5,550	52,170
			J	3,000	7,000	7,700	7,630	71,730	12,760	7,180	7,630	71,730
			N	10,000	10,200	11,200	11,100	104,340	16,680	9,380	11,000	104,340
			P†	10,000	13,400	14,700	14,570	136,940	22,580	12,700		
1.692	1.982	.....	N†	10,000	13,700	14,970	11,380	135,400	21,650	12,180		
			P†	10,000	18,000	19,650	14,930	177,710	29,300	16,480		
1.812	2.162	2.291	F	3,000	3,000	3,300	3,480	45,300	6,880	3,870		
			H	3,000	4,800	5,280	5,580	72,480	9,320	5,240	5,580	72,480
			J	3,000	6,600	7,260	7,670	99,660	12,090	6,800	7,670	9,9660
			N	9,700	9,700	10,570	11,150	144,960	15,820	8,900	11,150	144,960
			P†	10,000	12,700	13,870	14,640	190,260	21,400	12,040		
2.484	2.834	.....	N†	10,000	13,700	15,000	11,420	198,710	21,690	12,200		
			P†	10,000	18,000	19,690	14,990	260,810	29,330	16,500		
2.590	3.190	.....	F	2,900	2,900	3,180	3,480	64,760	6,540	3,680		
			H	3,000	4,600	5,080	5,570	103,610	8,980	5,050		
			J	3,000	6,400	6,980	7,660	142,460	11,660	6,560		
			N	9,300	9,300	10,160	11,140	207,220	15,250	8,580		
			P†	10,000	12,200	13,340	14,620	271,970	20,640	11,610		
3.682	4.282	.....	N†	10,000	13,700	15,000	11,370	294,530	21,690	12,200		
			P†	10,000	18,000	19,690	14,930	386,570	29,330	16,500		
3.077	3.761	.....	F	2,600	2,600	2,870	3,500	76,920	5,720	3,220		
			H	3,000	4,200	4,580	5,590	123,070	7,860	4,420		
			J	3,000	5,800	6,300	7,690	169,220	10,220	5,750		
			N	8,400	8,400	9,170	11,190	246,140	13,370	7,520		
3.600	4.369	.....	F	2,400	2,400	2,630	3,530	90,010	5,100	2,870		
			H	3,000	3,900	4,220	5,650	144,020	6,990	3,930		
			J	9,000	5,300	5,790	7,770	198,030	9,080	5,110		
			N	7,700	7,700	8,440	11,300	288,040	11,880	6,680		

[a] Since salt water is practically always encountered in drilling, the length of string is based upon 2 ft of water column to each pound of collapsing pressure. To obtain setting depths in collapse in fluids of other densities use chart on p. 2–47.

[b] High test pressures for tubing furnished with special clearance couplings are approximately 85 per cent of the listed pressures.

[c] Tension setting depths for tubing are not related to those for casing which are based on joint pull-out strength. Tension setting depths shown are determined as the product of the minimum yield strength for the grade and the area of the section under the root of the last perfect thread or the body of the pipe, whichever is smaller.

[d] Based on 87½ per cent for internal pressure at minimum yield strength.

[e] Root of the special clearance coupling thread at the first perfect thread on the pipe when made up to the power-tight position.

[f] On tubing furnished with special clearance couplings it is standard practice to furnish couplings in one steel grade higher than the tubing grade, but P-105 is the present highest grade.

Tubing Ranges

	Range		
	1	2	3
Total range length (incl.)...............	20–24	28–32	...
Range length for 100% of carload:			
Permissible variation (max)..........	2	2	...
Min permissible length..............	20	28	...

Jointers not permitted on tubing.

Gross Lineal Footage from Net Footage—Multiplication Factors
API Nonupset Tubing

Size, OD, in.	Nominal, wt./ft threads and coupling, lb	No. of threads per in.	Make-up loss per joint, in.	Multiplication factor*	
				Avg length of joint	
				20 ft	30 ft
1.900	2.75	10	1.375	1.0058	1.0038
2⅜	All	10	1.625	1.0068	1.0045
2⅞	All	10	2.063	1.0087	1.0058
3½	All	10	2.313	1.0097	1.0065
4	9.50	8	2.375	1.0100	1.0066
4½	12.60	8	2.563	1.0108	1.0072

* To obtain the gross or shipping length, multiply the net length in feet by the multiplication factor.

API External-upset Tubing

Size, OD, in.	Nominal, wt./ft threads and coupling, lb	No. of threads per in.	Make-up loss per joint, in.	Multiplication factor*	
				Avg length of joint	
				20 ft	30 ft
1.050	1.20	10	1.125	1.0047	1.0031
1.315	1.80	10	1.250	1.0052	1.0035
1.660	2.40	10	1.375	1.0058	1.0038
1.900	2.90	10	1.438	1.0060	1.0040
2⅜	All	8	1.938	1.0081	1.0054
2⅞	All	8	2.125	1.0089	1.0059
3½	All	8	2.375	1.0100	1.0066
4	11.00	8	2.500	1.0105	1.0070
4½	12.75	8	2.625	1.0111	1.0074

* To obtain the gross or shipping length, multiply the net length in feet by the multiplication factor.

Threading Data for API Nonupset Tubing

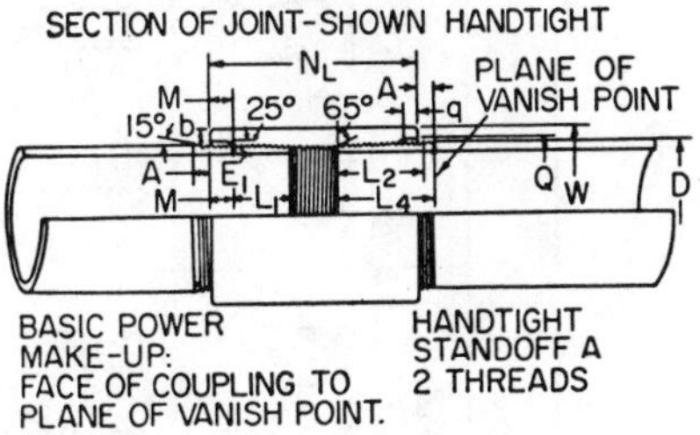
SECTION OF JOINT-SHOWN HANDTIGHT
NL
PLANE OF VANISH POINT
M
15°
b
25°
65°
A
q
A
E1
M
L1
L2
L4
Q
W
D
BASIC POWER MAKE-UP: FACE OF COUPLING TO PLANE OF VANISH POINT.
HANDTIGHT STANDOFF A 2 THREADS

Pipe		Threads†					Coupling					
									Recess			
Size, OD *D*, in.	Nominal, wt./ft threads and coupling, lb	No. per inch	Length, end of pipe to hand-tight plane L_1, in.	Effective length L_2, in.	Total length, end of pipe to vanish point L_4, in.	Pitch diam at hand-tight plane E_1, in.	OD *W*, in.	Length N_L, in.	Diam *Q*, in.	Depth *q*, in.	Bearing face width *b*, in.	Length face of coupling to hand-tight plane *M*, in.
1.900	2.75	10	0.729	1.206	1.375	1.83826	2.200	3¾	1.963	5/16	1/16	0.446
2⅜	4.00 4.60 5.80	10	0.979	1.456	1.625	2.31326	2.875	4¼	2.438	5/16	3/16	0.446
2⅞	6.40 8.60	10	1.417	1.894	2.063	2.81326	3.500	5⅛	2.938	5/16	3/16	0.446
3½	7.70 9.20 10.20* 12.70	10	1.667	2.144	2.313	3.43826	4.250	5⅝	3.563	5/16	3/16	0.446
4	9.50	8	1.591	2.140	2.375	3.91395	4.750	5¾	4.063	⅜	3/16	0.534
4½	12.60	8	1.779	2.328	2.563	4.41395	5.200	6⅛	5.563	⅜	3/16	0.534

For dimensions and performance properties see pp. 2–66 and 2–67.
For additional notes, see p. 2–68.
* On direct mill shipments only.
† Taper ¾ in./ft measured on the diameter.

Threading Data for API External-upset Tubing

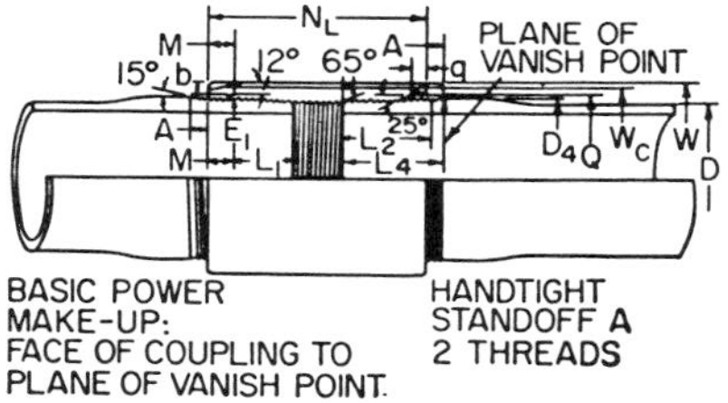
SECTION OF JOINT – SHOWN HANDTIGHT
N_L
M
15°
b
12°
65°
A
q
PLANE OF VANISH POINT
A
E_1
M
L_1
L_2
25°
L_4
D_4
Q
W_c
W
D
BASIC POWER MAKE-UP: FACE OF COUPLING TO PLANE OF VANISH POINT.
HANDTIGHT STANDOFF A 2 THREADS

Pipe		Threads*						Coupling						
								OD			Recess			
Size, OD D, in.	Nominal wt./ft threads and coupling, lb	No. per in.	Length, end of pipe to hand-tight plane L_1, in.	Effective length L_2, in.	Total length, end of pipe to vanish point L_4, in.	Pitch diam at hand-tight plane E_1, in.	OD external upset D_4, in.	Regular W, in.	Spec. clearance†,b,f W_c, in.	Length N_L, in.	Diam Q, in.	Depth q, in.	Bearing face width b, in.	Length, face of coupling to hand-tight plane M, in.
1.050	1.20	10	0.479	0.956	1.125	1.25328	1.315	1.660	.....	3¼	1.378	5/16	3/32	0.446
1.315	1.80	10	0.604	1.081	1.250	1.40706	1.469	1.900	.....	3½	1.531	5/16	3/32	0.446
1.660	2.40	10	0.729	1.206	1.375	1.75079	1.812	2.200	.....	3¾	1.875	5/16	⅛	0.446
1.900	2.90	10	0.792	1.269	1.438	2.03206	2.094	2.500	.....	3⅞	2.156	5/16	⅛	0.446
2⅜	4.70	8	1.154	1.703	1.938	2.50775	2.594	3.063	2.910	4⅞	2.656	⅜	5/32	0.534
2⅜	5.95	8	1.154	1.703	1.938	2.50775	2.594	3.063	.....	4⅞	2.656	⅜	5/32	0.534
2⅞	6.50	8	1.341	1.890	2.125	3.00775	3.094	3.668	3.460	5¼	3.156	⅜	7/32	0.534
2⅞	8.70	8	1.341	1.890	2.125	3.00775	3.094	3.668	.....	5¼	3.156	⅜	7/32	0.534
3½	9.30 12.95	8	1.591	2.140	2.375	3.66395	3.750	4.500	.....	5¾	3.813	⅜	¼	0.534
4	11.00	8	1.716	2.265	2.500	4.16395	4.250	5.000	.....	6	4.313	⅜	¼	0.534
4½	12.75	8	1.841	2.390	2.625	4.66395	4.750	5.563	.....	6¼	4.813	⅜	¼	0.534

For dimensions and performance properties see pp. 2–68 and 2–69.
For additional notes, see p. 2–68.
* Taper ¾ in./ft measured on the diameter.
† Sizes or values indicated are non-API.

Pipe-thread Dimensions

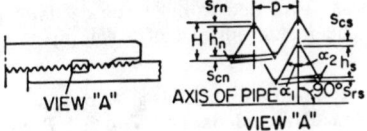

API Standard Round Thread

No. per in.	10	8
Thread element	in.	
$p =$	0.1000	0.1250
$H = 0.866p$	0.0866	0.1082
$h_n = h_s = 0.626p - 0.007$	0.0556	0.0712
$s_{rn} - s_{rs} = 0.120p + 0.002$	0.0140	0.0170
$s_{cn} = s_{cs} = 0.120p + 0.005$	0.0170	0.0200

$\alpha_1 = \alpha_2 = 30°.$

CEMENT-LINED TUBING

Cement-lined tubing was developed to meet the needs of the oil and gas industry requiring protection of the inside surface of steel pipe against unusual corrosive conditions.

Cement-lined Tubing—Nonupset
Weights, Dimensions, and Tension Properties

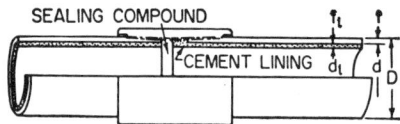

Size, OD D, in.	Unlined				Cement-lined				Grade	Joint yield load min, lb	Equiv. length, ft sf = 2
	Nom. wt./ft, lb	P.E. wt./ft, lb	Wall thickness t, in.	ID d, in.	Nom. wt./ft, lb	P.E. wt./ft, lb	Wall thickness t_l, in.	ID d_l, in.			
2⅜	4.00	3.94	0.167	2.041	4.86	4.79	0.1435	1.754	F	18,830	1,940
									H	30,130	3,100
									J	41,430	4,260
									N	60,260	6,200
	4.60	4.43	0.190	1.995	5.44	5.27	0.1435	1.708	F	22,480	2,070
									H	35,960	3,310
									J	49,440	4,550
									N	71,920	6,610
2⅞	6.40	6.16	0.217	2.441	7.52	7.22	0.1435	2.154	F	32,990	2,190
									H	52,780	3,510
									J	72,570	4,830
									N	105,560	7,020
3½	7.70	7.58	0.216	3.068	9.28	9.15	0.1715	2.725	F	40,670	2,190
									H	65,070	3,510
									J	89,470	4,820
									N	130,140	7,010
	9.20	8.81	0.254	2.992	10.75	10.36	0.1715	2.649	F	49,710	2,310
									H	79,540	3,710
									J	109,370	5,090
									N	159,080	7,400
	10.20	9.91	0.289	2.922	11.71	11.42	0.1715	2.579	F	57,840	2,470
									H	92,550	3,950
									J	127,250	5,440
									N	185,100	7,900
4	9.50	9.11	0.226	3.548	11.34	10.95	0.1715	3.205	F	45,000	1,980
									H	72,000	3,180
									J	99,010	4,370
									N	144,010	6,350
4½	12.60	12.24	0.271	3.958	15.03	14.67	0.2030	3.552	F	65,230	2,170
									H	104,360	3,470
									J	143,500	4,780
									N	208,730	6,940

Cement-lined tubing is supplied only in range 1 lengths
Unlined tubing joints conform in all details to API tubing; see p. 2–71.
Cement-lined tubing is lined integrally with coupling made up power-tight on mill end.
An adequate supply of sealing compound is supplied with each shipment to provide for making up field end.
For mill test pressures, collapsing pressures, and minimum internal yield pressures, see API tubing table, p. 2–66.
For method of calculating strengths and pressures, see performance section, p. 2–92.
The gross or shipping-length determination is identical with API nonupset tubing of the same size and weight; see p. 2–70.

Cement-lined Tubing
External-upset
Dimensions and Tension Properties

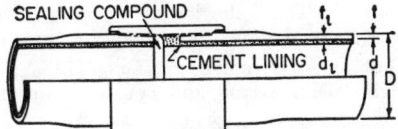

Size, OD D, in.	Unlined				Cement-lined				Grade	Joint yield load min, lb	Equiv. length, ft sf = 2
	Nom. wt./ft, lb	P.E. wt./ft, lb	Wall thickness t, in.	ID d, in.	Nom. wt./ft, lb	P.E. wt./ft, lb	Wall thickness t_l, in.	ID d_l, in.			
$2\frac{3}{8}$	4.70	4.43	0.190	1.995	5.54	5.27	0.1435	1.708	H	52,170	4,710
									J	71,730	6,470
									N	104,340	9,420
$2\frac{7}{8}$	6.50	6.16	0.217	2.441	7.56	7.22	0.1435	2.154	H	72,480	4,790
									J	99,660	6,590
									N	144,960	9,590
$3\frac{1}{2}$	9.30	8.81	0.254	2.992	10.85	10.36	0.1715	2.649	H	103,610	4,770
									J	142,460	6,560
									N	207,220	9,550
4	11.00	10.46	0.262	3.476	12.81	12.27	0.1715	3.133	H	123,070	4,800
									J	169,220	6,600
									N	246,140	9,610
$4\frac{1}{2}$	12.75	12.24	0.271	3.958	15.18	14.67	0.2030	3.552	H	144,020	4,740
									J	198,030	6,520
									N	288,040	9,490

Cement-lined tubing is supplied only in range 1 lengths.

Unlined tubing joints conform in all details to API tubing; see p. 2–71.

Cement-lined tubing is lined integrally with coupling made up power-tight on mill end.

An adequate supply of sealing compound is supplied with each shipment to provide for making up field end.

For mill test pressures, collapsing pressures, and minimum internal yield pressures, see API tubing table, p. 2–66.

For method of calculating strengths and pressures, see performance section, p. 2–92.

The gross or shipping-length determination is identical with API external-upset tubing of the same size and weight; see p. 2–70.

SPECIAL TUBING JOINTS

Extreme conditions at times arise in the production of oil and gas wells which result in the need for tubing with greater clearance or leak resistance than provided with standard API tubing joints. The following tables give dimensional and strength data on the special tubing joints designed to provide for these special conditions.

Hi-Pres-Sure Tubing—External-upset, Long Threads and Couplings
Weights, Dimensions, and Tension Properties

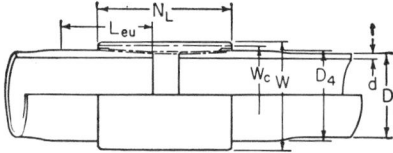

Size, OD D, in.	Nom. wt./ft, lb	Wall thickness t, in.	ID d, in.	Coupling OD Regular W, in.	Coupling OD Spec. clearance W_c, in.	Coupling Length Regular OD or spec. clearance N_L, in.	External-upset OD D_4, in.	External-upset Total length min L_{eu}, in.	Grade	Reg. OD coupling Joint yield load min, lb	Reg. OD coupling Equiv. length, ft sf = 2	Spec. clearance coupling Joint yield load min, lb	Spec. clearance coupling Equiv. length, ft sf = 2
2⅜	4.70	0.190	1.995	3.063	2.910	6⅛	2.594	3½	N	104,340	11,100	104,340	11,100
									P	136,940	14,570	136,940	14,570
	5.95	0.254	1.876	3.063	2.910	6⅛	2.594	3½	N	135,400	11,380	135,400	11,380
									P	177,710	14,930	177,710	14,930
2⅞	6.50	0.217	2.441	3.668	3.460	6¾	3.094	3¾	N	144,960	11,150	144,960	11,150
									P	190,260	14,640	190,260	14,640
	8.70	0.308	2.259	3.668	3.460	6¾	3.094	3¾	N	198,710	11,420	198,710	11,420
									P	260,810	14,990	260,810	14,990
3½	9.30	0.254	2.992	4.500	4.180	7¼	3.750	4	N	207,220	11,140	207,220	11,140
									P	271,970	14,620	271,970	14,620
	12.95	0.375	2.750	4.500	4.180	7¼	3.750	4	N	294,530	11,370	294,530	11,370
									P	386,570	14,930	386,570	14,930

8 round threads per inch; taper ¾ in./ft on the diameter.

For mill test pressures, collapsing pressures, and minimum internal yield pressures, see API tubing, external-upset table, p. 2–68.

For method of calculating strengths and pressures, see performance section, p. 2–92.

Gross Lineal Footage from Net Footage—Multiplication Factors
Hi-Pres-Sure Tubing—External-upset, Long Threads and Couplings

Size, OD, in.	Nom. wt./ft, lb	Make-up loss per joint, in.	Multiplication factors* Avg length of joint 20 ft	Multiplication factors* Avg length of joint 30 ft
2⅜	All	2.563	1.0108	1.0072
2⅞	All	2.875	1.0121	1.0081
3½	All	3.125	1.0132	1.0088

* To obtain the gross or shipping length, multiply net length in feet by the multiplication factor.

Extreme Line Tubing
Weights, Dimensions, and Tension Properties

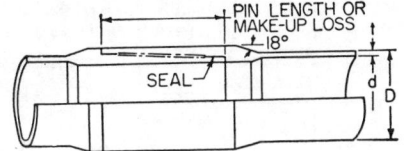

Size, OD D, in.	Nom. wt./ft, lb	Wall thickness t, in.	ID d, in.	Tubing drift diam, in.	Joint OD, in.	Grade	Joint yield load min, lb	Equiv. length, ft sf = 2
2⅜	4.70	0.190	1.995	1.901	3	J-55	71,730	7,630
						N-80	104,340	11,100
						P-105	136,940	14,570
2⅞	6.50	0.217	2.441	2.347	3½	J-55	99,660	7,670
						N-80	144,960	11,150
						P-105	190,260	14,640
	7.90	0.276	2.323	2.229	3⅝	J-55	123,940	7,840
						N-80	180,280	11,410
						P-105	236,620	14,980
	11.65	0.440	1.995	1.901	3¾	J-55	185,130	7,950
						N-80	269,270	11,560
						P-105	353,420	15,170
3½	9.30	0.254	2.992	2.867	4¼	J-55	142,460	7,660
						N-80	207,220	11,140
						P-105	271,970	14,620
	11.75	0.335	2.830	2.705	4¼	J-55	183,200	7,800
						N-80	266,480	11,340
						P-105	349,760	14,880
	17.05	0.530	2.440	2.347	4⅜	J-55	271,990	7,980
						N-80	395,620	11,600
						P-105	519,240	15,230

6 extreme line type threads per inch; taper ¾ in./ft on the diameter.
Standard weight sizes will pass corresponding API drift.
For mill test pressures, collapsing pressures, and minimum internal yield pressures, see API tubing table, p. 2–66.
For method of calculating strengths and pressures, see performance section, p. 2–92.

Gross Lineal Footage from Net Footage—Multiplication Factor
Extreme Line Tubing

Size, OD, in.	Nom. wt./ft, lb	Make-up loss per point, in.	Multiplication factors*	
			Avg length of joint	
			20 ft	30 ft
2⅜	4.70	2¹³⁄₁₆	1.0119	1.0079
2⅞	All	3	1.0127	1.0084
3½	All	3¾	1.0159	1.0105

* To obtain the gross or shipping length, multiply net length in feet by the multiplication factor.

Spangseal Tubing
Weights, Dimensions, and Tension Properties

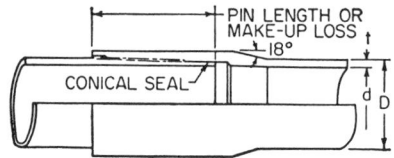

Size, OD D, in.	Nom. wt./ft, lb	Wall thickness t, in.	ID d, in.	Tubing drift diam, in.	Joint OD, in.	Grade	Joint yield load min, lb	Equiv. length, ft sf = 2
2⅜	4.70	0.190	1.995	1.901	3	J-55 N-80 P-105	71,730 104,340 136,940	7,630 11,110 14,570
2⅞	6.50	0.217	2.441	2.347	3¹⁷⁄₃₂	J-55 N-80 P-105	99,660 144,960 190,260	7,670 11,150 14,640

API threads, box will fit API pin; pin with seal cut off will fit API coupling.
For mill test pressures, collapsing pressures, and minimum internal yield pressures, see API tubing table, p. 2–66.
For method of calculating strengths and pressures, see performance section, p. 2–92.

Gross Lineal Footage from Net Footage—Multiplication Factors
Spangseal Tubing

Size, OD, in.	Nom. wt./ft, lb	Make-up loss per joint, in.	Multiplication factors*	
			Avg length of joint	
			20 ft	30 ft
2⅜ 2⅞	4.70 6.50	2.911 3.098	1.0123 1.0131	1.0082 1.0087

* To obtain the gross or shipping length, multiply net length in feet by the multiplication factor.

Hydril FJ Joint for Flush-joint Tubing
Weights, Dimensions, and Tension Properties

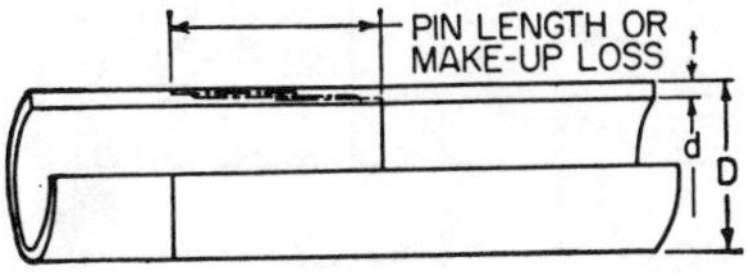

Size, OD D, in.	Nom. wt./ft, lb	Wall thickness t, in.	ID d, in.	Tubing drift diam, in.	Grade	Joint yield load min, 1,000 lb	Equiv. length, ft
2 3/8	4.60	0.190	1.995	1.901	J-55	34	3,840
					N-80	50	5,640
2 7/8	6.40	0.217	2.441	2.347	J-55	50	4,060
					N-80	72	5,840
3 1/2	9.20	0.254	2.992	2.867	J-55	74	4,200
					N-80	108	6,130
	10.20	0.289	2.922	2.797	J-55	86	4,340
					N-80	125	6,310
4	11.00	0.262	3.476	3.351	J-55	92	4,400
					N-80	133	6,630
	11.60	0.286	3.428	3.303	J-55	100	4,410
					N-80	146	6,440
	14.00	0.330	3.340	3.215	J-55	111	4,290
					N-80	161	6,230

Hydril threads are interchangeable between 4-in. 11- and 11.6-lb tubing.

For mill test pressures, collapsing pressures, and minimum internal yield pressures, see API tubing table, p. 2-66.

For method of calculating strengths and pressures, see performance section, p. 2-92.

Gross Lineal Footage from Net Footage—Multiplication Factors
Hydril FJ Joint for Flush-joint Tubing

Size, OD, in.	Nom. wt./ft, lb	Make-up loss per joint, in.	Multiplication factors* Avg length of joint 20 ft	30 ft
2 3/8	4.60	2 3/32	1.0088	1.0059
2 7/8	6.40	2 1/8	1.0089	1.0059
3 1/2	9.20	2 5/8	1.0111	1.0073
	10.20	2 21/32	1.0112	1.0074
4	11.00, 11.60	2 5/8	1.0111	1.0073
	14.00	2 11/16	1.0113	1.0075

* To obtain the gross or shipping length, multiply net length in feet by the multiplication factor.

Hydril A Joint for External-upset Tubing
Weights, Dimensions, and Tension Properties

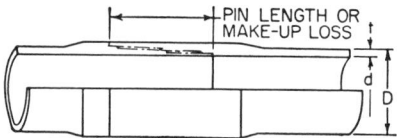

PIN LENGTH OR MAKE-UP LOSS t

Size, OD D, in.	Nom. wt./ft, lb	Wall thickness t, in.	ID d, in.	Tubing drift diam, in.	Joint* OD, in.	Grade	Joint yield load min, 1,000 lb	Equiv. length, ft sf = 2
2⅜	4.70	0.190	1.995	1.901	2¹⁹⁄₃₂	J-55 N-80	57 84	6,060 8,940
2⅞	6.50	0.217	2.441	2.347	3³⁄₃₂	J-55 N-80	80 116	6,150 8,920
3½	9.30	0.254	2.992	2.867	3¾	J-55 N-80	114 166	6,130 8,920
4	11.00	0.262	3.476	3.351	4¼	J-55 N-80	135 197	6,140 8,950
4½	12.75	0.271	3.958	3.833	4¾	J-55 N-80	159 230	6,240 9,020

Hydril A, CA, and CS threads are interchangeable.
Hydril 4½ in. OD, type A, CS, and EU (casing) threads are interchangeable.
For mill test pressures, collapsing pressures, and minimum internal yield pressures, see API tubing tables, pp. 2-66 to 2-67.
For method of calculating strengths and pressures, see performance section, p. 2-92.
* Tolerance +¹⁄₁₆ − 0 (API).

Gross Lineal Footage from Net Footage—Multiplication Factors
Hydril A Joint for External-upset Tubing

Size, OD, in.	Nom. wt./ft, lb	Make-up loss per joint, in.	Multiplication factors*	
			Avg length of joint	
			20 ft	30 ft
2⅜	4.70	2¼	1.0095	1.0063
2⅞	6.50	2¼	1.0095	1.0063
3½	9.30	2¹¹⁄₁₆	1.0113	1.0075
4	11.00	2¹¹⁄₁₆	1.0113	1.0075
4½	12.75	2¾	1.0116	1.0077

* To obtain the gross or shipping length, multiply net length in feet by the multiplication factor.

Hydril CA Tubing Joint
Weights, Dimensions, and Tension Properties

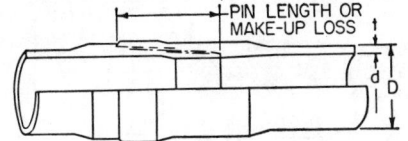

Size, OD, D, in.	Nom. wt./ft, lb	Wall thick- ness t, in.	ID d, in.	Tubing drift diam, in.	Joint			Grade	Joint yield load min, 1,000 lb	Equiv. length, ft sf = 2
					ID pin bored, in.	OD pin upset, in.	OD box machined, in.			
$2\frac{3}{8}$	4.70	0.190	1.995	1.901	1.945	$2^{19}\!/_{32}$	2.700	J-55 N-80 P-105	65 94 123	6,900 9,980 13,120
$2\frac{7}{8}$	6.50	0.217	2.441	2.347	2.375	$3^{3}\!/_{32}$	3.220	J-55 N-80 P-105	85 124 162	6,520 9,520 12,450
$3\frac{1}{2}$	9.30	0.254	2.992	2.867	2.920	$3\frac{3}{4}$	3.865	J-55 N-80 P-105	126 183 241	6,750 9,820 12,980

Hydril CA tubing is interchangeable with A and CS Hydril tubing.
For mill test pressures, collapsing pressures, and minimum internal yield pressures, see API tubing table, p. 2–66.
For method of calculating strengths and pressures, see performance section, p. 2–92.

Gross Lineal Footage from Net Footage—Multiplication Factors
Hydril CA Tubing Joint

Size, OD, in.	Nom. wt./ft, lb	Make-up loss per joint, in.	Multiplication factors*	
			Avg length of joint	
			20 ft	30 ft
$2\frac{3}{8}$	4.70	2.276	1.0096	1.0064
$2\frac{7}{8}$	6.50	2.348	1.0099	1.0066
$3\frac{1}{2}$	9.30	2.797	1.0118	1.0078

* To obtain the gross or shipping length, multiply net footage in feet by the multiplication factor.

Hydril CS Joint for External-upset Tubing
Weights, Dimensions, and Tension Properties

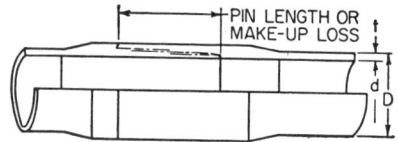

Size, OD, *D,* in.	Nom. wt./ft, lb	Wall thick-ness *t,* in.	ID *d,* in.	Tubing drift diam, in.	Joint			Grade	Yield load min, 1,000 lb	Equiv. length, ft sf = 2
					ID bored, in.	OD standard, in.	OD special, in.			
1.315	1.80	0.133	1.049	0.955	0.970	1.552	.....	J-55 N-80 P-105	27 40 52	7,500 11,110 14,440
1.660	2.40	0.140	1.380	1.286	1.300	1.883	.....	J-55 N-80 P-105	37 53 70	7,710 11,040 14,580
1.900	2.90	0.145	1.610	1.516	1.530	2.113	.....	J-55 N-80 P-105	44 64 84	7,590 11,030 14,480
2¹⁄₁₆	3.40	0.156	1.750	1.656	1.700	2.330	.....	J-55 N-80 P-105	51 75 98	7,500 11,030 14,410
2⅜	4.70	0.190	1.995	1.901	1.945	2.700	2.630	J-55 N-80 P-105	72 104 137	7,660 11,060 14,570
	5.30	0.218	1.939	1.845	1.890	2.700	.....	J-55 N-80 P-105	81 118 155	7,640 11,130 14,620
2⅞	6.50	0.217	2.441	2.347	2.375	3.220	3.155	J-55 N-80 P-105	100 145 190	7,690 11,150 14,620
3½	9.30	0.254	2.992	2.867	2.920	3.865	3.805	J-55 N-80 P-105	142 207 272	7,630 11,130 14,620
	10.30	0.289	2.922	2.797	2.878	3.865	.....	J-55 N-80 P-105	160 233 306	7,770 11,310 14,850
4	11.00	0.262	3.476	3.351	3.395	4.343	4.315	J-55 N-80 P-105	169 246 323	7,680 11,180 14,680
4½	12.75	0.271	3.958	3.833	3.865	4.855	4.825	J-55 N-80 P-105	198 288 378	7,760 11,290 14,820

Hydril A, CA, and CS threads are interchangeable.
Hydril 4½ in. OD type A, CS, and EU (casing) threads are interchangeable.
For mill test pressures, collapsing pressures, and minimum internal yield pressures, see API tubing table, p. 2-66.
For method of calculating strengths and pressures, see performance section, p. 2-92.

Gross Lineal Footage from Net Footage—Multiplication Factors
Hydril CS Joint for External-upset Tubing

Size, OD, in.	Nom. wt./ft, lb	Make-up loss per joint, in.	Multiplication factors*	
			Avg length of joint	
			20 ft	30 ft
1.315	1.80	2.187	1.0092	1.0061
1.660	2.40	2.187	1.0092	1.0061
1.900	2.90	2.187	1.0092	1.0061
2 1/16	3.40	2.187	1.0092	1.0061
2 3/8	4.70, 5.30	2.272	1.0096	1.0064
2 7/8	6.50	2.338	1.0098	1.0065
3 1/2	9.30, 10.30	2.787	1.0117	1.0078
4	11.00	2.787	1.0117	1.0078
4 1/2	12.75	2.830	1.0119	1.0079

* To obtain the gross or shipping length, multiply net footage in feet by the multiplication factor.

Hydril PH-6 Tubing Joint
Weights, Dimensions, and Tension Properties

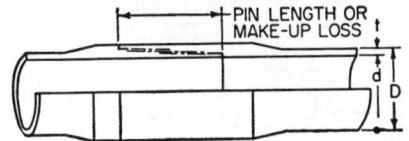

Size, OD D, in.	Nom. wt./ft, lb	Wall thickness t, in.	ID d, in.	Tubing drift diam, in.	Joint ID bored, in.	Joint OD machined, in.	Grade	Yield load min, 1,000 lb	Equiv. length, ft sf = 2
2 3/8	5.95	0.254	1.867	1.773	1.805	2 15/16	N-80	135	11,340
							P-105	178	14,960
	6.20	0.261	1.853	1.759	1.795	2 15/16	N-80	139	11,210
							P-105	182	14,680
	7.70	0.336	1.703	1.609	1.640	3 1/8	N-80	172	11,170
							P-105	226	14,680
2 7/8	7.90	0.276	2.323	2.229	2.265	3 3/8	N-80	180	11,390
							P-105	236	14,940
	8.70	0.308	2.259	2.165	2.200	3 1/2	N-80	198	11,380
							P-105	261	15,000
	8.90	0.316	2.243	2.149	2.180	3 1/2	N-80	203	11,400
							P-105	267	15,000
	9.50	0.340	2.195	2.101	2.130	3 5/8	N-80	217	11,420
							P-105	284	14,950
	11.00	0.405	2.065	1.971	2.000	3 3/4	N-80	251	11,410
							P-105	330	15,000
3 1/2	10.30	0.289	2.922	2.797	2.878	4 5/16	N-80	233	11,310
							P-105	306	14,850

For mill test pressures, collapsing pressures, and minimum internal yield pressures, see API tubing tables, p. 2–66.

For method of calculating strengths and pressures, see performance section, p. 2–92.

Gross Lineal Footage from Net Footage—Multiplication Factors
Hydril PH-6 Tubing Joint

Size, OD, in.	Nom. wt./ft, lb	Make-up loss per joint, in.	Multiplication factors* Avg length of joint	
			20 ft	30 ft
2⅜	5.95, 6.20	2.968	1.0125	1.0083
	7.70	2.936	1.0124	1.0082
2⅞	7.90	2.969	1.0125	1.0083
	8.70, 8.90	2.941	1.0124	1.0082
	9.50	2.918	1.0123	1.0082
	11.00	2.900	1.0122	1.0081
3½	10.30	3.236	1.0137	1.0091

* To obtain the gross or shipping length, multiply net footage in feet by the multiplication factor.

Hydril C-100 Tubing Joint
Weights, Dimensions, and Tension Properties

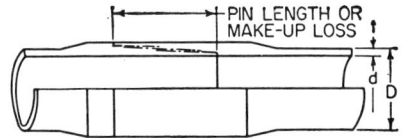

Size, OD D, in.	Nom. wt./ft, lb	Wall thickness t, in.	ID d, in.	Tubing drift diam, in.	Joint ID bored, in.	Joint OD machined, in.	Grade	Yield load min, 1,000 lb	Equiv. length, ft sf = 2
2⅜	4.70	0.190	1.995	1.901	1.945	2¹⁵⁄₁₆	J-55	72	7,660
							N-80	104	11,060
							P-105	137	14,570
2⅞	6.50	0.217	2.441	2.347	2.375	3½	J-55	100	7,690
							N-80	145	11,150
							P-105	190	14,620

For mill test pressures, collapsing pressures, and minimum internal yield pressures, see API tubing table, p. 2–66.

For method of calculating strengths and pressures, see performance section, p. 2–92.

Gross Lineal Footage from Net Footage—Multiplication Factors
Hydril C-100 Tubing Joint

Size, OD, in.	Nom. wt./ft, lb	Make-up loss per joint, in.	Multiplication factors*	
			Avg length of joint	
			20 ft	30 ft
$2\frac{3}{8}$	4.70	$3\frac{1}{8}$	1.0132	1.0088
$2\frac{7}{8}$	6.50	$3\frac{3}{16}$	1.0135	1 0089

* To obtain the gross or shipping length, multiply net footage in feet by the multiplication factor.

Integral-joint Tubing, External-upset
Weights, Dimensions, and Tension Properties

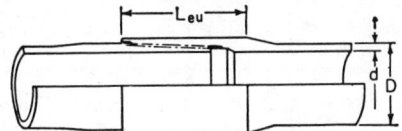

Size, OD D, in.	Nom. wt./ft, lb	Wall thick-ness t, in.	ID d, in.	Tubing drift diam, in.	Joint		Grade	Yield load min, lb	Equiv. length, ft sf = 2
					OD, in.	Length L_{eu}, in.			
$2\frac{3}{8}$	4.70	0.190	1.995	1.901	2.59375	3.000	J-55 N-80 P-105	71,730 104,340 136,940	7,630 11,100 14,570
	5.95	0.254	1.865	1.773	2.59375	3.000	N-80 P-105	135,400 177,710	11,380 14,930
$2\frac{7}{8}$	6.50	0.217	2.441	2.347	3.09375	3.750	J-55 N-80 P-105	99,660 144,960 190,260	7,670 11,150 14,640
	8.70	0.308	2.259	2.165	3.09375	3.750	N-80 P-105	198,710 260,810	11,420 14,990

Thread form and pin end is identical with and interchanges with API external-upset tubing, see p. 2-72.

For mill test pressures, collapsing pressures, and minimum internal yield pressures, see API tubing table, p. 2-66.

For method of calculating strengths and pressures, see performance section, p, 2-92.

The gross or shipping-length determination is identical with API external-upset tubing of the same size and weight; see p. 2-70.

Grayloc Tubing Joint
Weights, Dimensions, and Tension Properties

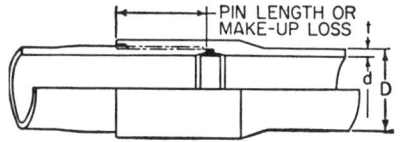

Size, OD D, in.	Nom. wt./ft, lb	Wall thickness t, in.	ID d, in.	Tubing drift diam, in.	Joint ID bored, in.	Joint OD, in.	Grade	Yield load min, lb	Equiv. length, ft sf = 2
2⅜	4.70	0.190	1.995	1.901	1.945	2.813	J-55	71,730	7,630
							N-80	104,340	11,100
							P-105	136,940	14,570
2⅞	6.50	0.217	2.441	2.347	2.370	3.375	J-55	99,660	7,670
							N-80	144,960	11,150
							P-105	190,260	14,640
	11.65	0.440	1.995	1.901	1.945	3.668	J-55	185,130	7,950
							N-80	269,270	11,550
							P-105	353,420	15,170
3½	9.30	0.254	2.992	2.896	2.920	4.125	J-55	142,460	7,660
							N-80	207,220	11,140
							P-105	271,970	14,620
	10.20	0.289	2.922	2.797	2.878	4.125	J-55	160,340	7,860
							N-80	233,220	11,430
							P-105	306,100	15,000

5 modified Acme-type threads per inch.
For mill test pressures, collapsing pressures, and minimum internal yield pressures, see API tubing table, p. 2–66.
For method of calculating strengths and pressures, see performance section, p. 2–92.

Gross Lineal Footage from Net Footage—Multiplication Factors
Grayloc Tubing Joint

Size, OD, in.	Nom. wt./ft, lb	Make-up loss per joint, in.	Multiplication factors* Avg length of joint 20 ft	30 ft
2⅜	4.70	2⅛	1.0089	1.0059
2⅞	6.50	2⅛	1.0089	1.0059
	11.65	2¾	1.0116	1.0077
3½	9.30, 10.20	2¾	1.0116	1.0077

* To obtain the gross or shipping length, multiply net footage in feet by the multiplication factor.

Atlas-Johnson AJ Tubing Joint
Weights, Dimensions, and Tension Properties

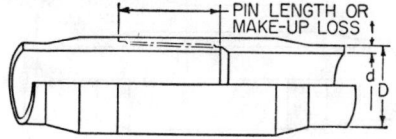

Size, OD D, in.	Nom. wt./ft, lb	Wall thick-ness t, in.	ID d, in.	Tubing drift diam, in.	Joint OD, in.	Grade	Yield load min, lb	Equiv. length, ft sf = 2
1.315	1.80	0.133	1.049	0.955	1.520	J-55	27,100	7,530
						N-80	39,600	11,000
1.660	2.40	0.140	1.380	1.286	1.858	J-55	36,700	7,650
						N-80	53,400	11,120
1.900	2.90	0.145	1.610	1.516	2.094	J-55	44,000	7,590
						N-80	63,900	11,020
2¹⁄₁₆	3.40	0.156	1.750	1.656	2.260	J-55	51,500	7,570
						N-80	75,000	11,030
2⅜	4.70	0.190	1.995	1.901	2.594	J-55	71,700	7,630
						N-80	104,000	11,060
2⅞	6.50	0.217	2.441	2.347	3.156	J-55	99,700	7,670
						N-80	145,000	11,150
3½	9.30	0.254	2.992	2.867	3.813	J-55	142,000	7,630
						N-80	207,000	11,130

8 modified buttress threads per inch on sizes 1.315 in. OD to 2⅜ in. OD, inclusive.
6 modified buttress threads per inch on sizes 2⅞ in. OD and 3½ in. OD.
Taper 1.125 in./ft on diameter.
For mill test pressures, collapsing pressures, and minimum internal yield pressures, see API tubing tables, p. 2-66.
For method of calculating strengths and pressures, see performance section, p. 2-92.

Gross Lineal Footage from Net Footage—Multiplication Factors
Atlas-Johnson AJ Tubing Joint

Size, OD, in.	Nom. wt./ft, lb	Make-up loss per joint, in.	Multiplication factors* Avg length of joint	
			20 ft	30 ft
1.315	1.80	1.250	1.0052	1.0035
1.660	2.40	1.500	1.0063	1.0042
1.900	2.90	1.687	1.0071	1.0047
2¹⁄₁₆	3.40	1.875	1.0079	1.0052
2⅜	4.70	2.375	1.0100	1.0066
2⅞	6.50	2.625	1.0111	1.0073
3½	9.30	3.000	1.0127	1.0084

* To obtain the gross or shipping length, multiply net footage in feet by the multiplication factor.

Dual Seal DS Tubing Joint
Weights, Dimensions, and Tension Properties

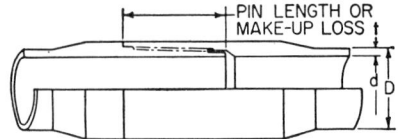

Size, OD D, in.	Nom. wt./ft, lb	Wall thickness t, in.	ID d, in.	Tubing drift diam, in.	Joint OD, in.	Grade	Yield load min, lb	Equiv. length, ft sf = 2
1.315	1.80	0.133	1.049	0.955	1.520	J-55 N-80	27,100 39,600	7,530 11,000
1.660	2.40	0.140	1.380	1.286	1.858	J-55 N-80	36,700 53,400	7,650 11,120
1.900	2.90	0.145	1.610	1.516	2.094	J-55 N-80	44,000 63,900	7,590 11,020
2 1/16	3.40	0.156	1 750	1.656	2.260	J-55 N-80	51,500 75,000	7,750 11,030
2 3/8	4.70	0.190	1.995	1.901	2.594	J-55 N-80	71,700 104,000	7,630 11,060
2 7/8	6.50	0.217	2.441	2.347	3.156	J-55 N-80	99,700 145,000	7,670 11,150
3 1/2	9.30	0.254	2.992	2.867	3.813	J-55 N-80	142,000 207,000	7,630 11,130

8 modified buttress threads per inch on sizes 1.315 in. OD to 2 3/8 in. OD, inclusive.
6 modified buttress threads per inch on sizes 2 7/8 in. OD and 3 1/2 in. OD.
Taper 1.125 in./ft on diameter.
For mill test pressures, collapsing pressures, and minimum internal yield pressures, see API tubing tables, p. 2–66.
For method of calculating strengths and pressures, see performance section, p. 2–92.

Gross Lineal Footage from Net Footage—Multiplication Factors
Dual Seal DS Tubing Joint

Size, OD, in.	Nom. wt./ft, lb	Make-up loss per joint, in.	Multiplication factors*	
			Avg length of joint	
			20 ft	30 ft
1.315	1.80	1.562	1.0066	1.0044
1.660	2.40	1.812	1.0076	1.0051
1.900	2.90	2.000	1.0084	1.0056
2 1/16	3.40	2.188	1.0092	1.0061
2 3/8	4.70	2.750	1.0116	1.0077
2 7/8	6.50	3.000	1.0127	1.0084
3 1/2	9.30	3.375	1.0143	1.0095

* To obtain the gross or shipping length, multiply net footage in feet by the multiplication factor.

Dual Seal Special DSS Tubing Joint
Weights, Dimensions, and Tension Properties

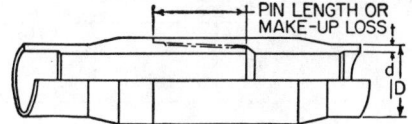

Size, OD D, in.	Nom. wt./ft, lb	Wall thickness t, in.	ID d, in.	Tubing drift diam, in.	Joint		Grade	Yield load min, lb	Equiv. length, ft sf = 2
					ID in.	OD, in.			
1.315	1.80	0.133	1.049	0.955	0.970	1.552	J-55 N-80 P-105	27,100 39,600 51,900	7,530 11,000 14,420
1.660	2.40	0.140	1.380	1.286	1.301	1.883	J-55 N-80 P-105	36,700 53,400 70,000	7,650 11,120 14,580
1.900	2.90	0.145	1.610	1.516	1.531	2.113	J-55 N-80 P-105	44,000 63,900 83,900	7,590 11,020 14,470
2 1/16	3.40	0.156	1.750	1.656	1.700	2.330	J-55 N-80 P-105	51,500 75,000 98,400	7,570 11,030 14,470
	4.70	0.190	1.995	1.901	1.945	2.700	J-55 N-80 P-105	71,700 104,000 137,000	7,630 11,060 14,570
	5.30	0.218	1.939	1.845	1.890	2.700	J-55 N-80 P-105	80,800 118,000 155,000	7,620 11,130 14,620
2 3/8	5.95	0.254	1.867	1.774	1.805	2.800	J-55 N-80 P-105	92,900 135,000 178,000	7,810 11,340 14,960
	6.20	0.261	1.853	1.760	1.795	2.800	J-55 N-80 P-105	95,300 139,000 182,000	7,690 11,210 14,680
	7.70	0.336	1.703	1.610	1.640	2.900	J-55 N-80 P-105	118,400 172,000 226,000	7,690 11,170 14,680
	6.50	0.218	2.441	2.347	2.375	3.220	J-55 N-80 P-105	99,700 145,000 190,000	7,670 11,150 14,620
	7.90	0.276	2.323	2.230	2.265	3.360	J-55 N-80 P-105	124,000 180,000 236,000	7,850 11,390 14,940
	8.70	0.308	2.259	2.166	2.200	3.440	J-55 N-80 P-105	136,000 199,000 261,000	7,820 11,440 15,000
2 7/8	8.90	0.316	2.243	2.150	2.180	3.440	J-55 N-80 P-105	139,800 203,000 267,000	7,850 11,400 15,000
	9.50	0.340	2.195	2.102	2.130	3.500	J-55 N-80 P-105	148,000 217,000 284,000	7,790 11,420 14,950

Dual Seal Special DSS Tubing Joint (*Continued*)

Size, OD *D*, in.	Nom. wt./ft, lb	Wall thick-ness *t*, in.	ID *d*, in.	Tubing drift diam, in.	Joint		Grade	Yield load min, lb	Equiv. length, ft sf = 2
					ID in.	OD, in.			
2⅞	11.00	0.405	2.065	1.972	2.000	3.625	J-55	172,000	7,820
							N-80	251,000	11,410
							P-105	330,000	15,000
3½	9.30	0.254	2.992	2.867	2.920	3.865	J-55	142,000	7,630
							N-80	207,000	11,130
							P-105	272,000	14,620
	10.30	0.289	2.922	2.797	2.878	3.937	J-55	160,000	7,700
							N-80	233,000	11,310
							P-105	306,000	14,850

8 modified buttress threads per inch on sizes 1.315 in. OD to 2⅜ in. OD, inclusive.
6 modified buttress threads per inch on sizes 2⅞ in. OD and 3½ in. OD.
Taper 1.125 in. ft on diameter.
For mill test pressures, collapsing pressures, and minimum internal yield pressures, see API tubing tables, p. 2-66.
For method of calculating strengths and pressures, see performance section, p. 2-92.

Gross Lineal Footage from Net Footage—Multiplication Factors
Dual Seal Special DSS Tubing Joint

Size, OD, in.	Nom. wt./ft, lb	Make-up loss per joint, in.	Multiplication factors*	
			Avg length of joint	
			20 ft	30 ft
1.315	1.80	1.562	1.0066	1.0044
1.660	2.40	1.812	1.0076	1.0051
1.900	2.90	2.000	1.0084	1.0056
2¹⁄₁₆	3.40	2.188	1.0092	1.0061
2⅜	All	2.750	1.0116	1.0077
2⅞	All	3.000	1.0127	1.0084
3½	All	3.375	1.0143	1.0095

* To obtain the gross or shipping length, multiply net footage in feet by the multiplication factor.

High-strength HS Tubing Joint
Weights, Dimensions, and Tension Properties

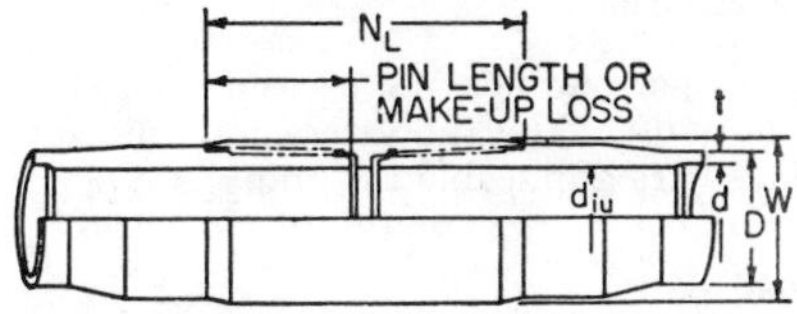

Size, OD D, in.	Nom. wt./ft, lb	Wall thickness t, in.	ID d, in.	Tubing drift diam, in.	Joint: ID bored d_{iu}, in.	Joint: OD W, in.	Joint: Length N_L, in.	Grade	Yield load min, lb	Equiv. length, ft sf = 2
2⅜	4.70	0.190	1.995	1.901	1.945	2.875	5½	P-105	137,000	14,570
	5.30	0.218	1.939	1.845	1.890	2.875	5½	P-105	155,000	14,620
	5.95	0.254	1.867	1.774	1.805	3.000	5½	P-105	178,000	14,960
	6.20	0.261	1.853	1.760	1.795	3.000	5½	P-105	182,000	14,680
	7.70	0.336	1.703	1.610	1.640	3.000	5½	P-105	226,000	14,680
2⅞	6.50	0.218	2.441	2.347	2.375	3.500	6⅛	P-105	190,000	14,620
	7.90	0.276	2.323	2.230	2.265	3.500	6⅛	P-105	236,000	14,940
	8.70	0.308	2.259	2.166	2.200	3.625	6⅛	P-105	261,000	15,000
	8.90	0.316	2.243	2.150	2.180	3.625	6⅛	P-105	267,000	15,000
	9.50	0.340	2.195	2.102	2.130	3.625	6⅛	P-105	284,000	14,950
	11.00	0.405	2.065	1.972	2.000	3.750	6⅛	P-105	330,000	15,000

For mill test pressures, collapsing pressures, and minimum internal yield pressures, see API tubing tables, p. 2–66.

For method of calculating strengths and pressures, see performance section, p. 2–92.

Gross Lineal Footage from Net Footage—Multiplication Factors
High-strength HS Tubing Joint

Size, OD, in.	Nom. wt./ft, lb	Make-up loss per joint, in.	Multiplication factors*: Avg length of joint 20 ft	Multiplication factors*: Avg length of joint 30 ft
2⅜	All	2.500	1.0105	1.0070
2⅞	All	2.813	1.0119	1.0079

* To obtain the gross or shipping length, multiply net footage in feet by the multiplication factors.

DESIGN FACTORS AND USE

Formulas for collapse resistance, internal yields pressures, and joint strengths for the various grades of tubing are for the purpose of providing minimum performance properties on which the design of tubing strings may be based and do not include factors of safety. In the design of tubing strings, factors of safety should be applied to suit the particular application.

Formulas Used in Determining Performance Properties of Tubing

Collapse and Internal Pressures

Values for collapse resistance and internal pressures for the various grades of tubing shown in the tables are minimum values and were determined by means of the formulas listed for casing, which also are applicable to tubing; see pages **2-36** and **2-37**.

Joint Strength-yield Load

Joint strength values for tubing are determined as the product of the specified minimum yield strength for the grade and the area of section under the root of the last perfect thread or of the body of the pipe, whichever is smaller. The formulas are as follows:

For nonupset tubing, the calculations are based on the cross-sectional area of the pipe wall at the thread root of the last perfect thread.

$$L_j = Y_m \times 0.7854[(D - 2h_s)^2 - d^2]$$

For external-upset tubing, the calculations are based on the plain-end area.

$$L_j = Y_m \times 0.7854(D^2 - d^2)$$

where L_j = minimum joint strength, lb
  D = tabulated outside diameter, in.
  h_s = height of thread, in., 0.05560 in. for 10 threads per inch, 0.07125 for 8 threads per inch
  d = tabulated inside diameter, in.
  Y_m = minimum yield strength, psi, as follows:

Grade F-25............	25,000
Grade H-40............	40,000
Grade J-55............	55,000
Grade N-80............	80,000
Grade P-105..........	105,000

Tensile Requirements

Grade	Yield strength, min, psi	Tensile strength, min, psi	Elongation, min, % in 2 in.	
			Strip speci- mens	Full- section speci- mens
Tubing:				
F-25	25,000	40,000	40*	45*
H-40	40,000	60,000	27	32
J-55	55,000	75,000	20	25
N-80	80,000	100,000	16	18
P-105	105,000	120,000	15	17

* The minimum elongation in 8 in. shall be 20 per cent for all grade F-25 material except wrought iron, for which the minimum elongation in 8 in. shall be 12 per cent.

Hydrostatic Tests

Test Pressures. Test pressures shall be the standard pressures listed in the tables on pages **2-66** to **2-69**, or a higher pressure as agreed upon between the purchaser and the manufacturer.

NOTE: The hydrostatic test pressures specified herein are mill-inspection test pressures, are not intended as a basis for design, and do not necessarily have any direct relationship to working pressures.

NOTE: The hydrostatic test pressures specified herein are based on the following formulas:

1. For grades F-25, H-40, and J-55,

$$P = \frac{2St}{D}$$

or 3,000, whichever is smaller.

2. For grades N-80 and P-105,

$$P = \frac{2St}{D}$$

or 10,000, whichever is smaller.

where P = hydrostatic test pressure, psi
S = fiber stress, as given below
t = tabulated wall thickness, in.
D = tabulated outside diameter, in.

Grade	Fiber stress, psi	
	Standard test pressures	Alternative test pressures, all sizes
F-25	20,000*	20,000*
H-40	32,000*	32,000*
J-55	44,000*	44,000*
N-80	64,000*	
P-105	84,000*	

* Based on 80 per cent of the specified minimum yield strength.

Correction Factors for Collapse in Fluids of Various Densities

The setting depths of tubing in fluids or other densities than salt water may be obtained by using the correction factors shown on page 2–47 for casing, which also are applicable to tubing.

Example of a Method for Designing a Typical 11,000-ft Single-weight and Grade String of 2⅞ in. OD API Nonupset Tubing to Meet Preselected Safety Factros for Collapse, Tension Yield Load, and Internal Yield Pressure When Based on Minimum Physical Properties

Safety factors:

Collapse........................ 1.125
Tension yield load............... 2.00
Internal yield pressure........... 1.00

Tabulated Design Data

Well depth, ft	Tubing						Safety factors			
	Wt./ft, lb	Steel grade	Type of joint		Amount required, ft	Wt. of string, lb		Col-lapse	Tension	Internal yield pressure
			Cou-pling	Type of thread		Section	Total		Yield load	
11,000	8.60	P-105	Reg.	API	11,000	34,600	94,600	3.00	2.21	3.58

Example of the design steps in setting up the string shown in the preceding table:

Calculations, Tension

Determine lightest weight and lowest grade of tubing that can be set in tension to 11,000 ft.

Referring to the tables of Tension Properties, page **2**–66, the equivalent-length column shows the maximum depths to which the tubing may be set with a safety factor of 2.

Read the figure for $2\frac{7}{8}$ in. OD which equals or closely exceeds total depths of 11,000 ft. 8.60-lb P-105 API nonupset tubing reads 12,160 ft. Select this tubing and determine the safety factor.

$$\text{Safety factor} = \frac{\text{min yield load}}{\text{wt. of string}}$$

$$= \frac{209,100}{11,000 \times 8.60} = 2.21$$

Collapse

Referring to the tables, the collapse column shows the maximum depth to which the tubing may be set.

Read the figure for $2\frac{7}{8}$ in. OD 8.60-lb P-105 API nonupset tubing which equals 29,330 ft with a safety factor of $1\frac{1}{8}$ and determine the safety factor for the selected string.

$$\text{Safety factor} = \frac{2 \times \text{min collapse resistance}}{\text{total depth of well}}$$

$$= \frac{2 \times 16,500}{11,000} = 3.00$$

Internal Yield Pressure

The safety factor for internal pressure based on minimum yield strength should never be less than 1.

It is usual practice to estimate the pressure encountered in drilling as equivalent to 1 psi for every 2 ft of depth, or $\frac{1}{2}$ psi for every foot of depth. However, if the formation pressure is known, this value should be divided into the internal yield strength to obtain the internal yield pressure safety factor. Determine the safety factor as follows:

$$\text{Safety factor} = \frac{\text{internal yield pressure, psi}}{0.5 \times \text{total depth of well}}$$

$$= \frac{19,690}{5,500} = 3.58$$

Stretch in Tubing When Freely Suspended in Fluid Media

When tubing is subjected to an axial stress, either tension or compression, which does not exceed the elastic limit of the material the stretch or contraction may be determined by the formulas shown on page **2**–53 for casing, which also are applicable to tubing.

Volume of Liquids in Tubing Strings, Gal

Size, OD / Wall thickness, in.

Length of tubing, ft	1.050	1.315	1.660	1.900	2⅜			2⅞		3½				4		4½
Wall thickness, in.	0.113	0.133	0.140	0.145	0.167	0.190	0.254	0.217	0.308	0.216	0.254	0.289	0.375	0.226	0.262	0.271
1	0.03	0.04	0.08	0.11	0.17	0.16	0.14	0.24	0.21	0.38	0.37	0.35	0.31	0.51	0.49	0.64
2	0.06	0.09	0.16	0.21	0.34	0.32	0.28	0.49	0.42	0.77	0.73	0.70	0.62	1.0	0.99	1.3
3	0.09	0.13	0.23	0.32	0.51	0.49	0.43	0.73	0.62	1.1	1.1	1.0	0.93	1.5	1.5	1.9
4	0.11	0.18	0.31	0.42	0.68	0.65	0.57	0.97	0.83	1.5	1.5	1.4	1.2	2.0	2.0	2.6
5	0.14	0.22	0.39	0.53	0.85	0.81	0.71	1.2	1.0	1.9	1.8	1.7	1.5	2.6	2.5	3.2
6	0.17	0.27	0.47	0.63	1.0	0.97	0.85	1.5	1.2	2.3	2.2	2.1	1.9	3.1	3.0	3.8
7	0.20	0.31	0.54	0.74	1.2	1.1	1.0	1.7	1.5	2.7	2.6	2.4	2.3	3.6	3.5	4.5
8	0.23	0.36	0.62	0.85	1.4	1.3	1.1	1.9	1.7	3.1	2.9	2.8	2.5	4.1	3.9	5.1
9	0.26	0.40	0.70	0.95	1.5	1.5	1.3	2.2	1.9	3.5	3.3	3.1	2.8	4.6	4.4	5.7
10	0.29	0.45	0.78	1.1	1.7	1.6	1.4	2.4	2.1	3.8	3.7	3.5	3.1	5.1	4.9	6.4
20	0.57	0.90	1.6	2.1	3.4	3.2	2.8	4.9	4.2	7.7	7.3	7.0	6.2	10.3	9.9	12.8
30	0.86	1.3	2.3	3.2	5.1	4.9	4.3	7.3	6.2	11.5	11.0	10.5	9.3	15.4	14.8	19.2
40	1.1	1.8	3.1	4.2	6.8	6.5	5.7	9.7	8.3	15.4	14.6	13.9	12.3	20.5	19.7	25.6
50	1.4	2.2	3.9	5.3	8.5	8.1	7.1	12.2	10.4	19.2	18.3	17.4	15.4	25.7	24.6	32.0
60	1.7	2.7	4.7	6.3	10.2	9.7	8.5	14.6	12.5	23.0	21.9	20.9	18.5	30.8	29.6	38.4
70	2.0	3.1	5.4	7.4	11.9	11.4	10.4	17.0	14.6	26.9	25.6	24.4	21.6	36.0	34.5	44.7
80	2.3	3.6	6.2	8.5	13.6	13.0	11.4	19.4	16.7	30.7	29.2	27.9	24.7	41.1	39.4	51.1
90	2.6	4.0	7.0	9.5	15.3	14.6	12.8	21.9	18.7	34.6	32.9	31.4	27.8	46.2	44.4	57.5
100	2.8	4.5	7.8	10.6	17.0	16.2	14.2	24.3	20.8	38.4	36.5	34.8	30.8	51.4	49.3	63.9
200	5.7	9.0	15.5	21.2	34.0	32.5	28.4	48.6	41.6	76.8	73.0	69.7	61.7	102.7	98.6	127.8
300	8.6	13.5	23.3	31.7	51.0	48.7	42.7	72.9	62.5	115.2	109.6	104.5	92.6	154.1	147.9	191.8
400	11.4	18.0	31.1	42.3	68.0	65.0	56.9	97.2	83.3	153.6	146.1	139.4	123.4	205.4	197.2	255.7
500	14.2	22.4	38.8	52.9	85.0	81.2	71.1	121.6	104.1	192.0	182.6	174.2	154.2	256.8	246.5	319.6
600	17.1	26.9	46.6	63.5	102.0	97.4	85.3	145.9	124.9	230.4	219.1	209.0	185.1	308.2	295.8	383.5
700	20.0	31.4	54.4	74.1	119.0	113.7	99.5	170.2	145.7	268.8	255.6	243.9	216.0	359.5	345.1	447.4
800	22.8	35.9	62.2	84.6	136.0	129.9	113.8	194.5	166.6	307.2	292.2	278.7	246.8	410.9	394.4	511.4
900	25.6	40.4	69.9	95.2	153.0	146.2	128.0	218.8	187.4	345.6	328.7	313.6	277.6	462.2	443.7	575.3
1,000	28.5	44.9	77.7	105.8	170.0	162.4	142.2	243.1	208.2	384.0	365.2	348.4	308.5	513.6	493.0	639.2

Example: What volume of acid will be contained in a 4,139-ft string of 4½-in. tubing? *Solution:* From table:

4,000 ft of 4½-in. tubing contains (4 × 639.2)	2,556.8 gal
100 ft of 4½-in. tubing contains	63.9 gal
30 ft of 4½-in. tubing contains	19.2 gal
9 ft of 4½-in. tubing contains	5.8 gal
4,139 ft of 4½-in. tubing contains	2,645.7 gal

API RECOMMENDED PRACTICE FOR CARE AND USE OF TUBING

Running and Pulling Tubing

Preparation and Inspection before Running

26. All tubing, whether new, used, or reconditioned, should always be handled with thread protectors in place.

27. Before running in the hole for the first time, tubing should be drifted with an API drift mandrel to ensure passage of pumps, swabs, and packers.

28. Elevators should be in good repair and should have links of equal length.

29. Heavy safety elevators and spiders are recommended for long strings.

30. Elevators should be examined to note if latch fitting is complete.

31. Spider slips which will not crush the tubing should be used. Slips should be examined before using to see that they are working together.

32. Tubing tongs which will not crush the tubing should be used on the body of the tubing and should fit properly to avoid unnecessary cutting of the pipe wall. The use of pipe wrenches is not recommended.

33. The following precautions should be taken in the preparation of tubing threads:
   a. Immediately before running, remove protectors from both field end and coupling end of a number of lengths of tubing in the top row and clean threads thoroughly, repeating as additional rows become uncovered.
   b. Carefully inspect the threads. Those found damaged, even slightly, should be laid aside unless satisfactory means are available for correcting thread damage.
   c. Place clean protectors on field end of the pipe so that thread will not be damaged while rolling pipe onto the rack and pulling into the derrick. Several thread protectors may be cleaned and used repeatedly for this operation.
   d. Before stabbing, apply ample thread compound over the entire threaded section of both external and internal threads.
   e. Check each coupling for make-up. If the stand-off is abnormally great check the joint for tightness. Loose couplings should be removed, the thread thoroughly cleaned, fresh compound applied over the entire thread surfaces, then the coupling replaced and tightened before pulling the tubing into the derrick.

34. For high-pressure or condensate walls, additional precautions should be taken to ensure tight joints, as follows:
   a. Couplings should be removed, and both the mill-end pipe thread and coupling thread thoroughly cleaned and inspected. To facilitate this operation, tubing may be ordered with couplings handling tight, which is approximately one turn beyond handtight, or may be ordered with the couplings shipped separately.
   b. Thread compound should be applied to both the external and internal threads and the coupling should be reapplied handling tight. Field-end threads and the mating coupling threads should have thread compound applied just before stabbing.

35. When tubing is pulled into the derrick, care should be taken that the tubing is not bent, or couplings or protectors bumped.

Stabbing, Making Up, and Lowering

36. Do not remove thread protector from field end of tubing until ready to stab. Just before stabbing, remove thread protector and apply thread compound over entire surface of threads. The brush or utensil used in applying thread compound should be kept free of foreign matter and the compound should never be thinned.

37. In stabbing, lower tubing carefully to avoid injuring threads. Stab vertically, preferably with assistance of man on stabbing board. If the tubing tilts to one side after stabbing, lift up, clean, and correct any damaged thread with three-cornered file; then carefully remove any fillings and reapply compound over thread surface. Care

should be exercised, especially when running doubles or thribbles, to prevent bowing and resulting errors in alignment when the tubing is allowed to rest too heavily on the coupling threads. Intermediate supports may be placed in the derrick to limit bowing of the tubing.

38. After stabbing, start screwing by hand or apply regular or power tubing tongs slowly. Power tubing tongs are recommended for high-pressure or condensate wells to ensure uniform make-up and tight joints. Joints should be made up tight, approximately two turns beyond the handtight position, with care being taken not to gall the threads. When the additional preparation and inspection precautions for high-pressure or condensate wells are taken, the coupling will "float" or make up simultaneously at both ends until the proper number of turns beyond the handtight position have been obtained. The handtight position may be determined by checking several joints on the rack and noting the number of threads exposed when a coupling is made up with a torque of 50 ft-lb.

39. Spider slips and elevators should be cleaned frequently and slips should be kept sharp.

40. Finding bottom should be accomplished with extreme caution. Do not set tubing down heavily.

Pulling Tubing

41. A caliper survey prior to pulling a worn string of tubing will provide a quick means of segregating badly worn lengths for removal.

42. Break-out tongs should be positioned close to the coupling. Hammering the coupling to break the joint is an injurious practice. When tapping is required, use the flat face, never the peen face, of the hammer, and tap lightly at the center and completely around the coupling, never near the end or on opposite sides only.

43. Great care should be exercised to disengage all the thread before lifting the tubing out of the coupling. Do not jump tubing out of the coupling.

44. Tubing stacked in derrick should be set on a firm wooden platform, *never* on concrete or earth.

45. Protect threads from dirt or injury when the tubing is out of the hole.

46. Tubing set back in the derrick should be properly supported to prevent undue bending. Tubing $2\frac{3}{8}$ in. outside diameter and larger, preferably should be pulled in stands approximately 60 ft long or in doubles of range 2. Stands of tubing 1.900 in. outside diameter or smaller, and stands longer than 60 ft, should have intermediate support.

47. Before leaving location, always firmly tie a setback of tubing in place.

48. Make sure threads are undamaged, clean, and well coated with compound before rerunning.

49. Distribute joint and tubing wear by moving a length from the top of the string to the bottom each time the tubing is pulled.

50. In order to avoid leaks, all joints should be retightened occasionally.

51. When tubing is stuck, the best practice is to use a calibrated weight indicator. Do not be misled, by stretching of the tubing string, into the assumption that the tubing is free.

52. After a hard pull to loosen a string of tubing, all joints pulled on should be retightened.

53. All threads should be cleaned and lubricated or should be coated with a material that will minimize corrosion. Clean protectors should be placed on the tubing before it is laid down.

54. Before tubing is stored or reused, pipe and threads should be inspected and defective joints marked for shipping and regauging.

Causes of Tubing Troubles

55. The more common causes of tubing troubles are as follows:

a. Improper selection for strength and life required, especially of nonupset tubing where upset tubing should be used.

b. Insufficient inspection of finished product at the mill and in the yard.
c. Careless loading, unloading, and cartage.
d. Damaged threads resulting from protectors loosening and falling off.
e. Lack of care in storage to give proper protection.
f. Excessive hammering on couplings.
g. Use of worn-out and wrong types of handling equipment, spiders, tongs, dies, and pipe wrenches.
h. Nonobservance of proper rules in running and pulling tubing.
i. Coupling wear and rod cutting.
j. Excessive sucker-rod breakage.
k. Fatigue, which often causes failure at the last engaged thread. There is no positive remedy, but using external-upset tubing in place of nonupset tubing greatly delays the start of this trouble.
l. Replacement of worn couplings with non-API couplings.
m. Dropping a string, even a short distance. This may loosen the couplings at the bottom of the string. The string should be pulled and rerun, examining all joints very carefully.
n. Leaky joints, under external or internal pressure, are a common trouble, and may be due to:
  1. Improper thread compound.
  2. Dirty threads, or threads contaminated with coating material used as protection from corrosion.
  3. Undertonging or overtonging.
  4. Galled threads due to dirt, careless stabbing, damaged threads, poor or diluted thread compound.
  5. Improperly cut field threads.
  6. Couplings that have been dented by hammering.
  7. Pulling too hard on string.
  8. Excessive rerunning.
o. *Corrosion.* Both the inside and outside of tubing can be damaged by corrosion, which can be recognized by the presence of pits or holes in the pipe. Corrosion products may or may not adhere to the tubing. Corrosion is usually caused by corrosive fluids and the damage can be aggravated by abrasive effects of pumping equipment and by high fluid velocities. Corrosion may be caused also by stray electric currents (electrolysis), by dissimilar metals in contact with each other (bimetallic galvanic corrosion), and by variations in the grain structure and surface finish in the same piece of steel (concentration cell corrosion). Because corrosion can result from so many different conditions, no simple or universal remedy can be given for its control. Each problem must be treated as an individual case, and a solution attempted in the light of the known corrosion factors and operating conditions. The condition of tubing can be determined by visual or optical-instrument inspections. Where this is not practical, the location, extent, and severity of damage to the inside of the tubing can be determined by means of a tubing-caliper survey. On the basis of the industry's experience to date, the following practices or measures can be used to control corrosion of tubing.
  1. Where internal or external tubing corrosion is known to exist and corrosive fluids are being produced, the following measures can be employed:
    a. In flowing wells, the annulus can be packed off and the corrosive fluid confined to the inside of the tubing. The inside surface of the tubing in this type of completion can be protected by using special coatings or by the use of inhibitors; also corrosion may be controlled by the use of alloy steel tubing. Alloy tubing containing 5 to 9 per cent nickel, baked-on phenolic resin and nickel-plated coatings are being tried but have not been completely evaluated. Alloy steels containing 5 per cent or more chromium may find economic use in special wells. Chemical inhibitors introduced periodically either in the form of sticks, solid granules, or liquids may provide adequate protection against corrosion.

b. In pumping and gas-lift wells, inhibitors can be introduced via the casing-tubing annulus and afford appreciable protection. In this type of completion, especially in pumping wells, better operating practices can also aid in extending the life of tubing, viz., through the use of rod protectors, rotation of tubing, and longer and slower pumping strokes.

2. To determine the value and effectiveness of the above practices and measures, cost and equipment failure records can be compared before and after application of control measures. Inhibitor effectiveness can also be checked by means of coupons, caliper surveys, and visual examinations of readily accessible pieces of equipment. Water analyses to determine the iron content before and after starting the inhibitor treatment may also serve as an indication of the comparative rates of corrosion. When lacking previous experience with any of the above measures, these should be used cautiously and on a limited scale until appraised for the particular operating conditions.

3. In general, all new areas should be considered as being potentially corrosive and investigations should be initiated early in the life of a field, and repeated periodically, to detect and localize corrosion before it has done destructive damage. These investigations should cover: (a) a complete chemical analysis of the effluent water, including pH, iron, hydrogen sulfide, organic acids, and any other substances which influence or indicate the degree of corrosion. An analysis of the produced gas for carbon dioxide and hydrogen sulfide is also desirable; (b) corrosion rate tests by using coupons of the same materials as in the well; and (c) the use of caliper or optical instrument inspections. Where conditions favorable to corrosion exist, a qualified corrosion engineer should be consulted. Particular attention should be given to mitigation of corrosion where the probable life of subsurface equipment is less than the time expected to deplete a well

PART 3: LINE PIPE

REFERENCES: API Standard 5L and 5LX, American Petroleum Institute. Bulletins and handbooks of the following companies: National Tube Division, United States Steel Corporation; The Youngstown Sheet and Tube Company; Jones & Laughlin Steel Corporation; The National Supply Company, Subsidiary of Armco Steel Corporation; Republic Steel Corporation; Johns-Manville; Aluminum Company of America.

REGULAR LINE PIPE

Line pipe is required by the oil and gas industry to convey oil, gas, and water in its operations.

The American Petroleum Institute with the cooperation of the American Gas Association has developed specifications meeting the needs of the oil and gas industry for steel and wrought-iron line pipe and published these in API Standards 5L and 5LX. These provide standard dimensions, strengths, and performance properties and the required thread gauging practice to ensure complete interchangeability. The following tables include dimensional and strength data of API line pipe.

In addition to API line pipe, line pipe to meet special conditions in regards to corrosion resistance, lines for temporary use, etc., have been developed. The cement-lined pipe, asbestos pipe, plastic pipe, and aluminum pipe shown in the following tables are intended for these special conditions.

API Butt-welded Plain-end Line Pipe
Dimensions, Weights, Internal Pressures, and Test Pressures

Size, nominal, in.	OD, in.	Wt./ft, lb	Wall thickness,* in.	ID,* in.	Internal pressure at min yield strength,† psi				Test pressures,‡ psi	
					Wrought iron	Elec. fce., class I O.H., or basic oxygen	Class II O.H. or basic oxygen	Bessemer	Wrought iron	Other classes
⅛	0.405	0.24	0.068 std.	0.269	4,840	5,040	5,640	6,040	700	700
		0.31	0.095 Xstg.	0.214	6,760	7,040	7,880	8,440	850	850
¼	0.540	0.42	0.088 std.	0.364	4,690	4,890	5,480	5,870	700	700
		0.54	0.119 Xstg.	0.302	6,350	6,610	7,400	7,930	850	850
⅜	0.675	0.57	0.091 std.	0.493	3,880	4,040	4,530	4,850	700	700
		0.74	0.126 Xstg.	0.423	5,380	5,600	6,270	6,720	850	850
½	0.840	0.85	0.109 std.	0.622	3,740	3,890	4,360	4,670	700	700
		1.09	0.147 Xstg.	0.546	5,040	5,250	5,880	6,300	850	850
		1.71	0.294 XXstg.	0.252	10,080	10,500	11,760	12,600	1,000	1,000

API Butt-welded Plain-end Line Pipe (*Continued*)

Size, nominal, in.	OD, in.	Wt./ft, lb	Wall thickness,* in.	ID,* in.	Internal pressure at min yield strength,† psi				Test pressures,‡ psi	
					Wrought iron	Elec. fce., class I O.H., or basic oxygen	Class II O.H. or basic oxygen	Bessemer	Wrought iron	Other classes
¾	1.050	1.13	0.113 std.	0.824	3,100	3,230	3,620	3,870	700	700
		1.47	0.154 Xstg.	0.742	4,220	4,400	4,930	5,280	850	850
		2.44	0.308 XXstg.	0.434	8,450	8,800	9,860	10,560	1,000	1,000
1	1.315	1.68	0.133 std.	1.049	2,910	3,030	3,400	3,640	700	700
		2.17	0.179 Xstg.	0.957	3,920	4,080	4,570	4,900	850	850
		3.66	0.358 XXstg.	0.599	7,840	8,170	9,150	9,800	1,000	1,000
1¼	1.660	2.27	0.140 std.	1.380	2,430	2,530	2,830	3,040	1,000	1,000
		3.00	0.191 Xstg.	1.278	3,310	3,450	3,870	4,140	1,400	1,300
		5.21	0.382 XXstg.	0.896	6,630	6,900	7,730	8,280	1,500	1,400
1½	1.900	2.72	0.145 std.	1.610	2,200	2,290	2,560	2,750	1,000	1,000
		3.63	0.200 Xstg.	1.500	3,030	3,160	3,540	3,790	1,400	1,300
		6.41	0.400 XXstg.	1.100	6,060	6,320	7,070	7,580	1,500	1,400
2	2.375	3.65	0.154 std.	2.067	1,870	1,940	2,180	2,330	1,000	1,000
		5.02	0.218 Xstg.	1.939	2,640	2,750	3,080	3,300	1,400	1,300
		9.03	0.436 XXstg.	1.503	4,190	5,510	6,170	6,610	1,500	1,400
2½	2.875	5.79	0.203 std.	2.469	2,030	2,120	2,370	2,540	.....	1,000
		7.66	0.276 Xstg.	2.323	2,760	2,880	3,230	3,460	1,400	1,300
		13.70	0.552 XXstg.	1.771	5,530	5,760	6,450	6,910	1,500	1,400
3	3.500	6.63	0.188§	3.124	.....	1,610	1,800	1,930	.....	1,000
		7.58	0.216 std.	3.068	.....	1,850	2,070	2,200	.....	1,000
		10.25	0.300 Xstg.	2.900	2,470	2,570	2,880	3,090	2,500	1,300
3½	4.000	7.63	0.188§	3.624	.....	1,410	1,580	1,690	.....	1,200
		9.11	0.226 std.	3.548	.....	1,700	1,900	2,030	.....	1,200
		12.51	0.318 Xstg.	3.364	2,290	2,380	2,670	2,860	2,300	1,700
4	4.500	8.64	0.188§	4.124	.....	1,250	1,400	1,500	.....	1,200
		10.00	0.219§	4.062	.....	1,460	1,640	1,750	.....	1,200
		10.79	0.237 std.	4.026	.....	1,580	1,770	1,900	.....	1,200
		14.98	0.337 Xstg.	3.826	2,160	2,250	2,520	2,700	2,200	1,700

* The weight per cubic inch is slightly less for wrought iron than for steel. Since wrought-iron pipe is made with the same weight per foot as steel pipe, the wall thickness of wrought-iron pipe is 2 to 3 per cent greater than the tabulated values above, and the inside diameter is correspondingly smaller.

† Internal-pressure values were calculated on basis of nominal dimensions; the fiber-stress values were reduced to 60 per cent in accordance with the longitudinal joint factor assigned by Section 8 of the Code for Pressure Piping (ASA B31.1.8-1955).

‡ Test-pressure values for sizes 3, 3½, and 4 in. X-strong wrought-iron pipe were calculated by the formula shown on p. 2–110; all other test pressures were established arbitrarily.

§ Wall thicknesses are not included in API listing and the test pressures are identical with those shown for standard wall thicknesses of the same size.

API Plain-end Line Pipe
Dimensions, Weights, Internal Pressures, and Test Pressures

Size, in.	OD, in.	Wt./ft, lb	Wall thickness,* in.	ID,* in.	Internal pressure at min yield strength, psi						Test pressures,¶ psi			
					Lap-welded wrought iron‡‡	Lap-welded steel§			Seamless and electric-welded		Wrought iron	Lap-welded steel	Grade A	Grade B
						Elec. fce., class I O.H. or basic oxygen	Class II O.H. or basic oxygen	Besse-mer	Grade A	Grade B				
⅛ nom.	0.405	0.24	0.068 std. wt.	0.269	.....	.....	.....	.....	10,070	11,750	.....	.....	700	700
		0.31	0.095 Xstg.	0.215	.....	.....	.....	.....	14,070	16,420	.....	.....	850	850
¼ nom.	0.540	0.42	0.088 std. wt.	0.364	.....	.....	.....	.....	9,780	11,410	.....	.....	700	700
		0.54	0.199 Xstg.	0.302	.....	.....	.....	.....	13,200	15,430	.....	.....	850	850
⅜ nom.	0.675	0.57	0.091 std. wt.	0.493	.....	.....	.....	.....	8,090	9,440	.....	.....	700	700
		0.74	0.126 Xstg.	0.423	.....	.....	.....	.....	11,200	13,070	.....	.....	850	850
½ nom.	0.840	0.85	0.109 std. wt.	0.622	.....	.....	.....	.....	7,790	9,080	.....	.....	700	700
		1.09	0.147 Xstg.	0.546	.....	.....	.....	.....	10,500	12,250	.....	.....	850	850
		1.71	0.294 XXstg.	0.252	.....	.....	.....	.....	21,000	24,500	.....	.....	1,000	1,000
¾ nom.	1.050	1.13	0.113 std. wt.	0.824	.....	.....	.....	.....	6,460	7,530	.....	.....	700	700
		1.47	0.147 Xstg.	0.742	.....	.....	.....	.....	8,400	9,800	.....	.....	850	850
		2.44	0.308 XXstg.	0.434	.....	.....	.....	.....	17,600	20,530	.....	.....	1,000	1,000
1 nom.	1.315	1.68	0.133 std. wt.	0.049	.....	.....	.....	.....	6,070	7,080	.....	.....	700	700
		2.17	0.179 Xstg.	0.957	.....	.....	.....	.....	8,170	9,530	.....	.....	850	850
		3.66	0.358 XXstg.	0.599	.....	.....	.....	.....	16,330	19,060	.....	.....	1,000	1,000
1¼ nom.	1.660	2.27	0.140 std. wt.	1.380	3,240	.....	.....	.....	5,060	5,900	1,000	.....	1,200	1,300
		3.00	0.191 Xstg.	1.278	4,420	.....	.....	.....	6,900	8,050	1,400	.....	1,800	1,900
		5.21	0.382 XXstg.	0.896	.....	.....	.....	.....	13,810	16,110	.....	.....	2,200	2,300
1½ nom.	1.900	2.72	0.145 std. wt.	1.610	2,930	.....	.....	.....	4,580	5,340	1,000	.....	1,200	1,300
		3.63	0.200 Xstg.	1.500	4,040	.....	.....	.....	6,320	7,370	1,400	.....	1,800	1,900
		6.41	0.400 XXstg.	1.100	.....	.....	.....	.....	12,630	14,740	.....	.....	2,200	2,300

Size	OD	Wt. per ft.	Wall thickness	I.D.	(1)	(2)	(3)	(4)	(5)	(6)	(7)	(8)	(9)	(10)
2 nom.	2.375	3.65	0.154 std. wt.	2.067	2,490	2,590	2,900	3,110	3,890	4,540	1,000	1,200	1,200	1,300
		5.02	0.218 Xstg.	1.939	3,520	3,670	4,110	4,410	5,510	6,430	1,400	1,800	1,800	1,900
		9.03	0.436 XXstg.	1.503	7,050	7,340	8,220	8,810	11,010	12,850	1,500	2,200	2,200	2,300
2½ nom.	2.875	5.79	0.203 std. wt.	2.469	2,710	2,820	3,160	3,390	4,240	4,940	1,000	1,200	1,200	1,300
		7.66	0.276 Xstg.	2.323	3,690	3,840	4,300	4,610	5,760	6,720	1,400	1,800	1,800	1,900
		13.70	0.552 XXstg.	1.771	7,370	7,680	8,600	9,220	11,520	13,440	1,500	2,200	2,200	2,300
3½ OD / 3 nom.	3.500	4.51	0.125 spec.	3.250	1,370	1,430	1,600	1,710	2,140	2,500	1,000	1,000	1,000	1,500
		5.58	0.156 spec.	3.188	1,710	1,780	2,000	2,140	2,670	3,120	1,300	1,300	1,300	1,900
		6.63	0.188 ref. wt.	3.124	2,060	2,150	2,410	2,580	3,220	3,760	1,500	1,600	1,600	2,200
		7.58	0.216 reg. wt.	3.068	2,370	2,470	2,760	2,960	3,700	4,320	1,800	1,900	1,900	2,500
		8.68	0.250 reg. wt.	3.000	2,740	2,860	3,200	3,430	4,290	5,000	2,100	2,200	2,200	2,500
		9.67	0.281 reg. wt.	2.938	3,080	3,210	3,600	3,850	4,820	5,620	2,300	2,500	2,500	2,500
		10.25	0.300 Xstg.	2.900	3,290	3,430	3,840	4,110	5,140	6,000	2,500	2,500	2,500	2,500
		18.58	0.600 XXstg.	2.300	6,580	6,860	7,680	8,230	10,290	12,000	2,500	2,500	2,500	2,500
4 OD / 3½ nom.	4.000	5.17	0.125 spec.	3.750	1,200	1,250	1,400	1,500	1,880	2,190	900	1,100	1,100	1,300
		6.41	0.156 spec.	3.688	1,500	1,560	1,750	1,870	2,340	2,730	1,100	1,400	1,400	1,600
		7.63	0.188 spec.	3.624	1,800	1,880	2,110	2,260	2,820	3,290	1,400	1,700	1,700	2,000
		9.11	0.226 spec.	3.548	2,170	2,260	2,530	2,701	3,390	3,960	1,600	2,000	2,000	2,400
		10.01	0.250 spec.	3.500	2,400	2,500	2,800	3,000	3,750	4,380	1,800	2,200	2,200	2,500
		11.17	0.281 spec.	3.438	2,700	2,810	3,150	3,370	4,220	4,920	2,000	2,500	2,500	2,500
		12.51	0.318 Xstg.	3.364	3,050	3,180	3,560	3,820	4,770	5,560	2,300	2,500	2,500	2,500
4½ OD / 4 nom.	4.500	5.84	0.125 spec.	4.250	1,070	1,110	1,240	1,330	1,670	1,940	800	1,000	1,000	1,200
		7.25	0.156 spec.	4.188	1,330	1,390	1,550	1,660	2,080	2,430	1,000	1,200	1,200	1,500
		8.64	0.188 reg. wt.	4.124	1,600	1,670	1,870	2,010	2,510	2,920	1,200	1,500	1,500	1,800
		10.00	0.219 reg. wt.	4.062	1,870	1,950	2,180	2,340	2,920	3,410	1,400	1,700	1,700	2,000
		10.79	0.237 reg. wt.	4.026	2,020	2,110	2,360	2,530	3,160	3,690	1,500	1,900	1,900	2,300
		11.35	0.250 reg. wt.	4.000	2,130	2,220	2,490	2,670	3,330	3,890	1,600	2,000	2,000	2,300
		12.67	0.281 reg. wt.	3.938	2,400	2,500	2,800	3,000	3,750	4,370	1,800	2,200	2,200	2,500
		13.98	0.312 reg. wt.	3.876	2,660	2,770	3,110	3,330	4,160	4,850	2,000	2,500	2,500	2,500
		14.98	0.337 Xstg.	3.826	2,800	3,000	3,360	3,590	4,490	5,240	2,200	2,500	2,500	2,500
		27.54	0.674 XXstg.	3.152	5,750	5,990	6,710	7,190	8,990	10,480	2,500	2,500	2,500	2,500
5 9⁄16 OD / 5 nom.	5.563	9.02	0.156 spec.	5.251	1,080	1,120	1,260	1,350	1,680	1,960	800	1,000	1,000	1,200
		10.76	0.188 spec.	5.186	1,300	1,350	1,510	1,620	2,030	2,370	950	1,200	1,200	1,400
		12.49	0.219 spec.	5.125	1,510	1,570	1,760	1,890	2,360	2,760	1,100	1,400	1,400	1,700
		14.62	0.258 spec.	5.047	1,780	1,860	2,080	2,230	2,780	3,250	1,300	1,700	1,700	1,900
		15.87	0.281 spec.	5.001	1,940	2,020	2,260	2,420	3,030	3,540	1,500	1,800	1,800	2,100
		17.52	0.312 spec.	4.939	2,150	2,240	2,510	2,690	3,370	3,930	1,600	2,000	2,000	2,400
		19.16	0.344 spec.	4.875	2,370	2,470	2,770	2,970	3,710	4,330	1,800	2,200	2,200	2,500
		20.78	0.375 Xstg.	4.813	2,590	2,700	3,020	3,240	4,040	4,720	1,900	2,400	2,400	2,500
		38.55	0.750 XXstg.	4.063	5,180	5,390	6,040	6,470	8,090	9,440	2,500	2,500	2,500	2,500

API Plain-end Line Pipe (*Continued*)

Size, in.	OD, in.	Wt./ft, lb	Wall thickness,* in.	ID,* in.	Internal pressure at min yield strength, psi						Test pressures,¶ psi			
					Lap-welded steel†§				Seamless and electric-welded		Wrought iron	Lap-welded steel	Grade A	Grade B
					Lap-welded wrought iron†‡	Elec. fce., class I O.H. or basic oxygen	Class II O.H. or basic oxygen	Bessemer	Grade A	Grade B				
6⅝ OD	6.625	12.89	0.188 reg. wt.	6.249	1,090	1,140	1,270	1,360	1,700	1,990	800	1,000	1,000	1,200
		14.97	0.219 reg. wt.	6.187	1,270	1,320	1,480	1,590	1,980	2,310	950	1,200	1,200	1,400
		17.02	0.250 reg. wt.	6.125	1,450	1,510	1,690	1,810	2,260	2,640	1,000	1,400	1,400	1,600
		18.97	0.280 reg. wt.	6.065	1,620	1,690	1,890	2,030	2,540	2,960	1,200	1,500	1,500	1,800
		21.77	0.312 reg. wt.	6.001	1,810	1,880	2,110	2,260	2,830	3,300	1,400	1,700	1,700	2,000
		23.06	0.344 reg. wt.	5.937	1,990	2,080	2,330	2,490	3,120	3,630	1,500	1,900	1,900	2,200
		25.03	0.375 reg. wt.	5.875	2,170	2,260	2,540	2,720	3,400	3,960	1,600	2,000	2,000	2,400
6 nom.	6.625	28.57	0.432 Xstg.	5.761	2,500	2,610	2,920	3,130	3,910	4,560	1,900	2,300	2,300	2,500
		53.16	0.864 X.Xstg.	4.897	5,010	5,220	5,840	6,260	7,820	9,130	2,500	2,500	2,500	2,500
8⅝ OD	8.625	16.90	0.188 reg. wt.	8.249	840	870	980	1,050	1,310	1,530	650	800	800	900
		19.64	0.219 reg. wt.	8.187	970	1,020	1,140	1,220	1,520	1,780	750	900	900	1,100
		22.36	0.250 reg. wt.	8.125	1,110	1,160	1,300	1,390	1,740	2,030	850	1,000	1,000	1,200
		24.70	0.277 reg. wt.	8.071	1,230	1,280	1,440	1,540	1,930	2,250	950	1,200	1,200	1,300
		27.74	0.312 reg. wt.	8.001	1,390	1,450	1,620	1,740	2,170	2,530	1,000	1,300	1,300	1,500
		28.55	0.322 reg. wt.	7.981	1,430	1,490	1,670	1,790	2,240	2,610	1,000	1,300	1,300	1,600
		30.40	0.344 reg. wt.	7.937	1,530	1,600	1,790	1,910	2,390	2,790	1,100	1,400	1,400	1,700
		33.04	0.375 reg. wt.	7.875	1,670	1,740	1,950	2,090	2,610	3,040	1,300	1,600	1,600	1,800
		38.26	0.438 reg. wt.	7.749	1,950	2,030	2,270	2,440	3,050	3,550	1,500	1,800	1,800	2,100
8 nom.	8.625	43.39	0.500 Xstg.	7.656	2,230	2,320	2,600	2,780	3,480	4,060	1,700	2,100	2,100	2,400
		72.42	0.875 X.Xstg.	6.875	3,900	4,060	4,540	4,870	6,090	7,100	2,500	2,500	2,500	2,500
10¾ OD	10.750	21.15	0.188 spec.	10.374	670	700	780	840	1,050	1,220	500	650	650	750
		24.60	0.219 reg. wt.	10.312	780	810	910	970	1,220	1,430	600	750	750	850
		28.04	0.250 reg. wt.	10.250	890	930	1,040	1,120	1,400	1,630	700	850	850	1,000
		31.20	0.279 reg. wt.	10.192	1,000	1,040	1,160	1,250	1,560	1,820	800	1,000	1,000	1,200
		34.24	0.307 reg. wt.	10.136	1,100	1,100	1,280	1,370	1,710	2,000	800	1,000	1,000	1,200
		38.20	0.344 reg. wt.	10.062	1,230	1,280	1,430	1,540	1,920	2,240	900	1,100	1,100	1,300

Pipe data table. Descriptive columns (Nom. size, O.D., Wt. per ft., Wall thickness & grade, I.D.) followed by ten pressure-rating columns (1)–(10).

Nom.	O.D.	Wt.	Wall / grade	I.D.	(1)	(2)	(3)	(4)	(5)	(6)	(7)	(8)	(9)	(10)
10 nom.	10.750	40.48	0.365 reg. wt.	10.020	1,400	1,200	1,200	1,000	2,380	2,040	1,630	1,520	1,360	1,300
		48.19	0.438 reg. wt.	9.874	1,600	1,500	1,500	1,200	2,850	2,440	1,960	1,830	1,630	1,560
		54.74	0.500 Xstg.	9.580	2,000	1,700	1,700	1,300	3,260	2,790	2,230	2,080	1,860	1,790
12¾ OD / 12 nom.	12.750	29.28	0.219 spec.	12.312	700	600	600	500	1,200	1,030	820	770	690	660
		33.38	0.250 reg. wt.	12.250	800	700	700	600	1,370	1,180	940	880	780	750
		37.45	0.281 reg. wt.	12.188	950	800	800	650	1,540	1,320	1,060	990	880	850
		41.51	0.312 reg. wt.	12.166	1,000	900	900	700	1,710	1,470	1,170	1,100	980	940
		43.77	0.330 reg. wt.	12.090	1,200	1,000	1,000	800	1,810	1,550	1,240	1,160	1,040	990
		45.55	0.344 reg. wt.	12.062	1,200	1,000	1,000	800	1,890	1,620	1,300	1,210	1,080	1,040
		49.56	0.375 reg. wt.	12.000	1,200	1,110	1,100	850	2,060	1,760	1,410	1,320	1,180	1,130
		57.53	0.438 reg. wt.	11.874	1,400	1,200	1,200	1,000	2,400	2,060	1,650	1,540	1,370	1,320
		65.42	0.500 Xstg.	11.750	1,600	1,400	1,400	1,100	2,750	2,350	1,880	1,760	1,570	1,510
14 OD	14.000	36.71	0.250 spec.	13.500	750	650	650	500	1,250	1,070	860	800	710	690
		41.21	0.281 spec.	13.438	850	700	700	600	1,400	1,200	960	900	800	770
		45.68	0.312 reg. wt.	13.376	950	800	800	650	1,560	1,340	1,070	1,000	890	860
		50.14	0.344 reg. wt.	13.312	1,000	900	900	700	1,720	1,470	1,180	1,100	980	940
		54.57	0.375 reg. wt.	13.250	1,100	950	950	750	1,880	1,610	1,290	1,200	1,070	1,030
		63.37	0.438 reg. wt.	13.124	1,300	1,100	1,100	900	2,190	1,880	1,500	1,400	1,250	1,200
		72.09	0.500 reg. wt.	13.000	1,500	1,300	1,300	1,000	2,500	2,140	1,710	1,600	1,430	1,370
16 OD	16.000	42.05	0.250 spec.	15.500	650	550	550	450	1,090	940	750	700	620	600
		47.22	0.281 spec.	15.438	750	650	650	500	1,230	1,050	840	790	700	670
		52.36	0.312 reg. wt.	15.376	800	700	700	550	1,360	1,170	940	870	780	750
		57.48	0.344 reg. wt.	15.312	900	750	750	600	1,500	1,290	1,030	960	860	830
		62.58	0.375 reg. wt.	15.250	1,000	850	850	700	1,640	1,410	1,130	1,050	940	900
		72.72	0.438 reg. wt.	15.124	1,100	1,100	1,000	800	1,920	1,640	1,310	1,230	1,100	1,050
		82.77	0.500 reg. wt.	15.000	1,300	1,100	1,110	900	2,190	1,880	1,500	1,400	1,250	1,200
18 OD	18.000	47.39	0.250 spec.	17.500	600	500			970	830				
		53.22	0.281 spec.	17.438	650	550			1,090	940				
		59.03	0.312 reg. wt.	17.376	750	600			1,210	1,040				
		64.82	0.344 reg. wt.	17.312	800	700			1,340	1,150				
		70.59	0.375 reg. wt.	17.250	900	750			1,460	1,250				
		82.06	0.438 reg. wt.	17.124	1,000	900			1,700	1,460				
		93.45	0.500 reg. wt.	17.000	1,200	1,000			1,940	1,670				
20 OD	20.000	52.73	0.250 spec.	19.500	500	450			880	750				
		59.23	0.281 spec.	19.438	600	500			980	840				
		65.71	0.312 reg. wt.	19.376	650	550			1,090	940				
		72.16	0.344 reg. wt.	19.312	700	600			1,210	1,030				
		78.60	0.375 reg. wt.	19.250	800	700			1,310	1,120				
		91.41	0.438 reg. wt.	19.124	900	800			1,530	1,310				
		104.13	0.500 reg. wt.	19.000	1,000	900			1,750	1,500				

API Plain-end Line Pipe (Continued)

Size, in.	OD, in.	Wt./ft, lb	Wall thickness,* in.	ID,* in.	Internal pressure at min yield strength, psi							Test pressures,¶ psi			
					Lap-welded steel†§				Seamless and electric-welded						
					Lap-welded wrought iron†,‡	Elec. fce., class I O.H. or basic oxygen	Class II O.H. or basic oxygen	Besse-mer	Grade A	Grade B		Wrought iron	Lap-welded steel	Grade A	Grade B
22 OD	22.000	72.38	0.312 spec.	21.376	. . . . .	. . . . .	. . . . .	. . . . .	850	990		. . . . .	. . . . .	500	600
		79.51	0.344 spec.	21.312	. . . . .	. . . . .	. . . . .	. . . . .	940	1,090		. . . . .	. . . . .	550	650
		86.61	0.375 spec.	21.250	. . . . .	. . . . .	. . . . .	. . . . .	1,020	1,190		. . . . .	. . . . .	600	700
		100.75	0.438 spec.	21.124	. . . . .	. . . . .	. . . . .	. . . . .	1,190	1,390		. . . . .	. . . . .	700	850
		114.81	0.500 spec.	21.000	. . . . .	. . . . .	. . . . .	. . . . .	1,360	1,590		. . . . .	. . . . .	800	950
24 OD	24.000	79.06	0.312 spec.	23.376	. . . . .	. . . . .	. . . . .	. . . . .	780	910		. . . . .	. . . . .	450	550
		86.85	0.344 spec.	23.312	. . . . .	. . . . .	. . . . .	. . . . .	860	1,000		. . . . .	. . . . .	500	600
		94.62	0.375 spec.	23.250	. . . . .	. . . . .	. . . . .	. . . . .	940	1,090		. . . . .	. . . . .	550	650
		110.10	0.438 spec.	23.124	. . . . .	. . . . .	. . . . .	. . . . .	1,100	1,280		. . . . .	. . . . .	650	750
		125.49	0.500 spec.	23.000	. . . . .	. . . . .	. . . . .	. . . . .	1,250	1,460		. . . . .	. . . . .	750	850

* The weight per cubic inch is slightly less for wrought iron than for steel. Since wrought-iron pipe is made with the same weight per foot as steel pipe, the wall thickness of wrought-iron pipe is 2 to 3 per cent greater than the tabulated values above, and the inside diameter is correspondingly smaller.
† Internal-pressure values for lap-welded pipe were calculated on basis of nominal dimensions; the fiber-stress values were reduced to 80 per cent in accordance with the longitudinal-joint factor assigned by Section 8 of the Code for Pressure Piping (ASA B31.1.8-1955).
‡ Lap-welded iron pipe is produced currently only in the following sizes:
Standard weight, special or regular weight, 1¼ in. nominal to 16 in. OD, inclusive.
X—strong 1¼ to 12 in. nominal, inclusive.
XX—strong 2 to 8 in. nominal, inclusive.
§ Lap-welded steel pipe is produced currently only in sizes 2 in. nominal to 16 in. OD, inclusive.
¶ Test pressures for sizes 3½ in. OD and larger were calculated by the formula shown on p. 2–110; all other test pressures were established arbitrarily.

API Threaded Line Pipe
Dimensions, Weights, and Test Pressures

Size, nominal, in.	Wt./ft, lb		Pipe				Couplings			Test pressures, psi			Iron,
	Nominal, threads and coupling	Plain end	Wall thickness, in.*	Diam, in.		No. of threads /in.	Length, in.	OD, in.	Calc. wt., lb	Steel			† wrought
				Outside	Inside*					Butt-welded	Lap-welded and grade A	Grade B	
⅛	0.25	0.24	0.068	0.405	0.269	27	1 1/16	0.563	0.04	700	0.700	0.700	700
¼	0.43	0.42	0.088	0.540	0.364	18	1⅝	0.719	0.09	700	0.700	0.700	700
⅜	0.57	0.57	0.091	0.675	0.493	18	1⅝	0.875	0.13	700	0.700	0.700	700
½	0.86	0.85	0.109	0.840	0.622	14	2⅛	1.063	0.24	700	0.700	0.700	700
¾	1.14	1.13	0.113	1.050	0.824	14	2⅛	1.313	0.34	700	0.700	0.700	700
1	1.70	1.68	0.133	1.315	1.049	11½	2⅝	1.576	0.54	700	0.700	0.700	700
1¼	2.30	2.27	0.140	1.660	1.380	11½	2¾	2.054	1.03	800	1,000	1,100	800
1½	2.75	2.72	0.145	1.900	1.610	11½	2¾	2.200	0.90	800	1,000	1,100	800
2	3.75	3.65	0.154	2.375	2.067	11½	3¼	2.875	1.86	800	1,000	1,100	800
2½	5.90	5.79	0.203	2.875	2.469	8	4⅛	3.375	3.27	800	1,000	1,100	800
3	7.70	7.58	0.216	3.500	3.068	8	4¼	4.000	4.09	800	1,000	1,100	800
3½	9.25	9.11	0.226	4.000	3.548	8	4⅜	4.625	5.92	1,200	1,200	1,300	950
4	11.00	10.79	0.237	4.500	4.026	8	4½	5.200	7.59	1,200	1,200	1,300	950
5	15.00	14.62	0.258	5.563	5.047	8	4⅝	6.296	9.98	.....	1,200	1,300	950
6	19.45	18.97	0.280	6.625	6.065	8	4⅞	7.390	12.92	.....	1,200	1,300	950
8	25.55	24.70	0.277	8.625	8.071	8	5¼	9.625	23.18	.....	1,200	1,300	950
8	29.35	28.55	0.322	8.625	7.981	8	5¼	9.625	23.18	.....	1,300	1,600	950
10	32.75	31.20	0.279	10.750	10.192	8	5¾	11.750	31.55	.....	1,000	1,200	800
10	35.75	34.24	0.307	10.750	10.136	8	5¾	11.750	31.55	.....	1,000	1,200	800
10	41.85	40.48	0.365	10.750	10.020	8	5¾	11.750	31.55	.....	1,200	1,400	800
12	45.45	43.77	0.330	12.750	12.090	8	6⅛	14.000	49.27	.....	1,000	1,200	800
12	51.15	49.56	0.375	12.750	12.000	8	6⅛	14.000	49.27	.....	1,100	1,200	800
14 D	57.00	54.57	0.375	14.000	13.250	8	6⅜	15.000	45.83	.....	950	1,100	750
16 D	65.30	62.58	0.375	16.000	15.250	8	6¾	17.000	55.83	.....	850	1,000	700
18 D	73.00	70.59	0.375	18.000	17.250	8	7⅛	19.000	66.53	.....	750	900	600
20 D	81.00	78.60	0.375	20.000	19.250	8	7⅝	21.000	79.37	.....	700	800	550

Internal pressures at minimum yield strength are the same as those shown for plain-end line pipe for the corresponding sizes and wall thicknesses; see pp. 2-100 to 2-106, inclusive.

The permissible variation in weight for any length of pipe is 10 per cent above and 3½ per cent below; but the carload weight shall not be more than 1¾ per cent under the calculated weight.

Furnished with threads and coupling and in random lengths, unless otherwise ordered. For tolerances on lengths see p. 2-110.

The weight per foot of pipe with threads and coupling is based on a length of 20 ft, including the coupling.

Taper ¾ in./ft measured on the diameter.

Sizes above 12 in. not regularly furnished with threads and coupling.

For illustration of joint and threading data, see p. 2-108.

* The weight per cubic inch is slightly less for wrought iron than for steel. Since wrought-iron pipe is made with the same weight per foot as steel pipe, the wall thickness of wrought-iron pipe is 2 to 3 per cent greater than the tabulated values above, and the inside diameter is correspondingly smaller.

† Test pressures shown apply to lap-welded wrought-iron pipe. Pressures shown for sizes 2 in. nominal and smaller apply also to butt-welded wrought-iron pipe.

Lap-welded pipe is produced currently in 2⅜ through 16 in. outside diameters.

Threading Data for API Threaded Line Pipe
Section of Joint—Shown Handtight

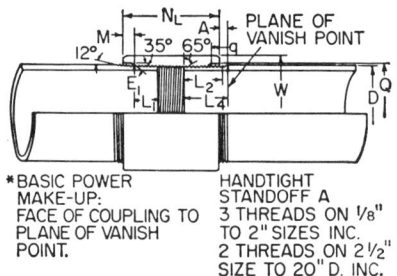

*BASIC POWER MAKE-UP: FACE OF COUPLING TO PLANE OF VANISH POINT.

HANDTIGHT STANDOFF A 3 THREADS ON ⅛" TO 2" SIZES INC. 2 THREADS ON 2½" SIZE TO 20" D. INC.

Pipe		Threads					Coupling		
Size, nominal, in.	OD D, in.	No. per inch	Length, end of pipe to hand-tight plane L_1, in.	Effec-tive length L_2, in.	Total length, end of pipe to vanish point L_4, in.	Pitch diam at hand-tight plane E_1, in.	Diam of recess Q, in.	Depth of recess q, in.	Length, face of coupling to hand-tight plane M, in.
⅛	0.405	27	0.180	0.2639	0.3924	0.37476	0.468	0.0347	0.1014
¼	0.540	18	0.200	0.4018	0.5946	0.48989	0.603	0.1471	0.2278
⅜	0.675	18	0.240	0.4078	0.6006	0.62701	0.738	0.1147	0.1938
½	0.840	14	0.320	0.5337	0.7815	0.77843	0.903	0.1582	0.2473
¾	1.050	14	0.339	0.5457	0.7935	0.98887	1.113	0.1516	0.2403
1	1.315	11½	0.400	0.6828	0.9845	1.23863	1.378	0.2241	0.3235
1¼	1.660	11½	0.420	0.7068	1.0085	1.58338	1.723	0.2279	0.3275
1½	1.900	11½	0.420	0.7235	1.0252	1.82234	1.963	0.2439	0.3442
2	2.375	11½	0.436	0.7565	1.0582	2.29627	2.469	2.2379	0.3611
2½	2.875	8	0.682	1.1375	1.5712	2.76216	2.969	0.4915	0.6392
3	3.500	8	0.766	1.2000	1.6337	3.38850	3.594	0.4710	0.6177
3½	4.000	8	0.821	1.2500	1.6837	3.88881	4.094	0.4662	0.6127
4	4.500	8	0.844	1.3000	1.7337	4.38713	4.594	0.4920	0.6397
5	5.563	8	0.937	1.4063	1.8400	5.44929	5.657	0.5047	0.6530
6	6.625	8	0.958	1.5125	1.9462	6.50597	6.719	0.5861	0.7382
8	8.625	8	1.063	1.7125	2.1462	8.50003	8.719	0.6768	0.8332
10	10.750	8	1.210	1.9250	2.3587	10.62094	10.844	0.7394	0.8987
12	12.750	8	1.360	2.1250	2.5587	12.61781	12.844	0.7872	0.9487
14D	14.000	8	1.562	2.2500	2.6837	13.87263	14.094	0.7136	0.8717
16D	16.000	8	1.812	2.4500	2.8837	15.87575	16.094	0.6658	0.8217
18D	18.000	8	2.000	2.6500	3.0837	17.87500	18.094	0.6773	0.8337
20D	20.000	8	2.125	2.8500	3.2837	19.87031	20.094	0.7490	0.9087

Taper of threads ¾ in./ft on diameter, all sizes.
For weights and dimensions, see p. 2–107.
  * Standard practice is to furnish "handling-tight" unless otherwise specified. "Handling-tight" is a make-up position between handtight and power-tight.

Pipe-thread Dimensions

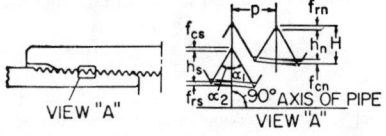

VIEW "A"

API Standard Sharp Thread

Number per inch...	27	18	14	11½	10	8
Thread element	Inches					
$p =$	0.0370	0.0556	0.0714	0.0870	0.1000	0.1250
$H = 0.866p$	0.0321	0.0481	0.0619	0.0753	0.0866	0.1082
$h_n = h_s = 0.760p$	0.0281	0.0422	0.0543	0.0661	0.0760	0.0950
$f_{rn} = f_{rs} = 0.033p$	0.0012	0.0018	0.0024	0.0029	0.0033	0.0041
$f_{cn} = f_{cs} = 0.073p$	0.0027	0.0041	0.0052	0.0063	0.0073	0.0091

$\alpha_1 = \alpha_2 = 30°.$

Tensile Requirements

	Yield strength, min, psi	Tensile strength, min, psi	Elongation, min, % in	
			2 in.	8 in.
Steel pipe				
Seamless, electric-flash or electric-resistance welded:				
Electric-furnace, open-hearth, or basic-oxygen,* grade A.	30,000	48,000	†	
Electric-furnace, open-hearth, basic-oxygen,* or besse-mer, grade B....................................	35,000	60,000	†	
Electric induction-welded:*				
Electric-furnace, open-hearth, basic-oxygen,* or besse-mer, grade B....................................	35,000	60,000	†	
Lap-welded or butt-welded:				
Electric-furnace...............................	25,000	45,000	...	22‡
Class I open-hearth or basic-oxygen*.............	25,000	45,000	...	22‡
Class II open-hearth or basic-oxygen*............	28,000	48,000	...	20‡
Bessemer......................................	30,000	50,000	...	18‡
Iron pipe				
Lap-welded or butt-welded:				
Wrought.......................................	24,000	42,000	...	12

* Tentative.   ‡ See footnotes on following page.
† Elongation requirements for grades A and B seamless and electric-welded steel line pipe shall be as follows:

Tabulated wall thickness, in.	Elongation in 2 in., min, %	
	Grade A	Grade B
0.312 and larger	35.00	30.00
0.281	33.25	28.50
0.250	31.50	27.00
0.219	29.75	25.50
0.188	28.00	24.00
0.156	26.25	22.50
0.125	24.50	21.00
0.094	22.75	19.50
0.062	21.00	18.00

The preceding table gives the computed minimum-elongation values for each $\frac{1}{32}$-in. decrease in wall thickness. If the tabulated wall thickness is less than 0.312 in. and other than shown above, the minimum-elongation requirement shall be determined by the following formulas.

Grade	Formula
A	$E = 56t + 17.50$
B	$E = 48t + 15.00$

where E = per cent elongation
     t = tabulated wall thickness of specimen, in.

‡ The elongation and gauge-length requirements for butt-welded pipe, 1,050 in. outside diameter ($\frac{3}{4}$ in. nominal) and smaller, shall be as follows:

OD, in.	Nominal size, in.	Gauge length, in.	Elongation, min, %
1.050, 0.840	$\frac{3}{4}$, $\frac{1}{2}$	6	18
0.675, 0.540	$\frac{3}{8}$, $\frac{1}{4}$	4	18
0.405	$\frac{1}{8}$	2	18

Hydrostatic Tests

Test Pressures. Test pressures shall be as listed in the tables on pages **2–100** through **2–106**.

NOTE: The hydrostatic test pressures specified herein are mill-inspection test pressures, are not intended as a basis for design, and do not necessarily have any direct relationship to working pressures.

NOTE: With the exception of butt-welded pipe, the test pressures for plain-end pipe $3\frac{1}{2}$ in. and larger were computed by the following formula. All other test pressures were established arbitrarily.

$$P = \frac{2St}{D}$$

or 2,500, whichever is smaller
where P = hydrostatic test pressure, psi
    S = fiber stress, as given below
    t = tabulated wall thickness, in.
    D = tabulated outside diameter, in.

Grade	Fiber stress, psi
Grade A steel pipe	18,000
Grade B steel pipe	21,000
Lap-welded steel pipe	18,000
Wrought-iron pipe	14,400

These fiber-stress values are 60 per cent of the specified minimum yield strengths shown in the table on page **2–109**; the fiber-stress value for lap-welded pipe is based on the specified minimum yield strength for bessemer steel (30,000 psi).

Tolerances on Lengths*

	Shortest length in entire shipment	Shortest length in 95% of entire shipment	Shortest length in 90% of entire shipment	Min avg length entire shipment
Threaded-and-coupled pipe:				
Single random lengths	16 ft 0 in.	18 ft 0 in.		
Double random lengths	22 ft 0 in.	....	....	35 ft 0 in.
Plain-end pipe:				
Single random lengths	9 ft 0 in.	....	....	17 ft 6 in.
Double random lengths	14 ft 0 in.	....	26 ft 3 in.	35 ft 0 in.
As agreed upon lengths in excess of 20 ft	40% of avg agreed upon	....	75% of avg agreed upon	

* By agreement between the purchaser and the manufacturer, these tolerances shall apply to each carload.

API High-test Line Pipe
Dimensions, Weights, and Pressures

Size, OD, in.	Wt./ft plain ends, lb	Wall thickness, in.	Net wt./ mile, tons	Internal pressure at min yield strength, psi				Mill test pressure, psi			
				X-42	X-46	X-52	X-56	X-42	X-46	X-52	X-56
6⅝	12.89	0.188	34.03	2,390	2,620	2,960	3,180	1,790	1,960	2,220	2,390
6⅝	14.97	0.219	39.52	2,780	3,050	3,440	3,710	2,090	2,290	2,580	2,780
6⅝	17.02	0.250	44.93	3,170	3,480	3,930	4,230	2,380	2,610	2,950	3,000
6⅝	18.97	0.280	50.08	3,550	3,890	4,400	4,740	2,670	2,920	3,000	3,000
6⅝	21.07	0.312	55.62	3,960	4,340	4,900	5,280	2,970	3,000	3,000	3,000
6⅝	23.06	0.344	60.88	4,370	4,780	5,400	5,820	3,000	3,000	3,000	3,000
6⅝	25.03	0.375	66.08	4,760	5,210	5,890	6,340	3,000	3,000	3,000	3,000
6⅝	28.57	0.432	75.42	5,480	6,000	6,790	7,310	3,000	3,000	3,000	3,000
8⅝	16.90	0.188	44.62	1,840	2,010	2,270	2,450	1,380	1,510	1,710	1,840
8⅝	18.27	0.203	48.23	1,980	2,170	2,450	2,640	1,490	1,630	1,840	1,980
8⅝	19.64	0.219	51.85	2,140	2,340	2,650	2,850	1,600	1,760	1,990	2,140
8⅝	22.36	0.250	59.03	2,440	2,670	3,020	3,250	1,830	2,010	2,270	2,440
8⅝	24.70	0.277	65.21	2,700	2,960	3,340	3,600	2,030	2,220	2,510	2,700
8⅝	27.74	0.312	73.23	3,040	3,230	3,770	4,060	2,280	2,500	2,830	3,000
8⅝	28.55	0.322	75.37	3,140	3,440	3,890	4,190	2,360	2,580	2,920	3,000
8⅝	30.40	0.344	80.26	3,350	3,670	4,150	4,470	2,520	2,760	3,000	3,000
8⅝	33.04	0.375	87.23	3,660	4,000	4,530	4,870	2,740	3,000	3,000	3,000
8⅝	38.26	0.438	101.01	4,270	4,680	5,290	5,690	3,000	3,000	3,000	3,000
8⅝	43.39	0.500	114.55	4,870	5,340	6,030	6,500	3,000	3,000	3,000	3,000
10¾	21.15	0.188	55.84	1,470	1,610	1,820	1,960	1,250	1,370	1,550	1,670
10¾	22.88	0.203	60.40	1,590	1,740	1,970	2,120	1,350	1,480	1,670	1,800
10¾	24.60	0.219	64.94	1,720	1,880	2,120	2,290	1,460	1,600	1,810	1,940
10¾	28.04	0.250	74.03	1,960	2,140	2,420	2,610	1,670	1,820	2,060	2,220
10¾	31.20	0.279	82.37	2,180	2,390	2,700	2,910	1,860	2,030	2,300	2,480
10¾	34.24	0.307	90.39	2,400	2,630	2,970	3,200	2,040	2,240	2,530	2,720
10¾	38.20	0.344	100.85	2,690	2,950	3,330	3,590	2,290	2,510	2,830	3,000
10¾	40.48	0.365	106.87	2,860	3,130	3,540	3,810	2,430	2,660	3,000	3,000
10¾	48.19	0.438	127.22	3,430	3,750	4,240	4,570	2,910	3,000	3,000	3,000
10¾	54.74	0.500	144.51	3,910	4,280	4,840	5,210	3,000	3,000	3,000	3,000
12¾	27.22	0.203	71.86	1,340	1,470	1,660	1,790	1,140	1,250	1,410	1,520
12¾	29.28	0.219	77.30	1,450	1,590	1,790	1,930	1,230	1,350	1,520	1,640
12¾	33.38	0.250	88.12	1,650	1,810	2,040	2,200	1,410	1,540	1,740	1,870
12¾	37.45	0.281	98.87	1,860	2,030	2,300	2,470	1,580	1,730	1,950	2,100
12¾	41.51	0.312	109.59	2,060	2,260	2,550	2,750	1,750	1,920	2,170	2,330
12¾	43.77	0.330	115.55	2,180	2,390	2,700	2,900	1,850	2,030	2,290	2,470
12¾	45.55	0.344	120.25	2,270	2,490	2,810	3,030	1,930	2,110	2,390	2,570
12¾	49.56	0.375	130.84	2,470	2,710	3,060	3,300	2,100	2,300	2,600	2,800
12¾	53.56	0.406	141.40	2,680	2,930	3,320	3,570	2,280	2,490	2,820	3,000
12¾	57.53	0.438	151.88	2,890	3,160	3,580	3,850	2,460	2,690	3,000	3,000
12¾	65.42	0.500	172.71	3,300	3,610	4,080	4,400	2,810	3,000	3,000	3,000
14	30.93	0.210	81.66	1,260	1,380	1,560	1,680	1,080	1,180	1,330	1,430
14	32.20	0.219	85.01	1,320	1,440	1,630	1,760	1,120	1,230	1,390	1,490
14	36.71	0.250	96.91	1,500	1,650	1,860	2,010	1,280	1,400	1,580	1,710
14	41.21	0.281	108.79	1,690	1,850	2,090	2,250	1,440	1,570	1,780	1,920
14	45.68	0.312	120.60	1,880	2,060	2,320	2,500	1,600	1,750	1,980	2,130
14	50.14	0.344	132.37	2,070	2,260	2,560	2,760	1,760	1,930	2,180	2,340
14	54.57	0.375	144.06	2,250	2,470	2,790	3,010	1,920	2,100	2,370	2,560
14	63.37	0.438	167.30	2,630	2,880	3,260	3,510	2,240	2,450	2,770	2,980
14	67.78	0.469	178.94	2,810	3,080	3,480	3,760	2,400	2,620	2,970	3,000
14	72.09	0.500	190.32	3,000	3,290	3,720	4,000	2,550	2,800	3,000	3,000

PRODUCTION EQUIPMENT

API High-test Line Pipe (Continued)

Size, OD, in.	Wt./ft plain ends, lb	Wall thickness, in.	Net wt./ mile, tons	Internal pressure at min yield strength, psi				Mill test pressure, psi			
				X-42	X-46	X-52	X-56	X-42	X-46	X-52	X-56
16	36.87	0.219	97.34	1,150	1,260	1,430	1,540	980	1,080	1,220	1,310
16	42.05	0.250	111.01	1,320	1,440	1,630	1,750	1,120	1,230	1,390	1,490
16	47.22	0.281	124.66	1,480	1,620	1,830	1,970	1,260	1,380	1,560	1,680
16	52.36	0.312	138.23	1,640	1,800	2,030	2,190	1,400	1,530	1,730	1,860
16	57.48	0.344	151.75	1,810	1,980	2,240	2,410	1,540	1,690	1,910	2,050
16	62.58	0.375	165.21	1,970	2,160	2,440	2,630	1,680	1,840	2,080	2,240
16	72.72	0.438	191.98	2,300	2,520	2,850	3,070	1,960	2,150	2,430	2,610
16	77.75	0.469	205.26	2,460	2,700	3,050	3,290	2,100	2,300	2,600	2,800
16	82.77	0.500	218.51	2,630	2,880	3,250	3,500	2,240	2,450	2,770	2,980
18	47.39	0.250	125.11	1,170	1,280	1,450	1,560	1,000	1,090	1,230	1,330
18	53.22	0.281	140.50	1,320	1,440	1,630	1,750	1,120	1,230	1,380	1,490
18	59.03	0.312	155.84	1,460	1,600	1,810	1,950	1,240	1,360	1,540	1,650
18	64.82	0.344	171.12	1,610	1,760	1,990	2,150	1,370	1,500	1,690	1,820
18	70.59	0.375	186.36	1,750	1,920	2,170	2,340	1,490	1,630	1,850	1,990
18	76.34	0.406	201.54	1,900	2,080	2,350	2,530	1,620	1,770	2,000	2,150
18	82.06	0.438	216.64	2,050	2,240	2,530	2,730	1,740	1,910	2,160	2,320
18	87.77	0.469	231.71	2,190	2,400	2,710	2,920	1,870	2,040	2,310	2,490
18	93.45	0.500	246.71	2,340	2,560	2,890	3,120	1,990	2,180	2,460	2,650
20	52.73	0.250	139.21	1,050	1,150	1,300	1,400	950	1,040	1,170	1,260
20	59.23	0.281	156.37	1,180	1,300	1,470	1,580	1,070	1,170	1,320	1,420
20	65.71	0.312	173.47	1,310	1,440	1,630	1,750	1,180	1,300	1,470	1,580
20	72.16	0.344	190.50	1,450	1,590	1,790	1,930	1,310	1,430	1,610	1,740
20	78.60	0.375	207.50	1,580	1,730	1,950	2,100	1,420	1,560	1,760	1,890
20	85.01	0.406	224.43	1,710	1,870	2,120	2,280	1,540	1,690	1,910	2,050
20	91.41	0.438	241.32	1,840	2,020	2,280	2,460	1,660	1,820	2,050	2,210
20	97.78	0.469	258.14	1,970	2,160	2,440	2,630	1,780	1,950	2,200	2,370
20	104.13	0.500	274.90	2,100	2,300	2,600	2,800	1,890	2,070	2,340	2,520
22	58.07	0.250	153.30	960	1,050	1,190	1,280	860	950	1,070	1,150
22	65.24	0.281	172.23	1,080	1,180	1,330	1,440	970	1,060	1,200	1,290
22	72.38	0.312	191.08	1,200	1,310	1,480	1,590	1,080	1,180	1,330	1,430
22	79.51	0.344	209.91	1,320	1,440	1,630	1,760	1,190	1,300	1,470	1,580
22	86.61	0.375	228.65	1,440	1,570	1,780	1,910	1,290	1,420	1,600	1,720
22	93.69	0.406	247.34	1,550	1,700	1,920	2,070	1,400	1,530	1,730	1,860
22	100.75	0.438	265.98	1,680	1,840	2,080	2,230	1,510	1,650	1,870	2,010
22	107.79	0.469	284.57	1,790	1,960	2,220	2,390	1,620	1,770	2,000	2,150
22	114.81	0.500	303.10	1,910	2,100	2,370	2,550	1,720	1,890	2,130	2,300
24	63.41	0.250	·167.40	880	960	1,090	1,170	790	870	980	1,060
24	71.25	0.281	188.10	990	1,080	1,220	1,320	890	970	1,100	1,190
24	79.06	0.312	208.72	1,100	1,200	1,360	1,460	990	1,080	1,220	1,320
24	86.85	0.344	229.28	1,210	1,320	1,490	1,610	1,090	1,190	1,350	1,450
24	94.62	0.375	249.80	1,320	1,440	1,630	1,750	1,190	1,300	1,470	1,580
24	102.37	0.406	270.26	1,430	1,560	1,760	1,900	1,280	1,410	1,590	1,710
24	110.10	0.438	290.66	1,540	1,680	1,900	2,050	1,380	1,520	1,710	1,840
24	117.81	0.469	311.02	1,640	1,800	2,030	2,190	1,480	1,620	1,830	1,970
24	125.49	0.500	331.29	1,750	1,920	2,170	2,340	1,580	1,730	1,950	2,100
26	68.75	0.250	181.50	810	890	1,000	1,080	730	800	910	970
26	77.25	0.281	203.94	910	1,000	1,130	1,220	820	900	1,020	1,090
26	85.73	0.312	226.33	1,010	1,110	1,250	1,350	910	1,000	1,130	1,210
26	94.19	0.344	248.66	1,110	1,220	1,380	1,490	1,010	1,100	1,240	1,340
26	102.63	0.375	270.94	1,220	1,330	1,500	1,620	1,100	1,200	1,350	1,460
26	111.05	0.406	293.17	1,320	1,440	1,630	1,750	1,190	1,300	1,470	1,580
26	119.44	0.438	315.32	1,420	1,550	1,750	1,890	1,280	1,400	1,580	1,700

API High-test Line Pipe (*Continued*)

Size, OD, in.	Wt./ft plain ends, lb	Wall thickness, in.	Net wt./ mile, tons	Internal pressure at min yield strength, psi				Mill test pressure, psi			
				X-42	X-46	X-52	X-56	X-42	X-46	X-52	X-56
26	127.82	0.469	337.44	1,520	1,660	1,880	2,030	1,370	1,500	1,690	1,820
26	136.17	0.500	359.49	1,620	1,770	2,000	2,160	1,460	1,600	1,800	1,940
28	74.09	0.250	195.60	750	830	930	1,010	680	740	840	910
28	83.26	0.281	219.81	850	930	1,050	1,130	760	840	940	1,020
28	92.41	0.312	243.96	940	1,030	1,170	1,250	850	930	1,050	1,130
28	101.53	0.344	268.04	1,040	1,130	1,280	1,380	930	1,020	1,160	1,240
28	110.64	0.375	292.09	1,130	1,240	1,400	1,500	1,020	1,110	1,260	1,350
28	119.72	0.406	316.06	1,220	1,340	1,510	1,630	1,100	1,210	1,360	1,470
28	128.79	0.438	340.01	1,320	1,440	1,630	1,760	1,190	1,300	1,470	1,580
28	137.83	0.469	363.87	1,410	1,540	1,740	1,880	1,270	1,390	1,570	1,690
28	146.85	0.500	387.68	1,500	1,650	1,860	2,010	1,360	1,480	1,680	1,810
30	79.43	0.250	209.70	700	770	870	940	630	690	780	840
30	89.27	0.281	235.67	790	870	980	1,050	710	780	880	950
30	99.08	0.312	261.57	880	960	1,090	1,170	790	870	980	1,050
30	108.88	0.344	287.44	970	1,060	1,200	1,290	870	950	1,080	1,160
30	118.65	0.375	313.24	1,050	1,150	1,300	1,400	950	1,040	1,170	1,260
30	128.40	0.406	338.98	1,140	1,250	1,410	1,520	1,030	1,130	1,270	1,370
30	138.13	0.438	364.66	1,230	1,350	1,520	1,640	1,110	1,210	1,370	1,480
30	147.84	0.469	390.30	1,310	1,440	1,630	1,760	1,190	1,300	1,470	1,580
30	157.53	0.500	415.88	1,400	1,540	1,740	1,870	1,270	1,390	1,570	1,690
32	84.77	0.250	223.79	660	720	820	880	600	650	740	790
32	95.28	0.281	251.54	740	810	920	990	670	730	830	890
32	105.76	0.312	279.21	830	900	1,020	1,100	740	810	920	990
32	116.22	0.344	306.82	910	990	1,120	1,210	820	900	1,010	1,090
32	126.66	0.375	334.38	990	1,080	1,220	1,320	890	980	1,100	1,190
32	137.08	0.406	361.89	1,070	1,170	1,330	1,430	960	1,060	1,190	1,280
32	147.48	0.438	389.35	1,150	1,260	1,430	1,540	1,040	1,140	1,290	1,380
32	157.86	0.469	416.75	1,230	1,350	1,520	1,650	1,110	1,220	1,380	1,480
32	168.21	0.500	444.07	1,320	1,440	1,630	1,750	1,190	1,300	1,470	1,580
34	90.11	0.250	237.89	620	680	770	830	560	610	690	750
34	101.28	0.281	267.38	700	770	860	930	630	690	780	840
34	112.43	0.312	296.82	780	850	960	1,030	700	770	860	930
34	123.56	0.344	326.20	850	930	1,060	1,140	770	840	950	1,030
34	134.67	0.375	355.53	930	1,020	1,150	1,240	840	920	1,040	1,120
34	145.76	0.406	384.81	1,010	1,100	1,250	1,340	910	990	1,120	1,210
34	156.82	0.438	414.00	1,090	1,190	1,340	1,450	980	1,070	1,210	1,300
34	167.87	0.469	443.18	1,160	1,270	1,430	1,550	1,050	1,150	1,300	1,400·
34	178.89	0.500	472.27	1,240	1,360	1,530	1,650	1,120	1,220	1,380	1,490
36	95.45	0.250	251.99	590	640	730	780	530	580	650	700
36	107.29	0.281	283.25	660	720	820	880	600	650	740	790
36	119.11	0.312	314.45	730	800	910	980	660	720	820	880
36	130.90	0.344	345.58	810	880	1,000	1,080	730	800	900	970
36	142.68	0.375	376.68	880	960	1,090	1,170	790	870	980	1,060
36	154.43	0.406	407.70	950	1,040	1,180	1,270	860	940	1,060	1,140
36	166.17	0.438	438.69	1,030	1,120	1,270	1,370	830	1,010	1,140	1,230
36	177.88	0.469	469.60	1,090	1,200	1,360	1,460	990	1,080	1,220	1,320
36	189.57	0.500	500.47	1,170	1,280	1,450	1,560	1,060	1,160	1,310	1,410

Tensile Requirements

Grade	Yield strength, min, psi	Tensile strength, min, psi	Elongation in 2 in., min, %				
			Tabulated wall thickness, in.‡				
			0.500–0.312, incl.	0.281	0.250	0.219	0.188
X-42	42,000	60,000	25.00	23.75	22.50	21.25	20.00
X-46	46,000	63,000	23.00	21.50	20.00	18.50	17.00
X-52	52,000	66,000*	22.00	20.00	18.00	16.00	14.00
X-56	56,000	68,000†	20.00	18.00	16.00	14.00	12.00

NOTE: The tensile-strength values of 68,000 and 74,000 psi in note † have not yet been approved by API.

* For grade X-52 pipe in sizes 20 in. and larger, with wall thickness 0.375 in. and smaller, the minimum tensile strength shall be 72,000 psi.

† For grade X-56 pipe in sizes 20 in. and larger, with wall thickness 0.375 in. and smaller, the minimum tensile strength shall be 74,000 psi.

‡ If the tabulated wall thickness is less than 0.312 in. and other than shown above, the minimum-elongation requirement shall be determined by the following formula:

Grade	Formula
X-42	$E = 40t + 12.50$
X-46	$E = 48t + 8.00$
X-52	$E = 64t + 2.00$
X-56	$E = 64t$

where E = per cent elongation
t = tabulated wall thickness of specimen, in.

Hydrostatic Tests

The test pressures for grades X-42, X-46, X-52, and X-56 shall be as listed in the table on pages 2-111 to 2-113. The minimum test pressures for other grades shall be computed by the formula given below.

NOTE: The hydrostatic test pressures given herein are mill-inspection pressures, are not intended as a basis for design, and do not necessarily have any direct relationship to working pressures.

NOTE: The test pressures given in the table on pages 2-111 to 2-113 were computed by the following formula:

$$P = \frac{2St}{D}$$

or 3,000, whichever is smaller

where P = hydrostatic test pressure, psi
S = fiber stress, psi, equal to 75 per cent of the specified minimum yield strength for pipe in sizes 8⅝ in. and smaller, 85 per cent for pipe in sizes 10¾ to 18 in., inclusive, and 90 per cent for pipe in sizes 20 in. and larger
t = tabulated wall thickness, in.
D = tabulated outside diameter, in.

Lengths

Length. Unless otherwise agreed upon between the purchaser and manufacturer, pipe shall be furnished in single random lengths or double random lengths as specified on the purchase order. If single random length is specified, the average length shall not be less than 17 ft 6 in., and no piece shall be shorter than 9 ft 0 in. If double random length is specified, the average length shall not be less than 35 ft 0 in., not more than 10 per cent of the lengths shall be shorter than 26 ft 3 in., and no piece shall be shorter than 14 ft 0 in. If the average length agreed upon is in excess of 20 ft, not more than 10 per cent of the lengths shall be shorter than 75 per cent of the average length agreed upon and no length shall be shorter than 40 per cent of the average length agreed upon. By agreement between the purchaser and the manufacturer, these stipulations shall apply to each carload.

Unlined and Cement-lined Line Pipe

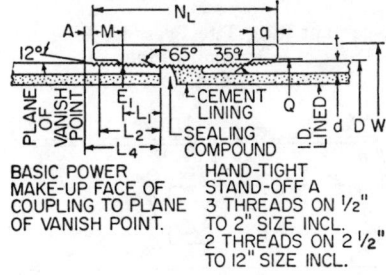

BASIC POWER
MAKE-UP FACE OF
COUPLING TO PLANE
OF VANISH POINT.

HAND-TIGHT
STAND-OFF A
3 THREADS ON ½"
TO 2" SIZE INCL.
2 THREADS ON 2½"
TO 12" SIZE INCL.

Nom. size, in.	Unlined pipe					Cement-lined pipe							
	Wt./ft, lb		Wall thick- ness, in.	OD, in.	ID, in.	Wt./ft, lb		Nom. lining thick- ness, in.	Nom. ID, in.	Threads		Couplings	
	Nom. T & C	Plain end,				Nom. T & C	Plain end			No./in.	Total length, in.	OD, in.	Length, in.
½	0.86	0.85	0.109	0.840	0.622	0.98	0.97	0.0690	0.484	14	0.7815	1.063	2⅛
¾	1.14	1.13	0.113	1.050	0.824	1.30	1.29	0.0690	0.686	14	0.7935	1.313	2⅛
1	1.70	1.68	0.133	1.315	1.049	1.93	1.91	0.0765	0.896	11½	0.9845	1.576	2⅝
1¼	2.30	2.27	0.140	1.660	1.380	2.71	2.68	0.1025	1.175	11½	1.0085	2.054	2¾
1½	2.75	2.72	0.145	1.900	1.610	3.24	3.20	0.1025	1.405	11½	1.0252	2.200	2¾
2	3.75	3.65	0.154	2.375	2.067	4.62	4.53	0.1435	1.780	11½	1.0582	2.875	2⅞
2½	5.90	5.79	0.203	2.875	2.469	6.96	6.85	0.1435	2.182	8	1.5712	3.375	4⅛
3	7.70	7.58	0.216	3.500	3.068	9.28	9.15	0.1715	2.725	8	1.6337	4.000	4¼
3½	9.25	9.11	0.226	4.000	3.548	11.09	10.95	0.1715	3.205	8	1.6837	4.625	4⅜
4	11.00	10.79	0.237	4.500	4.026	13.47	13.26	0.2030	3.620	8	1.7337	5.200	4½
5	15.00	14.62	0.258	5.563	5.047	18.81	18.43	0.2495	4.548	8	1.8400	6.296	4⅝
6	19.45	18.97	0.280	6.625	6.065	25.17	24.70	0.3125	5.440	8	1.9462	7.390	4⅞
8	25.55	24.70	0.277	8.625	8.071	33.27	32.41	0.3125	7.446	8	2.1462	9.625	5¼
8	29.35	28.55	0.322	8.625	7.981	36.98	36.18	0.3125	7.356	8	2.1462	9.625	5¼
10	32.75	31.20	0.279	01.750	10.192	44.46	42.91	0.3745	9.443	8	2.3587	11.750	5¾
10	35.75	34.24	0.307	10.750	10.136	47.39	45.88	0.3745	9.387	8	2.3587	11.750	5¾
10	41.85	40.48	0.365	10.750	10.020	53.35	51.99	0.3745	9.271	8	2.3587	11.750	5¾
12	45.45	43.77	0.330	12.750	12.090	59.42	57.74	0.3745	11.341	8	2.5587	14.000	6⅛
12	51.15	49.56	0.375	12.750	12.000	65.01	63.43	0.3745	11.251	8	2.5587	14.000	6⅛

All weights and dimensions are nominal.

This type of material, threaded and coupled, is supplied with API line pipe threads and couplings and, except for the lining, conforms to API specifications 5L.

For hydrostatic test pressures, see pp. 2-102 to 2-105.

ASBESTOS-CEMENT PIPE

Transite Asbestos-cement Ring-Tite Pressure Pipe and Asbestos-cement Pressure Pipe
Dimensions and Test Pressures

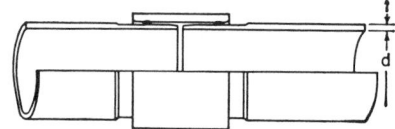

Nom. pipe size, in.	Class 100			Class 150			Class 200		
	Wall thickness t, in.	ID d, in.	Test pressure, psi	Wall thickness t, in.	ID d, in.	Test pressure, psi	Wall thickness t, in.	ID d, in.	Test pressure, psi
4	0.445	3.95	350	0.510	3.95	525	0.660	3.95	700
6	0.530	5.85	350	0.610	5.85	525	0.780	5.70	700
8	0.590	7.85	350	0.710	7.85	525	0.920	7.60	700
10	0.660	9.85	350	0.910	10.00	525	1.095	9.63	700
12	0.750	11.70	350	1.040	12.00	525	1.260	11.56	700
14	0.820	13.59	350	1.190	14.00	525	1.470	13.59	700
16	0.905	15.50	350	1.310	16.00	525	1.670	15.50	700

Standard nominal length, 13 ft.

PLASTIC PIPE

Standard Polyethylene Pipe

Nom. size, in.	OD, in.	ID, in.	Wall thickness, in.	Max operating pressure at 75°F, psi*	Nom. wt./ft, lb	Shipping length, ft
2	2.375	2.067	0.154	66	0.436	100 or 250 (coiled)
3	3.500	3.068	0.216	66	0.904	100 (coiled)
4	4.500	4.026	0.237	54	1.29	25 (straight)
6	6.625	6.065	0.280	47	2.26	25 (straight)

* The maximum operating temperature for polyethylene pipe is 120°F.

75-psi Pressure-rated Polyethylene Pipe

Nom. size, in.	OD, in.	ID, in.	Wall thickness, in.	Max operating pressure at 75°F, psi*	Nom. wt./ft, lb	Shipping length (coiled), ft
½	0.732	0.622	0.055	75	0.047	100 or 400
¾	0.966	0.824	0.071	75	0.081	100 or 400
1	1.232	1.050	0.091	75	0.132	100 or 300
1¼	1.618	1.380	0.119	75	0.228	100 or 300
1½	1.888	1.610	0.139	75	0.310	100 or 250
2	2.423	2.067	0.178	75	0.510	100 or 200

* The maximum operating temperature for polyethylene pipe is 120°F.

100-psi Pressure-rated Polyethylene Pipe

Nom. size, in.	OD, in.	ID, in.	Wall thickness, in.	Max operating pressure at 75°F, psi*	Nom. wt./ft, lb	Shipping length (coiled), ft
½	0.782	0.622	0.080	100	0.071	100 or 400
¾	1.024	0.824	0.100	100	0.118	100 or 400
1	1.300	1.050	0.125	100	0.187	100 or 300
1¼	1.710	1.380	0.165	100	0.324	100 or 300
1½	2.000	1.610	0.195	100	0.449	100 or 250
2	2.567	2.067	0.250	100	0.737	100 or 200

* The maximum operating temperature for polyethylene pipe is 120°F.

Double-duct Polyethylene Pipe for Jet-well Installations Weights and Dimensions

Nom. size, in.	Pressure pipe			Suction pipe			Nom. wt./ft, lb	Shipping lengths, (coiled), ft
	OD, in.	ID, in.	Wall thickness, in.	OD, in.	ID, in.	Wall thickness, in.		
1 × 1¼	1.232	1.050	0.091	1.618	1.380	0.119	0.366	120 or 240
1¼ × 1¼	1.618	1.380	0.119	1.618	1.380	0.119	0.462	120 or 240
1¼ × 1½	1.618	1.380	0.119	1.888	1.610	0.139	0.542	120 or 240

Maximum Setting Depths in Feet at Given Shut-off Pressures for Water at 60°F

Nom. size, in.	Shut-off pressure		
	40 psi	50 psi	60 psi
1 × 1¼	110	87	64
1¼ × 1¼	110	87	64
1¼ × 1½	110	87	64

The table above gives recommendations for maximum setting depths at the given pump shut-off pressures.

Double-duct polyethylene pipe consists of two separately extruded joined pipes. Double-duct pipe is expressly designed for well installations utilizing jet pumps. This design facilitates easy attachment of the pipe to the venturi and, in addition, makes it easy to feed the drop pipes into the casing.

Two single polyethylene pipes may be used in jet-well installations.

PRODUCTION EQUIPMENT

Polyvinyl Chloride Pipe—Normal Impact
Schedule 40

Nom. size, in.	OD, in.	ID, in.	Wall thickness, in.	Max operating pressure at 75°F, plain end only, psi*	Max operating pressure at max temp. of 150°F, plain end only, psi*	Nom. wt./ft, lb
½	0.840	0.622	0.109	410	220	0.150
¾	1.050	0.824	0.113	335	180	0.199
1	1.315	1.049	0.133	310	170	0.295
1¼	1.660	1.380	0.140	255	140	0.400
1½	1.900	1.610	0.145	230	125	0.478
2	2.375	2.067	0.154	195	110	0.643
2½	2.875	2.469	0.203	200	110	1.020
3	3.500	3.068	0.216	185	100	1.333
4	4.500	4.026	0.237	155	85	1.899
6	6.625	6.065	0.280	125	65	3.339
8	8.625	7.981	0.322	110	60	5.021
10	10.750	10.020	0.365	100	55	7.118
12	12.750	11.938	0.406	90	50	9.412
	14.000	13.126	0.437	90	50	11.131

* Threaded joints are not recommended for schedule 40 pipe.

Schedule 80

Nom. size, in.	OD, in.	ID, in.	Wall thickness, in.	Max operating pressure at 75°F, psi		Max operating pressure at max temp. of 150°F, psi		Nom. wt./ft, lb
				Plain end	Threaded	Plain end	Threaded	
½	0.840	0.546	0.147	575	330	310	175	0.191
¾	1.050	0.742	0.154	470	285	250	150	0.259
1	1.315	0.957	0.179	435	255	235	140	0.382
1¼	1.660	1.278	0.191	360	220	195	120	0.527
1½	1.900	1.500	0.200	325	205	175	110	0.639
2	2.375	1.939	0.218	280	190	150	100	0.884
2½	2.875	2.323	0.276	270	190	140	100	1.349
3	3.500	2.900	0.300	260	170	140	95	1.804
4	4.500	3.826	0.337	225	160	120	85	2.636
6	6.625	5.761	0.432	195	150	110	80	5.028
8	8.625	7.625	0.500	170	135	90	70	7.630

Schedule 120

Nom. size, in.	OD, in.	ID, in.	Wall thick-ness, in.	Max operating pressure at 75°F, psi		Max operating pressure at max temp. of 150°F, psi		Nom. wt./ft, lb
				Plain end	Threaded	Plain end	Threaded	
½	0.840	0.500	0.170	680	425	360	225	0.214
¾	1.050	0.710	0.170	520	330	275	175	0.281
1	1.315	0.915	0.200	485	300	255	160	0.419
1¼	1.660	1.230	0.215	405	260	215	135	0.584
1½	1.900	1.450	0.225	365	245	190	130	0.708
2	2.375	1.875	0.250	320	225	170	120	0.999
2½	2.875	2.275	0.300	320	205	170	110	1.452
3	3.500	2.800	0.350	305	210	160	110	2.072
4	4.500	3.624	0.438	295	225	155	120	3.343
6	6.625	5.501	0.562	255	205	145	110	6.403

Schedule A

Nom. size, in.	OD, in.	ID, in.	Wall thick-ness, in.	Max operating pressure at 75°F, plain end only, psi*	Max operating pressure at max temp. of 150°F, plain end only, psi*	Nom. wt./ft, lb
½	0.840	0.750	0.045	155	80	0.067
¾	1.050	0.940	0.055	155	80	0.103
1	1.315	1.195	0.060	135	70	0.141
1¼	1.660	1.520	0.070	120	65	0.210
1½	1.900	1.740	0.080	120	65	0.274
2	2.375	2.175	0.100	120	65	0.427
2½	2.875	2.635	0.120	120	65	0.621
3	3.500	3.220	0.140	120	65	0.884
4	4.500	4.110	0.195	120	65	1.579

* Threaded joints are not recommended for schedule A pipe.

Polyvinyl Chloride Pipe—High Impact
Schedule 40

Nom. size, in.	OD, in.	ID, in.	Wall thick-ness, in.	Max operating pressure at 75°F, plain end only, psi*	Max operating pressure at max temp. of 130°F, plain end only, psi*	Nom. wt./ft, lb
½	0.840	0.622	0.109	335	90	0.146
¾	1.050	0.824	0.113	275	70	0.195
1	1.315	1.049	0.133	255	70	0.289
1¼	1.660	1.380	0.140	210	50	0.391
1½	1.900	1.610	0.145	190	45	0.468
2	2.375	2.067	0.154	160	45	0.629
2½	2.875	2.469	0.203	165	50	0.998
3	3.500	3.068	0.216	150	40	1.304
4	4.500	4.026	0.237	130	30	1.857
6	6.625	6.065	0.280	105	30	3.266
8	8.625	7.981	0.322	90	30	4.912
10	10.750	10.020	0.365	80	25	6.963
12	12.750	11.938	0.406	75	25	9.207

* Threaded joints are not recommended for schedule 40 pipe.

Schedule 80

Nom. size, in.	OD, in.	ID, in.	Wall thick-ness, in.	Max operating pressure at 75°F, psi		Max operating pressure at max temp. of 130°F, psi		Nom. wt./ft, lb
				Plain end	Threaded	Plain end	Threaded	
½	0.840	0.546	0.147	470	270	120	70	0.187
¾	1.050	0.742	0.154	385	230	100	60	0.254
1	1.315	0.957	0.179	355	205	95	55	0.374
1¼	1.660	1.278	0.191	295	180	80	50	0.516
1½	1.900	1.500	0.200	265	170	70	45	0.625
2	2.375	1.939	0.218	230	155	60	40	0.864
2½	2.875	2.323	0.276	225	160	60	40	1.320
3	3.500	2.900	0.300	215	140	55	35	1.765
4	4.500	3.826	0.337	185	130	50	35	2.579
6	6.625	5.761	0.432	160	125	40	30	4.918
8	8.625	7.625	0.500	140	110	45	35	7.464

Schedule 120

Nom. size, in.	OD, in.	ID, in.	Wall thick-ness, in.	Max operating pressure at 75°F, psi		Max operating pressure at max temp. of 130°F, psi		Nom. wt./ft, lb
				Plain end	Threaded	Plain end	Threaded	
½	0.840	0.500	0.170	560	350	145	90	0.209
¾	1.050	0.710	0.170	430	270	110	70	0.275
1	1.315	0.915	0.200	400	250	105	65	0.410
1¼	1.660	1.230	0.215	335	205	85	55	0.571
1½	1.900	1.450	0.225	300	205	80	55	0.693
2	2.375	1.875	0.250	265	185	70	50	0.977
2½	2.875	2.275	0.300	265	170	70	45	1.420
3	3.500	2.800	0.350	250	175	65	45	2.027
4	4.500	3.624	0.438	245	185	65	50	3.271
6	6.625	5.501	0.562	210	170	55	45	6.265

Schedule A

Nom. size, in.	OD, in.	ID, in.	Wall thick-ness, in.	Max operating pressure at 75°F, plain end only, psi*	Max operating pressure at max temp. of 130°F, plain end only, psi*	Nom. wt./ft, lb
½	0.840	0.750	0.045	130	35	0.066
¾	1.050	0.940	0.055	130	35	0.101
1	1.315	1.195	0.060	110	30	0.138
1¼	1.660	1.520	0.070	100	25	0.205
1½	1.900	1.740	0.080	100	25	0.268
2	2.375	2.175	0.100	100	25	0.418
2½	2.875	2.635	0.120	100	25	0.608
3	3.500	3.220	0.140	100	25	0.865
4	4.500	4.110	0.195	100	25	1.545

* Threaded joints are not recommended for schedule A pipe.

Aluminum Pipe
Dimensions and Weights

Nom. pipe size, in.	Schedule No.*	OD, in.	ID, in.	Wall thickness, in.	Wt./lin ft, lb, plain ends†
⅛	40‡	0.405	0.269	0.068	0.085
¼	40‡	0.540	0.364	0.088	0.147
⅜	40‡	0.675	0.493	0.091	0.196
½	40‡	0.840	0.622	0.109	0.294
¾	10	1.050	0.884	0.083	0.297
	40‡	1.050	0.824	0.113	0.391
1	5	1.315	1.185	0.065	0.300
	10	1.315	1.097	0.109	0.486
	40‡	1.315	1.049	0.133	0.581
1¼	5	1.660	1.530	0.065	0.383
	10	1.660	1.442	0.109	0.625
	40‡	1.660	1.380	0.140	0.786
1½	5	1.900	1.770	0.065	0.441
	10	1.900	1.682	0.109	0.721
	40‡	1.900	1.610	0.145	0.940
2	5	2.375	2.245	0.065	0.555
	10	2.375	2.157	0.109	0.913
	40‡	2.375	2.067	0.154	1.264
2½	5	2.875	2.709	0.083	0.856
	10	2.875	2.635	0.120	1.221
	40‡	2.875	2.469	0.203	2.004
3	5	3.500	3.334	0.083	1.048
	10	3.500	3.260	0.120	1.498
	40‡	3.500	3.068	0.216	2.621
3½	5	4.000	3.834	0.083	1.201
	10	4.000	3.760	0.120	1.720
	40‡	4.000	3.548	0.226	3.151
4	5	4.500	4.334	0.083	1.354
	10	4.500	4.260	0.120	1.942
	40‡	4.500	4.026	0.237	3.733
5	5	5.563	5.345	0.109	2.195
	10	5.563	5.295	0.134	2.686
	40‡	5.563	5.047	0.258	5.057
6	5	6.625	6.407	0.109	2.623
	10	6.625	6.357	0.134	3.214
	40‡	6.625	6.065	0.280	6.564
8	30	8.625	8.071	0.277	8.543
	40‡	8.625	7.981	0.322	9.878
10	...	10.750	10.192	0.279	10.79
	30	10.750	10.136	0.307	11.84
	40‡	10.750	10.020	0.365	14.00
12	30	12.750	12.090	0.330	15.14
	...‡	12.750	12.000	0.375	17.14

All calculations based on nominal dimensions.
    * Schedule numbers 30 and 40 conform to American Standard for Wrought Iron and Wrought Steel Pipe, ASA B36.10. Schedule numbers for schedule 5 and schedule 10 conform to American Standard for Stainless Steel Pipe, ASA B36.19.
    † Weights calculated for 6061 and 6063. For 3003 multiply by 1.010.
    ‡ Also designated as standard pipe.

PRODUCTION EQUIPMENT

Aluminum Pipe—Not Welded
Bursting Pressures

Nom. pipe size, in.	Schedule No.	Bursting pressure, psi		
		3003-H112*	6063-T6	6061-T6
⅛	40	. . . . .	11,900	15,020
¼	40	. . . . .	11,490	14,490
⅜	40	. . . . .	9,270	11,730
½	40	. . . . .	8,880	11,220
¾	10	. . . . .	5,180	
	40	. . . . .	7,220	9,130
1	5	. . . . .	3,160	
	10	. . . . .	5,450	
	40	2,630	6,750	8,560
1¼	5	. . . . .	2,480	
	10	. . . . .	4,250	
	40	2,160	5,550	7,030
1½	5	. . . . .	2,160	
	10	. . . . .	3,690	
	40	1,940	4,990	6,320
2	5	. . . . .	1,720	
	10	. . . . .	2,920	
	40	1,630	4,190	5,320
2½	5	. . . . .	1,810	
	10	. . . . .	2,650	
	40	1,790	4,590	5,820
3	5	. . . . .	1,480	
	10	. . . . .	2,160	
	40	1,550	3,980	5,050
3½	40	1,420	3,630	4,600
4	5	. . . . .	1,150	
	10	. . . . .	1,670	
	40	1,320	3,370	4,280
5	5	. . . . .	1,190	
	10	. . . . .	1,470	
	40	1,150	2,950	3,750
6	5	. . . . .	1,160	
	10	. . . . .	1,230	
	40	1,050	2,680	3,410
8 (0.277)	30	790	2,020	2,560
8 (0.322)	40	920	2,360	2,990
10 (0.279)	. . .	630	1,630	2,070
10 (0.307)	30	700	1,790	2,280
10 (0.365)	40	835	2,140	2,720
12 (0.375)	. . .	720	1,850	2,340

* Computed bursting and yielding pressures and conversion factors for 3003-H112 alloy also apply to 3003-F alloy. They are based on the properties of the 3003-0 alloy.

Aluminum Pipe
Conversion Factors for Bursting Pressures at Various Temperatures for Not Welded and Circumferentially Welded Pipe

Temp., °F	3003-H112		6063-T6		6061-T6	
	Not welded	As welded	Not welded	As welded	Not welded	As welded
100 and under	1.00	1.00	1.00	0.57	1.00	0.63
150	0.91	0.91	0.95	0.56	0.98	0.62
200	0.85	0.85	0.91	0.53	0.95	0.60
250	0.79	0.79	0.84	0.49	0.91	0.57
300	0.70	0.70	0.61	0.45	0.76	0.53
350	0.63	0.63	0.39	0.36	0.58	0.44
400	0.55	0.55	0.25	0.24	0.41	0.34
450	0.47	0.47	0.17	0.17	0.25	0.25
500	0.40	0.40	0.13	0.13	0.15	0.15

Aluminum Pipe—Not Welded
Yielding Pressures

Nom. pipe size, in.	Schedule No.	Yielding pressure, psi		
		3003-H112*	6063-T6	6061-T6
⅛	40	. . . . .	9,750	13,640
¼	40	. . . . .	9,440	13,210
⅜	40	. . . . .	7,620	10,660
½	40	. . . . .	7,300	10,220
¾	10	. . . . .	4,260	
	40	. . . . .	5,940	8,310
1	5	. . . . .	2,590	
	10	. . . . .	4,490	
	40	1,110	5,560	7,780
1¼	5	. . . . .	2,040	
	10	. . . . .	3,500	
	40	910	4,570	6,400
1½	5	. . . . .	1,770	
	10	. . . . .	3,030	
	40	820	4,100	5,740
2	5	. . . . .	1,410	
	10	. . . . .	2,400	
	40	690	3,450	4,830
2½	5	. . . . .	1,490	
	10	. . . . .	2,180	
	40	760	3,780	5,290
3	5	. . . . .	1,210	
	10	. . . . .	1,770	
	40	660	3,270	4,580
3½	40	600	2,980	4,180
4	5	. . . . .	940	
	10	. . . . .	1,370	
	40	550	2,770	3,880
5	5	. . . . .	1,000	
	10	. . . . .	1,230	
	40	490	2,430	3,400
6	5	170	840	1,180
	10	. . . . .	1,030	
	40	440	2,200	3,080
8 (0.277)	30	330	1,660	2,320
8 (0.322)	40	390	1,940	2,710
10 (0.279)	. . .	270	1,330	1,860
10 (0.307)	30	290	1,470	2,060
10 (0.365)	40	350	1,760	2,460
12 (0.375)	. . .	300	1,510	2,120

* Computed bursting and yielding pressures and conversion factors for 3003-H112 alloy also apply to 3003-F alloy.   They are based on the properties of the 3003-0 alloy.

Aluminum Pipe
Conversion Factors for Yielding Pressures at Various Temperatures
for Not Welded and Circumferentially Welded Pipe

Temp., °F	3003-H112		6063-T6		6061-T6	
	Not welded	As welded	Not welded	As welded	Not welded	As welded
100 and under	1.00	1.00	1.00	0.45	1.00	0.50
150	0.97	0.97	0.96	0.45	0.98	0.50
200	0.94	0.94	0.92	0.45	0.96	0.50
250	0.89	0.89	0.86	0.45	0.94	0.50
300	0.83	0.83	0.64	0.41	0.74	0.49
350	0.78	0.78	0.33	0.24	0.57	0.44
400	0.72	0.72	0.20	0.18	0.40	0.35
450	0.64	0.64	0.14	0.14	0.25	0.25
500	0.58	0.58	0.12	0.12	0.12	0.12

Notes for Tables on Pages 2-122 and 2-124

The calculated internal bursting and yielding pressures in the tables on pages 2-122 and 2-124 are based on a maximum operating temperature of 100°F and the nominal dimensions of the pipe with no allowance for the effects of joints or fittings. The following formulas were used:

Bursting

$$P = \frac{K \, 2 S u t}{D - 0.8 t}$$

Yielding

$$P = \frac{S y (D^2 - d^2)}{D^2 + d^2}$$

where D = outside diameter, in.

d = inside diameter, in.

t = wall thickness, in.

K = correlation factor (given below)

Su and Sy = mechanical properties for the not-welded condition (given below)

The conversion factors in the tables on pages 2-122 and 2-124 for not-welded pipe at various temperatures are the ratios of the not-welded values of Su and Sy at the specified temperature to the not-welded values of Su and Sy, respectively, at 100°F. The conversion factors for as-welded pipe at various temperatures are the ratios of the welded values of Su and Sy at the specified temperature to the not-welded values of Su and Sy, respectively, at 100°F. The 100°F values are listed below.

Alloy	K	Not welded		Welded	
		Su[a]	Sy[b]	Su[c]	Sy[d]
3003-H112	0.85	14,000[e]	5,000[f]	14,000	5,000
6063-T6	1.02	30,000	25,000	17,000	11,300
6061-T6	1.02	38,000[g]	35,000	24,000	17,500

[a] Specified minimum longitudinal tensile strength.
[b] Specified minimum longitudinal yield strength.
[c] Specified in ASME Boiler and Pressure Vessel Code, Section IX.
[d] Based on bursting tests of pipe.
[e] Specified value is 14,500 psi; value shown is for −0 temperature.
[f] Specified value is 6,000 psi; value shown is for −0 temperature.
[g] Specified value for sizes under 1 in. is 42,000 psi; value shown was used in calculations for all sizes.

Aluminum Pipe
Minimum Mechanical Properties

	3003-H112	6063-T6	6061-T6
Tensile strength, psi..........	14,500	30,000	38,000*
Yield strength, psi............	6,000	25,000	35,000
Elongation, % in 2 in.........	......	8	8

* 42,000 for sizes under 1 in.

Lengths

Schedule 5 and 10 pipe:
   All sizes 20, 30, or 40 ft
Schedule 30 and 40 pipe:
   Sizes ⅛ through ⅜ in............ 12 ft
   Sizes ½ through 10 in........... 20 ft
   12-in. size.................... 12 ft
In many sizes 40-ft lengths can be supplied

Chapter 3

WELLHEAD EQUIPMENT
AND FLOW-CONTROL DEVICES

By JAMES H. FOSTER

Western Regional Manager
McEvoy Company

WELLHEAD EQUIPMENT

Wellhead equipment is a term used to describe, in general, equipment attached to the top of the tubular materials used in a well to support the strings, provide seals between strings, and control production from the well.

Since the American Petroleum Institute is an active organization set up for the purpose of establishing standards in sizes, grades, designs, dimensions, and quality, to provide safe interchangeable equipment for the industry, this section is confined to equipment covered by API standards. The only non-API equipment discussed in this section is for pressure applications below those presently covered by the API.

API WELLHEAD EQUIPMENT

Working-pressure Terminology

Working pressures of equipment components were at one time referred to by an API series designation, such as series 600—meaning a working pressure of 2,000 psi. Such series designations have been discontinued and replaced with more easily remembered terms indicating the actual allowable cold-working pressures in pounds per square inch.

Standard API cold-working-pressure ratings, test-pressure ratings, and former series designations follow:

Max cold-working pressure, psi	Hydrostatic test pressure, psi	Former corresponding series designation
960	1,440	Series 400
2,000	4,000	Series 600
3,000	6,000	Series 900
5,000	10,000	Series 1500
10,000	15,000	Series 2900
10,000*	15,000	
15,000	22,500	

* For special large-sized extreme-pressure flanges.
These working pressures are applicable for temperatures not exceeding 250°F.

The maximum working pressure is the maximum operating pressure to which the equipment should be subjected. The hydrostatic test pressure is the static body test pressure imposed by the manufacturer to prove adequacy in design, materials, and workmanship.

Occasionally wellhead equipment and valves are accidentally or purposely subjected to pressures in excess of design working pressures during high-pressure remedial work. Although the equipment often withstands the mistreatment, such practices should be avoided.

All manufacturers build safety factors into their product based on sound engineering and past experience, but the stresses caused by vibration, impact loads, and temperature variations are impossible to predict.

Equipment should never be subjected to pressures above the recommended working pressure unless the manufacturer is relieved of all responsibility, and the possible results due to failure are expected.

Physical Properties

All API wellhead equipment is made of steel having tensile properties equal to or exceeding those specified in Table 3-1.

Table 3-1 Minimum Tensile Properties*

	960 psi, API working pressure	2,000, 3,000 5,000, 10,000 psi, API working pressure	10,000 psi, API working pressure†	15,000 psi, API working pressure
Tensile strength, psi...............	70,000	90,000	90,000	100,000
Yield strength, psi.................	36,000	60,000	60,000	75,000
Elongation in 2 in., %.............	22	18	18	17
Reduction in area, %.............	30	30	35	35

* Reproduced by permission from API Standard 6E, Specification for Wellhead and Drilling-through Equipment, 5th ed., March, 1958; and API Standard 6BX, Specification for Ring Joint Flanges for Drilling and Production Service for Extreme Pressures. 2d ed., December, 1958.
† For special large-sized extreme-pressure flanges.

Lowermost Casing Heads

The lowermost casing head is a unit or housing attached to the top end of the surface pipe to provide a means for supporting the next string of casing, and sealing the annular space between the two strings of casing. It is composed of a casing-hanger bowl to receive the casing hanger necessary to support the next string of casing, a top flange for attaching blowout preventers, other intermediate casing heads or tubing heads, and a lower connection.

The lower connection may be a female thread, a male thread, or a slip-on for welding socket. Most common is the female-threaded lower connection, although the slip-on socket connection provides the strongest joint unless the surface casing is of such composition that welding causes serious weakening. The male lower thread is the weakest of the three connections because of the thin cross section necessary to provide full opening. It is used in most cases only to prevent removing the coupling on the surface pipe. The welded connection is most frequently used on deep wells to give the additional strength needed to suspend heavy casing loads without overstressing the threads on the surface pipe.

A landing base is sometimes used with the lowermost casing head to provide additional support for extremely heavy casing strings. The landing base is a separate unit welded to the lowermost casing head and to the surface pipe with a lower flange or skirt to transfer part of the weight to conductor strings, pilings, or a concrete foundation.

The lower connection is usually the weakest vertical load-supporting connection in an API wellhead assembly.   The body-wall thickness of the lowest-working-pressure lowermost casing head is sufficient to support the most extreme casing loads.   Therefore, it is not necessary to increase the working pressure of the head because heavy casing loads are anticipated.

Most lower casing heads are furnished with two 2-in. line-pipe threaded outlets, although studded or extended flanged outlets are sometimes used to provide additional strength for attaching valves.

Internal valve-removal threads should be included in the studded or extended flanged outlets to provide a means for seating a plug to seal the outlet while installing or removing a valve under pressure.

In the event a valve cuts out or it is desirable to install or remove a valve under pressure, after the well is completed, a special tool can be attached to the outlet or the valve and a plug can be inserted into the valve-removal thread to seal the pressure while necessary adjustments are made.   A full-opening valve must be used for this application to provide clearance for the plug.

In case threaded outlets are used, a valve-removal nipple may be used to provide the same facility.   Internal threads inside the valve-removal nipple provide a receptacle to seat the plug for removing, installing, or replacing the valve.

Lowermost casing heads are available with or without lock screws in the flange. Lock screws are normally used only to hold the casing hanger down against pressures which may occur during nipple-up operations or when casing-string weights are light enough to require a holddown to seal.

Sizes and Working Pressures.   Lowermost casing heads range in sizes from nominal 6 to nominal 20 in. to support casing in sizes from 4½ to 16 in., as indicated in Table 3-2.   Table 3-2 shows the various casing-head sizes needed for common surface, intermediate, and production string sizes.   The sizes of lowermost casing heads are desig-

Table 3-2. API Casing-head and Tubing-head Flange*
Sizes 1,000, 2,000, 3,000, 5,000 lb WOG (Water, Oil, or Gas)†

Surface pipe size	To support pipe size	API flange size, lower casing head	Nominal BOD bore	First intermediate casing-head flange size			Second intermediate casing			Tubing-head flange size	
				Bottom	Top	To support pipe size	Bottom	Top	To support pipe size	Bottom	Top‡
7	4, 4½, 5	6	7 1/16	...	......	....	......	....	....	6	6
8⅝	4, 4½, 5, 5½	8	9	...	......	....	......	....	....	8	6
9⅝	4½, 5, 5½, 6⅝, 7	10	11	...	......	....	......	....	....	10	6
10¾	5½, 6⅝, 7, 7⅝	10	11	...	......	....	......	....	....	10	6
11¾	5½, 6⅝, 7, 7⅝	12	13⅝	...	......	....	......	....	....	12	6
11¾	7⅝	12	13⅝	12	10-8	4, 4½, 5	......	....	....	10-8	6
11¾	8⅝	12	13⅝	12	10-8	4, 4½, 5, 5½	......	....	....	10-8	6
13⅜	8⅝	12	13⅝	12	10-8	4½, 5, 5½	......	....	....	10-8	6
13⅜	9⅝	12	13⅝	12	10	5½, 6⅝, 7	......	....	....	10	6
16	8⅝	16	16¾	16	10-8	4½, 5½	......	....	....	10-8	6
16	9⅝	16	16¾	16	10	5½, 6⅝, 7	......	....	....	10	6
16	10¾	16	16¾	16	12-10	5½, 6⅝, 7, 7⅝	......	....	....	12-10	6
16	10¾	16	16¾	16	12-10	7⅝	12-10	10-8	4, 4½, 5	10-8	6
16	13⅜	16	16¾	16	12	8⅝	12	10-8	4½, 5½	10-8	6
16	13⅜	16	16¾	16	12	9⅝	12	10	4½, 5½, 7	10	6
20	13⅜	20	20¼	20	12	8⅝	12	10	4½, 5½	10	6
20	13⅜	20	20¼	20	12	9⅝	12	10	4½, 5½, 7	10	6
20	16	20	20¼	20	16	10¾	16	10	5½, 7	10	6
20	16	20	20¼	20	20	13⅜	20	12	8⅝, 9⅝§	12	10

* All dimensions in inches.

† Sizes not applicable for 10,000-lb WOG equipment, which is designated by actual through-bore dimension.

‡ Top tubing-head flange sized for single tubing string completions (see Table 3-8 for multiple completions).

§ Third intermediate head can be used with 12-in. bottom flange and 10-in. top flange to support 5½ in. in 8⅝ in. with 10- by 6-in. tubing head; 5½ or 7 in. in 9⅝ in. with 10- by 6-in. tubing head.

nated by the nominal size of the API flanged-end connection on 960-, 2,000-, 3,000-, and 5,000-psi equipment, and the nominal size of the lower connection.   In 10,000-psi equipment, sizes are designated by the actual minimum size of the bore (Table 3-3).

Since the wellhead equipment used above tubular materials should be full-opening in order to pass full-sized in-hole tools, the bore of the tubular materials below an equipment component determines the minimum nominal size of the flange providing access to that tube.   A wellhead component must have a minimum internal diameter approximately $\frac{1}{32}$ in. larger than the drift diameter of the tube over·which it is used in order to be considered full-opening.

Table 3-3 gives the minimum nominal flange size to give full-opening access to each standard tube size.

Table 3-3. Minimum Full-opening Nominal Flange Size*

Nominal flange size, in.	Line pipe size nominal, in.	Tubing OD, in.	Casing OD, in.
960-, 2,000-, 3,000-, 5,000-psi working pressure			
$1\frac{1}{2}$†	$1\frac{1}{2}$	1.660 and 1.900	
2	2	1.600 through $2\frac{3}{8}$	
$2\frac{1}{2}$	$2\frac{1}{2}$	$2\frac{7}{8}$	
3	3	$3\frac{1}{2}$	
4	4	4 and $4\frac{1}{2}$	$4\frac{1}{2}$
6	6	....	$4\frac{1}{2}$ through 7
8	8	....	$7\frac{5}{8}$ and $8\frac{5}{8}$
10	10	....	$9\frac{5}{8}$ and $10\frac{3}{4}$
12‡	12	....	$11\frac{3}{4}$ and $13\frac{3}{8}$
14§	14	....	$11\frac{3}{4}$ and $13\frac{3}{8}$
16	16	....	16
20	20	....	20
10,000-psi working pressure¶			
$11\frac{3}{32}$†	$1\frac{1}{2}$	1.660 and smaller	
$1\frac{5}{8}$	2	1.900	
$12\frac{9}{32}$†	$2\frac{1}{2}$	1.900	
$2\frac{1}{16}$	3	$2\frac{3}{8}$	
$2\frac{9}{16}$	$3\frac{1}{2}$	$2\frac{7}{8}$	
$3\frac{1}{8}$†	4	$3\frac{1}{2}$	
$4\frac{1}{16}$†	5	4 and $4\frac{1}{2}$	$4\frac{1}{2}$
$7\frac{1}{16}$	10	....	$4\frac{1}{2}$ through 7
15,000-psi working pressure			
See separate discussion of 15,000-psi working pressure			

* Reproduced by permission from API Standard 6E, Specification for Wellhead and Drilling-through Equipment, 5th ed., March, 1958.
† Generally nonstock size.
‡ 12-in. nominal flange is limited to 3,000-psi working pressure when used over $11\frac{3}{4}$ and $13\frac{3}{8}$ casing.
§ 14-in. nominal flange required for $11\frac{3}{4}$ and $13\frac{3}{8}$ in 5,000-psi-maximum-working-pressure rating to give full opening.
¶ 10,000-psi valves, fittings, and flanges are designated by their actual through-bore dimensions.

Because of the problems encountered in sealing large threaded connections at high pressures in field make-up, Table 3-4 gives the maximum recommended thread ratings for various pipe sizes.

Selection.   In selecting a lowermost casing head for a particular application, the following factors should be considered.

1. *Design.*   The casing head should be designed to receive a casing hanger which will not damage the casing string to be suspended when supporting full-joint-strength casing load with a pack-off pressure equal to the minimum yield of the supported casing or the working pressure of the casing head, whichever is the smaller.

2. *Working Pressure.*   The minimum working pressure should be at least equal to the anticipated formation breakdown pressure at the bottom of the surface pipe, or

Table 3-4. Thread Ratings*

Type of thread	Size of thread, in.	Max working-pressure thread rating, psi
Casing........................	16 in. and larger	2,000
Casing........................	5 to 14 in., inclusive	3,000
Line pipe......................	2½ in. nominal and larger	3,000
Nonupset tubing................	2⅞ in. and larger	3,000
External upset tubing...........	3½ in. and larger	5,000

* Reproduced by permission from API Standard 6E, Specification for Wellhead and Drilling-through Equipment, 5th ed., March, 1958.

equal to or greater than the internal pressure rating of the surface pipe.   Maximum working pressure should be at least equal to the formation pressure at the bottom of the next smaller casing string.

3. *Lock Screws.* Lock screws in the casing-head flange may be used as an added safety precaution if the annulus pressures are expected during nipple-up or if a very light casing load is to be suspended.

4. *Size.* Nominal flange size should normally be the smallest permissible size to provide full-opening access to the surface pipe (Table 3-3) and should fit a standard out-of-stock intermediate head or tubing head and blowout preventer. It should have the necessary size and type of lower connection to fit the surface pipe.

Casing Hangers

A casing hanger is a device which seats in the bowl of a lowermost casing head or an intermediate casing head to suspend the next smaller casing string securely and provide a seal between the suspended casing and the casing-head bowl.

The size of a casing hanger is determined by the nominal outside diameter, which is the same as the nominal size of the mating casing-head flange. The nominal inside diameter is the same as the nominal outside diameter of the casing it is designed to suspend.

Sizes range from nominal 6 through 20 in. to support 4½- through 16-in. casing. Popular sizes are nominal 8 in. for 4½- through 5½-in. casing; nominal 10 in. for 4½- through 7⅝-in. casing; nominal 12 in. for 5½- through 9⅝-in. casing, as indicated in Table 3-2.

Casing hangers are generally available for all casing sizes in the following types:

1. *Automatic* (most popular type). The automatic casing hanger is a unitized assembly composed of a set of slips and a sealing mechanism. It can be latched around the casing and dropped through the blowout preventers to set and seal automatically when the casing is slacked off to set. This type is normally used when annulus pressures are expected during nipple-up operations.

2. *Manual.* The manual casing hanger is normally used in preference to the automatic type only as a matter of economics when pressure is not expected in the annulus during nipple-up. It is composed of a set of slips and a separate pack-off element. The slips can usually be latched around the casing and dropped through the blowout preventers, but the pack-off is installed after the preventers have been removed and the casing cut off.

3. *Slip-weld.* The slip-weld hanger is usually composed of a set of slips to support the casing weight and a spider or ring which can be welded to the casing to seal the hanger to the casing. The hanger is usually sealed in the head by a resilient compression-type seal. The hanger can be dropped through the blowout preventers to support casing weight, but final seal is made by welding after the preventers have been removed and the casing cut off. Particular care must be taken in preheating the casing and the casing head to ensure an adequate weld. Some casing is permanently damaged by improper welding.

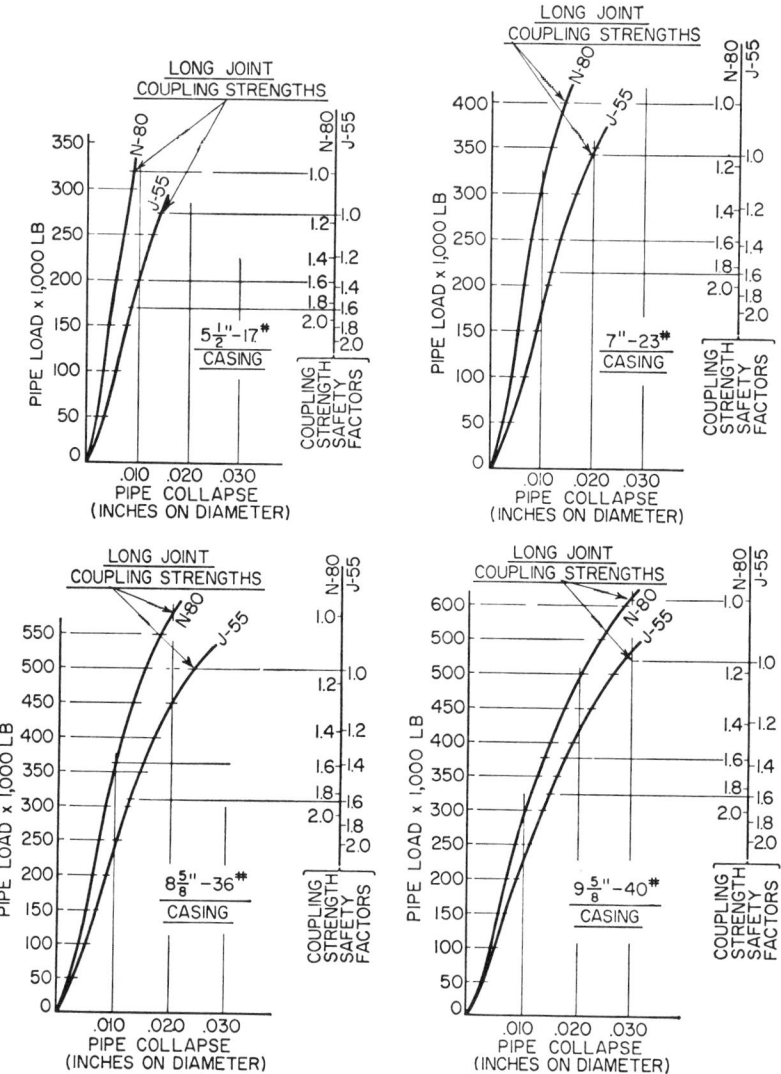

Fig. 3-1. Casing-hanger pull curves. (*McEroy Company, General Catalog 58–59, January, 1959.*)

4. *Boll Weevil.* The boll-weevil casing hanger is a simple mandrel-type hanger which screws onto the casing to be supported, and seats in the casing-head bowl. This type of hanger is not recommended if there is any question about getting the casing to bottom and obtaining the accurate spacing required.

An adequate casing hanger is one that will suspend full joint strength of the casing without sufficient deformation to restrict full-sized in-hole tools. Maximum permissible deformation at joint strength of the casing has been set at 0.030 in. by some manufacturers to provide adequate clearance.

The casing hanger should also provide an effective pack-off of such construction that the slip capacity is not affected by pressure from above the pack-off due to well pressure or test pressure.   To provide maximum utility, the pack-off should also be adjustable and removable, without moving the casing string, after it has been set.

Casing hangers are generally rated by their capacity to support casing weight rather than by working pressure. Some manufacturers furnish actual pull curves which show the deformation that can be expected in the slip area, for any casing load, up to joint strength, for all standard casing sizes, weights, and grades.

Figure 3-1 shows acceptable pull curves for a heavy-duty casing hanger with a pressure of 5,000 psi on the pack-off.

Casing-hanger Selection

In selecting a casing hanger, after establishing which type of hanger is most practical, the following factors should be considered:

1. The hanger should be capable of hanging full joint strength of the casing to be used, without sufficient reduction in diameter to obstruct full-sized in-hole tools.

2. The pack-off or primary seal should be of such construction that well pressure, flange test pressure, or fracture pressure cannot force the pack-off down and reduce the casing-hanger capacity.

3. The pack-off should be adjustable and removable (without moving the suspended casing string) after it has been set.

4. The hanger should be of the proper design and size to fit the mating casing-head bowl, and properly sized to support the casing to be used.

Intermediate Casing Heads

An intermediate casing head is a spool-type unit or housing attached to the top flange of the underlying casing head to provide a means of supporting the next smaller casing string and sealing the annular space between the two casing strings. It is composed of a lower flange, one or two side outlets, and a top flange with an internal casing-hanger bowl.

The lower flange of an intermediate casing head is counterbored with a recess to accommodate a removable bit guide, or a bit guide and secondary-seal assembly.   The purpose of the bit guide is to protect the top end of the intermediate casing string from damage by bits and tools going in the hole.

The counterbore is usually constructed to provide a fixed internal bit guide for the largest-sized intermediate casing string that can be suspended beneath that particular flange size.   A removable bit guide must be used to protect smaller-sized intermediate casing.

A removable bit guide and secondary-seal assembly may also be used in place of a removable bit guide to seal the annular space between the intermediate casing and the lower flange of the intermediate casing head.

By using a secondary seal, well fluids are confined to the body of the intermediate casing head and not allowed to contact the ring gasket or the pack-off on the casing hanger below.

If the well fluids are corrosive, use of a dependable secondary seal is particularly important to protect the ring gasket.

Also, by using a secondary seal and confining well fluids to a diameter approximately equal to the outside diameter of the intermediate casing, the piston load or thrust on the flanges and flange studs is greatly reduced. This permits use of an intermediate casing head with a top flange one working pressure rating higher than the lower flange. Of course, the body, the top flange, and the outlets must be of the appropriate dimensions to give the additional pressure rating.

Available secondary seals are generally of three types: (1) the unitized pressure-energized type; (2) the plastic-packed type; (3) the externally adjustable type. The externally adjustable type offers the advantage of being adjustable to stop a leak at any time during the life of a well.   A leak in the pressure-energized type or the plastic-packed type may be sealed by injecting a plugging material into the seal under pressure or by replacement.

Intermediate casing heads are available with one or two side outlets which may be threaded, studded, or extended flanged, depending on the working pressure and particular application. The side outlets should be equipped with valve-removal provisions as discussed in connection with the lowermost casing heads.

Like a lowermost casing head, the top flange of an intermediate casing head may be equipped with lock screws if needed, because of expected annulus pressures during nipple-up or very light suspended casing loads.

The design features for an intermediate casing-head bowl are identical to those discussed for a lowermost casing-head bowl. The bowl should be designed to receive a casing hanger which will suspend the next smaller casing string without damage to the pipe.

When a relatively short intermediate casing string is used, it is sometimes desirable to use a less expensive casing hanger with a lower load capacity for support, but a high-capacity casing hanger is usually required to suspend the next smaller casing string.

Sizes and Working Pressures. The lower and upper flanges on intermediate casing heads may range in size from nominal 6 to nominal 20 in. to support casing in sizes from $4\frac{1}{2}$ to $13\frac{3}{8}$ in. Table 3-2 shows the various intermediate head sizes required for standard casing sizes. Table 3-3 gives the minimum nominal flange size to give full-opening access to standard casing.

Intermediate casing heads are available in working pressures of 960, 2,000, 3,000, and 5,000 psi.

Generally, the minimum working pressure of the intermediate head should be equal to or greater than the maximum surface pressure required to break down the formation at the bottom of the intermediate casing string suspended below the intermediate casing head. The maximum working pressure should at least equal the shut-in formation pressure at the bottom of the casing string to be suspended in the intermediate casing head.

Selection. In selecting an intermediate casing head, the following factors should be considered:

1. Lower flange must be of the proper size and working pressure to fit the uppermost flange on the casing head below, or the crossover flange attached to the casing-head flange if one is used (Tables 3-2 and 3-3).

2. It must have the proper size of bit guide, or bit guide and secondary-seal assembly, to fit the casing suspended beneath it.

3. Top flange must be of the proper size and working pressure to suspend the next smaller casing string and fit the mating flange to be installed above (see working-pressure discussion and Tables 3-2 and 3-3).

4. It should have the proper size, type, and working pressure side outlets.

5. It must include a casing-hanger bowl designed to receive a casing hanger, with an effective pack-off mechanism that will support joint strength of the casing to be suspended without damage to the casing.

Intermediate Casing Hangers

Intermediate casing hangers are identical in every respect to casing hangers used in lowermost casing heads and are used to suspend the next smaller casing string in the intermediate casing head.

These hangers are selected on the same basis as casing hangers used in lowermost casing heads, as previously discussed.

Sizes are specified by the nominal diameter of the flange in which the hanger is to be used and the nominal size of the casing to be supported.

Tubing Heads

A tubing head is a spool-type unit or housing attached to the top flange on the uppermost casing head to provide a support for the tubing string and seal the annular space between the tubing string and production casing string. It also provides access to the casing-tubing annulus through side outlets. It is composed of a lower flange, one or two side outlets, and a top flange with an internal tubing hanger bowl.

Tubing heads are generally of two types: the unit with the flanged bottom and the flanged top, and one with the flanged top and threaded bottom. The unit with the threaded bottom is usually screwed directly on the production casing string, and the top flange is used for the same purpose as the double-flanged head.

The lower flange, on the double-flanged type, is constructed in much the same way as the lower flange on an intermediate casing head in that a recess is provided to accommodate a bit guide or a bit guide and secondary seal. The design, purpose, types, and application of bit guides and secondary seals are explained in the discussion of the intermediate casing head.

Tubing heads are available with one or two side outlets which may be threaded, studded, or extended flanged. Usually studded side outlets are used on units with a body working pressure of 3,000 psi and higher. Threaded side outlets are commonly used on units of 2,000-psi working pressure and lower. Extended flanged outlets are used on the higher-working-pressure and large-sized side outlet valves. All outlets should be equipped for valve-removal service, as explained in the discussion of the lowermost casing head.

The top flange of a tubing head must be equipped with an internal bowl of the proper design to receive the required tubing hanger. Lock screws must be included in the top flange to hold the tubing hanger in place when manipulating the tubing under pressure. Lock screws are also used to compress the tubing-hanger seal and seal the annular space between the tubing and casing. Most tubing heads offered by a manufacturer will receive any of the various types of single-completion tubing hangers of the same manufacturer. If multiple-tubing strings are to be installed, a tubing head with a special bowl may be required. This subject is explained in greater detail under the discussion of multiple completion.

Sizes and Working Pressures. The lower flange on a tubing head may range in size from a nominal 6 to a 20 in., and the upper flange may vary from nominal 6 to 12 in. for installation over production strings varying in size from $4\frac{1}{2}$ to $10\frac{3}{4}$ in.

Table 3-2 gives the various standard tubing-head sizes used over common casing sizes.

Tubing heads are available in working pressures of 960, 2,000, 3,000, 5,000, and 10,000 psi. A 15,000-psi-working-pressure tubing head is also available and is explained in a separate discussion on 15,000-psi-working-pressure equipment.

The upper and lower flanges on a tubing head are usually of the same working pressure unless a secondary seal is used to cross over to a higher-working-pressure top flange. By using a secondary seal to reduce the piston area exposed to well pressure, a top flange may be used with a working pressure one rating above the lower flange, provided the body and outlet dimensions also correspond to the higher rating.

The working pressure of a tubing head for a particular application should be at least equal to the anticipated surface shut-in pressure of the well. In most cases, it is considered more economical to install a tubing head with a working pressure equal to the formation breakdown rather than to replace the tubing head with higher-pressure equipment during high-pressure treatment.

A standard tubing head with a 6-in. top flange has a minimum bore of approximately $6\frac{5}{16}$ in., which is considered full-opening for a 7-in. or smaller production string. If a $7\frac{5}{8}$-in. production string is used, special care should be taken to select a full-opening tubing head for a $6\frac{3}{4}$-in. bit. Special tubing heads are available for this purpose. In using a special-bore tubing head, a corresponding special full-bore blowout preventer, and other drilling equipment, must be used to maintain complete control over the well during completion.

Selection. In selecting a tubing head, the following factors should be considered in order to maintain positive control over the well at all times:

1. The lower flange must be of the proper size and working pressure to fit the uppermost flange on the casing head below or the crossover flange attached to the casing-head flange, if one is used (Table 3-2).

2. The bit guide, or bit guide and secondary-seal assembly, must be sized to fit the production casing string.

3. The side outlets must be of the proper design, size, and working pressure.

4. The working pressure of the unit must be equal to or greater than the anticipated shut-in surface pressure.

5. The top flange must be sized to receive the required tubing hanger, and of the correct working pressure to fit the adapter flange on the Christmas-tree assembly. Lock screws must also be included in the top flange.

6. The tubing head should be full-opening to provide full-sized access to the production casing string below and be adaptable to future remedial operations, as well as artificial lift.

Tubing Hangers

A tubing hanger is a device used to provide a seal between the tubing and the tubing head.

Several types of tubing hangers are available, and each has a particular application. A brief discussion of the most popular types follows:

1. *Wrap-around.* The popular wrap-around hanger is composed of two hinged halves, which include a resilient sealing element between two steel mandrels.

The hanger can be latched around the tubing, dropped into the tubing-head bowl, and secured in place by the tubing-head lock screws. The lock screws force the top steel mandrel or plate down to compress the sealing element and form a seal between the tubing and tubing head.

Full tubing weight can be temporarily supported on the tubing hanger, but permanent support is provided by threading the top tubing thread into the adapter flange on top of the tubing head. The hanger then acts as a seal only.

The tubing can be stripped through the hanger, between upsets, under pressure. After the Christmas-tree assembly has been attached to the top tubing thread, the well can be circulated and a packer set under full control.

This type of hanger is frequently used as a blowout preventer when running tubing in a low-pressure well loaded with mud. If the well kicks, the tubing hanger can be latched around the tubing and lowered into the tubing-head bowl. A seal is made by tubing weight and by use of the lock screws. After circulation, it can be lifted out of the bowl with the first upset below the hanger.

2. *Polished-joint Hangers.* This type of hanger is slipped over or assembled around the top tubing joint, and the internal chevron seals are adjusted to provide a seal on the tubing body. The hanger is sealed against the tubing head with hydraulic packing or O rings. After the hanger is set, the Christmas tree can be attached to the top tubing thread and the well circulated under full control. The top tubing joint can be stripped through the hanger, between upsets, under pressure.

3. *Boll-weevil Hangers.* This is a doughnut- or mandrel-type hanger attached to the top tubing thread and supported in the tubing-head bowl. A seal between the mandrel and tubing head is provided by hydraulic packing or O rings. It is the only hanger designed to support the tubing weight permanently.

4. *Stripper Rubber.* A stripper rubber is a pressure-actuated sealing element used to control annulus pressures while running or pulling tubing in a low-pressure well. Tubing weight is supported by the adapter flange, a boll-weevil hanger, or slips located above the stripper rubber. In most cases, the stripper rubber should be used in conjunction with a blowout preventer and is not intended to replace the blowout preventer.

Selection. In selecting a tubing hanger, the particular application should dictate the type required.

In general, the hanger should provide an adequate seal between the tubing and tubing head and should be of standard size suitable for lowering through full-opening drilling equipment.

Back-pressure Valves

A back-pressure valve is a check valve installed in the tubing hanger, or in a mandrel above the tubing hanger, to seal the bore of the tubing while removing the blowout preventers and installing the Christmas tree. After the Christmas tree has been attached to the top tubing thread and the tubing hanger landed in the tubing head, the tubing can be circulated, through the back-pressure valve, and the packer set before flanging the Christmas-tree assembly to the tubing head.   The back-pressure valve can then be retrieved through the Christmas tree with a lubricator attachment.

Available back-pressure valves are generally of two types.   One type is secured into place with threads, and the other is secured with an expanding-lock mechanism.

In selecting a back-pressure valve, the following factors should be considered:

1. The valve should be so designed that an oversize Christmas-tree assembly is not needed to provide vertical access to the back-pressure valve.

2. A positive mechanism for securing the back-pressure valve in place should be provided.   The seating recess should offer as much protection from corrosion and erosion as possible.

3. The valve should have an opening of sufficient size to allow circulation through the valve at low rates.

Adapter

An adapter is a unit used to join connections of different dimensions.

The adapter may be used to connect two flanges of different dimensions or connect a flange to a thread.

An adapter used to connect two flanges with different dimensions may be studded and grooved on one side for a certain flange size, and studded and grooved on the other side for a different flange size.   A unit of this type is called a "double-studded adapter."

Crossover Flange

A crossover flange is an intermediate flange used to connect flanges of different working pressures.

Crossover flanges are usually available in two types:

1. A double-studded crossover flange is studded and grooved on one side for one working pressure, and studded and grooved on the other side for the next higher

Table 3-5. Crossover Flanges with Restricted-ring-groove Areas

Size, nominal flange, in.	Normal working-pressure rating, psi	Normal ring No.	Restricted-area ring No.	Working-pressure rating using restricted-area ring, psi
8	960	R49	R99	2,000
	2,000	R49	R99	3,000
	3,000	R49	R99	5,000
	5,000	R50	R47	10,000
10	960	R53	R49	2,000
	2,000	R53	R49	3,000
	3,000	R53	R49	5,000
	5,000	R54	R50	10,000
12	960	R57	R53	2,000
	2,000	R57	R53	3,000
	3,000	R57	R53	5,000
14	3,000*	R62	R53	5,000
	5,000	R63	R54	10,000
16	960	R65	R57	2,000
	2,000	R65	R57	3,000
	3,000	R66	R57	5,000
20	960	R73	R65	2,000
	2,000	R73	R65	3,000

* Dimensions for this flange do not appear in API Standard 6B.   Applicable dimensions are those given in ASA B16.5 for 14-in. 900-lb ring-joint flanges.

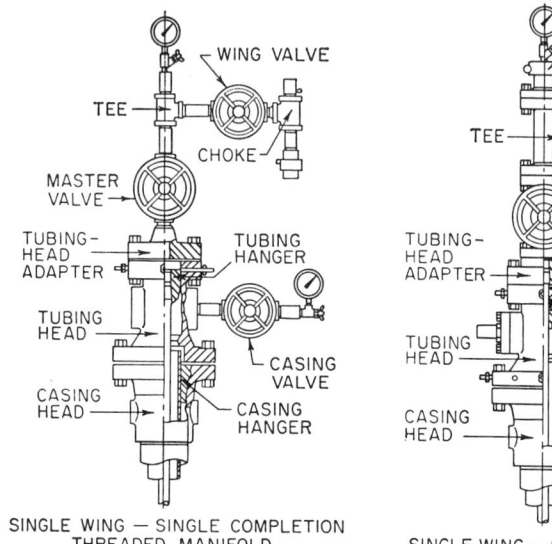

SINGLE WING — SINGLE COMPLETION
THREADED MANIFOLD

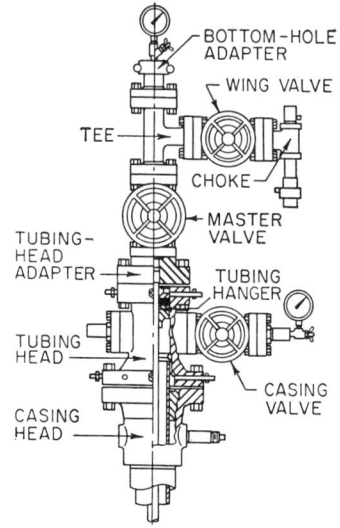

SINGLE WING — SINGLE COMPLETION

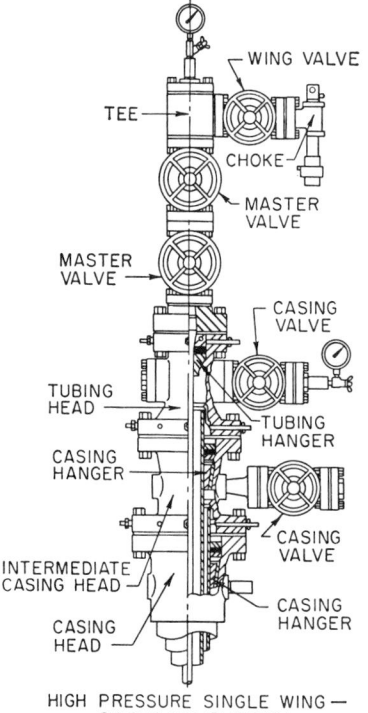

HIGH PRESSURE SINGLE WING —
SINGLE COMPLETION

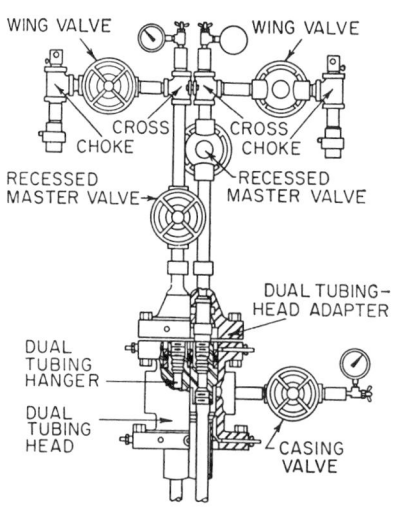

THREADED PARALLEL STRING
DUAL (OR TRIPLE) COMPLETION

Fig. 3-2. Typical

working-pressure rating. The flange must also include a seal around the inner string of pipe to prevent pressure from the higher-working-pressure side reaching the lower-working-pressure side. The seal may be of the resilient type, plastic-packed type, or welded type.

2. Another type of crossover flange includes a restricted ring groove in the top side of the flange to fit a corresponding restricted ring groove in the mating head. The restricted ring groove and the seal between the flange and the inner casing string act to restrict the pressure to a smaller area, thereby allowing a higher pressure rating.

Most intermediate casing heads and tubing heads have a restricted ring groove in the lower flange for this purpose. The body, side outlets, and top flange must also have the higher pressure rating.

Table 3-5 gives restricted-ring-groove ring-gasket numbers for corresponding standard ring gaskets.

Christmas-tree Assembly

A Christmas tree is an assembly of valves and fittings used to control production and provide access to the producing tubing string. It includes all equipment above the tubing-head top flange. Many variations in arrangement of these fittings are available to satisfy the needs of any particular application. Figure 3-2 shows several typical assemblies.

Tubing-head Adapter Flange

The tubing-head adapter flange is an intermediate flange used to connect the top tubing-head flange to the master valve and provide a support for the tubing.

Standard adapter flanges of the following three types are available:

1. *Studded Type.* This unit consists of a lower flange with a ring groove and boltholes to fit the top tubing-head flange, an internal thread in the bottom of the flange to receive and support the tubing weight, and a studded top connection to accommodate a flanged master valve.

2. *Spool Type.* This type is similar to the studded type except that the top connection is a separate flange to accommodate the master valve, and a top internal thread may be provided to act as a tubing landing or lift thread. It is also available with internal provisions for a back-pressure-valve mandrel.

3. *Threaded Adapter Flange.* This type of adapter flange is used to connect the top tubing-head flange to a threaded master valve. It is composed of a lower flange with a ring groove and boltholes to fit the top tubing-head flange, an internal thread in the bottom to support the tubing string, and a male thread on top to connect the

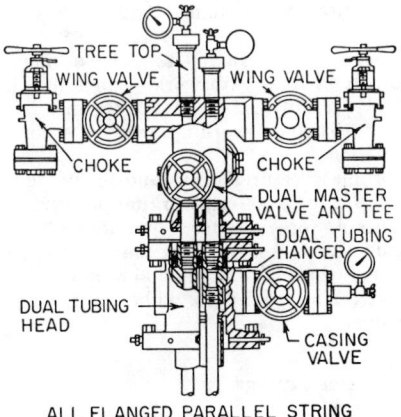

ALL FLANGED PARALLEL STRING
DUAL COMPLETION

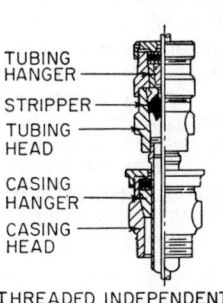

THREADED INDEPENDENT
WELLHEAD

Christmas-tree assemblies.

threaded master valve. The top male thread is usually an upset thread to give added strength.

A tubing-head adapter flange is described by specifying the lower flange size and working pressure, the bottom internal thread size and type, and the top-connection type, size, and working pressure.

The lower flange must be of the same size and working pressure as the tubing-head top flange. The top connection must be of the same size and working pressure as the master valve.

On Christmas trees with 960-, 2,000-, 3,000-, and 5,000-psi working pressures, the top flange on the tubing-head adapter and vertical run is usually the same nominal size as the tubing. However, on a 10,000-psi Christmas tree, the top flange on the adapter and the vertical run must have a larger nominal size than the tubing in order to provide a full-opening access to the tubing.

For example, a nominal 3-in. 10,000-psi master valve and vertical run must be used with $2\frac{3}{8}$-in. tubing, and a nominal $3\frac{1}{2}$-in. 10,000-psi vertical run must be provided for $2\frac{7}{8}$-in. tubing.

On a 15,000-psi Christmas tree, all fittings, including the master valves, are described by the actual bore, which is also the nominal size (see the discussion of 15,000-psi working pressure). In the new editions of the API Standards on Wellhead Equipment, this nomenclature will be used for 10,000-psi equipment also.

Valves

API valves, like API wellhead equipment, are made of high-strength alloy steels to give safe dependable service. ASA valves are made of carbon steel and should not be used for wellhead service.

Valves used on wellheads are basically of two types—gate valves and plug valves. Both are available with flanged end connections. Gate valves can be divided into lubricated and nonlubricated, wedging and nonwedging types.

Full-opening valves must be used in the vertical run of the Christmas-tree assembly to provide access to the tubing. Full-opening valves must also be used on tubing-head outlets and casing-head outlets equipped for valve-removal service.

Restricted-opening valves may often be used as wing valves, without loss of efficiency or utility, to effect an economic saving of 20 to 30 per cent of full-opening valve cost.

Threaded valves are available in sizes from $1\frac{1}{4}$ through 4 in., with working pressures from 960 through 5,000 psi. Upset tubing threads are usually used on valves in the vertical run of a Christmas tree to provide maximum strength. Valves with line-pipe threads are used on tubing wings, threaded tubing-head side outlets, and threaded casing-head side outlets. Most users prefer flanged valves on applications of 3,000 psi working pressure and above.

Flanged-end valves are available in sizes from 2 through 4 in. with working pressures of 960, 2,000, 3,000, 5,000, and 10,000 psi. Valves with working pressures of 15,000 psi are available with actual bores of $1\frac{11}{16}$, $1\frac{13}{16}$, $2\frac{1}{16}$, and $2\frac{9}{16}$ in. The actual bore and nominal size are the same in 15,000-psi-working-pressure equipment, as covered in the separate 15,000-psi discussion.

The nominal bore in valves with working pressures up to and including 5,000 psi is the same as the nominal valve size. A 2-in. 5,000-psi-working-pressure valve has a minimum bore of $2\frac{3}{32}$ in. and is suitable for a master valve above 2-in. tubing. However, the bore through a 10,000-psi valve is smaller than the nominal size.

To identify a 10,000-psi valve accurately, the flange size and bore must be specified. A full-opening 10,000-psi valve for use with 2-in. tubing should be described as a 3- by $2\frac{1}{16}$-in. 10,000-psi-working-pressure valve.

Christmas-tree Fittings

Other Christmas-tree fittings include tees, crosses, and other connections necessary to provide the most desirable arrangement for the particular application.

The size of the vertical run may vary from 2 to 4 in. but must be consistent with the master-valve and tubing-head adapter-flange size to give full-opening access to the tubing for wire-line tools and instruments.

The outlet on the tee or cross and wing assembly must be of sufficient size to handle the production requirements without undue restriction.   Outlets vary in size from 2 to 4 in., although the 2-in. size is normally adequate and is most commonly used in the United States.

All Christmas-tree assemblies should be assembled, pressure-tested to hydro-static test pressure, and checked with a drift mandrel to assure full opening before installation.

Table 3-6 shows the drift diameter for each standard tubing size, and Table 3-7 shows the minimum vertical bore of standard Christmas-tree sizes.

Table 3-6. Full-opening Christmas-tree Drift Size*

Tubing size OD, in.	Drift mandrel† diam, in.
1.660 (1¼)	1.286
1.900 (1½)	1.516
2⅜	1.901
2⅞	2.347
3½	2.867
4	3.351
4½	3.833

* Reproduced by permission from API Standard 6E, Specification for Wellhead and Drilling-through Equipment, 5th ed., March, 1958.
† Cylindrical drift 42 in. long with diameter as shown.

Table 3-7. Minimum Vertical Through-bore for Christmas-tree Assemblies*

Nominal size, in. (end flange)	Working-pressure rating, psi (end flange)	Min vertical through-bore, in.
1½	2,000 through 5,000	1⅝
2	2,000 through 5,000	2¹⁄₁₆
2½	2,000 through 5,000	2⁹⁄₁₆
3	2,000 through 5,000	3⅛
4	2,000 through 5,000	4¹⁄₁₆
1⅝	10,000	1⅝
1²⁵⁄₃₂	10,000	1²⁵⁄₃₂
2¹⁄₁₆	10,000	2¹⁄₁₆
2⁹⁄₁₆	10,000	2⁹⁄₁₆
3⅛	10,000	3⅛
4¹⁄₁₆	10,000	4¹⁄₁₆

* Reproduced by permission from API Standard 6E, Specification for Welhead and Drilling-through Equipment, 5th ed., March, 1958.

Bottom-hole Test Adapter

A bottom-hole test adapter is a device attached to the top of a Christmas-tree assembly to provide fast and safe adaptation of a lubricator for swabbing or testing. It may also include an internal thread to act as a lift thread for setting or raising the Christmas tree and tubing.

It is available in sizes from 2 to 4 in. and in working pressures from 960 to 10,000 psi.

Chokes

A choke is a device attached downstream from the wing valve to restrict, control, and regulate flow.   It may be of the positive or adjustable type.

A positive choke is composed of a body with internal provisions for receiving removable orifices of various sizes which are installed manually.

An adjustable choke is similar to a positive choke except that a stem with visible graduations indicating the effective orifice size is used to adjust the flow opening.

Both positive and adjustable chokes are available with threaded or flanged end connections.

Threaded chokes are available in working pressures of 1,500, 2,000, and 3,000 psi. Flanged chokes are available in 960-, 2,000-, 3,000-, 5,000-, 10,000-, and 15,000-psi working pressures.

Flow Control

A flow control is a device attached to the top of a master valve to act as a composite tee or cross, wing valve, choke, and bottom-hole test adapter. It is composed of a

Table 3-8. Multiple-parallel-tubing-string Data*†

Dual Completion

Tubing size	A	Min casing size	Min tubing-head flange size	
1.900 × 1.900	2 25/32	5½ in., 20 lb	6	
2 1/16 × 2 1/16	2 25/32	5½ in., 17 lb	6	
2⅜ × 2⅜	3 35/64	7 in., 38 lb	6	
2⅞ × 2⅞	4½	7⅝ in., 29.7 lb	8	
3½ × 3½	5 3/64	9⅝ in., 53.5 lb	10	

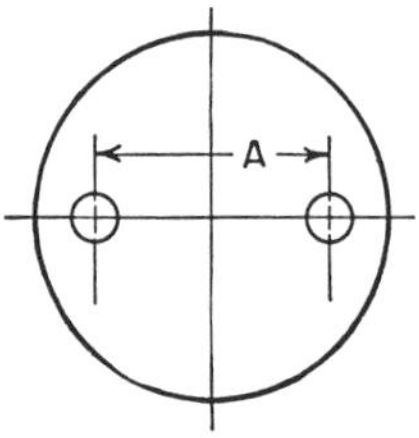

Triple Completion

Tubing size	Min casing size	A	B	C	Min tubing-head flange size	
1.900 × 1.900 × 1.900	6⅝ in., 32 lb	1⅞	1⅞	1⅞	6	
2 1/16 × 2 1/16 × 2 1/16	6⅝ in., 24 lb	1⅞	1⅞	1⅞	6	
2⅜ × 2⅜ × 2⅜	7 in., 26 lb	1 15/16	1 15/16	1 15/16	8	
2⅜ × 2⅜ × 2⅜	7⅝ in., 39 lb	2⅛	2⅛	2⅛	8	
2⅞ × 2⅞ × 2⅞	9⅝ in., 53. 5lb	2 13/16	2 13/16	2 13/16	10	

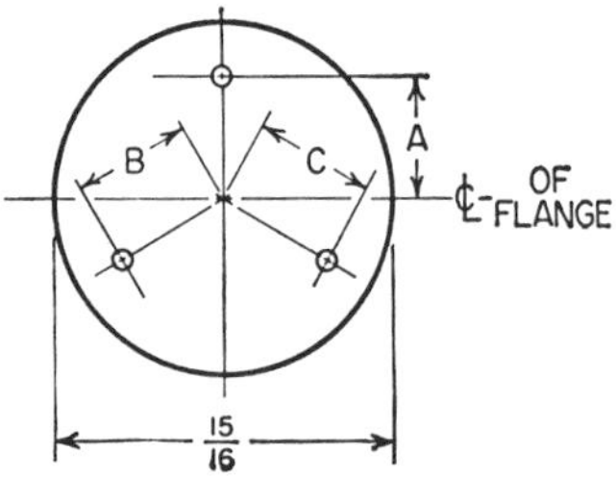

Quadruple Completion

Tubing size	Min casing size	A	Min tubing-head flange size	
1.900 × 1.900 × 1.900 × 1.900	8⅝ in., 36 lb	5¾	10	
2 1/16 × 2 1/16 × 2 1/16 × 2 1/16	8⅝ in., 36 lb	5¾	10	
2⅜ × 2⅜ × 2⅜ × 2⅜	9⅝ in., 53.5 lb	6⅛	10	
2⅞ × 2⅞ × 2⅞ × 2⅞ fabricated	11¾ in., 54 lb	8	12	
2⅞ × 2⅞ × 2⅞ × 2⅞ integral	10¾ in., 55.5 lb	6⅞	12	

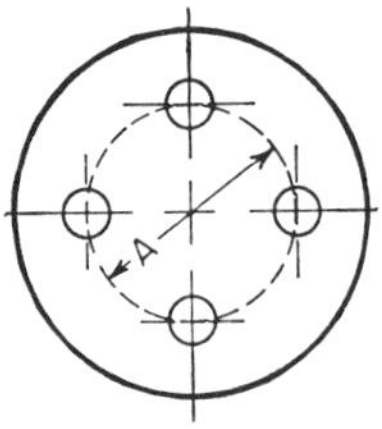

* Reproduced by permission from Robert Eichenberg, Design Consideration for AWHEM 15,000 psi Flanges, ASME Paper 57-PET-23, Sept. 22, 1957.

† Crossover joints or short tubing subs should be placed at least one full joint down the hole to reduce interference.

The above specifications include only those applications considered standard by most manufacturers. Equipment is available to accommodate many other tubing sizes, combinations, and center-line dimensions.

The following formula may be used to determine the minimum casing size necessary for any combination of multiple-parallel-tubing-string completions:

Duals and quadruples:

$$\text{Min casing size} = A + \text{tubing diam}$$

Triples:

$$\text{Min casing size} = 2\left[(A, B, \text{ or } C \text{ whichever is greatest}) + \frac{\text{tubing diam}}{2} \right]$$

Minimum casing size must also be sufficiently large to permit passage of API couplings unless one or more strings of integral-joint tubing are used.

body housing, an integral restricted-opening needle-type valve, a bottom-hole test-adapter top connection and a positive or adjustable choke assembly.

Flow controls are available in sizes from 2 to 3 in. and in working pressures from 960 through 5,000 psi.

Multiple-completion Equipment

Multiple completions or multiple-tubing-string completions require the same lowermost casing head, intermediate casing head, and tubing-head equipment as single-tubing-string completions with one exception. The tubing-head bowl must be designed and sized to accommodate the required size and number of tubing strings.

Figure 3-2 illustrates two types of dual parallel-string installations, and Table 3-8 gives a listing of common multiple-string applications and specifications.

Multiple-completion Tubing Heads

In selecting a tubing head for multiple parallel-tubing-string service, the same factors should be considered as previously suggested for selecting a single-completion tubing head, with the following additions: The tubing-head bowl

1. Should be of the required size and internal design to receive the desired tubing hanger
2. Should have the necessary nonrestrictive positioning or indexing devices to orient the tubing hanger accurately
3. Should be designed to receive an available tubing hanger which will suspend any lesser number of tubing strings and a single tubing string
4. Should be so designed that removal of the blowout preventers is not necessary until all tubing strings have been landed and sealed.

Multiple-completion Tubing Hangers

Multiple-completion tubing hangers perform the same function as single-completion tubing hangers, and as many types and variations in design are available.

A brief description of common available types and designs follows:

1. *Multiple-bore Mandrel Hanger.* This type of hanger consists of a large mandrel or doughnut with a separate bore for each tubing string. The individual tubing strings are landed in the large mandrel on landing collars. Back-pressure valves can be installed in the individual landing collars. This is the most simple and easily installed hanger but is limited to applications where gas-lift valves or tubing accessories with external diameters greater than tubing-joint diameters are not needed.

2. *Multiple-segment Hanger.* This type of hanger is composed of an individual hanger segment for each tubing string. Each segment seats in and occupies a part of the bowl when landed. Gas-lift valves and other tubing accessories may be installed on the tubing string. Each hanger segment may be equipped with provisions for back-pressure valves.

3. *Combination Mandrel and Boll-weevil Hanger.* This type of hanger is similar to the multiple-bore mandrel hanger except that one string of tubing is supported by threading into the large mandrel.

4. *Tension-type Hanger.* This type of hanger is constructed similar to the multiple-bore mandrel hanger and consists of a landing collar for each individual tubing string. The individual landing collars may be lowered through and lifted back up into the hanger mandrel, enabling the tubing strings to be set in tension through the blowout preventers. Back-pressure valves may be installed in the landing collars.

Selection. In selecting a multiple-completion tubing hanger, the following factors should be considered:

1. Seals on the individual hangers should not be exposed to damage by successive running of remaining tubing strings.

2. Positive pack-off elements or seals should be provided.

3. Design should allow passage of gas-lift valves if needed.

4. Center lines should be provided to suspend tubing in the casing without spreading at the top.

5. The hanger should be constructed to accommodate positive seating of back-pressure valves which do not require an oversize vertical run.

6. The hanger should be constructed for accurate, dependable pressure testing after tubing strings have been landed and sealed.

Multiple-completion Christmas-tree Assembly

The Christmas-tree assembly for a multiple-parallel-string wellhead includes all fittings above the tubing-head top flange.

Threaded, welded, independently flanged, and integrally flanged Christmas-tree assemblies are available for the installation of multiple tubing strings of $1\frac{1}{4}$-, $1\frac{3}{4}$-, $2\frac{3}{8}$-, $2\frac{7}{8}$-, 3-, and 4-in. sizes.

Threaded, welded, and independently flanged assemblies are furnished in working pressures of 2,000 and 3,000 psi, although threaded assemblies are rarely recommended for 3,000-psi applications. Welded assemblies are recommended for 3,000-psi service only on noncorrosive applications when pressures are expected to decline rapidly and economy is of great importance.

Integrally flanged assemblies are available in 2,000-, 3,000-, 5,000-, and 10,000-psi working pressures. These assemblies are preferred on severe or corrosive 2,000- and 3,000-psi service, and recommended for 5,000- and 10,000-psi applications.

15,000-psi-working-pressure Wellhead Equipment[1]

Casing heads and casing hangers on 15,000-psi-working-pressure wellhead assemblies are identical to those used on lower-working-pressure API equipment because pressures normally found at surface and intermediate string depths are well within standard API specifications. However, the tubing-head and Christmas-tree assemblies are different in that a different concept in design was used.

When well pressures approaching and exceeding 10,000 psi were found, manufacturers realized that flanges designed according to current code specifications would be impractical because of tremendous metal thicknesses and flange diameters.

Rather than wait for each manufacturer to develop a special design, the Standardization Committee of the Association of Wellhead Equipment Manufacturers (AWHEM) developed specifications for 15,000-psi-working-pressure ring-joint flange connections (Tables 3-9 and 3-10).

By increasing the strength of materials used, allowing greater permissible stresses, and using a different ring-gasket sealing method, the new specifications provide safe flanged connections which are smaller than API 10,000-psi-working-pressure flanges.

These AWHEM flanges were adopted by the API in 1957 and incorporated in the API Standard 6BX, Specification for Ring Joint Flanges for Drilling and Production Service for Extreme Pressures, 2d ed., December, 1958. This specification also includes three large 10,000-psi WOG (water, oil, or gas) flanges with 9-, 11-, and $13\frac{5}{8}$-in. bores.

Using the new 15,000-psi WOG connection in constructing a 15,000-psi-working-pressure wellhead, standard API flanges are used up through the top flange on the last intermediate casing head. A double-studded adapter with a 5,000-psi flange on bottom and a 15,000-psi WOG flange on top can then be used to convert to 15,000-psi working pressure. The double-studded adapter flange can be sealed against the casing with plastic-injected seals.

When specifying valves and other 15,000-psi wellhead connections, the actual through-bore must be given. For example, a $2\frac{1}{16}$-in. 15,000-psi-working-pressure valve would have a $2\frac{1}{16}$-in. bore and a $2\frac{1}{16}$-in. 15,000-psi WOG flange.

Flange and through-bore dimensions for API 15,000-psi-working-pressure flanges are given in Table 3-9. Ring-gasket specifications are given in Table 3-10.

Table 3-9. Flange Data*†

Standard API Flanges

10,000-psi- and 15,000-psi-maximum-working-pressure Flanges (API Standard 6BX)

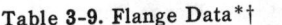

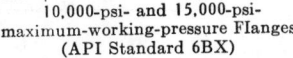

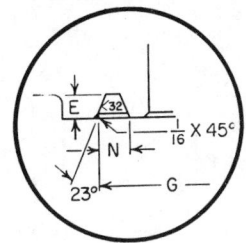

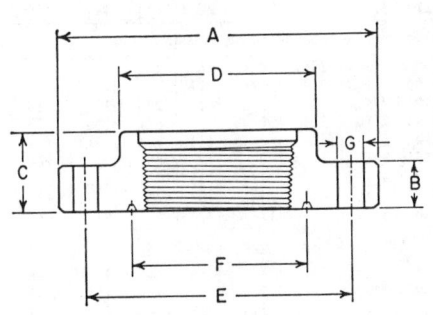

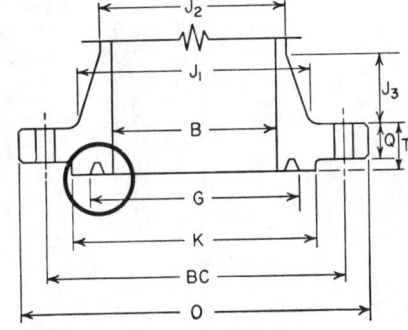

API Sizes and Specifications

Nominal size, in.	Studs with nuts			API ring No.	Flange							Approx wt., lb
	No.	Size	Approx wt., lb /set		A	B	C	D	E	F	G	
API 960 lb—1,440-psi test pressure, 960-psi working pressure												
2	8	5/8 × 4 3/4	4.4	R23	6 1/2	1 5/16	1 3/4	3 5/16	5	3 1/4	3/4	9
2 1/2	8	3/4 × 5 1/4	7.3	R26	7 1/2	1 7/16	1 15/16	3 15/16	5 7/8	4	7/8	13
3	8	3/4 × 5 1/2	7.5	R31	8 1/4	1 9/16	2 1/8	4 5/8	6 5/8	4 7/8	7/8	16
4	8	7/8 × 6	11.1	R37	10	1 11/16	2 5/16	5 3/4	7 7/8	5 7/8	1	26
5	8	7/8 × 6 1/4	11.4	R41	11	1 13/16	2 7/16	7	9 1/4	7 1/8	1	31
6	12	7/8 × 6 1/2	18.8	R45	12 1/2	1 15/16	2 9/16	8 1/8	10 5/8	8 5/16	1	44
8	12	1 × 7 3/8	26.5	R49	15	2 3/16	3	10 1/4	13	10 5/8	1 1/8	67
10	16	1 1/8 × 8 1/8	49.7	R53	17 1/2	2 7/16	3 3/16	12 5/8	15 1/4	12 3/4	1 1/4	91
12	16	1 1/4 × 9	70.9	R57	20 1/2	2 9/16	3 7/16	14 3/4	17 3/4	15	1 3/8	129
API 2,000 lb—4,000-psi test pressure, 2,000-psi working pressure												
2	8	5/8 × 4 3/4	4.4	R23	6 1/2	1 5/16	1 3/4	3 5/16	5	3 1/4	3/4	9
2 1/2	8	3/4 × 5 1/4	7.3	R26	7 1/2	1 7/16	1 15/16	3 15/16	5 7/8	4	7/8	13
3	8	3/4 × 5 1/2	7.5	R31	8 1/4	1 9/16	2 1/8	4 5/8	6 5/8	4 7/8	7/8	16
4	8	7/8 × 6 1/4	11.4	R37	10 3/4	1 13/16	2 7/16	6	8 1/2	5 7/8	1	37
5	8	1 × 7 1/8	17.3	R41	13	2 1/16	2 11/16	7 7/16	10 1/2	7 1/8	1 1/8	63
6	12	1 × 7 3/8	28.3	R45	14	2 3/16	2 15/16	8 3/4	11 1/2	8 5/16	1 1/8	80
8	12	1 1/8 × 8 3/8	38	R49	16 1/2	2 1/2	3 5/16	10 3/4	13 3/4	10 5/8	1 1/4	115
10	16	1 1/4 × 9 1/4	72.2	R53	20	2 13/16	3 11/16	13 1/2	17	12 3/4	1 3/8	177
12	20	1 1/4 × 9 1/2	90.2	R57	22	2 15/16	3 15/16	15 3/4	19 1/4	15	1 3/8	215
16	20	1 1/2 × 10 3/4	155.4	R65	27	3 5/16	4 1/2	19 1/2	23 3/4	18 1/2	1 5/8	366
20	24	1 5/8 × 12 1/4	210.0	R73	32	3 7/8	5 3/8	24	28 1/2	23	1 3/4	612

Table 3-9. Flange Data*† (*Continued*)

Nominal size, in.	Studs with nuts							Flange				
	No.	Size	Approx wt., lb /set	API ring No.	*A*	*B*	*C*	*D*	*E*	*F*	*G*	Approx wt., lb
API 3,000 lb—6,000-psi test pressure, 3,000-psi working pressure												
2	8	7/8 × 6 1/4	11.4	R24	8 1/2	1 13/16	2 9/16	4 1/8	6 1/2	3 3/4	1	25
2 1/2	8	1 × 6 7/8	16.9	R27	9 5/8	1 15/16	1 13/16	4 7/8	7 1/2	4 1/4	1 1/8	36
3	8	7/8 × 6 1/4	11.4	R31	9 1/2	1 13/16	2 7/16	5	7 1/2	4 7/8	1	31
4	8	1 1/8 × 7 3/8	23.4	R37	11 1/2	2 1/16	3 1/16	6 1/4	9 1/4	5 7/8	1 1/4	53
5	8	1 1/4 × 8 1/4	33.5	R41	13 3/4	2 5/16	3 7/16	7 1/2	11	7 1/8	1 3/8	83
6	12	1 1/8 × 8 3/8	39.2	R45	15	2 1/2	3 11/16	9 1/4	12 1/2	8 5/16	1 1/4	108
8	12	1 3/8 × 9 1/2	68.5	R49	18 1/2	2 13/16	4 5/16	11 3/4	15 1/2	10 5/8	1 1/2	172
10	16	1 3/8 × 10	94.5	R53	21 1/2	3 1/16	4 9/16	14 1/2	18 1/2	12 3/4	1 1/2	245
12	20	1 3/8 × 10 3/4	124.1	R57	24	3 7/16	4 15/16	16 1/2	21	15	1 1/2	326
16	20	1 5/8 × 12 1/4	175.0	R66	27 3/4	3 5/16	5 11/16	20	24 1/4	18 1/2	1 3/4	459
API 5,000 lb—10,000-psi test pressure, 5,000-psi working pressure												
2	8	7/8 × 6 1/4	11.4	R24	8 1/2	1 13/16	2 9/16	4 1/8	6 1/2	3 3/4	1	25
2 1/2	8	1 × 6 7/8	16.9	R27	9 5/8	1 15/16	2 13/16	4 7/8	7 1/2	4 1/4	1 1/8	36
3	8	1 1/8 × 7 5/8	23.9	R35	10 1/2	2 3/16	3 3/16	5 1/4	8	5 3/8	1 1/4	48
4	8	1 1/4 × 8 1/2	34.1	R39	12 1/4	2 7/16	3 7/8	6 3/8	9 1/2	6 3/8	1 3/8	73
5	8	1 1/2 × 10 1/2	60.2	R44	14 3/4	3 3/16	4 7/16	7 3/4	11 1/2	7 5/8	1 5/8	132
6	12	1 3/8 × 11 1/4	74.5	R46	15 1/2	3 5/8	5 1/16	9	12 1/2	8 5/16	1 1/2	164
8	12	1 5/8 × 12 1/2	123.9	R50	19	4 1/16	6 1/16	11 1/2	15 1/2	10 5/8	1 3/4	258
10	12	1 7/8 × 14 3/8	186.3	R54	23	4 11/16	6 11/16	14 1/2	19	12 3/4	2	436
12	16	2 × 15 3/4	320.5	R58	26 1/2	5 7/16	7 11/16	17 3/4	22 1/2	15	2 1/8	667
API 10,000 lb—15,000-psi test pressure, 10,000-psi working pressure												
2	8	7/8 × 7 1/4	12.5	R85	7 3/4	2 3/8	4 3/4	2 3/8	5 3/4	3 1/8	1	28
2 1/2	8	1 × 8 3/8	19.2	R86	8 7/8	2 3/4	5 1/16	2 7/8	6 5/8	3 9/16	1 1/8	45
3	8	1 1/8 × 9 1/4	26.9	R87	10	3 1/16	5 11/16	3 1/2	7 1/2	3 15/16	1 1/4	57
3 1/2	8	1 1/4 × 10 1/4	34.0	R89	11 1/2	3 3/8	5 1/2	4	8 1/2	4 1/2	1 3/8	100
4	8	1 3/8 × 11	50.4	R88	12 1/2	3 5/8	6 1/4	4 1/2	9 1/2	4 7/8	1 1/2	104
10	12	2 × 17	219.0	R91	20 3/4	5 11/16	11	10 3/4	16 3/4	10 1/4	2 1/8	600

15,000-psi-maximum-working-pressure Sizes and Specifications
API Standard 6BX

Nominal size and bore *B*	Studs with nuts			*O*	*T*	*Q*	J_1	J_2	J_3	*BC*	*K*	*G*	*N*	*E*
	No.	Size	Approx wt.											
1 11/16	8	3/4 × 5 3/4	7.8	7 5/8	1 3/4	1 1/2	3 11/16	2 11/16	1 7/8	6	3 13/16	2.893	0.450	7/32
1 13/16	8	7/8 × 5 3/4	11.1	8 3/16	1 25/32	1 9/16	3 27/32	2 13/16	1 7/8	6 5/16	4 3/16	3.062	0.466	7/32
2 1/16	8	7/8 × 6 1/4	11.4	8 3/4	2	1 3/4	4 3/8	3 1/4	2 1/8	6 7/8	4 1/2	3.395	0.498	15/64
2 9/16	8	1 × 7	17.1	10	2 1/4	2	5 1/16	3 15/16	2 1/4	7 7/8	5 1/4	4.046	0.554	17/64
3 1/16	8	1 1/8 × 8	49.6	11 5/16	2 17/32	2 1/4	6 1/16	4 13/16	2 1/2	9 1/16	6 1/16	4.685	0.606	19/64
7 1/16	16	1 1/2 × 13	188.0	19 7/8	4 11/16	4 1/4	12 13/16	10 7/8	3 5/8	16 7/8	12	9.521	0.921	17/16

10,000-psi-maximum-working-pressure Sizes and Specifications
API Standard 6BX

Nominal size and bore *B*	Studs with nuts			*O*	*T*	*Q*	J_1	J_2	J_3	*BC*	*K*	*G*	*N*	*E*	Ring No.
	No.	Size	Approx wt.												
9	16	1 1/2 × 13	93	21 3/4	4 7/8	4 3/8	14 3/4	12 7/8	3 11/16	18 3/4	14 1/8	11.774	1.039	1/2	0.157
11	16	1 3/4 × 15	182	25 3/4	5 9/16	5	17 3/4	15 3/4	4 1/16	22 1/4	16 7/8	14.064	1.149	9/16	0.158
13 5/8	20	1 7/8 × 17 1/4	219	30 1/4	6 5/8	6	21 3/4	19 1/2	4 1/2	26 1/2	20 3/8	17.033	1.279	5/8	0.159

* Reproduced by permission from Robert Eichenberg, Design Consideration for AWHEM 15,000 psi Flanges, ASME Paper 57-PET-23, Sept. 22, 1957.

† All dimensions in inches.

NON-API WELLHEAD EQUIPMENT

Non-API wellhead equipment, as covered in this discussion, includes the threaded independent wellhead assemblies of 2,000-psi working pressure and lower, used on shallow flowing or pumping wells. A typical arrangement of this equipment is shown in Fig. 3-2.

Lowermost Casing Heads

Lower casing heads are furnished with a lower thread, like API casing heads, which is threaded onto the surface pipe. Usually the top of the casing head is equipped with an external thread to receive a threaded cap used to compress the packing to

Table 3-10. Ring-joint Gasket Dimensions*†
Standard API Ring Gaskets

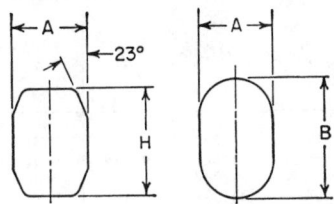

Standard Ring Gaskets
(Also Available in Stainless Steel)

API and ASA ring No.	Nominal size of flange	Flange series	Working pressure, psi	Pitch diam of groove	Width of ring A	Height of ring Oval B	Height of ring Octagonal H	Approx wt., lb
R-23	2	960, 2000	960, 2,000	3¼	7/16	1 1/16	5/8	0.8
R-24	2	3000, 5000	3,000, 5,000	3¾	7/16	1 1/16	5/8	1
R-85	2	10000	10,000	3⅛	½	....	1 1/16	0.8
R-26	2½	960, 2000	960, 2,000	4	7/16	1 1/16	5/8	1
R-27	2½	3000, 5000	3,000, 5,000	4¼	7/16	1 1/16	5/8	1.1
R-86	2½	10000	10,000	3 9/16	5/8	....	1 3/16	1.3
R-31	3	960, 2000, 3000	960, 2,000, 3,000	4⅞	7/16	1 1/16	5/8	1.3
R-35	3	5000	5,000	5⅜	7/16	1 1/16	5/8	1.3
R-87	3	10000	10,000	3 15/16	5/8	....	1 3/16	1.5
R-89	3½	10000	10,000	4½	¾	....	1 5/16	2
R-37	4	960, 2000, 3000	960, 2,000, 3,000	5⅞	7/16	1 1/16	5/8	1.5
R-39	4	5000	5,000	6⅜	7/16	1 1/16	5/8	1.6
R-88	4	10000	10,000	4⅞	¾	....	1 5/16	2.5
R-45	6	960, 2000, 3000	960, 2,000, 3,000	8 5/16	7/16	1 1/16	5/8	2
R-46	6	5000	5,000	8 5/16	½	¾	1 1/16	2.5
R-49	8	960, 2000, 3000	960, 2,000, 3,000	10⅝	7/16	1 1/16	5/8	2.5
R-50	8	5000	5,000	10⅝	5/8	7/8	1 3/16	4.5
R-53	10	960, 2000, 3000	960, 2,000, 3,000	12¾	7/16	1 1/16	5/8	3
R-54	10	5000	5,000	12¾	5/8	7/8	1 3/16	5.4
R-91	10	10000	10,000	10¼	1¼	....	1½	14.8
R-57	12	960, 2000, 3000	960, 2,000, 3,000	15	7/16	1 1/16	5/8	3.6
R-65	16	960, 2000	960, 2,000	18½	7/16	1 1/16	5/8	4.4
R-66	16	3000	3,000	18½	5/8	7/8	1 3/16	4.8
R-69	18	960, 2000	960, 2,000	21	7/16	1 1/16	5/8	5
R-70	18	3000	3,000	21	¾	1	1 5/16	11.6
R-73	20	960, 2000	960, 2,000	23	½	¾	1 1/16	6.5

* Reproduced by permission from Robert Eichenberg, Design Consideration for AWHEM 15,000 psi Flanges, ASME Paper 57-PET-23, Sept. 22, 1957.
† All dimensions in inches.

Table 3-10. Ring-joint Gasket Dimensions*† (*Continued*)
15,000-psi-maximum-working-pressure Ring Gaskets
API Standard 6BX

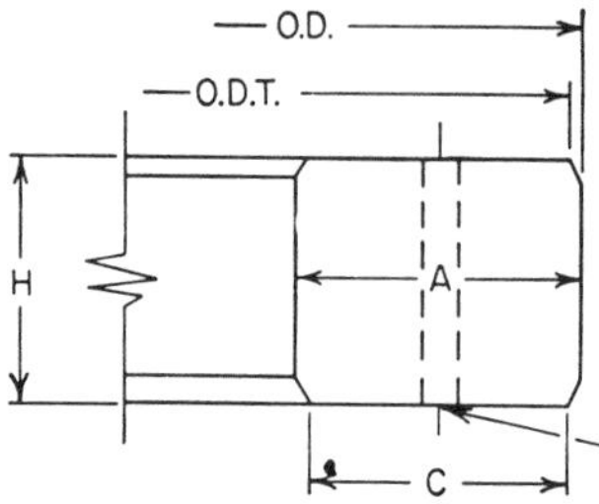
O.D.
O.D.T.
H
A
C
ONE PRESSURE EQUALIZING HOLE REQUIRED ON CENTER LINE

Ring No.	Size and bore of flange *B*	Working pressure	OD	Height *H*	Width *A*	Face diam *ODT*	Face width *C*	Hole size
BX-150	1 11/16	15,000 psi	2.842	0.366	0.366	2.790	0.314	1/16
BX-151	1 13/16	WOG working	3.008	0.379	0.379	2.954	0.325	1/16
BX-152	2 1/16	Pressure	3.334	0.403	0.403	3.277	0.346	1/16
BX-153	2 9/16	22,500 psi	3.974	0.448	0.448	3.910	0.385	1/16
BX-154	3 1/16	WOG test	4.600	0.488	0.488	4.531	0.419	1/16
BX-156	7 1/16	Pressure	9.367	0.733	0.733	9.263	0.629	1/16

10,000-psi-maximum-working-pressure Ring Gaskets
API Standard 6BX

Ring No.	Nominal size	OD	Height	Width	Face diam	Face width	Hole size
BX-157	9	11.593	0.826	0.826	11.476	0.709	1/8
BX-158	11	13.860	0.911	0.911	13.731	0.782	1/8
BX-159	13 5/8	16.800	1.012	1.012	16.567	0.869	1/8

make a seal and hold the slips down. The top thread can also be used to support a companion flange with an API ring groove and boltholes for attaching standard blowout preventers.

Casing Hanger

The casing-hanger slip segments are wrap-around type with a lower capacity than API casing hangers. Maximum capacity is usually about 15,000 lb of casing weight. The slips can be dropped through the blowout preventers to support the casing, but the seal must be placed around the suspended casing after the cutoff has been made.

Intermediate Casing Heads

Intermediate casing heads in this class are identical in design to lower casing heads. If an intermediate casing string is used, it is usually suspended in the lower casing head with a thread positioned just above the lower casing head to permit easy installation of the intermediate casing head. If proper spacing is impractical, the intermediate casing may be cut off a few inches above the lower casing head and a socket-type nipple, with a top thread, welded to the intermediate casing. Then the intermediate casing head can be attached to the thread.

Tubing Heads

A tubing head threads onto the top thread of the production string to support and seal the tubing string. The tubing may be supported with a set of slips and sealed with a sealing element compressed with a cap screwed down on top of the tubing head. Maximum capacity of the slip-type tubing hanger is about 125,000 lb of tubing weight.

A mandrel or doughnut tubing hanger may be used to support the tubing if desirable. Maximum weight-supporting capacity of this type of tubing hanger is limited only to the weight-supporting strength of the tubing head.

A blowout preventer can be attached to the tubing head with a companion flange for protection while running tubing.

A stripper rubber may also be used to strip the tubing in or out of the hole under pressure if needed. If a stripper rubber is used, it can be placed in the tubing-head bowl and a separate bowl can be attached to the tubing head to support the slip assembly or mandrel hanger.

Casing heads are available in all standard sizes with working pressures of 960 psi and lower. Tubing heads are available in working pressures of 960 and 2,000 psi. Both units are usually furnished with two 2-in. line-pipe outlets, although 3-in. outlets are available.

Christmas-tree Assembly

Christmas-tree assemblies for this type of equipment are usually very simple. If the well is expected to flow, a master valve is screwed onto the top tubing thread, a nipple and tee are screwed into the master valve, and a wing valve and choke are screwed into the tee.

If the well is expected to require immediate rod pumping, a pumping tee can be screwed directly onto the top tubing thread.

Selection

In selecting this class of equipment, the following factors should be considered:

1. Casing-head and tubing-head components should be constructed of cast steel or forged steel and should be full-opening.

2. Casing-hanger slips should be of drop-through type.

3. Caps used to hold down the suspension members and provide a seal should have hammer lugs for easy effective installation.

4. Both casing heads and tubing heads should be easily adaptable, with a full-opening adapter, to a standard blowout preventer.

FLOW-CONTROL DEVICES

Surface-control Devices

Surface Safety Valves. A surface safety valve is an automatic fail-safe valve designed to close when pressures, temperatures, or fluid levels vary above or below predetermined limits.

Typical applications of these valves are:

1. Installed between the wing valve and choke on a Christmas tree, the valve may be used to shut the well in when pressures vary above or below safe or practical limits. In the event the flow line freezes, or a valve on the flow line is closed, the surface safety valve will close and prevent damage due to full well pressure being applied to the flow line or other surface equipment. In case of a flow-line break, the surface safety valve will shut the well in because of low pressure and prevent loss of production, damage by production, and fire hazards.

The high-pressure limit is usually set about 10 per cent above normal flowing pressure. The low-pressure limit may be set 10 to 15 per cent below normal flowing pressure.

Valves for this type of service are available in several different arrangements, some of which are as follows: (1) actuated and controlled by pressure within the valve body; (2) actuated by pressure within the valve body and controlled by pressure from an external source; (3) actuated and controlled by pressure from an external source; (4) actuated by pressure from an internal source and controlled by electrical power; (5) actuated by pressure from an external source and controlled by electrical power.

2. Installed on lines at a flow-line header, the valve can be set to close in case of a flow-line break or if separator pressure or fluid level varies above or below predetermined limits.

3. Installed on the suction, discharge, and bypass on a compressor, automatic valves can be used to open the bypass, close the suction, and close the discharge lines in case pressures or temperatures become excessive.

4. Installed in any pressure system, automatic valves, controlled electrically or with pressure, may be used for remote emergency-shutdown purposes.

In general, surface safety valves are designed to close when pressures, temperatures, or fluid levels vary above or below predetermined conditions; however, valves which open under these conditions are also available.

Most surface safety valves must be opened manually after closing automatically; however, valves which can be opened automatically are available but do not include the fail-safe feature.

Sizes and Working Pressures. Surface safety valves are available in 2- through 4-in. sizes in working pressures from 125 through 10,000 psi. Larger sizes are available on special order.

Selection. In selecting a surface safety valve for a particular application, the following characteristics should be considered:

1. Flow passage may be full- or restricted-opening.

2. They may be designed to open or close in the event of control-source failure.

3. They may be designed to open or close automatically after the control source has been restored to normal.

Automatic Flow-control Devices

An automatic flow control is a device designed to act as a variable automatic choke to maintain greater fluid loads in the tubing. On some low-pressure wells, it is useful in controlling surges, improving gas-oil ratios, and reducing the tendency of the well to load with fluid and die.

The device is so constructed that normal flow passes through a fixed orifice. When the well loads and the tubing pressure drop, a spring- or pressure-actuated valve opens a larger flow area to assist in unloading the fluid.

Installed on a well susceptible to loading and dying when shut in, the automatic flow control may be used to flow the well continuously at low rates and unload fluid automatically. This application often eliminates the need for shutting a well in and allowing it to die after producing the allowable.

In selecting the proper fixed orifice size for this application, a bean size which will load the well must be used. This causes the reduction in tubing pressure necessary to cause the larger valve to open and unload the tubing. The distance the larger valve moves off the seat must be adjusted for the particular well to provide the desired results.

A valve of this type may also be used on pumping wells susceptible to surges to control surges and improve gas-oil ratios.

Automatic flow-control valves are normally furnished in 2-in. sizes with a body working pressure of 3,000 psi. Other sizes are available on special order.

Subsurface Control Devices.[2]   Subsurface Safety Valves

A subsurface safety valve is a full-opening safety device for installation in the tubing string below the surface.

The purpose of this type of safety valve is to shut off flow through the tubing should surface pressures vary above or below predetermined limits because of surface-equipment damage, a flow-line break, or excessive flow-line pressure. The valve may also be closed manually with a surface control.

The device consists of a tubular housing, made up as a part of the tubing string, which contains a spring-operated, pressure-controlled, rotating ball-type valve.

Control pressure is directed to the safety-valve assembly through a 1/8-in. tube, attached to the production tubing, from a surface-control manifold.

These valves are available in full-opening sizes for 2½- and 3-in. tubing in 5½- and 7-in. casing, respectively.

Removable Tubing Safety Valve (Storm Choke)

A tubing safety valve, or storm choke, is a device installed in the tubing string, below the surface, to shut the well in when flow reaches a predetermined rate.

Primarily used on offshore, bay, or townsite locations, the tubing safety valve acts as a safety shut-off in case the Christmas tree or control valves are damaged.

The valve can be seated in a pump-seating nipple, a special landing nipple, or on slips. It can be installed and retrieved with wire-line tools.

With the slip-suspension type, the valve can be set at any point in the tubing string without prior installation of a seating nipple; however, the slip suspension is not recommended for pressure differentials in excess of 1,500 psi. Suspension in a seating nipple is more positive and dependable.

The valve is operated by pressure differential and is composed of a spring-loaded sleeve-type valve with an attached flow bean. The valve is held in an open position by the spring until the force of the pressure differential, caused by a high flow rate, exceeds the preset force of the compressed spring.

Closure of the valve at different flow rates may be adjusted by varying the size of the flow bean and adjusting the spring compression.

The valve should be adjusted to remain open when the well is producing at a maximum desired rate. A flow rate above this predetermined maximum will cause the valve to close.

After the valve has closed because of excessive flow rates, it can be opened by equalizing pressure across it. If pressure to equalize the valve is not readily available, wire-line tools may be used to open an equalizing valve located in the assembly which allows pressures to equalize across the tool.

Tubing safety valves are available in 1¼-, 1½-, 1¾-, 2-, 2½-, and 3-in. nominal tubing sizes.

When ordering a tubing safety valve, the following data should be given:

1. Tubing size
2. Setting depth (or depth to landing nipple) at which tool is to be landed
3. Rate of oil and/or gas flow, maximum desired
4. Flowing pressure at maximum desired rate
5. Flow rate at which the valve should close
6. Gas-oil-water ratios
7. Specific gravity of produced fluids
8. Bottom-hole temperature

Removable Tubing Input Safety Valve

The removable input tubing safety valve is designed for installation in injection wells to plug the tubing automatically to prevent reversal of flow in case surface connections or input pressures fail.

This type of safety valve is designed similar to the removable tubing safety valve and installed and suspended the same way. It is available in 2-, 2½-, 3-, and 3½-in. sizes.

When ordering a removable input safety valve, the same data are required as previously described for ordering a removable tubing safety valve or storm choke, except that flow rates will become injection rates in this instance.

Removable Bottom-hole Choke

A removable bottom-hole choke is, as the name implies, a removable choke designed for installation in the bore of the tubing below the surface.

The choke assembly can be landed in a pump-seating nipple, a special landing nipple, or on slips, and can be installed or retrieved with wire-line tools.

Installation with a slip suspension is not recommended for pressure differentials in excess of 1,750 psi. For greater differentials, a special landing nipple or pump-seating nipple should be used.

The purpose of a bottom-hole choke is as follows:

1. To reduce the surface pressure and the attendant temperature drop caused by large pressure reductions through the surface choke, thereby reducing the tendency for freezing in the tubing and surface controls.

By placing the choke sufficiently low in the tubing, formation temperature can be used to reduce freezing resulting from the temperature drop caused by the pressure drop across the choke.

In cases where it is necessary to take a large pressure drop across the bottom-hole choke, which lowers the temperature far below the hydrate point, it may be necessary to install more than one choke. By reducing the pressure in stages, the formation temperature can often add sufficient heat to each stage to prevent freezing.

2. The flowing life of a well may be increased by breaking gas out of solution at the bottom of the hole to lighten the oil column and increase the flowing velocity of the fluids in the tubing.

3. To maintain a more constant bottom-hole pressure which can retard water encroachment by tending to hold a consistent water-oil contact.

4. To cause a fluid seal and reduce the flow of free gas into the wellbore, thus reducing the gas-oil ratio.

Bottom-hole chokes are available in 1½-, 2-, 2½-, and 3-in. sizes. When ordering a bottom-hole choke, the following data should be furnished:

1. Tubing size
2. Well depth
3. Volume of oil, water, and/or gas flow
4. Bottom-hole flowing pressure
5. Desired pressure reduction across choke

Removable Bottom-hole Regulator

A removable bottom-hole regulator is a device installed in the tubing string, below the surface, to act as a choke and maintain a constant pressure differential low in the tubing string. It is primarily designed to prevent freezing in the tubing by the same means as previously described in the discussion on removable bottom-hole chokes.

The bottom-hole regulator differs from the bottom-hole choke in that the bottom-hole regulator maintains a constant pressure drop across the regulator assembly regardless of the surface pressure.

By maintaining a constant pressure differential at a low level in the tubing, tubing pressure can often be maintained at a pressure sufficiently low to prevent the formation of hydrates when the well is shut in. Surface choke adjustments automatically change the rate of flow through the regulator.

Before the regulator is installed, the valve mechanism is set to give the desired pressure differential. The setting may be changed by adjusting compression in the spring.

Pressure differentials up to 1,500 psi may be maintained across the regulator assembly. Greater pressure differentials may be maintained by the use of more than one regulator assembly. This may be accomplished by placing two regulator body assemblies in tandem and using only one landing and locking mechanism, or by placing the regulators on separate landing and locking mechanisms. The latter course may be necessary where the temperature, pressure, and fluid contents of the tubing limit the differential pressures available because of the hydrate formation conditions.

A bottom-hole regulator m:.y be landed in a special landing nipple, a pump-seating nipple, or on slips. It can be installed and retrieved with wire-line tools.

Removable bottom-hole regulators are available in 1½-, 2-, and 3-in. sizes.

When ordering a removable bottom-hole regulator, the following data must be furnished:

1. Tubing size
2. Well depth at which regulator may be placed
3. Rate of oil, water, and/or gas flow
4. Bottom-hole flowing pressure
5. Shut-in static pressure
6. Desired pressure drop across the regulator

WELLHEAD CORROSION ASPECTS[2]

Corrosion has often been defined as the destruction of a metal by reactions with its environment. The attack may be internal or external and may result from chemical or electrochemical action.

Internal attack is usually due to "sweet corrosion" caused by the presence of CO_2 and organic acids, or "sour corrosion" caused by the presence of H_2S, or a combination of the two.

External attack is usually due to "oxygen corrosion" caused by exposure to atmospheric oxygen, "electrochemical corrosion" caused by the flow of electric currents, or a combination of the two.

To control corrosion in wellhead equipment, one or more of the following methods may be employed, depending on the type of corrosion present and the economics involved:

1. Use of special corrosion-resistant alloys
2. Injection of an effective inhibitor
3. Application of effective coatings
4. Properly applied and maintained cathodic protection

Although a detailed discussion of corrosion is not the purpose of this section, it is necessary to describe briefly the various types of corrosion encountered in wellhead equipment in order to explain the various methods of control.

Internal and external corrosion are controlled differently and are discussed separately.

Internal Corrosion

Sweet Corrosion. Sweet corrosion is usually defined as corrosion occurring in oil or gas wells where no iron sulfide corrosion product or H_2S odor exists.

Corrosion of this type in gas-condensate wells is often attributed to carbon dioxide and organic acids. Although noncorrosive in the absence of moisture, when moisture is present, CO_2 dissolves and forms carbonic acid. Carbonic acid with the organic acids contributes to corrosion. The quantity of CO_2 dissolved in the corroding fluid determines the severity of corrosion.

Generally, corrosion can be expected when the partial pressure of the CO_2, at bottom-hole conditions, exceeds 30 psi.

The partial pressure of CO_2 can be easily determined by the formula

$$\text{Partial pressure} = (\text{total pressure})(\text{per cent } CO_2)$$

Wellhead Protective Methods

1. An effective inhibitor, protective coatings, or special-alloy equipment are generally required when the CO_2 partial pressure, at bottom-hole conditions, exceeds 30 psi.

2. Special-alloy equipment is generally required when the CO_2 partial pressure, at bottom-hole conditions, exceeds 100 psi.

Sour Corrosion. Sour corrosion is defined as corrosion occurring in oil or gas wells when hydrogen sulfide and the iron sulfide corrosion product are present. Iron sulfide appears as a black powder or scale.

Hydrogen sulfide, like carbon dioxide, is not corrosive in the absence of moisture. If moisture is present, the gas becomes corrosive. If CO_2 is also present, the gas is more severely corrosive.

Attack by H_2S causes the formation of iron sulfide, and the adherence of the iron sulfide to steel surfaces creates an electrolytic cell. The iron sulfide is cathodic to the steel and accelerates local corrosion. Hydrogen sulfide also causes hydrogen embrittlement by releasing hydrogen into the steel grain structure to reduce ductility and cause extreme brittleness.

Wellhead-protection Methods

1. Special-alloy equipment is generally required when pressures exceed 1,000 psi and H_2S content exceeds 1 per cent.

2. Proper injection of effective inhibitor.

3. Proper application of hydrogen sulfide impermeable coatings.

External Corrosion

Oxygen Corrosion. Oxygen corrosion is caused by the oxidation or rusting of steel due to exposure to atmospheric oxygen or a corrosive atmosphere. The severity of corrosion depends on temperature, erosion of the metal surface, property of corrosion product, surface films, and the availability and type of electrolyte. Salt water causes a very rapid increase in corrosion rate.

On offshore installations, wellhead equipment is often subjected to one or more of the following three zones of attack:

1. The underwater or submerged zone
2. The splash zone—most severe
3. The spray zone

Wellhead-protection Methods

1. Use of special-alloy equipment
2. Application of effective external protective coatings of metallic or nonmetallic materials
3. Cathodic protection of underwater zone

Electrochemical Corrosion. There are two major types of electrochemical corrosion. One type is somewhat of a reverse plating reaction caused by stray direct electric currents flowing from the steel anode to a cathode. Another type of electrochemical corrosion occurs when pipe or a wellhead is exposed to certain types of moist soil.

Bimetallic corrosion or another form of electrochemical corrosion, aggravated by use of dissimilar metals, is often called galvanic corrosion.

Wellhead-protection Methods

1. Properly applied and maintained cathodic protection
2. Application of effective external surface coatings
3. Avoiding use of dissimilar metals
4. Electrical insulation of surface lines from wellhead assembly

Application of Special-alloy Components

Proper alloys used in making corrosion-resistant wellhead components are as follows:

1. Stainless steels with 12 per cent or higher chromium content
2. Inconel
3. Monel
4. Magnetic steels with a hardness equal to or less than Rockwell C 22, for resistance to hydrogen embrittlement

Wellhead-component Arrangements

The extent to which special-alloy wellhead components are used depends on the severity of corrosion. The following arrangements, listed in order of ascending protection, are often used.

Single Completion with Packer

1. Special-alloy ring gaskets in all connections above the top tubing-head flange.
2. Special-alloy ring gaskets in all connections above the top tubing-head flange and a special-alloy master valve. All other components of standard-alloy steel.
3. Special-alloy ring gasket in all connections above the top tubing-head flange and a special-alloy Christmas-tree assembly. All other components of standard-alloy steel.

Multiple Tubing String Completion

1. Special-alloy ring gaskets in all connections above the top tubing-head flange.
2. Special-alloy tubing hanger and other parts in contact with well fluid, special-alloy ring gaskets in all connections above the top tubing-head flange, and a special alloy master valve. All other components of standard alloy.
3. Special-alloy tubing hanger and other parts in contact with well fluid, special-alloy ring gasket in all connections above the top tubing-head flange, and a special-alloy Christmas-tree assembly. All other components of standard alloy.

References

1. Eichenberg, Robert: Design Considerations for AWHEM 15,000 psi Flanges, ASME Paper 57-PET-23, Sept. 22, 1957.
2. NACE-API: *Corrosion of Oil and Gas Well Equipment*, Boyd Printing Company, Dallas, Tex., 1958.

Chapter 4

PRODUCTION PACKERS

By W. B. BLEAKLEY

Production Editor
The Oil and Gas Journal

A production packer is a down-hole tool designed to assist in the efficient production of oil and gas from a well with one or more productive horizons.

FUNCTION

A production packer is used to provide a seal between the outside of the tubing and the inside of the casing, to prevent the movement of fluids due to a pressure differential above and below the sealing point.

The packer has these requirements:

1. It should be connected to the tubing.

2. Its OD should be sufficiently less than the ID of the casing to provide clearance for running in the hole.

3. It must be designed so that when it is in the proper position, some surface control can be used to cause it to seal off the annulus between the tubing and casing.

In addition to contributing to efficient production operations, the packer relieves the casing of high well pressures. This is important because the casing, being of larger diameter than the tubing and having thinner walls, is usually more susceptible to high-pressure damage than the tubing.

Flowing-well Efficiency. A new well completed without a packer may have sufficient energy and volume to maintain steady flow through the tubing for a long period of time. Eventually, however, the reservoir energy will decline to the point where the well will not flow on a continuous basis but will begin to flow by surges, a period of no-flow followed by a flowing part of a cycle. These cycles become longer, until the well starts flowing by "heads."

"Surging" and "heading" are the normal results of declining well productivity and reduced velocity of flow through the tubing. The open annular space between the tubing and casing in a well completed without a packer acts as a surge chamber for gas that comes out of solution. The gas in the annulus must be compressed by a build-up in bottom-hole pressure before the well will "kick off." A slug of oil and gas is then produced until the pressure in the annulus has declined, and the build-up starts over again.

This cyclic operation, besides being inefficient, is detrimental to the sand face, particularly if the producing formation is incompetent. Much more sand will be produced in a well of this type than in one producing at a steady rate.

The efficiency of a surging well can frequently be increased by the installation of a packer. With the annulus sealed off, there is no surge-chamber effect, and the energy of the expanding gas is used to move the oil up the tubing.

There are many cases on record where a well, considered dead, or on the pump, has been returned to a flowing status by the installation of a packer. Since the cost of a packer on an initial installation can be fairly nominal, there is very little reason to gamble the cost of a workover to install one at a later date.

Surface Control. It was mentioned that one of the requirements of a packer is that it must be set by some surface operation. There are certain limitations regarding the methods which can be utilized to control a packer from the surface. Because the tubing is attached to the packer, it must be used in some way to bring about the setting of the packer. There are only five ways in which surface control can be transmitted to the packer through the tubing:

1. The tubing can be rotated an unlimited number of turns to the right.

2. The tubing can be safely rotated approximately one turn to the left (further rotation might act to unscrew a tubing joint).

3. The tubing can be raised upward an unlimited distance, and a strain applied within the limits of the tensile strength of the tubing and the strength of the rig equipment.

4. The tubing can be lowered and a force equal to the tubing weight imposed on the packer.

5. Pressure may be applied inside the tubing within the limits of the burst strength of the tubing. It may be necessary, with some packer models, to drop a plug or a ball to seat somewhere in the tool before pressure can be built up.

There are important exceptions to the foregoing limitations on surface control: (1) some packers are designed to be set by the detonation of an explosive, and (2) some packers require special setting tools that may incorporate features that will permit operations other than those mentioned.

Many packer applications are temporary. Packers are used during cementing, fracturing, and testing operations, but the tool is retrieved when the servicing job is completed. The packers used for this type of work are called "retrievable packers" because they are designed for easy recovery. The other major packer application is in permanent well completions. The packers used in this application are known as "permanent completion packers" and are designed to be left in the well over a long period of time Some of these are designed for eventual removal, and others are constructed of materials that will drill easily, if necessary.

Another major application of packers is in multiple completions. Packers are used to separate the production from two or more zones producing from the same well.

Applications will be covered in more detail after the various parts of packers are described.

PACKER COMPONENTS

To perform its several functions properly, a packer assembly is made up of many parts. Among these are the sealing element, the circulating valve, slips, friction springs and blocks, safety joints, and hydraulic holddown. Some of these features may not be found in certain packers because the particular application may not require them. Descriptions and functions of these various parts follow.

Sealing Element. In conventional packers, the seal is provided by a hollow rubber cylinder that is compressed longitudinally. This causes the rubber to expand laterally to come in contact with the casing. The application of sufficient force will seat the rubber tightly to prevent movement of fluids around it.

Multiple Packing Elements permit the use of rubber of different degrees of hardness. Under certain conditions, this provides a more effective pack-off with less pressure or upstrain than a single element. In a three-element packer, for example, the uppermost and lowermost elements are usually harder than the middle element. These outside elements will bear most of the abrasion while the tool is being run in the hole, and the softer middle element will not be damaged. Most of the sealing action is obtained as a result of compression of the center element.

Slips. The slips are used to support the packer against the casing while the force is applied to expand the rubber element. These are similar to the slips used to support drill pipe when making a trip in the hole, except that they are designed to work on the inside of the casing. There are usually three or more segments, having serrated surfaces, that are pressed against the casing, by a slip-and-cone arrangement. As the weight of the tubing or drill pipe is applied, the slips move outward on a cone-shaped device and dig into the casing, and downward movement is prevented. The pipe weight is then picked up by the packer assembly, and the sealing element expands. Some packers have two sets of slips, working in opposite directions so that the packer will not move up or down, regardless of the direction of applied pressure differential.

Circulating Valve. Once the sealing element is expanded, the hole below the packer is isolated from the casing annulus. This may be a disadvantage if (1) it is desired to circulate drilling mud out of the annulus; (2) it is desired to equalize pressures before unseating the packer; (3) it is desired to circulate fluids while cementing, fracturing, treating, or testing a well. For these reasons, most packers are equipped with a circulating valve (sometimes called an equalizing valve) located above the sealing element. This valve can be opened by drill pipe or tubing manipulation (rotation, pulling up, pushing down, or a combination of these operations). With the valve open, communication is established between the inside of the tubing and the casing annulus.

Friction Springs. These are similar to the springs on casing centralizers. They serve a different purpose, however. On packers, the slips are held in a closed position until the packer has been lowered to the proper position in the well. The slips are then released, usually by rotation of the tubing in a right-hand direction. Normally, the packer body would rotate at the same time, but the friction springs provide sufficient drag on the casing so that the packer does not turn as the tubing is rotated. Thus the release mechanism is actuated, and the slips are allowed to spread out against the casing. Application of tubing weight will complete the setting of the slips as described above.

Friction Blocks. These perform the same function as friction springs but are thin blocks having cylindrical surfaces that drag on the inside of the casing and prevent rotation of the packer during the slip-release operation.

Safety Joint. Packers that are used for well testing or treating are called retrievable packers. They are removed from the hole when the work is completed. If the tool becomes stuck, an expensive fishing job may be required. To facilitate removal operations, the tubing or drill pipe can be removed from the packer by backing off at the safety joint. These joints are constructed so that separation will not occur accidentally, but with proper manipulation of the drill pipe, separation will occur easily. One type, for example, requires an upward pull on the drill pipe along with right-hand rotation. This eliminates the possibility of unscrewing a tool joint in the process.

Most packers are manufactured of brass and cast-iron parts below the safety joint so that they may be drilled out if necessary.

Hydraulic Holddown. One of the functions of a packer is to isolate the well's pressure inside the tubing and relieve the casing of any internal strain. This imposes a large pressure differential across the packer in most cases. This differential is large enough, in some wells, that the packer will be forced upward in the casing. To prevent this, a hydraulic holddown, or anchor, is used below the packer.

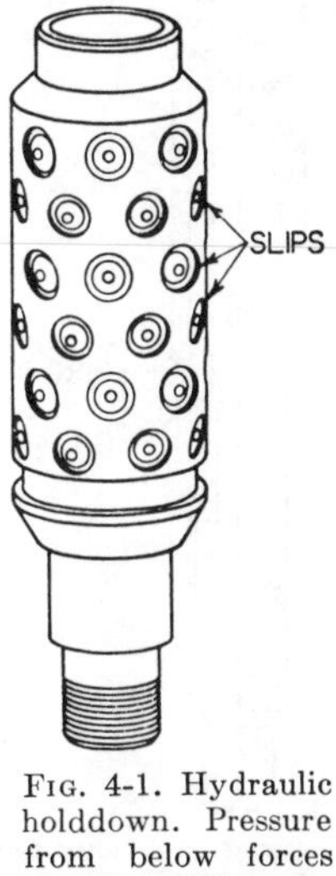

Fig. 4-1. Hydraulic holddown. Pressure from below forces the slips against the casing, preventing upward movement. (*Courtesy of The Guiberson Corp.*)

The hydraulic anchor uses the pressure differential across the tubing as a working force. As the pressure in the tubing increases, the holding action of the anchor increases. The anchor consists of a series of slips or serrated buttons on the outside of a cylindrical surface (Fig. 4-1). These slips are free to move in and out, radially, as the pressure varies. A pressure increase will cause the slips to move out and bear against the inside of the casing. Further pressure increase causes the slips to be forced more tightly against the casing, preventing upward movement of the anchor and the packer.

Opening the circulating valve on the packer will equalize the pressure across the tubing and the anchor, and the slips on the anchor will retract, permitting the packer to be moved.

PACKER TYPES

The several types of packers are:

1. Anchor packers
2. Hook-wall packers
3. Disk-wall packers
4. Tension packers
5. Permanent-completion packers
6. Hydraulic packers

These are described in detail below.

Anchor Packers. This type is expanded by the application of drill pipe or tubing weight. It is supported by the bottom of the hole. It can be set on bottom or it can be set at any place in the hole by using a piece of pipe below the packer that will reach bottom. The setting depth depends on the length of this anchor pipe.

In its usual application, the anchor packer is run on tubing to form a seal between the tubing and casing. The packer is held in its extended position by shear pins and the weight of the anchor pipe when running in the hole.

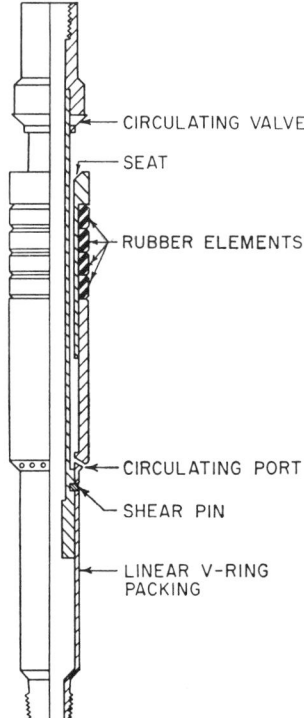

After the packer reaches the setting position, the weight of the tubing or drill pipe is allowed to bear on the packer. Since the packer is supported from below by the anchor pipe, the applied weight shears the pins and collapses the assembly, forcing the packing element outward against the casing.

An anchor packer can generally be retrieved by lifting the tubing. This extends the packer and releases the compressed rubber.

Figure 4-2 shows a typical anchor-packer arrangement with a double packing element. Many models differ from this simplified design. Some use several separate rubber cylinders. Each cylinder becomes an individual packer.

One important modification of the basic anchor packer can be released by applying fluid pressure in the tubing after dropping a special valve in the tubing. The valve seats in the inner mandrel of the compressed packer. Pressure in the tubing exerts a force on the movable mandrel, forcing it up and out of the packer rubber until the packer is fully extended.

If production comes from below the packer, as it usually does, the anchor pipe should be slotted or perforated.

Bottom-hole Packer. Because of application, the anchor packer is frequently called a bottom-hole packer. In open-hole completions, the anchor

Fig. 4-2. Anchor packer. Tubing weight shears the shear pins and collapses the packer, causing extrusion of the sealing element.

CIRCULATING VALVE

SEAT

RUBBER ELEMENTS

CIRCULATING PORT

SHEAR PIN

LINEAR V-RING PACKING

packer can be used to shut off bottom water. The packer is set in the same manner as if the tool were to be used to provide a seal between the tubing and casing, except that the inside is blanked off to prevent water from entering the well bore. Most packers used for this purpose are shorter than conventional anchor packers, and they are usually used without a tailpipe.

One of the earliest developments along this line is the lead plug for water shut-off (Fig. 4-3). It is still in use in open holes where high pressures are not anticipated. A lead plug is fitted with a steel mandrel that is driven into the plug when the tool is located at the bottom of the well. This causes the lead to expand against the wall of the well and prevent water from entering the well bore.

Hook-wall Packers. This type is more versatile than the anchor packer. After it is set in one position, it can be moved easily to another position, either above or below, and reset. The casing or tubing or both may extend below the packer.

The hook-wall packer is so constructed that hooks hold the slips in a closed position (Fig. 4-4). The hooks can be disengaged at will. Friction springs are used on hook-wall packers to aid in setting the slips. The packing element is located above the slips, usually.

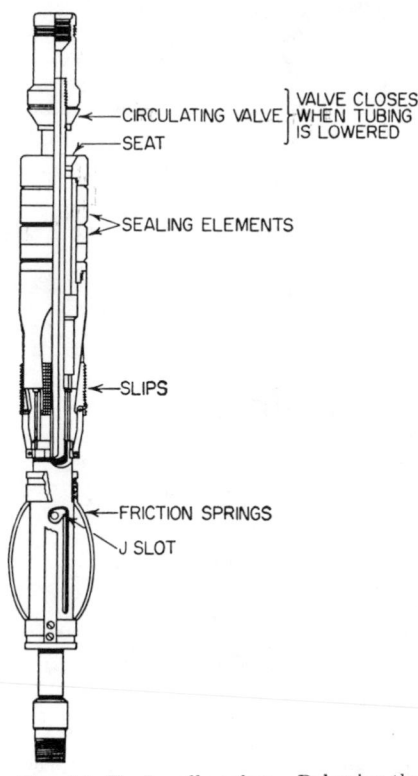

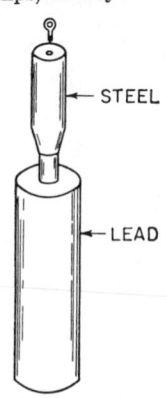

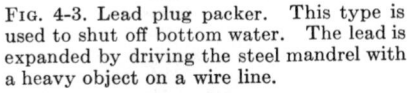

Fig. 4-3. Lead plug packer. This type is used to shut off bottom water. The lead is expanded by driving the steel mandrel with a heavy object on a wire line.

Fig. 4-4. Hook-wall packer. Releasing the J hooks permits the slips to expand against the casing. Application of tubing weight expands the sealing element. (*Courtesy of Lane-Wells Co.*)

To set the packer, it is lowered into the well to a point about 1 ft above the desired location. The tubing is then rotated enough to disengage the hooks. During this operation the friction springs prevent the slip assembly from turning. Disengaging the hooks lets the slips expand and engage the casing. Lowering the pipe seats the slips so they will support weight. Further lowering of the pipe expands the packing element, seating the packer.

After it is set, a hook-wall packer may be raised to a higher position simply by pulling it upward and reseating. To move it to a lower position, it must be raised to unseat the slips. The pipe is then rotated in a reverse direction to engage the hooks. Then the packer can be moved to a lower position and seated as before.

It is important to note that, in seating a hook-wall packer, the number of turns required, the direction of rotation, and the distance above the setting position that seating operations should begin are different for each manufacturer. His procedure and recommendations should be followed closely to ensure satisfactory results.

Disk-wall Packers. The disk-wall packer (Fig. 4-5) has a certain advantage over the hook-wall type because of the apparent ease and certainty with which it can be set. It cannot be moved so easily as the hook-wall type after it is set.

The slips in a disk-wall packer are held in the closed position by a frangible disk. The disk must be broken after the packer is in the setting position. This is usually accomplished by (1) dropping a go-devil or piece of pipe 6 or 8 in. long into the well or (2) lowering a heavy object on a wire line.

When the disk breaks, a spring forces the slips upward. They then expand about a tapered cone until they engage the casing. Lowering the pipe seats the slips and expands the packing element, just as in the hook-wall type.

The disk-wall packer may be moved readily to a higher position in the well. It cannot be moved to a lower one unless it is pulled completely out of the well and a new disk is installed.

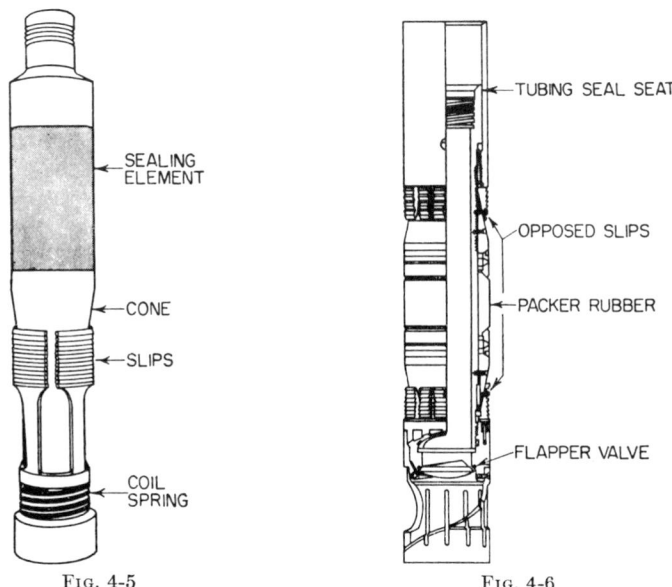

FIG. 4-5 FIG. 4-6

FIG. 4-5. Disk-wall packer. Slips expand against the casing when a frangible disk inside the packer is broken. Tubing weight is used to seat the packer. (*Courtesy of Larkin of Butler.*)

FIG. 4-6. Baker retainer production packer. Opposed slips are set by a special tool.

One manufacturer offers a combination wall and anchor packer. It includes design features of both types. The setting depth is determined by the anchor length, as in the anchor type of packer. Contact with the bottom of the hole sets the slips. These slips pick up the pipe load above the packer, causing the packing element to expand.

Once this combination type of packer is set, its ability to hold is not affected by changes in the bottom of the hole such as erosion or washing, because the anchor pipe has no other function once the slips are set. If production comes from below the packer, as in the usual case, the anchor pipe would be slotted or perforated.

Both anchor and wall packers may be used in several combinations to accomplish certain jobs. For example, an anchor packer could be set near bottom to isolate a productive zone below it while acidizing a higher zone, using a wall packer above the upper zone. There is practically no limit to the versatility of the various combinations that can be used.

Upstrain or Tension Packers. These are a modification of some of the types already mentioned. They differ only in that the packer is set by pulling up on the tubing instead of allowing the tubing weight to act downward on the packer. A few simple mechanical changes in the J-slot mechanism of a hook-wall packer plus reversal of the cone-and-slip device will provide all the elements of a tension packer. Packers of this type have one distinct advantage; they will hold higher pressures from below because the pressure merely acts to set the packer tighter.

Permanent-completion Packers. Though the ordinary wall packer may remain in place during the life of a well, it is designed for removal and relocation. But in modern production practice, large pressure differentials are met frequently. These may be exerted from above or below. Under such conditions, the usual retrievable production packer may fail to perform satisfactorily under all conditions. Thus the permanent type of production packer is becoming increasingly important. It is designed for installation in a well for the duration of the well's productive life.

The Baker retainer production packer (see Fig. 4-6) has two sets of opposing slips with a compressible packing element between, designed to provide a leakproof packer-to-casing seal. The inside surface of the packer is accurately honed so a packer-to-tubing seal can be obtained by using an accessory tubing-seal assembly. This assembly contains 20 V-type packing rings. Ten of these seal off pressure from above. The remaining 10 seal off pressure from below.

The packer body is equipped at the bottom with a flapper type of check valve opened by inserting the tubing or a perforated production tube. The valve automatically closes when the tubing is withdrawn, sealing off pressure from below (see Figs. 4-7 and 4-8).

The manufacturer claims considerable versatility for this packer because of the two opposed sets of slips and the packer-to-casing and packer-to-tubing seals. The packer permits normal production from a zone below the packer as in Fig. 4-7. With this same equipment setup, acid or cement squeeze, formation fracture, and

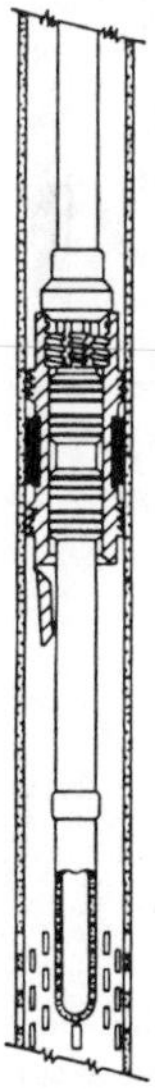

Fig. 4-7 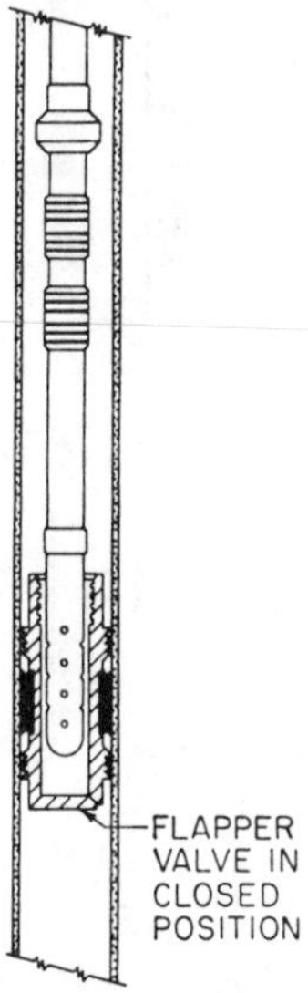   Fig. 4-8 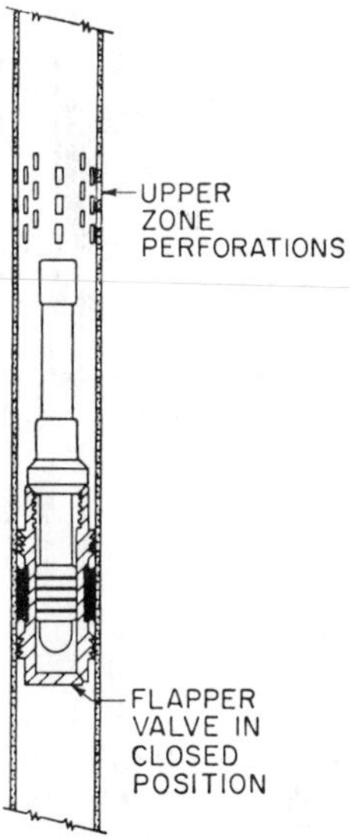   Fig. 4-9 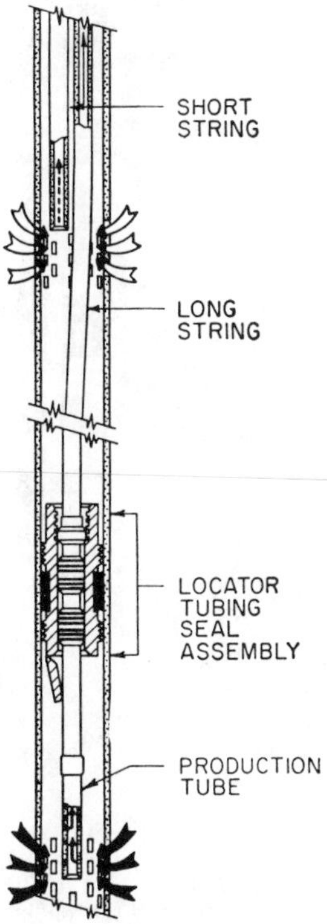   Fig. 4-10

gas or water injection can be accomplished. With the arrangement in Fig. 4-8 the zone below the packer is isolated. The tubing may then be removed without killing the well.

Using the hookup in Fig. 4-9, an upper zone may be worked over without exposing the lower zone to high mud pressure. This prevents loss of potential from the lower zone. Figure 4-10 shows the adaptability of this type of packer to a dually completed well with a parallel-string hookup. Other types of dual-zone completions using two chokes and parallel or crossover flow devices are also possible.

In the Baker tools, extrusion of the rubber packer under pressure from above or below is prevented by a combination of lead, cast-iron, and ductile-cast-iron retaining rings. These expand as the rubber packing element expands, and they provide support for the rubber element.

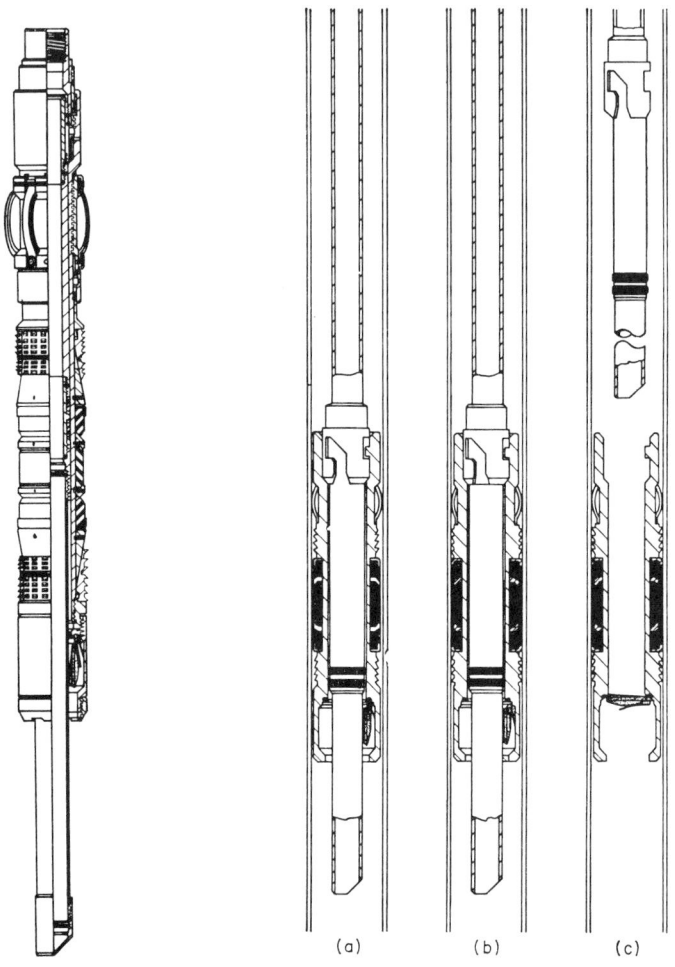

FIG. 4-11   (a)   (b)   (c)

                                  FIG. 4-12

FIG. 4-11. Halliburton type C production packer.

FIG. 4-12. Operation of the Halliburton type C packer. (*a*) Going in hole. Tubing will fill with fluid as the packer is lowered since there is no restriction in the packer. Back-pressure valve is held open to allow fluid passage in either direction. (*b*) Packer set, and fluid is being produced from the formation. (*c*) Tubing picked up until seals are clear of packer bore. Fluid can be circulated in the annulus, treating fluid can be spotted in the tubing, and other operations can be performed without disturbing the producing zone. Back-pressure valve closes automatically when tubing is pulled to shut in the formation.

Halliburton's type C production packer (Fig. 4-11) is a full-opening permanent-type drillable casing packer run in on tubing and set in the casing above the formation to be produced. It serves as a production casing packer for single- or dual-zone completions. This packer will accommodate flush-joint and coupled tubing. Operation of this packer is illustrated in Fig. 4-12.

To set the packer, the tubing is first rotated 25 turns to the right.   The drag springs prevent the packer itself from turning.   This rotation releases the slips, which are then set by pulling upward on the tubing.

Halliburton production packers use an expanding-shoe-type sealing element to provide a positive seal in the casing (Fig. 4-13).   A center packer rubber made of soft-durometer oil-resistant synthetic rubber is enclosed on each end by a cup-type shoe. Brass shear pins in the shoes stabilize the soft center packer rubber, reducing the possibility of swabbing action while running in.   End packers are high-strength hard-durometer oil-resistant synthetic rubber.   They expand out to the casing inside diameter and help prevent the soft positive-sealing center packer from flowing over the

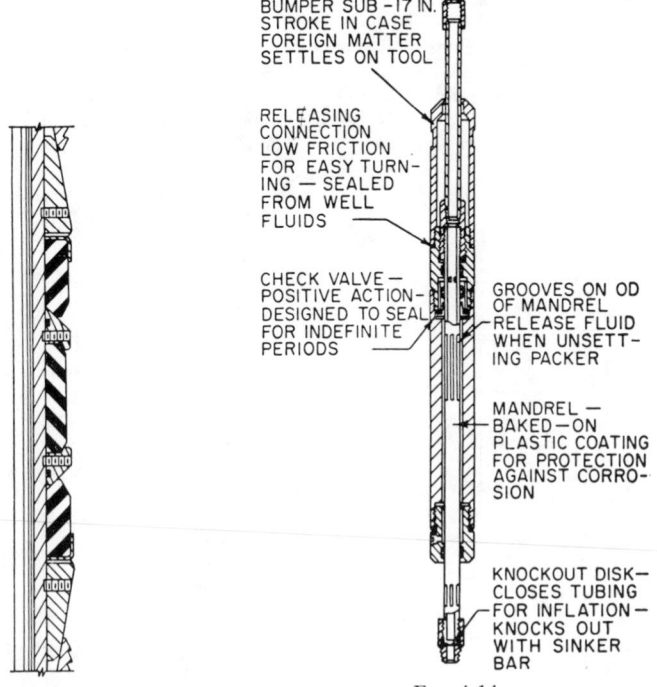

FIG. 4-13.

FIG. 4-14.

FIG. 4-13. Expanding-shoe-type sealing element to prevent extrusion of packer rubber. (*Courtesy of Halliburton Co.*)

FIG. 4-14. Elements of an inflatable packer.   (*Courtesy of Lynes, Inc.*)

shoes when subjected to extremely high pressures.   Forty-five-degree angles on the shoes cause the hard-durometer end packers to be expanded out to the casing inside diameter as the center packer is being set.   A brass cup-type shoe on each end packer expands out to the casing inside diameter.   This action forms a metallic container that helps prevent extrusion of the rubber.   The shoes also act as a shield to assist in preventing attack of corrosive fluids on the rubber sealing elements.

To summarize, the permanent-completion type of packer permits normal single-zone production, squeeze, or injection; dual completion with pressure differential operating from above or below; workover or squeeze in an upper zone; tubing removal from a well with a single zone below the packer, and many other applications in flowing or pumping wells.   If it is desired to deepen the well, or otherwise remove the packer, the packer can be easily drilled up because of the materials used and the construction design.

Inflatable Packers.   The packers described earlier are set by mechanical action. The packing element is expanded by applying weight to the packer.   A recent development of different design is the inflatable packer (Fig. 4-14). This one is set by application of hydraulic pressure to the inside of the packing element. When the element is expanded, check valves hold the fluid inside the packer under pressure, so that production operations can be carried on in the well without disturbing the inflated element.

A knockout disk is located in the bottom of the tubing so that pressure can be built up in the packer to expand the rubber element. This knockout disk can be removed with a sinker bar after the packer is set.

The packer also features a bumper sub with a 17-in. stroke so that the packer may be jarred loose in case foreign matter settles around the tool while in the hole.

The packer is released by rotating the tubing and pulling upward. This causes grooves in the mandrel to move opposite the check-valve portion of the tool, and the pressure in the inflated element is released. When the element collapses, the tool can be removed from the well.

The inflatable packer can be used in open hole or casing, except that abrasive particles are embedded in the cover to obtain anchoring friction in casing (Fig. 4-15). A hydraulic holddown is not required when the abrasive particles are used.

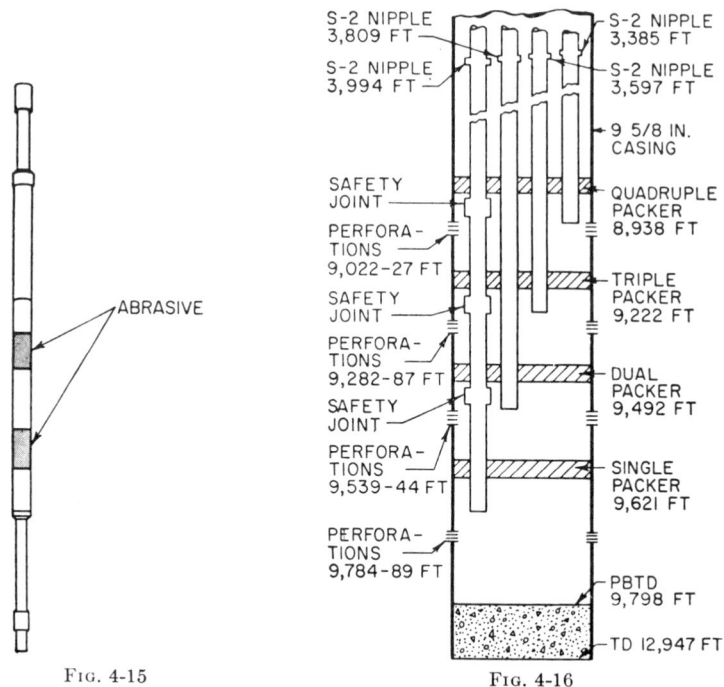

Fɪɢ. 4-15   Fɪɢ. 4-16

Fɪɢ. **4-15.** Exterior of inflatable packer showing embedded abrasive particles. These prevent packer movement under high differential pressures. (*Courtesy of Lynes, Inc.*)

Fɪɢ. **4-16.** Quadruple completion as used in a Gulf of Mexico well. Annulus was not used as a production string because this is prohibited in offshore wells.

PACKERS IN MULTIPLE COMPLETIONS

The packers discussed so far can be easily adapted to dual completions. The simplest of these, of course, is the type of completion where the production from the lower zone goes through the packer and up the tubing. Production from the upper zone then goes through the annular space between the tubing and casing. This can be altered by using a crossover device that transfers the lower-zone production to the annular space and the upper-zone production goes through the tubing.

Either of these arrangements is satisfactory over a long period of time if either one or both zones produce gas. The gas zone can then be produced through the annulus, with no lift problems involved. If, however, both zones are productive of oil, and tubing is necessary for efficient flowing, or pumping is required, then a second string of tubing is needed.

The simplest installation of this type utilizes one string of tubing set through the packer, producing from the lower zone, with a short string, hung above the packer producing from the upper zone. This arrangement is satisfactory unless it is desired to set the upper-zone tubing on a packer to relieve the casing of formation pressure, or to confine corrosive fluids to the tubing, in which case a second packer is needed.

Recent developments in packer design have led to the production of packers that may be used to produce from as many as four zones simultaneously through four parallel strings of small-diameter tubing. The first application of this technique was in a well in the Gulf of Mexico, where regulations prevent the production of oil or gas through the annulus. Four productive zones were discovered, and a four-string completion was required (Fig. 4-16).

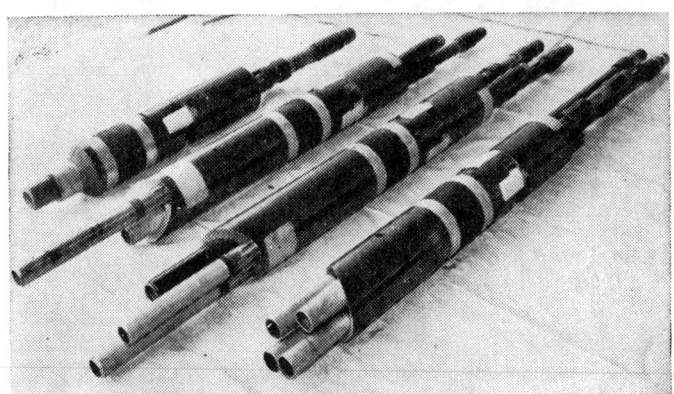

FIG. 4-17. Four packers of the type used in the first quadruple completion using four parallel strings of tubing. From left to right the packers will accommodate one, two, three, and four strings of tubing and are placed in the well in that order starting at the bottom. (*Courtesy of Brown Oil Tools, Inc.*)

The same procedure has been used in an onshore well, with three strings of tubing with the fourth zone being produced through the annulus.

The lower packer in a multiple completion must accommodate one string of tubing. The second packer from the bottom must accommodate two strings of tubing, the third three, etc.

The packers used in the offshore quadruple completion in Fig. 4-17 were of the type set by hydraulic pressure. A piston-and-cylinder arrangement under the action of a pressure differential in excess of 4,000 psi causes the pins to shear, the slips to set, and the sealing element to collapse.

Production packers were used recently in an unusual well-testing program. In some very deep wells in west Texas, the operator did not wish to use conventional drill-stem test techniques because of the exceptionally high temperatures and pressure that were encountered. To eliminate the possibility of blowouts, a production packer was set, and the zone below the packer was tested. When it was decided to abandon this zone, a cement retainer was placed in the well and a cement plug was run to the bottom of the next zone to be tested. Another production packer was located above the zone, and tests were run between the packer and the cement plug. On abandoning this zone, the procedure was repeated. As an additional safety measure, a second packer was installed, in each case a few feet above the first.

CHOOSING THE RIGHT PACKER

Deciding which packer to use is a job for an expert. The manufacturer's catalogs in most cases list well over 300 packers from which a choice must be made. A large number of these can be eliminated immediately when some of the well dimensions are specified, but there are still many other conditions that must be considered. Among these are:

1. Casing size
2. Tubing size
3. Nature of fluid in the hole
4. Setting location
5. Production mechanism: flowing, pumping, or gas lift
6. Single or multiple completion
7. Setting depth
8. Pressure and temperature to be encountered

The type of packer to be used, hook wall, disk wall, permanent completion, etc., can be decided from the packer application and the characteristics of the tools from the preceding sections. Manufacturer's engineers are usually well qualified to assist in the selection of the right tool for the right job.

INSPECT PACKERS BEFORE RUNNING

An expensive repair job can be prevented by careful inspection of a packer before it is run in the hole. Be sure to look for broken slips, loose screws, and damaged elements. Determine that the packer has the correct size of gauge rings. Be sure that all moving parts are free to move.

If full opening is required, check the packer to be sure that sufficient opening is available for perforating guns and other tools that may have to go through the packer.

Be sure the bypass valve is open or closed, as desired.

PRECAUTIONS

Running a packer under ideal conditions can be a hazardous job, and ideal conditions are rare in oil and gas wells. It is therefore necessary to take precautions to ensure a successful operation. Here are a few suggestions:

1. Inspect the packer for correct size. Casing size and weight range will be found stenciled on the packer, or stamped on the nameplate, or in some other conspicuous location.

2. Be sure the hole is free of junk and debris. Scale, salt, pieces of rubber from swab cups, and other material will prevent satisfactory seating of the packer rubber.

3. A properly selected packer will have a minimum of clearance inside the casing in the unset condition. For this reason, it is important that the casing be in good condition, free of obstructions and protrusions that might damage the sealing element. If there is any doubt, a "feeler" should be run down the casing to determine if any tight spots exist. If any obstructions are found, a casing scraper should be used to remove them. In the long run, this extra precaution will save both time and money.

Most oil strings are designed with tapered pipe; that is, the casing at the surface will be thick-walled, that near the center of the hole will have thinner walls, and that on the bottom will again be thick. This is done to overcome the various forces that are at work in the well and that will be encountered during the casing-running procedure. If a packer is chosen that will have just the right clearance at the surface, there may be too much clearance if this packer is to be set near the center of the hole. For this reason, it is a wise idea to plan ahead on the casing program and install a couple of joints of heavy-walled casing where packer setting is anticipated.

4. Check the J slot or other type of setting mechanism for right- or left-hand rotation and travel required to actuate the packer. Check for the required amount of weight or tension to set the packer.

5. Be sure the packer is right side up!

6. The packer should be run in the hole at slow or moderate speed. This is especially true if a hydraulic holddown is being used. High speed will create high pressure on the underside of the tools, and the holddown slips might be expanded prematurely. If the fluid level is not at the top of the casing, care should be taken that the rate of descent is slow when the fluid level is reached, so that there will be no impact on striking the fluid surface.

7. Avoid jerking the pipe when running the packer. Avoid sudden stops.

8. Avoid turning the tubing when running the packer unless instructions for the specific packer being run suggest turning to keep pins in the J slots.

9. If a safety joint is used, or if the packer assembly has left-hand threads that need to be unscrewed after the packer is set, be sure that these threads are not made up too tight.

HOW TO TEST PACKERS.

When a packer is set, it is evident that the packing element is expanded if the packer will support the weight of the tubing. In the case of a tension packer, the element is expanded if the tension on the line or tubing is greater than that required to lift the tools in the hole.

Seating of the packing element alone is not enough to verify that the packer will not leak, however. The packer may be tested by applying pressure to the annulus and observing any pressure decline, which will be an indication of a leak. Or pressure may be applied in the tubing if the casing has not been perforated, and a pressure decline will indicate a leak. If the tubing is put under pressure, the casing pressure can be observed also. An increase in casing pressure would mean that fluid is leaking around the packer from the tubing to the casing.

PACKER LIMITATIONS

It has been shown that the function of a hydraulic holddown device is to prevent the upward movement of a hook-wall or similar packer when exposed to high pressure from below. Here is an indication then of possible trouble that may be experienced if too much is expected of a packer installation.

At the outset, conventional packers should have opposed slips if pressure differentials are to be held from above or below. A hook-wall packer will not hold high differential pressure from below unless a holddown is used; a tension packer will not hold high differential pressure from above unless it is equipped with opposed slips; an anchor packer will not hold high differential pressure from above because of buckling of the tailpipe and will hold high differential from below only if a holddown is used.

In a high-pressure well equipped with a hook-wall packer, the differential across the packer can be reduced by loading the annulus with fluid. Depending on the completion technique, the annular space between the tubing and casing may be full of drilling fluid or oil, or it could be empty. If high differentials are anticipated, lease crude can be used to load the annulus, and the possibility of packer movement will be reduced.

Conventional packing elements cannot be expected to give satisfactory service when exposed to temperature extremes. Some wells that have been drilled have encountered temperatures in the range of 300 to 400°F. These conditions require that special packing elements be used. Unusual conditions such as high temperature should be made known to the manufacturer when the packer is ordered.

HOW MUCH WEIGHT ON THE PACKER

In setting an anchor packer or a wall-type packer, most of the weight available from the setting string is used to ensure that the packer is properly seated and that the packer rubber is expanded tightly against the casing.

The amount of weight to be left on the packer when the tubing is hooked up is another matter and introduces some rather complex considerations.

Temperature Effect. When the tubing is run, the hole will probably be full of drilling fluid that has been in place long enough to come to equilibrium temperature, with the temperature gradually increasing with depth. If the tubing is put in compression, by allowing most of the tubing weight to bear on the packer, then additional forces will be imposed on the tubing when the well is put on production. Produced fluid will be at reservoir temperature and will probably increase the average temperature of the tubing when the well is flowing. This will cause the tubing to expand or attempt to expand, and increased compressive forces will result. Because of the clearance in the annulus between the tubing and casing, the tubing will be free to "corkscrew," thus taking up part of the expansion due to increased temperature.

Suppose the well, with tubing in compression, is to be treated with a chemical, say acid, after it has been on production. The injected fluid will be at normal surface temperature, which will be considerably below the average temperature of the tubing. This will cause the tubing to contract, relieving the compressive forces, and perhaps putting the tubing in tension. The magnitude and direction of the forces will depend on the amount of weight imposed on the packer when the well was completed initially.

If the tension forces are large, a packer of the wall or anchor type will possibly be moved up the hole, under the influence of the shrinking tubing. This movement will depend on the operation of any holddown device that may be in place. When the well is again put on production, the compressive forces will be magnified because the packer will be in a higher position than previously and will not yield to downward forces.

Production from a high-pressure gas well equipped with a bottom-hole choke or other restriction will produce a cooling effect that can be of importance in determining the forces on tubing. Expansion of the gas will result in a temperature drop that will create a local cooling effect.

If a well is equipped with a tension packer, the tubing will be in tension initially, and any decrease in temperature due to injection of cold fluid will increase the amount of tension in the tubing.

It has been found that, for steel held firmly at both ends, a stress of 207 psi is produced for each degree change in temperature (H. G. Texter, Casing Strain after Cementing, *Oil and Gas Journal*, Apr. 8, 1948). The coefficient of thermal expansion for steel is 0.0000069 per degree Fahrenheit, and the modulus of elasticity is 30,000,000 psi. Then, for each degree of temperature change, the stress is

$$S = 0.0000069 \times 1 \times 30,000000 = 207 \text{ psi}$$

The force, in pounds, imposed on a packer due to temperature change can be calculated from the formula

$$F = K(T_1 - T_2)$$

where F = force produced by thermal contraction or expansion, lb
K = constant for each size tubing, lb/°F
= 270 for $2\frac{3}{8}$-in. 4.7-lb tubing
= 375 for $2\frac{7}{8}$-in. 6.5-lb tubing
= 539 for $3\frac{1}{2}$-in. 9.3-lb tubing
T_1 = average temperature of the tubing at the time packer is set, °F
T_2 = average temperature of the tubing at the time forces are determined, °F

Thus a temperature change of 50°F in a well equipped with $2\frac{3}{8}$-in. 4.7-lb tubing would produce a net force on the packer of

$$F = 270 \times 50 = 13,500 \text{ lb}$$

Temperature Changes with Permanent Completion Packers. In the permanent-completion-type packers previously described, the tubing is not fastened directly to the packer but maintains a seal through sealing rings against the smooth inside surface of the packer body. This gives the tubing another degree of freedom under the influence of temperature change.

Assuming that the tubing is installed in the well without initial loading, then a temperature drop will cause the tubing to contract, and sealing rings on the bottom part of the sealing mandrel will be pulled up into the packer body to maintain the seal. If the average tubing temperature increases, the tubing will tend to expand, and if clearance is available, the sealing rings normally above the packer will move down into the packer body to maintain the seal. If the tubing is so located that there are no sealing rings above the packer, then an increase in temperature will impose a compressive stress in the tubing.

The situation in a producing well is quite different from what the foregoing simplified description would indicate. The amount of contraction that may develop in the tubing could easily require several feet of extra sealing-ring sections to ensure that a seal is maintained at all times. At the outset this may not seem to be a difficult problem to overcome, but consider these conditions: A well is completed with a permanent-completion-type packer, with extra sealing rings. This is a high-temperature deep well. After being on production for several months or a year, some corrosion is detected, and an inhibitor squeeze job is indicated. The inhibitor, with overflush, at normal surface temperature is pumped down the tubing. The cool fluid reduces the temperature of the tubing and contraction takes place. This pulls some of the extra sealing rings into the body of the packer. But these sealing rings have been idle for a long period of time, exposed to high temperatures, and have deteriorated. They are no longer able to maintain an effective seal, and a workover may be required.

The practical answer to this problem is to impose a load on the tubing at installation by placing the tubing in compression; a temperature drop will only relieve some of the compressive load or all of it without changing the physical length of the tubing string. The question to be answered then is how much weight must be set on the packer when the tubing is installed.

Calculating the temperature effect on steel, using the coefficient of thermal expansion, is not a difficult problem if the average temperature is known. In an oil or gas well, this presents an almost impossible problem, because of:

1. The geothermal gradient
2. The fluid in the annulus, if any
3. The condition of the pipe surface, because corrosion, scale, etc., make the heat-transfer coefficients indeterminable
4. Various specific heats, if more than one fluid is involved
5. Possible variation in the flow rate in the tubing

This problem is currently under study by most manufacturers of permanent-completion-type packers, but at the time of writing, there was no workable formula available with which to solve the problem. Major oil company engineers are cooperating in an effort to arrive at a solution. The best answer so far is to follow the recommendations of the packer manufacturer, who can call on experience in estimating the amount of weight required on the tubing when it is installed.

ACKNOWLEDGMENT

The preparation of this manuscript was made possible through the courtesy of these manufacturers whose catalogs and technical literature were used as a source of information: Baker Oil Tools, Inc.; Brown Oil Tools, Inc.; Halliburton Co.; Larkin of Butler; Lane Wells; and Lynes, Inc.

Chapter 5

GAS LIFT

By C. V. KIRKPATRICK

Chairman, Division of Chemical and Petroleum Engineering
University of Houston

INTRODUCTION

Gas lift has been applied to every type of producing well. In the past, lift gas was available at little or no cost but the increasing emphasis on gas conservation and gas sales has resulted in a much closer look at lift-gas costs. Gas lift, however, has in many instances continued to maintain an economic and operating advantage over other methods of artificial lift because of its simplicity, relatively trouble-free operation, and improved equipment and design technology.

The gas lifting of liquids is accomplished in one of two ways: (1) by continuous injection of gas into the tubing string (or casing annulus) at some predetermined depth so as to lower the formation pressure and allow fluids to flow continuously from the well or (2) by the intermittent injection of gas into the well at a high instantaneous rate and for a short period of time to surface a column of fluid at regularly controlled time intervals. The former means of operation is designated as continuous flow, while the latter is referred to as intermittent flow. Continuous-flow gas lift can be satisfactorily applied to most wells having a reasonable degree of bottom-hole pressure maintenance, and a productivity index (PI) of approximately 0.5 bbl of liquid/day/psi or greater. (The PI can be as low as 0.20 bbl of liquid/day/psi if the injection gas is available at a sufficiently high pressure.) Intermittent gas lift is usually applied to wells with PIs of less than 0.50. A well with a low bottom-hole pressure (BHP) and a high PI is generally not applicable to the gas-lift operation.

It has been determined that there is a sharp increase in flowing BHP required for continuous-flow rates less than 250 B/D, while there is a decrease in the flowing BHP required for continuous-flow rates of 250 through 800 B/D. This is a general statement and is influenced somewhat by tubing size. The type of gas-lift system selected, continuous or intermittent, is governed by the volume of fluids to be produced, the available lift gas as to both volume and pressure, and the well-reservoir conditions such as the case when the high instantaneous BHP drawdown encountered with intermittent flow would cause excessive sand production or the coning of water and/or gas into the well bore.

For the proper selection, installation, and operation of gas-lift systems the operator must know the equipment and the fundamentals of gas-lift design technology. Equipment includes the main operating valves, wire-line adaptations, check valves, mandrels, surface control equipment, and compressors. Design technology involves system mechanics, valve-spacing principles, continuous-flow systems, intermittent-flow systems, and miscellaneous categories such as chamber design, closed rotative systems, and dually completed wells on gas lift.

As the understanding of gas-lift-valve operation and equipment function is paramount, this phase will be discussed first. Since the question is often raised as to why use gas-lift valves at all, it would seem appropriate to give some of the reasons at this point. There are four principal advantages to be gained by the use of valves in gas-lift systems. These are:

1. Deeper injection depths can be achieved by the use of valves for wells with fixed surface-injection-gas pressures.

2. Variation in the well's productivity can be accounted for by selective gas injection at a "higher" or "lower" valve, as the case may be.

3. Controlled gas volumes can be "metered" into the well.

4. Intermittent gas injection can be accomplished, thereby allowing the well to build up a fluid head between injections.

Gas-lift valves are used in a multiplicity of operations. They are used for unloading wells, for continuous-flow production, for intermittent-flow production, for the removal of water and condensate from gas wells, for water-supply wells in pressure-maintenance systems, for both production of water and kicking off logged-up water wells which have been "backflowed," and for the injection of chemical corrosion inhibitors.

The most significant aspect of gas-lift design technology has been the development of a technique which will allow accurate calculation of a flowing well's pressure gradient from surface production data. This technique allows the determination of the PI of a well prior to the installation of artificial lift equipment. Since continuous-flow gas lift is merely an extension of natural flow, the ability to calculate the pressure gradient will enable accurate prediction of the optimum injection depth, surface-gas-injection pressure, gas volume, and choke sizes for the gas-lift valves and the field gas system.

In the face of continuously increasing producing costs, a demand exists for improved techniques and efficiency in gas-lift operations. Close study should be given each proposed installation to ensure that the well can be satisfactorily lifted to depletion. This is principally a matter of correct design. Gas lift usually shows the clearest advantage over other artificial lift in high-capacity high-water-cut wells but can also handle the lift requirements of the other well categories.

It is well to note that the fundamentals presented in the design-technology section have applications which far exceed that of just the gas lifting of well fluids.

EQUIPMENT

Main Operating Valves

Basic Operating Principle. All gas-lift valves, regardless of make, perform in accordance with the same basic operating principle. Recognition of this basic princi-

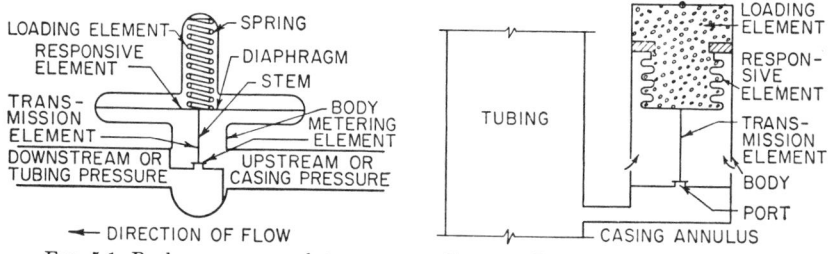

FIG. 5-1. Back-pressure regulator.   FIG. 5-2. Pressure-charged gas-lift valve.

ple should enable one to follow the mechanics of any type of gas-lift valve. The simplest comparison is with a pressure regulator. Two general headings mark the comparison: (1) component parts and (2) valve response.

1. *Component Parts*

   a. Body

   b. Loading element (gas, spring, combination gas and spring)

c. Responsive element (metal bellows, piston, rubber diaphragm)

d. Transmission element (metal rod, rubber diaphragm)

e. Metering element (orifice or port)

2. *Valve Response.* Note that the controlling pressure in both the regulator and gas-lift valve shown in Figs. 5-1 and 5-2 acts over the large responsive-element area (diaphragm for regulator, bellows for valve). If this area is large compared with the valve-port size then the tubing back-pressure effect, helping to open the valve, will be small. A larger valve port for the same bellows size (or other responsive elements) simply means more help from the tubing in opening the valve and, consequently, less pressure requirement in the casing. This principle is used in the continuous-flow-type valve, wherein a large port is used to get maximum tubing sensitivity and either a

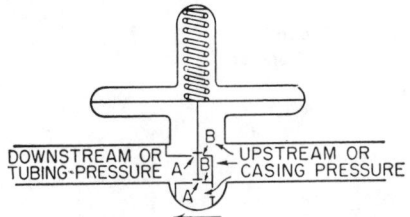

FIG. 5-3. Back-pressure balanced valve regulator.

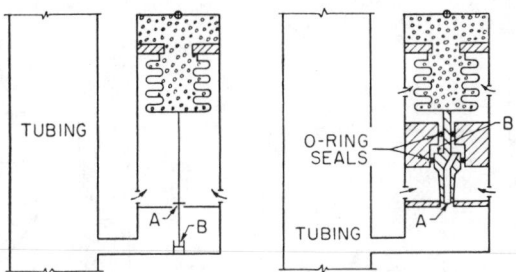

FIG. 5-4. Gas-lift valve with tubing pressure balanced.

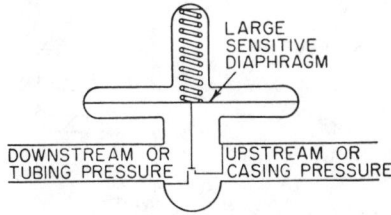

FIG. 5-5. Pressure regulator sensitive to downstream pressure.

tapered valve stem or a fixed small orifice is used to restrict the input gas. A large port may be desirable in intermitting valves for transmitting high instantaneous gas volumes into the tubing. For certain installations, the tubing-pressure effect must be "balanced" out or the valve will have an excessive spread (i.e., pass too much gas before closing off). Spread is defined as the difference between the opening and closing pressure of the valve. This "balancing" of the tubing-pressure effect is illustrated in Figs. 5-3 and 5-4.

In the tubing-sensitive valve, commonly called "fluid-operated," the tubing pressure becomes the controlling pressure. In order to achieve this result, the smaller tubing pressure is directed against the larger area of the responsive element (bellows) rather than the smaller valve-stem end. Hence, for a given constant casing pressure, the valve can be set to be opened by a predetermined tubing-head build-up. Figures 5-5 and 5-6 illustrate this type of valve.

The spring-loaded differential valve, like the "fluid-operated" valve, makes use of the tubing pressure to help open the valve. It differs, in principle, in that both the

Fig. 5-6. Principle of the fluid-operated valve.

Fig. 5-7. Spring-loaded differential-type valve.

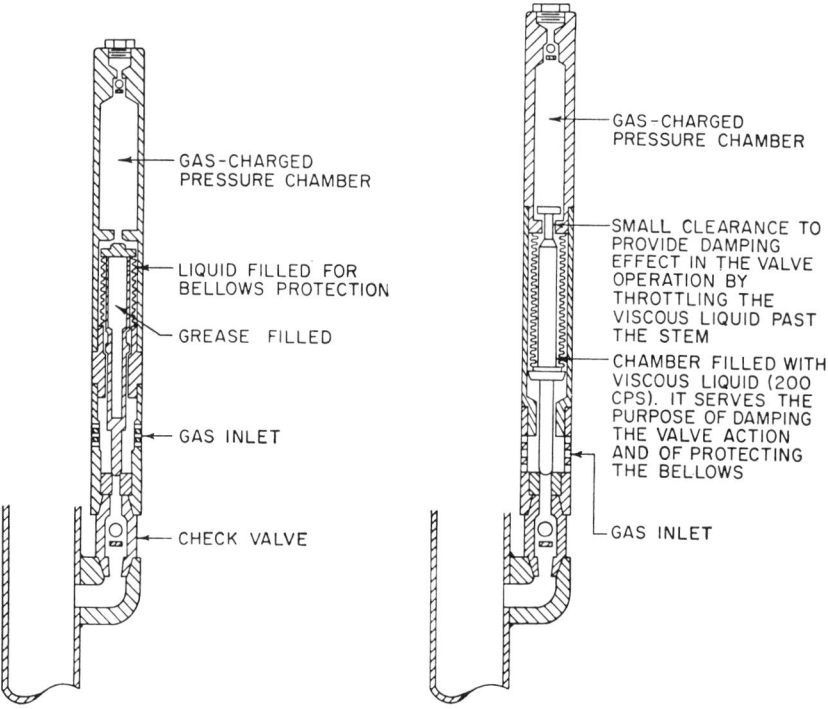

Fig. 5-8. Gas-charged bellows intermitting valve.

Fig. 5-9. Gas-charged bellows intermitting valve.

loading force (spring) and tubing force serve to open the valve. The casing pressure furnishes the only closing force (see Fig. 5-7).

Aside from certain retrievable features, the mechanics of all gas-lift valves fall into two categories:

1. Pressure-loaded (including the spring as a loading force)
2. Mechanically operated (Nixon and Acme types)

In general, with slight modifications, valves from the pressure-loaded group may be used for either continuous or intermittent flow. The single exception is the automatic continuous-flow valve, shown in Fig. 5-23, which can be used only on continuously flowing wells. Some in the mechanically operated group are restricted to continuous flow, whereas others may be used for either continuous- or intermittent-flow operations.

Valve Auxiliary Elements. It is to be noted that certain mechanical refinements are used by the various valve manufacturers in order to improve performance. The metal bellows must be protected against excessive differential pressures. Some of the methods used are shown in the valve illustrations.

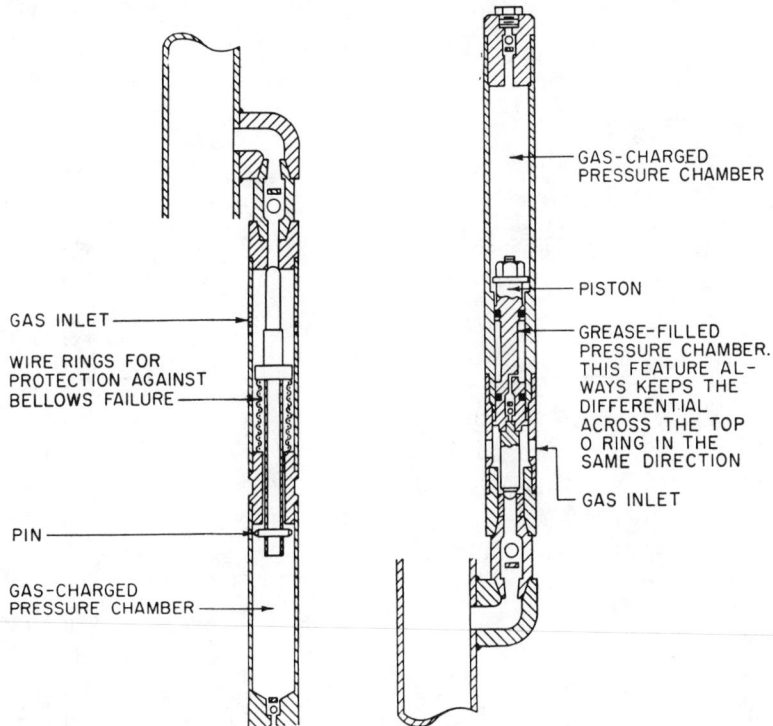

GAS INLET

WIRE RINGS FOR PROTECTION AGAINST BELLOWS FAILURE

PIN

GAS-CHARGED PRESSURE CHAMBER

GAS-CHARGED PRESSURE CHAMBER

PISTON

GREASE-FILLED PRESSURE CHAMBER. THIS FEATURE AL- WAYS KEEPS THE DIFFERENTIAL ACROSS THE TOP O RING IN THE SAME DIRECTION

GAS INLET

FIG. 5-10. Gas-charged bellows intermitting valve.

FIG. 5-11. Gas-charged piston intermitting valve.

A damping action of the valve's response just before closing off is desirable to prevent valve "chatter" and consequent damage to the ball and seat. Figures 5-9 and 5-14 show some ways in which this may be achieved.

In order to protect the ball and seat of the valve from excessive wear and more readily to ensure positive gas shut-off, certain valve designs will feature tungsten carbide ball and seats, tungsten carbide ball and monel seat, and monel ball and Teflon seat.

The operating principles of several of the pressure-loaded gas-lift valves are shown in Figs. 5-8 to 5-25. These include conventional intermitting, tubing-sensitive (fluid weight), and continuous-flow types. Also shown are the various loading elements such as gas, spring, gas-spring combination, and the different types of transmission elements such as metal bellows, rubber diaphragm, and piston. Figure 5-15 illustrates the "pilot" type of gas-lift valve.

Wire-line Adaptations

The most significant development in gas-lift equipment in the past decade has been that of the eccentric mandrel which allows the running and pulling of gas-lift valves by wire line. Full-open tubing is realized by the use of this equipment. Figure 5-26 shows the schematic principle of this operation. Concentric-retrievable-valve designs are also available but do not provide the full-open-tubing feature. Figure 5-27 illustrates a special eccentric wire-line retrievable-orifice-type valve. This valve can be

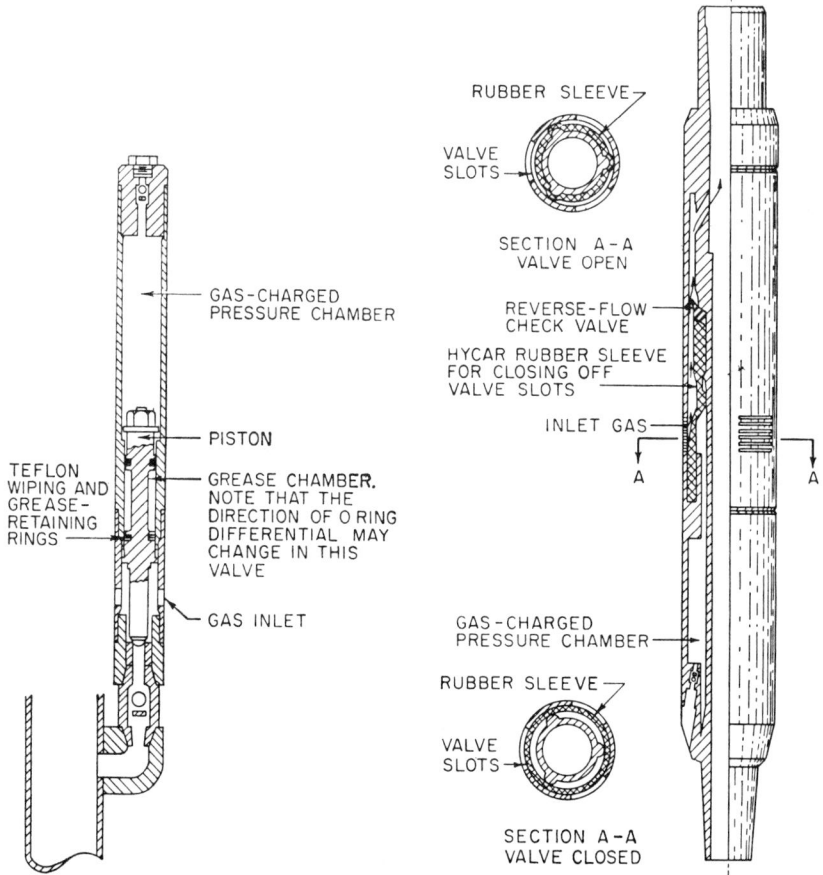

FIG. 5-12. Gas-charged piston intermitting valve.

FIG. 5-13. Gas-charged rubber-diaphragm intermitting valve.

positively opened or closed while in place in the well by wire-line techniques. Figure 5-28 shows another wire-line adaptation using the sliding-sleeve principle.

Check Valves

Check valves have an important place in gas-lift equipment installations. Although the main valves can be purchased without them, their function is important enough that they should be considered an integral part of the valve system. The prime purpose of the check valve is to prevent fluid backflow from the tubing to the casing annulus or vice versa in a casing-flow installation. Serious erosion and accelerated corrosion problems arise when they are not used.

Several different principles are used in the design of check valves. The designs incorporate spring loading, velocity, gravity, and the magnetic principle. The check-valve principle is illustrated in each of the main valve figures.

Mandrels. Mandrels are available in the conventional type, the wire-line eccentric type, the wire-line concentric type, and the capsule type, in which the mandrel completely surrounds the valve. They are adapted to provide either tubing or casing flow. Special designs feature a "wrap-around" principle which channels the injection gas spirally upward to eliminate the erosional effect of high-velocity gas blasting straight across the tubing, ceramic coating to counter further the erosional effect, and corrosion insulators to minimize galvanic corrosion resulting from dissimilar metals.

Dual-well Equipment. Equipment for dually completed wells on gas lift is essentially the same as that for single wells in so far as valves and mandrels are concerned. Special packers and crossovers are available for different dual-well conditions. Both concentric- and parallel-type installations are common. Figures 5-29 and 5-30 show

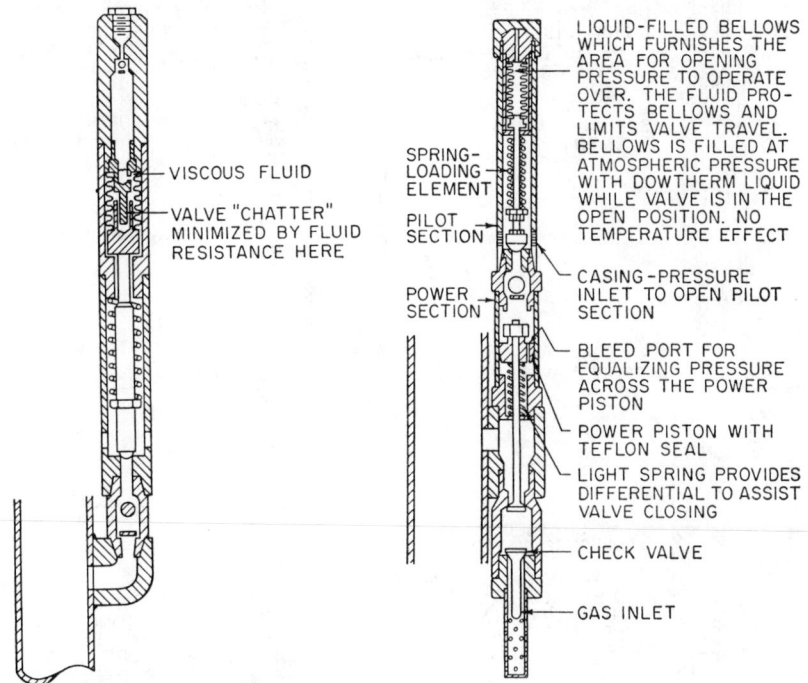

FIG. 5-14. Combination gas-charged bellows and spring-loaded intermitting valve with a "fluid-cushioning principle."

FIG. 5-15. Spring-loaded pilot-type intermitting valve.

two types of dual-gas-lift installations. Figures 5-67 and 5-68 illustrate certain dual-installation surface controls.

Surface Gas-injection Control Equipment. The surface control of injection gas is dependent upon the type of installation being operated. Figure 5-31 illustrates the schematic principle of how some of this equipment is applied. Figure 5-32 distinguishes between "line" and "casing" pressures. A dual-well gas-lift system will require different control from that of a single-well gas-lift system. Intermittently flowing wells have different requirements. The equipment used for surface control may be a choke, regulator, time-cycle motor-valve controller, a tubing or casing flow cutoff, or any combination of the above. If a motor valve is to be used on an installation for continuous flow as opposed to intermittent flow, a smaller controller port should be used. Also bleeding gas from the motor-valve dome should be accomplished with a minimum waste of power gas. When intermitting, it is desirable to bleed gas from the controller during the shorter injection period rather than the longer period

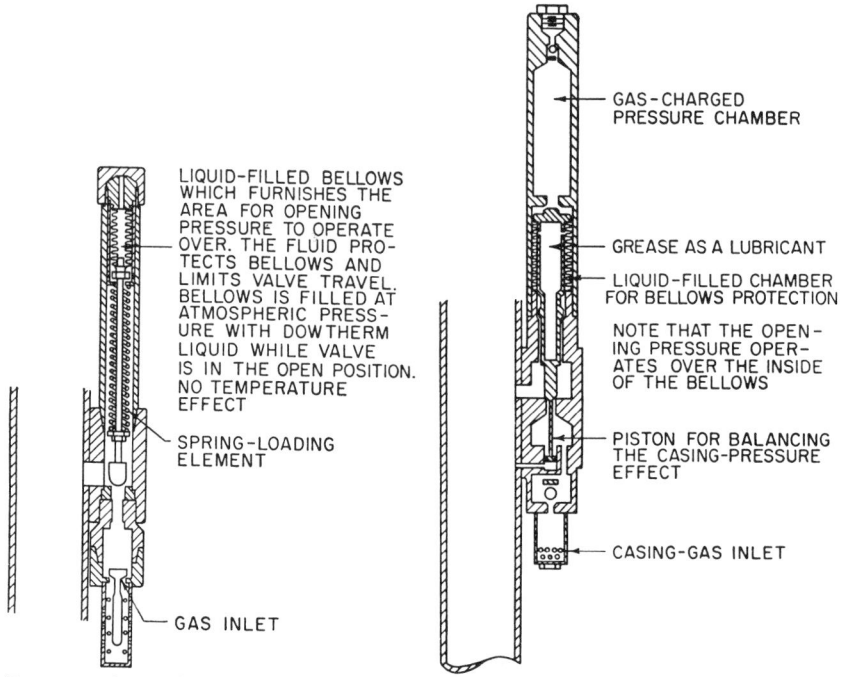

LIQUID-FILLED BELLOWS
WHICH FURNISHES THE
AREA FOR OPENING
PRESSURE TO OPERATE
OVER. THE FLUID PRO-
TECTS BELLOWS AND
LIMITS VALVE TRAVEL.
BELLOWS IS FILLED AT
ATMOSPHERIC PRESS-
URE WITH DOWTHERM
LIQUID WHILE VALVE
IS IN THE OPEN POSITION.
NO TEMPERATURE
EFFECT

SPRING-LOADING
ELEMENT

GAS INLET

FIG. 5-16. Spring-loaded "fluid-operated" valve.

GAS-CHARGED
PRESSURE CHAMBER

GREASE AS A LUBRICANT

LIQUID-FILLED CHAMBER
FOR BELLOWS PROTECTION

NOTE THAT THE OPEN-
ING PRESSURE OPER-
ATES OVER THE INSIDE
OF THE BELLOWS

PISTON FOR BALANCING
THE CASING-PRESSURE
EFFECT

CASING-GAS INLET

FIG. 5-17. Gas-charged bellows "fluid-operated" valve.

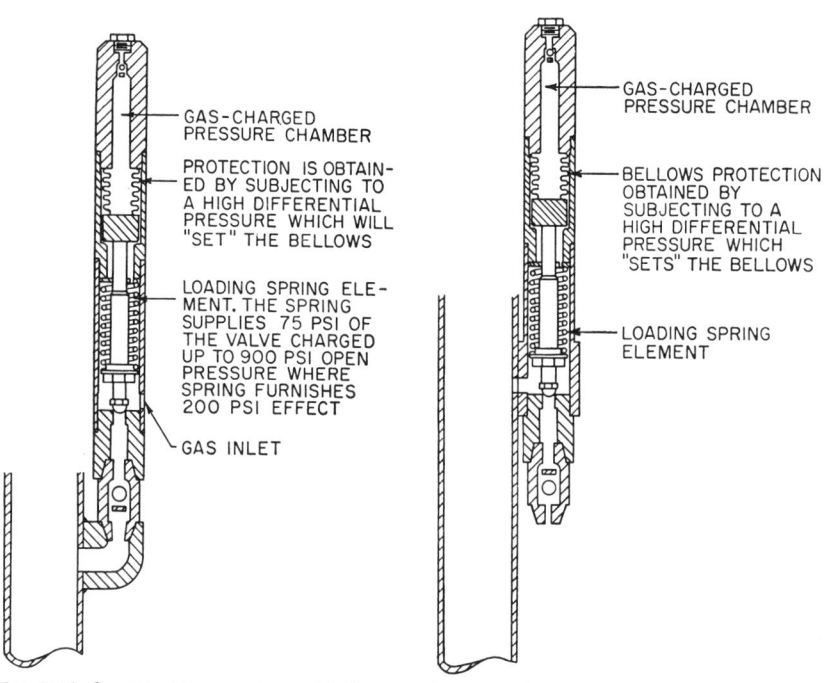

GAS-CHARGED
PRESSURE CHAMBER

PROTECTION IS OBTAIN-
ED BY SUBJECTING TO
A HIGH DIFFERENTIAL
PRESSURE WHICH WILL
"SET" THE BELLOWS

LOADING SPRING ELE-
MENT. THE SPRING
SUPPLIES 75 PSI OF
THE VALVE CHARGED
UP TO 900 PSI OPEN
PRESSURE WHERE
SPRING FURNISHES
200 PSI EFFECT

GAS INLET

FIG. 5-18. Combination gas-charged bellows and spring-loaded intermitting valve.

GAS-CHARGED
PRESSURE CHAMBER

BELLOWS PROTECTION
OBTAINED BY
SUBJECTING TO A
HIGH DIFFERENTIAL
PRESSURE WHICH
"SETS" THE BELLOWS

LOADING SPRING
ELEMENT

FIG. 5-19. Combination gas-charged bellows and spring-loaded "fluid-operated" valve.

between injections, as this gas is normally vented to atmosphere. This would be a pressure-closing-type motor valve. For continuous flow the opposite combination would be desired. Use of the pressure-closing-type motor valve should be considered against the possibility of power-gas failure. In the event this occurs, the controller will remain in the open position and full line pressure will pass into the casing.

Although not items of control equipment, two- and three-pen (for dual wells) surface-pressure recorders will materially aid the "trouble shooting" of wells not producing as expected. Figure 5-33 shows a field record of one of these units. Additional information on surface controls is given in Figs. 5-67 and 5-68.

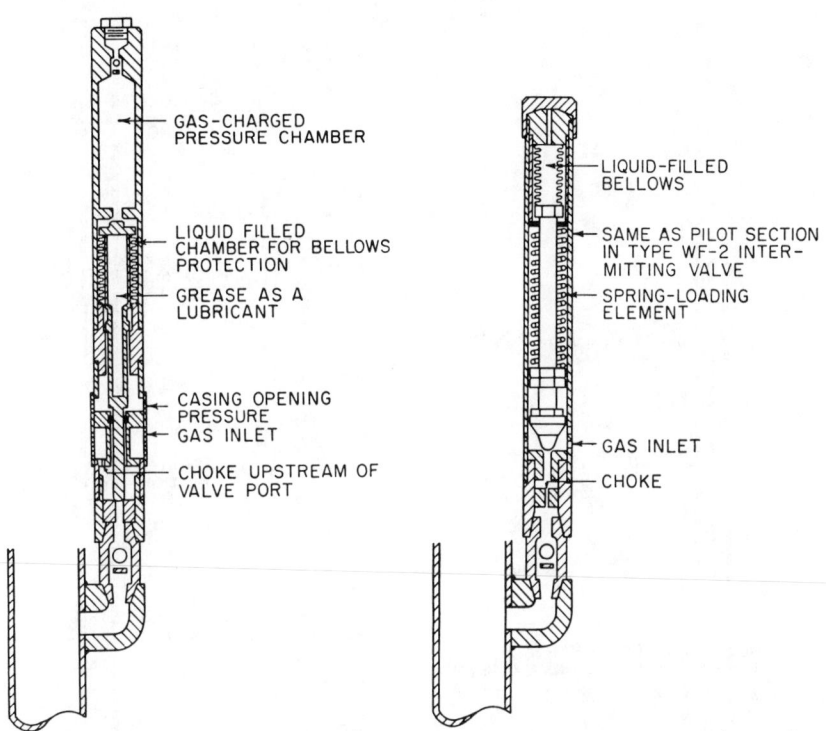

GAS-CHARGED
PRESSURE CHAMBER

LIQUID FILLED
CHAMBER FOR BELLOWS
PROTECTION

GREASE AS A
LUBRICANT

CASING OPENING
PRESSURE
GAS INLET

CHOKE UPSTREAM OF
VALVE PORT

LIQUID-FILLED
BELLOWS

SAME AS PILOT SECTION
IN TYPE WF-2 INTER-
MITTING VALVE

SPRING-LOADING
ELEMENT

GAS INLET

CHOKE

Fig. 5-20. Gas-charged bellows continuous-flow valve (choke upstream of valve port).

Fig. 5-21. Spring-loaded continuous-flow valve (choke downstream of valve port).

The Gas-lift Plunger. The plunger or free piston should be considered an auxiliary tool in the gas-lift operation. Its most widespread applications are restricted to a rather narrow well category. This category is low-volume relatively shallow wells making only moderate amounts of gas and with limited surface injection-gas pressures. Another application is that for automatic unloading of liquid heads in oil and gas wells by utilizing the reservoir gas pressure built up in the casing between cycles. Plunger operation may be controlled by casing pressure, tubing pressure, or a surface time-cycle controller. A plunger will keep the well string free of paraffin, and in certain installations, it may be completely wire-line installed and serviced.

It is important to recognize the relation between a plunger installation and a conventional intermitting system. The conventional intermitting system requires a certain amount of "priming" fluid. That is, only about 60 per cent of a given fluid slug is recovered per cycle. However, once this priming fluid has been fed into the well, the conventional installation will then recover the reservoir fluid as fast as it feeds into the well bore. For example, if on a 5-bbl build-up 3 bbl are recovered at the surface in a conventional intermitting system, then as soon as the reservoir feeds in another 3 bbl, the well is ready to trigger again.   This factor is the basis for an important misconception in the comparative performance between a plunger installation and a conventional intermitting one   The plunger will, of course, experience less slippage and fallback of the well fluids, but it can produce no more liquid phase per day than a properly designed conventional intermitting installation, nor can it carry a given well to a lower stage of depletion.

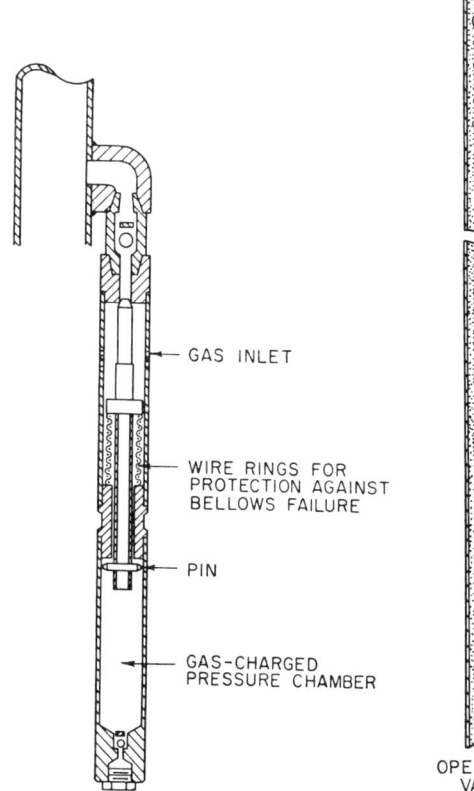

Fig. 5-22. Gas-charged bellows continuous-flow valve (with tapered valve stem).

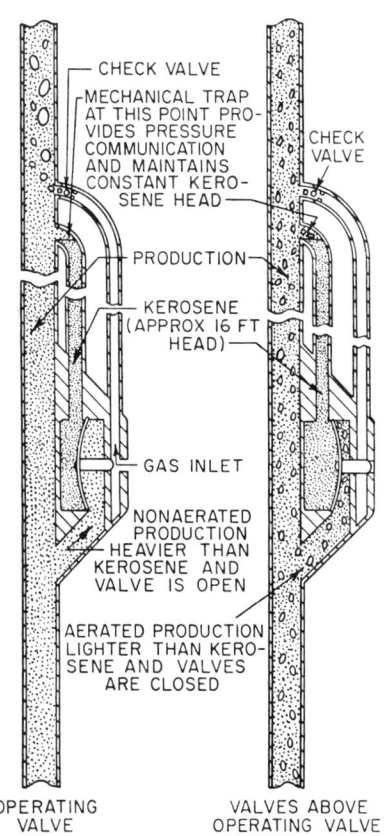

Fig. 5-23. Automatic continuous-flow valve using rubber diaphragm and fluid-density differences for operation.   Commonly called a "specific-gravity" valve.

The plunger will show a distinct gas-oil ratio (GOR) advantage in wells of low volume and low surface gas-injection pressure.   The minimum amount of gas required per cycle in any intermitting installation, be it plunger or conventional, is that required to fill the tubing from the injection depth to the surface at the average slug-expulsion pressure and temperature.   For a given liquid slug, it takes a lower pressure differential when a solid interface is used between the gas and liquid (plunger) than when it is not (conventional).   Therefore, a lower gas-oil ratio should be expected with a plunger installation.

Extreme mechanical demands present a foremost plunger-operating problem.   For example, one operating every two hours from a depth of 8,000 ft travels approximately 36 miles per 24-hour day.   This is over 1,000 miles per month and in rather close mechanical confines. Depending upon design and type, plunger wear can present critical operating and production problems.

Operational ruggedness, fall time of the piston, and fairly elaborate surface controls, in some systems, serve to limit the application.

The necessity for operational ruggedness in the piston is shown by failures in the shock-absorber mechanism, springs, rubber sealing element, and guide fins. It would appear that the simpler more rugged designs would be less subject to mechanical failure.

The fall time of the piston can be quite important. This fall time is a function of the piston design, wellhead pressure, and the extent to which the well is making free gas.

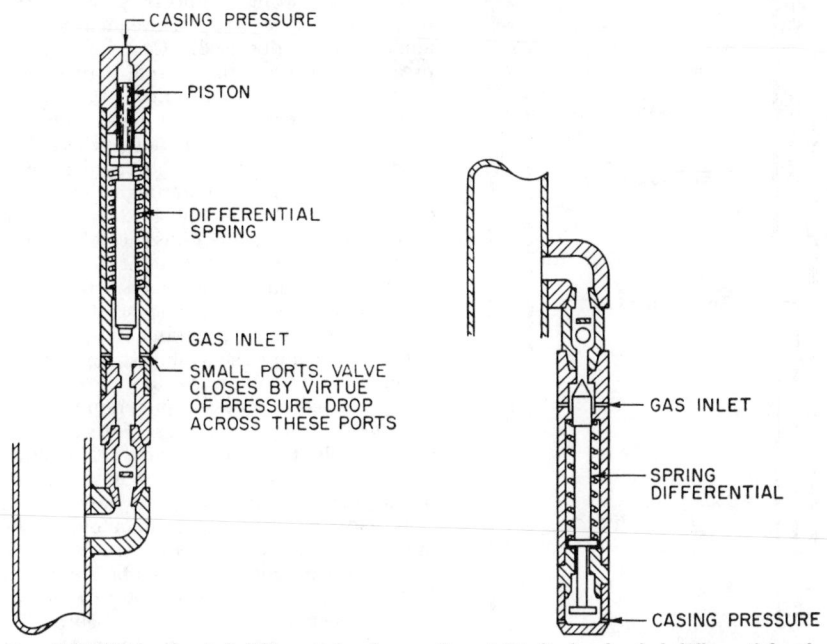

FIG. 5-24. Spring-loaded differential valve.   FIG. 5-25. Spring-loaded differential valve.

Figures 5-34, 5-35, and 5-36 show simplified versions of three types of plungers, and Fig. 5-37 illustrates one type of plunger operation. Other more elaborate installations are common in certain oil-producing areas. Nomographs which will allow the estimation of operating pressures and gas requirements for certain types of plunger systems designs are available from the manufacturer. These nomographs together with a comprehensive discussion on gas-lift plunger design have been published in a series of articles in *The Petroleum Engineer*, vol. 30, June, 1958.

Compressors

The source of lift gas for gas-lift systems was first provided by either gas wells or large-scale cycling and gas-repressuring plants. The increasing economic value of natural gas together with more rigorous gas-conservation practices has resulted in a widespread application of small compressor plants designed specifically for gas-lift purposes. Operators are recognizing that closed rotative gas-lift systems can be properly designed for rapid pay-out. This type of installation is quite flexible in that excess gas produced with the oil can be directed to sales-gas channels. Further, once the maximum lift-gas requirements of the system have been fulfilled, only a nominal amount of make-up gas (available from production) is all that is necessary to be added to the system.

Accordingly, the compressor manufactures have made available high-quality packaged compressor units in the low- to medium-horsepower range. These may be the integrally driven type (400 to 600 rpm) in which the compressor is directly connected to the prime-mover drive, or of the high-speed (900 to 1,600 rpm) belt-driven type. Both single and multistage units are offered. The applications are generally for high over-all compression ratios (12 to 16). Two-stage reciprocating compressors best fit the basic conditions and, consequently, are almost universally used. Centrifugal compressors, on the other hand, have high-volume low-compression-ratio characteristics and are therefore not suited for the job.

For compressor applications where less than 150 hp is required, the popular trend has been toward the lighter high-speed belt-driven units. In the 150- to 250-hp range there is a considerable difference of opinion as to which type of unit is better suited. As this is the horsepower range most frequently encountered, the designer must closely observe all factors: fuel, maintenance, salvage, relocation, compression stages, and others which relate to compressor life.

A packaged compressor unit simply means that all components necessary to make a complete plant are unitized on a skid mounting. A typical packaged compressor plant includes the compressor, prime mover, steel skid, gas- and water-piping manifolds, radiator, gas-cooling section, and scrubber.

The integral compressor can be purchased installed, less housing, for $200 to $300 per brake horsepower (1958) and the belt-driven type for about one-half this amount. The over-all cost will vary, depending upon the geography, climate, size, and type of the unit. The important factor is that a wide selection of high-quality units is available which will offer attractive pay-outs for correctly designed gas-lift systems.

In choosing compressors, it is desirable to consult with the compressor manufacturers before final selection. All manufacturers have literature available upon request, which will assist in the design of a compressor installation. There are, however, certain fundamental relations which are helpful in any given case. Rapid estimates of over-all horsepower requirements can be accomplished with a good degree of accuracy without the use of charts and tables.

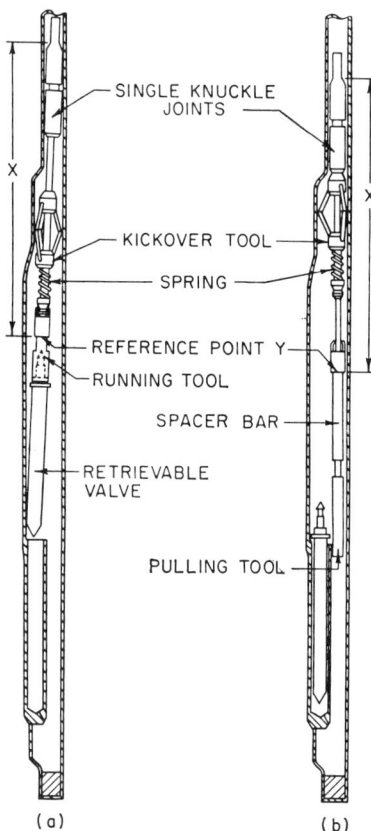

SINGLE KNUCKLE JOINTS

X

KICKOVER TOOL

SPRING

REFERENCE POINT Y

RUNNING TOOL

SPACER BAR

RETRIEVABLE VALVE

PULLING TOOL

X

(a)   (b)

FIG. 5-26. Wire-line retrievable gas-lift valve with eccentric mandrel. (a) Running valve; (b) pulling valve. Note that the dimension X is the same for both running and pulling the valve. Note also the position of the spring on the kickover tool in reference to point Y. When running and retrieving valve the pulling tool must first be run past the valve and then pulled back up as shown in (b).

A principal requisite in compressor-performance calculations is that absolute pressures must be used. Basic relations between suction pressure, discharge pressure, compression ratio, and the number of compression stages are as follows:

$$C = (C')^{1/n} = \left(\frac{P_d}{P_s}\right)^{1/n} \tag{1}$$

where C = absolute compression ratio *per stage*
C' = over-all absolute compression ratio
n = number of stages
P_d = absolute discharge pressure, psia
P_s = absolute suction pressure, psia

$$P_d = P_s C^n = P_s C' \qquad (2)$$

where the terms are as defined above

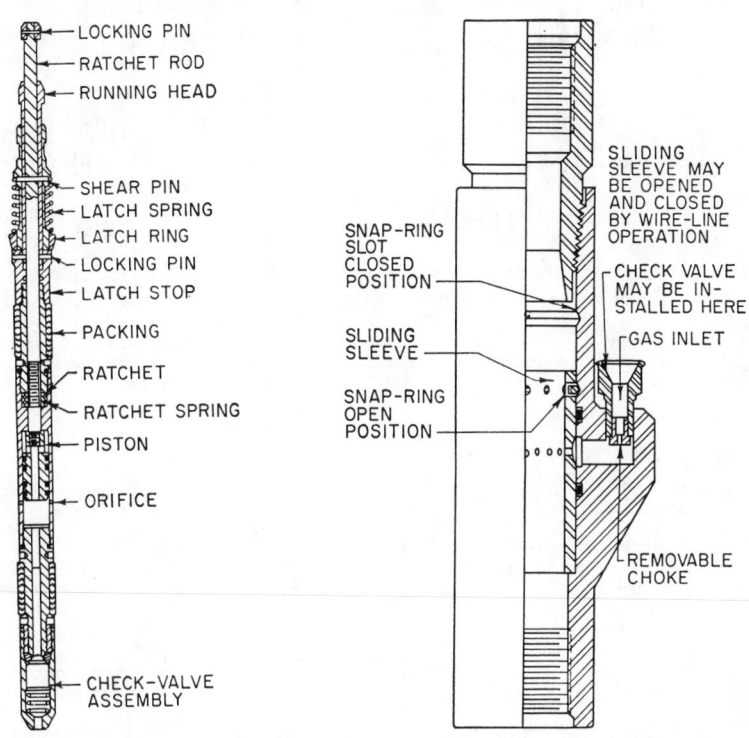

FIG. 5-27. Mechanically operated orifice valve (for use with eccentric mandrel).

FIG. 5-28. Wire-line operated sliding-sleeve-type valve.

A simplified method for estimating compressor horsepower requirements for an integrally driven compressor is given by Clark Brothers Co. as follows:

1. Find the per stage compression ratio.
2. Multiply by 1.05 to correct for pressure drop and imperfect gas cooling.
3. Multiply the corrected ratio by 23.
4. Multiply the result by the number of stages to get the brake horsepower per million cubic feet of gas at standard conditions (bhp/MMcf).

Problem Example
Suction pressure P_s = 45 psig = 60 psia
Discharge pressure P_d = 685 psig = 700 psia
Volume of gas to be compressed = 1.5 MMcf/D
Suction temperature = 80°F measured at 15.025 psia

1. $C = \left(\dfrac{700}{60}\right)^{\frac{1}{2}} = 3.42$
2. $1.05 \times 3.42 = 3.60$
3. $23 \times 3.60 = 82.8$
4. $2 \times 82.8 \times 1.5 = 250$ bhp/1.5 MMcf/D

For belt-driven units the horsepower should be increased by about 5 per cent.

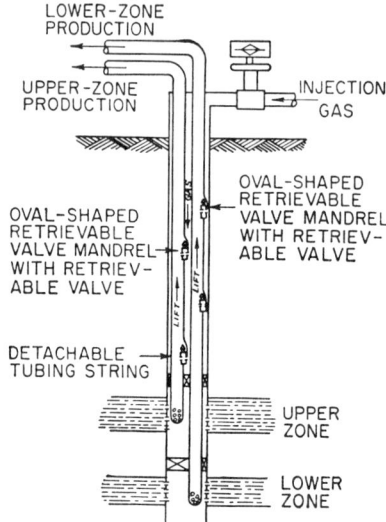

FIG. 5-29. Gas lifting both zones of a dually completed well with a common injection-gas source.

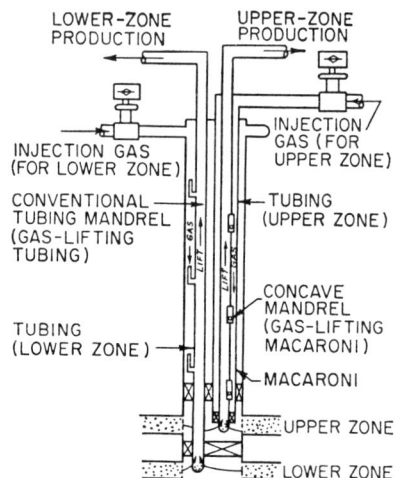

FIG. 5-30. Gas lifting two zones of a dually completed well combination concentric- and parallel-type installation with separate injection-gas sources.

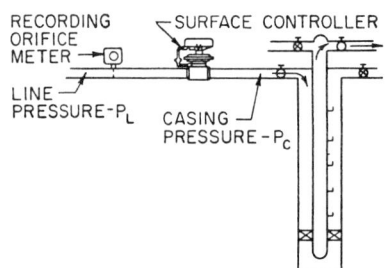

FIG. 5-31. Sketch illustrating a type of surface control for an intermitting well.

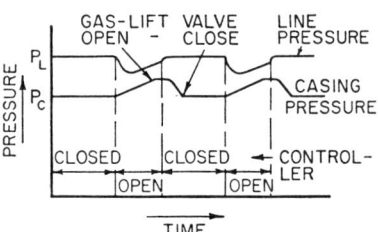

FIG. 5-32. Sketch differentiating between "line" and "casing" pressure as the surface controller operates.

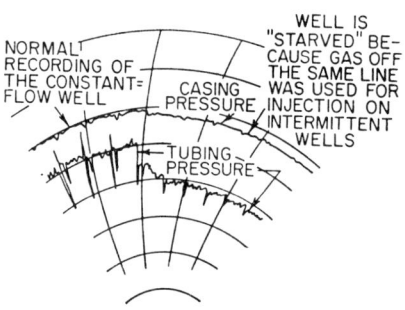

FIG. 5-33. Field-recorded pressure chart of a continuous flow well illustrating the problem resulting from supplying lower-pressure intermittent wells from the same injection-gas source as this higher-pressure operating continuous-flow well.

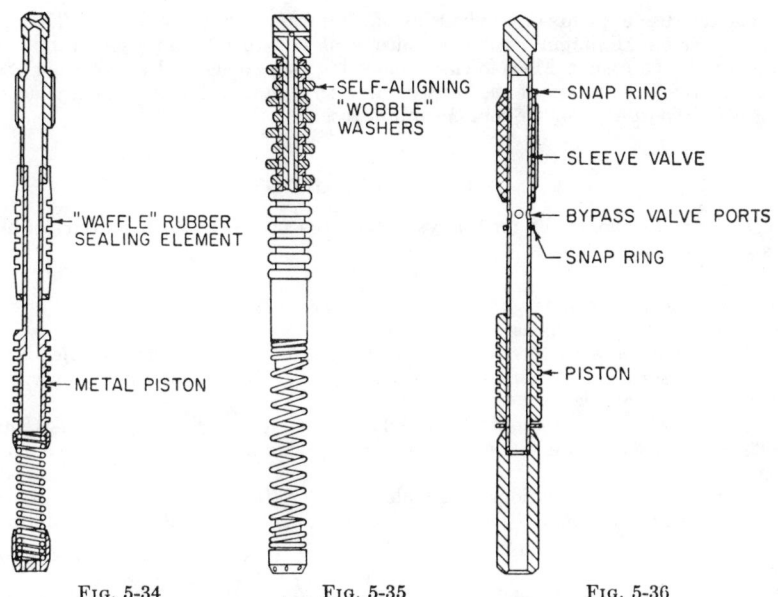

FIG. 5-34.   FIG. 5-35.   FIG. 5-36.

FIG. 5-34. Gas-lift plunger with "waffle" rubber sealing element.
FIG. 5-35. Gas-lift plunger with self-adjusting washers as the sealing element.
FIG. 5-36. Gas-lift plunger with piston sealing element.

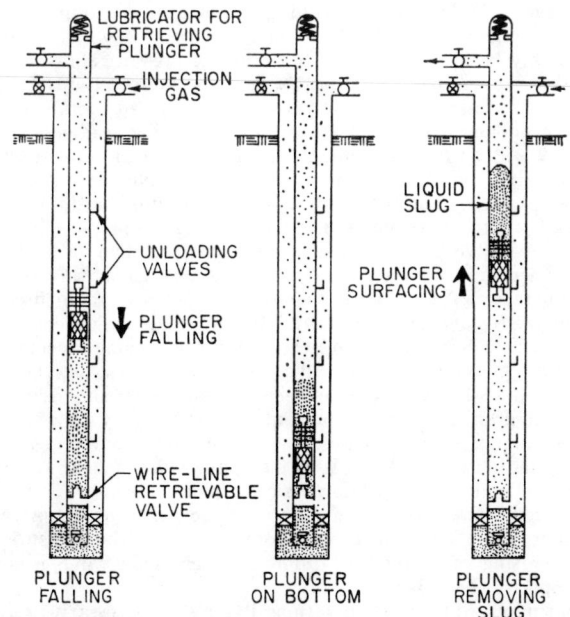

FIG. 5-37. Illustration of one type of gas-lift plunger operation using a centrally wire-line retrievable gas-lift valve.

Some very useful points on the housing of compressors are given by B. S. Thompson in his paper on Minimum Practical Housing of Low-cost Compressor Station, presented at the Petroleum Mechanical Engineering Conference in Denver, Colo., Sept. 21–24, 1958. Orientation of the equipment with regard to the prevailing wind is of particular importance for air-cooled compressors.

DESIGN TECHNOLOGY

The design technology of gas-lift systems can be set out under five principal headings. These are:

1. Mechanics, to include system and valve mechanics
2. Valve-spacing principles
3. Continuous-flow well systems in which optimum injection depth, injection-gas volume, and surface injection-gas pressures are determined; also correct selection of valve type and port size
4. Intermitting-well systems which include theoretical and optimum gas requirements, optimum pressure requirements, correct valve selection, and surface control methods
5. Miscellaneous applications to include closed-rotative-system design, dually completed wells, small-conduit gas-lift problems, chamber installations, and trouble shooting.

Mechanics—System Mechanics. *The Unloading Operation—Continuous.* Consider the well installation shown in Fig. 5-38*a*, *b*, and *c*. As casing pressure is applied to the annulus all valves in the string are open and the fluid is "forced" or U-tubed into the tubing through the open valves. As the first valve is uncovered, gas will be injected into the solid liquid column above the valve in the tubing. The tendency will be for this head to be removed first as a slug and then as an aerated column. As the casing pressure is higher than the tubing pressure at any common level, the liquid will continue to be depressed until the second valve is uncovered. The BHP at this point will probably be in excess of the bottom-hole pressure shut-in (BHPSI) of the well but liquid phase will be feeding past valve 1 because of the transfer through the lower open valves. Therefore, just as valve 2 is uncovered there will be a two-phase flowing gradient above valve 1 and an unaerated flowing gradient between valves 1 and 2. Valve 2 will now go into operation and both 1 and 2 will temporarily pass gas. (This operation is not necessarily true for all valve-spacing designs.) With a choke in the input casing line the gas will be passing into the tubing at a higher rate than it is being fed into the casing and, consequently, the pressure in the annulus will begin to drop. As valve 1 has a higher pressure setting than valve 2, it will close off and valve 2 will continue to pass gas. Valve 2 will pass gas until valve 3 is uncovered and begins to operate. The cycle will then repeat itself. At some intermediate valve-operating point the reservoir will "kick off" (if the well is to flow continuously). The location of this point will be important in certain valve-spacing procedures. Throughout this unloading phase, successive valves are spaced closer together because of the heavy unaerated unloading gradient between valves. After the reservoir has "kicked off," however, the gradient between valves becomes partially aerated and, depending on the well producing characteristics, the valves may sometimes be spaced with *increasing* distances between them. It is to be pointed out that this degree of aeration is much less in wells making appreciable amounts of water.

The well will now work down automatically to the operating valve where gas will be injected continuously. This will be the point at which the pressure in the tubing opposite the operating valve, plus the differential across the valve, is equal to the casing pressure opposite the valve.

In some continuous-unloading operations it may be necessary to drop the casing injection pressure as each successive valve is uncovered in order to close off the upper valves. Also, a tubing standing valve may be required for certain wells whose highly permeable formations will take fluid readily.

The Unloading Operation—Intermittent. Certain wells have to be unloaded intermittently. These wells are usually those which are to be operated intermittently from
the final operating valve but are not necessarily confined to this type of well. Neither
is it to be inferred that all intermittent wells must be unloaded in this manner. Selection of the unloading method depends essentially upon the available operating pressure, the type of unloading valve used, and the characteristics of the well. Intermittent unloading is required when the rate of the liquid-phase feed-in into the tubing is
insufficient to maintain a flowing gradient above the operating valve. When this
condition is evident, continuous unloading will cause the gas to "blow" around.

A common intermittent-unloading problem is characteristic of wells whose reservoir
pressure will not support a column of liquid to the surface. Enough submergence cannot be obtained when unloading from the upper valves to maintain a two-phase aerated
gradient. Large-port unloading valves are necessary in this operation to ensure
unloading by slugs. Use of choked valves in this instance will merely bubble the gas
through the fluid. A standing valve in the tubing will assist unloading operations for
this type of well.

The mechanics of the intermittent-unloading operation is accomplished by injecting
gas into the casing periodically, allowing sufficient time between injections for a large
liquid-phase slug to be U-tubed from the annulus to the tubing.

The well will work down to a final operating valve, the location of which will depend
upon the continuously available casing pressure and the rate of well fluid feed-in.

Valve Mechanics. *Introduction.* The mechanical operating characteristics of the
gas-lift valve must be thoroughly understood before valve-string design can be considered. Accordingly, this section defines "spread" and derives the opening and closing formulas for pressure-loaded gas-lift valves.

Spread. For the purpose of convenience in application, spread may be defined as
the difference in the casing pressure, as reflected at the surface, for open and closed
positions of a pressure-loaded valve. Spread is simply a measure of the unbalanced
area over which the opening and closing pressures operate. The same force can be
achieved by a small pressure and large area as by a large pressure and small area.
When a straight bellows-charged valve (bellows is the only pressure-charged element)
is open, the opening pressure operates over the total effective bellows area, which
includes the valve stem. The pressure sealed in the bellows is acting over the same
effective area and consequently the valve will close when these two pressures become
equal. Just before opening, however, and neglecting the pressure in the tubing, the
opening casing pressure acts over a smaller area (the total effective area of the bellows
less the area of the valve port). Therefore, a higher pressure is required to force the
valve off its seat than that which will allow it to return. The effect of the back pressure in the tubing toward opening the valve can be balanced out to any desired degree.
That is, the tubing effect can vary from some maximum value to zero (see Fig. 5-4).

The full significance of the spread characteristic is principally twofold. First, it
must be correctly selected so as to produce with a minimum GOR (for intermitting
wells); and secondly, it must be properly considered when spacing the valves. If the
well installation has a large annulus volume (i.e., deep well with a small tubing and
large casing), then a valve with a small spread should be used. If the annulus volume
is small, than a correspondingly larger valve spread may be selected.

In valve spacing, spread affects the operating closing pressure of the valves. They
should be so spaced as to give a decreasing surface closing pressure under operating
conditions for each lower valve. For gas-charged valves, this closing pressure is
dependent upon the geothermal temperature gradient of the area in question, the
influence of producing rate upon this gradient, the opening pressure of the valve at
60°F, and the valve spread.

Derivation of the operating opening and closing pressures will now be given. A
combination bellows and spring-loaded valve will be used in the derivation. This
type of valve involves all forces, and therefore, it is a simple matter to eliminate either
the bellows or the spring for valves that are not of the combination type.

Opening Pressure of Valve under Operating Conditions. Refer to Fig. 5-39.
Using a force balance, we may write

$$F_c = F_o$$

where F_c = force, lb, keeping valve closed

F_o = force, lb, trying to open valve

and from Fig. 5-39b

$$F_c = P_B A_B + S_T(A_B - A_V)$$
$$F_o = P_V(A_B - A_V) + P_T(A_V)$$

where P_B = pressure inside valve bellows

P_V = pressure *in casing opposite valve* just before opening

P_T = pressure *in tubing opposite valve* just before opening

S_T = effective spring tension, psi. (Note that the spring *effect* is given in psi and not pounds of force. Strictly speaking, a spring exerts a force in pounds per unit length of compression. However, the travel of the valve between the open and closed positions is small and is offset by the additional area exposed by the valve stem on opening.)

A_B = total effective bellows area

A_V = area of valve port

Now, equating, dividing both sides by A_B, and solving for P_V,

$$P_V = \frac{P_B}{1 - A_V/A_B} + S_T - \frac{P_T(A_V/A_B)}{1 - A_V/A_B} \tag{3}$$

Note from this relation the following:

1. The term $\dfrac{P_B}{1 - A_V/A_B}$ is simply the pressure necessary to *overcome* the bellows charge *alone* at operating temperature. That is, at 60°F it is the opening pressure of the valve minus the spring effect in psi.

2. The *full psi* effect of the spring S_T must be overcome.

3. The tubing effect in opening the valve is somewhat *greater* than just the tubing pressure multiplied by the A_V/A_B ratio. This effect is given by the expression $P_E = P_T\left(\dfrac{A_V/A_B}{1 - A_V/A_B}\right)$, where P_E is the direct tubing-pressure effect in psi if this pressure were applied over the same bellows area as the casing pressure (i.e., $A_B - A_V$). In other words, $P_E(A_B - A_V)$ will give the same opening force as $P_T A_V$.

4. The opening pressure at the casing wellhead can be determined from

$$P_C = \frac{P_V}{e^{\left(\frac{GL}{53.3TZ}\right)}} \tag{4}$$

where P_C = casing pressure at surface necessary to give a pressure of P_V opposite valve

P_V = pressure in casing opposite valve required to open it

G = lift-gas gravity

L = depth to valve, ft

T = average temperature in the casing, °R

Z = compressibility factor at average temperature T and average pressure in the casing

e = Napierian or natural logarithm base, approximately 2.72

Closing Pressure of the Valve under Operating Conditions. For the closing-pressure derivation consider that the valve is open and the casing pressure is operating over the total effective bellows area. Refer to Fig. 5-39c. Hence

$$F_c = F_o$$
$$F_c = P_B A_B + S_T(A_B - A_V)$$
$$F_o = P_V A_B$$

and equating, dividing by A_B, and solving for P_V,

$$P_V = P_B + S_T\left(1 - \frac{A_V}{A_B}\right) \tag{5}$$

and can also be written as

$$P_V = \left(\frac{P_B}{1 - A_V/A_B} + S_T \right) \left(1 - \frac{A_V}{A_B} \right)$$ (6)

Note from this relation:

1. The closing pressure of the valve is a constant because it is dependent only upon the pressure inside the bellows (which is constant at the operating temperature) and a constant fractional effect of the spring pressure.

2. The pressure inside the bellows can readily be determined by multiplying the pressure necessary to overcome the bellows charge alone (i.e., valve-opening pressure at 60°F minus spring), corrected to operating temperature, by the $(1 - A_V/A_B)$ term.

3. The closing pressure opposite the valve can be converted to surface-casing pressure.

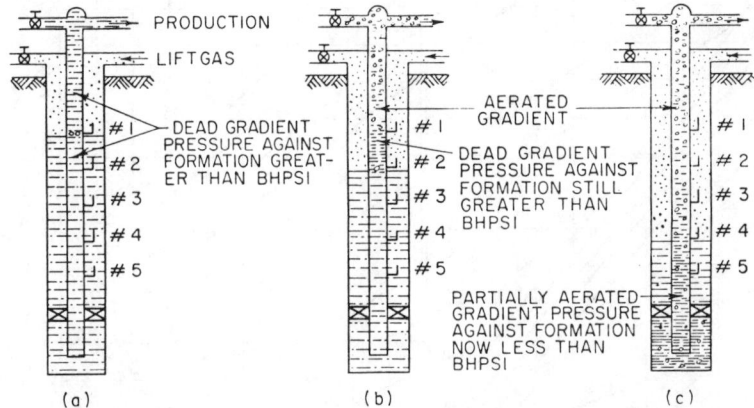

FIG. 5-38. Illustration of continuous unloading where well "kicks off" during the unloading process. Well "kicked off" when valve 3 went into operation. (a) Valve 1 uncovered, just beginning to inject gas. Dead lift. (b) Valve 2 uncovered, just beginning to inject gas. Dead fluid between valves 1 and 2. (c) Valve 4 uncovered, just beginning to inject gas. Note that well has "kicked-off" and that there is now a partially aerated gradient between valves 4 and 5.

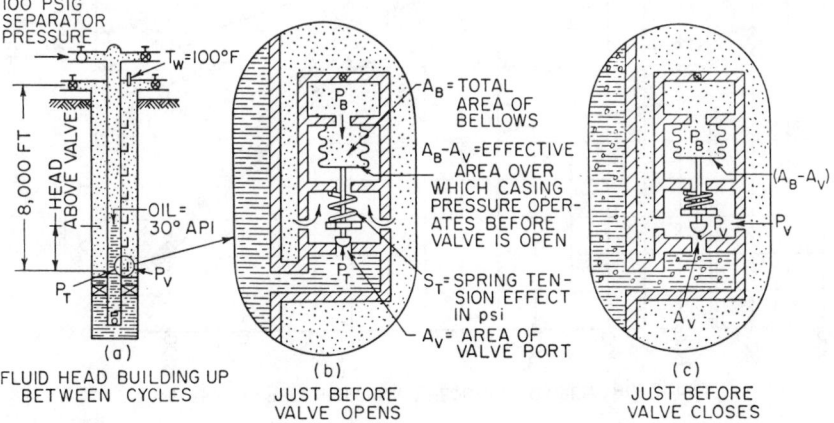

FIG. 5-39. Illustration for determination of open and close formulas for pressure-charged valves.

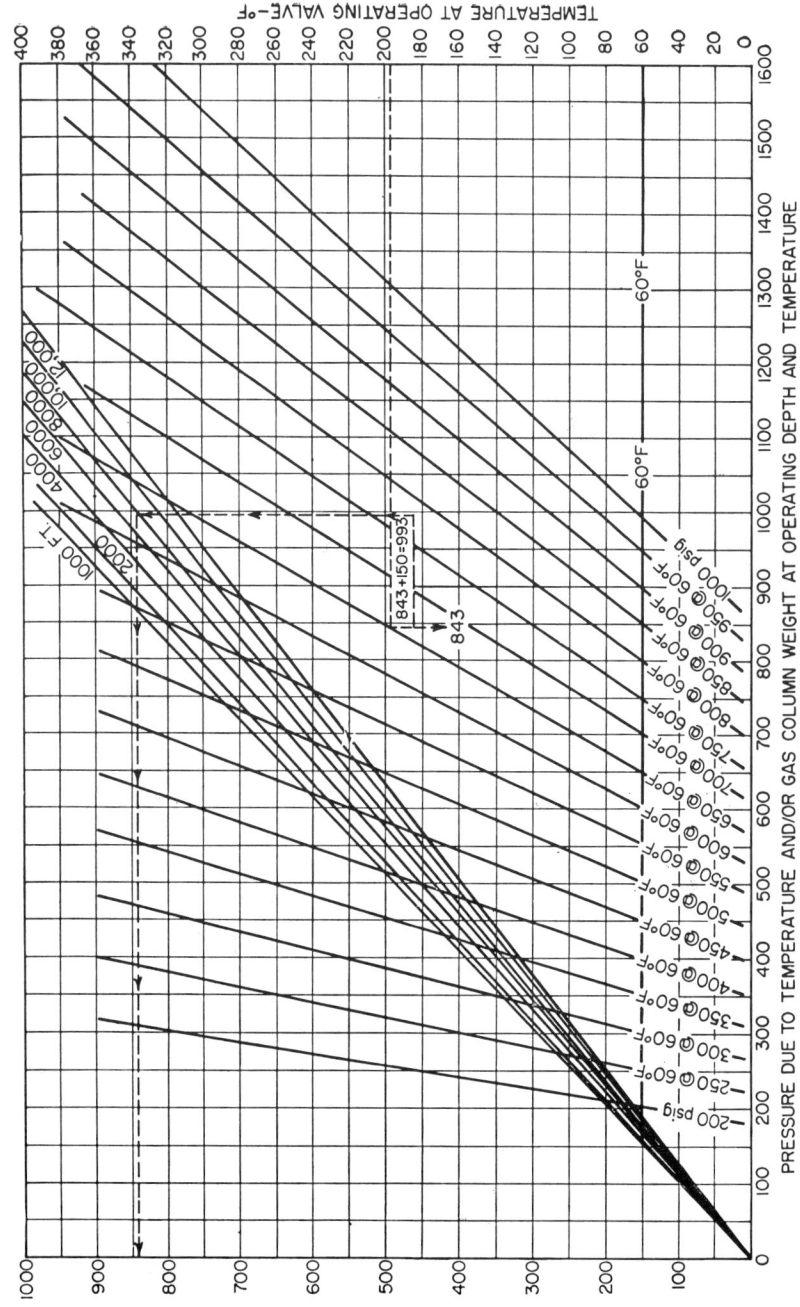

Fig. 5-40. Composite chart for determining the effect of gas gradient and/or temperature on gas-lift valve operation. (See opposite page for remainder of legend)

TEMPERATURE AT OPERATING VALVE—°F

PRESSURE DUE TO TEMPERATURE AND/OR GAS COLUMN WEIGHT AT OPERATING DEPTH AND TEMPERATURE (NO TUBING EFFECT)

WELLHEAD PRESSURE (CASING) REQUIRED TO OPEN VALVE—psig

843+150=993

843

1000 FT.

5–20

4. The fact that the closing pressure is constant means that, if the valves can be charged with an appreciable difference in their operating closing pressures, the operating valve can be determined from surface pressures.

5. The closing-pressure relation will apply to both intermitting- and continuous-flow-type valves with two exceptions. The exceptions are continuous-flow valves which are choked upstream of the main valve port and fluid-operated valves.

The combination chart shown in Fig. 5-40 allows a rapid estimate of these terms.

Valve-spacing Principles

Because of the wide variation in gas-lift application and individual well performance, no one valve-spacing technique will cover all problems. An understanding of the fundamental factors that control valve spacings is essential for good spacing designs. The section on valve and system mechanics has emphasized these fundamentals. It

---

Problem Example for Fig. 5-40

Given
1. 800 psig combination bellows and spring-loaded intermitting valve set at 8,000 ft
2. Spring tension = 150 psi.
3. Gravity of lift gas = 0.70.
4. Normal temperature gradient.
5. Wellhead temperature = 70°F.
6. Back pressure from tubing completely balanced.

Required. Minimum casing pressure at wellhead to open valve.

Solution
1. Temperature of valve at 8,000 ft = $70 + 1.6 \times 80 = 198°F = 658°R$.
2. Pressure necessary to overcome bellows alone at 60°F = $800 - 150 = 650$ psig.
3. Enter the chart of the 198°F point and proceed to the intersection of the 650 psig valve curve. Mentally note the reading on the abscissa as 843 psig. This is the pressure necessary to overcome the bellows alone for chart conditions.
4. Mentally add 150 psi to the 843 psi and get 993 psig, which is the pressure required opposite the valve to open it under chart conditions and with no help from the tubing.
5. Proceed up from the 993 psig abscissa point to the intersection of the 8,000-ft depth curve and read across to the ordinate. Read a valve of 843 as the casing pressure necessary to open the valve under chart conditions and with no help from the tubing.
6. Now to correct from chart conditions to actual conditions: Chart conditions: $G = 0.60$, average temperature = $(100 + 198)/2 = 149°F = 609°R$. Actual conditions: $G = 0.70$, average temperature = $(70 + 198)/2 = 134 = 594°R$.

(a) From figure determine the pressure due to the weight of a column of gas for chart conditions, a wellhead pressure of 843 psig and a depth of 8,000 ft to be 148 psi.

(b) Correct this pressure due to the weight of the column of gas from chart conditions to actual conditions: = $(148)(0.70/0.60)(609/594) = 177$ psi.

7. Now the actual wellhead pressure requirement will be equal to the chart value (843 psig) minus the difference in the pressure due to the weight of the column of gas for actual and chart conditions: = $843 - (177 - 148) = 814$ psig.

8. To apply a tubing effect:

$$P_c = 814 - P_T \frac{A_V/A_B}{1 - (A_V/A_B)}$$

where P_c = minimum casing pressure required at the wellhead
P_T = pressure in the tubing opposite the valve
$\dfrac{A_V}{A_B}$ = valve port to effective bellows area ratio

Chart basis for Fig. 5-40:
1. Nitrogen gas in bellows.
2. Gravity of lift gas = 0.60.
3. Temperature of valve bellows = $tv = 70 + (1.6)$ (depth of valve in hundreds of feet).
4. Temperature at wellhead = $tw = 100°F$.
5. Average temperature in casing annulus = $(tw + tv)/2 = (100 + tv)/2$.
6. No pressure from tubing helping to open valve.
7. Corrections can easily be made for other gas gravities and average temperatures.
8. Valve pressures as given are opening pressures at 60°F psig.

is noted that this section is devoted to valve spacing and not valve location for operations. Methods for determining the optimum operating depth are given in the continuous- and intermittent-flow design sections.

In the case of the continuous unloading operation described in Fig. 5-38, it can be seen that the pressure in the tubing opposite valve 2, just before it is exposed to casing-annulus gas, is made up as follows:

1. The tubing-wellhead pressure
2. The aerated flowing gradient above valve 1
3. The unaerated *flowing* gradient between valves 1 and 2

Therefore, in spacing valve 2 an approximation of these gradients must be made. This is most often a dead lift at this point. That is, the reservoir has not "kicked off" (i.e., the BHPF is greater than the BHPSI) and the aerated gradient is being sustained above valve 1 only by the transfer of *dead* liquid phase from the casing annulus. The aerated gradient is light because of a high volume per cent of gas phase. It is significantly less than the aerated gradient resulting when design production is obtained from the final operating valve.

The flowing gradient between valves 1 and 2 is a heavy gradient. It is approximately a dead-liquid gradient for wells whose reservoirs do not kick off from the first valve.

The gradient picture becomes quite different, however, once the reservoir kicks off and the well continues to work down toward the final operating valve. At this point, the aerated flowing gradient begins to increase because the higher average pressure in this section of the tubing keeps more formation gas in solution and there is a greater volume rate of liquid phase since the formation is now adding to that still being transferred from the annulus.

The flowing gradient between the valve passing gas and the one below that just before coming into operation is now a partially aerated gradient and much lighter than that for the dead unloading liquid.

Therefore, the flow gradients that govern valve spacing for continuous unloading are constantly changing as each successive valve goes into operation. The aerated gradient becomes progressively heavier and the unaerated gradient becomes progressively lighter.

The flow gradients (aerated) for wells that unload intermittently are even *lighter* than those in continuous unloading. The reason for this difference is essentially the absence of liquid phase. The liquid is removed in slugs and the tubing gradient above the operating valve will be predominantly gas phase and much lighter than a corresponding continuous unloading gradient. The unaerated gradient in the intermittent-unloading well will approach the dead-fluid gradient.

Valve-spacing Formulas. The derivation of valve-spacing formulas must take into account two conditions:

1. Those conditions in which the pressure build-up in the tubing controls the operation of the valve, such as the "fluid-operated" and spring-loaded differential types of valves
2. Those conditions in which the casing pressure controls the valve operation, such as the conventional pressure-loaded valves

A basic valve-spacing requirement for all classes of valves and all types of wells is one which must recognize the nominal wellhead unloading gas pressures generally available. The vast majority of gas-lift installations do not have high unloading and operating gas pressures. Therefore, in order to work down to a maximum operating depth, upper valves must close off once a lower valve goes into operation. Otherwise, for large-port unloading valves where the upper valves do not close off, the annulus gas will "blow" around, increasing the tubing pressure and preventing transfer of fluid into the tubing.

The position of the first valve, regardless of valve type, depends upon the gas pressure available, the static unloading fluid gradient, and the static fluid level of the well. If the static fluid level is near the surface and the well is unloading into the separator, the position of the first valve is given by (see Fig. 5-41)

$$L_1 = \frac{P_c - P_s}{G_s} \tag{7}$$

where L_1 = distance to first valve, ft
P_c = casing pressure at surface
P_s = surface tubing pressure
G_s = static fluid gradient, psi/ft

The location of the first valve when the static fluid level is down the well bore is given by (see Fig. 5-42)

$$L_1 = L_S + \frac{P_C}{1 + (A_A/A_T)\, G_s} \tag{8}$$

where L_S = depth to static fluid level
A_A = area of annulus
A_T = area of tubing
and the other terms are as previously defined.

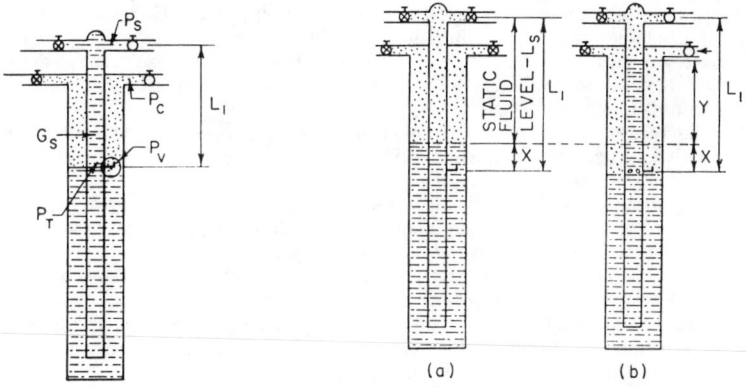

FIG. 5-41. Valve spacing—first valve—high static fluid level.

FIG. 5-42. Valve spacing—first valve—low static fluid level.

The limit of the fluid-level depth for the applicability of the above formula is determined by the maximum casing pressure available. The valve should not be placed at a depth where the hydrostatic head above the valve, after fluid transfer from the casing, would be greater than the available casing pressure. This condition would obviously prevent uncovering the valve.

Differential Valve. For spring-loaded differential valves the distance between valves is given by

$$L_2 = \frac{D_V}{G_s} \tag{9}$$

where D_V is the valve-spring differential in psi and the other terms are as defined. For a detailed derivation of this relation, see *The Power of Gas*, Camco, Inc.

The straight spring-loaded differential valve is normally used with a minimum of back pressure at the tubing wellhead. Liquid-phase transfer through lower valves causes high differentials because of the chokes (see Fig. 5-7) and this subjects the well to a prolonged intermittent-unloading process. Further, well installations which have packers may experience unloading difficulties if these valves are spaced too far apart in a well using a packer. The valve-closing force (pressure in the casing) will exceed the valve-opening force (pressure in the tubing and the spring differential pressure), and the fluid in the annulus cannot be transferred into the tubing.

"Fluid-operated" Valve. The "fluid-operated" valve is a "differential" valve but differs from the conventional principally in that the "loading" pressure acts to close the valve.

The conventional spacing procedure for this valve is as follows:

1. The first valve is spaced as given above.

2. The second and subsequent valves are spaced with the same distances between them, assuming a dead unaerated fluid gradient between valves and allowing for a suitable differential pressure from casing to tubing for the valve just going into operation. This differential should be on the order of 150 to 200 psi. Hence, if the "kick-off" casing pressure is reduced by this amount and a dead unloading gradient is assumed, each successive valve after the first will be spaced at the same distance apart and equal to the casing pressure minus the differential divided by the dead unloading gradient.

A graphical analysis of this operation will materially aid understanding and result in a more efficient design.

Several precautions should be noted in the fluid-operated valve application.

1. If gas-charged valves are used, the temperature effect must be considered and the valve "trigger pressure" set for operating conditions.

2. Higher valve charge settings mean the valves can be spaced farther apart, whereas lower charge settings result in closer valve spacing. Hence a balance must be achieved between the two settings in that higher valve charges will result in a lower produced gas-oil ratio (i.e., larger liquid heads) but may likewise give fewer cycles per day and hence less production when operating from the final valve because of the longer build-up time required.

3. The valves should not be dropped in pressure charge down the wellbore. Each upper valve will kick open as the liquid slug passes it, irrespective of whether or not a nominal drop in pressure between valves has been used.

4. Very little surface control can be experienced over this valve once it is in the well.

5. A combination string of conventional and fluid-operated valves should be used in the deeper wells in order to reduce the total number required.

6. Excessive back pressure at the wellhead should be avoided (such as long flow lines, etc.) to prevent high gas-fluid ratios.

7. The application of the "fluid-operated" principle should not be confined to the conventional fluid-operated valves. Large-port conventional intermitting valves should be considered in fluid-operated designs.

Pressure-loaded Valve—Conventional Spacing Method. For pressure-loaded valves the spacing of the first valve, for both high and low static fluid levels, is as previously given. For detailed derivations of pressure-loaded valve spacing, see *The Power of Gas*, Camco, Inc.

The second and subsequent valves can be spaced by the formula given below (refer to Fig. 5-43).

$$L_2 = \frac{P_{V-2} - (P_S + L_1 G_F)}{G_s} \tag{10}$$

$$L_3 = \frac{P_{V-3} - [P_S + (L_1 + L_2)G_F]}{G_s} \qquad \text{etc.} \tag{11}$$

where P_{V-2}, P_{V-3} is actually the pressure in the casing opposite valve 2 under operating conditions.

L_2, L_3 is the distance between valves 1-2, 2-3, etc. P_{V-2}, P_{V-3} should be taken, however, for use in the above formula as the opening pressure at 60°F of the valve being spaced, if it is a gas-pressure-charged type. If it is a straight spring-loaded type then P_{V-2}, P_{V-3} should be taken as the closing pressure of the valve above.

The other terms are as defined.

Theoretically it is desirable for the valve above to close off just as the one below goes into operation. Hence P_{V-2} would normally represent the *operating* closing pressure of the valve above. In conventional spacing and valve charging for gas-charged valves, the opening pressure at 60°F of the valve being spaced closely approximates the operating closing pressure of the valve above.

The conventional spacing technique is recommended for conditions of high available surface gas pressure so that lower valves may be set at appreciable lower pressure to ensure operation from a single valve.

In summary, use this technique as follows:

1. Select the opening pressure at 60°F of the first valve the same as the available casing kick-off pressure. Drop the pressures in succeeding valves by approximately 25 psi at 60°F until near operating depth where the increment should be increased to 40 psi or greater. Depending upon the geothermal gradient of the area in question, this 25-psi increment between valves may be reduced to 0 psi for the *unloading valves*.

2. Select the static gradient used in the conventional spacing formula the same as that of the fluid with which the well was killed.

3. Select the unloading aerated gradient above the operating valve, as used in the conventional formula, as follows: (*a*) If the final design flowing gradient is known,

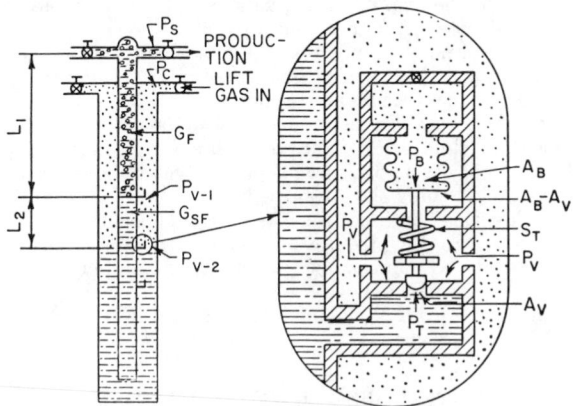

FIG. 5-43. Pressure-loaded valve spacing and spacing terms.

select the unloading aerated gradient as 50 per cent of the final gradient. (*b*) If the final design flowing gradient is unknown, select the unloading aerated gradient as 0.08 psi/ft if the well is to unload continuously, and 0.04 psi/ft if the well is to unload intermittently.

4. Space the first valve in accordance with the procedure already given, considering whether or not the well has a high static fluid level, a low static fluid level, or a low static fluid level and a formation that takes fluid readily.

5. Space the second and subsequent valves by the conventional formula given.

6. Set valve to intended operating depth and bracket this point with valves set at a 25 to 50 psi difference in opening pressures at 60°F.

7. Be sure that the final surface casing operating pressure is approximately equal to the surface closing pressure of the valve above the operating valve.

8. Select the proper port size for the operating valve from a chart such as Fig. 5-59.

Pressure-loaded Valve Spacing—Surface-closing Method. Many wells have only nominal gas-injection pressures available, and hence the drop in valve-pressure settings down the well, as in the conventional spacing method, seriously limits the operation. In the conventional spacing method the first valve is set to open at 60°F at the same pressure as that of the available kick-off pressure. A procedure will now be detailed whereby a more representative pressure setting of this first valve can be realized. This setting will be higher than that of the conventional method for the same available injection pressure, and therefore a greater injection depth can be reached.

This spacing technique is recommended for both continuous and intermittent wells, nominal available injection pressures, and all well conditions wherein maximum working depth for the available injection pressure is desired.

The steps in the surface-closing spacing method are as follows:

1. Space valve 1 in the conventional manner and select its surface-closing pressure as 30 psi less than the available kick-off pressure. This 30 psi is an arbitrary selection that has proved reliable for many valve-spacing problems. It should not be regarded as the absolute selection in every case. Operating experience will influence subsequent modifications of this selection, if they are found necessary.

2. Determine the closing pressure of the first valve at its operating depth and convert this figure to the valve-opening pressure at 60°F [Eq. (5)].

3. Find the tubing pressure needed to open the first valve under operating conditions [see Eq. (3) and item 3, page 5–18].

4. Select the opening pressure of the other valves at 60°F. This selection is dependent upon the geothermal gradient of the well, the type of well, continuous or intermittent flow, and the flow rate to be obtained. Larger increments of pressure decrease should be used between the final operating valve and the valve above (25 to 50 psi). This will ensure gas injection from only one valve.

5. If the reservoir will not kick off from the first valve (bottom-hole pressure less than reservoir shut-in pressure), space the second valve by pressure balance. This will ensure unloading without a pressure stymie.

6. Space other valves by the pressure-balance method down to the depth in the tubing where the static fluid level of the well will ensure a high enough hydrostatic head in the tubing for the casing pressure to open the valve above the uncovered valve. This will generally include only the second valve.

7. For valves below this depth use the conventional spacing formula.

8. Check the surface casing pressure necessary to operate from the final valve. This pressure should not be appreciably greater and preferably equal to or less than the closing pressure of the valve above.

9. Select the choke size for the final operating valve if it is to be a continuous-flow well (Fig. 5-59).

CONTINUOUS-FLOW-WELL SYSTEMS

Correct design of continuous-flow gas-lift systems will allow determination of the following information prior to running the valve string:

1. Optimum injection depth
2. Optimum injection gas-fluid ratio
3. Required surface gas-injection pressure
4. Selection of proper choke size in the valve to pass the correct amount of gas

Once the injection depth has been found, valves are placed 200 to 500 ft (depending upon the capacity of the well) above and below this point and charged so as to ensure single-valve injection. Suitable valve-spacing procedures are then employed to work down to and operate from the selected depth.

Figure 5-44 illustrates a well producing continuously by gas lift. This sketch also contains most of the common terms used in gas-lift performance.

To determine the four factors listed above, it is necessary to produce the flowing-pressure-gradient graph shown in Fig. 5-44 *before* the well is put on production. In order to do this, one must know or be able reasonably to estimate the following:

1. Bottom-hole pressure shut-in (usually known or can be reasonably estimated)
2. Productivity index of the well. If not known, it can be estimated by a procedure given below
3. Desired gross fluid-producing rate (known)
4. WOR (known or reasonably estimated)
5. GFR (assumed)
6. Back pressure at the tubing (P_s, known)

7. Well producing depth (known)

8. Flowing gradients above and below the final operating valve (unknown, but can be calculated)

A knowledge of the flowing pressure gradients then will allow a solution of the problem, including a correct estimation of the current PI as well as the rate of PI decline.

A technique will now be presented for calculating flowing-well pressure gradients. This will be followed by problem examples, illustrating the application to continuous-flow gas-lift systems.

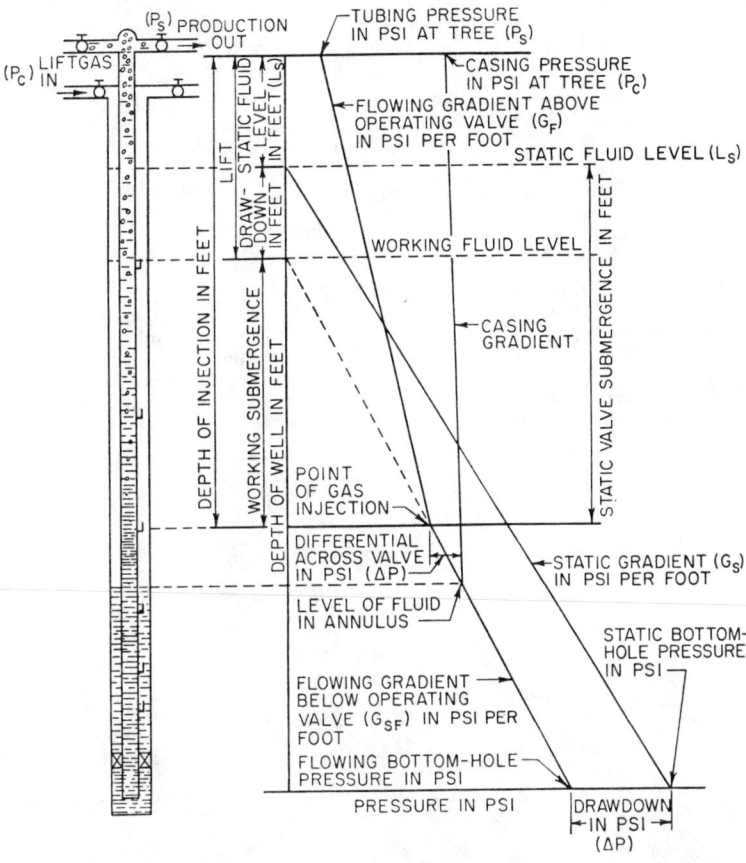

FIG. 5-44. Graphical presentation of basic gas-lift terms, continuous-flow well on gas lift.

Data Required for Pressure-gradient-traverse Calculation

1. Accurately metered oil, water, and gas production
2. Tubing wellhead pressure at the time of the test
3. Gravity of oil, water, and gas
4. Wellhead and bottom-hole temperature

These can be estimated with the aid of Fig. 5-48, but temperatures should be measured if possible. The composite volume factor charts used in the calculation are sensitive to temperature.

5. Size of tubing and depth set
6. Depth of mid-point of well completion interval
7. Shut-in bottom-hole pressure

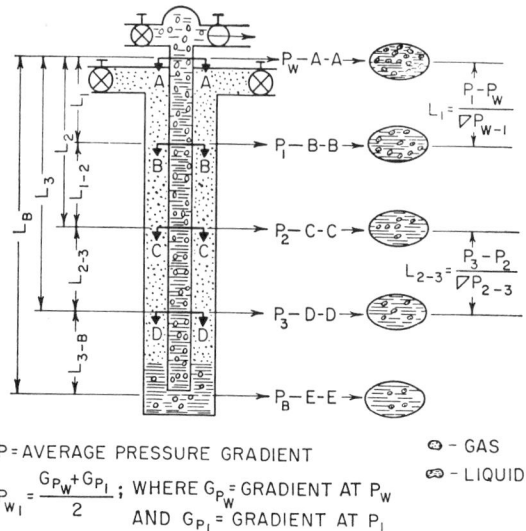

$$\nabla P = \text{AVERAGE PRESSURE GRADIENT}$$

○ – GAS
◎ – LIQUID

$$\nabla P_{W_I} = \frac{G_{P_W} + G_{P_I}}{2} \; ; \; \text{WHERE } G_{P_W} = \text{GRADIENT AT } P_W$$
$$\text{AND } G_{P_I} = \text{GRADIENT AT } P_I$$

FIG. 5-45. Sketch illustrating two-phase flow at different pressure points in the flow string. The mass flow rate is the same at all four sections (pounds of production gas, oil, water per barrel of sto = M), but the respective volumes of gas and liquid (composite volume factor = B_t) are different. Consequently the density of production (M/B_t) is different for each pressure point or section. By use of Standing's composite volume factor chart shown in Fig. 5-47 metered fluid volumes at the surface, and Phillips' gradient curves for the particular tubing size, the flowing gradient can be determined.

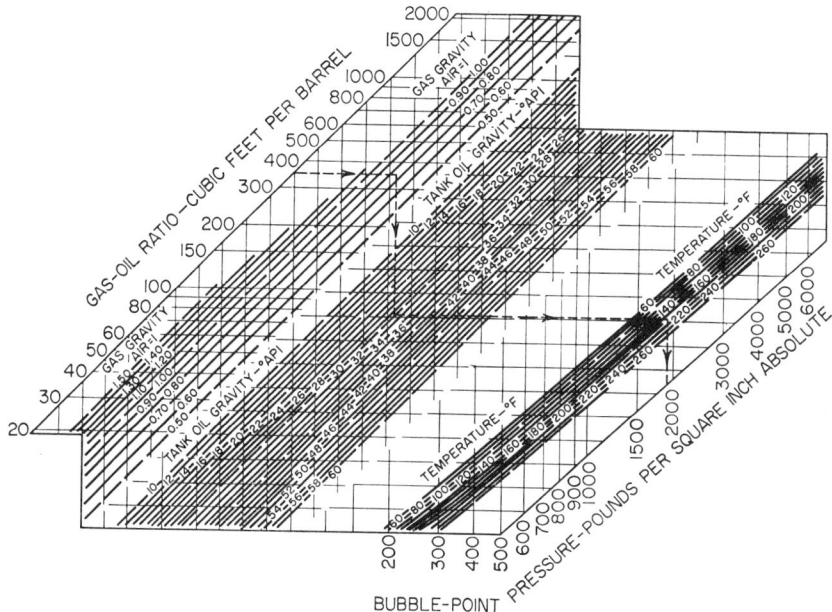

FIG. 5-46. Standing's solution GOR chart. (*Reprinted by permission of California Research Corporation.*)

Example of Properties of Natural Hydrocarbon Mixtures of Gas and Liquid. Bubble-point Pressure:

Required. Bubble-point pressure at 200°F of a liquid having a gas-oil ratio of 350 cu ft/bbl, a gas gravity of 0.75, and a tank oil gravity of 30°API.

Procedure. Starting at the left side of the chart, proceed horizontally along the 350 cu ft/bbl line to a gas gravity of 0.75. From this point drop vertically to the 30°API line. Proceed horizontally from the tank-oil-gravity scale to the 200°F line. The required pressure is found to be 1,930 psia.

Procedure (Refer to Fig. 5-45)

1. Compare the metered producing gas-fluid ratio against the solution gas-oil ratio determined from Fig. 5-46. The purpose is to check the reliability of the metered rates. From values of shut-in bottom-hole pressure, bottom-hole temperature, oil gravity, and gas gravity, Fig. 5-46 will give the solution GOR. Note that this chart is sensitive to gas gravity and temperature, and therefore these two items should be accurately determined.

2. Calculate the mass M which is the total pounds of production per barrel of stock-tank oil (weight in pounds of 1 bbl of stock-tank oil plus pounds of water per barrel of stock-tank oil plus pounds of gas per barrel of stock-tank oil, see Fig. 5-45).

3. Calculate the mass rate $Q_o M$ which is the total pounds of production per day (barrels of stock-tank oil per day Q_o times pounds of production per barrel of stock-tank oil M).

4. Assume pressure points in even increments added to the wellhead pressure (see Fig. 5-45) and read the composite volume factors B_t from Fig. 5-47. The temperature

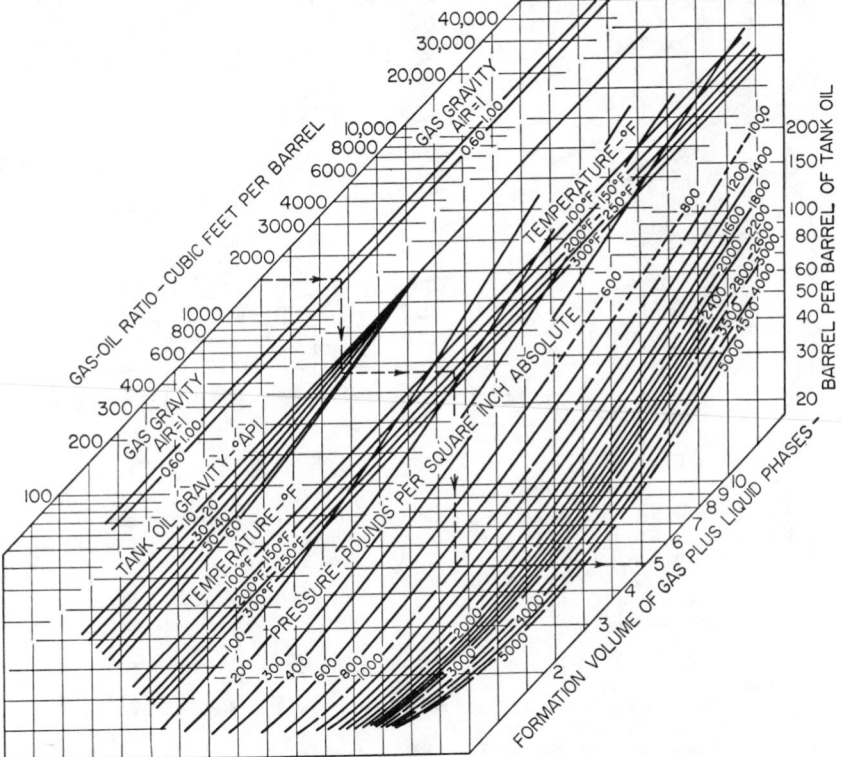

FIG. 5-47. Standing's composite volume factor. (*Reprinted by permission of California Research Corporation.*) The 100, 200, and 300 psia curves have been added to the original chart by proportional extrapolation.

Example of Properties of Natural Hydrocarbon Mixtures of Gas and Liquid. Formation Volume of Gas plus Liquid Phases:

Required. Formation volume of the gas plus liquid phases of a 1,500 cu ft/bbl mixture, gas gravity = 0.80, tank oil gravity = 40°API, at 200°F and 1,000 psia.

Procedure. Starting at the left side of the chart, proceed horizontally along the 1,500 cu ft/bbl line to the 0.80 gas gravity line. From this point drop vertically to the 40°API line. Proceed horizontally to 200°F and from that point drop to the 1,000 psia pressure line. The required formation volume is found to be 5.0 bbl/bbl of tank oil.

used in this determination should be the average temperature in the tubing under flowing conditions. Figure 5-48 can be helpful in estimating either surface or bottom-hole temperature when either one or the other is known.

5. To the volume factor for each assumed pressure point for oil and gas add the barrels of water produced per barrel of stock-tank oil (WOR). This is the composite volume factor for oil, water, and gas.

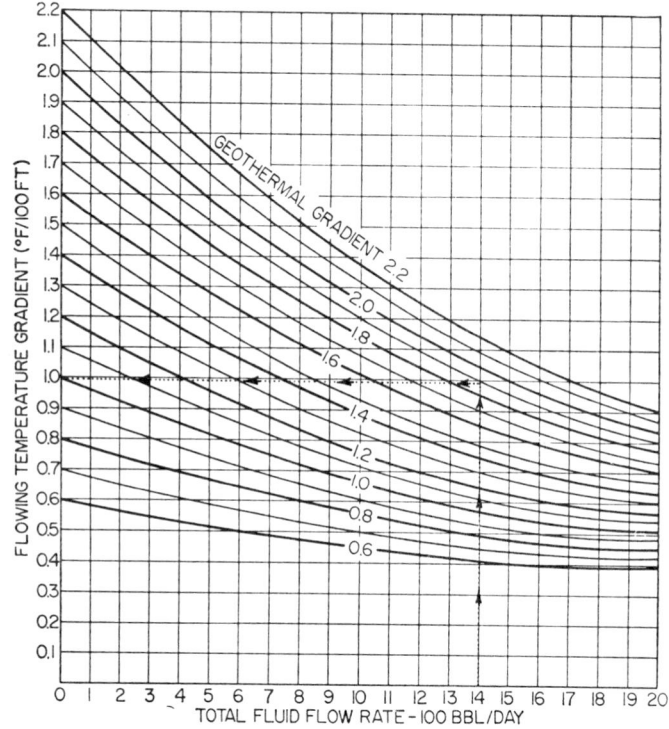

FIG. 5-48 Flowing-temperature gradient for different flow rates, geothermal gradients, and tubing sizes. Chart to be used directly for 2½-in. tubing. For 2-in tubing multiply the actual flow rate by 2. For 3-in. tubing divide the actual flow rate by 1.5.

Problem Example for Fig. 5-48

Given. 700 B/D total fluid to be produced through 2-in. tubing from 5,500 ft geothermal gradient for area is 1.9°F/100 ft, and BHT is 175°F. Determine surface flowing temperature.

Solution. 1. 700 B/D in 2-in. tubing is approximately equivalent to 1,400 B/D in 2½-in. tubing.

2. At the intersection of 1,400 B/D and the 1.9 geothermal gradient line read a gradient on the ordinate of 1°F/100 ft depth.

3. Surface flowing temperature = $175 - 1.0 \times 55 = 120°F$.

6. Obtain the density of production at each assumed pressure point by dividing M by the composite volume factor at each pressure point and convert to pounds per cubic foot by dividing by 5.615 cu ft per barrel.

7. Determine the pressure gradient at each assumed pressure point from the appropriate Phillips friction factor chart, see Fig. 5-49b. Using Q_oM total mass rate calculated in item 3 as ordinate and the density at each pressure point (curved lines), drop *vertically* to abscissa for the gradient.

8. Calculate the average gradient between each successive pair of pressure points.

9. Divide this average gradient into the pressure difference between the two respective pressure points to obtain the distance between them.

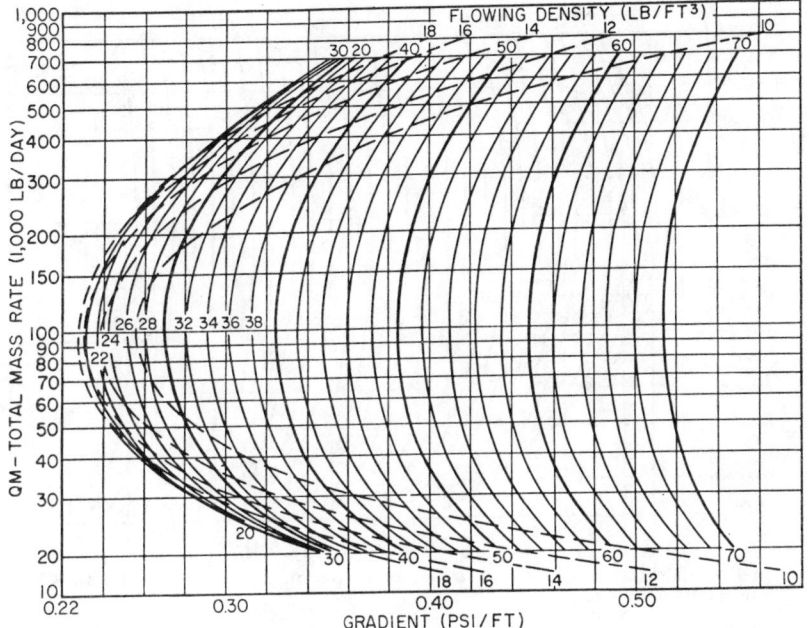

FIG. 5-49. Calculation of pressure traverse for 1¼-in. tubing (1.380 in. ID).

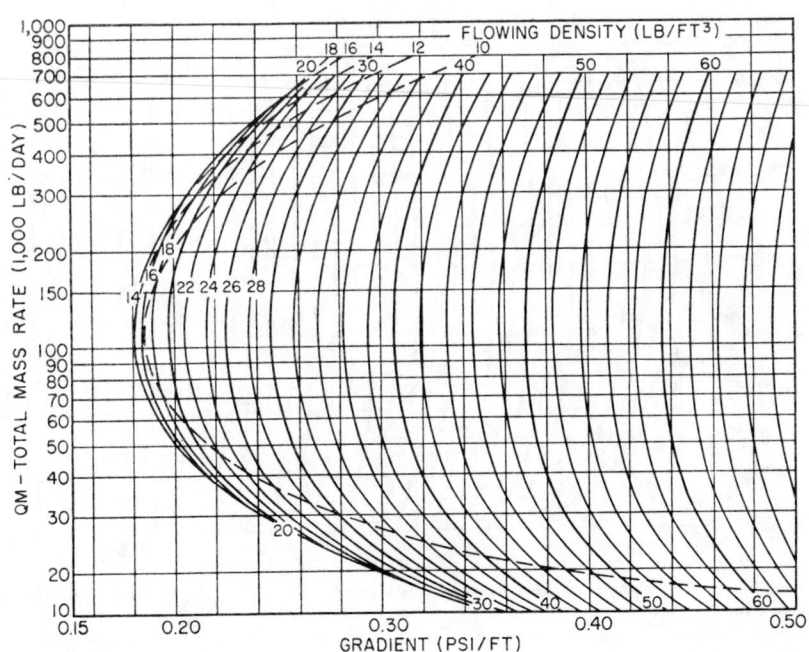

FIG. 5-49a. Calculation of pressure traverse for 1½-in. tubing (1.610 in. ID).

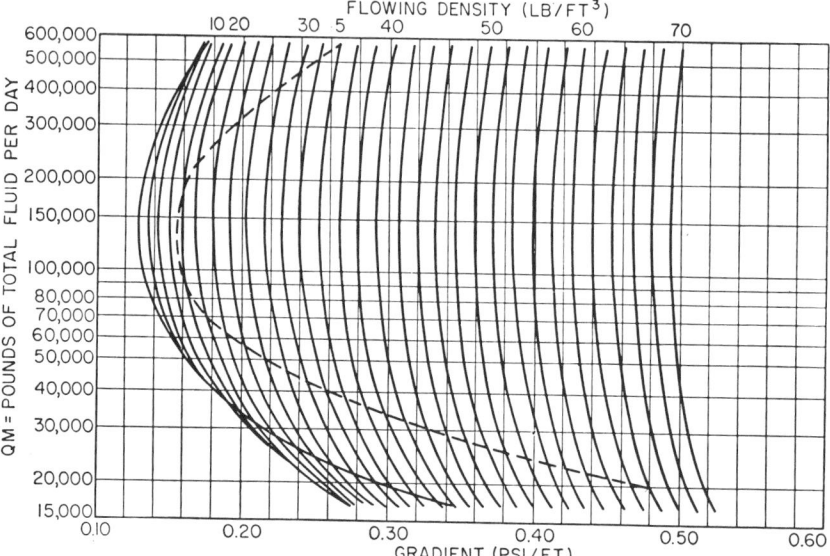

Fɪɢ. 5-49b. Calculation of pressure traverses for nominal size 2.0-in. (4.5 to 4.7 lb/ft, 1.995 in. ID) tubing size.

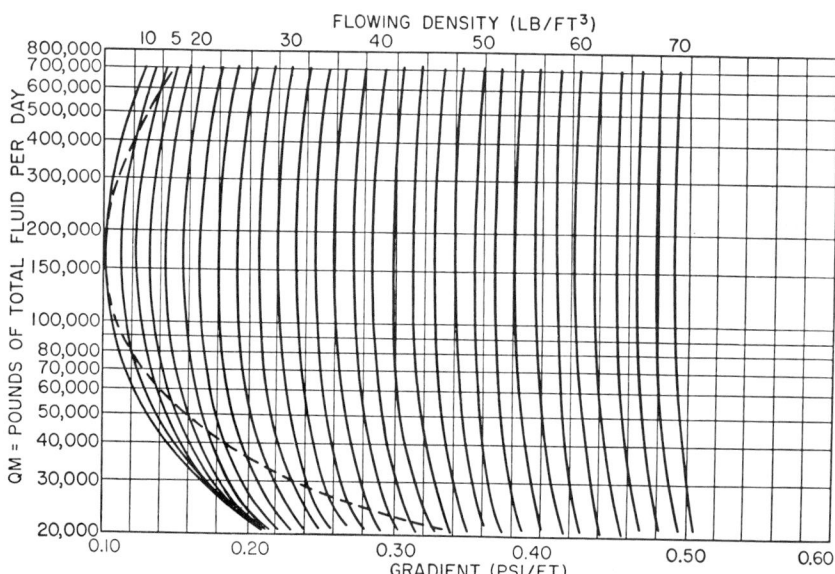

Fɪɢ. 5-49c. Calculation of pressure traverses for nominal size 2½-in. (6.25 to 6.5 lb/ft, 2.441 in. ID) tubing size.

10. If the surface tubing pressure is high enough to yield a density readable on the Phillips gradient chart (Fig. 5-49b, minimum of 10 lb/cu ft for 2-in. tubing) the distance between pressure points may be cumulatively added to determine the depth of each. Start with tubing pressure at zero depth. If the density is too low to be read from the charts then an extrapolation technique must be used for this low-pressure region. An explanation of this procedure is given below.

11. Plot pressure vs. depth in the same manner that subsurface pressure-gauge data are plotted and extend the curve to total depth.

12. From the producing rate and the flowing bottom-hole pressure the productivity index may be calculated. Accurate production data must be used if accurate check results with actual pressure-bomb surveys are to be obtained.

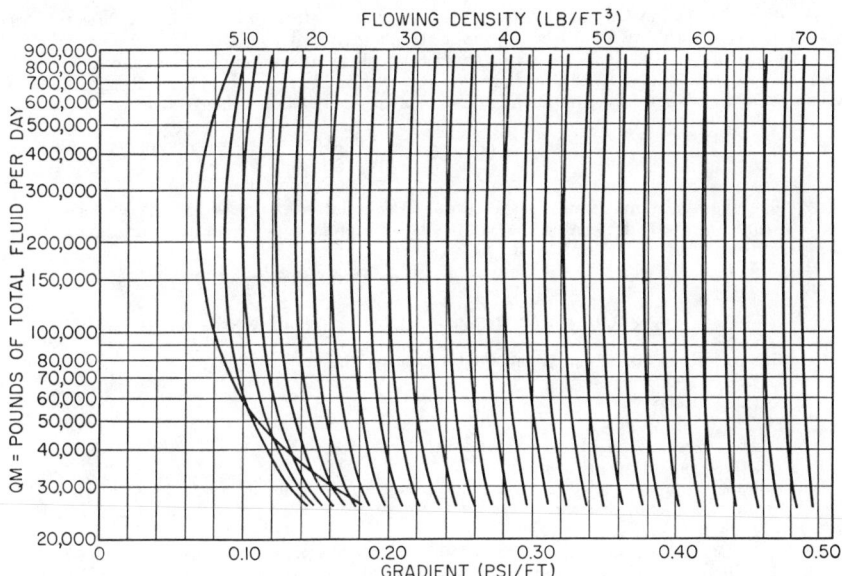

FIG. 5-49d. Calculation of pressure traverses for nominal size 3.0-in. (7.694 lb/ft, 3.068 in. ID) tubing size.

Limitations of the Phillips Flow-resistance Correlation. The Phillips correlation is based on 2.0-, 2½-, and 3.0-in.-diameter nominal-size tubing; gas-liquid ratios up to 5,000 cu ft/bbl of total fluid; liquid rates from 60 to 1,500 bbl of total liquid per day; water-oil ratios up to 56 bbl of water per barrel of oil (98 per cent cut); oil gravities from 30 to 56°API; and well depths to 11,000 ft. The correlation is presented for the multiphase flow of gas and liquid through vertical tubing only. Good results can be obtained with GORs up to 2,000 cu ft/bbl. In general, however, high GORs and low wellhead pressures limit the accuracy of the correlation.

A problem example will now be given:

Well Conditions

1. Producing rate = 400 B/D gross fluid
2. WOR = 1:1; GOR = 500 cu ft/bbl; GFR = 250 cu ft/bbl
3. Back pressure at tubing = 200 psig
4. Depth = 6,000 ft
5. Tubing = 2 in.
6. Oil = 40 API
7. Water = 1.05 sp gr
8. Geothermal gradient = 70 + (1.6)(depth/100) = 166°F at 6,000 ft

9. Flowing-temperature gradient = 99 + 1.11 (depth/100) (determined by means of Fig. 5-48)

10. Gas gravity = 0.65

11. Shut-in bottom-hole pressure = 2,057 psig

12. Flowing bottom-hole pressure—to be determined

13. PI—to be determined

Estimate

a. Well PI.

b. To illustrate the calculated-gradient technique for low wellhead pressures, assume the same conditions as above, except that the back pressure at the tubing is 50 psig.

Solution a

1. First determine the flowing-temperature gradient from Fig. 5-48. A flow rate of 400 B/D in 2-in. tubing would be approximately equivalent to 800 B/D in 2½-in.; at the intersection of the 800 B/D rate and the 1.6 geothermal-gradient curve read a flowing-temperature gradient of 1.11°/100 ft of depth. Surface temperature when flowing then is given as 99°F. Therefore, the flowing temperature at any depth is given by

$$T_V = 99 + (1.11)\left(\frac{\text{depth}}{100}\right)$$

2. The average temperature in the tubing is calculated as (99 + 166)/2 = 133°F.

3. From Fig. 5-47, determine the composite volume factors for oil at an average tubing temperature of 133°F, for each assumed pressure point (see Table 5-1).

4. Calculate M, which is the pounds of total production (oil + water + gas) per bbl STO.

$$M = 0.825 \times 350 + 1.05 \times 350 + 0.0764 \times 0.65 \times 500 = 682 \text{ lb/bbl}$$

where 0.0764 = density of air, lb/cu ft at 14.65 psi and 60°F
      0.65 = gas gravity
      500 = GOR
    0.825 = oil sp gr
     350 = weight of bbl of fresh water
    1.05 = water sp gr

5. Determine density in pounds per cubic foot by dividing M by 5.615 B_t (Table 5-1).

6. From Fig. 5-49b, determine gradients for each pressure-point density and a Q_oM of 136,400 lb/day.

7. Calculate the numerical-average gradient between pressure points.

8. Get the distance between pressure points by dividing the pressure increment between pressure points by the average gradient. Note that the first pressure increment in this example is 185 psi.

9. Obtain the depth to each pressure point and plot the gradient curve (see graph, Fig. 5-50).

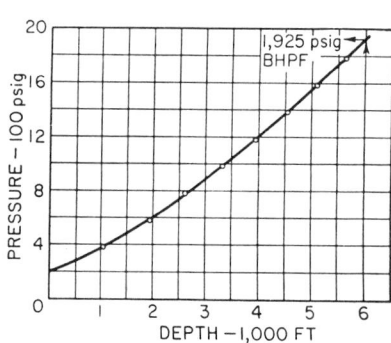

Fig. 5-50. Problem Example a. Calculated gradient.

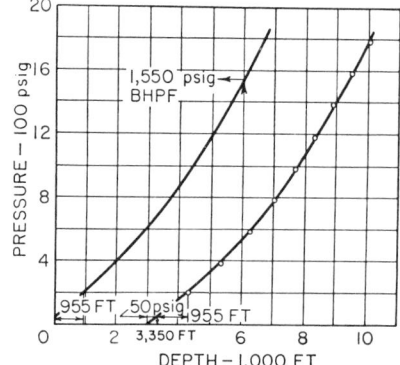

Fig. 5-51. Problem Example b.

10. Pick flowing bottom-hole pressure from graph as 1,925 psig at 6,000 ft.

11. Estimate PI:

$$PI = \frac{400}{2,058 - 1,925} = 3.0 \text{ B/D/psi}$$

Solution b. **Back Pressure at Tubing = 50 psig**

1. The composite-volume-factor chart cannot be read for pressures under 100 psig on the surface, and hence the distance between the tubing wellhead pressure (50 psig) and the first assumed pressure point (200 psig) must be determined by plotting pressure against an arbitrary depth datum.

2. Arbitrarily assume the 1,800-psig pressure point (see Table 5-1) to be located at a depth of 10,000 ft.

Table 5-1. Problem a. **200 psig Wellhead Pressure**

P, psia	GOR, cu ft/bbl	B_t	B_t+B_w WOR 1:1	Density, lb/cu ft	Gradient	Avg gradient	Distance	Depth
215	500	6.30	7.30	16.6	0.152	.....	....	0
400	500	3.80	4.80	25.3	0.200	0.176	1,050	1,050
600	500	2.72	3.72	32.6	0.243	0.222	902	1,952
800	500	2.15	3.15	38.5	0.282	0.263	761	2,713
1,000	500	1.82	2.82	43.0	0.312	0.297	674	3,327
1,200	500	1.62	2.62	46.3	0.333	0.323	620	3,947
1,400	500	1.48	2.48	49.0	0.351	0.342	585	4,532
1,600	500	1.38	2.38	51.0	0.365	0.358	559	5,091
1,800	500	1.32	3.32	52.3	0.372	0.368	544	5,635

3. The distance between all other pressure points except the 50- and 200-psig points will remain the same as in part a. Therefore, locate each pressure depth by cumulative subtraction from 10,000 ft (see Table 5-2).

Table 5-2. Problem b. **50 psig Wellhead Pressure**

P, psia	GOR, cu ft/bbl	True-depth figures		Arbitrary-depth datum figures (see Fig. 5-2)	
		Distance	Depth	Distance	Depth
65	...	.....	0 Start		
215	500	.....	975	1,050	4,305
400	500	1,050	2,025	902	5,355
600	500	902	2,927	761	6,257
800	500	761	3,688 Cumulative additions	674	7,018 Cumulative subtractions
1,000	500	674	4,362	620	7,692
1,200	500	620	4,982	585	8,312
1,400	500	585	5,567	559	8,897
1,600	500	559	6,126	544	9,456
1,800	500	544	6,670	.....	10,000 Start

$M = 0.0764 \times 0.65 \times 500 + 0.825 \times 350 + 1.05 \times 350 = 682$ lb/bbl.

4. Now plot results and extrapolate the curve to the 50-psig pressure and determine the distance between 50- and 200-psig pressure points to be $4,305 - 3,350 = 955$ ft (Fig. 5-51). This extrapolation should always be made on a condensed depth scale. A ratio of 2 psi/ 10 ft for 20 squares to an inch paper should be the minimum scale used.

5. Shift the curve to the ordinate by moving each plotted point 3,350 ft to the left, or determine the distances as in the first part of the problem between the pressure points and plot the curve (Fig. 5-51).

6. Pick flowing bottom-hole pressure from the graph as 1,545 psig at 6,000 ft. Estimate PI:

$$PI = \frac{400}{2,058 - 1,550} = 0.787 \text{ B/D/psi}$$

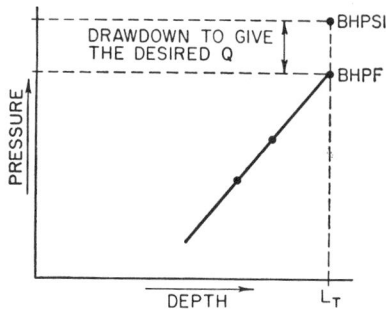

FIG. 5-52. Flowing gradient below the point of injection.

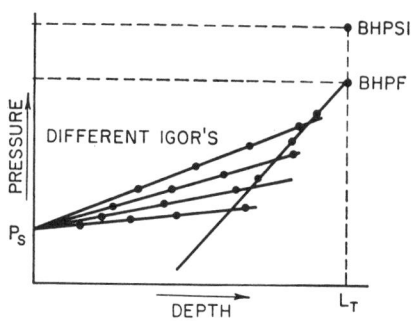

FIG. 5-53. Flowing gradients both above and below the point of injection.

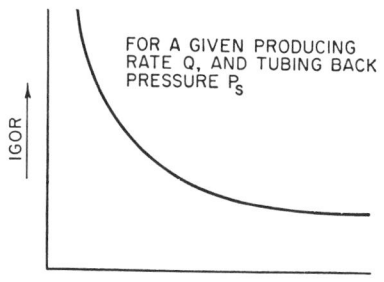

FIG. 5-54. Injection pressure vs. injection gas-fluid-ratio (IGFR).

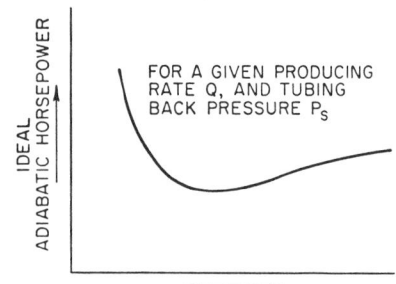

FIG. 5-55. Ideal adiabatic horsepower vs. injection pressure

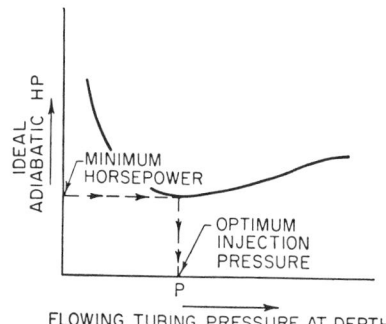

FIG. 5-56

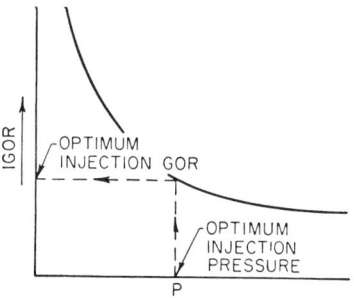

FIG. 5-57

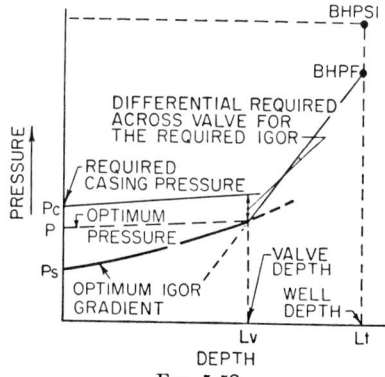

FIG. 5-58

FIGS. 5-56, 5-57, 5-58. Graphs illustrating the determination of the optimum injection point.

5-36

The procedure for optimum design of continuous-flow gas-lift systems is now given:

1. For the producing rate desired and from a knowledge of well productivity index, depth, solution gas-oil ratio, and shut-in bottom-hole pressure, calculate and plot in the manner previously described the flowing gradient below the point of gas injection (see Fig. 5-52).

2. Calculate and plot the flowing gradient above the point of gas injection for different *assumed* injection-gas-fluid ratios and for the required tubing wellhead pressure P_S. These gradients are calculated on the basis of the total gas-fluid ratio, which is solution gas plus injection gas (see Fig. 5-53).

3. The intersection of each of the flowing gradients above the point of injection and the flowing gradient below the point of injection shown in Fig. 5-53 furnishes the necessary data for a plot of injection-gas-fluid ratio vs. injection pressure (see Fig. 5-54).

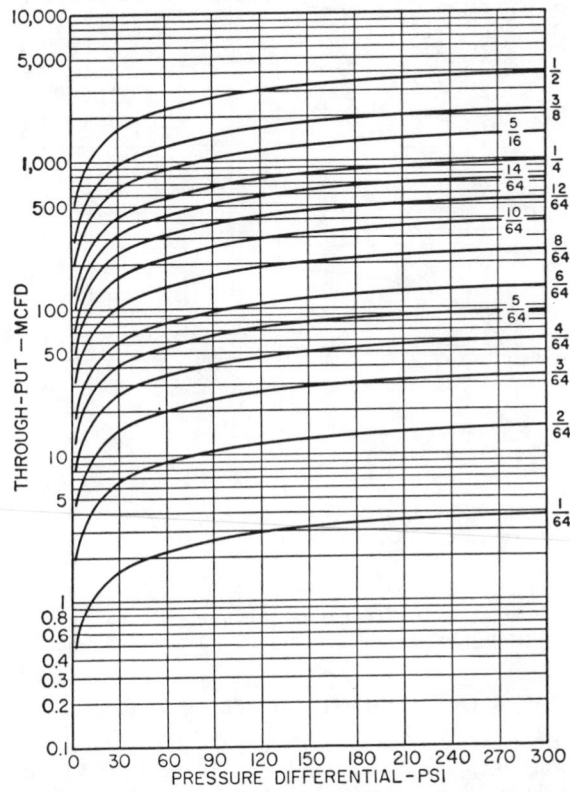

FIG. 5-59. Typical gas-lift valve-choke capacity chart—upstream pressure 500 psig.

4. The same data used to plot Fig. 5-54 can also be used to calculate ideal adiabatic horsepower, and a plot can be made of horsepower vs. pressure (see Fig. 5-55).

5. The optimum injection pressure is at the point of minimum horsepower. This optimum injection pressure, applied to the injection-gas-fluid ratio vs. pressure graph in Fig. 5-54, will give the optimum injection gas fluid ratio. This optimum injection-gas-fluid ratio can then be singled out from the gradient curves shown in Fig. 5-53, and the depth of injection as well as required casing pressure becomes fixed (see Figs. 5-56, 5-57, and 5-58). All wells analyzed for optimum gas-lift conditions will not show a positive minimum on the ideal adiabatic horsepower injection-pressure plot. The graph will, however, assist in the selection of an injection pressure which will ensure operation in the most efficient operating range.

6. The proper choke size for the valve is selected from a chart such as Fig. 5-59.

Most gas-lift installations are marked by limiting conditions of injection pressure and injection-gas volume. For these cases it is necessary to determine the injection-

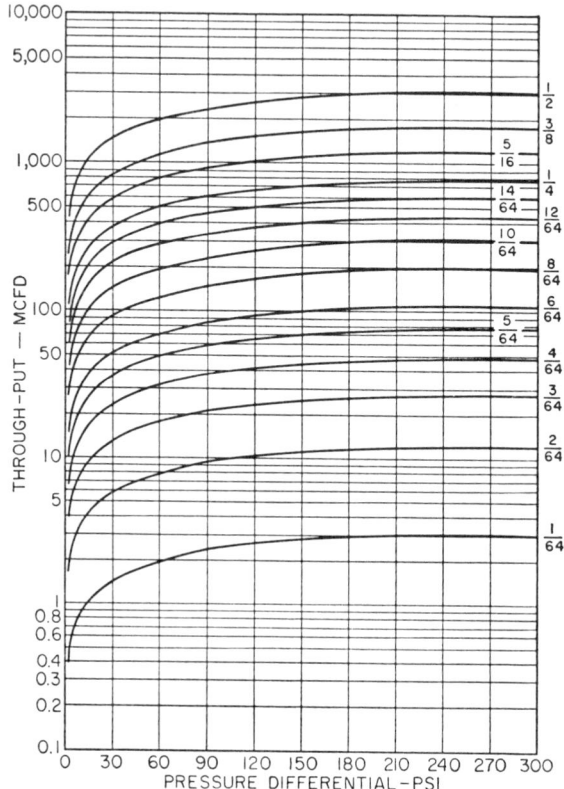

FIG. 5-59a. Typical gas-lift valve-choke capacity chart—upstream pressure 550 psig.

gas-fluid ratio which will allow injection at the greatest depth consistent with the maximum continuously available casing pressure. Hence these systems may be rapidly designed simply by sketching a graph similar to Fig. 5-58.

DESIGN OF INTERMITTENT-FLOW INSTALLATIONS

The intermittent-flow mechanism is considerably different from that of continuous flow. It is normally applicable in either high BHP low PI or low BHP low PI types of wells. In either case, an excessive high drawdown resulting in a prohibitive GOR is required to produce the desired amount of oil by continuous flow. And in many instances, the reservoir simply is not capable of giving up the desired liquid regardless of the drawdown. Figure 5-60 illustrates one possible type of conventional intermittent or ballistic flow. From this illustration, the two principal factors that contribute to the complexity of the process can be analyzed. These two factors are (1) the complex flowing gradient and (2) the contribution of the PI of the well to the well's actual deliverability under intermittently operating conditions.

Figures 5-61 and 5-62 illustrate qualitatively the effect of absolute pressure on well PI.

It is well to note, however, that in discussing intermitting-well performance the effect of maximum drawdown should be mentioned. Many wells have a straight-line build-up curve. Others which *apparently* exhibit this characteristic will often show a *rapid* build-up at very low drawdowns. Wells of this type should definitely be valved

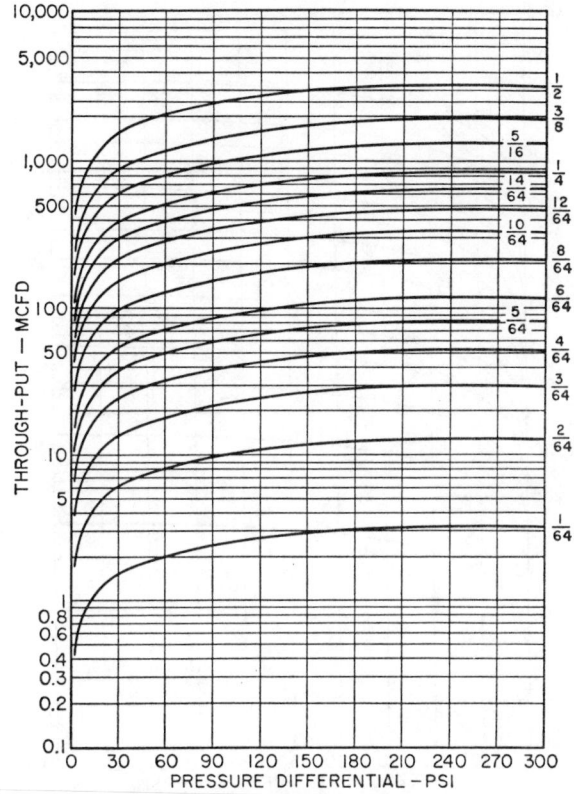

Fig. 5-59b. Typical gas-lift valve-choke capacity chart—upstream pressure 600 psig.

to bottom for maximum production. Those in the former category need not be valved to bottom as increased production will not be realized with increasing drawdown.

A problem example will now be given. This problem will illustrate the design technique which locates the operating valve for a well with low productivity index and relatively high bottom-hole pressure. Normally, wells of this type would be valved to bottom; however, in order to illustrate the effect of all factors in the intermittent operation, a specific depth short of bottom for the operating valve is given.

The procedure for calculation of the theoretical minimum injection gas-oil ratio is also given.

Well Conditions

1. Depth = 8,000 ft
2. Available surface operating pressure = 800 psig
3. Tubing = 2-in.; casing = 5½-in., 20 lb
4. No water, none anticipated
5. Oil = 30 API, sp gr = 0.875
6. Production desired = 100 B/D
7. BHPSI = 2,000 psig
8. Well PI = 0.10 (calculated from offset intermitting well)
9. Tubing pressure at wellhead = 50 psig
10. Minimum cycle time = 45 minutes, estimated

Required

a. Location of operating valve for above conditions
b. The theoretical minimum injection gas-oil ratio for an average temperature in the tubing of 127°F

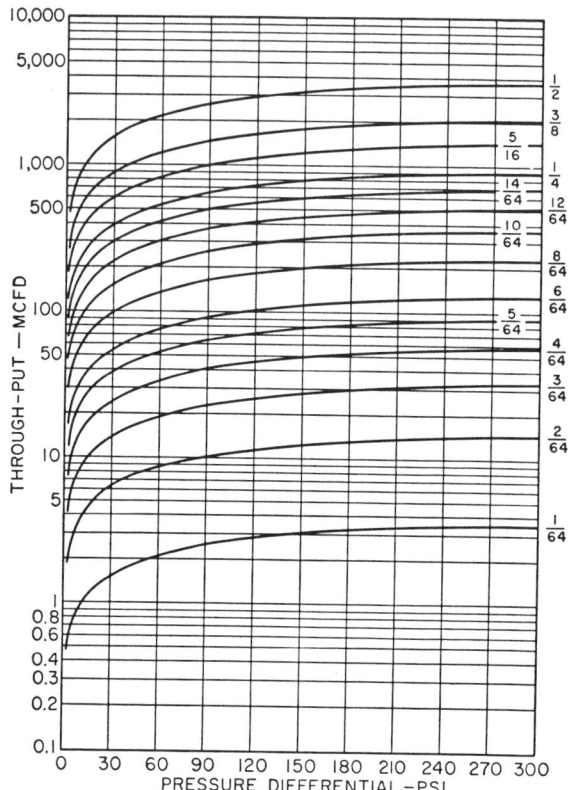

Fig. 5-59c. Typical gas-lift valve-choke capacity chart—upstream pressure 650 psig.

Solution

1. As the well is making no water, the design should be based on an oil gradient of 0.379 psi/ft.

2. A production rate of 100 B/D and a PI of 0.10 will require a BHP drawdown of 1,000 psig. This means an average BHPF of 1,000 psig must be maintained.

3. The SFL of the well with 50-psig surface tubing pressure will be 2,826 ft.

4. A 1,000-psi drawdown is equivalent to a hydrostatic head of oil of 2,640 ft. Therefore, the working fluid level would be located at a depth of 5,500 ft (2,860 + 2,640). This is the mid-point of the fluid-slug build-up.

5. Calculate the operating head required for 100 B/D, 45-minute cycle.

a. A 45-minute cycle is equivalent to 32 cycles/day. 1,440/45 = 32, where 1,440 = minutes/24 hours.

b. Thirty-two cycles would require production of 3 + bbl/cycle for a 100 B/D rate.

c. Operating experience shows approximately 60 per cent of the starting head is produced in properly designed conventional intermittent installations. Therefore, the operating hydrostatic column or fluid slug should be equivalent to 5 bbl of oil (3/0.6 = 5). This is a hydrostatic head of 1,292 ft

$$\left(\frac{5}{3.87}\right)(1,000) = 1,292 \text{ ft}$$

where 3.87 is 2-in. tubing capacity in bbl/1,000 ft.

d. The operating head pressure required for 50 psig on the surface is 540 psig (1,292 × 0.379) + 50 = 540.

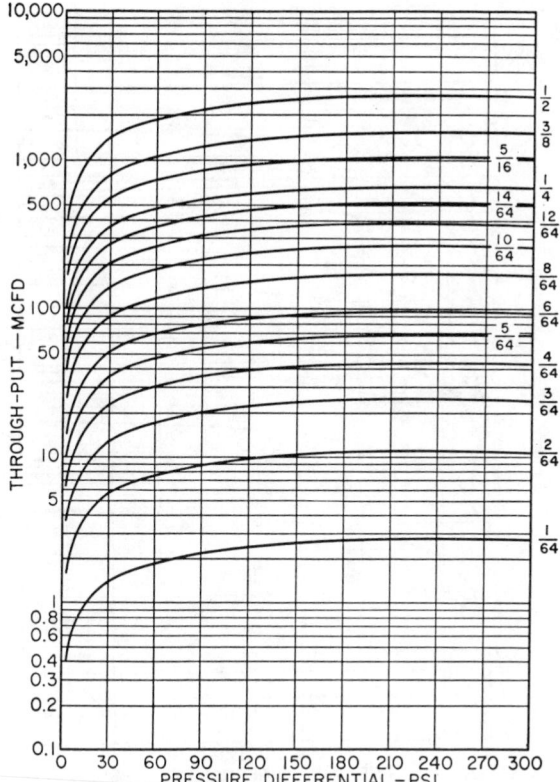

Fig. 5-59d. Typical gas-lift valve-choke capacity chart—upstream pressure 700 psig.

6. The operating valve should be located 646 ft (1,292/2) below the working fluid level determined in step 4 above. This is a depth of 6,146 ft. Figure 5-63 illustrates these calculations.

7. Limited observation has shown that for minimum slippage and fallback in conventional intermitting the pressure differential across the slug should be approximately 50 per cent of the head operating pressure with a minimum differential of 200 psi. Therefore, for 540 psig operating head a minimum operating pressure in the tubing opposite the valve at 6,146 ft will be 810 psig (540 + $^{54}\!\%\!_2$ = 810). Considering the pressure drop across the valve, a casing pressure of approximately 835 psig opposite the valve would be desirable. At a depth of 6,146 ft, 835 psig casing pressure opposite the valve would require a surface operating pressure of about 725 psig.

To estimate the theoretical minimum injection GOR, proceed as follows:

The minimum amount of gas necessary to surface the slug will be that required to fill the tubing from the injection depth to the surface, less that volume occupied by the liquid slug. The gas will be at a pressure which is the average between the slug head (less slippage and fallback), including trap pressure, and the pressure at injection depth.

Two-inch tubing has a capacity of 3.87 bbl/1,000 ft, and if the injection depth is 6,146 feet (see 6 above), then there are 6.146 × 3.87 = 23.75 bbl of space in the tubing.

The slug occupies approximately 5 bbl of space in a distance of 1,292 ft. The pressure opposite the injection valve in the tubing at a depth of 6,146 ft is 810 psig.

Therefore, the space occupied by gas just as the top of the 5 bbl starting slug hits the surface is 18.75 bbl, or 105.5 cu ft.

From Fig. 5-40, with 810 psig at 6,146 ft the pressure at 1,292 ft (the approximate bottom of the slug) is 730 psig. Therefore, the average pressure on the 105.5 cu ft of gas is 770 psig

$$\text{Minimum gas} = 105.5 \times \frac{770}{14.65} \times \frac{520}{587} \times \frac{1}{0.921} = 5,330 \text{ scf}$$

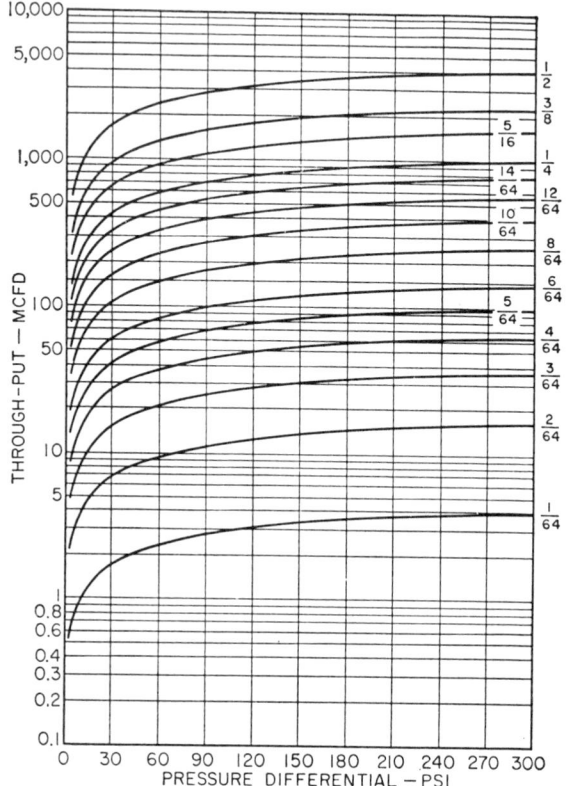

Fɪɢ. 5-59e. Typical gas-lift valve-choke capacity chart—upstream pressure 750 psig.

where 0.921 is the gas-deviation factor. See Fig. 5-69 for a simplified chart for the gas-deviation factor. Minimum IGOR = 5,330/3 = 1,776 cu ft/bbl.

MISCELLANEOUS

This section, though headed Miscellaneous, may well prove the opposite in any given case. It is listed as such only because, in the gross picture, the fundamental problems of design have been covered. As chamber installations are merely a special application of intermitting systems and can be readily designed by inspection, this section will cover only closed rotative installations and dual completions. Figures 5-64 and 5-65 illustrate two types of chamber designs.

Closed Rotative Gas-lift System Design. A closed rotative gas-lift system may be defined as one in which high-pressure gas from a compressor is delivered to a well or wells for lifting fluid, and the spent lift gas and formation gas are returned in a continuous cycle to the compressor for recompression. The only gas intentionally diverted from the system is excess formation gas and the only gas entering the system is make-up gas to compensate for compressor fuel and line losses. Within economic limits, it is desirable to design a system which requires a minimum of make-up gas regardless of whether this make-up gas is obtained from an outside source or from the system's wells.

There are four basic considerations in the design of a rotative gas-lift system: (1) The gas requirements, both current and ultimate; once the system is filled for maximum requirements, only small amounts of make-up gas are required to keep the system

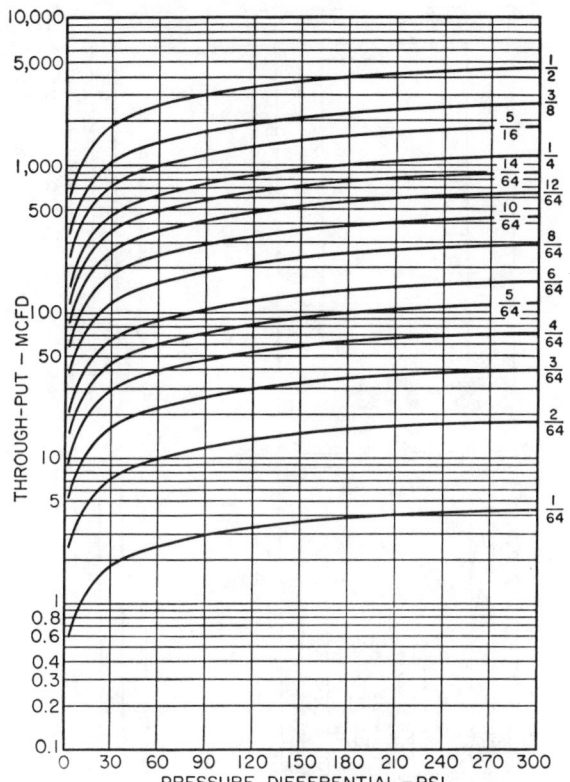

FIG. 5-59f. Typical gas-lift valve-choke capacity chart—upstream pressure 800 psig.

operative. (2) The design of the injection and gathering lines. Consideration should be given to the provision of storage capacity in both the injection system and the compressor suction system, and to additional wells which may be included at a later date. (3) Selection of the compressors and compressor-plant design (see the section on compressors, page **5**-11). (4) The selection of gas-lift equipment and equipment auxiliaries. This includes valves and mandrels, packers, standing valves, surface intermitting control equipment, and surface-pressure recorders. Special attention must be given to the rotative gas-lift system which contains a high percentage of intermitting wells. Gas storage in this type of system is much more critical than that for continuous-flow wells.

Estimation of Gas Requirements and Optimum Injection Pressure. The estimation of gas requirements and of optimum injection pressures should be made for individual wells in the manner previously presented in the sections on continuous- and intermittent-flow system design.

Design of the Injection and Gathering Line Systems. In the design of the injection system, maximum gas requirements must include future wells which may be added to the system. Economics will usually favor looping the lines to meet ultimate requirements. The trunk lines, taking the discharge of the compressors, should be adequately sized to handle these maximum anticipated gas requirements.

Adequate storage must be available to minimize pressure surges occasioned by fluctuations in gas demand. This is particularly true when intermittent wells are included. This storage space could be provided by an abandoned well, the annulus of wells not on gas lift, or a shallow well with large-diameter casing drilled specifically for this purpose.

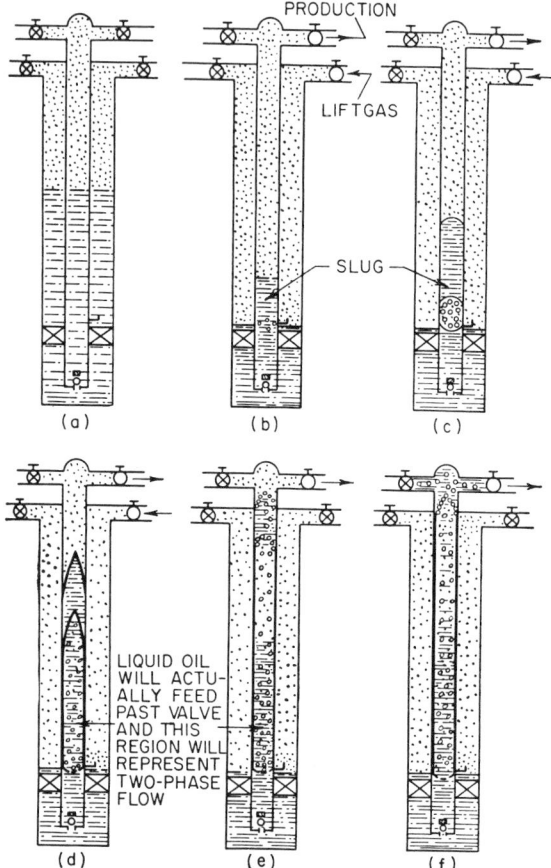

FIG. 5-60. Sketches illustrating intermittent or ballistic-type flow.   (a) Well shut in; (b) the instant after valve opens; (c) slug starting to move; (d) slug profile becomes more pointed as lift gas seeks to channel through; (e) slug breaks over into completely tubulent flow as velocity reaches peak; (f) some fallback as slug bits wellhead.

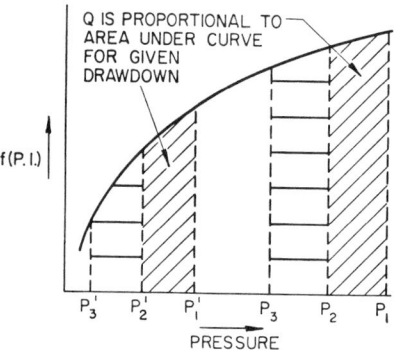

FIG. 5-61. Illustrating relative ability of reservoir to deliver fluid at high vs. low absolute pressures.

For the continuous-flow rotative system, the first step in the design is to list the maximum gas requirements for each well. The second step is to show the length of each line segment on a sketch with the maximum gas which it will be required to deliver. The maximum gas requirement for a segment is the cumulative sum of individual well volume requirements from the end of the line back to the compressors.

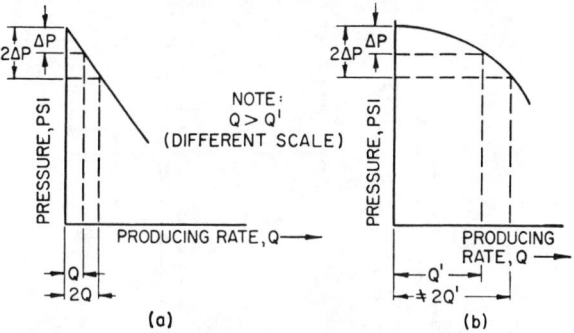

Fig. 5-62. Production vs. drawdown for a constant and a variable PI well. (a) Constant PI. (b) Variable PI.

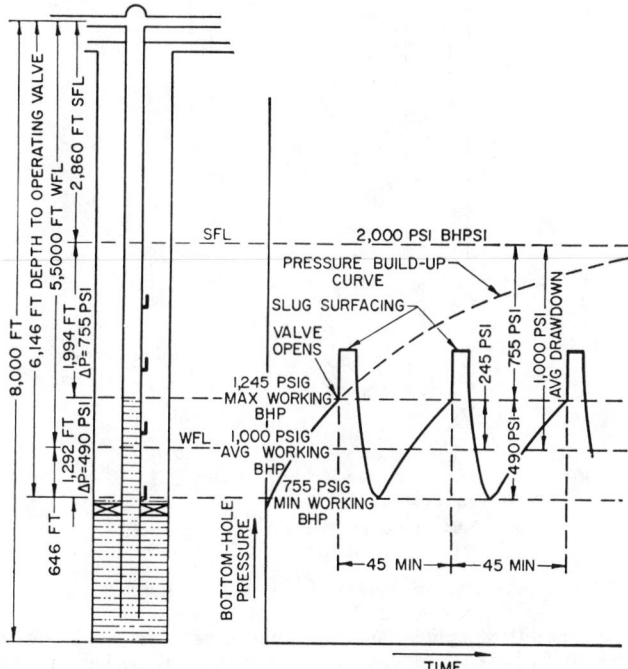

Fig. 5-63. Illustration of bottom-hole pressure recording for slug build-up and surfacing in intermittent-well problem example.

The third step is to size the lines for maximum capacity and allowable pressure drop. This can be conveniently accomplished by reference to a nomograph produced in the *Natural Gasoline Supply Men's Association Handbook*. This nomograph is based on Weymouth's formula and gives the pressure drop per mile of length for various sizes of pipe and various rates of flow. Weymouth's formula normally gives a pressure drop which is somewhat higher than actual; therefore lines sized by this nomograph will represent a conservative choice.

The gathering or suction system will be designed in the same manner as the injection system with allowance for the most economical use of any existing gathering or field fuel system. Looping the lines should be considered where convenient. It is to be noted that the intake system must handle a larger volume of gas (injected plus formation) at a lower pressure than the injection line system.

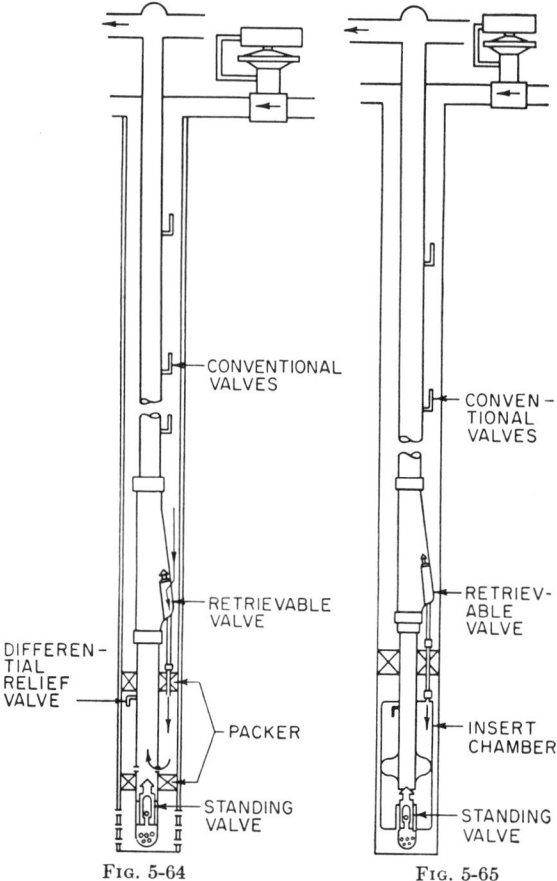

FIG. 5-64   FIG. 5-65

FIG. 5-64. Accumulation-chamber installation.
FIG. 5-65. Insert accumulation-chamber installation.

Selection of Compressors. Selection of compressors depends upon many factors and has been discussed in the equipment section, page **5**–11.

Selection of Gas-lift Equipment and Equipment Auxiliaries. The selection of gas-lift valves, mandrels, and surface controllers and the need for packers or chamber installations should be tailored to fit individual field and well requirements as in any proper gas-lift design. The need for careful selection and application of gas-lift equipment for a rotative system is more critical than for the usual installation because of the limitations imposed by capacity of the compressor plant and the gathering and injection systems.

Rotative Systems for Intermitting Wells. The design of a rotative gas-lift system which contains intermitting wells is considerably more complex than one in which all wells are being produced by continuous flow. The gas demand for continuous-flow wells is one which is relatively constant for a prolonged period of time. As the compressor is a constant-rate device, the problem of gas storage within the system for continuous flow (constant demand) is complicated only by the suction side of the compressor. The size of this low-pressure storage is a function of the formation gas-oil ratio. If the formation gas-oil ratio is low, the storage may be neglected and the excess gas sold or flared.

The intermittent well, however, presents a different problem. This well requires high instantaneous gas-injection rates for short time intervals followed by a much longer period of no gas demand. These demands are contrary to optimum compressor performance, and the system must be given special consideration in designing both the injection and suction lines so as to provide adequate storage space.

Multiwell System Example. The general relations for a solution to the problem for a multiwell closed rotative system will now be derived. Refer to Fig. 5-66.

The condition of maximum instantaneous gas demand can be expressed as

$$G_m = W_m Q_A T \qquad (12)$$

where G_m = maximum instantaneous gas demand
W_m = maximum number of wells injecting gas simultaneously
Q_A = average per well injection rate, cu ft/min
T = injection time, min/cycle

The gas lost from storage

$$G_L = W_m Q_A T - Q_m T = T(W_m Q_A - Q_m) \qquad (13)$$

where G_L = gas lost from storage
Q_m = maximum compressor-gas injection rate, cu ft/min

The gas lost from storage must also equal

$$G_L = \frac{P_D - P_C}{14.65} S_D \qquad (14)$$

where S_D = discharge-system storage, cu ft
P_D = compressor discharge pressure, psig
P_C = line pressure or maximum required well surface injection pressure, psig

Equating Eqs. (13) and (14) and solving for S_D,

$$S_D = \frac{(W_m Q_A - Q_m)14.65T}{P_D - P_C} \qquad (15)$$

The maximum instantaneous gas demand plus formation gas passes through the separator and returns to the suction system. For continuous compressor operation, and neglecting the formation gas, the net gain in the suction system can be expressed as

$$\text{Net gain in suction system} = W_m Q_A T - Q_m t$$

where t = time, minutes, it takes for the gas to pass the separator

And if none of the gas is blown off, the suction-system storage can be expressed as

$$S_L = \frac{(W_m Q_A T - Q_m t)14.65}{P_L - P_{ci}} \qquad (16)$$

where S_L = low-pressure or suction-system storage
P_L = low pressure or suction storage pressure
P_{ci} = compressor intake or suction pressure

Under these design considerations all the rotative gas is fed back into the compressor and the formation gas may either be discharged to the atmosphere for field usage or pipeline sales. Only make-up gas to compensate for line losses and plant and field fuel will be required for the rotative system.

With the aid of Fig. 5-66, let us now apply this design to a multiwell intermittent rotative system. There are three possible systems to consider, and the one selected will depend primarily on the pay-out time. The selection will be influenced, however, by factors which cannot be brought in the problem example as such: (1) the terrain, (2) future wells to be connected to the system, (3) the proximity of a gas pipeline for sale of formation gas, and (4) the volume and richness of the gas to be handled.

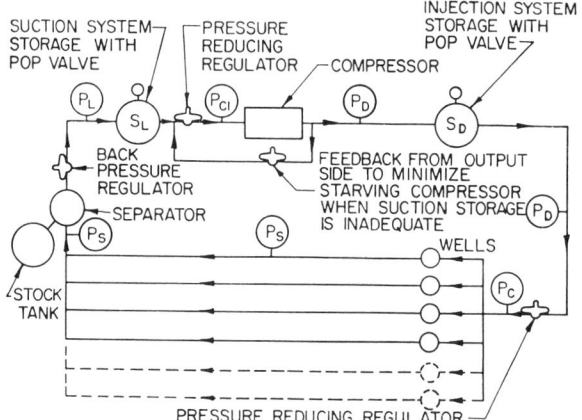

FIG. 5-66. Multiwell closed rotative system–intermitting wells problem example. P_C = casing injection pressure; P_D = compressor discharge pressure (available injection pressure); P_{ci} = compressor intake pressure; P_L = low-pressure or suction-storage pressure; P_S = separator pressure; S_D = high-pressure or compressor-discharge storage; S_L = low-pressure or suction storage.

The three possible systems to be considered are
1. Maximum storage required, the condition wherein the compressor output pressure and the well's injection-pressure requirements are essentially the same
2. Moderate storage requirements and nominally increased compressor discharge pressure
3. Minimum storage and a high-pressure discharge system
Assume the following conditions for the multiwell system:
1. Total number of wells, all on intermittent lift = 10 (W_T)
2. Estimated injection gas required 150 Mcf/D/well = 1.5 MMcf/D total
3. Maximum number of wells that will inject gas simultaneously (50 per cent) = 5 (W_m) (assumed)
4. Mean gas-injection rate per well = 2,400 cu ft/min (Q_A) (for 60 B/D, 2 bbl/cycle, IGOR of 2,400 cu ft/bbl)
5. Mean injection time 2 minutes (T)
6. Minimum operating-line pressure 580 psig (P_C)
7. Compressor discharge pressure 600 psig (P_D)
8. Compressor discharge rate 1.5 MMcf/D = 1,040 cu ft/min (Q_m)
Solution for System 1. Maximum storage required. Assume the discharge-system pressure to be kept constant to within 20 psi.
From Eq. (15), the discharge-system storage can be calculated

$$S_D = \frac{(5 \times 2,400 - 1,040) \times 14.65 \times 2}{600 - 580} = 16,050 \text{ cu ft}$$

or, in terms of 7-in. casing equivalent, (16,050/21.9)100 = 73,300 ft, or 13.9 miles.
Solution for System 2. Moderate storage and nominally increased compressor output pressure. Assume a total line-pressure drop of 120 psi. This will give a 700 psig compressor discharge pressure. Then

$$S_D = \frac{(5 \times 2,400 - 1,040) \times 14.65 \times 2}{700 - 580} = 2,675 \text{ cu ft}$$

or, in terms of 7-in. casing, (2,675/21.9)100 = 12,200 ft, or 2.31 miles.

Solution for System 3. Minimum storage and high-pressure discharge system. Assume the compressor output pressure is 800 psig. Then

$$S_D = \frac{(5 \times 2,400 - 1,040) \times 14.65 \times 2}{800 - 580} = 1,460 \text{ cu ft}$$

or, in terms of 7-in. casing, $(1,460/21.9)100 = 6,600$ ft, or $1\frac{1}{8}$ miles.

The suction-system storage for each of the three systems will depend upon the operating conditions. However, for comparison, assume a 50 psig separator pressure in each of the three cases and a compressor suction pressure which will allow the compressor to operate at an approximate 4.5:1 compression ratio per stage with two-stage compression. For these conditions, the suction pressure of each of the three systems discussed would be (1) $P = 15$ psig; (2) $P = 20$ psig; and (3) $P = 25$ psig. Assuming five minutes' time for the gas to pass the separator in each case, the suction-system storage can be calculated by means of Eq. (16). The results are (1) 7,880 cu ft; (2) 9,200 cu ft; and (3) 11,050 cu ft.

GAS-LIFTING DUAL COMPLETIONS

The design of gas-lift installations for dual completions requires special considerations. The technology involved in effective design of single-zone well strings must first be thoroughly understood for both continuous and intermittently flowing conditions. The advantages and limitations of using tubing-sensitive (fluid-weight) valves as opposed to casing-pressure-operated valves should be recognized. Slim-hole completions using macaroni strings pose special problems.

It is the purpose of this section to signal out specifically the more significant aspects of this problem as well as to give some general operating hints which will prove helpful in any given well operation. The problem is developed under six major headings as follows:

1. Introduction to the problem
2. Dual gas lift—both zones on continuous flow
3. Dual gas lift—one zone continuous and the other intermittent
4. Dual gas lift—both zones intermittent
5. Dual gas lift—probable producing characteristics of both zones unknown
6. Dual gas lift—general operating principles

Introduction to the Problem. Many dual-gas-lift installations do not have the problem of restricted conduit flow and therefore represent somewhat simpler designs. The principles set out below apply to all dual-gas-lift installations except where otherwise noted. For the small-conduit wells ($\frac{3}{4}$, 1-, and 2-in. combinations), where the pressure drop of the lift gas becomes critical, specific designs must consider the pressure drop of the injected gas. The high-pressure drop of the lift gas (usually associated with intermittent lift and sometimes as a high-instantaneous-rate requirement in unloading) requires higher valve-charge settings and larger differences in pressure settings of the successive valves in the same string. Recognition of the limited volumes of fluid which can be produced from the smaller conduits particularly under intermitting conditions is necessary.

Aside from these special considerations, the operating problems are similar for both large- and small-conduit duals. Figures 5-29 and 5-30 illustrate two typical dual installations. Much of the material presented here has been taken from the paper on More Efficient Dual Gas Lift Installations by H. W. Winkler of Camco, Inc., published in the May, 1958, issue of *World Oil*.

Both Zones Continuous Flow

1. Select pressure-operated valves for both strings provided no problem is anticipated in working down to each zone's operating fluid level.

2. Choke the lower-capacity zone and leave the higher capacity unchoked.

3. The pressure differential across the choked valve should be greater than 100 psi (the operating depth and injection-gas requirement including choke size are determined in the manner previously presented in the section on continuous-flow design). Select the valve-choke size to pass approximately 25 per cent more gas than estimated with a differential greater than 100 psi.

4. The unchoked operating valve should have an operating closing pressure less than the flowing pressure in the tubing opposite the valve. This will allow surface control of gas injection to this zone without materially affecting production from the other zone.

One Zone Continuous Flow and the Other Intermittent Flow. *Both Strings Pressure-operated*

1. The continuous-flow-zone operating valve should be choked so as to obtain an operating pressure differential in excess of 100 psi.

2. The intermitting-zone valve should have a higher surface closing pressure than that required to operate the continuous-flow zone (see Fig. 5-67).

3. A bypass (around the surface intermitter) with a regulator and choke is necessary for this type of installation. The regulator is set at the continuous operating pressure of the continuous-flow zone. This pressure is less than the surface closing pressure of the operating intermitting valve. The purpose of the regulator is to assure a constant maximum build-up pressure for the intermitting zone which would otherwise be affected by fluctuating operating pressures in the continuous-flow zone (see Fig. 5-68).

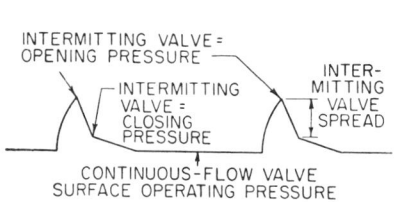

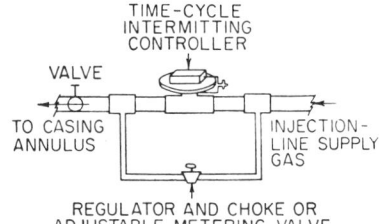

Fɪɢ. 5-67. Surface casing injection pressure recording for correct operation of dual-zone gas lift—one zone intermittent flow, the other continuous flow. (*After Winkler.*)

Fɪɢ. 5-68. Injection-gas bypass with regulator and choke or adjustable metering valve. (*After Winkler.*)

One String Pressure-operated and the Other Fluid-operated

1. The continuous-flow zone should be produced with the pressure-operated valve, and it should be choked for a high-pressure differential across the valve (greater than 100 psi).

2. The intermittent zone should use the fluid-weight valve with the tubing "trigger" pressure selected in accordance with the zone's ability to produce. (This trigger pressure must not be too high so that an adequate slug-surfacing pressure differential may be obtained. A differential of at least 150 to 200 psi is desirable.)

3. A "balanced" fluid-weight valve should be used so that it will be insensitive to lift-gas pressure fluctuations.

4. Any of the following surface controls may be used: (1) regulator, (2) regulator and choke, (3) metering valve, or (4) choke.

Both Zones Intermittent Flow. *One String Pressure-operated and the Other Fluid-operated*

1. The pressure-operated valve should be used on the higher-capacity zone, unless the weaker formation does not have a rapid enough build-up (to "trigger" the fluid-operated valve) to get the desired production from this zone.

2. A bypass with regulator is necessary to ensure proper operation of the pressure-controlled valve when the fluid-weight valve is in operation. The surface intermitter will then build up the casing pressure to the same maximum value on each cycle regardless of whether or not both valves come into operation at the same time (see Fig. 5-68).

3. Use a "balanced" fluid-weight valve.

Both Strings Fluid-operated

1. The higher-capacity zone should be set to trigger at a higher tubing pressure consistent with the available lift pressure which will provide an adequate slug-surfacing differential. This will result in lower injection gas-fluid ratios.

2. Retrievable-type valves are preferred.

3. A choke or a regulator and choke may be used for surface control. If difficulty is anticipated in working down, use a surface intermitter with the fluid-weight valves. The intermitter control will minimize pressure drawdown in the lift gas and ensure the closing off of the upper valves.

4. If it is known that either or both tubing strings will operate below the second valve, conventional pressure-charged valves should be used in combination with the fluid weight in order to reduce the total number of valves required.

Both Zones Produced through the Same Valve String

If the allowable for each zone can be produced in two weeks, a special crossover tool will allow production of both zones through the same valve string.

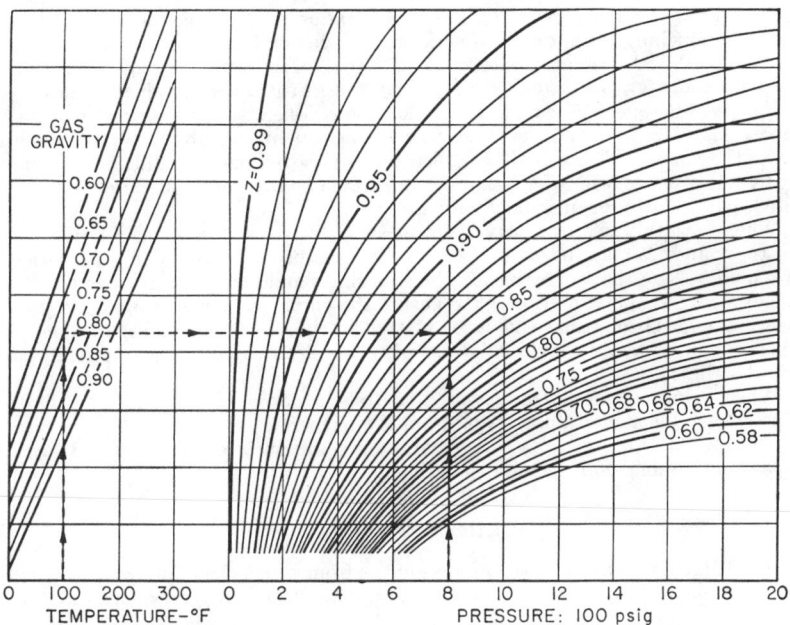

Fig. 5-69. Simplified gas-deviation chart for 0.60 to 0.90 gravity gas-lift gas. (*Data from Standing and Katz.*) A 0.70 gravity gas at a temperature of 100°F and a pressure of 800 psig has a deviation of 0.861.

Producing Characteristics of Either or Both Zones Unknown

Both valve strings should be fluid-operated with retrievable valves. The advantages of fluid-operated valves in this case are:

1. A greater number of valves will be required, thereby increasing the probability of working from the desired deliverability depth of the well.

2. The automatic "trigger" feature of these valves will allow both zones to adjust to a producing cycle and depth consistent with the optimum characteristics of each reservoir.

3. The fluid-operated valves used in conjunction with a surface intermitter will ensure working to a maximum depth in the well.

A Summary of Significant Operating Principles

1. Consider the use of a retrievable production tube between packers. This item of equipment, when applicable, will permit workover of either zone by wireline and without pipe-handling equipment. Further, the retrievable production tube will allow production of the upper or lower zone through either valve string, thus minimizing the effects of an incorrect estimate of the relative producing ability of the two zones.

2. Recognize that it is possible to unload through only one valve string if both zones are to be operated near bottom. This is possible with either retrievable equipment or by swabbing and should be considered particularly where two valve strings will make working down difficult.

3. When using fluid-weight valves in deep wells, use conventional pressure-charged valves in the upper portion of the string in order to reduce the total number of valves required.

4. Where unloading difficulties are expected and fluid-weight valves are used, consider the use of a surface intermitter in order to offset the effects of casing-pressure drawdown and to ensure the closing of the upper valves.

5. When using fluid-operated valves in a dual with two different tubing sizes, the following considerations are significant: (a) When used on the smaller tubing, fluid-weight valves will result in more frequent injection cycles with the possibility of starving the other zone for lift gas. (b) The consideration in (a) above must be weighed against the possibility of not achieving desired producing rates when the fluid-weight valves are used with the larger-sized tubing. If the zone is of very low capacity, it may result in too few operating cycles per day for a satisfactory production rate.

6. For pressure-operated valves, continuous-flow design, set the closing pressure of the operating valve at a value less than that of the anticipated tubing flowing pressure opposite the valve. This will allow a near zero operating pressure differential across the valve and hence will afford significant surface control over the amount of gas injected, particularly for unchoked valves.

7. When both tubing strings have nonconcentric valve mandrels, the relative spacing of the mandrels must be given special consideration. When running the strings, no two mandrels on the shorter or detachable string should pass mandrels on the fixed or longer string at the same time. To ensure the elimination of this difficulty, mandrel spacings for both strings should be plotted to the same scale on separate graphs and possible interference should be observed as the detachable string is lowered past the fixed string.

8. When using nonconcentric gas-lift mandrels, a nonrotating holddown must be used to release the short tubing string from the packer.

9. The use of three pen-pressure recorders at the surface will materially assist trouble-shooting dual-zone gas-lift operations

ACKNOWLEDGMENT

Acknowledgment is made of the many sources from which the information has been drawn, and particularly to the Humble Oil & Refining Co. and Camco Gas Lift Corp.

References

1. Babson, E. C.: The Range of Application of Gas Lift Methods, *Drill. and Prod. Prac., API, Annual*, vol. 266, 1939.
2. Baxendell, P. B.: Producing Wells on Casing Flow—An Analysis of Flowing Pressure Gradients, *Trans. AIME*, vol. 213, p. 202, 1958.
3. Buthod and Whitely: Fluid Flow, *Oil and Gas J.*, Dec. 7, 1945.
4. Camco, Inc.: *Multiphase Vertical Flowing Tubing Pressure Gradients*, Houston, Tex.
5. Gilbert, W. E.: Flowing and Gas Lift Well Performance, API Paper 801–30H, 1954.
6. Kemler, Emory, and G. A. Poole: A Preliminary Investigation of Flowing Wells, *Drill. and Prod. Prac., API, Annual*, vol. 140, 1936.
7. Kirkpatrick, C. V.: *The Power of Gas*, Camco, Inc., Houston, Tex., 1953, 1955.
8. Kirkpatrick, C. V.: Advances in Gas Lift Technology, *Drill. and Prod. Prac., API, Annual*, 1959.
9. Massey, William P.: Intermittent Gas Lift Operation Is Successful, *World Oil*, December, 1958.
10. May, C. J., and A. Laird: The Efficiency of Flowing Wells, *Pet. Tech.*, vol. 20, p. 214, 1934.
11. May, C. J.: Efficiency of Flowing Wells, *Trans. AIME*, vol. 114, p. 99, 1935.
12. Moore, T. V., and H. D. Wilde: Experimental Measurements of Slippage in Flow through Vertical Pipes, *Trans. AIME*, vol. 296, 1931.

13. Poettman, F. H., and P. G. Carpenter: The Multiphase Flow of Oil, Gas, and Water through Vertical Flow Strings with Application to the Design of Gas Lift Installations, *Drill. and Prod. Proc., API, Annual*, 1952.
14. Shaw, S. F.: *Gas Lift Principles and Practices*, The Gulf Publishing Company, Houston, Tex., 1939.
15. Versluys, J.: Mathematical Development of the Theory of Flowing Wells, *Trans. AIME*, vol. 192, 1930.
16. Winkler, H. W.: Downhole Chambers Increase Gas Lift Efficiency, *Pet. Engr.*, June–August, 1956.
17. Winkler, H. W.: How to Design a Closed Rotative Gas Lift System, *Pet. Engr.*, May, 1957.
18. Winkler, H. W.: Flow Valve Selection for Gas Lifting Duals, West Texas Oil Lifting Short Course, Fifth Annual, Texas Technological College, April, 1958.
19. Winkler, H. W.: More Efficient Dual Gas Lift Installations, *World Oil*, May, 1958.
20. Winkler, H. W.: *Gas Lift Manual*, Camco, Inc., Houston, Tex., 1958.
21. Winkler, H. W.: The Application of Pressure and Temperature Surveys to Gas Lift, *World Oil*, May, 1959.
22. Zaba and Doherty: *Practical Petroleum Engineer's Handbook*, 4th ed., The Gulf Publishing Company, Houston, Tex., 1956.
23. Beeson, Carrol M., Donald G. Knox, and John H. Stoddard: The Plunger Lift Method of Oil Production, *Pet. Engr.*, vol. 30, 1958.

Chapter 6

HYDRAULIC PUMPS

By C. J. Coberly

President, Kobe, Inc.

and

F. Barton Brown

Chief Mechanical Engineer
Product Research and Development Division
Kobe, Inc.

BOTTOM-HOLE APPLICATION OF HYDRAULIC POWER

In the broad definition *hydraulic bottom-hole pumps* are fluid-power-operated, which would include both liquid and gas as the power-transmitting means. At the present time the only commercial pumps are liquid-operated and the liquid is generally the well oil with the gas, water, and sand removed to a point substantially better than required for pipeline oil. Water has been used experimentally as the power-transmitting fluid.

The basic difference between hydraulic well pumps and the time-accepted sucker-rod type is in the power-transmitting medium. Oil under moderately high pressure is pumped to the bottom of the well, usually as a continuous unidirectional flow, as contrasted to the reciprocating-rod system. This fluid operates an engine in the bottom of the well which is mechanically connected with a pump.

Types

The type of hydraulic pump which has come into use is a *reciprocating engine* having directly connected to it a *reciprocating pump*, but the same basic principle applies to a rotary engine connected to a rotary pump. Since the pressures are high and the volumes are small, positive-displacement devices are best adapted, although a multistage turbine connected to a multistage centrifugal pump would be feasible for high-volume low-head conditions.

The jet pump has been proposed for oil-field applications and tested to a limited extent.

History

The basic *principle* of hydraulic pumps was first applied to pumping oil by Faucett in 1875. While this device was steam-operated and required a large-diameter borehole, it incorporated most, if not all, of the features of present-day pumps. No commercial use of the Faucett pump is of record, and it was not until after 1920 that increasing well depths led various engineers to study the problem seriously. Humphreys, Crum, and Gage are names which will be recorded in the history of the development. The first sustained commercial effort was made by Kobe, Inc., starting in 1932, and until recently Kobe pumps were the only hydraulic pumps available. Since 1945, the principle has become generally accepted by the oil industry, and by 1959, Dempsey (Byron-Jackson), Sargent, National, and Fluid Packed Pump had entered the field commercially.

GENERAL DESCRIPTION

Basic Systems

Two basic *systems* have been applied to hydraulic pumping, first, the oscillating-column system, in which there is an intermittent application of pressure to the fluid in one or more tubes extending from the wellhead to the pump; and second, a system in which *fluid* is supplied under pressure *continuously* to the *bottom-hole unit* where a valve controls its application to give a reciprocating motion. The difference between the two is in the length of the passage between the control point and the pump. In the first case this is the entire length of the tubing; and in the latter it is the distance of a few feet at the most from the engine valve to the ends of the cylinder.

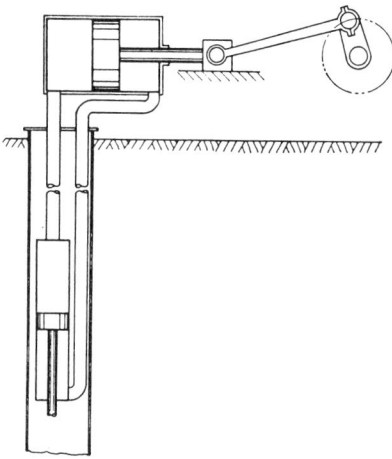

FIG. 6-1. Oscillating-column hydraulic pumping system.

Oscillating Columns

In its simplest form the oscillating-column system may be a crank-and-flywheel-operated cylinder at the wellhead, having the two tubes connecting the ends of this cylinder to a bottom-hole cylinder, as shown in Fig. 6-1. The ratio of surface-cylinder and bottom-hole-cylinder areas may be selected to give any desired stroke multiplication. In place of the crank-and-flywheel device at the surface, sources of high and low pressure may be provided and a timed valve used to control the alternate application of these pressures to the tubings.

This type of device has not come into commercial use because of the limitations imposed by the compressibility of the fluid in the tubing columns.

Direct Flow in a Closed Circuit

All commercial hydraulic oil-well pumps today use a system having a continuous flow of power fluid in a closed circuit to transmit power to the bottom-hole pump.

A prime mover, as shown in Fig. 6-2, operates a triplex or other positive-displacement pump, which takes settled oil from a supply tank and delivers it to a high-pressure distribution system having individual flow controls or throttle valves which divide the fluid, directing the required amount to each well. This system may be for one well or for an entire lease, sometimes involving hundreds of wells. Where it is for an individual well, control is accomplished by the speed and size of or by intermitting the triplex pump. The well tubing may be arranged in a variety of ways, which are described in detail on page 6-51. The insert pump uses concentric tubes and the pump is run inside the production tubing on a string of small-diameter tubing. It is seated in a shoe at the bottom having a port for entrance of the well fluid. Power oil is pumped down the inner string to the pump unit, and the mixed spent power oil and production return together in the tubing annulus. At the wellhead a lead line returns this fluid to the supply tank, where the water and sand are separated and the settled oil is returned to the intake of the triplex. The well or lease production is drawn from this tank to gauge tanks or to main collection lines.

The bottom-hole unit has a bottom intake for well fluid and a top intake for power fluid. The pump intakes fluid at formation pressure and discharges it into the well tubing against the column pressure. The net pressure on the pump is the column pressure minus the formation pressure, and when the engine and pump pistons have the same diameter the differential pressure on the engine is equal to the net pressure on the pump. With power oil and pumped fluid of equal density, the engine and pump column pressures are balanced. The engine takes power oil at column pressure plus the differential pressure and discharges into column pressure. The power of the engine and pump is determined by the differential and net pressures, respectively,

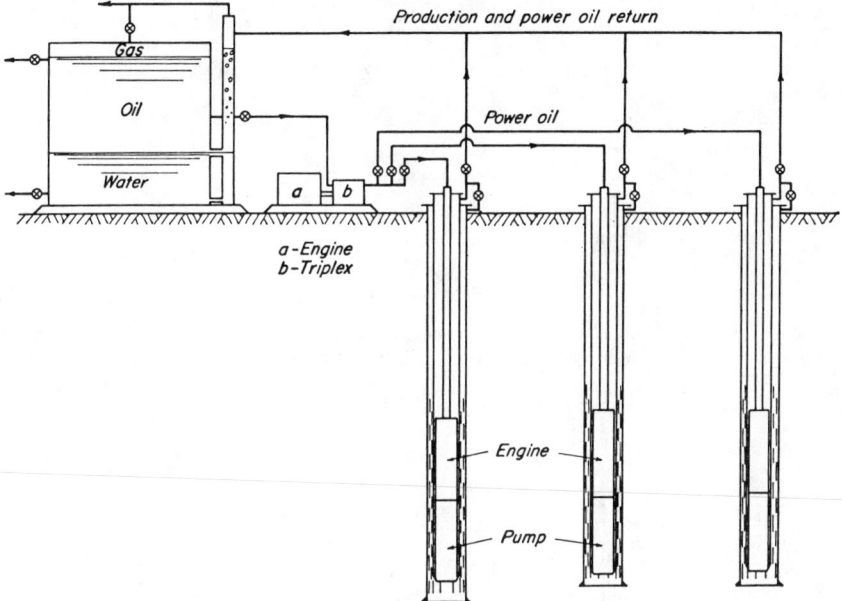

FIG. 6-2. Direct-flow hydraulic pumping system.

and the absolute value of the pressures is of interest only in determining the hydraulic and mechanical designs. If the well or submergence pressure is low, the net pressure on the pump is substantially the full column pressure and the absolute pressure at the engine intake with a 1:1 area ratio is double the column pressure.

DESIGN PRINCIPLES

The *bottom-hole unit* has *three elements* which may be combined in various ways—an engine, a control valve, and a pump. To understand the construction and operation of the complete unit, some variations in each of the elements are given below.

Cylinder

The cylinder with its associated piston and piston rod and the pressures applied to produce the up- and downstrokes are illustrated in Fig. 6-3a to f where

U = upstroke P_1 = operating pressure P_3 = well pressure
D = downstroke P_2 = engine discharge pressure P_4 = pump discharge pressure

In open systems $P_2 = P_4$.

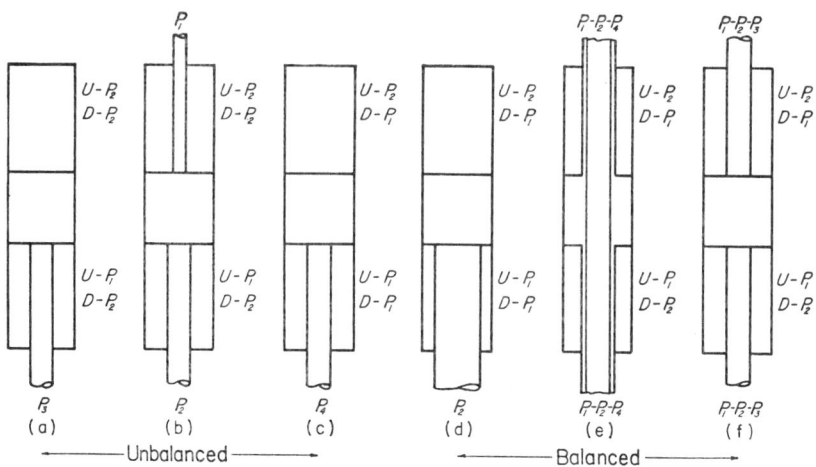

Fig. 6-3. Cylinder types.   Note that in e and f the pressure P_1, P_2, P_3, or P_4 applied to the rod area must be the same on the top and bottom.

Figures 6-3a, b, and c are applicable to single-acting pumps, and d, e, and f may be best applied to double-acting pumps.

Engine Valve

With cylinders 3a, b, c, and d a three-way valve is required and with e and f a four-way valve is used.   Such valves are illustrated in principle in Fig. 6-4a and b.

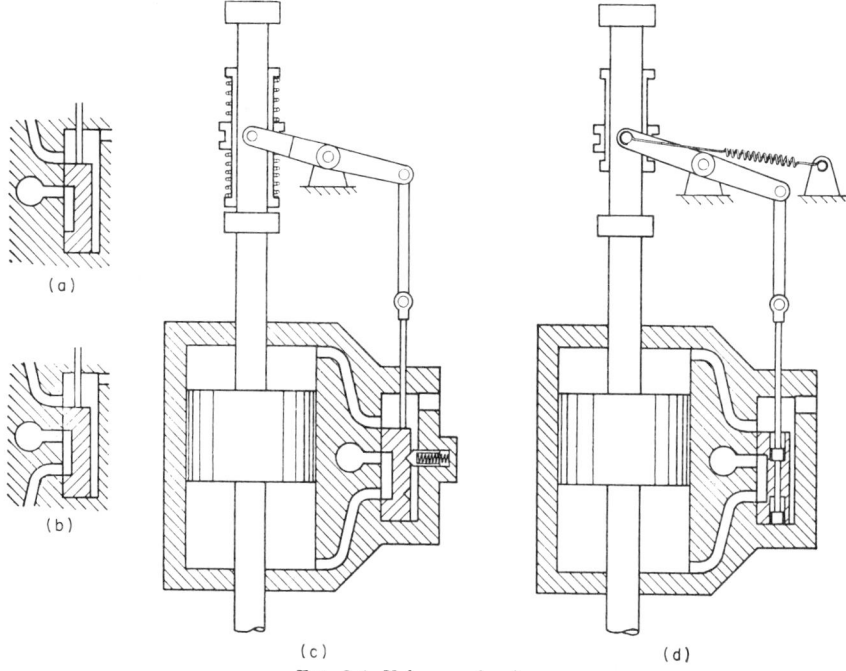

Fig. 6-4. Valve mechanisms.

With these valves the upper and lower ports are connected to the ends of the cylinders of Fig. 6-3, as indicated by the pressures. The valve is connected to the piston rod with lost motion; so that as the rod approaches the end of the stroke it actuates the valve.

If the valve is mechanically operated in this way, means of avoiding dead-center position is provided, such as by means of a spring-toggle action or spring and triggered detent.

The most satisfactory valve operation is obtained by use of a pilot valve, which controls the fluid to a cylinder having a piston connected to and operating the main valve. The pilot valve is either mechanically or hydraulically actuated and has a mechanical or hydraulic detent, or it may have a mechanical or hydraulic toggle action.

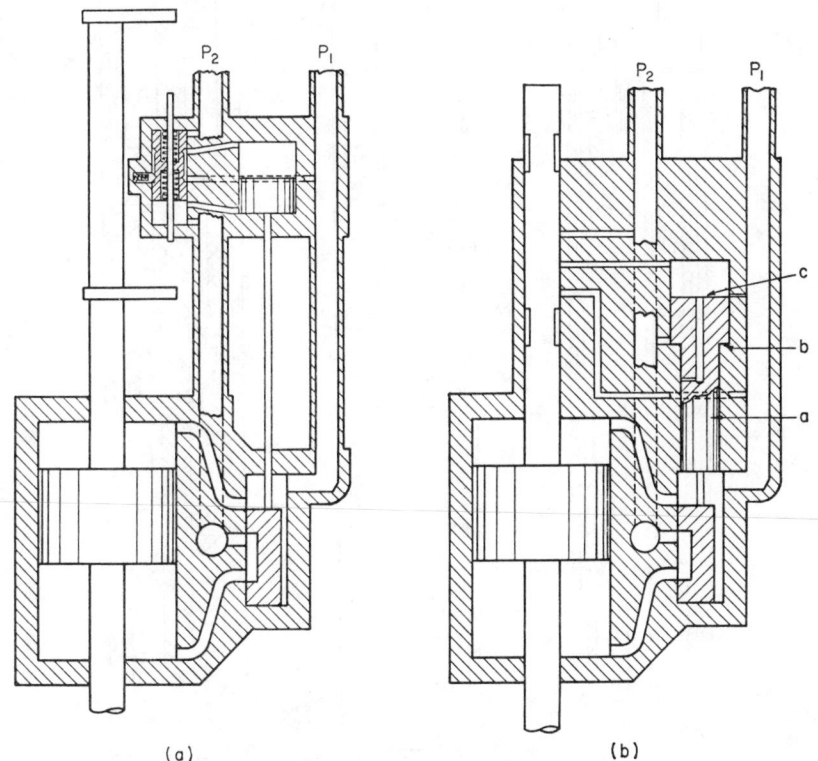

(a)   (b)

Fig. 6-5. Valve mechanisms.

Figure 6-4c shows the principle of a direct-acting valve with spring snap action and detent, and Fig. 6-4d the spring-toggle action.

Figure 6-5a shows a main valve operated by a pilot piston which is controlled by a four-way pilot valve. The pilot valve is mechanically operated at the ends of the main piston stroke by the snap-action springs and the spring detent. Figure 6-5b shows a pilot-controlled and fluid-operated main valve. The pilot piston illustrated is a differential-area type, as illustrated in Fig. 6-3d, and therefore requires only a three-way pilot valve. For equal force in each direction the small area of the pilot-valve rod a and annular area b are equal and are constantly connected to pressure and exhaust, respectively. The pilot piston area c is the sum of the areas of a and b. Therefore, when the operating pressure P_1 is applied to c the force is *down* and equal to

$$F = P_1c - P_1a - P_2b$$

but $P_1c = P_1a + P_1b$

$$F = (P_1 - P_2)b$$

When exhaust pressure P_2 is applied to c the force is *up* and equal to

$$F = P_2c - P_1a - P_2b$$
$$F = -(P_1 - P_2)a$$

Since the areas a and b are equal, the forces are equal to move the main valve up or down.

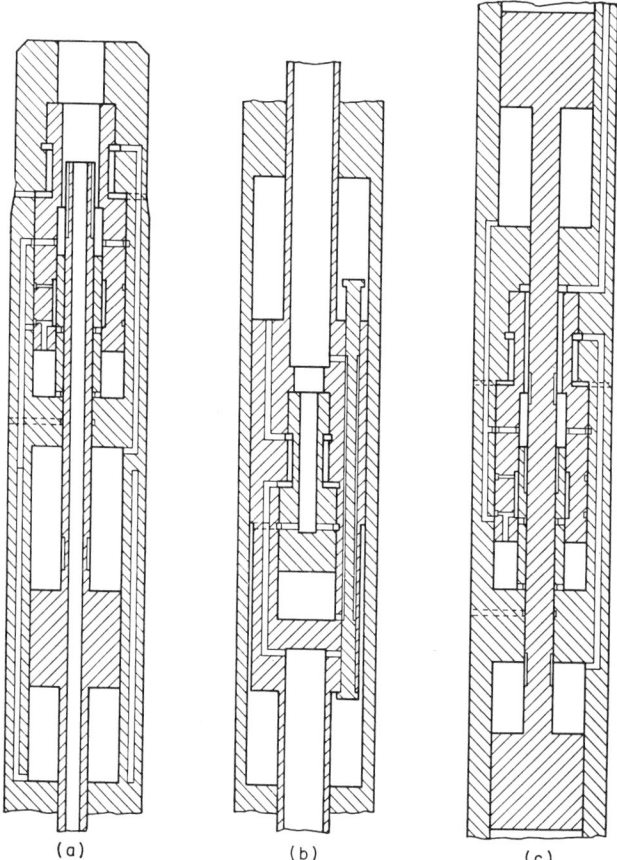

(a) (b) (c)

Fig. 6-6. Valve location.

By combining one of the engine principles illustrated in Fig. 6-3 with the valve principles of Fig. 6-4 or 6-5 any desired form of hydraulic engine may be produced suitable for applying to bottom-hole pumps.

Because of space limitations practical constructions using these principles usually have the main valve and engine piston coaxial and may have the pilot valve coaxial also but, since this valve is small, it may be parallel to the axis of the main valve and piston.

The main valve and pilot valve are located at either the top or bottom end of the engine cylinder, or in the engine piston. These three valve locations, as applied to full double-acting engines, are illustrated in Fig. 6-6a to c in simplified form. For single action one main valve port is omitted. Figure 6-6a shows the valve on top. Figure 6-6b shows a valve in the piston with the piston rod and extension tubular and used for the power-oil supply and exhaust.   In this case the pilot valve is mechanically actuated and has a hydraulic detent.   Figure 6-6c shows the valve below the engine cylinder.

Pump

The bottom-hole pump for hydraulic operation is single-acting, differential double-acting, or full double-acting and may use any of the cylinder types illustrated in Fig. 6-3a to f.

Single-acting.   The single-acting pump corresponds in principle and construction to the sucker-rod pump.   This type has a pumping stroke which is usually upward and a downward return stroke.   Since it pumps in only one direction, the force required for the return stroke is low, and if the return is downward, it may use either gravity alone or a combination of gravity and a small hydraulic force.   The latter construction is usually used, as the weight of the moving parts of the pump does not provide sufficient force for positive and fast action.   Figure 6-7a shows a differential-area engine connected to a single-acting pump.   The engine valve is not shown but may be any one of those illustrated in Fig. 6-6a, b, or c.   The pump may be located either below or above the engine or may be concentric with it.   Figure 6-7a has the engine above the pump and in axial alignment.   This is the most common arrangement, since it is desirable for the pump to have bottom intake and with power oil supplied from above it is best for the engine to be on top.   The intake or standing valve may be a single-ball or poppet type of large size.   The working valve, in this case carried by the plunger, is also a single-ball or poppet type.   On the upstroke the pump load is applied to the full piston diameter.   The effective engine area is the piston area minus the rod area, and the force is this area times the pressure $P_1 - P_2$.   On the downstroke P_1 is applied to both sides of the engine piston, and since the pump standing valve is closed, the downward force is $P_1 - P_2$ times the area of the rod.

This same construction may be used for gravity return, by changing the engine valve porting so that the top of the engine piston is constantly open to P_2 and the annulus below the piston is open to P_1 on the upstroke and P_2 on the downstroke.

Figure 6-7b shows a concentric arrangement of engine and pump for single-acting operation.   In this case P_1 is constantly applied to a small-diameter piston extension a.   The annulus b between this extension and the full piston diameter is open to P_2.   The annulus c between the pump piston and the engine piston is open to P_1 on the upstroke and to P_2 on the downstroke.   The upward force is $P_1 - P_2$ times the area of the engine annulus c minus P_1 times the area of the piston extension a.   On the downstroke the force equals $P_1 - P_2$ times the extension area a.

Differential Double-acting.   Figure 6-7c illustrates the principle of a concentric full double-acting engine connected to a differential double-acting pump.   This type of pump uses single intake and discharge valves.   It does, however, have double-acting withdrawal from the formation and double-acting discharge.   The net displacement of the pump is the differential area double-acting or the full area of the pump piston single-acting.   For a given pump cylinder diameter it therefore has the same capacity as a single-acting pump.   As illustrated P_1 is applied to the tubing annulus with P_2 in the inner tube.   This, however, may be reversed by a suitable crossover above the engine.   The pump discharge in this illustration is through the hollow piston rod of both the pump and the engine.

Figure 6-7d illustrates the construction of a differential double-acting engine connected to a differential double-acting pump.   In this case the engine valve is a three-way differential-area type and is located in the engine piston.

Figure 6-7e shows a differential double-acting pump in which the differential area constantly open to well pressure is above the engine piston.   A four-way engine valve (not shown) would be used and located in the middle plug, which would direct fluid alternately to the annulus under the engine piston or the annulus over the pump piston.

Full Double-acting.   Figure 6-7f illustrates a fully balanced full double-acting engine connected with a full double-acting pump.   The two pistons are connected with a hollow piston rod and have a lower rod and an upper rod extending through the cylinder heads to balance the areas. The upper rod is subjected to the pressure P_1, and since it is hollow, P_1 is also applied to the end of the lower rod. The upper rod acts as a pilot valve, having ports which alternately apply pressure and exhaust to the lower end of the main valve, which is a differential-area type as shown in Fig. 6-6a. Since the pump is full double-acting, an intake and exhaust valve is required for each end of the pump cylinder. With this construction pressure surges in the power-oil

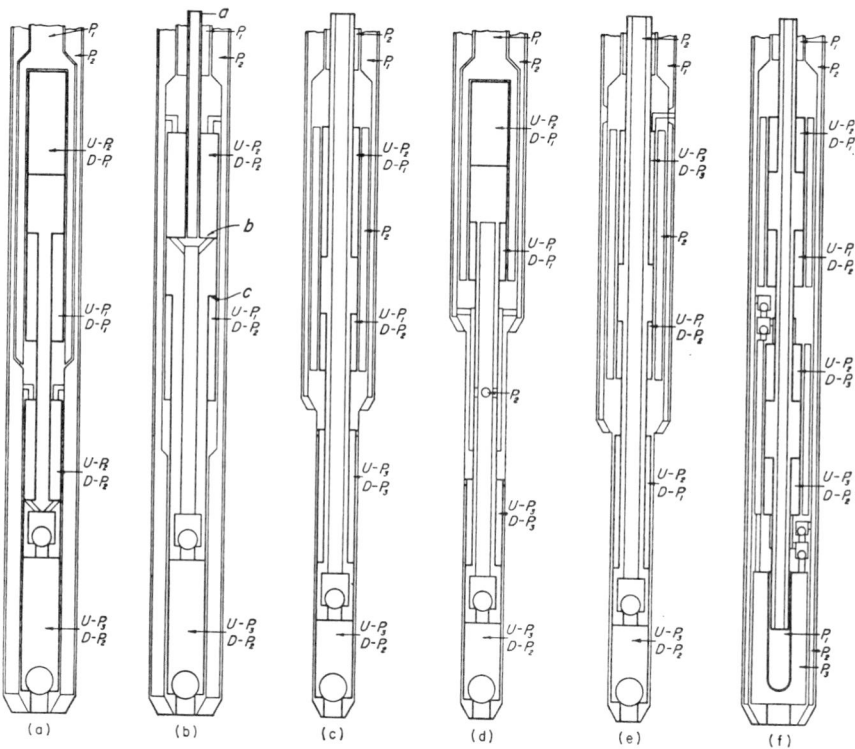

FIG. 6-7. Pump and engine combinations. In open systems the pump discharge pressure $P_4 = P_2$ and is designated as P_2 here.

system and in the pump-discharge column are reduced to a minimum and an even withdrawal from the formation is obtained.

Closed System

Figures 6-7a to f are illustrated as "open" system pumps in which the discharge fluid from the engine is mixed with the discharge from the pump. In the "closed" system the operating fluid is separated from the pumped fluid, both in the pump and in the tubing system. In this case an additional tube passage is required in which the engine discharge pressure is P_2, and may differ from the pump discharge pressure P_4 due to the difference in density of the operating fluid selected and the produced fluid.

The closed system has advantages over the open system where the produced fluid is sandy, corrosive, or has poor lubricating properties. This is covered in more detail under power-oil systems, pages **6**–27 to **6**–38.

DESIGN DETAILS

Valve

The engine valve has a primary function of *reversing* the *fluid* to the ends of the engine cylinder when the piston approaches the end of its stroke. It has other important requirements also—namely, *speed control* and *acceleration control*. To best accomplish these additional functions the valve is provided with multiple speeds and stroke control at each speed.

Figure 6-8 shows the construction of the Kobe differential-area valve which has three speeds in each direction. The valve is shown in five positions; in Fig. 6-8*a* the

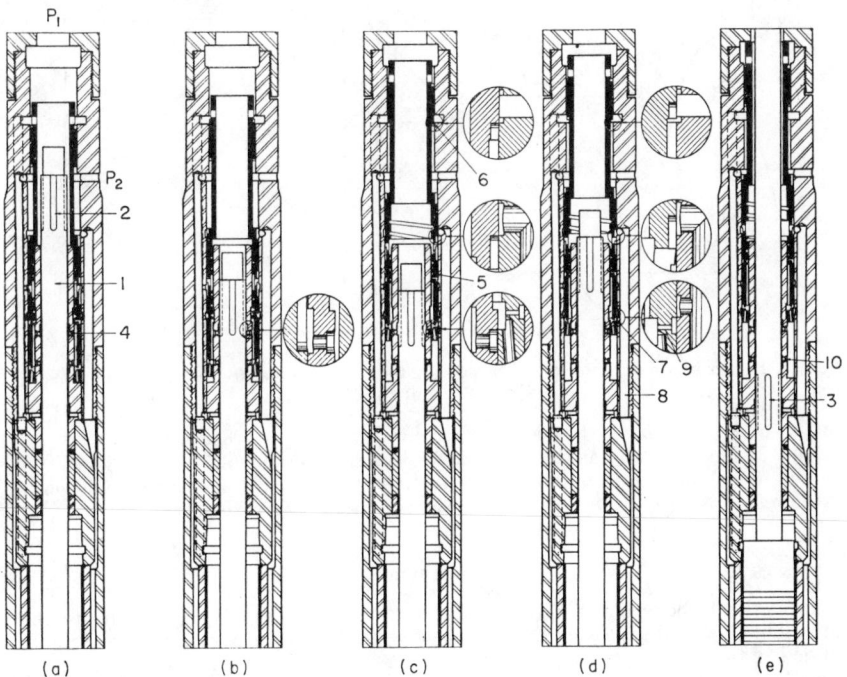

FIG. 6-8. Three-speed governing valve.

valve is down, the ports are fully open, and the pressure P_1 is being directed through the upper valve port to the top of the piston which is moving down at full speed; in Fig. 6-8*e* the valve is in the up position with the ports from the top of the piston open to exhaust P_2 and the piston is moving up at full speed. The valve rod (1) is attached to the piston and has upper and lower ports (2) and (3) which connect the operating area of the valve to pressure and exhaust, respectively, to cause the first or high-speed motion of the valve.

In Fig. 6-8*b* the valve rod has opened the upper port (4) to pressure and the valve is moving up at the first speed. The ports of the valve have not closed; so the piston continues down to the bottom of the stroke as shown in Fig. 6-8*c* controlled by a lower dashpot (not shown).

When the valve is in the position shown in Fig. 6-8*c* the valve land has cut off the port (4), stopping the high-speed movement, leaving only the control thread (5) open to pressure, which causes the valve to move at a very slow speed. At this point the throttling grooves (6) are just starting to open; so that both power-oil inlet and exhaust are throttled, giving a dwell and a slow start to the piston. The throttle grooves (6) are graduated so that, as the valve continues to move at slow speed, a controlled acceleration is obtained.

In the position shown in Fig. 6-8d the upper throttling grooves have just passed the edge of the port and the lower grooves are in their mid-position. In this position the valve port (7) is starting to open to the passage (8) which is supplying power fluid to the underside of the engine piston. The control orifice (9) controls the rate of admission to the valve of the power fluid from this source and this control is sized to give a valve speed of four times the slow speed. The valve then continues at this speed to the end of its upward motion, as shown in Fig. 6-8e.

In Fig. 6-8e the piston is starting to enter the upper dashpot and the lower valve-rod port (3) is approaching the port (10) which will open the area under the valve to

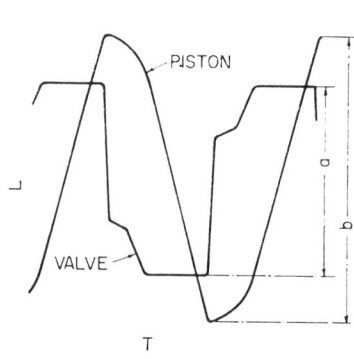

FIG. 6-9. Piston and valve motion of three-speed governing valve.

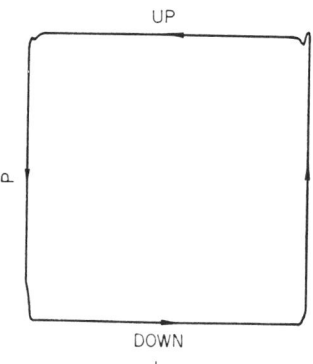

FIG. 6-10. Indicator card for conditions of of Fig. 6-9.

exhaust and start the high-speed movement down. The other controls "down" function in the same way as the "up" controls described above.

Figure 6-9 shows the piston and valve motion under normal operating conditions. Figure 6-10 is an indicator card under the conditions of Fig. 6-9.

Governing

As described above under Fig. 6-8d, the passage (8) is supplying pressure to the piston, but this fluid is passing through the lower throttling grooves and the pressure will be less than the supply pressure due to pressure drop. When this pressure drop is one-half the supply pressure, the valve will not move beyond this point, as the valve is a differential-area type with a 2:1 area ratio. The maximum rate the piston can move under these conditions is proportional to $\sqrt{P_1 - P_2}$ times the area of the throttling grooves at this mid-point. If there is no load on the pump the piston speed will be limited to this rate. This is called the *governing speed* and the throttle area is selected to give full rated speed under these conditions at 2,500 psi operating pressure. Figure 6-11 gives the governing speed vs. operating pressure with no pump load. When the pump picks up load, the piston will slow down, reducing the pressure drop, increasing the pressure in passage (8) to more than one-half pressure, and the valve will again move to complete its stroke.

Figure 6-12 shows the valve and piston on a time base with no load on the pump for the entire "up" stroke and with half filling on the downstroke.

Figure 6-13 is an indicator card for pressure under the piston for these same conditions. It should be noted that as soon as the piston hits fluid the valve opens and the pump resumes normal speed. The valve will thus throttle for any part of the stroke that the pump is not loaded.

This governing action is very important in hydraulic-pump operation. In a closely coupled hydraulic system the speed of the engine is determined by the volume of fluid supplied and is independent of the load on the engine. However, in a well pumping system a large amount of energy is stored in the compressed fluid in the tubing, and the engine speed is limited only by the rate of expansion of this compressed fluid. The instantaneous engine speed therefore could be extremely high if, during one stroke or a part of a stroke, the pump is not filled with fluid, as occurs in "pump-off." The amount of stored energy depends on the volume of oil and the

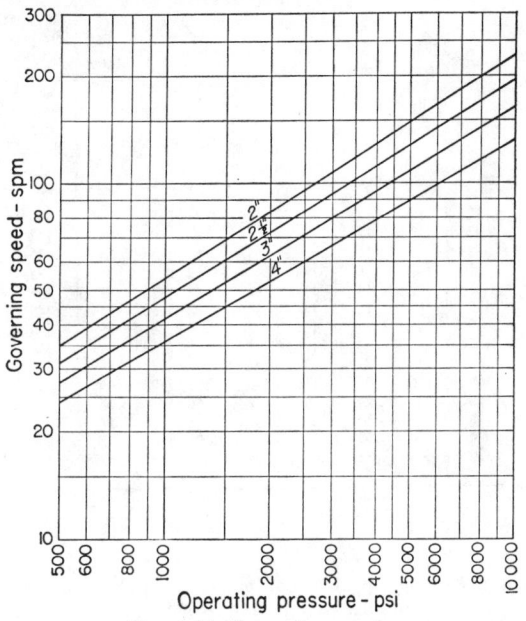

FIG. 6-11. Governing speed.

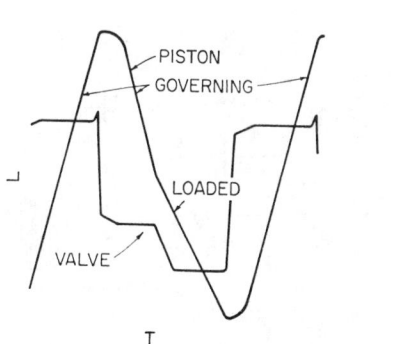

FIG. 6-12. Piston and valve motion with governing.

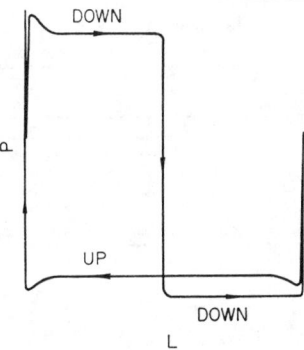

FIG. 6-13. Indicator card with governing of Fig. 6-12.

bulk modulus (see Fig. 6-69). With oil having a bulk modulus of 200,000 psi and an operating pressure of 2,500 psi and with 6,000 ft of 2½-in. tubing, the volume of compressed fluid, if expanded to zero pressure, would operate a 2½-in. pump (1¼-in. piston, 18-in. stroke) 148 complete strokes. Therefore, during the first stroke the pressure would drop only 17 psi and the speed would be limited only by hydraulic friction in the tubing and engine passages, which could be many times the normal speed. With a governing valve the maximum speed at "pump-off" is limited to its design speed, as shown in Fig. 6-11, which in this case is full rated speed at 2,500 psi. At 5,000 psi the governing speed would be limited to approximately 40 per cent above full rated speed.

Table 6-1. Specifications of Kobe Production Units

Nominal pump size	OD	Pump length, in.	Approx wt., lb	Shipping wt., lb	Stroke, in.	Piston sizes		Area ratios		Rated speed, spm	Pump displacement at rated speed, B/D	Capacity, B/D per spm		Max setting depth
						Engine	Pump	E/P	P/E			Power oil required engine end	Displacement pump end	
2 × 1³⁄₁₆	1⅞	78½	42	80	12	1	1³⁄₁₆	1.83	0.55	83	95	2.15	1.14	15,000
2 × 1	1⅞	78½	42	80	12	1	1	1.00	1.00	83	174	2.15	2.10	10,000
2 × 1³⁄₁₆	1⅞	78½	42	80	12	1	1³⁄₁₆	0.63	1.55	83	270	2.15	3.25	6,300
2½ × 1	2⁵⁄₁₆	105	85	147	18	1¼	1	1.92	0.52	71	182	5.02	2.56	15,000
2½ × 1⅛	2⁵⁄₁₆	105	85	147	18	1¼	1⅛	1.34	0.75	71	261	5.02	3.67	13,400
2½ × 1¼	2⁵⁄₁₆	105	85	147	18	1¼	1¼	1.00	1.00	71	349	5.02	4.92	10,000
2½ × 1⁷⁄₁₆	2⁵⁄₁₆	105	85	147	18	1¼	1⁷⁄₁₆	0.70	1.43	71	500	5.02	7.04	7,000
3 × 1¼	2¹³⁄₁₆	136½	168	256	24	1½	1¼	1.69	0.59	64	358	9.61	5.59	15,000
3 × 1⅜	2¹³⁄₁₆	136½	168	256	24	1½	1⅜	1.27	0.79	64	475	9.61	7.42	12,700
3 × 1½	2¹³⁄₁₆	136½	168	256	24	1½	1½	1.00	1.00	64	604	9.61	9.44	10,000
3 × 1¾	2¹³⁄₁₆	136½	168	256	24	1½	1¾	0.68	1.48	64	896	9.61	14.0	6,800
4 × 1¾	3¹³⁄₁₆	173	370	540	30	2	1¾	1.46	0.69	57	822	21.44	14 4	14,600
4 × 2	3¹³⁄₁₆	173	370	540	30	2	2	1.00	1.00	57	1,200	21.44	21.0	10,000
4 × 2⅜	3¹³⁄₁₆	173	370	540	30	2	2⅜	0.65	1.55	57	1,850	21.44	32.5	6,500

National Pump

The hydraulic pump made by the National Supply Company is illustrated in Figs. 6-14 and 6-15. This pump uses the principle of Fig. 6-7d, which is a differential-area engine connected to a differential-area pump, with the areas selected for equal work on the up- and downstroke.

The valve is located at the top end of the engine cylinder and is controlled by

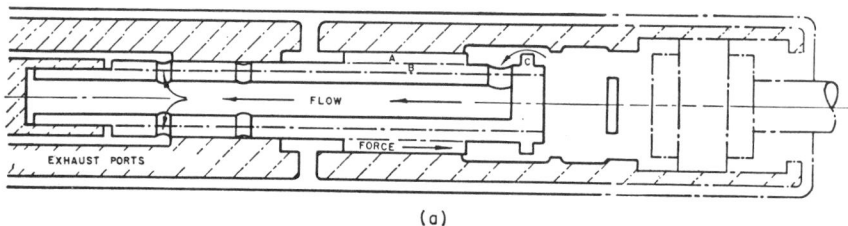

(a)

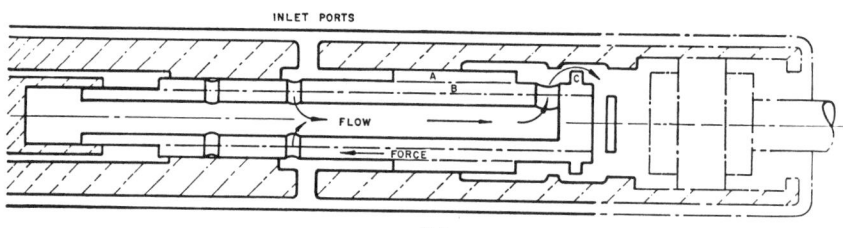

(b)

FIG. 6-14. National engine valve. (a) Upstroke; (b) downstroke.

pressure differential and fluid velocity. No pilot valve is required and there are no mechanical linkages. When the valve is in the up position, as shown in Fig. 6-14a, the flow of fluid by the spool head C holds the valve in this position by opposing the downward force of the pressure differential on the area A. At the end of the stroke

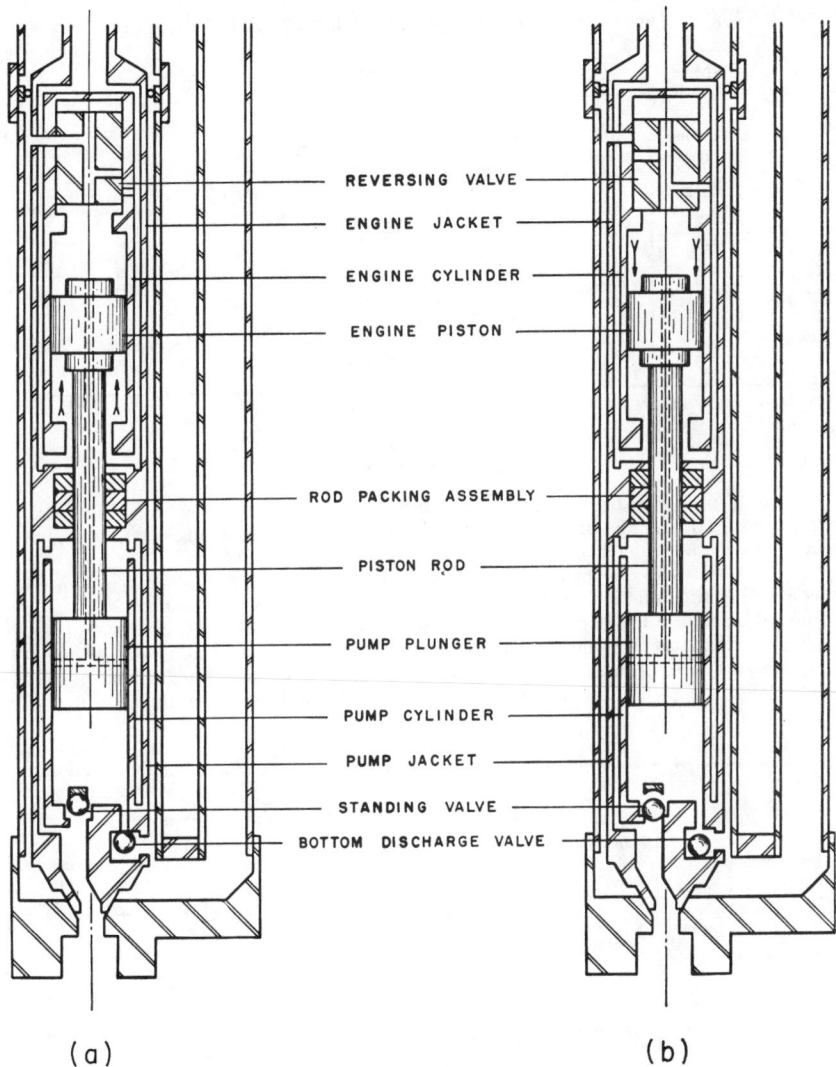

REVERSING VALVE

ENGINE JACKET

ENGINE CYLINDER

ENGINE PISTON

ROD PACKING ASSEMBLY

PISTON ROD

PUMP PLUNGER

PUMP CYLINDER

PUMP JACKET

STANDING VALVE

BOTTOM DISCHARGE VALVE

(a)   (b)

Fig. 6-15. National pump. (a) Upstroke; (b) downstroke.

the valve is shifted to its down position by this force. The pressure differential is now upward on the area B but is again opposed by the flow by the spool head C. When the spool valve is shifted to either extreme position, it is held in place by the flow of fluid.

Figure 6-15 is a simplified drawing showing the construction of the engine and pump. The annular area below the engine piston is exposed to power-oil pressure at all times, and the top of the piston is alternately exposed to pressure and exhaust.

The annular area above the pump plunger is exposed to well pressure at all times, and the bottom of the plunger is alternately exposed to well pressure through the standing valve and to the pump column pressure through the discharge valve. When the ratio is 1:1 the two pistons have the same diameter and the piston rod area is one-half the piston area.

Table 6-2 gives the capacity, ratios, and principal dimension of this pump.

Table 6-2. Specifications of National Hydraulic Pumping Units

Nominal pump size	Engine piston diam, in.	Pump plunger diam, in.	Pack-off length	Area ratio pump/engine	Balance pressure* at surface, psi/1,000 ft	Displacement, B/D per spm		Rated speed, spm	Stroke length	Displacement, B/D at rated spm	
						Engine	Pump			Engine	Pump
2	1¼	1 1/16	78½	0.72	312	2.91	2.10	73	16	212	153
2	1¼	1⅛	78½	0.80	346	2.91	2.36	73	16	212	172
2	1¼	1¼	78½	1.00	433	2.91	2.91	73	16	212	212
2½	1⅝	1⅛	105	0.48	208	7.90	3.80	62	26	490	236
2½	1⅝	1⅜	105	0.72	312	7.90	5.65	62	26	490	350
2½	1⅝	1⅝	105	1.00	433	7.90	7.90	62	26	490	490

* Per 1,000-ft lift, specific gravity = 1.0.

Sargent Pump

The pump produced by the Sargent Engineering Company, as shown in Fig. 6-16, uses a combination of the principles of Fig. 6-7*a* and *b*, which is a single-acting engine connected with a single-acting pump.

The three-way valve is located in the engine piston and has a pilot valve operated by contacting the cylinder head, as illustrated in principle in Fig. 6-6*b*.

The engine piston has exhaust pressure applied to the annular area over the piston at all times, and the annular area under the piston is alternately subjected to operating pressure and exhaust pressure. Operating pressure is supplied to the piston through the upper tubular piston rod, and a downward force is produced equal to

Table 6-3. Sargent Rodless-pump Data

Pump size			Piston rod diam	Length of stroke	Displacement, B/D per spm		Max rated speed	Max displacement at max rated speed, B/D		Power ratio		Approx max setting depth
Tubing size	Engine plunger diam	Prod. plunger diam			Power oil	Prod.		Power oil	Prod.	Eng. prod.	Prod. eng.	
2	1⅝	1	1 1/16	52 9/16	13.3	6.2	27	359	167	1.68	0.59	16,500
2	1⅝	1¼	1 1/16	52 9/16	13.3	9.6	27	359	259	1.08	0.93	10,700
2	1⅝	1½	1 1/16	52 9/16	13.3	13.8	27	359	372	0.75	1.33	7,500
2½	2 1/16	1¼	⅞	52	21.2	9.5	27	572	256	1.74	0.58	17,000
2½	2 1/16	1½	⅞	52	21.2	13.7	27	572	370	1.21	0.83	12,000
2½	2 1/16	1¾	⅞	52	21.2	18.6	27	572	502	0.89	1.13	8,800
2½	2 1/16	2	⅞	52	21.2	24.2	27	572	654	0.68	1.47	6,800
3	2½	1½	1	59	36.1	15.5	27	975	419	1.88	0.53	18,000
3	2½	1¾	1	59	36.1	21.1	27	975	570	1.38	0.72	13,500
3	2½	2	1	59	36.1	27.5	27	975	743	1.06	0.94	10,500
3	2½	2¼	1	59	36.1	34.8	27	975	940	0.84	1.20	8,300
3	2½	2½	1	59	36.1	43.0	27	975	1160	0.68	1.47	6,800
4	3 5/16	2¼	1 5/16	59	63.5	34.8	27	1715	940	1.48	0.68	14,500
4	3 5/16	2¾	1 5/16	59	63.5	52.0	27	1715	1400	0.99	1.01	9,900
4	3 5/16	3¼	1 5/16	59	63.5	72.6	27	1715	1960	0.71	1.41	7,100

the operating pressure minus the pump discharge pressure applied to the area of this piston rod.   This engine unit is attached to and operates a standard-type sucker-rod pump.

Table 6-3 gives the important dimensions and operating data.

Dempsey Pump

The Dempsey pump is made by the Byron-Jackson division of the Borg Warner Company.   This unit is similar in some respects to the Sargent pump.   It is single-acting, using the principle of Fig. 6-7a.   Figure 6-17 illustrates its construction.

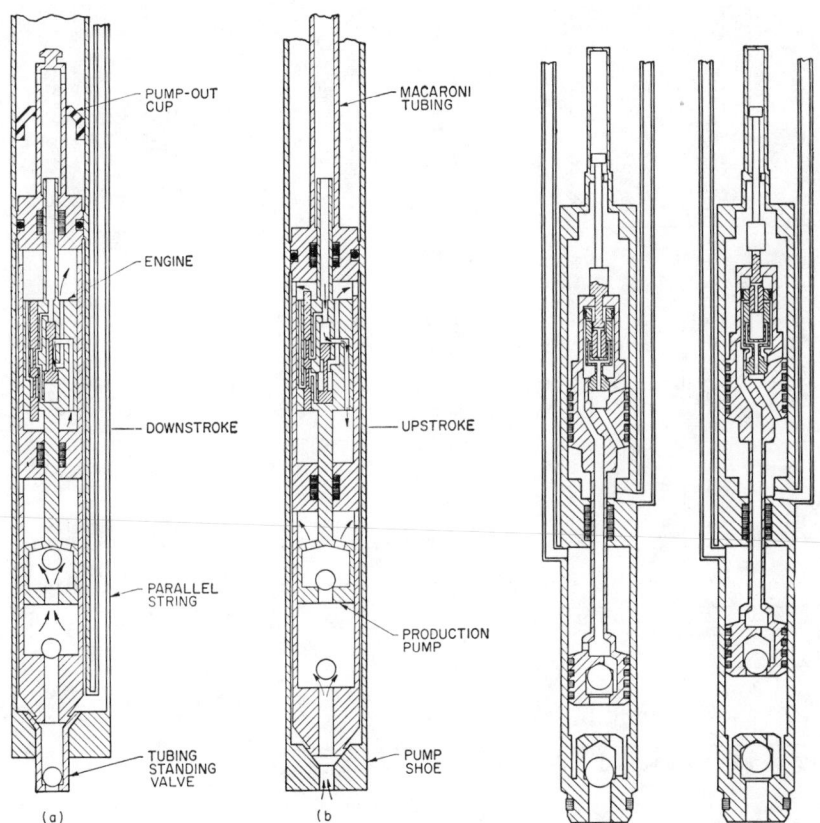

FIG. 6-16. Sargent pump.   (a) Parallel free type; (b) insert type.

FIG. 6-17. Dempsey pump.

The valve is a pilot-operated three-way poppet type located in the engine piston. The pilot valve is mechanically operated by a rod extension equal in length to the pump stroke and sliding in a tubular extension of the engine cylinder.   Collars at both ends of the rod contact an internal shoulder in this tube as the piston approaches the end of its stroke which shifts the pilot valve controlling the main valve.

The downward force is obtained by the operating pressure minus the pump-discharge pressure applied to the projected area of the piston rod.   The piston rod is tubular and handles the engine discharge.

The dimension and displacement data are given in Table 6-4.

Table 6-4. Standard BJ Hydraulic Production Units Sizes and Specifications

Nominal tubing and pump size	OD of pump, in	Plunger diam, in. Engine	Plunger diam, in. Pump	Plunger area, sq in. Engine	Plunger area, sq in. Pump	Middle rod Nominal pipe size	Middle rod Area, sq in.	Displacement, B/D per spm Engine	Displacement, B/D per spm Pump	Effective ratio engine to pump
					Insert pumps					
2	1⅞	*1¼	1¼	1.227	1.227	¼	0.229	11.0	11.0	1.22
2	1⅞	*1¼	1⅟₁₆	1.227	0.887	¼	0.229	11.0	7.9	0.88
2½	2¼	1½	1½	1.767	1.767	⅜	0.358	15.8	15.8	1.26
2½	2¼	1½	1¼	1.767	1.227	⅜	0.358	15.8	11.0	0.87
2½	2¼	1½	1⅟₁₆	1.767	0.887	⅜	0.358	15.8	7.9	0.63
3	2¾	2	2	3.142	3.142	½	0.554	28.0	28.0	1.21
3	2¾	2	1¾	3.142	2.406	½	0.554	28.0	21.4	0.93
3	2¾	2	1½	3.142	1.787	⅜	0.358	28.0	15.8	0.63
3	2¾	2	1¼	3.142	1.227	⅜	0.358	28.0	11.0	0.42
					Fluid-retrievable pumps					
2	1⅞	1¼	1¼	1.227	1.227	¼	0.229	11.0	11.0	1.22
2	1⅞	1¼	1⅟₁₆	1.227	0.887	¼	0.229	11.0	7.9	0.88
2	1¾	1½	1½	1.767	1.767	⅜	0.358	15.8	15.8	1.26
2	1¾	1½	1¼	1.767	1.767	⅜	0.358	15.8	11.0	0.87
2	1¾	1½	1⅟₁₆	1.767	0.887	⅜	0.358	15.8	7.9	0.63
2½	2¼	1½	1½	1.767	1.767	⅜	0.358	15.8	15.8	1.26
2½	2¼	1½	1¼	1.767	1.227	⅜	0.358	15.8	11.0	0.87
2½	2¼	1½	1⅟₁₆	1.767	0.887	⅜	0.358	15.8	7.9	0.63
2½	2¼	2	2	3.142	3.142	½	0.554	28.0	28.0	1.21
2½	2¼	2	1¾	3.142	2.406	½	0.554	28.0	21.4	0.93
2½	2¼	2	1½	3.142	1.767	⅜	0.358	28.0	15.8	0.63
2½	2¼	2	1¼	3.142	1.227	⅜	0.358	28.0	11.0	0.42
					Casing pumps					
4½	4½	3¼	3¼	8.290	8.290	¾	0.885	73.8	73.8	1.12
4½	4½	3¼	2¾	8.290	5.940	¾	0.885	73.8	52.8	0.788

* These models can be used with centering guides in 2½-in. tubing.

Engine Efficiency

The losses in a hydraulic engine can be divided into two classes: first, the *pressure losses* which are increases in operating pressure due to the frictional effects of *boundary lubrication, viscous drag* of sliding fits, and the *fluid friction* of the power oil flowing through the ports and passages of the unit; and second, the *volumetric losses*, which include the nonproductive power oil used to operate the *engine valve* or to return the *single-acting piston* and the *leakages* by the sliding fits of the valve, piston, and rods.

Boundary Lubrication. The loss from this cause is *indeterminate*, as any misalignment of parts may produce excessive bearing pressures and increase the loss. Friction of rings or other packing which produce high bearing pressures will also have poor lubrication. This is particularly true under slow speed and at the ends of the stroke and gives the "stick-start" action noted under conditions of boundary lubrication.

Viscous Drag. Closely fitted parts show a *fluid* shear *drag* which usually is *small* but may become significant with heavy oils. The drag force expressed in pounds is determined by the relation

$$PA = \frac{3.644\mu VL}{(C/D) \times 10^7}$$

where PA = drag force (engine piston + pump piston), lb
 P = drag pressure, psi
 A = area of engine piston, sq in.
 L = piston length (engine and pump piston lengths equal), in.
 μ = viscosity, cp
 V = piston velocity, ft/min
 C = diametral clearance, thousandths of an inch
 D = piston diameter, in.

Figure 6-18 gives the drag loss for the engine piston plus the pump piston as a function of diametral clearance, viscosity, and piston speed.

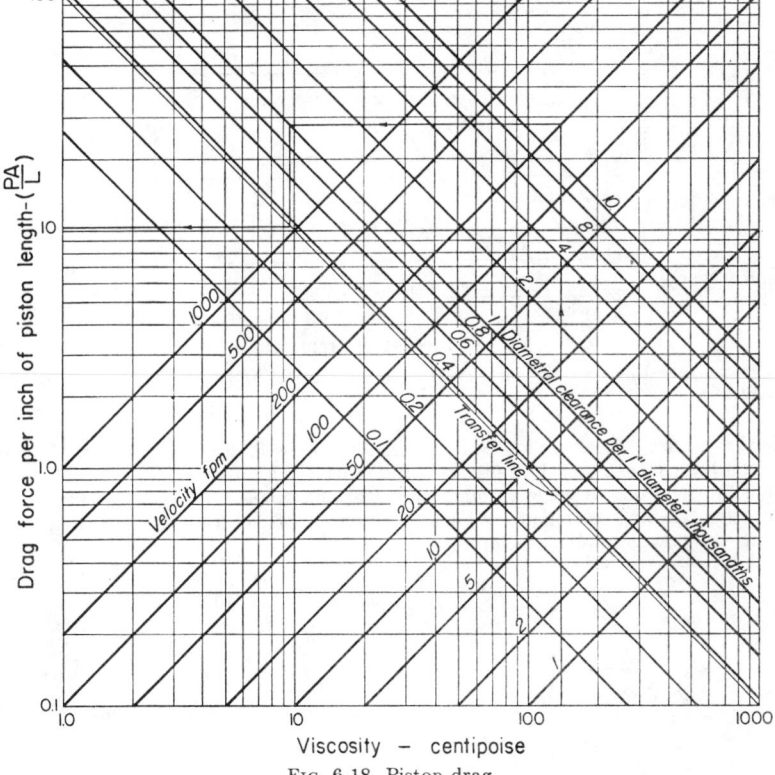

Fig. 6-18. Piston drag.

Fluid Friction. Hydraulic losses depend primarily on the *velocity* in the ports and passages of the engine and to a limited extent on the *viscosity* of the power fluid (see page 6–70). The velocities are usually held to a maximum of 20 ft/sec, which is turbulent flow with the oils generally handled. Piston speeds are usually under 5 ft/sec. The total loss due to mechanical friction, viscous drag, and fluid friction is shown in Fig. 6-19. This chart is from tests with power oil having a viscosity of 10 cs at 100°F.

Valve Loss. It is usual to charge against the engine efficiency the fluid used to operate the engine valve. This varies with the design but usually is not more than a few per cent of the engine displacement. In the valve used by Kobe this loss is approximately 2 per cent.

Single-acting Loss. In single-acting pumps using *operating fluid* applied to the *rod area* for the return stroke, a substantial loss occurs. The rod area must be sufficient to limit the stress to a reasonable value on the power stroke, and the full displacement of this area is lost. In some cases this is over 20 per cent of the total operating fluid.

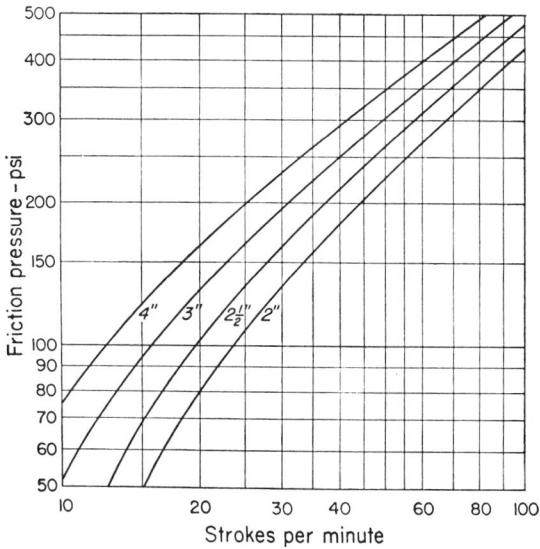

FIG. 6-19. Operating-pressure increase due to mechanical and hydraulic friction of engine and pump.

Leakage Loss. Leakage losses are a function of the fluid *viscosity* and the *clearance* between the parts subject to a pressure differential. Exline[7] and Tao and Donovan[27] derive the relations for flow through the clearance space between close-fitting parts such as valves and plungers for both stationary and rotating seals. For practical designs the flow is in all cases laminar.

$$Q = \frac{\pi P}{8 \mu L} \left[(R^4 - r^4) - \frac{(R^2 - r^2)^2}{\log_e R/r} \right]$$

where Q = volume rate of flow
P = total pressure drop
L = length of flow path
r = radius of inner cylinder
R = radius of outer cylinder
h = radial clearance $(R - r)$
μ = viscosity

This can be reduced to

$$Q = \frac{\pi}{6} \frac{r h^3 P}{\mu L} \left(1 + \frac{1}{2} \frac{h}{r} + \frac{1}{60} \frac{h^2}{r^2} - \frac{1}{120} \frac{h^3}{r^3} \cdots \right)$$

and since h/r is usually so small that the h/r terms in the parentheses can be neglected, the relation can be further reduced to

$$Q = \frac{\pi}{6} \frac{rh^3P}{\mu L}$$

For the leakage between flat parallel plates such as in flat valves

$$Q = \frac{Wh^3P}{12\mu L}$$

where W = width of plates
These equations are more convenient to use by substituting D for $2r$ and C for $2h$ in which D is then the diameter of the piston and C is the diametral clearance between the piston and cylinder. Using these terms, the relation becomes

$$Q = \frac{\pi D C^3 P}{96\mu L}$$

When the piston is not concentric with the cylinder the leakage is increased. If the amount that the piston is off center is expressed as a ratio to the clearance, or e,

$$Q = \frac{\pi D C^3 P}{96\mu L} (1 + 1.5e^2)$$

With Q in barrels per day, P in thousands of psi, C in thousandths of an inch, D in inches, L in inches, and μ in centipoise this relation becomes

$$Q = \frac{\pi D C^3 P}{96\mu L} (1 + 1.5e^2)\, 61.4$$

When the piston is on center $e = 0$ and when piston is in line contact with the cylinder wall $e = 1$ and the term in the parentheses becomes 2.5.

In using these relations correction must be made for the change in viscosity due to the mean pressure and temperature in the leakage path and for dimensional changes due to deformation of parts under load.

Figure 6-20 gives the leakage by a cylindrical plunger in a cylinder, assuming no change in dimensions under pressure. As can be seen from this chart, leakage increases rapidly with clearance and closely fitted parts are essential. In the Kobe pump the normal loss at 10 cp and 2,500 psi is approximately 6 per cent of the displacement. This includes the leakages into the pump end for lubrication. The over-all volumetric loss including the valve-operating fluid is approximately 8 per cent.

Since *close fits* are important to *high efficiency* these losses will increase as the parts wear and the clearances become greater. The life under field conditions depends upon the amount of foreign material in the power oil. This material may be water, salt, sand, scale, iron oxide, or other corrosion products. The effect of these materials may be sufficient to require pump repairs in a period as short as 30 days. Under favorable conditions the frequency of repairs may be several years, and the average is approximately one year. Power-oil systems and cleaning methods which have an important bearing on this matter are discussed on page **6**-27.

Pump End

Plungers and Liners. *Pumps* adapted to *hydraulic pumping* may be standard *API* rod pumps connected to a hydraulic operating engine or may be a special design built with the engine as a complete unit. Sargent is an example of the former type, while National, Kobe, Fluid, and Byron-Jackson use the latter construction.

Close Fits. All pumps except Kobe and Byron-Jackson use close fits with *clearances* and *lengths* derived from practice with rod pumps. See Chap. 8 for plunger and liner lengths and clearances used for rod pumps. In Kobe the combination of close fits and piston rings is used and the length of fit is much shorter than has been the practice with rod pumps.

Lubrication. Lubrication with *power oil* is provided by all manufacturers for the seal between the engine and pump, and in Kobe and National this lubrication is extended to all sliding fits in both the engine and pump. Lubrication reduces the wear and permits closer fits and lower total leakage to the extent that the power fluid is better than the well fluid being pumped. This may be from *equal* to *many times better* when the pump is handling *corrosive water* or *sand*. Figure 6-21 shows the pump and engine-piston construction used by Kobe.

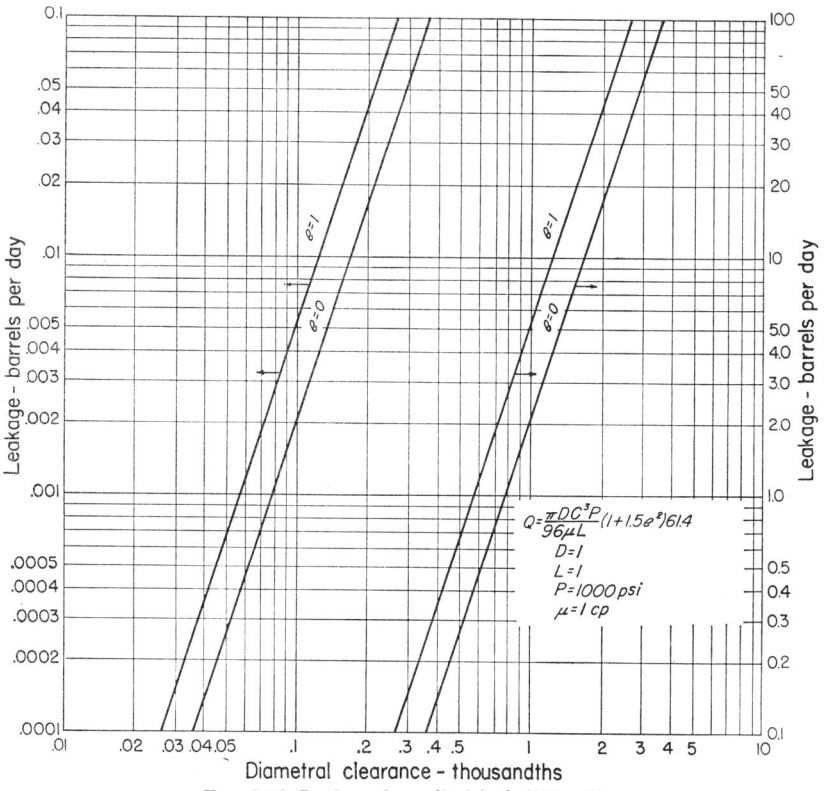

FIG. 6-20. Leakage by cylindrical sliding fits.

Valves. Most manufacturers use valves the same or similar to those used in API *rod pumps*, which are given under that heading in Chap. 7. Kobe uses ball valves of special design with a multiple-ball arrangement in place of the single ball of rod-pump practice. Also Kobe, being double-acting, has an intake and exhaust valve at each end of the pump cylinder. All valves are spring-loaded with a common follower for the three balls in parallel, making the valve action independent of gravity. Figure 6-22 shows a pump-valve assembly of this type.

Special valves have been proposed using flat valves, poppet valves, and slide valves, both fluid and mechanically operated, but none has been used commercially.

Clearance Volume. Since the *stroke length* of hydraulic pumps is *positive*, close spacing of the piston relative to the end of the cylinder is possible and the clearance volume can be reduced to that of the valve cage. This volume ranges from 5 to 10 per cent of pump displacement. This gives a high compression ratio, which is essential with gassy fluid to prevent excessive loss of efficiency. Where lubricated plungers are used, this clearance volume is further reduced and complete gas lock is impossible, as the leakage of lubrication fluid into the pump cylinder will completely fill the clearance volume and give an infinite compression ratio on the top end and an increase in compression ratio on the lower end of the double-acting pump.

FIG. 6-21. Engine and pump piston construc-   FIG. 6-22. Pump valve construction (Kobe).
tion (Kobe).

Limitations

Engine and Pump Size. Restricted diameter is the most serious design limitation in hydraulic bottom-hole pumps. Units to run inside 2- and 4-in. tubings must deliver as much as 15 and 100 hp, respectively.

This power requirement at reasonable piston speeds dictates the use of high pressure, which produces high stress and high elastic deformation. With close-fitting parts in sliding contact deformation must be limited or compensated for. Also the fluid passages must be adequate to handle the power oil and produced fluid with low pressure loss. Therefore, the optimum design must carefully balance all these factors and properly utilize the limited cross-sectional area. The hydraulic design should not introduce shock loading and the mechanical design should give special attention to the shape of parts to avoid stress concentrations.

Oscillating-column Pumps. In this type of pump the fluid in the operating column must be *compressed* on each stroke to produce full operating pressure before any motion is obtained in the bottom-hole cylinder. Because of space limitations, the well cylinder and tubings must be small in diameter, and hence high pressure is required to apply a reasonable amount of power. For example, with tubes 2,000 ft in length and with oil having a bulk modulus of 200,000 psi, the fluid column is compressed lengthwise 1,000/200,000 × 2,000, or 10 ft 0 in., to produce a pressure of 1,000 psi. If the stroke of the piston also requires a volume of fluid equal to that held by 10 ft 0 in. of tubing, the maximum stroke efficiency would be 50 per cent. At 8,000 ft the volume of fluid to be compressed would be four times as large and the pressure would also be increased by a factor of 4. Therefore, the linear column compression to build the full operating pressure would be 160 ft. If the same-sized bottom-hole cylinder is used, the stroke efficiency would be 10/170, or 5.9 per cent, which is too low to have practical value.

This low stroke efficiency may be *avoided* by operating at a speed equal to the *natural frequency* of the hydraulic system or at a harmonic. The natural frequency of a tube closed at both ends, neglecting the elasticity of the tube, is

$$t = \frac{2L}{c} \quad \text{and} \quad c = \sqrt{\frac{Gg}{w}}$$

where t = time for one cycle, sec
   t_1, t_2 = time for second and third harmonics, sec
   L = length of tubing, ft
   c = velocity of sound in the liquid, ft/sec
   G = bulk modulus of liquid, lb/sq ft
   g = acceleration of gravity = 32.2 ft/sec
   w = weight of liquid, lb/cu ft
The harmonics are

$$t_1 = \frac{2L}{2c} \quad t_2 = \frac{2L}{3c} \quad \text{etc.}$$

The *elasticity* of the *tube* reduces the effective modulus of the system and reduces c and therefore increases t. With tubing used for production its effect is not over 10 per cent.

With a fixed speed as determined by these factors, the only means of adjusting the pump capacity is to vary the stroke length. This is difficult to attain with a practical design for conditions encountered in producing oil.

Another important limitation is that c is not constant because both G and w vary with the amount of water and gas in the oil and also with the temperature and pressure. The bulk modulus G also varies with the fluid and with temperature and pressure. Bulk modulus is important to all hydraulic pumping systems. See page 6-56 for bulk modulus of fluids used for power oil and for well fluids.

Direct-flow Hydraulic Pumps. All commercial hydraulic pumps today are of this type, in which a return system is provided for the power fluid, either separately or mixed with the production, and the flow of power fluid is substantially constant and in one direction. The following limitations apply to pumps using this system.

Depth. The depth limitation is determined by the tubing used in the well for power oil and production. Setting depths and internal pressure limits for various grades of tubing are given in Chap. 2. Small tubings have t/d ratios (wall thickness over diameter) which permit internal pressures greater than normally required for setting depths which are limited be the tension strength of the tubing or the threaded coupling. Pumps can be designed for the maximum pressures the tubing can withstand with some reduction in displacement due to increased wall thickness of cylinders, valves, etc. Present Kobe designs are for maximum depths of 15,000 ft, but this can be increased as required. Since present drilling methods use drill pipe and casing having the same tensile limitations as the production tubing, the depth limitations of rotary drilling and hydraulic pumping are substantially the same. The limitation with tubular goods of maximum strength now available is approximately 30,000 ft with reasonable safety factors.

Power vs. Ratio of Pump Area to Engine Area and Tubing Size. The *power*-handling capacity of tubing used for hydraulic pumps compares very favorably with other means of transmitting power. The use of high pressure is of importance, as the per cent friction loss at a given horsepower capacity varies inversely as P^3. The fluid capacity at constant per cent friction loss varies directly as $P^{1/2}$. The power capacity of a tubing system with an assumed value of per cent power loss varies directly as $P^{3/2}$. Figure 6-23 gives the power capacity for closed systems with the same tubing size for power oil and power-oil return as a function of pump-to-engienarea ratio and the depth. The ultimate limit for a given tubing size depends on the allowable internal pressure and this depends on pump-to-engine-area ratio times the depth. This chart gives the capacity of power-oil tubing expressed in horsepower per 1,000 ft of lift with 1,000 ft of power-oil tubing and 1,000 ft of power-oil-return tubing of the same diameter, with a friction loss of 10 per cent of the power input at a specific gravity of 1.0, and with pump-to-engine ratios of 0.5 to 5.0. From the net power available at the pump the fluid-handling capacity is established and may be read on the upper scale. For the example given on the chart 1-in. tubing will transmit 4.4 hp at a 1.8:1 ratio per 1,000 ft of lift or 44.0 hp at 10,000 ft. The pump fluid-handling capacity with this ratio would be 560 B/D at any depth within the pressure limitation of the tubing and the bottom-hole pump.

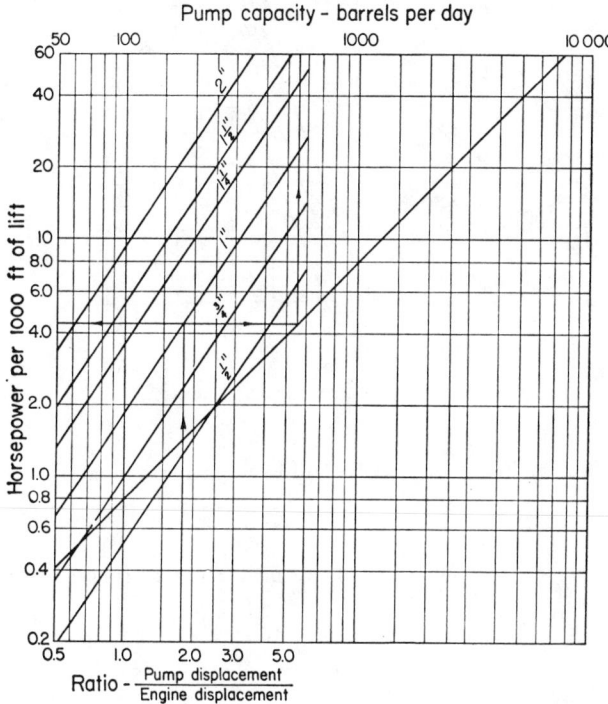

FIG. 6-23. Power-transmitting capacity of tubing. Power oil and power-oil return tubings of same diameter and length equal to lift.

Speed. Pump *speeds* are limited to values that will permit satisfactory *filling* of the pump end. This depends upon the viscosity of the oil under bottom-hole conditions and the submergence pressure. If the pressure is sufficient to fill the pump cylinder, speeds of 1.5 to 2.0 times normal can be used without damage to the equipment. The normal speed rating used by Kobe is

$$N^2L = 100,000$$

where N = pump speed, spm
L = pump stroke, in.

This rating with a pump-to-engine ratio of 1:1 gives fluid velocity in the pump section of less than 10 ft/sec and in the pump-discharge and engine passages of less than 20 ft/sec.

Capacity. On the above *basis* of *speed*, the capacity of the presently available Kobe standard sizes is given in Table 6-1. The capacity of Sargent, National, and Byron-Jackson, as recommended by each manufacturer, is given in Tables 6-2 to 6-4.

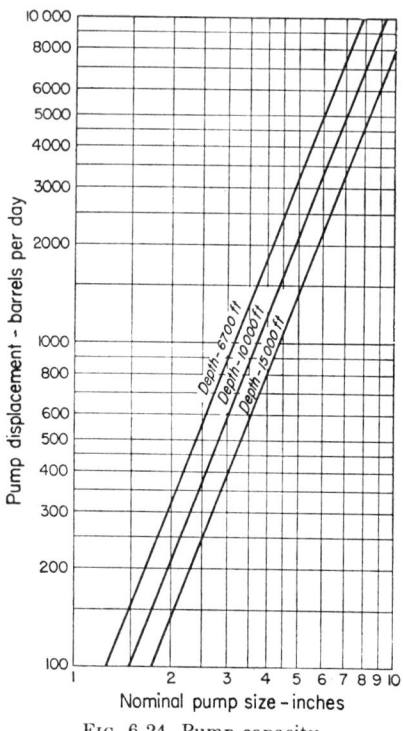

FIG. 6-24. Pump capacity.

Figure 6-24 gives the capacity of standard Kobe pumps at rated speed as determined by the relation:

$$N^2L = 100,000$$

The proportions of the standard pump on which this chart is based are:

$$L = 7.5d$$

$$\text{Engine-piston diameter} = \frac{d}{2.0}$$

$$\text{Pump-piston diameters} = \frac{d}{1.75}, \frac{d}{2.0}, \text{ or } \frac{d}{2.5}$$

$$\text{Rod diameter} = \frac{d}{4}$$

where d = nominal pipe size, i.e., the tubing size in which the pump is run

The three ratings on the chart are for pump-to-engine ratios which will permit maximum lifts of 6,700, 10,000, and 15,000 ft, respectively.

FREE-PUMP SYSTEM

The free-pump system differs from the insert or tubing type in that the pump is *not attached* to the tubing and can be removed without disturbing the tubing. The pump used is the same except for adapters added to obtain a pressure seal in the tubing. Figure 6-25 illustrates the principle of the free pump.

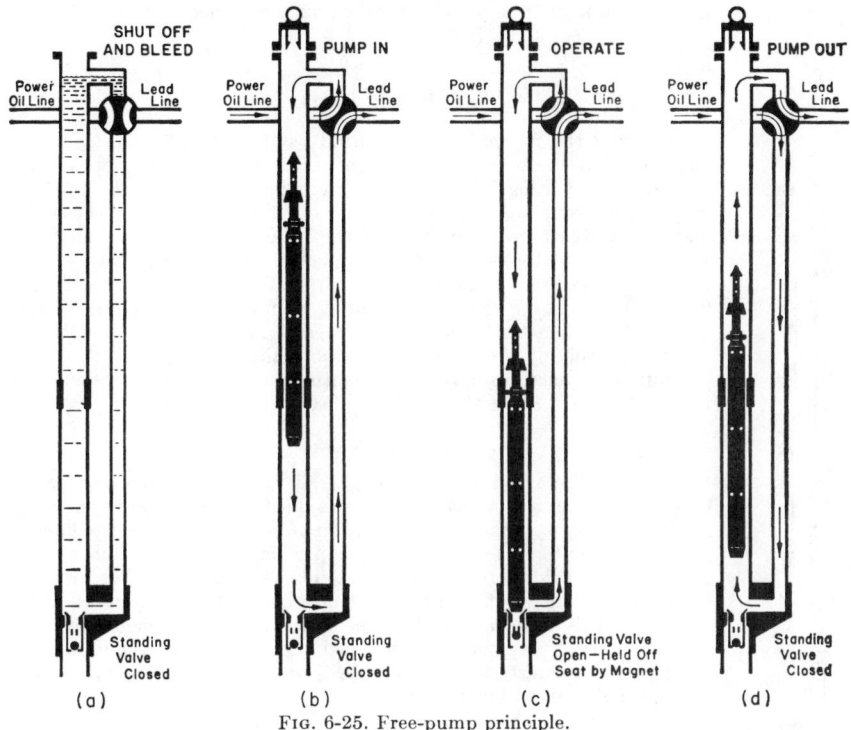

FIG. 6-25. Free-pump principle.

Tubings

With this system the *two tubings* used for *power oil* and *production* are normally in *parallel*, but in casing-type installations or for small pumps they may be concentric. In either case the two tubings are connected together at the lower end to form a U tube. The bottom of this U tube has a standing valve so that the system may be filled with fluid.

Standing Valve

Figure 6-26 shows the standing valve, which may be pulled with a wire line and which provides a means of holding the valve in a normally open position when the pump is in operation. It also has a drain means for bleeding the tubing before pulling the standing valve.

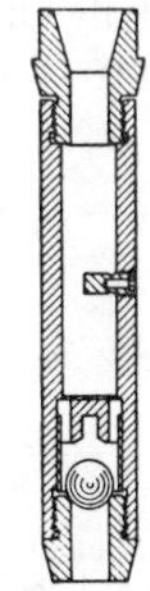

Running Pump

With the *tubings filled* with fluid as shown in Fig. 6-25a the pump is inserted into the tube through the tubing head. The cap is put in place and the tubing-head valve placed in the operating position, which applies fluid on top of the pump and circulates it to bottom as shown in Fig. 6-25b. The fluid under the pump returns in the other leg of the U tube and is discharged into the lead line. When the pump reaches bottom it seats in the taper shoe of the standing valve. In this position the pressure seal on top of the engine is in the sealing collar as shown in Fig. 6-25c, and power fluid is directed to the engine for pump operation. The power-fluid exhaust

FIG. 6-26. Standing valve.

PRODUCTION EQUIPMENT

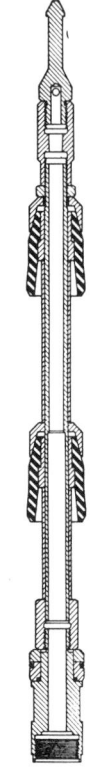

is below the sealing collar in open systems and thus mixes with the production in the pump-housing tube and is returned to the wellhead in the other leg of the U tube.

Pulling Pump

To *remove* the *pump,* the tubing-head valve is placed in the "pump out" position as shown in Fig. 6-25d, which reverses the application of pressure in the legs of the U tube building pressure under the pump, which applies an upward force to the annular area between the seal diameter of the pump seat in the shoe of the standing valve and the seal diameter of the sealing collar above the pump. The downward force on the pump is the column pressure in the tubing above the fluid level in the well applied to the sealing diameter of the pump seat. This sealing diameter is selected to give any desired ratio of unseating pressure to column pressure. This is normally selected at 25 per cent of column pressure but may be substantially more than this in shallow wells.

Swab Cups

To *reduce* the amount of *fluid bypassing* the pump when being removed from the well, *swab cups* are provided on the packer-nose assembly as shown in Fig. 6-27. The top of this assembly has a latch point which enters the tubing-head cap when the pump reaches the surface and is held there by a spring latch. The tubing-head valve can be turned to "shut off" position, which bleeds the pressure off the tubing, and the pump may then be pulled from the tubing with the cap. The latch cap has a breach-lock type of connection and is released by a quarter turn. The pressure required to remove the pump is determined by the rate of removal, as it is largely due to the tubing friction. The pressure due to the weight of the pump itself amounts to only 13 psi for the 2-in. and 30 psi for the 4-in.

F I G . 6 - 2 7 .
Packer-nose
a s s e m b l y
with swab
cups.

Time Required

The pump-out *time* depends upon the *power-fluid supply* available and setting *depth* and is usually in the range of 30 minutes to 2 hours. The maximum rate depends upon the supply pressure and volume, as the energy is practically all used to overcome tubing friction. Figure 6-28 gives the pump-out rate vs. pressure at the depths shown and with the tubing combinations listed. This

Table 6-5

	Pump size			
	2 in.	2½ in.	3 in.	4 in.
Open system:				
Tubing combination........	2 by 1	2½ by 1¼	3 by 1½	4 by 2
Diam of bundle, in.........	4.51	5.58	6.79	8.375
Min casing size.............	5½ in., 20 lb	6⅝ in., 24 lb	7⅝ in., 24 lb	9⅝ in., 47 lb
Closed system:				
Tubing combination........	2 by ¾ by ¾	2½ by 1 by 1	3 by 1¼ by 1¼	4 by 1½ by 1½
Diam of bundle, in.........	4.437	5.46	6.87	8.000
Min casing size............	5½ in., 23 lb	6⅝ in., 28 lb	8⅝ in., 49 lb	9⅝ in., 53.5 lb

Nominal tubing size given in inches.
Largest tube is external upset and small tubes are line pipe clamped to the large tube as shown in Fig. 6-63.

chart is for oil having a viscosity of 10 cs and specific gravity of 0.90 and the pressure drop is in psi per 1,000 ft of tubing. With casing pumps the friction is low, as it is largely in the main tubing, which is also shown in Fig. 6-28, and in this case the operating fluid capacity will govern the pump-out rate.

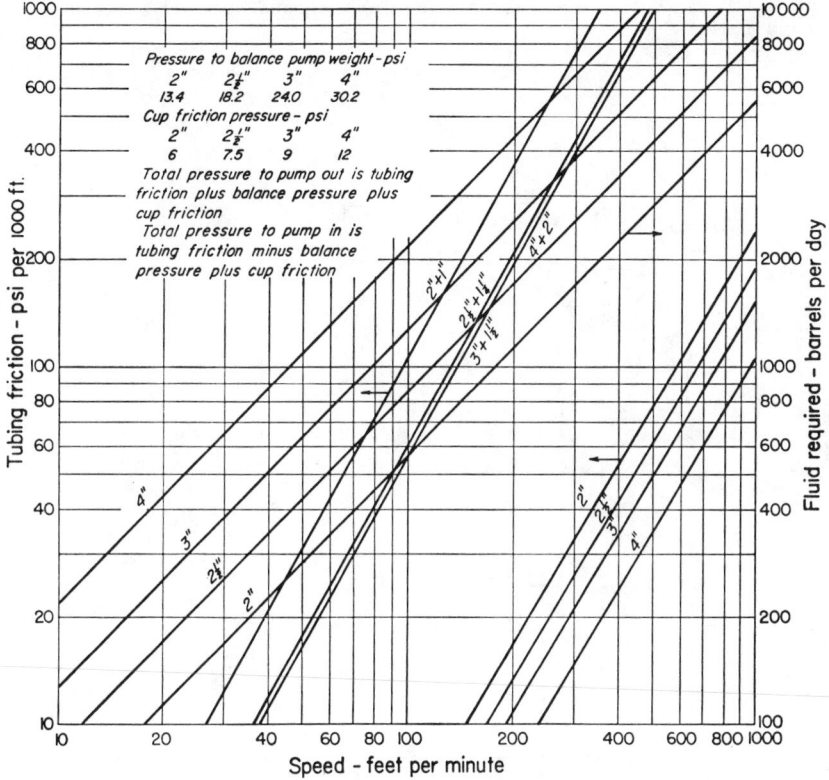

FIG. 6-28. Free pump pulling rate and pressure.

The size of free pump which may be installed depends on the casing size and the tubing combination used. Table 6-5 gives the range of pump sizes which may be used.

POWER-OIL SUPPLY

Power-oil *requirements vary* widely in both amount and conditions of operation, depending on the type of system used. The function of the power-oil system is primarily to remove from the oil a large part of the *water* and *abrasives* to obtain an oil with reasonable lubricating properties and free from any impurities which would cause excessive corrosion or wear of the pump parts. Since the fluid produced from the well may range from 100 per cent oil to 100 per cent water and with varying amounts of salt, sand, and iron oxide, the severity of the clean-up problem varies widely.

There are two systems for power fluid used—the *open system* in which the power oil and production are mixed, and the *closed system* in which they are entirely separated except for minor leakages in the bottom-hole unit. In the open system when the well fluid is 100 per cent water the maximum cut in the return fluid is approximately 50 per cent. With the closed system the only fluid added is for leakage make-up, as there is no contamination of the power oil in its normal use. The amount of make-up required is 1 to 2 per cent of the engine displacement, and hence the capacity of the power-oil-cleaning system is greatly reduced as compared with an open system.

Single Well—Open System

Single-well installations may use a simple *surge tank* for power-oil supply when the production is clean. Surge tanks may also be used for well testing regardless of the quality of the produced fluid at some sacrifice of pump life if the oil contains sand or corrosive water. The type and size of surge tank recommended are shown in Fig. 6-29 and Table 6-6.

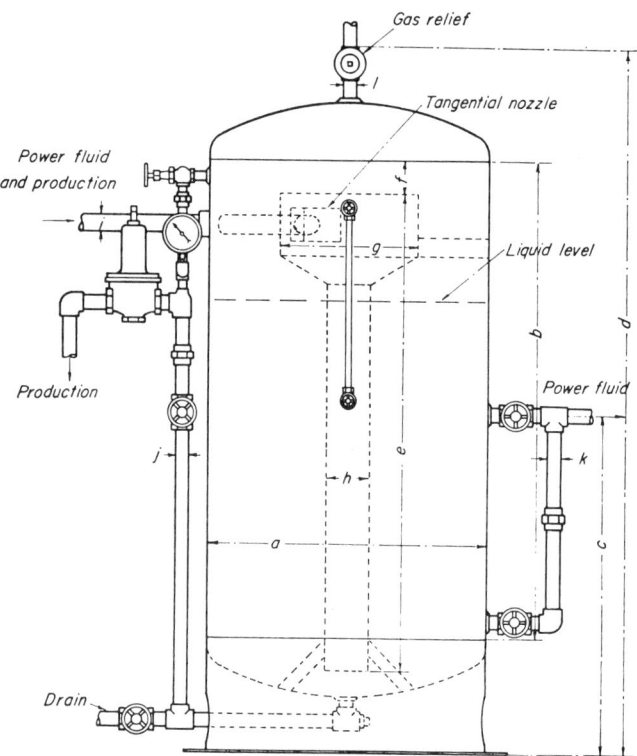

FIG. 6-29. Open-system surge tank.

Table 6-6. Open-system Surge Tank
(All dimensions in inches)

	Size and capacity and principal dimensions			
Pump size	2	$2\frac{1}{2}$	3	4
Power oil, B/D	200	400	800	1,600
a	30	36	48	60
b	48	60	84	96
c	36	43	58	72
d	72	90	126	144
e	48	60	84	96
f	3	4	5	6
g	15	18	24	30
h	4	5	6	8
i	$1\frac{1}{4}$	2	3	4
j	1	$1\frac{1}{4}$	2	3
k	$1\frac{1}{4}$	2	3	4
l	1	$1\frac{1}{4}$	2	3

Filter

Self-contained filter units were used extensively in early installations and under favorable conditions give excellent results. The important requirement of a filter system which periodically cleans or regenerates the filter medium is first to eliminate or reduce to a minimum the amount of wax and emulsion in suspension in the oil. This usually requires heating the oil to a temperature that will put all the wax in solution, which will at the same time assist in breaking emulsion. This is covered

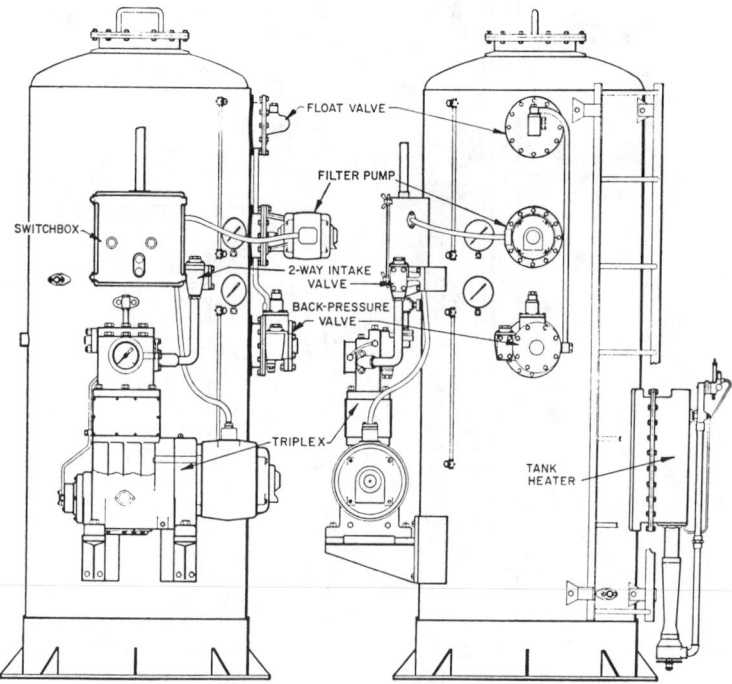

FIG. 6-30. Filter tank.

in more detail under wash tanks. Filter units use either a heater which may be directly gas-fired or a heat exchanger taking heat from the engine-cooling water. Figure 6-30 shows the type of unit used.

Heater-Treaters

Heater-treaters may also be used, usually with a power-oil tank and sometimes with a wash tank ahead of the unit as a free-water knockout. Figure 6-31 shows the construction of a type of heater-treater made by National Tank, which has a temperature-controlled gas-fired heater with built-in heat exchangers, gas separation, hay tank, etc. Table 6-7 gives the specifications and important dimensions of these units.

Multiple Well—Open System

With a multiple-well open system several methods of cleaning power oil have been used, but the generally accepted method is a well-designed wash tank and in some cases with a power-oil storage tank having a capacity equal to the power oil required for 24 hours of operation.

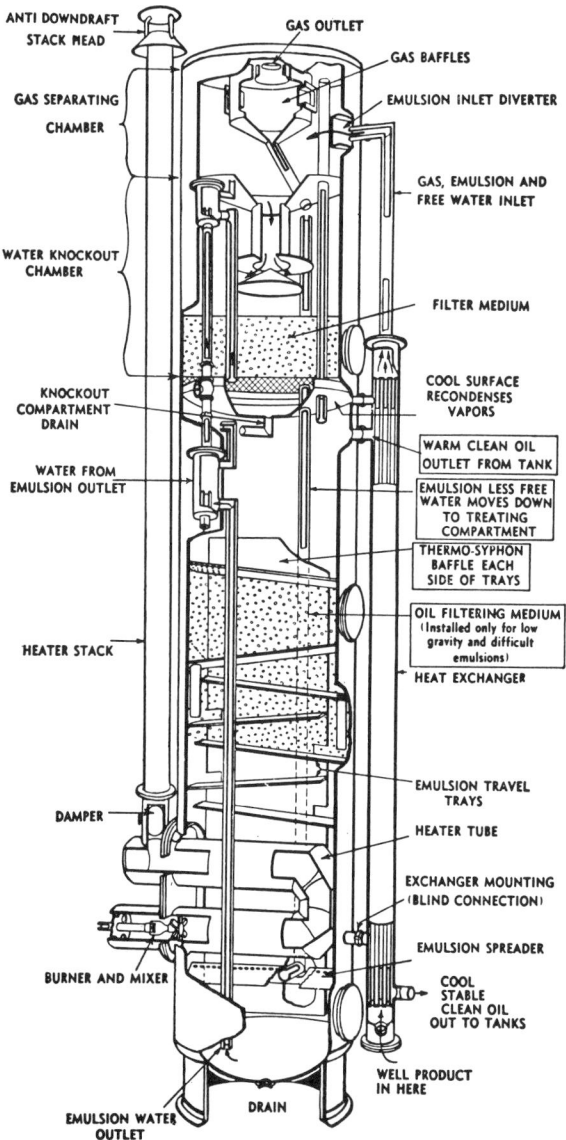

FIG. 6-31. Heater-treater.

Wash Tank

Figure 6-32 and Table 6-8 show the construction and principal dimensions of wash tanks used with hydraulic pumps. The wash tank is essentially a *gravity separator* divided into three parts: first, a bulk separator for free gas; second, a bulk separator for free water; and third, a quiescent tank for settling of suspended solids and water droplets or small-diameter gas bubbles not removed in the bulk separators.

The volume of free gas is usually small, as it is tubing gas only, and this could not be a large amount except in wells having high fluid levels which may tend to

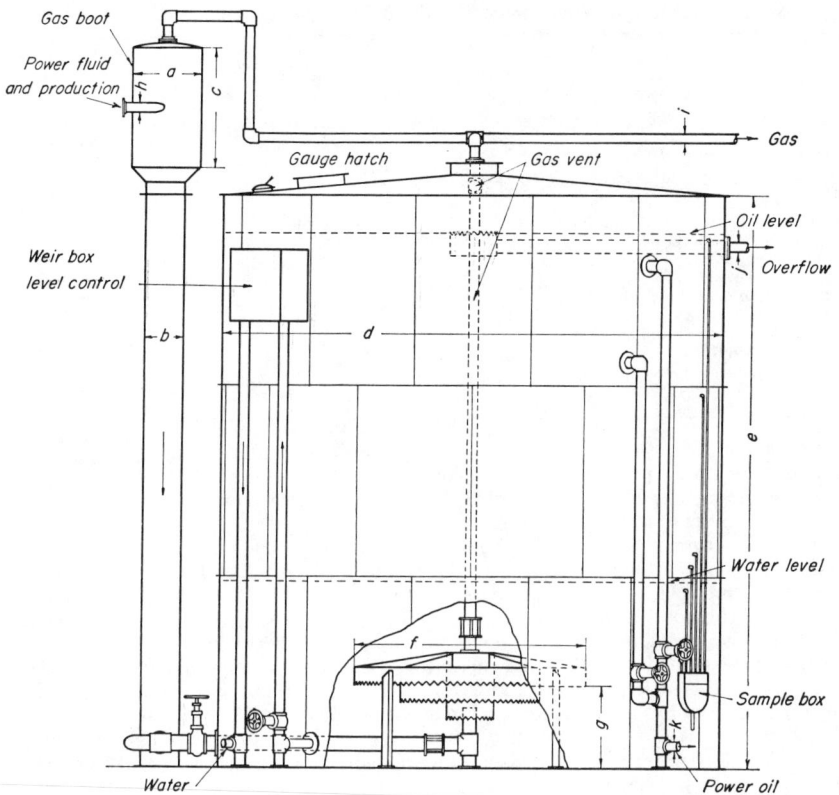

FIG. 6-32. Wash tank.

Table 6-7

Nominal size, diam by shell length, ft..........	4 × 27½	6 × 27½	8 × 27½	10 × 27½
Capacity,* bbl treated oil per hour............	5–30	10–50	20–100	35–150
Capacity,† gas MMcf/D.....................	1–2	2–4	3–6	4–8
Capacity,‡ free water, B/D.................	250–1,800	550–4,000	1,000–7,000	1,500–10,000
Rated WP of tank, psi......................	25	25	25	25
Steel in tank shell, thickness, in...............	¼	¼	¼	¼
Steel in tank heads, thickness, in.............	¼	¼	¼	⅜
Heating capacity, Btu/hr....................	350,000	500,000	1,000,000	1,350,000
Heater tube, diam, in.......................	18	18	24	24
Size of stack, in............................	8⅝	8⅝	12¾	12¾
Gas burner, size, in. LF.....................	2	2	5	5
Temperature control (112 to 190°F), in........	¾	¾	¾	¾
Fuel-gas consumption (cu ft/hr max)..........	583	833	1,538	2,080
OD of heat exchanger, 22 ft long, in..........	8⅝	10¾	10¾	10¾
No. of 1- by 20-in. tubes in exchanger........	14	24	30	30

* Capacities for oil depend on variable conditions such as necessary treating temperature, ratio of oil to water, relative viscosities and densities of the oil and water, rate of chemical action, and other factors.

† Capacities for gas depend on flowing characteristics. Capacities for steady flowing volumes will be greater than for heading flows.

‡ Capacities for free water depend upon relative viscosities and densities of the oil and water and the size of the water line, leading away from the treater.

Table 6-8. Wash-tank Sizes and Principal Dimensions

Dimension	Capacity, B/D			
	300	750	1,500	3,000
a. Diam of boot—top section, in...........	20	36	36	36
b. Diam of boot—bottom section, in........	8	20	20	20
c. Height of boot, in.....................	32	60	60	60
d. Diam of wash tank....................	9 ft 2¾ in.	15 ft 4⅝ in.	21 ft 6½ in.	29 ft 8⅝ in.
e. Height of wash tank, ft...............	24	24	24	24
f. Diam of spreader, ft.................	4	8	10	12
g. Location of spreader from bottom........	3 ft 6 in.	3 ft 6 in.	3 ft 6 in.	3 ft 6 in.
h. Inlet line, in........................	3	3	4	4
i. Gas line from boot and tank, in........	3	4	4	6
j. Stock draw-off, in....................	3	4	4	6
k. Triplex supply, in....................	3	4	4	6
l. Vertical velocity, ft/hr...............	1.1	0.94	0.95	1.0

flow by heads through the pump (see page 6-83 for gas-handling capacity of pumps). In wells which have previously been produced by natural flow or gas lift, the production goes through a gas trap ahead of the wash tank, which limits the gas to solution gas at trap pressure and temperature.

The *bulk separator* for *gas* is a "boot" ahead of the wash tank proper, having a tangential entrance for well fluid near the top and a top outlet for gas. The boot usually has an enlarged section at the top to prevent carry-over of foam into the gas lines. The boot is either external and adjacent to the wash tank or internal, in which case it is usually in the center of the wash tank with the standpipe leading directly to the spreader of the water separator. The external boot has the advantage that corrosion is easily detected and repairs made without disturbing the tank. The internal boot has less heat loss and gives better distribution of liquid in the tank. Where heavy oils are produced, froth is difficult to separate and sometimes a top section of full wash-tank diameter is used with a cone bottom and a central downpipe for liquid to the bulk-water separator.

The *bulk separator* for *water* is the lower section of the wash tank. The water level is controlled by an overflow water leg which may be adjustable if desired. Usually about one-third of the wash tank is for bulk-water separation. The oil-water mixture from the boot is discharged into the water with a spreader which distributes the flow as uniformly as possible over the cross section of the tank. The free water drops out and the oil rises through the water.

Emulsion Layer

The line of separation of oil and water is not sharp, as water in oil emulsion is present in varying amounts and forms a layer between the water and oil. The thickness of the emulsion layer varies widely, depending upon the characteristics of the oil, and particularly upon the surface tension. Surface tension at the oil-water interface is influenced largely by the amount of colloidal solid material in the oil or water. Separation takes place slowly in the emulsion layer, and the holding time required in this layer determines the capacity of the tank. The use of heat and chemical is frequently required to assist in breaking this emulsion.

Stokes' Law

Gravity separation of small bubbles of gas, drops of water, or sand grains follows Stokes' law when the Reynolds number is ≤ 1.85. The terminal velocity of settling of these small particles limits the fluid-handling capacity of the wash tank, or at a given fluid rate the size of the wash tank determines the particle size of solids or liquids that remain in the fluid. Any particles having a terminal velocity of settling less than the vertical velocity of the fluid in the wash tank will be carried over. The size of the wash tank therefore determines the minimum grain size of sand in the power oil. According to Stokes' law, the velocity of settling is determined by the following relation:

$$R_e \leqq 1.85$$

$$V_s = 4.146 \frac{d^2(\rho_s - \rho)}{\mu}$$

where V_s = velocity of settling, ft/hr
d = diameter of particles, in. $\times 10^{-3}$
μ = viscosity of liquid, cp
ρ_s = specific gravity of suspended particles
ρ = specific gravity of liquid
k = shape factor; spheres = 1.0, sand = 0.65

when $R_e \lessgtr 1.85$ the deviation from Stokes' law is appreciable and the following relation designated as the "intermediate" may be used:[13]

$$R_e > 1.85$$

$$V_s = \frac{19.1d^{1.14}(\rho_s - \rho)^{0.71}k}{\mu^{0.43}\rho_s^{0.29}}$$

Table 6-9 gives the velocity of separation of gas bubbles ($\rho = 0.0$), water drops ($\rho = 1.0$ to 1.15), and sand grains ($\rho = 2.0$ to 4.0) in oil having a viscosity of 10 cp and a specific gravity of 0.87.

Table 6-9. Gravity Separation
Velocity of Settling (Separation), Feet per Hour, in Oil
($\mu = 10$ cp; $\rho = 0.87$)

Particle diameter: Inches $\times 10^{-3}$ Microns			100 2,540	50 1,270	10 254	5 127	1 25.4	0.5 12.7	0.1 2.54
Type	ρ_s	$\rho_s - \rho$							
Gas*	0.0	−0.87	1,276	579	36.0	9.00	0.360	0.0900	0.00360
Water	1.0	0.13	331	135	5.4	1.35	0.054	0.0135	0.00054
	1.05	0.18	417	186	7.5	1.86	0.075	0.0186	0.00075
	1.10	0.23	496	224	9.5	2.38	0.095	0.0238	0.00095
	1.15	0.28	571	258	11.6	2.90	0.116	0.0290	0.00116
Solids	2.0	1.13	1,000	453	30.8	7.60	0.308	0.0760	0.00308
	2.5	1.63	1,295	587	43.9	10.98	0.439	0.1100	0.00439
	3.0	2.13	1,565	709	57.4	14.35	0.574	0.1430	0.00574
	4.0	3.13	2,060	934	84.4	21.20	0.844	0.2120	0.00844

* For this table the density of gas is assumed to be 0.0.

Wash tanks shown in Fig. 6-32 and Table 6-8 are selected to give a vertical velocity of 1.0 ft/hr, assuming uniform distribution across the tank. With this velocity Table 6-9 shows that any water droplets smaller than 0.005 in. diameter or any sand grains smaller than 0.001 in. diameter will be carried over. Some benefit, however, is derived from the tendency of water drops to coalesce and for small sand grains to be attached by surface tension to water droplets and to each other, so that separation is not dependent entirely on the settling of individual grains.

Effect of Viscosity

Table 6-9 is for an oil having a viscosity of 10 cp, which would be an oil of 30 to 35°API at normal temperatures. Stokes' law shows the rate of settling to vary inversely as the viscosity. If the viscosity were lowered to 2 cp, the grain size carried would be reduced in the ratio $1/\sqrt{5}$.

Heaters

To reduce the viscosity of low-gravity oils, heaters are required which also reduce the surface tension at the oil-water interface. Both these factors are important in breaking of emulsions and settling of water. With oils requiring only a small amount of heat, the engine-cooling water may be used to heat the power oil. With engines having water-cooled exhaust manifolds, approximately two-thirds of the heat value of the fuel burned by the engine may be transferred to the oil. The temperature obtained in the oil will then depend upon the power applied per unit of volume. The temperature rise will be approximately 13°F/1,000 psi of operating pressure.

To obtain the best results any heat which is added should be ahead of the boot, so that all the gas release will occur in the boot rather than in the wash tank. If chemical is used to assist in water removal, it should be added preferably in the power oil distributed to the wells, but if it is not added to the power oil, it should be injected into the lead line ahead of the heater.

Table 6-10 gives the temperature required to reduce the viscosity to the values shown. For good separation the oil viscosity should be less than 10 cp.

Table 6-10. Tank Temperatures, °F

Oil gravity		Viscosity, cp				
°API	Sp gr	50	20	10	5	2
10	1.000	250	305	355		
15	0.9659	175	215	260	320	
20	0.9340	120	160	200	255	365
25	0.9042	65	105	140	190	285
30	0.8762	...	55	90	135	220
35	0.8498	...	...	45	85	170

Wax

When wax is in suspension in the oil the crystal size is small and the specific gravity is so close to that of the oil that good separation does not occur. Also the wax tends to hold both the water and small sand particles in suspension and interferes with their settling. Therefore, to obtain good settling of water and sand the temperature

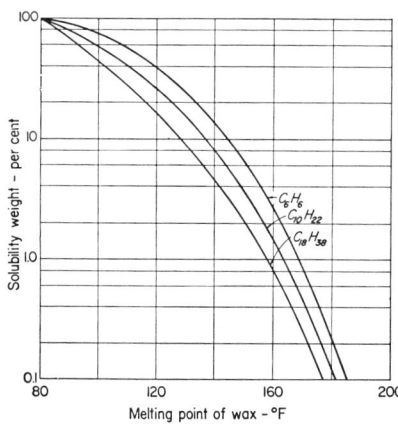

FIG. 6-33. Solubility of wax vs. melting point at 80°F.

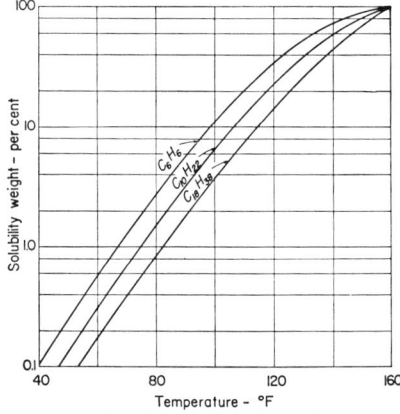

FIG. 6-34. Solubility of 160°F melting point wax vs. temperature.

must be sufficiently high to put all the wax in solution. This varies with the amount and solubility of the wax involved but is usually less than 100°F. Figure 6-33 gives the solubility of wax at 80°F as a function of the melting point, and Fig. 6-34 gives the solubility of a 160° melting point wax as a function of temperature. Some oils have been found to contain wax with melting points as high as 190°F.

Electric Dehydrators

Electrical dehydrators are described in Chap. 11, but one type which has been found particularly suited to treating power oil utilizes high-voltage direct current. This has been found capable of removing water and sediment under favorable condition down to 2 ppm and grain sizes of 2μ. The use of electric d-c units has been found

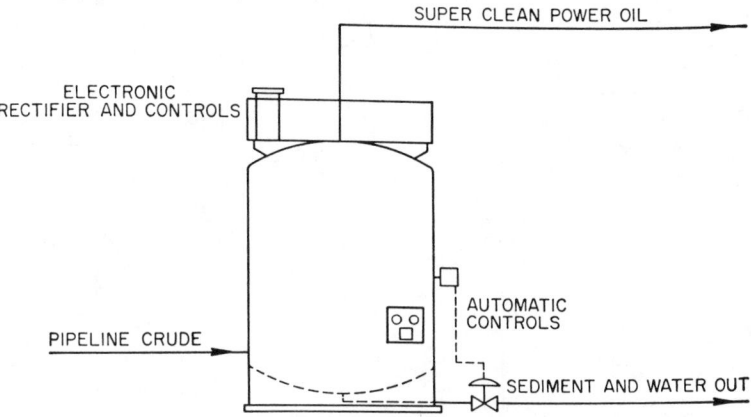

Fig. 6-35. Petreco sediment separator (Petrolite Corp.).

to increase pump life substantially.[14] Figure 6-35 and Table 6-11 give dimensions and capacities of these units.

Table 6-11. Electrical Separators

	Vertical tank		Horizontal tank	
Rated capacity, B/D, 35°API............	850	3,500	11,000	22,000
Diameter, ft............................	5	10	12	12
Height or length, ft.....................	10	15	25	45

Centrifugal Cleaners

Continuous centrifuges such as the Sharples Nozljector have been used experimentally for cleaning power oil. This unit is self-cleaning and has a continuous discharge of water and sediment. The capacity of this type of centrifuge is well fitted to large-volume installations.

Combination of Equipment

Large installations for multiple-well operation sometimes utilize a combination of equipment with *gas traps, wash tanks, heaters, electrical dehydrators, storage tanks,* and *pumps* for delivering oil to the triplex pumps under pressure. The location of these units usually is at the main tank battery with a number of triplex pumps at the same location. In this case the power oil may be distributed to the wells in individual lines. If the lease is large or the well spacing 40 acres or more, it is sometimes more economical to distribute in a large line serving a number of control centers, each handling any convenient number of wells. In some cases the well controls have been at each wellhead.

Closed System

Power-oil Selection. One of the advantages of the closed system is that power oil may be selected which has good lubricity and a viscosity which will give good engine-valve action and low leakage losses under bottom-hole conditions of temperature and

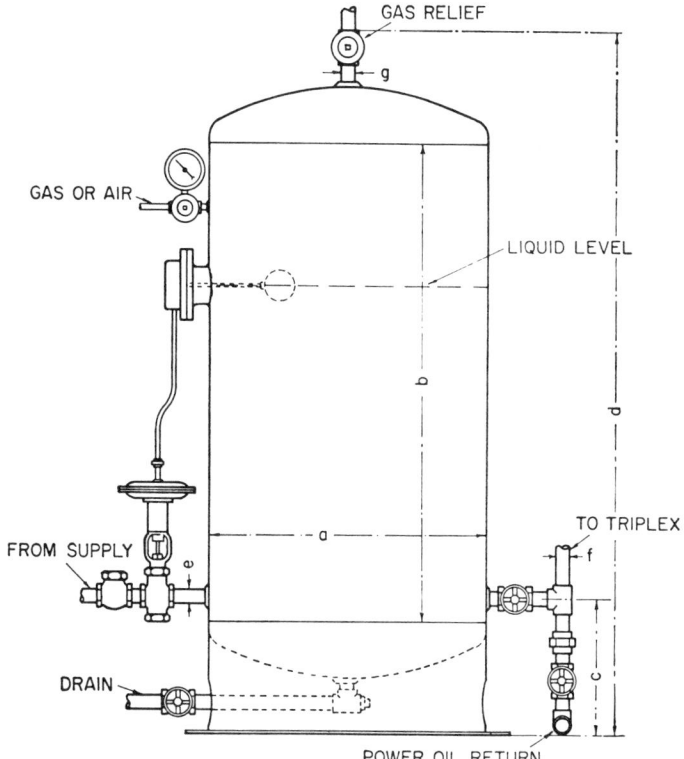

FIG. 6-36. Closed-system surge tank.

pressure. This reduces the number of variables to which the engine is subjected and simplifies its design. The closed system is particularly advantageous when the produced oil is either under 20°API or over 50°API. In the first case the viscosity is too high and in the second the lubricating value of the oil is apt to be poor. An oil of approximately 30°API and having a viscosity of 10 to 20 cs at 100°F is to be preferred for wells less than 5,000 ft in depth. Heavier oils are preferred for deep wells, in order to obtain a bottom-hole viscosity in the order of 10 cs.

Single-well Closed System. The simplest system consists of a small surge tank, preferably under sufficient pressure to give good charging of the triplex pump. This should be from 20 to 100 psi with a level control and gas or air over the fluid. A make-up pump maintains the fluid level in the surge tank from a clean-oil-supply tank. This should have two to three times the volume of the well tubing to permit removing and reinstalling free pumps. Figure 6-36 and Table 6-12 show the type and size of surge tank recommended for various pump sizes and well depths. Closed-system power supply may use any or a combination of the equipment described above for cleaning the make-up oil. The capacity of the cleaning system should allow for the maximum make-up rate to be expected. Two per cent of the power-oil circulation rate has been found adequate. Any of the cleaning methods given above may be used, but gravity settling is the simplest.

Table 6-12. Closed-system Surge Tank—Size, Capacity, and Principal Dimensions
(All dimensions in inches)

Pump size	2	2½	3	4
Capacity, bbl*	3	6	12	24
a	30	36	48	60
b	48	60	84	96
c	15	18	24	30
d	72	90	126	144
e	1	1¼	2	3
f	1¼	2	3	4
g	1	1¼	2	3

* Capacity at float control.

In place of an individual supply tank, a central tank may be used for any desired number of single-well installations, with a centrifugal or rotary pump for delivering oil to the individual surge tanks. The line and pump capacities should be sufficient to supply the triplex displacement when the well pump is being surfaced. This capacity will depend upon the probability of servicing more than one well at a time and the desired pump-out rate.

An alternate for single wells is a supply tank at atmospheric pressure but covered to prevent weathering of the oil. This tank may be used for settling as well as storage. Based on three times the surfacing requirement would give tank capacities as shown in Table 6-13. Tank capacities based on three times the volume required to surface free pumps are shown in Table 6-13.

Table 6-13. Capacity of Supply Tank, bbl

Pump size, in.	Depth, ft				
	2,000	5,000	7,500	10,000	15,000
2	100	100	100	100	200
2½	100	100	100	100	250
3	100	100	200	250	500
4	100	250	300	500	750

In this case the return power oil goes directly to the charging pump with the supply tank floating on the line to make up leakage. A meter may be placed in this line, to show the volume of power oil used. It can be seen from the above tank sizes that the vertical velocity in the tank for normal make-up is low compared with wash-tank designs and should give good cleaning.

Multiple-well Closed Systems. In multiple-well closed systems the same methods are employed as for individual wells but may be more elaborate to ensure uniform high-quality power fluid. The basic cleaning system should be sized for a capacity corresponding to the number of wells. Supply tanks, transfer pump, etc., do not need to be selected to meet the summation of the maximum requirements of each well but rather should be selected for the expected maximum which the system will require.

With multiple-well installations it is best to have the supply tank at the gauge-tank battery so that it can take oil from the normal wash tank. The oil from the supply tank can be transferred to the triplex with a centrifugal or rotary pump with each triplex or each battery of triplexes and supplied through a meter to check leakage losses. These pumps may also act as charging pumps for the triplex so that individual pumps at each triplex are not required.

In very large installations it is desirable to have all important parts of the system in multiple units or with standbys for emergency to avoid possible down time caused by failure of any of the equipment.

POWER-OIL PUMPS

Pressure Requirements

The *operating pressure* required *depends* upon the *pumping head*, the engine-to-*pump ratio* of the bottom-hole unit, and the *friction loss* in the system. See page **6**–65 for friction loss. For estimating it is usually sufficient to use 0.5 psi/ft of lift times engine-to-pump ratio as given in Tables 6-1 to 6-4 for the total pressure including friction. In multiple-well systems this pressure must be sufficient for the heaviest well in the system. This should also include an allowance of 100 to 300 psi for the flow control. Throttle valves shown in Fig. 6-46 require a higher pressure drop to get good regulation than the flow-control valves of Fig. 6-45. The trend is toward smaller ratios of engine to pump and hence higher operating pressures. By use of higher pressure the power-transmitting capacity of tubing is increased (see page **6**–69). The present maximum pressure is approximately 5,000 psi.

Volume Requirements

Over-all volumetric efficiencies on which volume and power requirements are based may run as high as 90 per cent, but for the purpose of selecting equipment an efficiency of 50 per cent should be assumed. This covers the surface pump losses and those of both the engine and pump of the bottom-hole unit. Where large volumes are required, as in multiple-well installation, it is the practice to use a number of triplex pumps in parallel. If the central plant services wells of different depths, the piping is arranged so that one or more triplex pumps may be used at each pressure and shifted as required by changes in volume demand of the low-operating-pressure and high-operating-pressure wells. A multiple triplex system gives flexibility and at the same time permits standardizing on a popular size of unit with low cost per installed horsepower.

Horsepower Requirements

The horsepower required is established by the pressure requirement, the volume requirement, and the efficiency of the triplex pump.

The following relations are useful in computing power requirements:

$$\text{Theoretical hydraulic hp} = \frac{Ql\delta}{135,800} \text{ or } \frac{QP}{58,700}$$

where Q = volume, B/D
l = depth to pumping fluid level, ft
δ = specific gravity of fluid
P = pressure, psi

or
$$\text{hp} = Q \times P \times 0.0005833$$

where Q = volume, gal/min
P = pressure, psi

To determine the volume of power fluid required,

$$Q_p = \frac{\text{spm} \times C_p}{E_p} \quad \text{or} \quad \text{spm} = \frac{Q_p \times E_p}{C_p}$$

$$Q_e = \frac{\text{spm} \times C_e}{E_e} \quad \frac{C_e}{C_p} = \text{engine-to-pump ratio}$$

or
$$Q_e = \frac{Q_p \times \dfrac{C_e}{C_p}}{E_p \times E_e}$$

where Q_p = capacity of pump, B/D
$\qquad Q_e$ = power oil required by engine, B/D
$\qquad C_p$ = pump displacement factor, B/D/spm
$\qquad C_e$ = engine power oil, B/D/spm
$\qquad E_p$ = volumetric efficiency of pump
$\qquad E_e$ = volumetric efficiency of engine

Operating pressure, open system:

$$P_c = 0.4331\delta_p l$$

$$P_e = (0.4331\delta_p l + P_{f1})\frac{C_p}{C_e} + 0.4331\delta_p l + P_{f1} + P_{f2}$$

$$P_t = (0.4331\delta_p l + P_{f1})\frac{C_p}{C_e} + P_{f2} + P_{f3} + P_{f4} + P_{f5} - 0.4331(\delta_e - \delta_p)l + P_{f1}$$

Operating pressure, closed system:

$$P_c = 0.4331\delta_p l$$

$$P_e = (0.4331\delta_p l + P_{f1})\frac{C_p}{C_e} + 0.4331\delta_r l + P_{f6} + P_{f2}$$

$$P_t = (0.4331\delta_p l + P_{f1})\frac{C_p}{C_e} + P_{f6} + P_{f2} + P_{f3} + P_{f4} + P_{f5} - 0.4331(\delta_e - \delta_r)l$$

where P_{f1} = friction in pump column
$\qquad P_{f2}$ = mechanical and hydraulic friction of bottom hole unit, psi (see Fig. 6-19)
$\qquad P_{f3}$ = friction in power-oil tube, psi
$\qquad P_{f4}$ = surface line friction, psi
$\qquad P_{f5}$ = control-valve pressure drop, psi
$\qquad P_{f6}$ = friction power-oil return tube, psi
$\qquad \delta_p$ = specific gravity of produced fluid
$\qquad \delta_e$ = specific gravity of power oil
$\qquad \delta_r$ = specific gravity of power-oil return
$\qquad P_c$ = pump column pressure, psi
$\qquad P_e$ = engine pressure at unit, psi
$\qquad P_t$ = triplex pressure, psi

See properties of fluids for δ_p, δ_e, and δ_r, page 6–55. See friction loss in tubing, page 6–65 for P_{f1}, P_{f3}, P_{f4}, and P_{f6}.

Pump Types

The type of unit usually applied to hydraulic pumping is the triplex, although duplex, quintuplex, and other types could be used. The size of the units which have been used ranges from 1 to 100 hp. The most common sizes are 15 and 60 hp. These ratings are based upon hydraulic horsepower output and are usually driven by gas engines having displacements of 220 and 800 cu in., respectively. Motor-driven units are used on the smaller sizes or in locations where gas is not available or where absence of noise or fire hazards make electric power desirable.

Figure 6-37 shows the construction of an integral motor-drive triplex designed for heavy-duty application. This pump has antifriction bearings, heavy heat-treated crankshaft, hardened-tooth helical double-reduction gear train, weatherproof motor, close-fitting interchangeable plungers and liners with no packing required, force-feed lubrication to all bearings, connecting rods, and crossheads, scavenger pump for plunger leakage, pressure gauge and pressure-relief valve integrally mounted.

Figure 6-38 shows the skid-mounted engine-drive unit with all required auxiliaries driven by the same engine.

The use of closely fitted plungers and liners results in a higher efficiency than is obtained with packing. Also, being nonadjustable, it is not subject to damage by overtightening.   When liners are worn enough to cause excessive leakage, they are removed and exchanged for rehoned assemblies.

The selection of the plunger-liner fit to be used is determined by balancing the leakage power loss and viscous-drag loss to obtain a minimum total loss.   The leakage with the plunger in motion and with the plunger stationary is the same, and the relations given on page 6–18 may be applied to determine this loss.

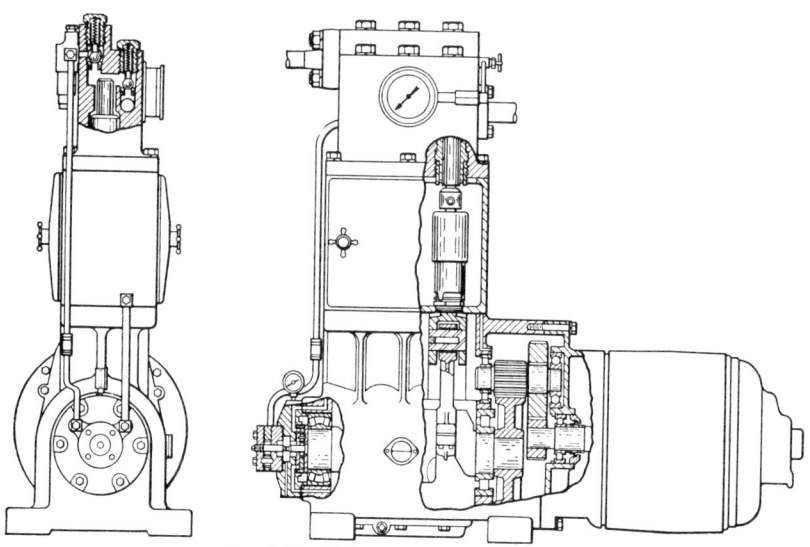

Fig. 6-37. Kobe integral-motor triplex.

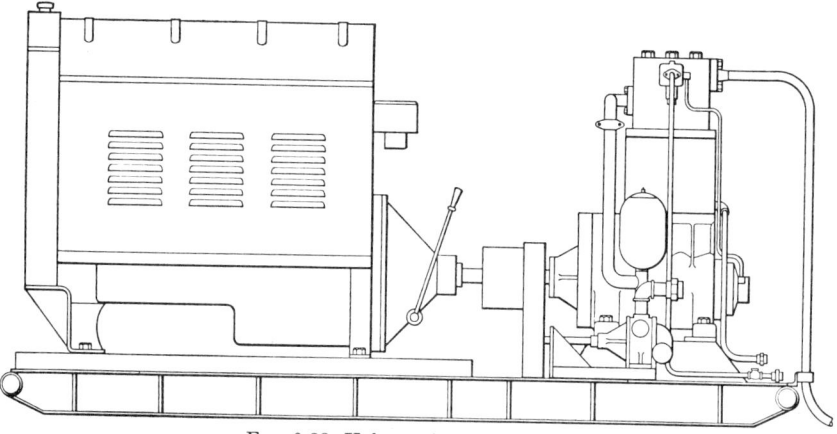

Fig. 6-38. Kobe engine-drive triplex.

The drag force follows the basic relation given on page 6–17 for bottom-hole engine plungers modified to correct for the varying velocity of the crank-driven plunger. The power loss is the integral of the instantaneous loss at any point in the stroke with the velocity following simple harmonic motion corrected for the connecting-rod crank-throw ratio $1/r$.

$$W = 1.268 \times 10^{-9} \frac{DL\mu n r^2}{C} \left[1 + \frac{1}{4} \left(\frac{l}{r} \right)^2 \right]$$

where W = loss per plunger per revolution, ft-lb
$\quad\quad D$ = plunger diameter, in.
$\quad\quad L$ = fit length, in.
$\quad\quad \mu$ = viscosity, cp
$\quad\quad n$ = speed, rpm
$\quad\quad r$ = crank radius, in.
$\quad\quad l$ = connecting-rod length, in.
$\quad\quad C$ = clearance, thousandths of an inch
$\quad\quad s$ = stroke = $2r$, in.

With l/r of 4.5,

$$\left[1 + \frac{1}{4} \left(\frac{l}{r}\right)^2 \right] = 1.012$$

Table 6-14. Kobe Triplex Pumps
Size 2

Plunger			Max press., psi	Triplex crankshaft speed											
				100 rpm			200 rpm			300 rpm			350 rpm		
P and L size	Area, sq in.	Stroke, in.		Gal/min	B/D	Hyd. hp	Gal/min	B/D	Hyd. hp	Gal/min	B/D	Hyd. hp	Gal/min	B/D	Hyd. hp
1 1/16 *	0.371	3	4,720	1.44	49.3	3.97	2.88	98.6	7.94	4.32	148	11.9	5.04	173	13.9
3/4	0.442	3	3,960	1.71	58.6	3.97	3.42	117	7.94	5.13	176	11.9	5.98	205	13.9
1 3/16 *	0.518	3	3,380	2.01	68.9	3.97	4.02	138	7.94	6.03	207	11.9	7.03	241	13.9
7/8	0.601	3	2,910	2.33	79.9	3.97	4.66	160	7.94	6.99	240	11.9	8.16	280	13.9
1 5/16 *	0.690	3	2,540	2.68	91.9	3.97	5.36	184	7.94	8.04	276	11.9	9.38	322	13.9
1	0.785	3	2,230	3.05	105	3.97	6.11	209	7.94	9.15	314	11.9	10.7	366	13.9
1 1/8	0.994	3	1,760	3.85	132	3.97	7.70	264	7.94	11.6	396	11.9	13.5	462	13.9
1 1/4	1.227	3	1,430	4.76	163	3.97	9.52	326	7.94	14.3	490	11.9	16.7	571	13.9

To obtain brake horsepower, divide hydraulic horsepower by 0.95.
Standard gear ratio for gas engine drive is 3.986; other ratio available is 5.204.
* Plungers and liners are available on special order only.

Size 3

Plunger			Max press, psi	Triplex crankshaft speed											
				100 rpm			200 rpm			300 rpm			400 rpm		
Diam, in.	Area, sq in.	Stroke, in.		Gal/min	B/D	Hyd. hp	Gal/min	B/D	Hyd. hp	Gal/min	B/D	Hyd. hp	Gal/min	B/D	Hyd. hp
3/4	0.442	4	5,000	2.29	78.6	6.68	4.59	157	13.4	6.90	237	20.2	9.18	315	26.8
7/8	0.601	4	5,000	3.12	107	9.10	6.24	214	18.2	9.36	321	27.2	12.5	428	36.5
1	0.785	4	5,000	4.08	140	11.9	8.16	280	23.8	12.2	420	35.6	16.3	560	47.6
1 1/8	0.994	4	5,000	5.16	177	15.1	10.3	354	30.0	15.5	531	45.8	20.7	708	60.2
1 1/4	1.227	4	4,120	6.38	219	15.3	12.8	437	30.6	19.1	656	45.8	25.5	874	61.3
1 3/8	1.485	4	3,400	7.72	265	15.3	15.4	529	30.6	23.1	794	45.8	30.9	1,058	61.3
1 1/2	1.767	4	2,860	9.18	315	15.3	18.4	630	30.6	27.5	945	45.8	36.7	1,259	61.3
1 5/8	2.074	4	2,440	10.8	370	15.3	21.6	740	30.6	32.3	1,109	45.8	43.1	1,478	61.3
1 3/4	2.405	4	2,100	12.5	429	15.3	25.0	858	30.6	37.5	1,286	45.8	50.0	1,714	61.3
1 7/8 *	2.761	4	1,830	14.4	492	15.3	28.7	984	30.6	43.0	1,475	45.8	57.4	1,967	61.3
2 *	3.142	4	1,610	16.3	560	15.3	32.6	1,118	30.6	49.0	1,679	45.8	65.3	2,239	61.3
2 1/8 *	3.546	4	1,420	18.4	632	15.3	36.8	1,263	30.6	55.3	1,895	45.8	73.7	2,527	61.3
2 1/4 *	3.976	4	1,270	20.7	708	15.3	41.3	1,416	30.6	62.0	2,125	45.8	82.6	2,833	61.3

Available gear ratios are 3.079, 3.579, 4.330, and 4.864.
* Cylinder blocks and plungers available on special order only.

Therefore the horsepower loss per plunger is

$$\mathrm{hp} = 7.58 \times 10^{-13} \frac{DL\mu n^2 r^2}{C} \times 1.012$$

The leakage power loss from page 6–19 is

$$\mathrm{hp} = 17.06 \frac{C^3 D P^2}{\mu L}$$

where P = pressure, psi

Total horsepower loss per plunger is

$$\mathrm{hp} = 7.67 \times 10^{-13} \frac{DL\mu n^2 r^2}{C} + 17.06 \frac{C^3 D P^2}{\mu L}$$

From this relation the optimum clearance for any assumed conditions can be determined. Figure 6-39 gives the clearance for minimum horsepower loss and also the horsepower per plunger at this clearance.

With a viscosity of 10 cp and other factors normal for the pumps used, the optimum clearance will be approximately 0.001 in./in. of diameter and at this clearance from Fig. 6-20 the leakage with 1-in. plungers at 5,000 psi is 0.01 gal/min, or less than 0.07 per cent of the displacement.

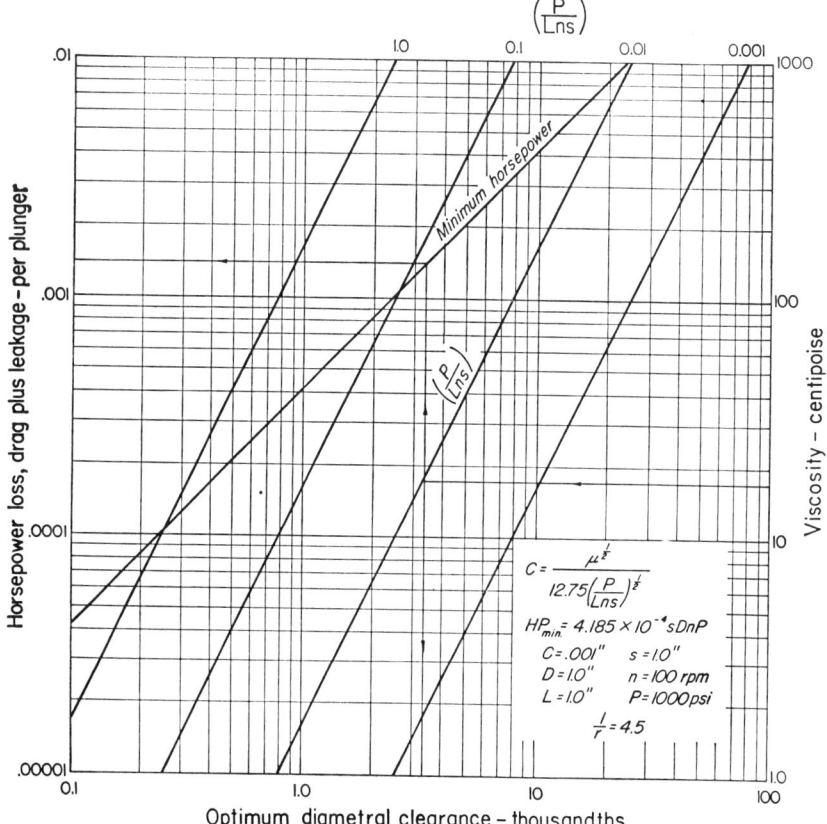

FIG. 6-39. Clearance vs. viscosity for minimum horsepower loss.

Figure 6-40 shows the typical performance of a small motor-driven unit using the close-fitting plunger construction.

Table 6-14 gives the capacity and important characteristics of the Kobe triplex pump.

Figure 6-41 shows the construction of an Aldridge vertical quintuplex pump. Table 6-16 gives the capacities of these units and principal dimensions.

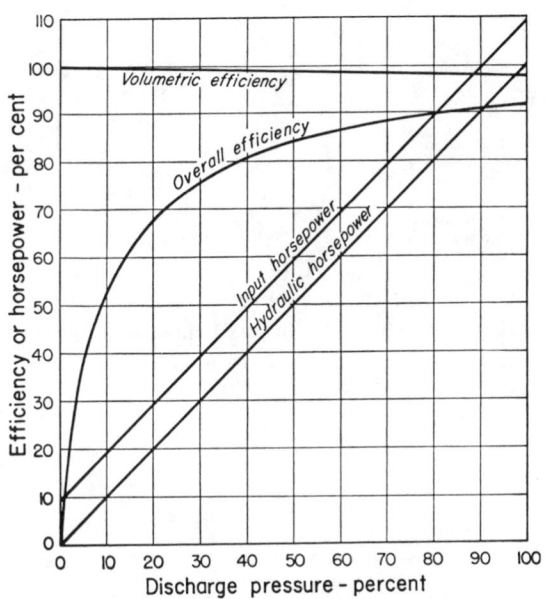

FIG. 6-40. Typical performance of small motor-driven triplex.

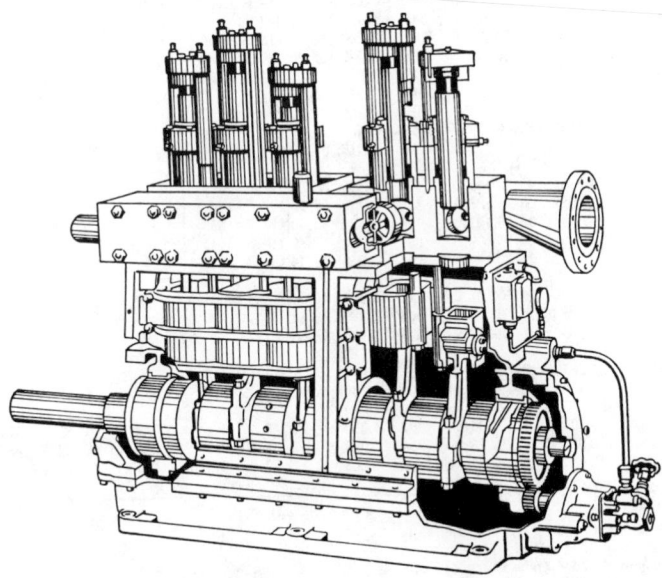

FIG. 6-41. Aldridge quintuplex pump.

PRODUCTION EQUIPMENT

Table 6-15. "National" Triplex Plunger Pumps

Size	J-125	F-60	F-30	F-15
Rated output at rated speed, hydraulic hp............	113	60	30	15
Rated speed, rpm..................	400	400	450	500
Stroke, in..........................	5	4	3	2
Low-pressure cylinder:				
Plunger sizes, in....................	$2\frac{3}{4}$–4	2–$2\frac{3}{4}$	$1\frac{3}{4}$–$2\frac{1}{2}$	$1\frac{3}{4}$–$2\frac{1}{4}$
Output at rated speed, gal/min......	154–287	65–123	42–86	31–52
Max discharge pressure, psi..........	1,250–590	1,575–835	1,220–600	825–500
Medium-pressure cylinder:				
Plunger sizes, in....................	$1\frac{1}{2}$–$2\frac{3}{4}$	....	1–$1\frac{1}{2}$	1–$1\frac{1}{2}$
Output at rated speed, gal/min......	46–154	....	14–31	10–19
Max discharge pressure, psi..........	4,200–1,250	....	3,735–1,650	2,520–1,120
High-pressure cylinder:				
Plunger sizes, in....................	$1\frac{1}{8}$–$1\frac{5}{8}$	$1\frac{3}{8}$–2		
Output at rated speed, gal/min......	26–54	21–65		
Max discharge pressure, psi..........	7,470–3,580	4,975–1,578		
Max width by length of frame and cylinder, in......................	37 × 67	31 × 50	24 × 41	20 × 34

Table 6-16. Aldridge Multiplex Pumps, 5-in. Stroke

Fluid end	Plunger diam, in.	Press., psi	Quintuplex displacement				Septuplex displacement				Nonuplex displacement			
			100 rpm	360 rpm	100 rpm	360 rpm	100 rpm	360 rpm	100 rpm	360 rpm	100 rpm	360 rpm	100 rpm	360 rpm
			Gal/min	Gal/min	B/D	B/D	Gal/min	Gal/min	B/D	B/D	Gal/min	Gal/min	B/D	B/D
A	$3\frac{1}{2}$	775	104.0*	312.0*	3,567	10,700	146.0*	437.0*	4997	14,990	187.0*	562.0*	6433	19,300
	$3\frac{3}{8}$	835	96.9†	310.0†	3,319	10,620	135.6†	434.0†	4650	14,880	174.0†	557.0†	5969	19,100
	$3\frac{1}{4}$	900	89.7‡	305.0‡	3,079	10,470	125.6‡	427.0‡	4312	14,660	161.5‡	549.0‡	5535	18,820
	$3\frac{1}{8}$	975	83.00	299.0	2,850	10,260	116.20	418.0	3990	14,350	149.3	537.0	5130	18,400
	3	1 055	76.50	275.5	2,620	9,440	107.10	385.5	3680	13,210	137.8	496.0	4730	17,000
	$2\frac{7}{8}$	1 150	70.30	253.0	2,410	8,680	98.40	354.3	3380	12,180	126.5	456.0	4340	15,650
	$2\frac{3}{4}$	1 260	64.30	231.5	2,200	7,940	90.00	324.0	3090	11,110	115.8	417.0	3970	14,300
	$2\frac{5}{8}$	1 380	58.70	211.5	2,010	7,250	82.20	296.0	2820	10,180	105.8	382.0	3630	13,100
	$2\frac{1}{2}$	1 520	53.20	191.7	1,828	6,580	74.40	268.0	2550	9,200	95.80	345.0	3290	11,830
	$2\frac{3}{8}$	1 685	47.80	172.2	1,640	5,910	67.20	242.0	2300	8,300	86.30	310.5	2960	10,670
B	$2\frac{1}{4}$	1 875	43.00	155.0	1,475	5,325	60.20	217.0	2063	7,450	77.40	279.0	2660	9,580
	$2\frac{1}{8}$	2 105	38.40	138.2	1,320	4,750	53.75	193.8	1845	6,650	69.10	248.5	2370	8,550
	2	2,375	34.00	122.3	1,168	4,200	47.60	171.2	1630	5,880	61.20	220.2	2100	7,570
	$1\frac{7}{8}$	2,705	29.93	107.8	1,027	3,700	41.80	150.8	1435	5,160	53.80	194.0	1850	6,670
	$1\frac{3}{4}$	3,105	26.20	94.3	900	3,230	36.44	131.3	1250	4,510	46.80	168.8	1610	5,800
C	$1\frac{5}{8}$	3,600	22.50	81.0	773	2,780	31.50	113.5	1080.0	3,900	40.50	146.0	1425	5,020
	$1\frac{1}{2}$	4,225	19.30	69.4	663	2,380	26.80	96.5	920.0	3,310	34.47	124.2	1182	4,270
	$1\frac{3}{8}$	5,025	16.10	57.9	553	1,990	22.56	81.2	773.0	2,790	29.00	104.4	995.0	3,580
D	$1\frac{1}{4}$	6,085	13.30	47.8	457	1,640	18.62	67.10	640.0	2,300	23.95	86.2	822.5	2,960
	$1\frac{1}{8}$	7,510	10.75	38.7	369	1,330	15.05	54.20	517.0	1,860	19.35	69.7	665.0	2,390
E	1	9,505	8.50	30.6	292	1,050	11.90	42.80	408.0	1,470	15.30	55.1	525.0	1,890
	$\frac{15}{16}$	10,815	7.48	26.9	256	923	10.47	37.62	359.0	1,290	13.46	48.4	462.0	1,660
	$\frac{7}{8}$	12,415	6.53	23.4	224	803	9.14	32.85	314.0	1,128	11.75	42.3	403.0	1,450

Aldridge quintuplex, septuplex, and nonuplex pumps are also made with 6- and $8\frac{1}{2}$-in. strokes. Triplex pumps are made by Aldridge with stroke lengths of $2\frac{1}{2}$, 3, 5, and 6 in.

* At maximum rpm of 300—applies to triplex and multiplex.
† At maximum rpm of 320—applies to triplex and multiplex.
‡ At maximum rpm of 340—applies to triplex and multiplex.

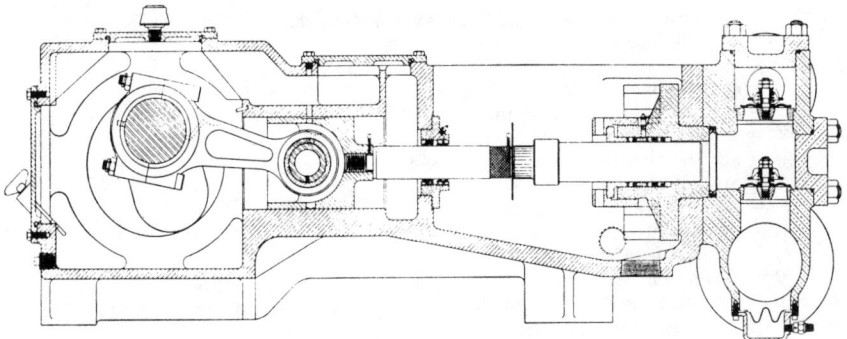

Fig. 6-42. National horizontal triplex.

Figure 6-42 shows a horizontal triplex which has been applied to hydraulic operation, and Table 6-15 gives the rated capacities of available units.

Auxiliaries

Charging Pump. To supply oil to the triplex where the storage and the pump are on the same level so no substantial head is available, a supercharger is used in the suction line. This may be a centrifugal pump or more commonly is a positive-displacement rotary pump with either variable displacement or a pressure-controlled bypass valve. This unit is usually belt-driven from the engine-triplex shaft, but with centrifugal pumps it may be a separate motor-driven unit.

The pressure required depends upon the condition of the oil and the speed of the triplex. When the oil is saturated with gas in the power-oil tank, which is usually the case in open systems, sufficient pressure must be applied to offset friction and velocity heads so that all points in the system will have a net pressure greater than the gas-saturation pressure of the oil. With gas-free dead oil it is desirable for the supply pressure to be sufficient to accelerate the plungers so they will follow the crosshead motion without depending on any threaded connection. Adequate excess pressure is provided by a charge pump delivering oil at 25 to 100 psi. To compute the pressure required the following relations apply:

Acceleration of plunger, simple harmonic motion

$$a = \omega^2 r$$

$$\omega = \frac{2\pi n}{60}$$

$$a = \frac{4\pi^2 n^2 r}{3{,}600 \times 12} = 9.14 \times 10^{-4} n^2 r$$

Correction for ratio of connecting-rod length to crank length

$$y = \sqrt{1 + \frac{r^2}{l^2}} \qquad \text{for } \frac{l}{r} = 4.5 \qquad y = 1.222$$

$$a = 9.14 \times 10^{-4} n^2 r \sqrt{1 + \frac{r^2}{l^2}}$$

$$P = \frac{W}{g}\frac{a}{A} \qquad W = A l_p d \qquad P = \frac{l_p \, d a}{g}$$

where a = acceleration in line of piston travel, ft/sec/sec
ω = angular velocity, radians/sec
r = crank radius, in.
n = speed, rpm
l = connecting-rod length, in.
W = weight of plunger, lb
g = acceleration of gravity, ft/sec/sec
A = area of plunger, sq in.
P = acceleration pressure, psi
d = density of plunger material, lb/cu in.
l_p = length of plunger, in.
y = correction to acceleration for ratio of connecting rod to crank length

For solid steel plungers 10 in. in length, a stroke of 4 in., and a connecting-rod–crank ratio of 4.5, this relation becomes

$$P = 1.96 \times 10^{-4} n^2$$

Chemical Pump. Skid-mounted units provide one or more chemical pumps and supply tanks for feeding chemicals into the oil to reduce corrosion in the system or to assist in water removal when the power oil and production reach the wash tank. This down-hole treatment utilizes the well temperature to assist in breaking oil emulsions.

POWER-OIL DISTRIBUTION

Main Lines

The distribution of the power fluid to the individual well is a simple piping problem. The important factors to be considered are convenient location of well controls and capital investment. Friction in the lines is usually not an important factor in design except with oils of 20°API gravity or heavier. Tubing-friction data which may be applied to surface lines are given on pages **6–75** and **6–76**. It is good practice to keep velocities under 3.0 ft/sec, in which case fluid friction will not be excessive.

Low-pressure lines from the power-oil tanks to the power pumps should be larger than the high-pressure lines with velocities under 1.0 ft/sec and with a minimum of pipe fittings.

Local Headers

Triplex discharge headers where a number of units are operated in parallel should be carefully designed for safety at high pressures. Particular attention should be given to prevent vibration of these lines, and it is recommended that where possible welding fittings should be used in place of threaded fittings. Each triplex outlet should be provided with a shut-off valve, preferably of the nonreturn check-valve type. This prevents feedback to any triplex not in operation and is a safety measure to prevent loss of oil or other hazard in the event of a failure of any part of the triplex fluid system. It is good practice to also have pressure-controlled governors on the engines driving the triplex pumps which serve to give the major control of fluid volumes within the engine-speed range recommended by the manufacturers.

Several different distribution patterns may be followed. On large leases it will be more economical to use large-sized main lines with control stations at convenient points. Each control station would be provided with a distribution manifold with flow-control valves, meter loops, and various other accessories described in detail on pages **6–47** to **6–49**. From these stations individual lines feed the wells.

Central Headers

Medium-sized leases are usually equipped with central distribution manifolds for all the wells. These are located near the lease-tank battery for convenience. If heated oil is used, the lines to the wells may be insulated, although this is usually not found to be economical. Buried lines are desirable, both to protect against mechanical damage and to add some heat insulation. The lines should be below the frost line in cold climates and preferably in dry soil. In some cases corrosion protection is used.

Lines for marine, lake, and river-bed installations must provide for protection from mechanical damage and from corrosion.

The length of lines is more a matter of cost than of power loss (see pages 6–75 and 6–76 for friction loss). Where conditions are unusual, such as in flood areas, it is not uncommon to have lines as much as 5,000 to 10,000 ft in length.

Flow-control Valves

Valves for this service should be pilot-operated with a differential across the pilot orifice of 25 to 75 psi to give adequate control force for the main valve with a reasonable diaphragm or piston size. Figure 6-43 shows the construction of such a valve

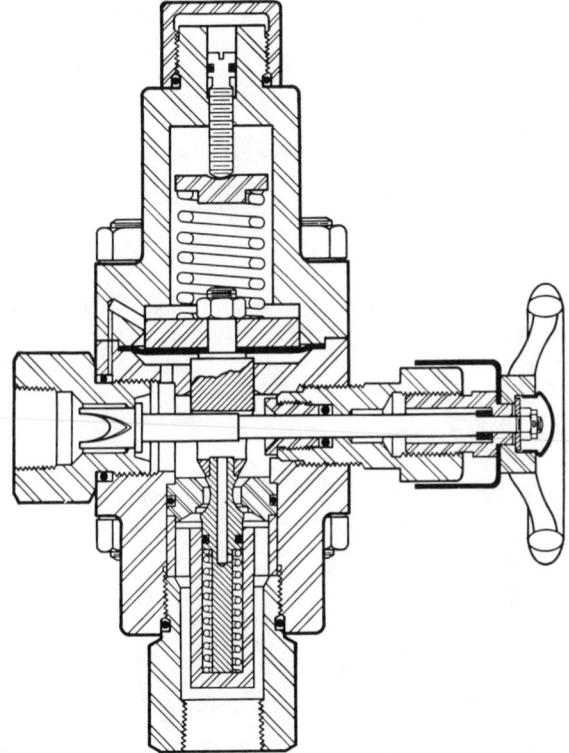

FIG. 6-43. Grove flow-control valve.

with a balanced main valve and a characterized adjustable pilot valve to give a wide range of adjustment and one that is not critical to set. This valve has a diaphragm motor to operate the main valve with an adjustable differential to permit selecting the best operation. The differential used is normally 75 psi. A graduated control is provided which may be calibrated in barrels per day, gallons per minute, or strokes per minute.

Throttle Valves

Common practice for a low-cost installation has been to use a V-notch throttle valve or similar device as shown in Fig. 6-44. Pump speed is subject to much greater variation with a throttle valve than with the flow controller shown in Fig. 6-43.   A plain needle valve is not so satisfactory as V-notch valves for low flow rates, as the adjustment is too sensitive and also any solids in the oil tend to plug the annulus between the valve and the seat, with the result that the flow will not remain constant. Where needle valves are used, the selection of the proper stem diameter and seat-orifice size is important, so that at the minimum setting the valve will be open a

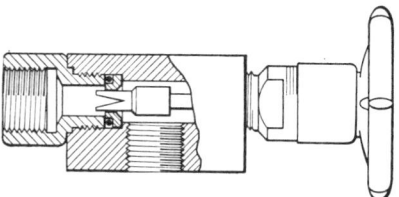

FIG. 6-44. V-notch throttle valve.

sufficient amount to avoid bridging.   Needle valves are usually carbide-trimmed to reduce erosion of the throttling members.

Both throttle valves and flow-control valves usually have a globe valve in series as a block valve for complete shut-off to permit maintenance of the flow control or the line to the well without releasing the pressure from the system.

Metering

Metering is often used in the power-oil system either with a displacement meter in each control line downstream from the flow-control valve or a meter loop valved

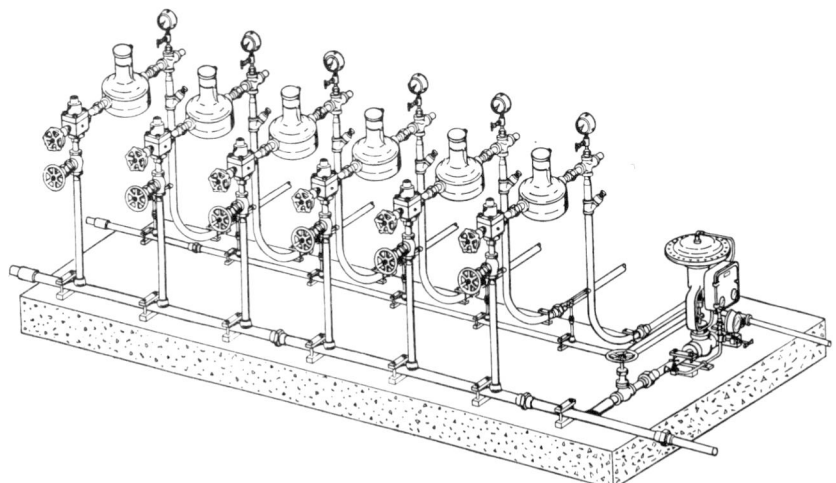

FIG. 6-45. Pump controls with individual meters.

in, so that any well may be operated on metered fluid for test purposes without disturbing the other wells.   Figure 6-45 shows the customary individual meter arrangement and Fig. 6-46 illustrates a typical meter loop for a number of wells.   Meter mechanisms are usually the standard type used for water or oil at low pressure with a case for 5,000 psi operating pressure.

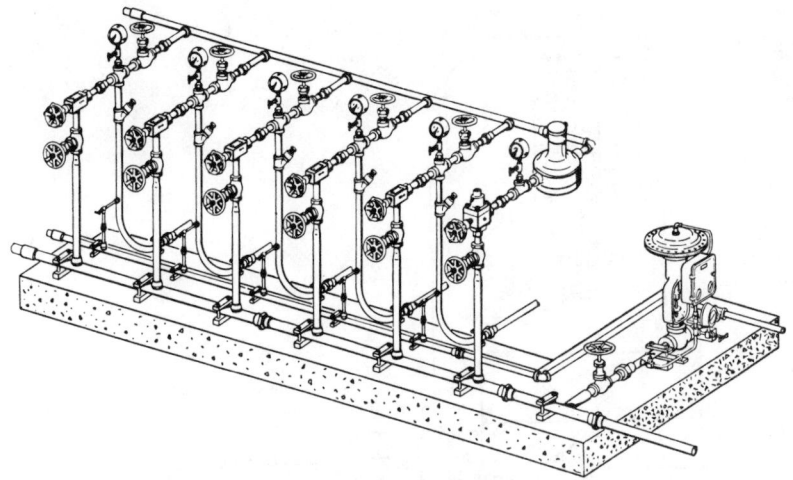

FIG. 6-46. Pump controls with meter loop.

Intermitting

In multiple-well installations intermitting may be accomplished in a number of different ways. Where flow-control valves are used the simplest control is accomplished through a pilot-solenoid control of the differential-pressure diaphragm of the flow valve shown in Fig. 6-43. Such a control may be an individual control for each valve, taking its operating fluid from the high-pressure source as shown in Fig. 6-47. The same basic control may be provided in a central control station with any desired number of controls and using either high-pressure fluid or a constant medium pressure from a reducing valve.

Where individual-well electric-driven triplexes are used an electric timer may be used which controls the main contactor of the triplex motor. With any intermitting device the cycle is selected to give the best well performance or to meet proration requirements. With high productivity or high water cuts it is desirable to use a short cycle to maintain substantially constant well conditions. In such cases the wells may be intermitted on a cycle as short as five minutes. In prorated fields the timing may be on a fixed schedule established for the field.

Air-operated controls may also be utilized with diaphragm motors and wizard-type orifice-valve controls. These may be either normally open or normally closed to meet requirements of safety, power-unit starting, etc.

Wellheads—Insert Pump

With this type of installation the wellhead consists of a simple tubing head usually carrying the power-oil tubing on slips with a packing to isolate the produced fluid Figure 6-48 shows a wellhead of this type.

Free Pump

With the free pump it is desirable to use a more elaborate tubing head which provides a pump catcher, a four-way valve to control the pump, a pressure gauge for operating and pump-out pressures, and other accessories. Figure 6-49 shows the construction of the type of valve commonly used for this purpose. In wells which "head," a lubricator is bolted to the valve block having a full-hole plug or gate valve

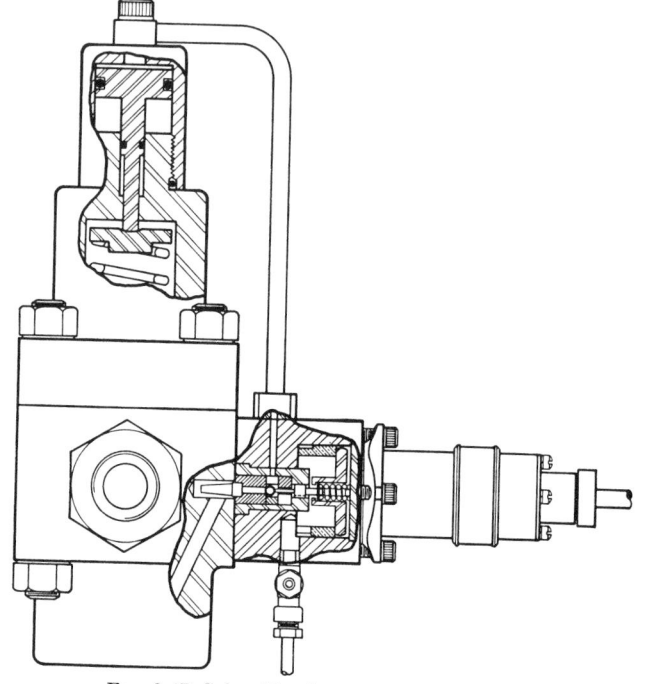

Fig. 6-47. Solenoid-valve-controlled flow valve.

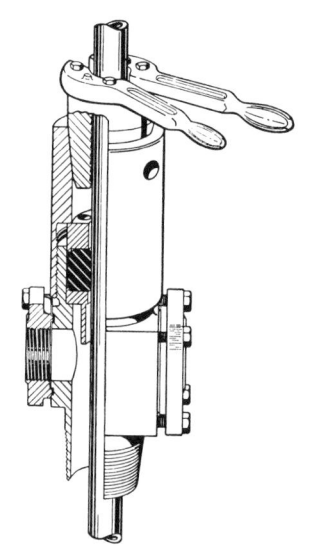

Fig. 6-48. Insert-pump tubing head.

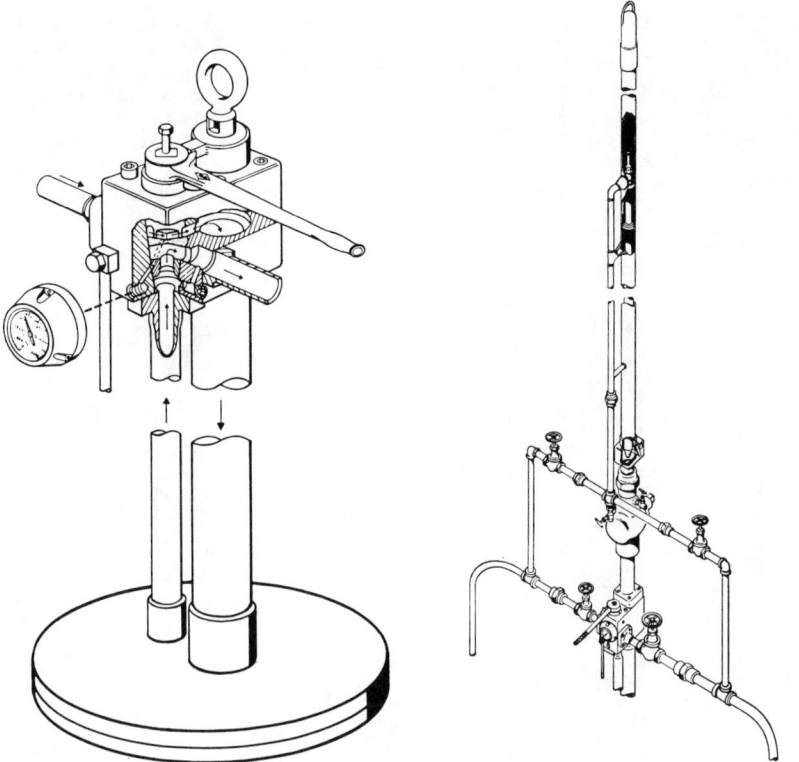

FIG. 6-49. Free-pump tubing head and four-   FIG. 6-50. High-pressure pump lubricator.
way valve.

which will allow the pump to enter the lubricator tube.   Figure 6-50 illustrates this
device.

Multiple Well

Where directionally drilled wells are produced with hydraulic pumps, the wellheads
and manifolding are close-coupled with either free-type or insert-type tubing heads.
High-pressure supply lines may be arranged for flow control at the wellhead or remote,
and each well has connections for oil and gas production arranged to suit the practice
of individual operators.

Subsurface

In some cases the entire system is installed in a trench or in individual cellars with
the piping and all controls below ground.

WELL TUBING

Tubing Pumps

Tubing pumps may be casing-type or with the power tube run separately.   Tubing
pumps are not common except in the casing type, because of the necessity of pulling
the tubings to retrieve the pump.   When the power tubing is run separately, the
pump is attached to the production tubing and may be of any diameter that will run

in the well casing. The power tube is run after the pump is in place and is stabbed into a socket with an O ring or other pack-off means, such as shown in Fig. 6-51.

With the casing-type installation the tubing to which the pump is attached is usually the power-oil tube and the production is returned in the casing annulus. A hook-wall packer is used to seal in the casing, which may either be attached to the bottom of the pump or carried by a J tool-setting adapter. In some cases the packer is run and pulled independently and has a taper shoe on top into which the pump seats to form a fluidtight joint. Where a J tool is used on the pump, the packer may

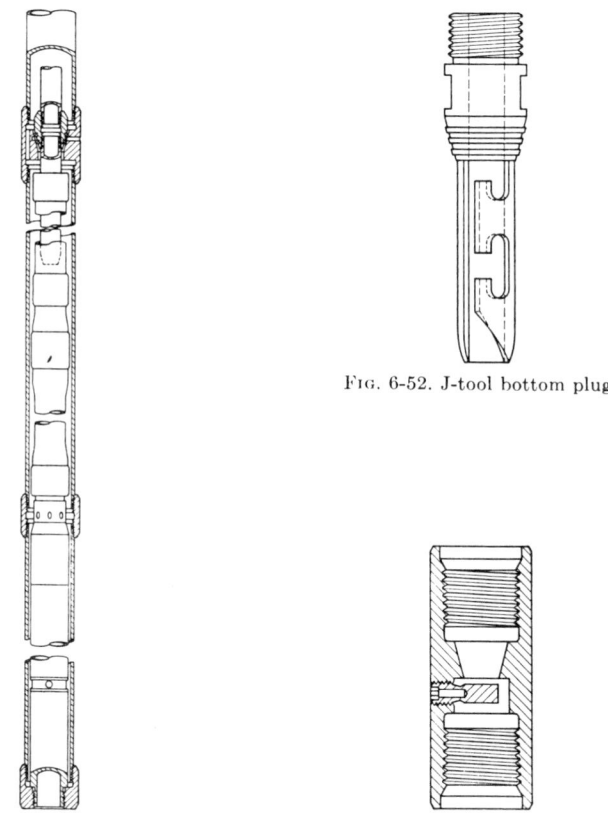

FIG. 6-52. J-tool bottom plug.

FIG. 6-51. Tubing pump.   FIG. 6-53. Knockout bleeder collar.

be either set and pulled with the pump or may be left in place when the pump is pulled. Figure 6-52 shows the J-tool bottom plug and Fig. 6-54 shows the bottom-hole assembly in the casing. A knockout plug, as shown in Fig. 6-53, is used in the power tubing to bleed the tubing before pulling.

Insert Pump

The insert-type pump is run on the power tube and seats in a shoe in the bottom of the production tubing. The power-oil return and the production are usually brought to the surface in the annulus between the power tube and the well tubing. The well tubing carries the gas anchor or in some cases a drop tube to get inside a small liner. Figure 6-55 shows the insert bottom-hole assembly with a down-pass gas anchor.

Closed System

Where closed power-oil systems are used with either insert or tubing pumps, several tubing arrangements may be selected. Figure 6-56 shows an insert pump with the production up the parallel tube. With both insert and tubing pumps either the production or the power-oil return may be handled through the tubing annulus or either one through the casing annulus. With high-volume production with low gas-oil ratio the casing annulus is usually used for the production. Figure 6-57 shows a

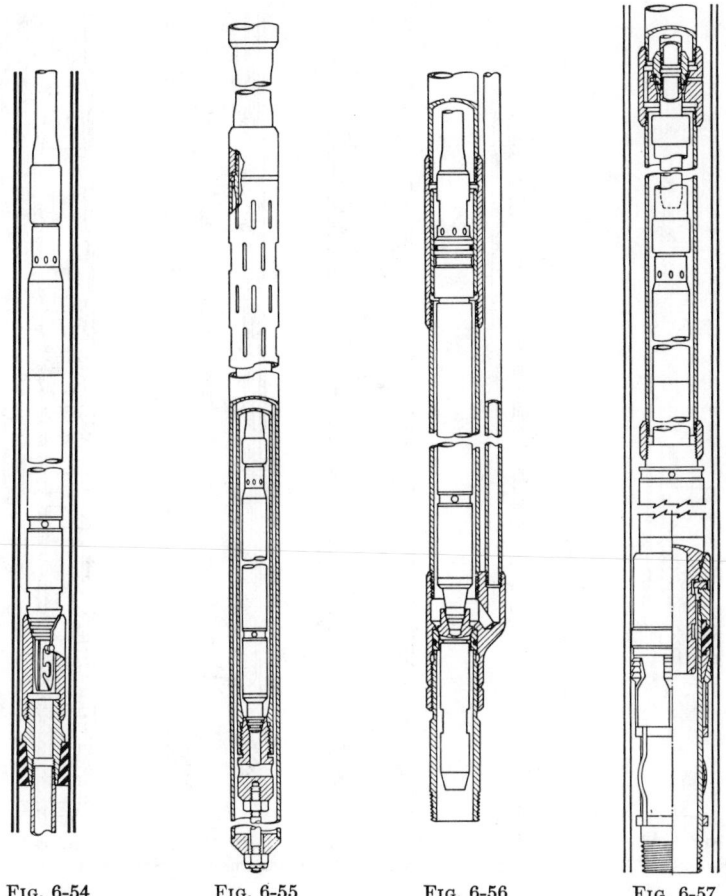

FIG. 6-54   FIG. 6-55   FIG. 6-56   FIG. 6-57
FIGS. 6-54 TO 6-57. Insert and casing pumps. See text for details.

high-volume tubing pump with the production up the casing. If too much gas is produced to be handled through the pump, a parallel gas string may be run to relieve the gas from below the packer.

Free Pump

The tubing arrangement for the free pump takes several forms, depending on the requirements. The most common arrangement is two tubes in parallel for the open system, as shown in Fig. 6-58, or three tubes in parallel for a closed system, as shown in Fig. 6-59. By suitable bottom-hole arrangements the tubes may be used in any combination for power oil, power-oil return, and production.   Where large volumes are produced or when the produced fluid is viscous, the largest tube is used for production and the two small tubes for power oil and power-oil return, respectively.

A casing-type free pump may be a single tube for the open system as in Fig. 6-60 or two tubes in parallel for the closed system as shown in Fig. 6-61, with the casing annulus used for the third passage.   As in the above case, the three passages may be used in any combination for power oil, power-oil return, and production.

It is also possible to use two tubes in parallel with a third tube inside one of the tubes.   This would not be an economical arrangement, but it does have certain

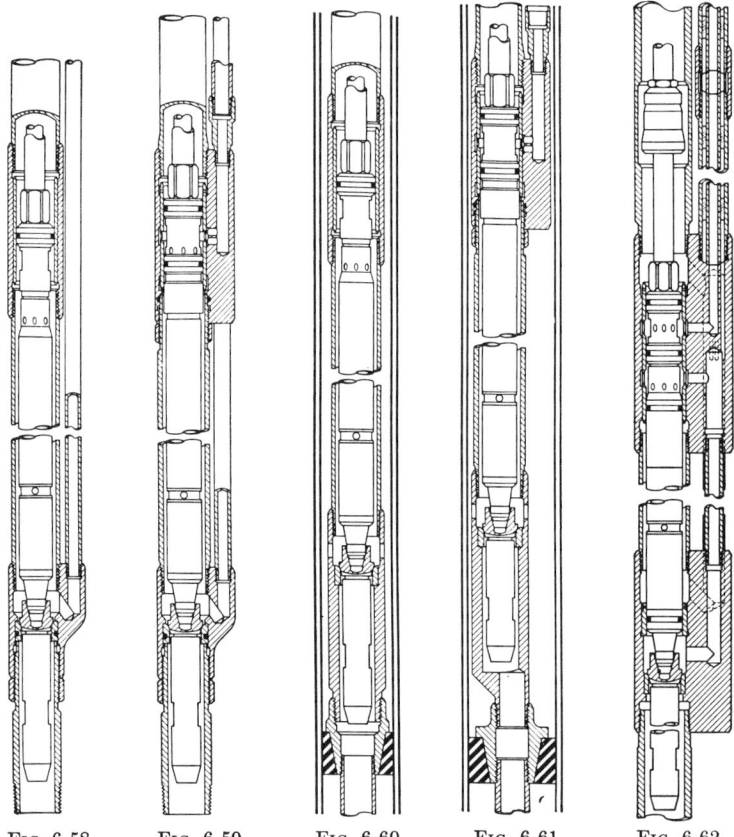

FIG. 6-58   FIG. 6-59   FIG. 6-60   FIG. 6-61   FIG. 6-62
FIGS. 6-58 TO 6-62. Free pump, bottom-hole arrangements.   See text for details.

advantages where the two tubes are nested and run together with a special joint which seals both the inner tube and the outer tube.   In this case the inner tube would be used for the power oil, so that it would be required to hold only the power-oil pressure rather than the power-oil plus the column pressure.   Figure 6-62 shows the nested tube with the special joint required.

Tubing Suspension

The production tubing may be either EU or plain, depending upon the depth, and carried on slips in the tubing head.

When parallel tubes are used, they may be carried by the production tubing with clamps of the type shown in Fig. 6-63. In this case the side tubes may be plain tubing, as the production tubing carries the entire tension load. It is also possible to run the side tube independently and stab into a taper socket as shown in Fig. 6-64. In this case the side tube would be EU except in shallow wells.

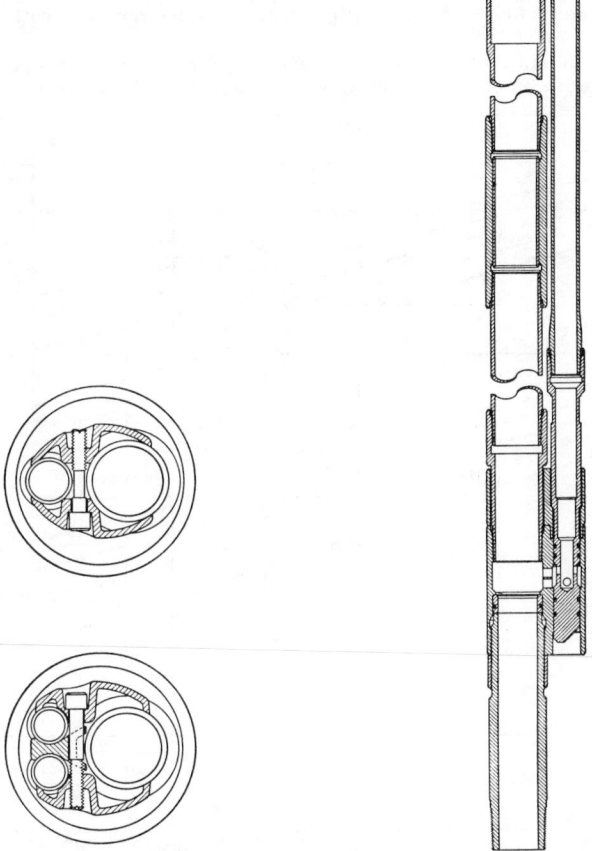

FIG. 6-63. Tubing clamps.   FIG. 6-64. Independent side string.

Tubing Sizes

For tubing sizes, weights, joints, allowable pressures, and setting depths, see Chap. 2.

PROPERTIES OF WELL FLUIDS

Gravity

The gravity of oils produced by pumping is usually in the range between 10 and 50°API or 1.000 and 0.7796 specific gravity at 60°F. The specific gravity of oils varies with temperature and pressure, the gravity at any temperature and pressure being expressed approximately by the following:

$$\delta = -3.2 \times 10^{-4}T + \delta_1 + 0.166 + P(0.01T - 6.43\delta_1 + 3.60)10^{-6}$$

where δ = specific gravity at P and T
δ_1 = specific gravity at 60°F
T = absolute temperature (t°F + 460)
P = pressure, psig

The compressibility of oils decreases with specific gravity and pressure and increases with temperature. Figures 6-65 and 6-66 give the specific gravity of a number of oils at temperatures from 0 to 300°F and 0 to 10,000 psi. The relation given above for the variation with temperature and pressure correlates very well with the experimental data.

Most oils are produced with varying amounts of water, usually as separate phases with some water in oil emulsion, depending in amount on the degree of agitation to

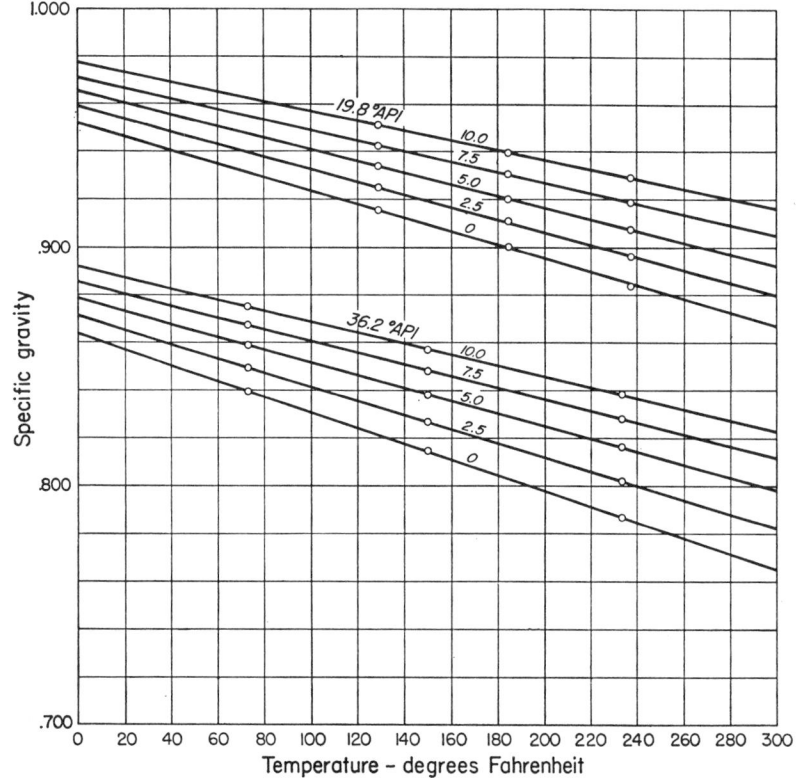

FIG. 6-65. Specific gravity of 19.8 and 36.2°API oil at 0 to 10,000 psi.

which the mixture has been subjected. The water will vary in gravity from 1.000 to 1.250 depending upon its salt content. Normal oil-field waters are usually in the range from 1.03 to 1.10 specific gravity.

The gravity of produced fluid can therefore vary from 0.70 to 1.25 and must be taken into consideration in evaluating the performance of pumps.

Bulk Modulus

Closely related with the specific gravity is the bulk modulus of fluids. Bulk modulus is expressed as the change in pressure required for a unit change in volume. It is usually given in psi but is sometimes expressed as pounds per square foot.

$$G = \frac{V_1(P_2 - P_1)}{V_1 - V_2} \quad \text{or} \quad G = \frac{\delta_2(P_2 - P_1)}{\delta_2 - \delta_1}$$

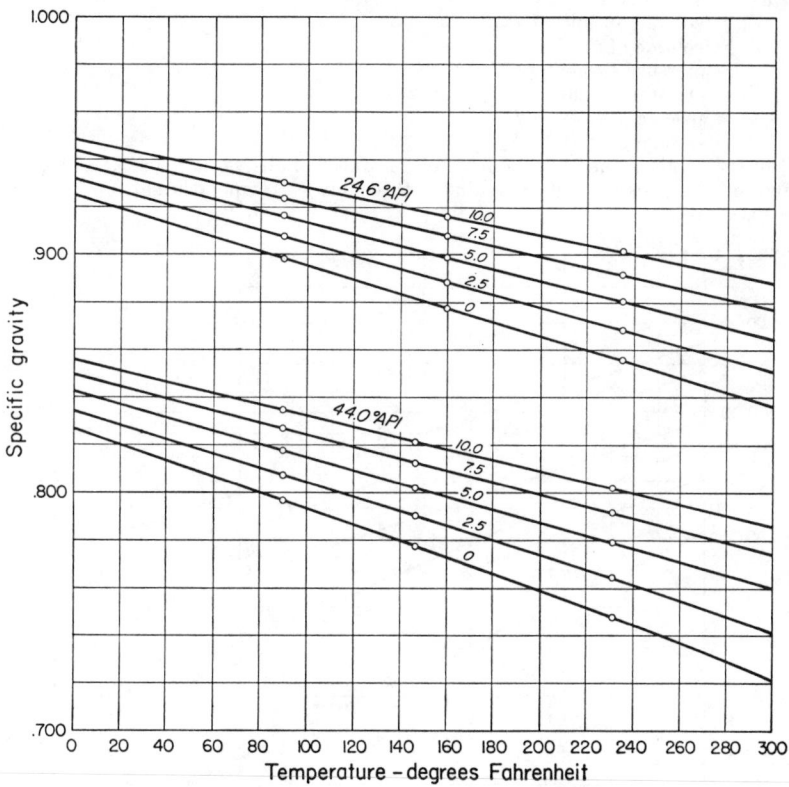

FIG. 6-66. Specific gravity of 24.6 and 44.0°API oil at 0 to 10,000 psi.

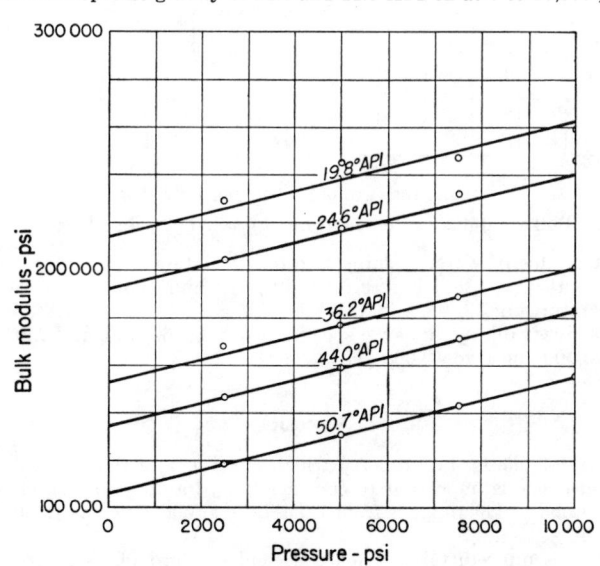

FIG. 6-67. Bulk modulus at 150°F vs. pressure.

where G = bulk modulus, psi
    V_1 = volume of fluid at P_1
    V_2 = volume of fluid at P_2
    P_1 = pressure (lower), psi
    P_2 = pressure (higher), psi
    δ_1 = specific gravity at P_1
    δ_2 = specific gravity at P_2

Figure 6-67 gives the bulk modulus of a number of oils vs. pressure at 150°F.
Figure 6-68 gives the bulk modulus of three oils vs. temperature at 0 to 2,500 and 0 to 10,000 psi.

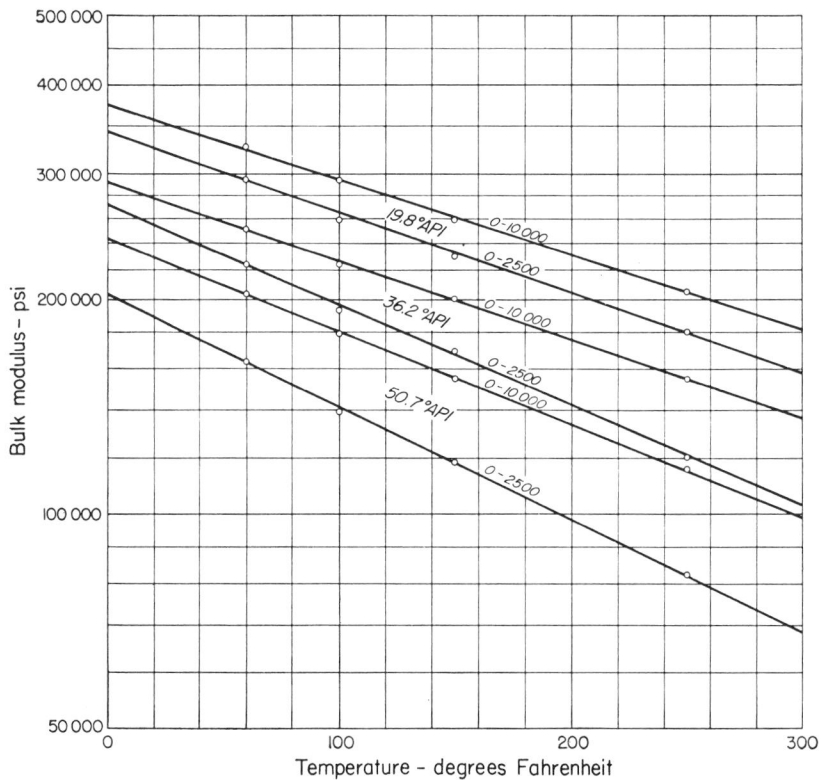

Fig. 6-68. Bulk modulus vs. temperature at 0 to 2,500 psi and 0 to 10,000 psi.

The bulk modulus of water is subject to less variation with temperature than oil but increases with pressure. Figure 6-70 gives the bulk modulus of water vs. pressure at temperatures of 32, 68, and 122°F.

Figure 6-69 gives bulk modulus vs. specific gravity at 60, 150, and 250°F with pressures of 0 to 2,500 and 0 to 10,000 psi.

Viscosity

The viscosity of oils is the property which is subject to the greatest variation in well fluids and hence is important to consider in hydraulic pumping or in any other production method. The range is from 1.0 cs or less to as much as 1,000,000 cs under well conditions.

Viscosity varies unpredictably when a second or third phase is present, such as

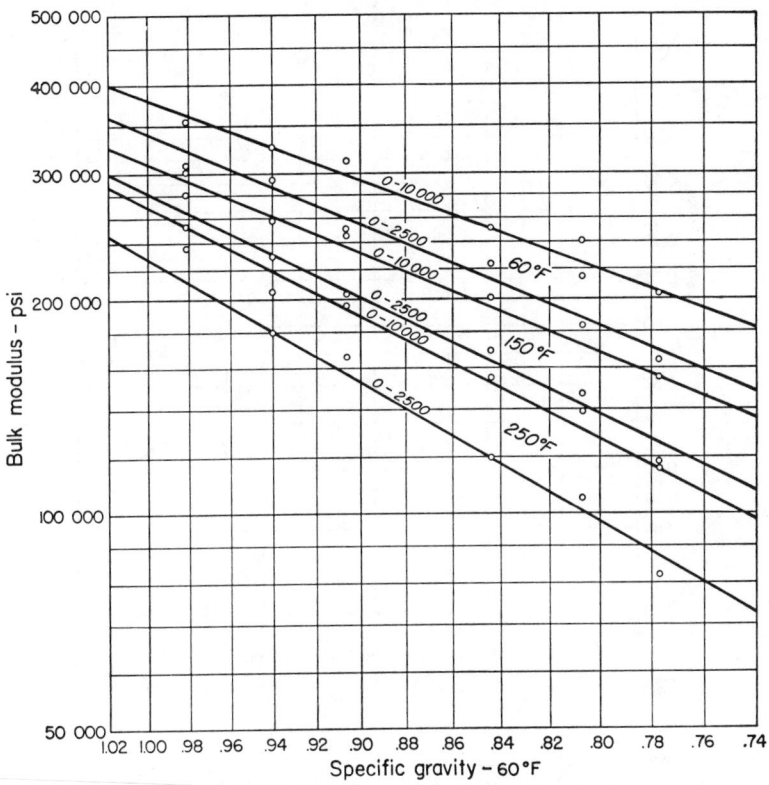

FIG. 6-69. Bulk modulus vs. specific gravity of oil.

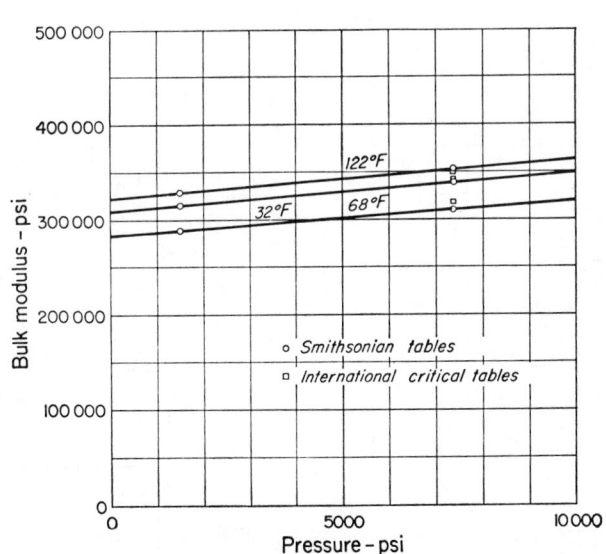

FIG. 6-70. Bulk modulus of water.

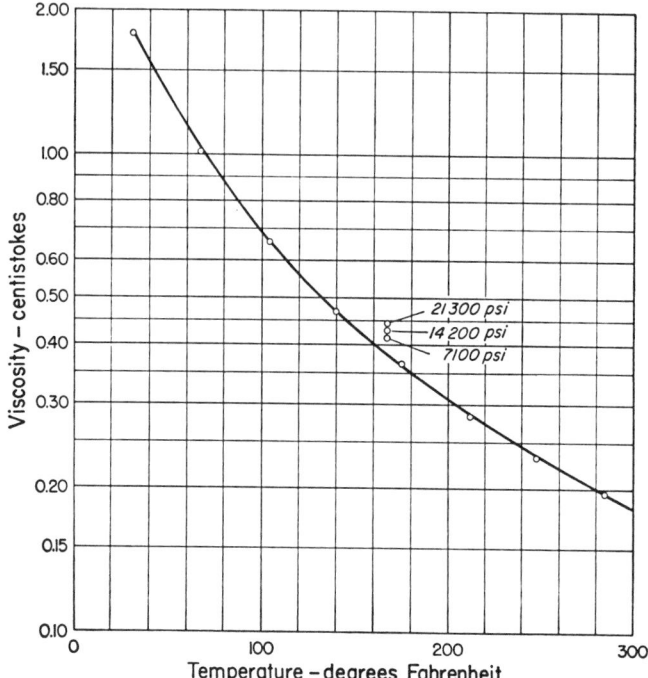

FIG. 6-71. Viscosity of water vs. temperature at 0 psi.

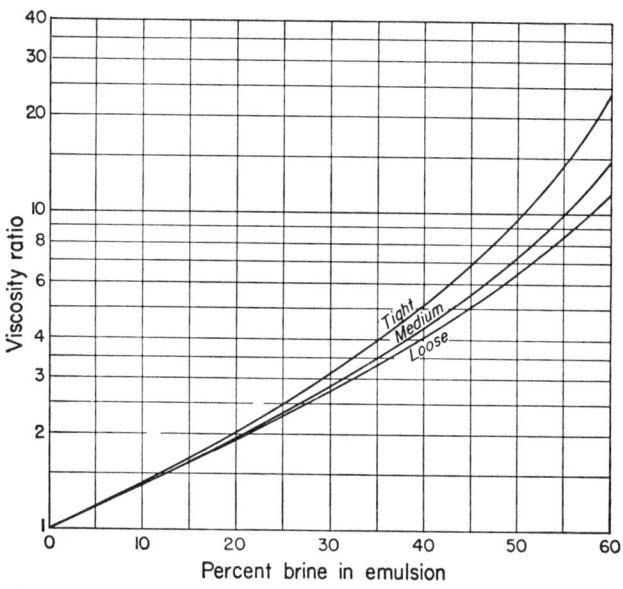

FIG. 6-72. Effect of emulsion on oil viscosity. (*William Woelflin, Drill. and Prod. Prac., API., 1942.*)

wax, water, and gas. Wax which is in suspension causes a substantial increase in viscosity and has a further property of jelling if allowed to stand at temperatures below the "cloud" or crystallization point. Very few crudes have sufficient wax to set up at normal tank or pipeline temperatures, but when this is the case steam coils and steam tracer lines must be provided to handle the oil. The handling of the wax problem is covered in more detail on pages 6–81 to 6–82.

Water has a viscosity of 1.124 cp at 60°F and decreases with temperature, as shown in Fig. 6-71. Water as a secondary phase has a marked effect on viscosity, depending largely upon the degree of emulsification rather than the quantity of water in the oil. Where the water is the primary phase, it wets the wall of the tubing and the viscosity will be dependent principally on the water properties. Figure 6-72 gives the effect of water emulsion on the viscosity of oil.

Gravity Factor

At normal temperature (usually 100°F for viscosity determinations) the viscosity of oils increases with specific gravity quite consistently, even though the compositions of the oils may differ. Paraffinic oils generally have somewhat higher viscosities than asphaltic crudes. Figure 6-73 is a plot of a large number of oils, paraffinic,

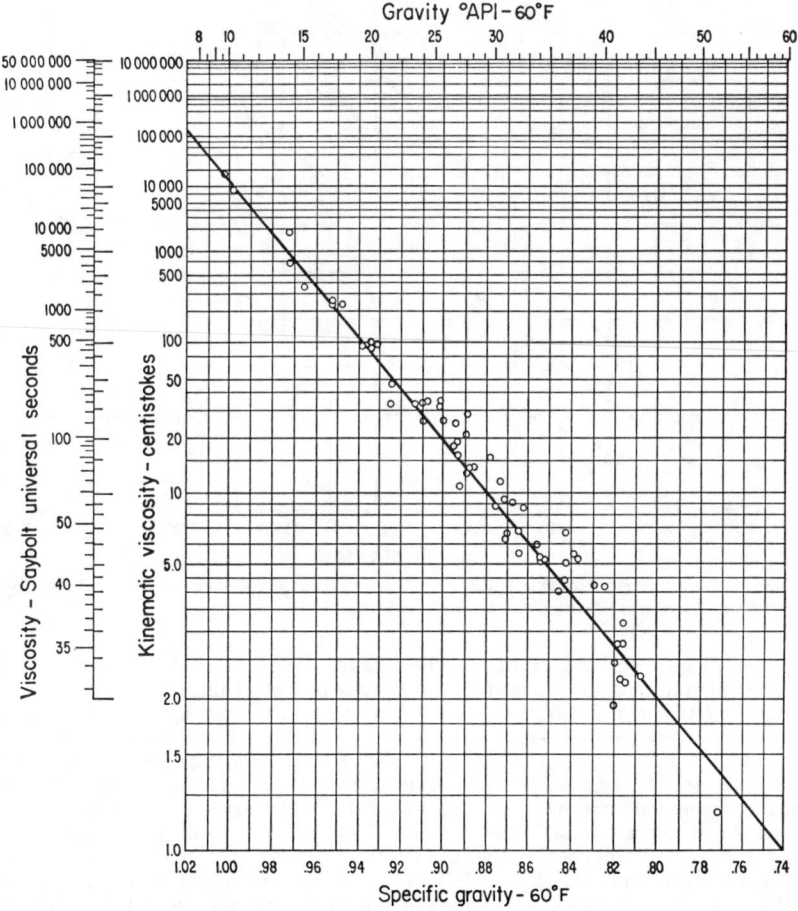

FIG. 6-73. Viscosity of oil vs. specific gravity (viscosity at 100°F).

asphaltic, and mixed base, from widely scattered fields, which show a good correlation with gravity. This chart has the log-log scale for kinematic viscosity as used for the ordinate of ASTM viscosity charts, and specific gravity as the abscissa. For oils on which actual viscosity determinations are not available, this chart may be used to obtain viscosities at 100°F for estimating friction losses.

Temperature Gradient

Well temperatures vary with geological conditions and may vary in a given field because of water strata and to a limited extent because of flow rates and gas expansion.

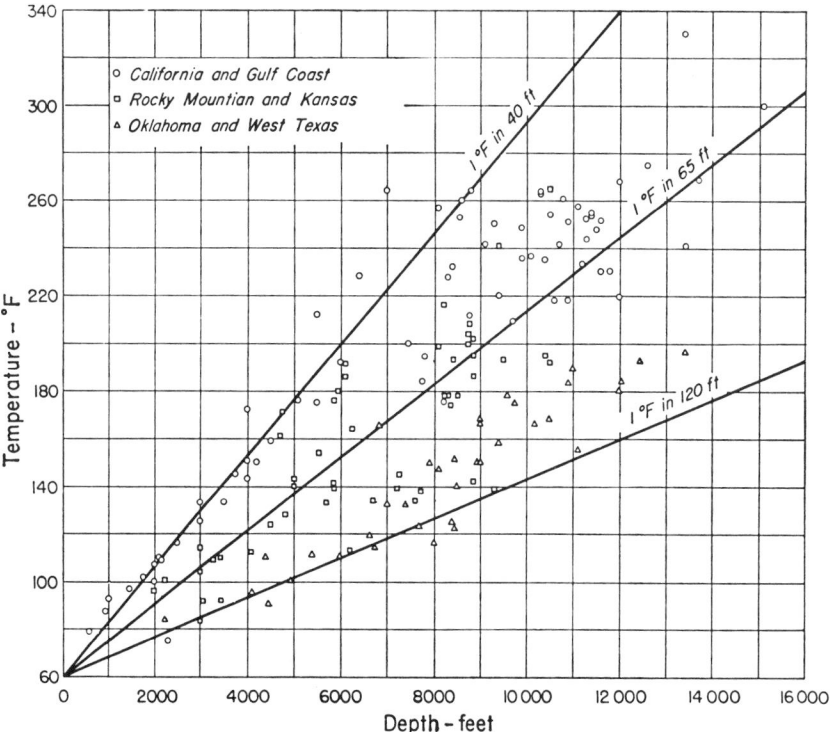

FIG. 6-74. Well temperature gradients. (*API Prod. Bull. 205, October, 1930; Carl Vogelsang, Selection of Type of Cement, API, 1958.*)

Figure 6-74 gives the temperature gradient as reported by a study made by the API and recent information obtained for deep wells in California, Mid-Continent, Gulf Coast, and the Rocky Mountain area. The temperature at any depth is generally taken as the mean ambient temperature plus 1°F for each 65 ft of depth. There are some notable exceptions on both sides of this relation ranging from 1°F in 40 ft to 1°F in 120 ft. Gulf Coast and California in general have temperatures higher than the average and are in the approximate range of 1°F increase in 50 ft of depth. Oklahoma, North Texas, West Texas, and the Panhandle are notably cool and average approximately 1°F increase in 100 ft of depth.

Since temperature has a large effect on viscosity, it is important to know the temperature gradient within a few degrees in computing friction loss in tubing, particularly if laminar flow is indicated for any appreciable part of the total tubing length.

Temperature Factor

Viscosity decreases with temperature and is represented by a straight-line relation for most oils when plotted on ASTM viscosity sheets having $\log_e \log_e$ of viscosity as the ordinate and $\log_e$ of absolute temperature T as the abscissa.

$$\log_e \log_e (\nu + A) = -B \log_e T + K$$

where ν = kinematic viscosity, cs
   A = 0.6 for viscosities over 1.5 cs, 0.65 from 1.0 to 1.5 cs, 0.70 from 0.7 to 1.0 cs, 0.75 from 0.4 to 0.7 cs
   B = temperature index
   K = a constant

The temperature index may be expressed as the angle between viscosity line and the abscissa, or the tangent of this angle. If the ASTM chart is used the scale factor must be taken into consideration. The scale factor of this chart is 5.064. The true slope of the viscosity line therefore is

$$B = 5.064 \tan \theta$$

where B = temperature index
   θ = angle between viscosity line and abscissa

The temperature index for the average oil in degrees is approximately 35° on the ASTM chart, or $B = 3.55$.

Figure 6-75 gives the viscosity of 13 oils from 10 to 50°API plotted on the ASTM chart. The range is from $B = 2.27$ to $B = 4.21$.

Pressure Factor

Viscosity increases substantially with pressure in the range used in hydraulic pumps. Bridgman, *Physics of High Pressures*, reports on the effect of pressure on viscosity to 170,000 psi with oils, water, and other liquids. The ASME lubrication studies report the viscosity of lubricating oils at pressures up to 100,000 psi and temperatures from 32 to 425°F.[2]

Crude oils have been found to follow the same general relation. A pressure of 10,000 psi causes an increase by a factor of 1.5 at a viscosity of 1 cs to 4.0 at 100 cs.

Bridgman reports that E. N. Da C. Andrade presents the viscosity relation in the form

$$\eta v^{\frac{1}{2}} = A e^{\left(p + \frac{r}{v^2}\right) \frac{s}{T}}$$

where v = specific volume
   r and s = constants

Following Andrade's relation a study of the data on crudes by F. B. Brown and C. J. Coberly (AIME, 1959) shows the following relation to express viscosity in terms of specific gravity, temperature, and pressure for crude oils from 10 to 50°API.

The general relation is given by

$$\nu + A = e^{CT^{-B}} e^{E\delta_1} e^{(G \log_e T + H\delta_1 + J)P^F}$$

For the above crudes this equation reduces to the form

$$\log_e \log_e (\nu + 0.6) = B(6.328 - \log_e T) + 11.53\delta_1 + DP - 9.254,$$
and
$$D = (5.47 \log_e T - 12.50\delta_1 - 20.46)10^{-5}$$

where T = absolute temperature ($t°F + 460$)
   P = pressure, psig
   δ_1 = specific gravity at 60°F
   B = temperature index

By means of this expression the viscosity of any crude oils is fully defined at any temperature and pressure in terms of its viscosity at 100°F, the temperature factor,

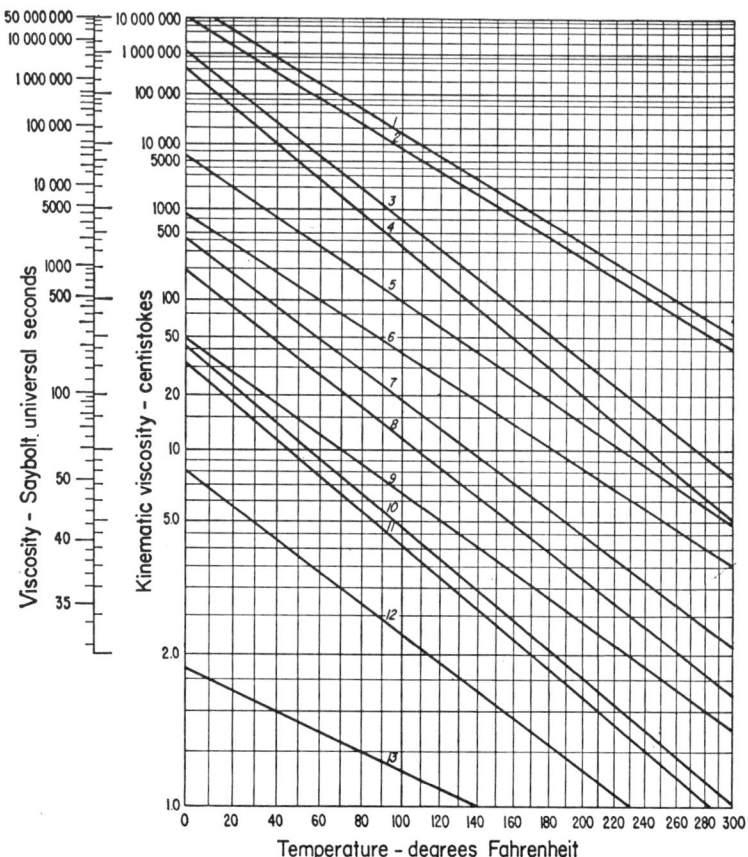

Temperature - degrees Fahrenheit
FIG. 6-75. Viscosity of oils.

°API		Temp index	Field	°API		Temp index	Field
1.	9.5	2.93	Boscan, Venezuela	8.	30.6	3.73	Ventura, Calif.
2.	10.7	2.92	Boscan, Venezuela	9.	31.1	3.44	Kettleman Hills, Calif.
3.	14.0	3.76	Maricopa, Calif.	10.	36.4	4.04	Oklahoma City, Okla.
4.	15.0	3.98	Wilmington, Calif.	11.	34.6	4.21	Kettleman Hills, Calif.
5.	19.8	3.24	Sansinena, Calif.	12.	44.0	3.65	Denton, N.M.
6.	25.6	3.09	Scholem Alecham, Okla.	13.	50.7	2.27	Kettleman Hills, Calif.
7.	26.8	3.61	Seal Beach, Calif.				

and specific gravity at 60°F. This relation is based on the viscosity-gravity plot of Fig. 6-73. If the oil in question falls on the line of this chart, the relation may be used with confidence. If it deviates from the chart, the gravity corresponding to the viscosity at 100°F is used as the true gravity in computing the viscosity at any other condition of temperature and pressure.

Figures 6-76 and 6-77 give the experimental values of viscosity measured with a rolling-ball viscosimeter for four crude oils from 20 to 50°API and at three temperatures and five pressures up to 10,000 psi. The lines on these charts are drawn using the above equation and show very good correlation with the experimental data.

The alignment chart of Fig. 6-78 is based on the above relation and may be used to determine viscosities at any temperature and pressure.

Figure 6-79 may be used to determine specific gravity and pressure gradient at any well depth and wellhead pressure.

For friction loss in vertical tubing subject to temperature gradients, the relation of Fig. 6-78 may be integrated between any two temperatures and the average viscosity determined for friction-loss computations. Absolute viscosity in centipoise

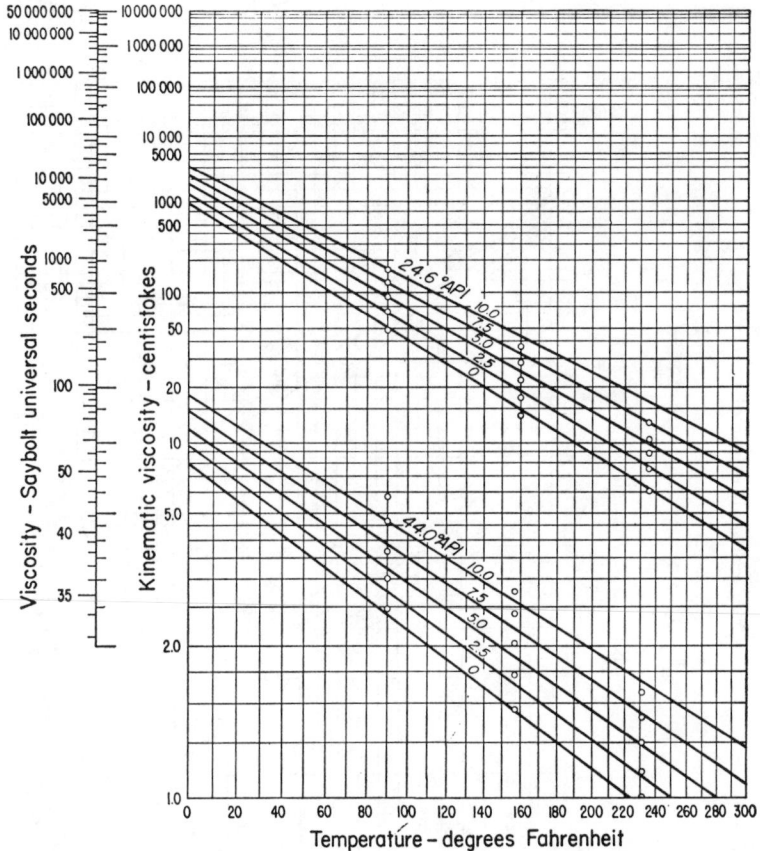

FIG. 6-76. Viscosity of 24.6 and 44.0°API oil at 0 to 10,000 psi.

is obtained by multiplying the kinematic viscosity from Fig. 6-78 by the specific gravity from Fig. 6-79.

When the temperature gradient is known, Fig. 6-80 may be used to determine the viscosity at any depth and also the value of (kinematic viscosity)$^{0.21}$ which is used in tubing friction-loss computations.

FRICTION LOSS IN TUBING

Friction loss in tubing and pipe is given on pages 6–75 and 6–76, and is reported by Kemler,[11] R. S. J. Pigott,[15] and others. The friction-loss relations given in these references are applicable to uniform conditions but introduce important errors when applied to the well tubing of hydraulic pumps, because of effects of temperature and

pressure gradients on the viscosity and density of the fluid. This is further complicated by the fact that the flow condition often changes from laminar to turbulent at
some point in the tubing, because of these viscosity and density changes. In the case
of flow in the annulus between concentric tubings, the usual flow relations must be
modified by empirical factors which have a substantial effect on pressure drop.

For rough selection of tubing sizes the conditions may be assumed to be constant
at an estimated average viscosity. The chart of Fig. 6-81 gives the fluid-handling
capacity of tubing with a pressure drop of 50 psi 1,000 ft, or approximately 10 per cent
of the static pressure.

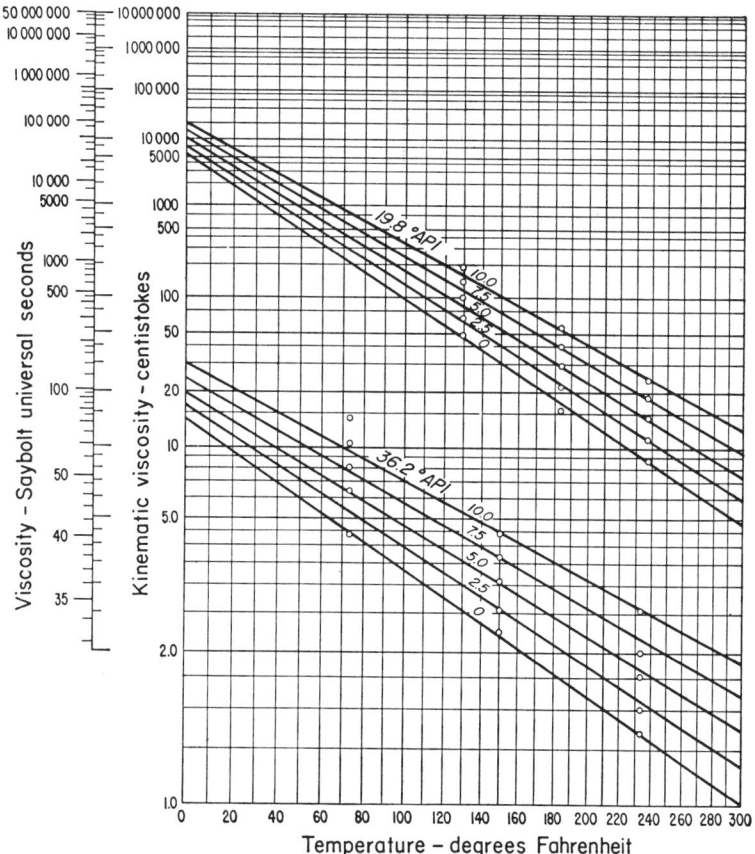

Fig. 6-77. Viscosity of 19.8 and 36.2°API oil at 0 to 10,000 psi.

To compute the friction loss more accurately the properties of the oil in question
must be known under the conditions existing in the tubing. In the absence of specific
information on the oil, the relations and data given on pages 6–55 to 6–65 may be used
to obtain a good approximation of the friction loss. A rational solution involving all
the variables is not available, but by first determining the type of flow and the point
of change from laminar to turbulent, the problem may be divided into two parts and
materially simplified. The relations given in this section are based upon this simplified approach. The important variables not considered in the usual friction-loss
relations are the well temperature gradient and the corresponding viscosity and

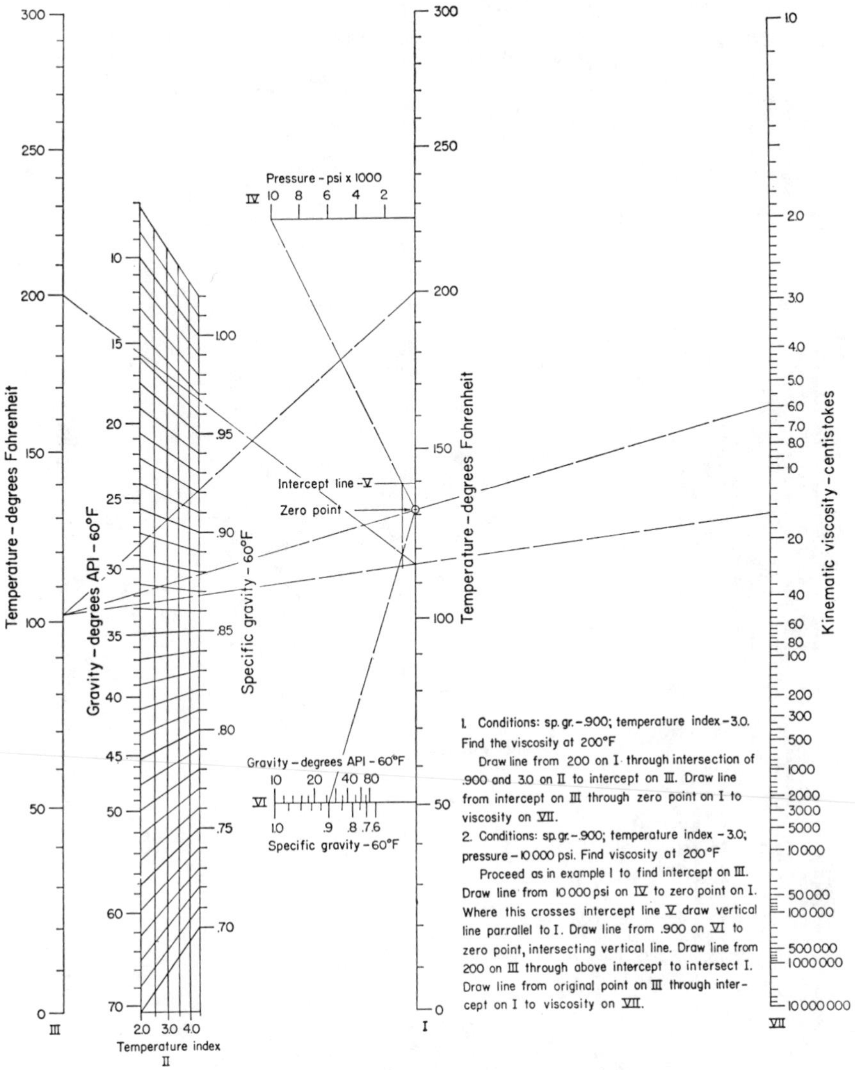

FIG. 6-78. Viscosity vs. temperature and pressure.

density gradients modified by both the column pressure and the superimposed operating pressure.

Pressure Gradient

The pressure gradient in a vertical column varies with both temperature and pressure. The density of the fluid at any point in the column is reduced by the expansion due to the temperature and is increased by compression resulting from the column pressure plus any superimposed pressure at the surface. The pressure at any depth from the surface is therefore an integrated value. The relation given on page **6**–55 and the well temperature gradient establish the column pressure at any point. (See the monograph in Fig. **6-79**.)

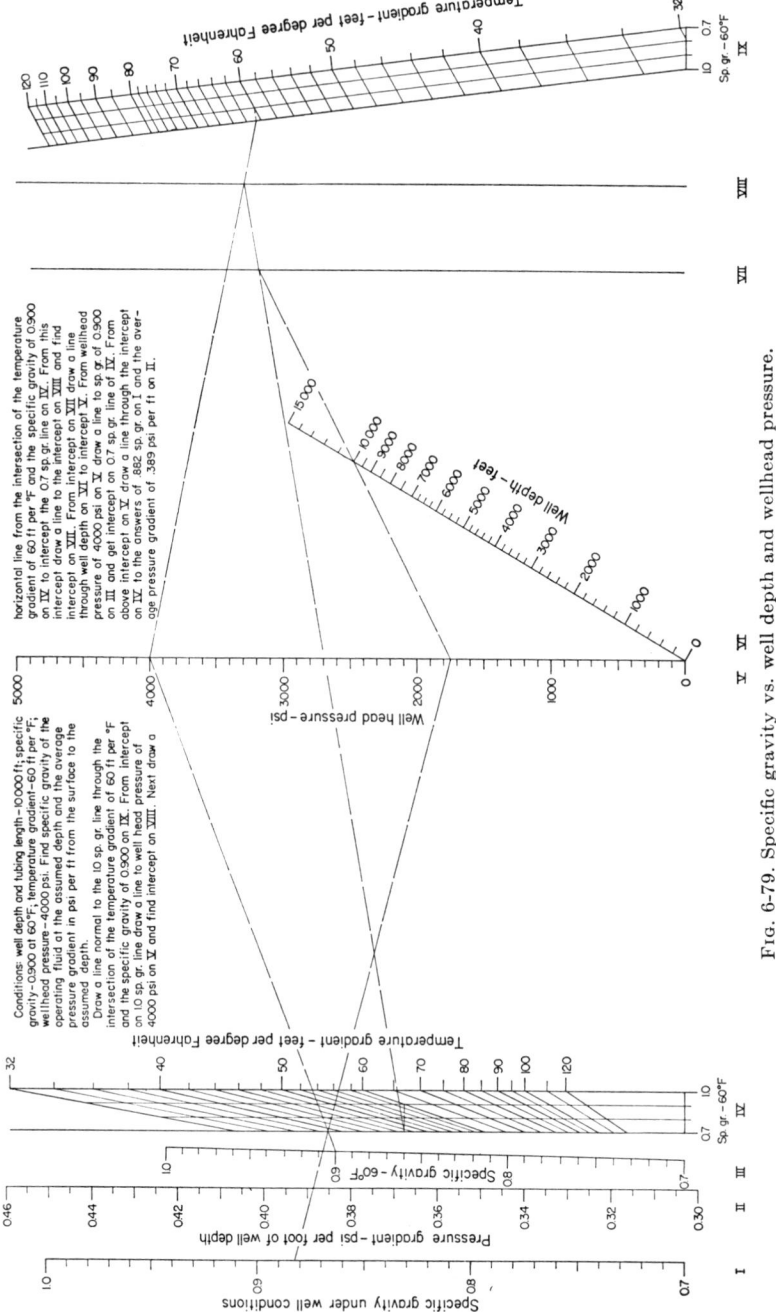

Conditions: well depth and tubing length—10,000 ft; specific gravity—0.900 at 60°F; temperature gradient—60 ft per °F; wellhead pressure—4000 psi. Find specific gravity of the operating fluid at the assumed depth and the average pressure gradient in psi per ft from the surface to the assumed depth.

Draw a line normal to the 1.0 sp. gr. line through the intersection of the temperature gradient of 60 ft per °F and the specific gravity of 0.900 on IX. From intercept on IX draw a line to well head pressure of 4000 psi on V and find intercept on VIII. Next draw a

horizontal line from the intersection of the temperature gradient of 60 ft per °F and the specific gravity of 0.900 on IV to intercept the 0.7 sp. gr. line on IV. From this intercept draw a line to the intercept on VIII and find intercept on VII. From intercept on VII draw a line through well depth on VI to intercept V. From wellhead pressure of 4000 psi on V draw a line to sp. gr. of 0.900 on III and get intercept on 0.7 sp. gr. line of IV. From above intercept on IV draw a line through the intercept on IV to the answers of .882 sp. gr. on I and the average pressure gradient of .389 psi per ft on II.

Fig. 6-79. Specific gravity vs. well depth and wellhead pressure.

6–68

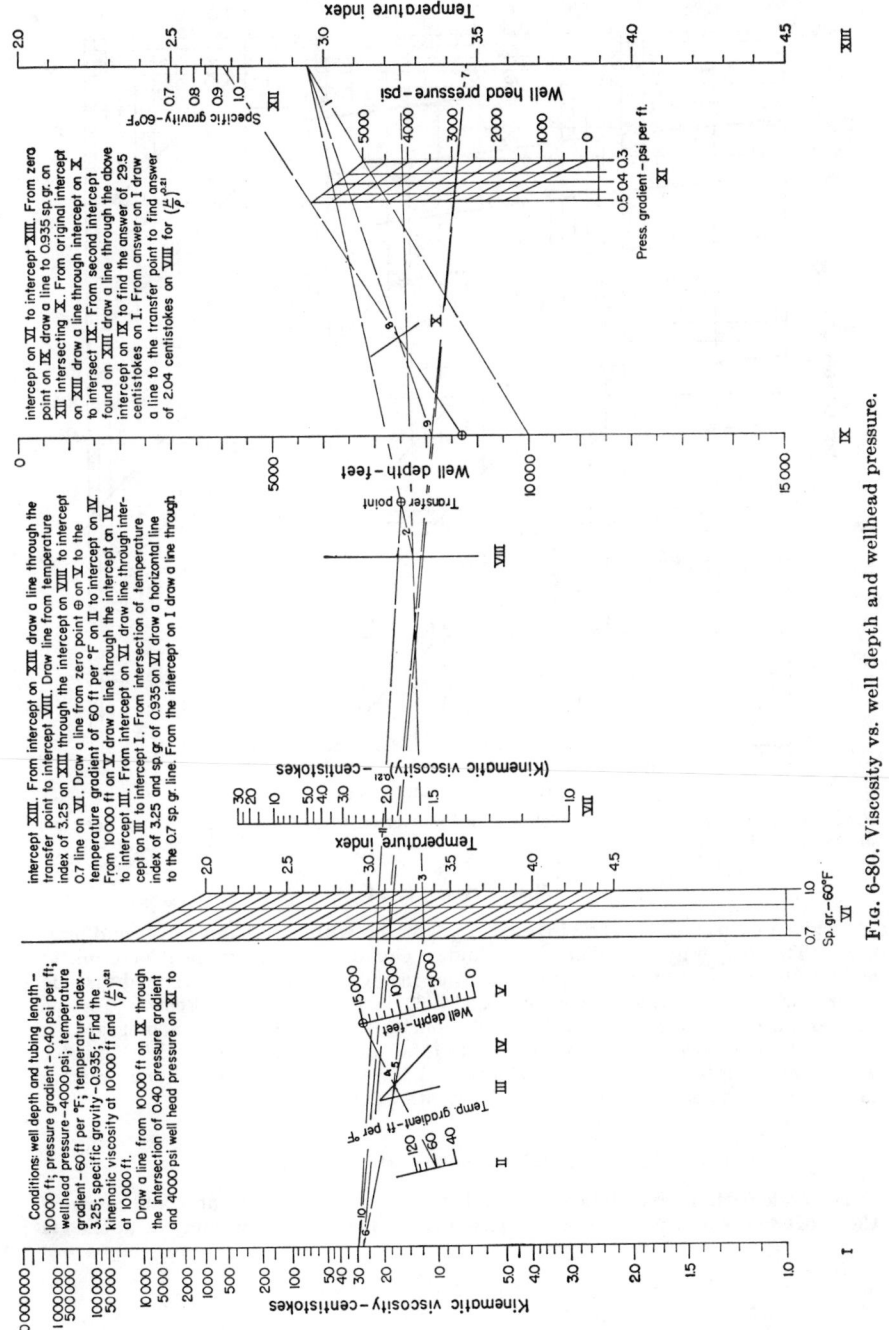

FIG. 6-80. Viscosity vs. well depth and wellhead pressure.

6-69

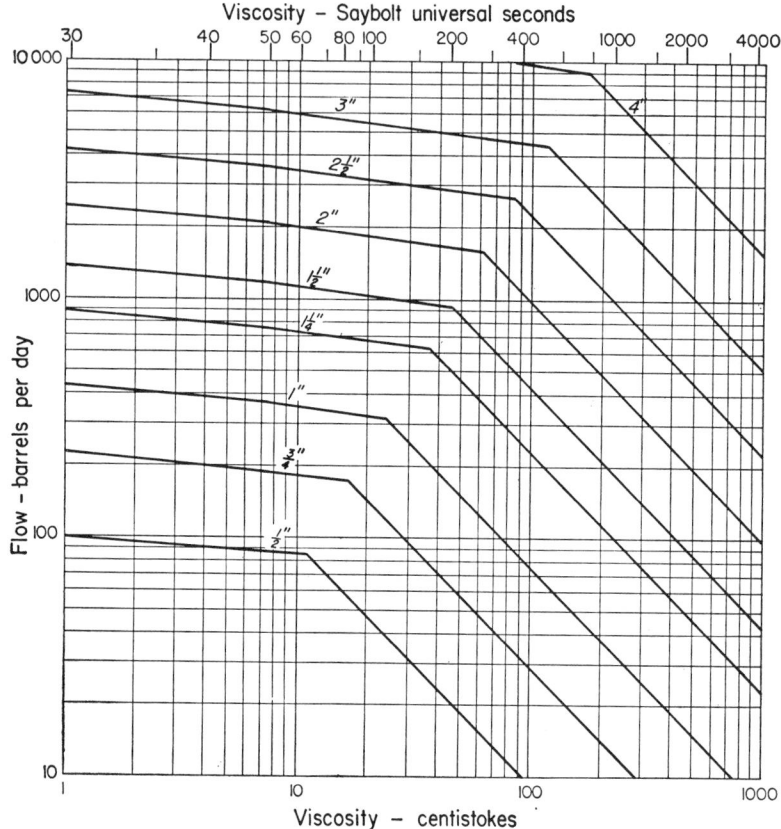

Fig. 6-81. Fluid-carrying capacity of tubing for friction loss of approximately 10 per cent of static head.

Viscosity Gradient

As given on page **6**–63, the viscosity of oils varies with both temperature and pressure. The temperature gradient being known and the pressure gradient determined as indicated above, the viscosity at any point in the vertical column of fluid may be determined. The relation given on page **6**–63 may be modified to correct for the temperature and pressure gradient, and from this equation or the nomograph in Fig. 6-80 the viscosity may be computed to a fair degree of accuracy. With oils for which the temperature-pressure-viscosity is known an integrated column-pressure factor may be determined and a viscosity-depth curve established.

Friction-loss Relations—Circular Section

The basic friction-loss relation applicable to the flow of fluids in tubes and to which the above temperature, pressure, and viscosity gradient corrections may be applied is

$$h_f = f \frac{l}{d} \frac{V^2}{2g}$$

where $f = \phi(R)$ and $R = \dfrac{dV\,\rho}{\mu}$

l = length of tubing, ft
h_f = friction loss, ft
d = ID, ft
V = velocity, ft/sec
g = acceleration of gravity = 32.2 ft/sec/sec

Where R is less than 1,200 the flow is laminar and $f = 64/R$. Between $R = 1,200$ and $R = 2,500$ is a transition zone and where R is greater than 2,500 flow is turbulent. The relation for R may be divided into two parts, dV and ρ/μ. dV expresses the assumed flow conditions of fluid quantity and tubing size. ρ/μ is the reciprocal of the kinematic viscosity. The lower and upper critical points therefore occur at viscosities of

$$\text{Lower critical } R = 1,200 \qquad \frac{\mu}{\rho} = \frac{dV}{1,200}$$

$$\text{Upper critical } R = 2,500 \qquad \frac{\mu}{\rho} = \frac{dV}{2,500}$$

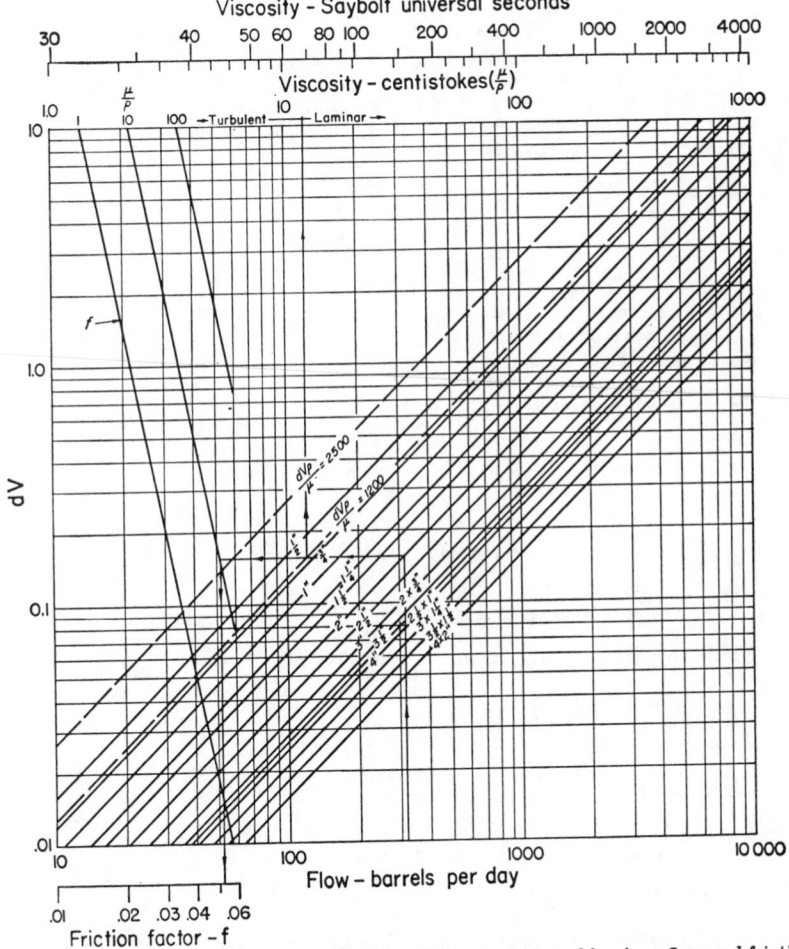

FIG. 6-82. Chart for determining viscosity limits for turbulent and laminar flow and friction factor for turbulent flow.

With assumed flow rates and tubing sizes μ/ρ may be determined for either the lower or upper critical point, and with the μ/ρ depth relations given above, the lengths of tubing subject to laminar and turbulent flow may be readily determined. The friction problem is then divided into two parts, laminar from the surface down to the point in the well where $R = 1,200$ and turbulent for the rest of the tubing. Figure 6-82 gives this relation for nominal-sized tubings from $\frac{1}{2}$ to 4 in. and for annular flow between tubings and flow rates of 10 to 10,000 B/D. This chart also gives f in the turbulent range for μ/ρ from 1.0 to 100.

From the kinematic-viscosity alignment chart of Fig. 6-80 and the specific-gravity alignment chart of Fig. 6-79 a weighted average value of absolute viscosity may be obtained applicable to the section of tubing subject to laminar flow.

The section of tubing subject to turbulent flow is treated in a similar manner using weighted average values of f and specific gravity. The friction factor f is a function of R, and for values from 1,200 to 50,000, which covers the range for pumping conditions and for tubing sizes from $\frac{1}{2}$ to 4 in., f may be expressed by the relation

$$f = \phi(R^{-0.21})$$

Since $R = dV\rho/\mu$ this may be divided into two parts, $(dV)^{-0.21}$ and $(\rho/\mu)^{-0.21}$. Figure 6-82 gives values of f from this relation for kinematic viscosities of 1, 10, and 100 cs. Since ρ/μ is the reciprocal of the kinematic viscosity the friction factor f of Fig. 6-82 may be corrected for other viscosities, by multiplying by the ratio $(\mu/\rho)^{0.21}/10^{0.21}$ or $0.616(\mu/\rho)^{0.21}$. See page 6-74 for determination of $(\mu/\rho)^{0.21}$.

In units particularly useful for friction problems of hydraulic pumping the following relations apply.

Circular Section

Velocity:

$$V = 0.01191 \frac{Q}{d^2}$$

where V = velocity, ft/sec
Q = quantity of oil flowing, B/D
d = diameter of tubing, in.

Friction:

Laminar flow:

$$P_L = 7.95 \times 10^{-6} \frac{\mu l Q}{d^4}$$

Turbulent flow:

$$P_L = 11.46 \times 10^{-6} \, \delta f \, l \, \frac{Q^2}{d^5}$$

where P_L = friction drop, psi
μ = weighted average viscosity, cp

$\dfrac{\mu}{\rho}$ = weighted average kinematic viscosity, cs

l = length of tubing, ft
Q = quantity of oil flowing, B/D
d = ID of tubing, in.
δ = weighted average specific gravity
f = weighted average friction factor

$$f = \phi\left(\frac{dV\,\rho}{\mu}\right)$$

$$f = 0.0361 \frac{(\mu/\rho)^{0.21}}{(dV)^{0.21}}$$

Table 6-17 gives the important computation factors for friction in circular-cross-section tubing for nominal sizes ranging from $\frac{1}{2}$ to 4 in.

Table 6-17. Tubing-friction Computation Factors, Circular Section

Tube size					V $\dfrac{11.91}{d_1{}^2}$ 1,000 B/D	$\dfrac{dV}{12}$ 1,000 B/D	P_L	
Nominal in.	ID d_1, in.	$d_1{}^2$	$d_1{}^4$	$d_1{}^5$			Laminar 1,000 B/D 1,000 ft $\mu = 10$ cp	Turbulent 1,000 B/D 1,000 ft $f = 0.054; \delta = 1.0$
½	0.622	0.387	0.150	0.093	30.785	1.596	530	6,654
¾	0.824	0.679	0.461	0.380	17.541	1.204	172	1,628
1	1.049	1.100	1.211	1.270	10.823	0.946	65.6	487
1¼	1.380	1.904	3.627	5.000	6.254	0.719	21.9	123.8
1½	1.610	2.592	6.719	10.817	4.595	0.616	11.83	57.2
2	1.995	3.980	15.841	31.602	2.992	0.497	5.02	19.6
2½	2.441	5.958	35.503	86.664	1.999	0.407	2.24	7.14
3	2.992	8.952	80.139	239.777	1.330	0.332	0.992	2.58
3½	3.476	12.083	145.989	507.456	0.986	0.286	0.545	1.219
4	3.958	15.666	245.416	971.357	0.760	0.251	0.324	0.637

Friction-loss Relations—Annular Section

For friction loss in annular passages Atherton[1] used $d_e = d_1 - d_2$ where d_e is the diameter of a circular pipe having the same hydraulic radius as the annulus between a tube of d_1 inside diameter and a tube of d_2 outside diameter. Davis[6] applied an empirical correction factor to the Atherton relation, which made it fit the published data more accurately.

Exline[7] shows the flow in an annulus to depend on the eccentricity in the laminar range.

Tao and Donovan[27] give the relation for the effect of eccentricity in the turbulent range. This relation is too complex for application to friction problems, but the simple correction given below follows the Tao and Donovan relation within ±5 per cent.

$$P_L = \phi \left[\frac{1}{(1 + 1.5e^2)^{0.25}} \right]$$

Annular Section. Applying these factors to the friction-flow relation gives the following for flow in annular passages.

Velocity:

$$V = 0.01191 \frac{Q}{d_1{}^2 - d_2{}^2}$$

Friction laminar:

$$P_L = \frac{7.95 \times 10^{-6} \mu l Q}{(d_1 - d_2)^2 (d_1{}^2 - d_2{}^2)} \qquad \text{Atherton}$$

Davis correction:

$$\left(\frac{d_1}{d_1 - d_2} \right)^{0.1}$$

Exline correction:

$$\frac{1}{1 + 1.5_e{}^2}$$

Friction with Davis and Exline corrections:

$$P_L = \frac{7.95 \times 10^{-6} \mu l Q \left(\dfrac{d_1}{d_1 - d_2} \right)^{0.1}}{(d_1 - d_2)^2 (d_1{}^2 - d_2{}^2) (1 + 1.5e^2)}$$

where P_L = pressure drop, psi
  μ = weighted average viscosity, cp
  l = length of annulus, ft
  Q = flow, B/D
  d_1 = inside diameter of outer tube, in.
  d_2 = outside diameter of inner tube, in.

  e = eccentricity of tubes = $\dfrac{d_3}{d_1 - d_2}$

  d_3 = distance inner tube is off center, in.

Friction Turbulent. Using the equivalent-diameter relation of Atherton, the relation given above for circular-cross-section tubing becomes

$$P_L = \frac{11.46 \times 10^{-6}\ \delta f\ Q^2\ 1}{(d_1 - d_2)\ (d_1{}^2 - d_2{}^2)^2}$$

The Davis correction factor is

$$\frac{1}{\left(\dfrac{d_1}{d_1 - d_2}\right)^{0.1}}$$

The Tao and Donovan correction (modified) factor is

$$\frac{1}{(1 + 1.5e^2)^{0.25}}$$

Combining the above relations, the friction loss is

$$P_L = \frac{11.46 \times 10^{-6}\ \delta f\ Q^2 l}{(d_1 - d_2)\ (d_1{}^2 - d_2{}^2)^2 \left(\dfrac{d_1}{d_1 - d_2}\right)^{0.1} (1 + 1.5e^2)^{0.25}}$$

where P = pressure drop, psi.
  Q = flow, B/D
  l = length of annulus, ft
  δ = specific gravity of water = 1.0
  d_1 = ID of outer tube, in.
  d_2 = OD of inner tube, in.
  d_3 = OD of coupling (inner tube), in.

  e = eccentricity = $\dfrac{d_1 - d_3}{d_1 - d_2}$

  $f = \phi\left(\dfrac{dV\ \rho}{\mu}\right) = 0.0361 \dfrac{\left(\dfrac{\mu}{\rho}\right)^{0.21}}{(dV)^{0.21}}$

  $\dfrac{\mu}{\rho}$ = kinematic viscosity, cs

Table 6-18 gives the important computation factors for friction in tubing annuli with combinations of tubing sizes normally used with insert-type hydraulic pumps.

The alignment chart in Fig. 6-83 is based on the above relations and may be used to determine the friction loss in the section of tubing subject to laminar flow. For accurate determination the absolute viscosity in centipoise is determined at several points to obtain a weighted average value. The charts in Figs. 6-79 and 6-80 are used to obtain kinematic viscosity and specific gravity at any point in the tubing from which absolute viscosity is determined.

The alignment chart in Fig. 6-84 is used in the same way for friction loss in the turbulent range. To correct the friction factor for variation in viscosity Fig. 6-80 gives $(\mu/\rho)^{0.21}$ at any point in the tubing.

The charts in Figs. 6-83 and 6-84 are applicable to the determination of friction loss

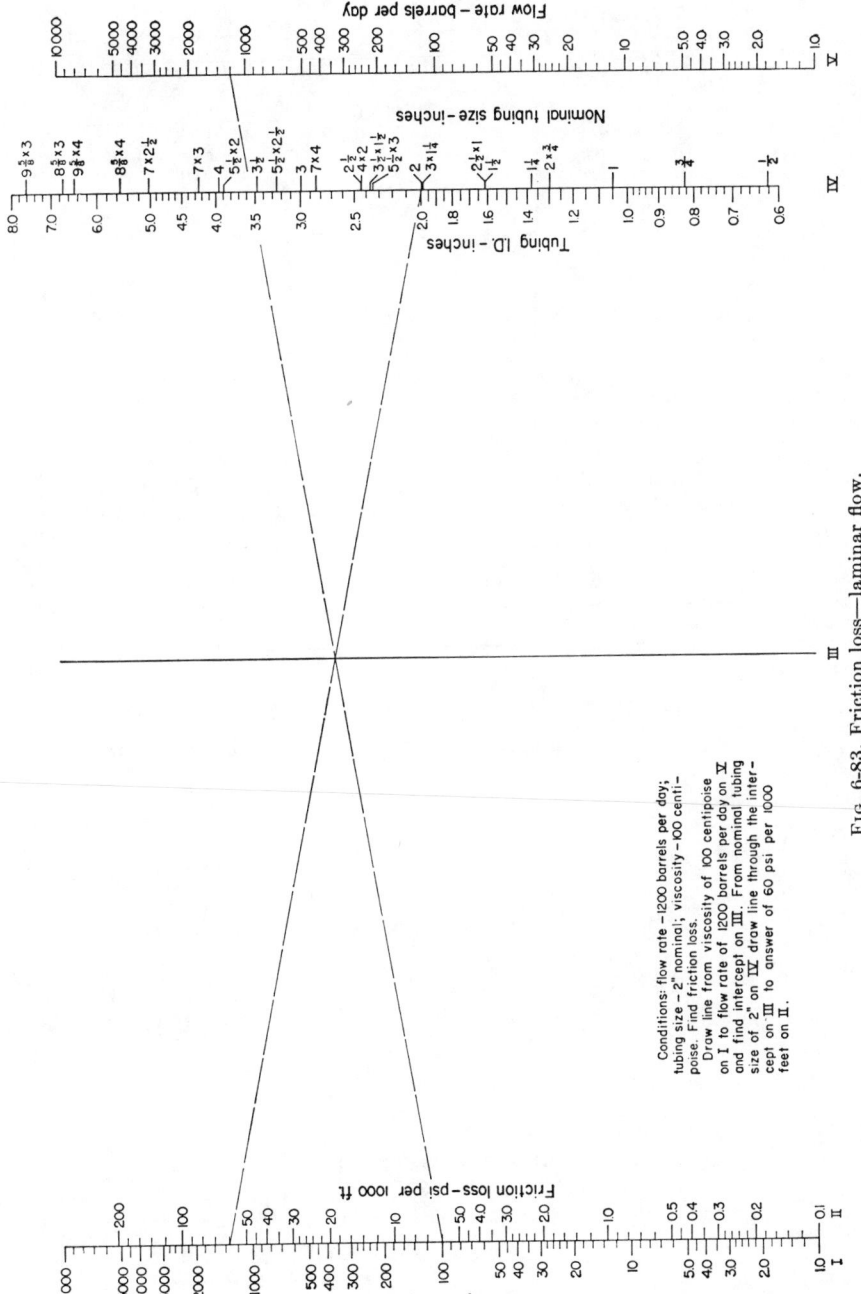

Fig. 6-83. Friction loss—laminar flow.

I Flow rate – barrels per day

IV Nominal tubing size – inches

Tubing I.D. – inches

III

Conditions: flow rate –1200 barrels per day; tubing size – 2" nominal; viscosity –100 centipoise. Find friction loss.

Draw line from viscosity of 100 centipoise on I to flow rate of 1200 barrels per day on V and find intercept on III. From nominal tubing size of 2" on IV draw line through the intercept on III to answer of 60 psi per 1000 feet on II.

Friction loss–psi per 1000 ft

II

I

Viscosity – centipoise

6–75

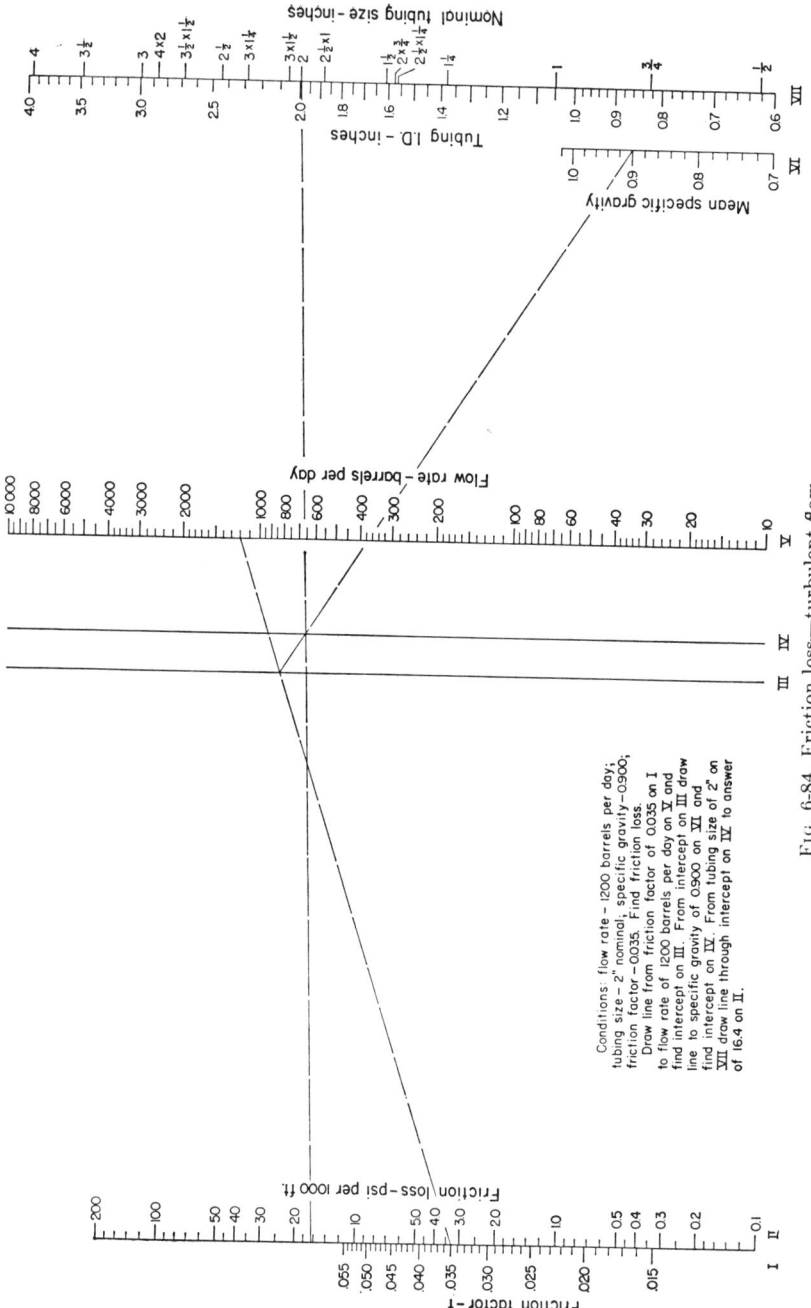

Fig. 6-84. Friction loss—turbulent flow.

Table 6-18. Tubing-friction Computation Factors, Annular Section

| Nominal, in. | Tube sizes | | | $d_1 - d_2$ | $d_1 - d_3$ | $d_1{}^2$ | $d_2{}^2$ | $d_1{}^2 - d_2{}^2$ | $(d_1{}^2 - d_2{}^2)^2$ |
	d_1 ID outer, in.	d_2 OD inner, in.	d_3 OD EU coup, in.						
2 × ¾	1.995	1.050	1.660	0.945	0.335	3.980	1.103	2.878	8.28
2½ × 1	2.441	1.315	1.900	1.126	0.541	5.958	1.729	4.229	17.88
3 × 1¼	2.992	1.660	2.200	1.332	0.792	8.952	2.756	6.196	38.39
3½ × 1½	3.476	1.900	2.500	1.576	0.976	12.083	3.610	8.472	71.77
4 × 2	3.958	2.375	3.063	1.583	0.895	15.666	5.641	10.025	100.50

| Nominal, in. | Velocity $\dfrac{11.91}{d_1{}^2 - d_2{}^2}$ 1,000 B/D | $\dfrac{(d_1 - d_2)V}{12}$ 1,000 B/D | $\left(\dfrac{d_1}{d_1 - d_2}\right)^{0.1}$ | e $\dfrac{d_1 - d_3}{d_1 - d_2}$ | e^2 | $(1 + 1.5e^2)$ | $(1 + 1.5e^2)^{0.25}$ | P_L | |
								Laminar 1,000 B/D 1,000 ft $\mu = 10$ cp	Turbulent 1,000 B/D 1,000 ft $f = 0.054$; $\delta = 1.0$
2 × ¾	4.139	0.326	1.078	0.354	0.126	1.188	1.044	28.1	70.3
2½ × 1	2.816	0.264	1.080	0.480	0.231	1.346	1.076	11.9	26.4
3 × 1¼	1.922	0.192	1.084	0.595	0.353	1.495	1.112	5.12	10.0
3½ × 1½	1.406	0.185	1.082	0.619	0.383	1.575	1.120	2.60	4.51
4 × 2	1.188	0.157	1.096	0.565	0.320	1.479	1.102	2.34	3.22

in both circular and annular passages for the tubing sizes normally used with hydraulic pumps.

APPLICATIONS

Extreme Depth

Table 6-1 gives the depth limitation of Kobe pumps of standard design at 15,000 ft. This may be increased in several ways. First, by increasing the operating pressure with present designs, the power capacity may be increased and the depth limit increased. It is estimated that with presently available materials and present designs the maximum operating pressure could be raised from the present limit of 5,000 to 7,500 psi. By reducing the engine displacement 25 per cent the pressure could be further increased to 10,000 psi. By a combination of these changes, depths of 30,000 ft can be pumped with the following approximate capacities: 2 in., 75 B/D; 2½ in., 150 B/D; 3 in., 300 B/D; 4 in., 600 B/D.

Other methods include two or more units with engines in parallel with the pumps in series. The same parallel-series arrangement may be incorporated in a single unit with minor design changes.

High Capacity

By using two or more pumps arranged in tandem in the tubing and with suitable porting in the bottom-hole assembly, they may be operated with both the engines and pumps in parallel. By combining subassemblies with suitable adapters, two or more pumps may be operated in parallel with a single engine with a corresponding reduction in maximum depth. Two pumps would give the following capacities and depth limitation with the largest pump liner for each pump size:

	Pump size, in.			
	2	2½	3	4
Capacity, B/D..........	540	1,000	1,800	3,700
Depth limit............	3,150	3,500	3,400	3,250

Where well conditions permit the use of casing-type pumps, the engine and pump may be a combination of sizes such as 3 by 4, 4 by 6, etc., depending upon the requirements. A 4- by 6-in. pump with the largest standard pump cylinder has a capacity limitation of 4,500 B/D and a depth limitation of 2,700 ft.

Combination of gas-lift with hydraulic pumps may be used to extend the capacity by use of a large pump end with a small engine, in which case the limit of operation would be the pump load, which would depend on the productive formation thickness and the gas-lift pressure. The pump in this case is set near bottom with a discharge pipe extending to a packer set in the casing just above the producing formation. The engine is direct-connected to the pump with power oil discharging into the production and is of a size that with normal operating pressure would lift the fluid above the packer and discharge against the gas-lift pressure. Figure 6-85 shows the general arrangement of this type of pump. The maximum displacement provided with a unit having a 3-in. engine and 6½-in. OD pump is 7,300 B/D. Such combinations have been operated to depths of 6,500 ft.

Multiple Zone

Single Pump. Figure 6-86 shows the arrangement of a single pump adapted for alternate operation of two zones by lifting the tubing to shift the intake from the lower zone to the upper. A hydraulic cylinder is provided at the wellhead to move the tubing and may be controlled manually or on a timed cycle with automatic control. In the case illustrated, the gas is shut in on the lower zone but could be relieved by a small string of tubing connected to the packer. The pump in this case is insert-type and either one or both tubing strings may be moved to shift zones.

Figure 6-87 shows a free-pump closed-system arrangement for pumping two zones with a single pump, in which the inlet is shifted hydraulically with a bottom-hole device. In this case the two zones alternately feed into a casing-type anchor above the upper zone. The shift is made by reversing the direction of operation of the power oil in the closed system. To remove the pump, power oil is directed down both power-oil tubes at the same time. Gas is released from both zones alternately and produced through the casing. The cycle can readily be made automatic and of any desired duration on each zone.

Figure 6-88 illustrates a two-zone free pump in which the pump is removed from the well and the bottom fitting is changed to select the two zones. The gas is shut in on the lower zone but could be released with another parallel tubing string. This system is not adapted to automatic operation or to short cycle but is applicable where wells are prorated and can be produced for a number of days on each zone.

Multiple Pump. Figure 6-89 shows an insert type of installation with two separate pumps in parallel tubings and a fifth tube to release the gas from the lower zone. This gives two completely independent pumps, one for each zone, with separate controls, isolated production, and independent running and pulling of the pumps from either zone. This requires two tubes large enough to insert the pumps and therefore limits the pump size to 2-in. in 7-in. casing or 2½-in. in 8⅝-in. casing.

Figure 6-90 shows multiple free pumps in tandem with porting in the bottom-hole assembly to open each pump to the separate zones. The power oil is conducted down a side string and the production from the upper zone is up the tubing with the production from the lower zone produced up the casing annulus. Gas from both zones is shut in. The speed control of the bottom-hole pumps is accomplished by throttling the outlets of the tubing and the casing annulus.

Figure 6-91 also shows multiple free pumps in tandem with power oil down the well tubing and with the power oil and production from one pump up a first parallel

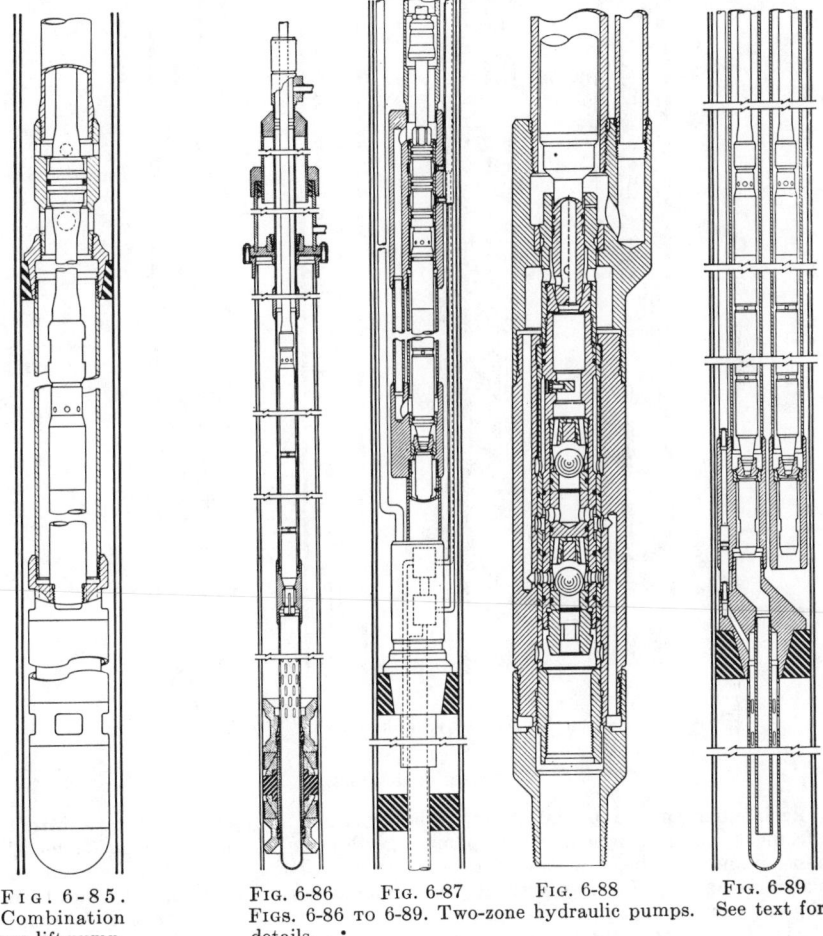

FIG. 6-85. Combination gas-lift pump.

FIG. 6-86   FIG. 6-87   FIG. 6-88   FIG. 6-89. See text for
FIGS. 6-86 TO 6-89. Two-zone hydraulic pumps.
details.

string and the power oil and production from the second pump up the second parallel string. In this case the gas is shut in on the lower zone.

Figure 6-92 shows an insert pump with a mixing valve below the pump which may be operated by raising or lowering the macaroni tubing to open either zone or to mix the production from the two zones in any desired proportions.

Figure 6-93 shows a single engine with two pumps each connected to its respective zone. This requires two small tubes parallel with the pump tube and will require a third tube if it is necessary to vent the gas from the lower zone. The pumps for each must in this case run at the same speed but could have different capacities by using different plunger sizes.

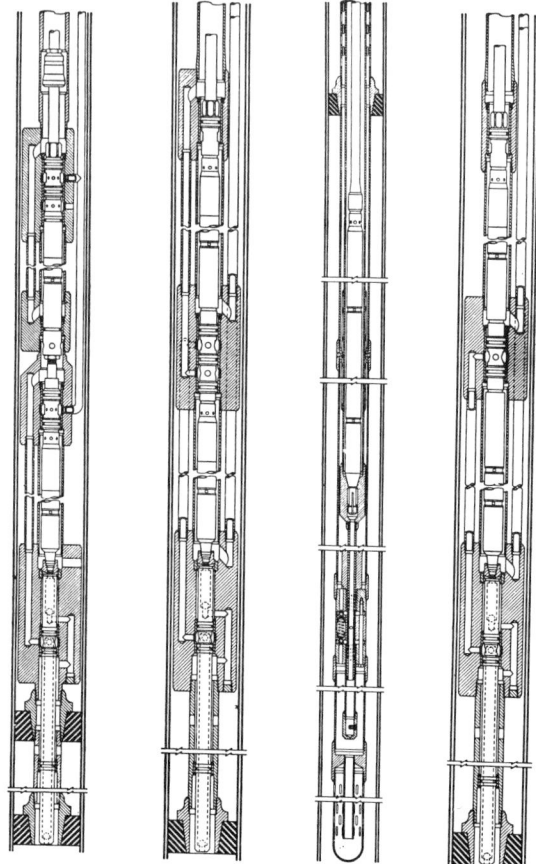

FIG. 6-90   FIG. 6-91   FIG. 6-92   FIG. 6-93
FIGS. 6-90 TO 6-93. Two-zone hydraulic pumps.   See text for details.

Directional Wells

Residential and Industrial Areas. The efficiency of hydraulic pumps is not affected by well deviation. Some pumps are designed to operate in a horizontal position and have been operated for long periods without trouble in wells having a maximum angle of 70° from vertical. This application to directional wells has been of great value in industrial, residential, and beach areas by concentrating the wells, placing the wellheads underground, and locating the power supply at a point that would have the least effect on the surroundings.

Marine. Hydraulic pumping is particularly suited to offshore installations. With multiple wells drilled from islands or platforms, one centralized power-oil installation can operate all the wells and may be located at any convenient point so that drilling and pumping may be carried out on adjacent wells. Where wells are near shore, the power may be conducted to the wells in pipeline with all gauge tanks, treating system, and triplex units at an onshore location.

Surface Hazards. Hydraulic free pumps are located in lakes or flood areas with the wellhead above high water so that the pump can be pulled and replaced by a single pumper with a small boat. Normal operation such as controlling and checking pump speed and productions and checking efficiencies and approximate fluid levels may all be done at a control station located on high ground.

Snow, wind, dust, rain, or even a landslide has little or no effect on the operation of the pump unless it is sufficiently severe to damage the well casing.

Viscosity Control. Where oils of extreme viscosities are produced, hydraulic pumps may be used with closed power-oil systems using oil of selected viscosity. Where open systems are used a low-viscosity power oil may be used which will blend with the production and reduce its viscosity to a value that will limit the fluid friction to reasonable values. Standard ASTM blending charts may be used to obtain the resultant viscosity of mixed oils.

Wax Control

Scrapers. Wax deposits in tubing and surface lines may be controlled in several ways. This deposit may be in the interior of the tubing or in the tubing annulus of insert pump. In the circular tubes, scrapers may be used operated periodically with a

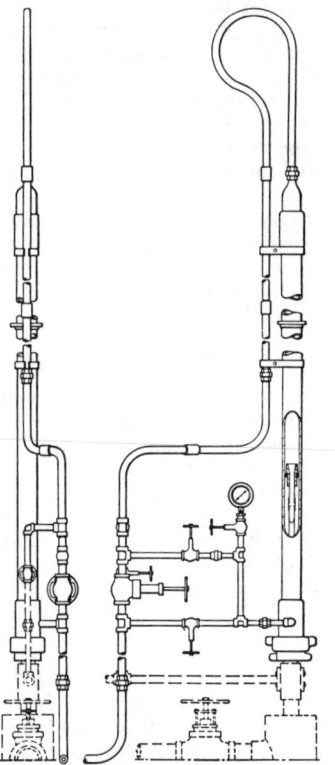

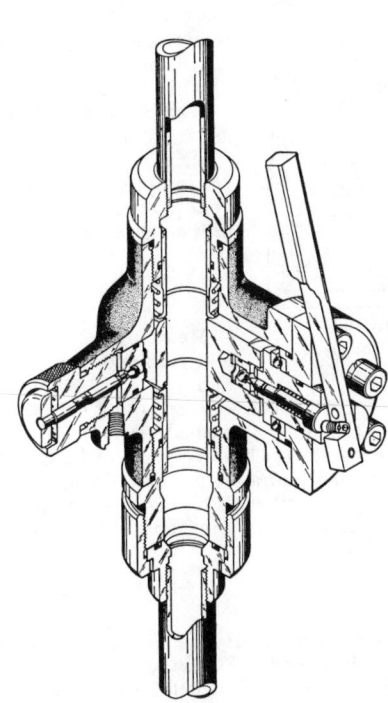

Fig. 6-94. Hydraulic lift for operating wax scrapers.

Fig. 6-95. Soluble-plug injector valve.

wire line, or automatic scrapers have been made by Garrett and others which drop from the wellhead to a trip point below the wax deposit, which closes the fluid passage of the scraper so that it is pumped to the surface with the wax ahead of it.

Annulus scrapers are usually applied to the inner tube, or in some cases it has been found that lifting the tubing a distance equal to coupling spacing will free the wax. Hydraulic lifts over the wellhead have been provided for this purpose, using the power oil to operate the lift periodically. Figure 6-94 shows the construction of a hydraulic lift.

Soluble Plugs. Soluble plugs are another scraping means, in which a soft pliable cylindrical plug about 1½ diameters long having a fairly high solution rate in the crude is pumped through the tubing. The solution rate increases with temperature, so that the plug is either dissolved or sufficiently softened when it reaches the bottom-hole unit that it will pass through without any trouble. Plugs will go through elbows and tees and are used in surface lines as well as in well tubing. The plug is inserted into the tubing with a special valve shown in Fig. 6-95.

Hot Oil. Hot oil is also used both continuously and by batch. In the former case it is effective only when pumping rates are high and when the wax is deposited in the first 1,000 ft from the surface or less. Where wax is deposited at 3,000 ft or deeper, heat is not effective, because of the heat exchange between the two tubings. Hot oil may be batched successfully if applied before excessive friction is built up. Reverse-flow check vales such as that shown in Fig. 6-96 are helpful for hot-oil circulation in insert installations and by special adaptation may be applied to parallel tubings. The valve is placed just below the wax point to conserve the heat and reduce the circulation friction.

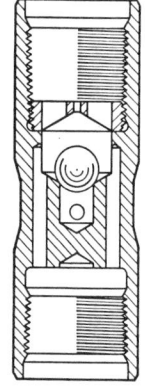

Tubing Coatings. Tubing coatings have also been used. Phenolic resins have been found best. This application is quite successful in some cases but has not been found to be a complete answer in all cases. Epoxy resins have also been used, and sometimes applied in the field, although it is generally considered to be best to do the work in a shop under well-controlled conditions. Several coats are applied with one or more baking operations in the process.

Wax Solvents. Numerous wax solvents and inhibitors have been used, but not with general success. Batch treatment is sometimes successful, but the cost of treatment is high with effective solvents. No inhibitors have so far been found which can be relied on to prevent wax deposits entirely. Some inhibitors change the character of the deposit so that it is more readily removed by other treatments.

Corrosion Control

Fig. 6-96. Reverse-flow check valve.

Metallurgy. Hydraulic pumps use a relatively small amount of material, and hence costly material may be applied in their construction. It has been found that nickel, chromium, cobalt, and their alloys are effective in retarding corrosion, and these are used extensively.

Inhibitors. Chemical inhibitors of the type that preferentially wet the surfaces of the metal have been very successful for protecting bottom-hole equipment of all kinds, including hydraulic pumps. In hydraulic pumping the inhibitor may be applied in the power oil with a chemical pump, which is normally built into the power unit. To protect the casing and outside of the tubing, the inhibitor is batched into the casing.

Sand Production

Lubrication. Hydraulic pumps have several features that make them effective in handling sand. First, the sliding surfaces of the bottom-hole unit may be lubricated with the power oil which tends to exclude the sand and reduce the wear.

Table 6-19. Velocity in Tubing

Pump size, in.	Capacity		Tube size, in.	Velocity, ft/sec		Tube size, in.	Velocity, ft/sec	
	Min	Max		Min	Max		Min	Max
2	274	449	1	2.97	4.87	2	0.82	1.35
2½	538	856	1¼	3.36	5.35	2½	1.08	1.71
3	973	1,511	1½	4.47	6.96	3	1.30	2.02
4	2,042	2,672	2	6.12	8.00	4	1.55	2.03

Velocity. Where open systems are used, the power oil dilutes the production and gives a steady continuous flow at about double the production rate, which increases the sand-carrying power of the fluid. With fine sand carry power is not much of a problem, except in high-gravity oils or where the pump is shut down at intervals. The data given on page 6-33 give settling rates for different particle sizes and oils. If the settling rate approaches the fluid velocity in the tubing, sand will accumulate and give trouble. With parallel-tube free pumps the velocities are sufficiently high to have good carrying power. Table 6-19 gives the velocity in the tubing with an open system with the production in either the large tubing or the side string.

Gas Production

Formation Volume. Positive-displacement pumps do not lend themselves to handling gas through the pump except where submergence pressures are high. The effect of submergence is to reduce the volume of the gas and at the same time increase

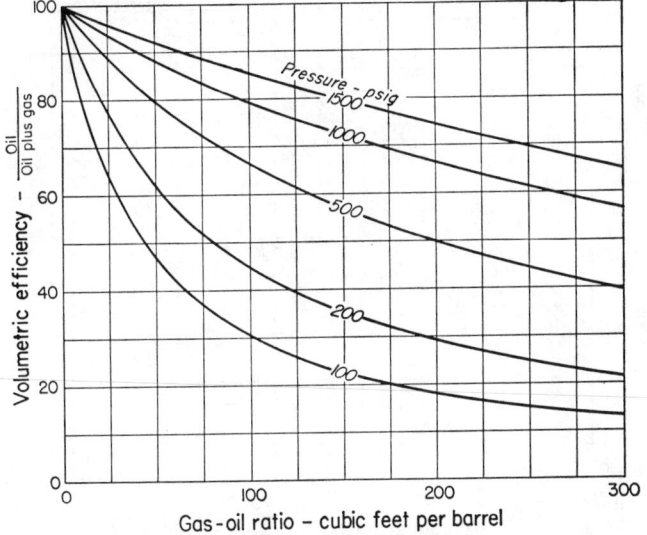

Fig. 6-97. Effect of gas on pump efficiency, not considering gas in solution in the oil.

the amount of gas in solution in the oil. Sage and Lacey (API Project 37) have established PVT relations and formation volumes of petroleum gases and liquids over a wide range. The specific volume of the liquid increases with gas in solution and with high fluid levels, and saturated oil must be taken into consideration in pump performance. Figure 6-97 gives the volumetric efficiency of pumps with oil and gas, assuming no absorption of gas in the liquid. M.B. Standing (API, 1947, p. 275, prepared a chart for formation volume of oil based on data of J. E. Gosline (API, 1928, p. 243) and C. R. Dodson (API, 1941, p. 326) and others. This is reproduced in Fig. 6-98 and gives formation volume of the bubble-point liquid as a function of temperature, pressure, and specific gravity of both the gas and liquid.

These charts indicate the necessity of separating the free gas from the liquid before it enters the pump to obtain good volumetric efficiencies. The condition of gas bubbles in the liquid is much less troublesome to handle than froth. Gas bubbles not in contact with each other would indicate efficiencies greater than 50 per cent in all cases, but with froth the efficiency may be less than 25 per cent. Density of fluid columns has been measured and sometimes gives column pressures of 10 psi/100 ft or less, indicating the presence of froth in the casing.

Gas Anchors. Figure 6-99 shows a number of types of gas separators used with hydraulic pumps but applicable as well to rod pumps. *a* is a poor man's anchor with a down pass which, if properly proportioned, will reduce the amount of gas carried in bubble form but will have no value in breaking froths. Being located below the pump, this device at the best gives saturated oil at the bottom of the quill, which would then be more than saturated in the pump barrel because of the difference in elevation and the pressure drop through the pump inlet. *b* is a down-pass anchor around the pump which can give a positive head on pump suction and is more effective than *a* in handling gas bubbles, but this also is not effective for froth. *c* is a casing anchor in which the production flows to a point above the pump and is directed against the casing wall, where it is spread on the wall to give a large surface. The device is effective in reducing froth if the discharge of the flow pipe is into gas. When froth is above this point, the effective area is that of the annular cross section and in

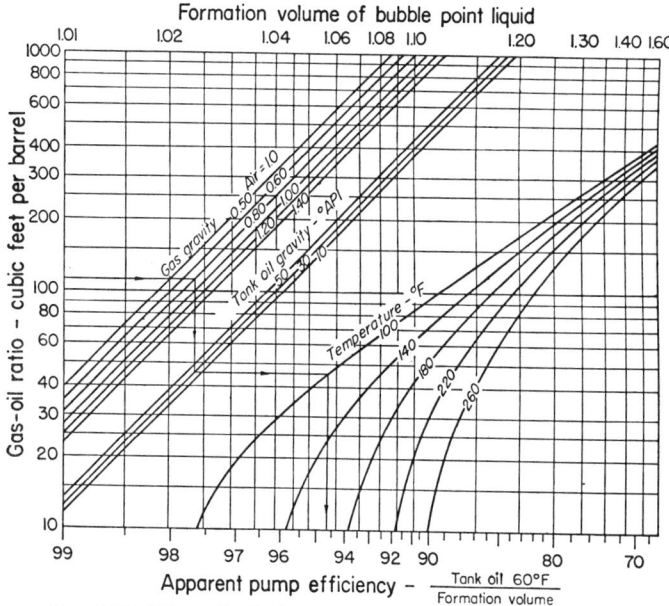

Fig. 6-98. Effect of solution gas on apparent pump efficiency.

this case its improvement over the down-pass anchor *b* is due only to the effect of the reduced velocity. To prevent froth from building above the discharge a throttle valve may be located in the flow line as in *d*, which is controlled by the pressure or liquid level in the casing annulus. This has been found effective but has the disadvantage that it involves valves and sensitive controls in the produced fluid.

Bottom-hole-pressure Determinations. The operating pressure of a hydraulic pump is a direct rough measure of the pumping head. By use of a test gauge and simple technique this may be refined to give bottom pressures with an accuracy of ±25 psi or possibly ±10 psi. The greatest accuracy is obtained in a closed system, which leaves the mean density of the produced column as the principal uncertainty. To eliminate the fluid-friction factor the pump is shut off and the pressure read at the "last stroke." Gas in the column can be held in solution with back pressure on the wellhead and corrected for. Determining the average water cut in the column presents the greatest difficulty as any bypassing of the oil through the water will give a column density greater than computed from tank gauges of water and oil production.

By using the free pump, a standard type of pressure bomb may be circulated in with the pump. Two methods are employed, one in which the bomb is below the

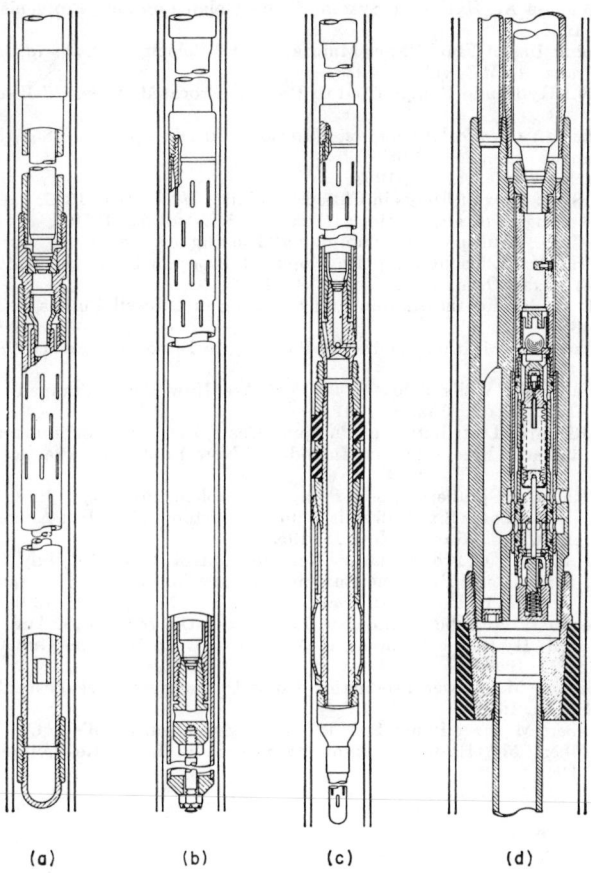

| (a) | (b) | (c) | (d) |

FIG. 6-99. Gas anchors.

pump, and a second in which it is above. When the bomb is below the pump it requires packing off in the tubing above the normal sealing collar and is not applicable to closed systems. When the bomb is placed above the pump, the standard sealing collar is used and the pressure is transmitted through the pump with a capillary steel tube. The bomb in this case is in a housing which forms an extension to the standard packer-nose assembly. With the bomb above the pump no obstruction is in the pump suction to change the pump operation and closed-system pumps can be used.

References

1. Atherton, D. H.: *Trans. ASME*, 1926, pp. 145–176.
2. ASME Viscosity Pressure Reports, 1953.
3. Coberly, C. J.: Hydraulic Power Applied to Oil-well Pumping, *Drill. and Prod. Prac. API*, 1935, pp. 79–90.
4. Coberly, C. J.: Problems in Modern Deep-well Pumping, *Trans. ASME*, vol. 60, pp. 561–571, 1938.
5. Cox, Dan: Hydraulic Pumping Cost Data, *Oil and Gas J.*, Oct. 3, 1940.
6. Davis, E. S.: *Trans. ASME*, vol. 65, pp. 755–759, 1943.
7. Exline, P. G.: *Prod. Eng.*, April, 1946.
8. Flood, H. Lee: Design and Installation of Hydraulic Well Pumping System, *Pet. Engr.*, August, 1941.

9. Gaviria, William A.: Hydraulic System Solves Galan Pumping Problems, *Petr. Engr.*, February, 1958.
10. Hurley, John: Use of Fluid Power Maintains Sand Velocity, *Pet. World*, January, 1946.
11. Kemler: *Trans. ASME*, vol. 55, 1933.
12. Miles, J. N.: Hydraulic Pumps Used to Produce Prorated Wells, *Oil Weekly*, Apr. 21, 1941.
13. Perry, John H.: *Chemical Engineers' Handbook*, 3d ed., pp. 1850–1854, McGraw-Hill Book Company, Inc., New York, 1950.
14. Phelan, R. E.: *Trans. AIME*, 1953.
15. Pigott, R. S. J.: Flow of Fluids in Closed Conduits, *Mech. Eng.*, 1933, p. 497; Pressure Losses in Tubing, Pipe and Fittings, *Trans. ASME*, vol. 72, 1950.
16. Robinson, J. D.: Multiple Well Pumping at Dominguez, *Pet. World*, April, 1939.
17. Short, E. H., Jr.: Efficient Deep Development Program Is Demonstrated in Russell Field, West Texas, *Oil and Gas J.*, Feb. 23, 1946.
18. Short, Ed: Hydraulic Installation and Servicing of Oil-well Pumps, *Oil and Gas J.*, Jan. 8, 1948.
19. Simons, Harry F.: Multiple Hydraulic Pumping in Illinois Oil Fields, *Oil and Gas J.*, Apr. 10, 1941.
20. Simons, Harry F.: Wells Below 9,000 Feet Are Now Being Pumped by Hydraulic Method, *Oil and Gas J.*, June 5, 1951.
21. Sneddon, Richard: Distribution of Pumping Costs, *Pet. Engr.*, September, 1948.
22. Sneddon, Richard: Free Pumping Introduces New Production Practices, *Pet. Engr.*, July, 1950.
23. Sneddon, Richard: Spraberry Poses Pumping Problem, *Pet. Engr.*, July, 1952.
24. Stormont, D. H.: These Six Hydraulic Pumping Systems Will Meet Almost Any Dual-zone Problem, *Oil and Gas J.*, Nov. 28, 1955.
25. Stovall, W. S., Jr.: Oil Production by Remote Control, *World Oil*, July 7, 1947.
26. Stumm, J. B.: Unusual Two-zone Pumping Installation, *Pet. Engr.*, September, 1954.
27. Tao, L. N., and W. F. Donovan: *Trans. ASME*, vol. 77, pp. 1291–1301, 1955.
28. Weber, George: Hydraulic Pumping in East Texas, *Oil and Gas J.*, Aug. 14, 1941.
29. Williams, Neil: Hydraulic Pumping Is Applied to Deep Wells on Gulf Cost, *Oil and Gas J.*, June 25, 1942.
30. Wilson, Gilbert M.: Lower Production Costs through Advance Lease Planning, *Oil Weekly*, May 11, 1942.
31. Wilson, Gilbert M.: Free Pump, Speeds Surfacing and Seating, *World Oil*, July 28, 1947.
32. Wilson, Gilbert M.: Hydraulic Pumping System in Lease Re-equipping Program, *World Oil*, Dec. 1, 1947.

Chapter 7

SUBSURFACE SUCKER-ROD PUMPS

By Roy L. Chenault

Chief Research Engineer, Oil Well Supply Division U.S. Steel Corporation

The general principles of sucker-rod pumps as used in oil wells are well known. Fundamentally, they consist of the usual simple combination of a cylinder and piston or plunger with a suitable intake valve and discharge valve for displacing the well fluid into the tubing and to the surface. However, the variety of problems encountered in pumping oil wells has resulted in a great number of modifications of this fundamentally simple unit to make it more effective for the various conditions encountered. In general, it can be said that the pumping of oil wells often presents the widest variety of adverse conditions to be met in a single installation of any pumping application with which the writer is familiar. These may include high discharge pressures; low intake pressures; severe abrasive conditions resulting from sand or other solids in suspension; severe corrosive conditions resulting from corrosive gases or salt waters; deposits of lime, salts, or other solids from the water pumped; paraffin deposits from the oil pumped; and the fact that the pump must handle liquids, permanent gases, and condensable vapors under the pressure and temperature conditions existing at the pump. Strong magnetic forces are often encountered that may interfere with valve action when the valves are made of magnetic material, and electrolytic corrosion is likely to occur as a result of using dissimilar materials.

The bores of reciprocating oil-well pumps commonly range from 1 to $4\frac{3}{4}$ in. diameter. The $4\frac{3}{4}$-in.-bore pump has a displacement about $22\frac{1}{2}$ times that of the 1-in. pump for a given speed and stroke length. This wide range of pump capacities is necessary to permit the selection of the most efficient and economical pumping equipment for all conditions encountered. It is pointed out that in many wells it is necessary to pump large volumes of water along with the oil; so that the pump has to have a capacity several times that indicated by the net oil production.

The following bores of subsurface pumps are now standardized by the American Petroleum Institute: 1, $1\frac{1}{16}$, $1\frac{1}{4}$, $1\frac{1}{2}$, $1\frac{3}{4}$, 2, $2\frac{1}{4}$, $2\frac{1}{2}$, $2\frac{3}{4}$, $3\frac{3}{4}$, and $4\frac{3}{4}$ in. Stroke lengths range from a few inches to more than 30 ft, and production rates with this type of pump range from a fraction of a barrel per day—with part-time operation—to approximately 3,000 B/D.

There are two broad classifications of pumps operated by sucker rods. The older type is now known as a "tubing pump." This term indicates that the pump barrel is attached directly to the tubing of a pumping well and lowered to the bottom of the well, or to any desired location for pumping, as the tubing is run into the well. The plunger, or traveling valve, of a tubing pump is run in on the lower end of the sucker rods until it contacts the lower valve, or "standing-valve" assembly. The rods are then raised sufficiently to prevent bumping bottom at the end of the downstroke and connected to a pumping unit, or jack, at the surface.

A more recent development is the "insert" or "rod" pump in which the entire assembly of barrel, traveling valve, plunger, and standing valve is installed with the sucker rods and seated in a special seating nipple, a tubing pump barrel, or other device designed for the purpose. The rod-type pump has the obvious advantage that the entire pump may be removed from the well for repair or replacement, with only a rod pulling job; whereas, with a tubing pump it is necessary to pull both rods and tubing to remove the pump barrel. The rod pump, however, is necessarily of smaller maximum capacity for a given tubing size.

Tubing-type pumps may have a standing valve seated in a coupling or seating shoe at the lower end of the barrel, or the standing valve may be seated in a coupling at the lower end of an "extension nipple" that extends below the lower end of the barrel. The ID of the extension nipple is somewhat larger than that of the barrel to permit the pump plunger to stroke out both top and bottom to produce uniform barrel wear and prevent accumulations of solids on the barrel wall.

Rod-type pumps may also be equipped with extension nipples above and below the barrel for similar reasons. In addition, rod pumps may be "top-seating" (pump suspended from top of barrel), "bottom-seating" (pump seated at bottom of barrel), "stationary-barrel" (traveling plunger), or "traveling-barrel."

Both tubing- and rod-type pumps may be equipped with one-piece "full barrels" or with either one-piece or sectional liner barrels. In the case of liner barrels the liners are clamped in position in an outer protecting jacket with suitable collars at each end of the jacket.

The American Petroleum Institute has adopted standard designations for the various combinations listed above. The following explanation of this classification system is taken from API Standard 11A, API Specifications for Oil Well Pumps.

Classification of API Oil-well Pumps

Type of pumps	Abbreviations	
	Full barrel	Liner barrel
(a) Tubing type, with shoe	TW	TL
(b) Tubing type, with extension shoe and nipple	TWE	TLE
(c) Rod type, stationary barrel, with top holddown	RWA	RLA
(d) Rod type, stationary barrel, with bottom holddown	RWB	RLB
(e) Rod type, traveling barrel	RWT	RLT

See explanatory diagrams (Fig. 7-1) numbered in accordance with above.
First letter:
T = tubing type; noninserted, run on tubing
R = rod or "inserted" type; run on the rods; through tubing
Second letter:
W = full barrel; supersedes "cold-drawn working barrel," also "cast-iron" type
L = liner barrel; includes sectional and full liners
Third letter:
E = tubing pump with extension nipple and shoe
A = stationary-barrel rod pump with top holddown
B = stationary-barrel rod pump with bottom holddown
T = traveling-barrel rod pump

The following definitions are provided to clarify some of the more important terms used in connection with oil-well pumps since a majority of these terms are peculiar to deep-well pumping terminology.

1. Barrel. The barrel of an oil-well pump is the cylinder into which the well fluid is admitted and displaced by a closely fitted piston or plunger.

2. Plunger. The pump plunger is a closely fitted tubular piston fitted with a check valve for displacing well fluid from the pump barrel. This may be all-metal or equipped with cups, rings, or other soft packing to form a seal with the barrel.

3. Standing Valve. This is the intake valve of the pump and generally consists of a ball-and-seat-type check valve. The valve assembly remains stationary during the pumping cycle.

4. Traveling Valve. This is the discharge valve and moves with the plunger of a stationary-barrel type of pump and with the barrel of a traveling-barrel type. The entire assembly of a cup-type plunger, or plunger equipped with other type of soft packing, along with the check valve, is often referred to as a "traveling valve."

5. Standing-valve Puller. This is a tool designed to attach to the standing-valve cage of a tubing-type pump when the sucker rods are lowered to bottom. The standing-valve assembly is then unseated by raising the rod string and is removed along with the pump plunger when the rods are pulled. This avoids the necessity for pulling tubing to remove the standing valve of the tubing-type pump.

6. Garbutt Rod. This is another arrangement sometimes used for pulling the standing valve of a tubing-type pump. It consists of a rod threaded on the lower end and attached to the standing-valve cage. The upper end of the rod is provided with a

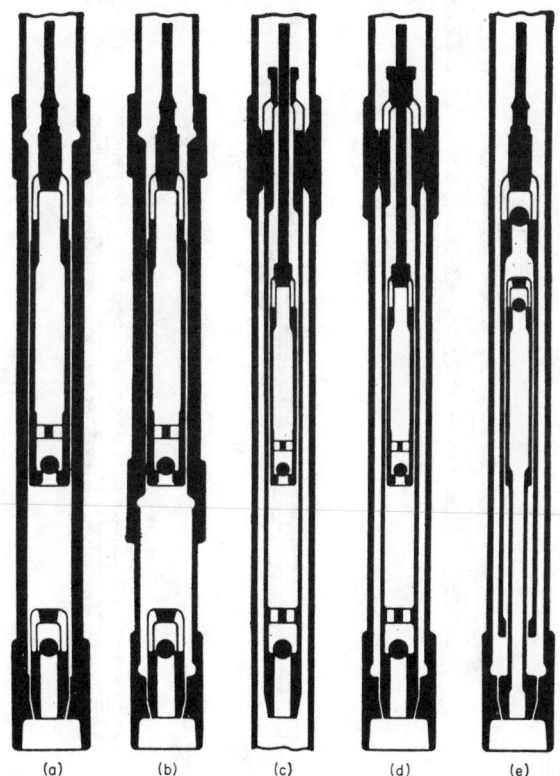

(a)   (b)   (c)   (d)   (e)

Fig. 7-1. Diagrams illustrating API pump classification. (*From API Standard 11A, 7th ed., p. 11, October, 1944.*)

crossbar that extends into the hollow pump plunger. The plunger is equipped with a hollow nut at the bottom that provides a shoulder to contact the crossbar of the garbutt rod when the plunger is raised to a point higher than the usual upper limit of the stroke. This unseats the standing valve, and it may be pulled and reinstalled with the plunger. This arrangement limits the stroke length to a value somewhat less than the length of the plunger. It also makes it necessary to locate the traveling valve at the top of the plunger, which is undesirable if free gas is a problem.

7. Valve Rod. Valve rods are used in rod-type stationary-barrel pumps to connect the lower end of the sucker-rod string to the pump plunger. The valve rod runs through a guide at the top of the pump. API valve-rod sizes range from $\frac{5}{8}$ to $1\frac{1}{16}$ in. diameter. Both straight threads and pipe threads are presently accepted as API standard on various sizes (see API Standard 11A, Supplement 5).

8. Pull Tube. Pull tubes are used in rod-type traveling-barrel pumps to connect the plunger with the seating anchor or "holddown." (See API Standard 11-A, Supplement 5, for thread dimensions for straight threads.) Tapered threads also are used on some sizes of pull tubes by some manufacturers.

9. Holddown. A holddown is an anchoring device for retaining a rod pump in its working position. The holddown may be located either at the top or bottom of a

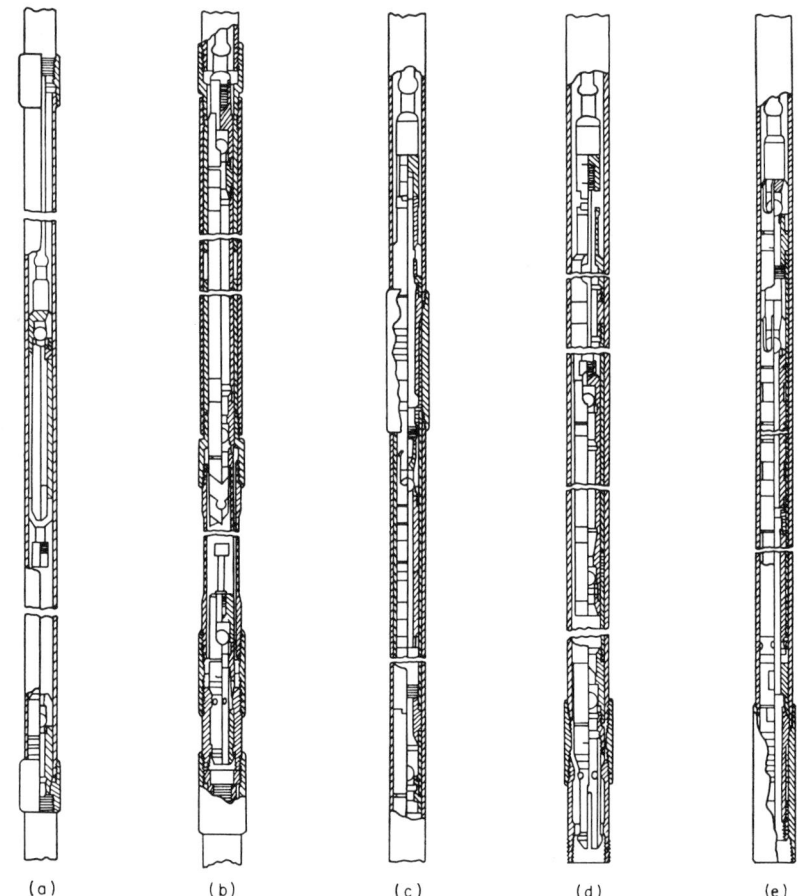

(a)   (b)   (c)   (d)   (e)

FIG. 7-2. Actual assemblies illustrating API pump classification. (*a*) Tubing pump with shoe. TW = full barrel. TL = liner barrel. (*b*) Tubing pump with extension nipple and shoe. TWE = full barrel. TLE = liner barrel. (*c*) Rod pump, stationary barrel with top-seating holddown. RWA = full barrel. RLA = liner barrel. (*d*) Rod pump, stationary barrel with bottom holddown. RWB = full barrel. RLB = liner barrel. (*e*) Rod pump, traveling barrel. RWT = full barrel. RLT = liner barrel.

stationary-barrel rod pump but can be located only at the bottom with a traveling-barrel pump. A holddown assembly may be equipped with composition cups or rings which form a tight fit in a seating nipple, or coupling, to hold the pump in its working position by friction, or it may be provided with spring clips that snap into position under a shoulder and require a definite pull upward on the rods to unlatch for removal. With the cup-type holddown the cups or rings also serve as a seal to prevent leakage of fluid from the tubing back to the well after it has passed through the pump. With the mechanical holddown an accurately ground, or babbitted, tapered mandrel seats on a mating taper to form a leakproof seal.

Figure 7-1 shows diagrams illustrating API pump classifications, and Fig. 7-2 shows actual assemblies of pumps representing these various classifications. The assemblies shown in Fig. 7-2 utilize a variety of different types of parts that are available for making up pump assemblies. For example, the first illustration on the left shows a tubing pump equipped with a plain metal plunger supplied with a standing-valve puller that is attached to the standing-valve cage by lowering the rods until a thread protector on the puller contacts the standing-valve cage. The rods are then turned to the right and the threaded end of the standing-valve puller screws into the top of the standing-valve cage so the valve assembly is removed when the rods are pulled. The standing valve shown in this illustration is equipped with composition cups that form a seal in the barrel to prevent leakage past the valve assembly. The second illustration shows a mechanical-holddown-type standing-valve assembly with a self-latching type of standing-valve puller that latches onto the extension above the standing-valve cage when the rods are lowered to bottom and the valve is then pulled when the rods are raised. The standing valve may be replaced by lowering the rods to bottom and rotating to the left.

The third illustration of Fig. 7-2 (RWA, RLA) shows a cup- or ring-type holddown used for top seating with a stationary-barrel rod pump. With this assembly a "closed cage" is used with the standing-valve assembly and an open cage is used above the plunger. With the fourth illustration (RWB, RLB) a mechanical-type bottom holddown is utilized with a stationary-barrel rod pump. In this case two traveling balls and seats are shown, one in an "open cage" at the top of the plunger and another in a "closed cage" at the bottom of the plunger. The last illustration of Fig. 7-2 shows a traveling-barrel rod-type pump with a friction-cup or ring-type holddown. The "standing valve" is mounted in an open cage at the top of the plunger and the "traveling valve" is mounted directly above the upper end of the barrel. The traveling-valve cage attaches directly to the sucker rods.

Figure 7-3 is an enlarged view showing the construction of a sectional-liner-type tubing-pump barrel. This particular barrel illustrates cast liner sections that are 12 in. long which are located in the liner jacket on an accurately machined mandrel after which they are clamped in place with the end collars, and the mandrel is removed. This illustration also shows a simple one-piece metallic plunger located within the barrel, but no additional fittings are shown.

Figure 7-4 shows a typical sectional-liner-type traveling-barrel rod-pump assembly with the various components labeled with their common names. The assembly is equipped with a mechanical bottom holddown assembly fitted with a babbitt seal. This type is installed in the well by attaching the sucker rods to the top valve cage and lowering the assembly into the well tubing until the holddown mandrel latches into its mating part (seating shoe) at the bottom of the tubing. During normal operation the pump is spaced so the "barrel"—consisting in this case of the liner jacket and liner assembly—moves up and down over the plunger, and the stroke must be adjusted so the "pull nut" works between the "lock holddown coupling" and the "plunger adapter." When the pump is to be removed from the well, the rods are disconnected from the pumping unit at the surface and lifted until the "pull nut" contacts the "plunger adapter" and a sufficient stress is put on the rods to unlatch the "lock holddown mandrel," after which the assembly is removed with the sucker rods.

PUMP SELECTION

The proper application of the various API pump designs illustrated generally in Figs. 7-1 and 7-2, as well as other "special pumps," is a matter that is subject to considerable difference of opinion among various operators. However, there are some generally accepted recommendations that are outlined below as a guide.

Tubing pumps, as shown in the first two illustrations of Figs. 7-1 and 7-2, have larger bores and correspondingly greater displacements for a given stroke length than rod pumps that can be used with the same size of tubing. Therefore, tubing pumps are

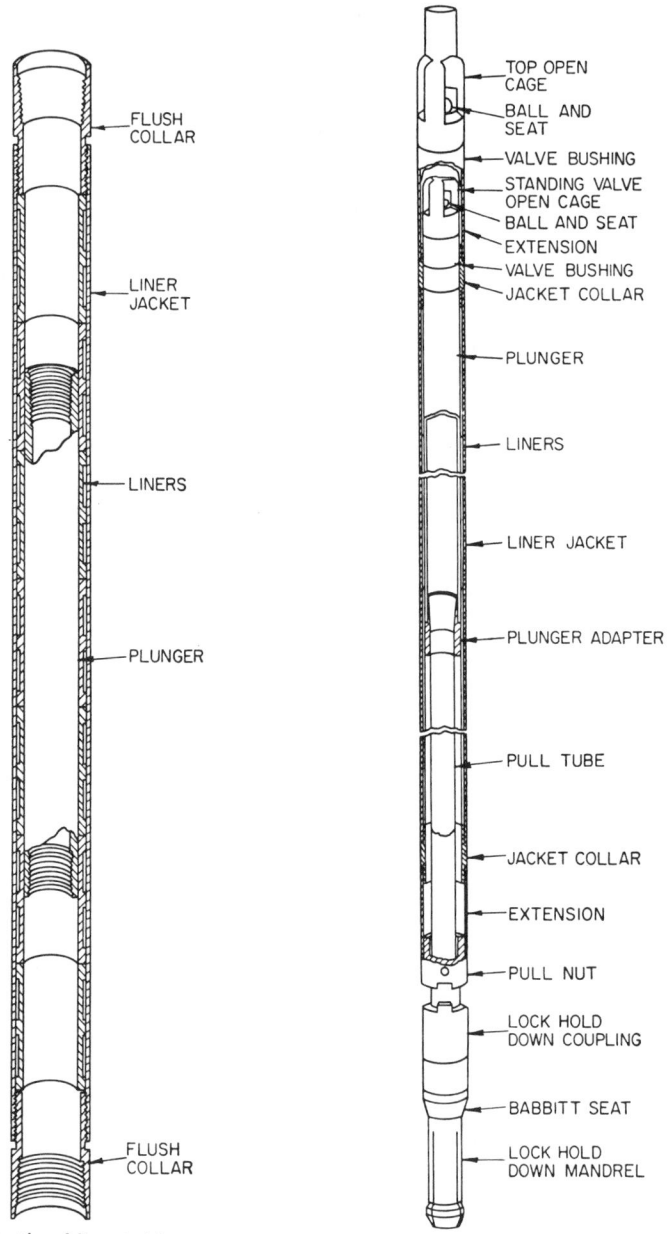

FIG. 7-3. Sectional-liner tubing-pump barrel with plunger.

FIG. 7-4. Sectional-liner traveling-barrel rod-pump assembly.

commonly used where it is necessary to lift large volumes of fluid and a pump of high displacement is required.   However, this greater volume results in a heavier fluid load on the sucker-rod string so that a portion or all of the capacity advantage may be lost in excessive rod and tubing stretch (see under Effect of Stretch of Sucker Rods and Tubing, page 7–17).   A tubing pump has fewer working parts and is often lower in cost than a rod pump of corresponding size.   A tubing pump with an extension nipple as shown in the second illustration of Figs. 7-1 and 7-2 permits the plunger to stroke partly out the bottom of the barrel, as well as the top of the barrel, and this arrangement is often used where solid deposits may form in the barrel where it is not contacted by the plunger.

The stationary-barrel rod pump with top seating, as shown in the third illustration of Figs. 7-1 and 7-2, is a very popular form of rod pump and is generally preferred for average conditions.   The top-seating holddown provides a seal just below the point where fluid is discharged to the tubing so sand or other solid particles are prevented from settling between the barrel and the tubing and the pump is not likely to become stuck in the tubing by packed sand.

The stationary-barrel rod pump with bottom holddown, as shown in the fourth illustration of Figs. 7-1 and 7-2, is recommended for deeper wells than the top holddown assembly since the barrel is not put in tension by the fluid load when the plunger is traveling downward.   Such high fluid loads in deep wells can result in high stresses in a thin-wall barrel, whicn may contribute to barrel failure.   With bottom seating the load is taken on the seating assembly and the barrel is relieved of this tensile stress. This assembly as illustrated is subject to pulling difficulties because of the probability of sand's settling around the barrel making it impossible to pull with the sucker rods. It is possible also to utilize a seal-off arrangement at the top of a bottom-seating pump to prevent sand from settling around the barrel, and this represents the ideal arrangement for deep wells producing sand with the well fluid.

The traveling-barrel pump as shown in the last illustration of Figs. 7-1 and 7-2 has the advantage of simplicity and relatively few working parts.   Many operators prefer this type of pump because of its simplicity and the fact that its construction also relieves the pump barrel of a tension load resulting from the weight of the fluid column.   A theoretical advantage of this type of pump is the fact that the pressure differential across the plunger is such that the high pressure is on the bottom of the plunger on the intake stroke and the direction of leakage, or slippage, past the plunger is opposite to the direction of the force of gravity which tends to cause sand to settle on the plunger.   For this reason there is less tendency for sand to be forced into the clearance space between the plunger and barrel and accelerate wear.   Although the traveling-barrel rod pump is bottom-seated, it is not so likely to become sanded in the tubing as is a bottom-seated stationary-barrel rod pump since there is a continual surging of the well fluid in and out of the lower end of the barrel while in operation. Also, the construction of this pump is such that sand cannot settle into the barrel when the pump is shut down.   A disadvantage of the traveling-barrel rod pump is the long and somewhat restricted inlet for oil to be admitted to the pump barrel.   This may result in a relatively high pressure drop through the "pull tube" and plunger to liberate excessive quantities of free gas or to cause the formation of condensable vapors which will adversely affect the volumetric efficiency of the pump.

Regarding the choice between sectional-liner-type barrels and one-piece barrels, the sectional-liner construction was devised primarily because of the difficulty in finishing the bores of long one-piece barrels with sufficient accuracy.   However, more recent developments in honing equipment have made it possible to finish one-piece barrels with accuracy approaching that of the 12-in. liner sections, and for this reason the one-piece barrel is becoming more popular for metal-to-metal-type plunger pumps. In the case of rod pumps, a larger bore for use in a given size of tubing can be supplied, and this often constitutes sufficient reason for using a one-piece barrel in preference to a sectional-liner barrel.   Sectional-liner barrels have advantages in reworking or rehoning to a larger size to economize on expensive materials since the sections can be measured and sorted to require a minimum amount of honing and a minimum material loss to recondition for additional use.   If such reworking is attempted with a one-piece barrel, the entire barrel must be rehoned to the diameter required to clean up the most severely worn or scored portion of the barrel. Special accurately finished mandrels must be utilized for aligning liner sections, and they are susceptible to misalignment as a result of field handling. Therefore, the one-piece barrel is generally preferred for use in areas where well-equipped pump shops are not readily available.

PLUNGERS

Figure 7-5 illustrates the two most common types of "metal-to-metal" plungers utilized for displacing well fluid in oil-well pumps. The left-hand illustration shows a plain plunger with "box-end" threads. This type of plunger generally is finished somewhat undersize at each end opposite the threads. This provides for the slight

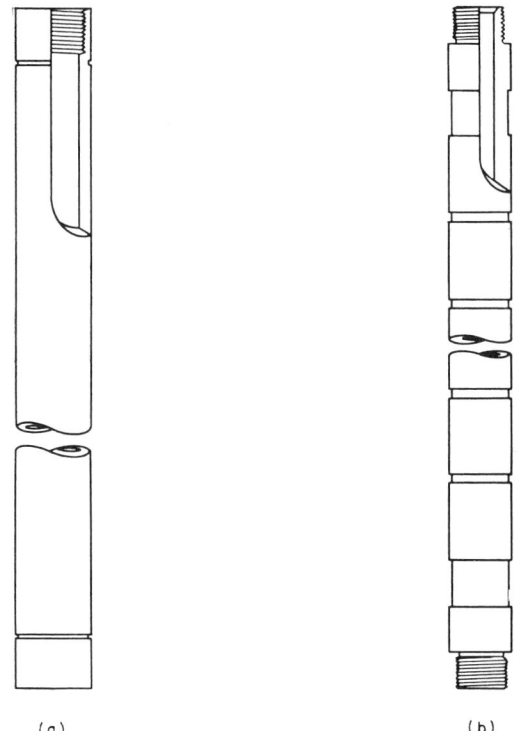

(a)   (b)

Fig. 7-5. Plain (a) and grooved (b) metal-to-metal plungers.

expansion of the plunger when tightened without causing binding of the plunger in the pump barrel. The right-hand illustration of Fig. 7-5 shows a grooved "pin-end" plunger.

Most subsurface pump manufacturers provide both plain and grooved plungers in various materials. It has never been conclusively demonstrated that either type of construction has any particular advantage over the other. Many operators feel that grooves facilitate lubrication of closely fitted plungers by providing spaces for the well fluid to accumulate in considerable quantities. However, there is considerable slippage past any plunger operating under usual conditions where the differential pressure across the plunger is several hundred or even thousands of pounds per square inch. This slippage will provide adequate lubrication with either type of plunger if the fluid has any lubricating value. One possible advantage of a grooved plunger is that any solid particle, such as a sand grain or a steel chip that gets between the plunger and the barrel, may become lodged in a groove and minimize scoring of the barrel and plunger. With a plain plunger particles cannot escape from the finished surfaces until they have traveled the full length of the plunger. On the other hand, a grooved plunger stroking out of a barrel increases the probability of picking up and carrying solid material into the barrel.

The high differential pressures encountered in pumping deep wells require an effective sealing or packing means on the plunger. For wells of extreme depth a closely fitted metallic plunger is almost always used to form a satisfactory seal with the barrel. Such plungers are commonly supplied with nominal clearances of 0.001, 0.002, 0.003, or 0.005 in. in the barrel. Such plunger fits are commonly referred to as −1, −2, −3, or −5 fits. The API tolerance for liner barrels is +0.0012 in., −0.0002 in. for all sizes, and the tolerance for plungers is +0.0000 in., −0.0005 in., making it possible for the fit of a −1 plunger, for example, to vary from 0.0008 to 0.0027 in. diametral clearance.

SLIPPAGE PAST PLUNGERS

In considering slippage past a closely fitted plunger, the flow between the plunger and the barrel is in the viscous range; so that leakage or slippage is inversely proportional to the absolute viscosity and to the plunger length. It is directly proportional to the plunger diameter, the differential pressure between the two ends of the plunger, and the cube of the diametral clearance.

The absolute viscosity of well fluids commonly pumped will range from approximately 1 to 100 cp at temperatures existing at the pump setting. In some cases the viscosity may be as high as 1,000 cp. As a result of viscosity variations the slippage past the plunger of a particular plunger-pump assembly with a given plunger fit, length, and diameter may vary by as much as 100 to 1 under fairly common conditions, and as much as 1,000 to 1 under extreme conditions with the same differential pressure across the plunger. Thus it is seen that a plunger pump may operate with acceptable efficiency in a well producing a highly viscous oil, whereas the same pump operated at the same speed and stroke may fail to deliver any oil to the surface when installed at the same depth in a well producing oil of low viscosity.

The following equation can be used to determine slippage losses past a pump plunger with sufficient accuracy for most purposes:

$$Q = \frac{\pi D P C^3}{\mu L \times 2.32 \times 10^{-7}} \tag{1}$$

where Q = slippage loss, cu in./min
D = plunger diameter, in.
P = differential pressure across plunger, psi
C = diametral clearance, in.
L = length of plunger, in.
μ = absolute viscosity, cp

A specific application of this equation will serve to illustrate the importance of plunger fits for a pump of a particular bore and stroke, operating with various plunger fits in fluids of various viscosities.

If we assume a $2\frac{1}{4}$-in.-bore pump having 0.003-in. diametral clearance operating with a pressure differential of 2,000 psi between the two ends of a 48-in. plunger, and at a rate of fifteen 48-in. strokes per minute in oil having a viscosity of 3 cp, then Eq. (1) becomes

$$Q = \frac{\pi \times 2.25 \times 2,000 \times 2.7 \times 10^{-8}}{3 \times 48 \times 2.32 \times 10^{-7}}$$

$$= 11.43 \text{ cu in./min}$$

Assuming that the volume of the barrel below the plunger is completely filled during the upstroke, this rate of leakage can occur only during the upstroke, or approximately one-half the total time. The net slippage past the plunger is 5.72 cu in./min. or 0.85 B/D. The displacement of a 2¼-in. pump operating at fifteen 48-in. strokes per minute is 426 B/D, and the slippage in this case is only about 0.2 per cent, which is insignificant. The results with this and other plunger clearances with 3-cp oil are shown in Table 7-1.

Table 7-1. Losses Resulting from Slippage of 3-cp Oil Past 2¼-in. Pump Plunger 48 in. Long with 2,000 psi Pressure Differential and Various Plunger Fits. Also Slippage in Percentage of Pump Displacement with Fifteen 48-in. Strokes per Min

Slippage past plunger		Slippage loss in pump at 15 strokes/min		
Diametral clearance, in.	Slippage rate, cu in./min	Cu in./min	B/D	% of pump displacement
0.003	11.43	5.72	0.85	0.2
0.006	91.5	45.8	6.8	1.6
0.010	424	212	31.5	7.4
0.020	3,390	1,695	251.8	59.2

In the case of 0.020-in. plunger clearance, the slippage loss when pumping water or oil with a viscosity of 1 cp would be 755 B/D, which is more than the pump displacement, and it would be impossible to pump water to the surface, or to a level requiring 2,000 psi pressure differential across the plunger. When pumping oil with a viscosity of 100 cp, however, the slippage would be only about 7.5 B/D, or less than 1.8 per cent of the pump displacement, and a clearance of 0.020 in. is reasonably satisfactory for these conditions.

It is pointed out that slippage losses result directly in power losses, since the same power is required to lift the plunger with 90 per cent of the fluid slipping past the plunger during the upstroke as is required with 1 per cent or less slippage. The energy dissipated in slippage losses results in an increase in temperature of the oil within the pump, and a decrease in viscosity which further increases slippage losses. Also, when water is produced with oil excessive slippage losses increase the chances of forming emulsions.

Close plunger clearances are relatively more important with small-bore pumps than with larger bores, inasmuch as the displacement for a given stroke length and speed varies as the square of the diameter, whereas slippage varies as the first power of the diameter. Close plunger clearances are especially important in small pumps operated at extremely low speeds, as used in stripper wells in some areas. It is believed that the method outlined above is satisfactory for evaluating maximum slippage to be expected in all cases.

PLUNGERS EQUIPPED WITH SOFT PACKING

Figure 7-6 shows various arrangements of composition cups, (a) where the cups constitute the entire packing means, (b) where they are used in combination with composition "valve rings," and (c) in combination with coiled soft packing (generally flax) which is commonly called a "repack." The applications of such soft-packing arrangements generally are limited to relatively shallow wells and where abrasive conditions are not excessively severe. Where this type of plunger is satisfactory it has the advantage of being easily and cheaply reconditioned with new cups or other types of packing and the flexible packing will compensate for considerable wear of the barrel as long as the barrel surface remains smooth.

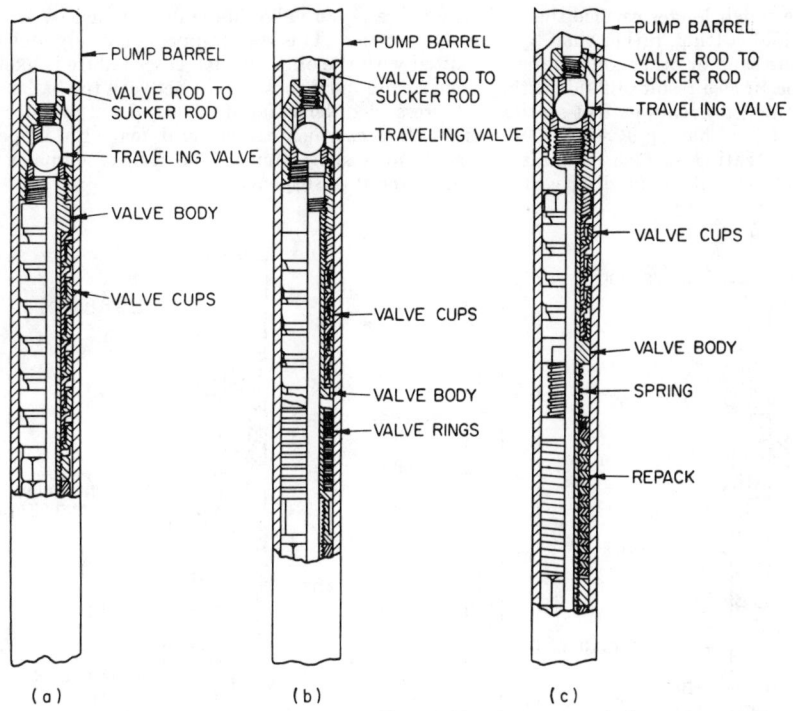

FIG. 7-6. Flexible plungers: (*a*) cup type; (*b*) combination cup and ring type; (*c*) repack type.

BALLS AND SEATS

Figure 7-7 illustrates the two types of ball-and-seat combinations commonly used for check valves in subsurface pumps. The "flat-type" seat is now the only standard seat recognized by the American Petroleum Institute, but the "ribbed type" was recognized until fairly recently and there are a great number of the ribbed-type seats

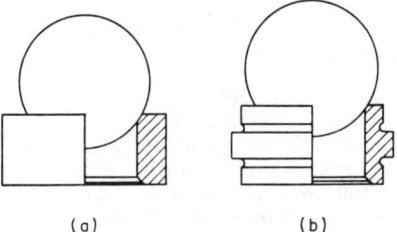

FIG. 7-7. Pump valve balls and seats: (*a*) flat type; (*b*) ribbed type.

still in use. Balls and seats for oil-well-pump check valves are made in a wide variety of materials to resist extremely abrasive and corrosive conditions. API Standard 11A lists the important dimensions of standard sizes along with the pump sizes with which they are commonly used.

DOUBLE VALVES

Figure 7-8 shows common arrangements of two valves in series used both as traveling valves and as standing valves. Experience has shown that two valves in series will give much longer service than a single valve if the valve life is determined by wear or fluid cutting, rather than by corrosive action.   This result appears entirely logical where sand or other solid material is lifted with the oil.   In such cases failure is likely to occur as a result of fluid cutting when a solid particle is caught between the ball and seat and prevents perfect seating.   A pressure differential of 2,000 psi will produce a jet of fluid having a velocity of over 500 ft/sec, which can easily damage the lapped valve-seating surface on balls and seats in a short time.   The rate of damage is accelerated if the fluid jet carries solid material in suspension.

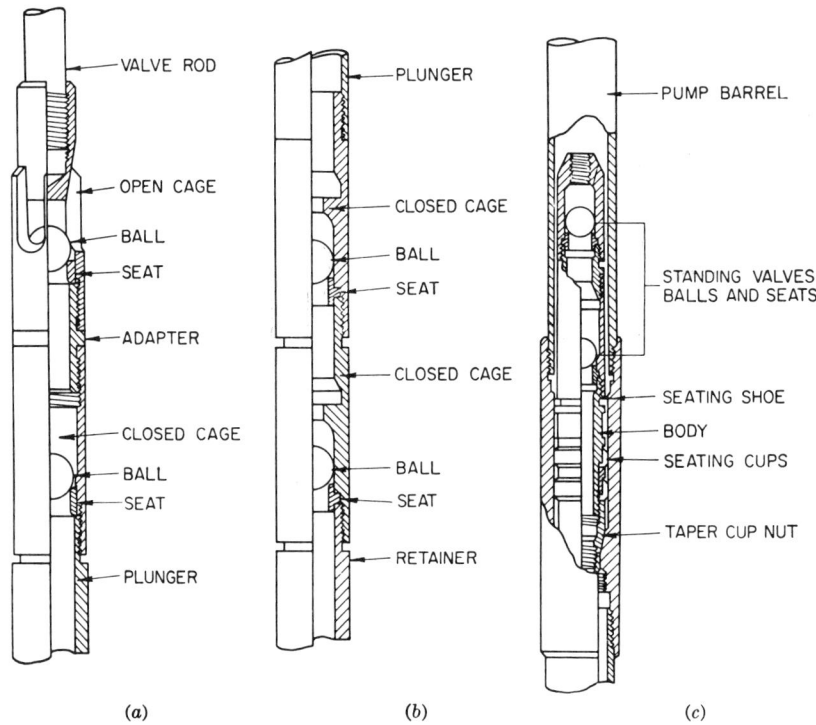

(a)   (b)   (c)

Fig. 7-8. Double-valve arrangements: (a) double valve on top of plunger; (b) double valve on bottom of plunger; (c) double standing valve.

The life of a ball and seat will depend largely on the number of times it is subjected to damage by fluid jets.   By the use of double valves this can be greatly decreased since a jet cannot occur until both balls are held off their seats during the same stroke. For example, if conditions are such that a single ball and seat is prevented from seating properly once out of each 100 strokes, the chances of both of two valves in series failing to seat properly wil be reduced to 1 in 10,000 strokes.   Furthermore, if the two valves fail to seat the pressure drop will be distributed between the two valves and the cutting action will be less severe than with a single valve.

BOTTOM-DISCHARGE VALVE

The bottom-discharge valve as illustrated in Fig. 7-9 is used in connection with bottom-seating stationary-barrel rod pumps and is designed to cause part of the fluid discharged from the pump to circulate up around the outside of the pump barrel. This is done to prevent sand from settling around the pump, which may make it impossible to pull the pump on the sucker rods.   The bottom-seating arrangement for a rod-type pump is desirable in wells of extreme depth since the pump barrel is relieved of the fluid load, which places the barrel in tension. When top seating is used the barrel is subjected to a high pressure which tends to expand the barrel.

Figure 7-10 illustrates another means for utilizing the advantages of bottom seating with a stationary-barrel rod pump and preventing sand from settling around the outside of the pump barrel. This assembly utilizes a mechanical bottom holddown, with

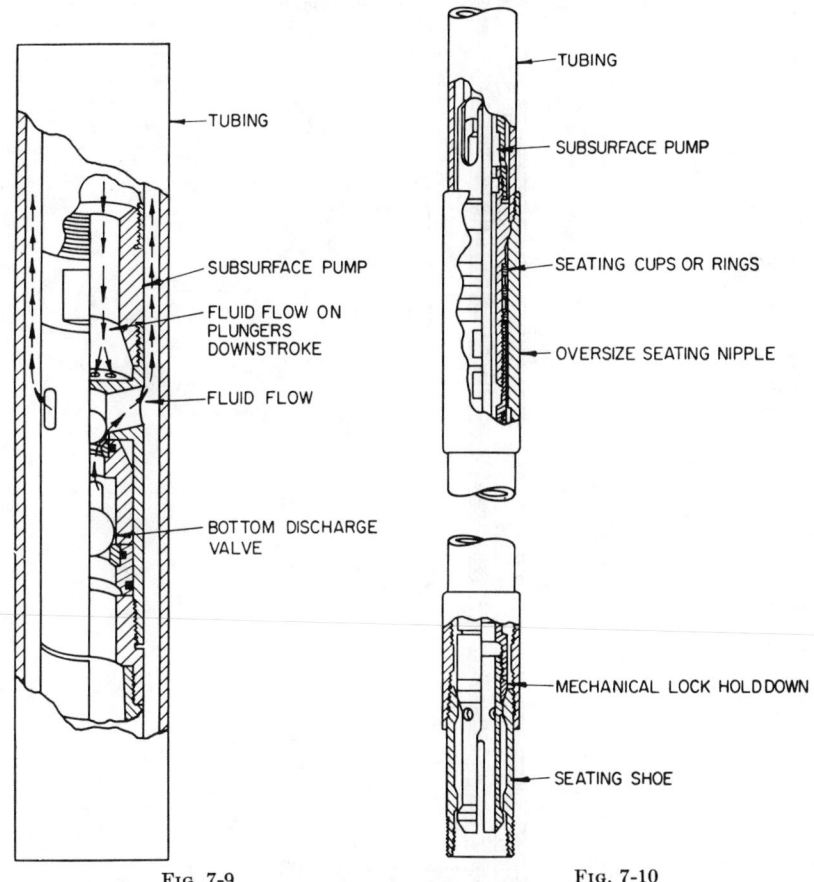

FIG. 7-9   FIG. 7-10

FIG. 7-9. Bottom-discharge valve for use with bottom-seating stationary-barrel rod pumps. This valve is attached to the bottom of a pump and through it part of the well fluid is diverted up the side of the pump to help dislodge sand that may have settled between the pump and the tubing.

FIG. 7-10. Top seal and bottom seating for stationary-barrel rod pumps.

seating cups or rings which fit into a slightly restricted seating nipple properly spaced in the tubing to form a seal at the top of the pump barrel.

THREE-TUBE PUMP

This type of pump is illustrated in Fig. 7-11 and gets its name from the three tubes used in its construction. The complete pump assembly is lowered into the well on the sucker-rod string and is positioned in the well by contacting either a cup-seating

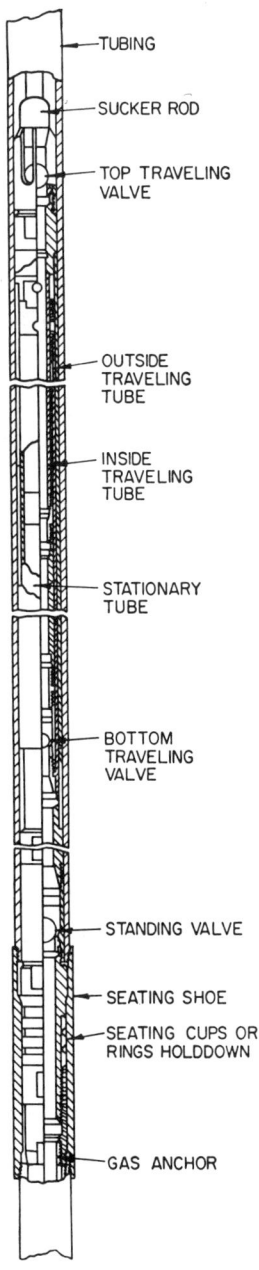

TUBING

SUCKER ROD

TOP TRAVELING VALVE

OUTSIDE TRAVELING TUBE

INSIDE TRAVELING TUBE

STATIONARY TUBE

BOTTOM TRAVELING VALVE

STANDING VALVE

SEATING SHOE

SEATING CUPS OR RINGS HOLDDOWN

GAS ANCHOR

FIG. 7-11. Three-tube pump.

assembly or a mechanical lock holddown.   The middle tube of the pump is stationary, being attached to the holddown.   The other two tubes attached to the sucker-rod string move over the middle stationary tube, one on the outside and one on the inside. The tubes used in this pump are relatively long and have a relatively large operating clearance in comparison with the usual pump plunger.   The resistance to flow between the tubes is adequate to create the seal necessary to displace the fluid past the standing valve and through the traveling valve against the tubing pressure.   The three-tube pump is relatively inexpensive because it is not necessary to work to such close toler- ances in the manufacture of the pump.   It is primarily designed to clean out wells after workover operations or formation-fracturing operations, which may make the well produce large quantities of sand for a considerable period of time.   It is also used in wells producing from loose-sand formations which consistently produce quantities of fine floating sand.

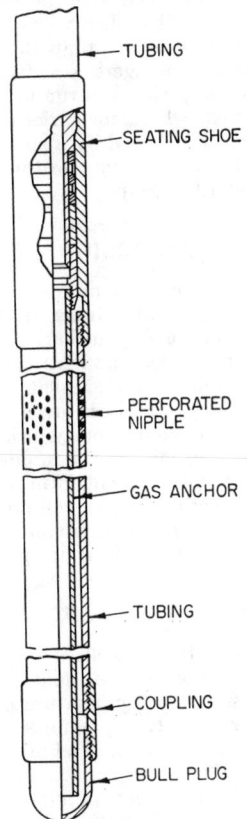

TUBING

SEATING SHOE

PERFORATED NIPPLE

GAS ANCHOR

TUBING

COUPLING

BULL PLUG

FIG. 7-12. Gas-anchor arrangement.

GAS ANCHORS

Where conditions are such that there is considerable free gas in the well fluid at the pump intake, it is desirable to prevent as much gas as possible from entering the pump and permit the gas to rise to the surface through the casing annulus rather than through the tubing.   Numerous so-called "gas anchors" are in use that are designed to separate the free gas and deflect it up the casing annulus.   Figure 7-12 illustrates a common type of gas-anchor arrangement in which the well fluid must enter the perforated nipple and circulate downward at a low velocity before entering the gas-anchor tube, which is attached to the pump intake.   This gives the free gas an opportunity to separate and rise to the uppermost ports in the perforated nipple where it may return to the casing.   A large portion of the gas will rise through the casing before passing through the perforated nipple.

SPECIAL PUMPS

Numerous other special types of pumps are in use, including casing pumps which are designed to be inserted directly in the casing without a string of tubing.   Such pumps are set in the casing on a packer or casing anchor, which grips the casing and holds the pump in position.   Such pumps are limited in size only by the casing size and can be made to have a very large capacity in relatively shallow wells.   However, with this arrangement all the gas produced with the well fluid must pass through the pump, and this may seriously limit the effective capacity in wells producing large quantities of gas.   Another special type of pump that is used to some extent is an arrangement where two displacing plungers are designed to act in series.   This increases the displacement of a pump that will run in a given size of tubing and at a given stroke length.   In some wells where, for various reasons, gas locking is a problem, the situation can sometimes be relieved by a special pump having two so-called "compression chambers" which serve to increase the compression ratio above that normally obtainable in a "standard" pump.

CORROSION

In some areas resistance to corrosion of the materials used in subsurface pumps is of major importance.   A wide variety of alloy irons, steels, nonferrous alloys, and elements have been used to combat corrosive conditions in various districts.   Some of the corrosive agents commonly found in various districts are hydrogen sulfide, carbon dioxide, salt waters containing sodium chloride, calcium chloride, magnesium chloride, and other salts.   Chemical corrosion inhibitors are now widely used by many operators.   Such inhibitors are fed either continuously or intermittently down the casing into the well.   Protective films are formed on the tubing and rods, as well as on pump parts.   However, since protective films cannot form on wearing surfaces the closely fitted pump parts in rubbing contact are not so well protected by corrosion inhibitors as are the rods and tubing.   For this reason it is more important to utilize corrosion-resistant materials in the construction of subsurface pumps.

EFFECT OF GASES AND VAPORS

In selecting pumping equipment for oil wells it should be remembered that in a majority of cases some of the constituents of the fluid being pumped are above or near their boiling points at the pressure and temperature conditions existing within the pump.   These conditions may release large volumes of dissolved gases and vapors with a slight drop in pressure of the well fluid, in addition to the free gas initially in the fluid.   For this reason it is very difficult to pump some wells down.   Many wells will apparently pump off with several hundred feet of fluid standing in the hole because the condensable vapors and gases occupy the entire displacement volume of the pump.   Under these conditions, without a relatively high intake pressure which decreases compression ratio, the pressure below the plunger cannot be raised to the tubing pressure. (This is necessary before the traveling valve can open and deliver oil to the tubing.) On the downstroke the vapors may condense and occupy a very small volume without an appreciable increase in pressure, and only the permanent gases are effective in increasing the pressure in accordance with the gas laws.

There are two precautions to take to minimize the adverse effects of vapors and gases:

1. The compression ratio should be made as high as possible.   This is accomplished by using a closed-cage-type valve below the plunger with a stationary-barrel pump, or a

valve above the plunger with a traveling-barrel-type pump. It is also important to space the pump so the traveling valve and standing valve come as near to each other as possible at the lowest position of the rods without making contact, and utilize as long a stroke as possible with the equipment available.

2. Flow velocities and turbulence at the pump inlet should be kept at a minimum. This is accomplished by using the largest standing valve possible and a suitable gas anchor with the largest possible flow passages.

EFFECT OF STRETCH OF SUCKER RODS AND TUBING

When a uniform string of sucker rods or tubing is run into a well, the length of the rods or tubing will increase by an amount proportional to the square of the length of the string, since the weight as well as the length increase in proportion to the depth to which the string of rods or tubing is run. This initial stretch of rods or tubing under their own weight remains constant under static conditions and does not complicate the spacing of pumps. However, during pump operation the fluid load which is alternately transferred from the tubing to the sucker rods causes the tubing to increase

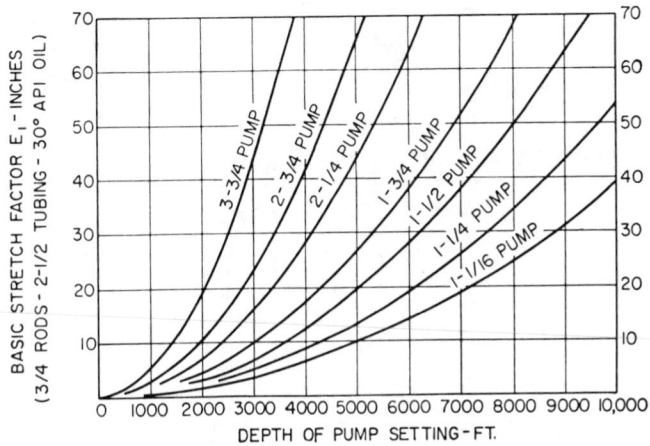

FIG. 7-13. Curves for determining length of plunger stroke.

in length on the downstroke when the tubing is supporting the fluid load, and a shortening of the tubing with an increase in length of the sucker rods when the rods are carrying the load on the upstroke. Both these effects tend to shorten the plunger stroke in the well pump in comparison with the polished-rod stroke at the surface. Pumping-unit stroke length may vary from approximately 1 to 30 ft in practice, and for relatively short strokes in relatively deep wells the actual plunger stroke may be a small fraction of the polished-rod stroke at the surface.

Figures 7-13 and 7-14 show curves that can be used with correction factors in Tables 7-2 and 7-3, and the accompanying explanations to determine plunger strokes and pump displacements corresponding to various polished-rod strokes for most common rod-and-tubing combinations and density of well fluids for seven commonly used pump bores. Note that tubing-size designations are based on tubing OD as recently adopted by the API.

It is pointed out that these curves do not take account of dynamic effects which vary with the pumping speed and may result in "overtravel" of the plunger at high speeds. The displacements given by the curves, therefore, can be considered as minimum values to be expected. The curves were computed on the assumption that some grade of steel sucker rods would be used, and a value of 29×10^6 for the modulus

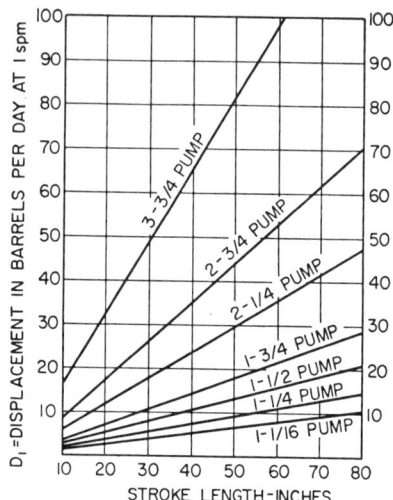

Fig. 7-14. Curves for determining displacement of sucker-rod pumps (displacement in barrels per 24-hour day = $D_1 \times$ spm).

Table 7-2. Correction for Rod-and-tubing Combinations

Rods, in.	Tubing, in.	Factor F_1
⅝	2⅜	1.44
	2⅞	1.36
	3½	1.30
¾	2⅜	1.08
	2⅞	1.00
	3½	0.941
⅞	2⅞	0.787
	3½	0.729
	4½	0.690
1	2⅞	0.648
	3½	0.590
	4½	0.551

Table 7-3. Correction for Gravity of Fluid

Sp gr	API gr	Factor F_2
1.25	...	1.43
1.20	...	1.37
1.15	...	1.31
1.10	...	1.26
1.00	10	1.14
0.966	15	1.10
0.933	20	1.07
0.902	25	1.03
0.875	30	1.00
0.850	35	0.972
0.825	40	0.943
0.802	45	0.916
0.780	50	0.892

of elasticity was assumed.   If nonferrous rods are used, an appropriate correction must be made for the modulus of the material.

The following notes and examples show methods for determining plunger strokes with uniform rod strings and with tapered rod strings.

To determine pump plunger stroke with uniform rod strings:

$$S_2 = S_1 - (E_1 F_1 F_2) \qquad (2)$$

where S_2 = actual plunger stroke

S_1 = polished-rod stroke

E_1 = basic stretch factor from Fig. 7-13 for proper depth and pump size

F_1 = correction factor from Table 7-2 for actual rod-and-tubing combination in well

F_2 = correction factor from Table 7-3 for gravity of fluid

To determine pump displacement:

1. Find value of D_1 (Fig. 7-14) corresponding to actual plunger stroke and pump size.

2. Displacement in barrels per day = $D_1 \times$ spm.

Example

Well data

Depth to pump, 4,500 ft

Pump size, 1¾ in. ID

Rods, ⅞ in.

Tubing, 2⅞ in.

Length of polished-rod stroke, 48 in. = S_1

Spm, 20

API gravity, 25

From Fig. 7-13, E_1 for 1¾-in. pump at 4,500 ft = 21.6 in.

From Table 7-2, F_1 for ⅞-in. rods, 2⅞-in. tubing = 0.787

From Table 7-3, F_2 for 25°API = 1.03

Plunger stroke S_2 = 48 − (21.6 × 0.787 × 1.03) = 30.5 in.

From Fig. 7-14, D_1 = 10.8 for 30.5-in. stroke, 1¾-in. pump

Displacement = 10.8 × 20 = 216 B/D

To determine plunger stroke with tapered sucker-rod string:

Let A = length of ⅝-in. rods in string

B = length of ¾-in. rods in string

C = length of ⅞-in. rods in string

D = length of 1-in. rods in string

Y = total length of rod string

$$\text{Plunger stroke } S_2 = S_1 - E_1 F_2 \left[\left(F_{1A} \frac{A}{Y} \right) + \left(F_{1B} \frac{B}{Y} \right) + \left(F_{1C} \frac{C}{Y} \right) + \left(F_{1D} \frac{D}{Y} \right) \right] \qquad (3)$$

where S_1 = polished-rod stroke

E_1 = basic stretch factor from Fig. 7-13 for depth and pump size

F_{1A} = correction factor from Table 7-2 for ⅝-in. rods in tubing used

F_{1B} = correction factor from Table 7-2 for ¾-in. rods in tubing used

F_{1C} = correction factor from Table 7-2 for ⅞-in. rods in tubing used

F_{1D} = correction factor from Table 7-2 for 1-in. rods in tubing used

F_2 = correction factor from Table 7-3 for gravity of fluid

Note that any particular term in parentheses is used only if there is a rod size in the string corresponding to the letter (A, B, C, or D) appearing in this term.   For example, if a tapered string consists only of ⅝- and ¾-in. rods Eq. (3) becomes

$$S_2 = S_1 - E_1 F_2 \left[\left(F_{1A} \frac{A}{Y} \right) + \left(F_{1B} \frac{B}{Y} \right) \right]$$

Example

Depth to pump, 4,500 ft

Pump size, 1¾ in.

Rods, 2,400 ft, ¾ in. = B

2,100 ft, ⅞ in. = C

Tubing, $2\frac{7}{8}$ in.
Length of polished-rod stroke, 48 in. = S_1
API gravity, 25°

From Fig. 7-13, E_1 for $1\frac{3}{4}$-in. pump at 4,500 ft = 21.6 in.
From Table 7-2

$$F_{1B} \text{ for } \tfrac{3}{4}\text{-in. rods and } 2\tfrac{7}{8}\text{-in. tubing} = 1.00$$
$$F_{1C} \text{ for } \tfrac{7}{8}\text{-in. rods and } 2\tfrac{7}{8}\text{-in. tubing} = 0.787$$

From Table 7-3, F_2 for 25°API oil = 1.03
Using $\frac{3}{4}$ in. and $\frac{7}{8}$ in. rods, Eq. (3) becomes

$$S_2 = S_1 - E_1 F_2 \left[\left(F_{1B} \frac{B}{Y} \right) + \left(F_{1C} \frac{C}{Y} \right) \right]$$

$$= 48 - (21.6 \times 1.03) \left[\left(1 \times \frac{2,400}{4,500} \right) + \left(0.787 \times \frac{2,100}{4,500} \right) \right]$$

$$= 48 - 22.25(0.533 + 0.367)$$
$$= 48 - (22.25 \times 0.90)$$
$$= 28\text{-in. plunger stroke}$$

OVERTRAVEL OF PUMP PLUNGER

As a result of dynamic effects and the inertia and elasticity of a long string of sucker rods, there will be some additional stretch in the rods over that determined for static conditions. This effect is a function of the length of the rod string, the length of the polished-rod stroke, and the speed (spm), and results in an *increase* in the stroke length at the pump. This effect is known as overtravel, and the theoretical value of the overtravel to be added to determine the actual plunger stroke is given by the following equation:

$$\text{Overtravel} = \frac{1.55(L/1,000)^2 \times S_1 \times \text{spm}^2}{70,500}$$

where L = length of sucker-rod string, ft
      S_1 = polished-rod stroke, in.
      spm = strokes/min

It is pointed out that miscellaneous sources of friction, such as rod friction, plunger friction, and fluid friction, may considerably reduce the calculated value of overtravel. However, in many installations considerable overtravel approaching the calculated value is observed.

It is suggested that anyone actively engaged in sucker-rod pumping activities contact the Division of Production, American Petroleum Institute, Dallas, Tex., for up-to-date information on API pump-standardization developments. Present standards are covered in API Standard 11A, API Specification for Oil Well Pumps. However, a special task group of the API subcommittee on pumps is currently working on a proposal for a drastic revision of the standards to assure complete interchangeability of parts between manufacturers of a number of the more popular classes of pumps.

Chapter 8

SUCKER RODS

By Walter H. Ritterbusch, Jr.

Northern Division Sales Manager
The S. M. Jones Company

The first all-metal sucker rod patent, No. 528168, was issued Oct. 30, 1894, to Samuel M. Jones of Toledo, Ohio. Since that time, the sucker rod has gone through many improvements because of vastly advanced manufacturing techniques and availability of new alloys.

Basically, however, the sucker rod is unchanged as it performs the original function for which it was designed in the same manner, that of lifting oil out of a cased hole by serving as a connecting rod between the subsurface pump and the lifting or pumping device on the surface.

In performing this service, a severe limitation is placed on the sucker rod by the inside diameter of the production string or tubing. This necessitates designing the outside diameter of the sucker-rod joint to provide clearance for passage of fluid up through the tubing to the surface.

ROD DIMENSIONS

To meet this requirement, various sizes of sucker rods have been standardized by the API. These standardization tables, published in API Standard 11B, dated May, 1957, are as shown in Tables 8-1 and 8-2 and Figs. 8-1 and 8-2.

Table 8-1. General Dimensions and Tolerances for Sucker Rods and Pony Rods

All dimensions in inches except rod lengths which are in feet. See Fig. 8-1

1	2	3	4	5	6	7	8	9	10
Size of rod	Nominal diam of pin	OD of pin shoulder and box D_f	Width of wrench square ± 1/32 W_s	Length of wrench square* W_l	Diam of bead D_u	Total length of rod box, min L_b	Length of box-and-pin rod† ± 2.0 in.	Length of pin-and-pin rod‡ ± 2.0 in.	Length of box-and-pin and pin-and-pin pony rods†‡ ± 2.0 in.
5/8	15/16	1.375 ± 0.015	7/8	1¼	Not to exceed D_f	2⅛	25	25, 30	1⅓, 2, 3, 4, 6, 8, 10, 12
¾	1 1/16	1.500 ± 0.015	1	1¼		2⅜	25	25, 30	1⅓, 2, 3, 4, 6, 8, 10, 12
⅞	1 3/16	1.625 + 0.005 −0.010	1	1¼		2⅜	...	25, 30	1⅓, 2, 3, 4, 6, 8, 10, 12
1	1⅜	2.000 + 0.005 − 0.010	1 5/16	1½		3	...	25, 30	1⅓, 2, 3, 4, 6, 8, 10, 12
1⅛	1 9/16	2.250 ± 0.015	1½	1⅝		3¼	...	25, 30	1⅓, 2, 3, 4, 6, 8, 10, 12

* Minimum length exclusive of fillet.
† The length of box-and-pin rods shall be measured from contact face of pin shoulder to contact face of box.
‡ The length of pin-and-pin rods shall be measured from contact face of pin shoulder to contact face on the field end of the coupling.

PRODUCTION EQUIPMENT

Table 8-2. Standard Couplings and Subcouplings
All dimensions in inches. See Fig. 8-2

1	2	3	4	5	6	7
	OD*		Length, min		Length† of wrench flat W_l	Distance between wrench flats, $+0, -\frac{1}{32}$ W_f
Rod size, also nominal size of coupling	Standard W	Alternative W	Standard coupling N_L	Sub-coupling N_L		
⅝	1½	....	4	Optional	1¼	1⅜
¾	1⅝	....	4	with	1¼	1½
⅞	1¹³⁄₁₆	1⅝‡	4	the	1¼‡	1⅝‡
1	2³⁄₁₆ §	2§	4	manu-	1½	1⅞
1⅛	2⅜ ¶	....	4½	facturer	1⅝	2⅛

* The outside diameter for type I subcouplings shall conform to the outside diameter stipulated for the larger connection. The outside diameter for type II subcouplings shall conform to the W dimension given in Table 8-2 except, when the pin connection is larger than the box connection the outside diameter shall conform to the pin-shoulder diameter D_f specified in Table 8-1.

† Minimum length, exclusive of fillets.

‡ Alternative couplings with an OD of 1⅝ in. are intended for use with ⅞ in. sucker rods in 2⅜ in. OD, 4.70 lb external-upset tubing. These couplings shall have no wrench flats. The OD of these couplings shall be subject to a tolerance of +0.005 in., −0.010 in.

§ The standard outside diameter of 1-in. couplings is intended for use in tubing 3½ in. OD and larger. The alternate outside diameter is intended for use in tubing 2⅞ in. OD.

¶ Couplings for 1⅛-in. rods are intended for use in tubing 3½ in. OD and larger.

In addition to the above sizes of rods, there are presently being manufactured hollow sucker rods and a ½-in.-diameter sucker rod. These are, by nature, for special application, and the demand is limited.

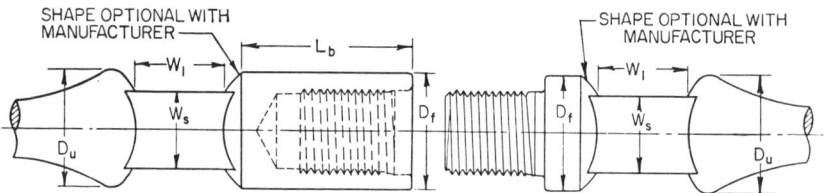

Fig. 8-1. General dimensions for sucker-rod box and pin ends. See Table 8-1.

HOLLOW SUCKER RODS

One type of hollow sucker rod was developed primarily so that various fluids can be injected down through the center of the rods for such purposes as paraffin treatment, chemical inhibitor treatment, and diluent injection for heavy crudes. They are presently manufactured in two sizes: ⅞ in. OD by ⅜ in. ID with 1³⁄₁₆-in.-diameter pin or 1 in. OD by ½ in. ID with 1³⁄₁₆-in.-diameter pin. The net weights (see Table 8-3) are closely related to ¾-in. solid rods in the former and ⅞-in. solid rods in the latter case. The load limitations are practically the same as that of a ¾-in. solid sucker rod.

Another more recent type of hollow sucker rod has been developed for producing relatively large quantities of fluid through their centers in tubingless well completions. These rods are made from standard seamless tubing with a sucker-rod pin and shoulder integrally forged on each end. They are currently manufactured in two sizes: 1.050 in. OD by ¾ in. ID with 1³⁄₁₆-in.-diameter pins and 1.315 in. OD by 1 in. ID with 1⅜-in.- diameter pins. The load limitations of the ¾- and 1-in. (ID) hollow rods are equivalent to the ⅝- and ¾-in. solid rods, respectively.

½-IN.-DIAMETER SUCKER ROD

One-half-inch-diameter sucker rods are presently manufactured in 25-ft lengths, with 1 in. OD couplings. This rod was developed for completions where the pump is set in $1\frac{1}{4}$-in. ID tubing and includes either single- or multiple-zone completions. These rods are designed to lift limited amounts of fluids from moderate to shallow depths.

COUPLING OD VS. TUBING

Most manufacturers have for years offered alternate coupling ODs, available on special order. These are, for the most part, not listed in API Standard 11B, because it is the primary function of the API to assure interchangeability of product and not to serve as a listing of all available joint combinations.

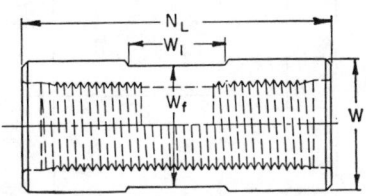

Fig. 8-2. Standard couplings and subcouplings. See Table 8-2. (*Reproduced, by permission, from API Standard 11B: Specification for Sucker Rods.*)

To summarize what is available dimensionally in sucker rods, we may say that sucker rods are now available in either 25- or 30-ft lengths, in double pin or in box and pin ($\frac{5}{8}$ in. only), in diameter from $\frac{1}{2}$ to $1\frac{1}{8}$ in. and with the coupling ODs in Table 8-3, either casehardened, through-hardened, or nonhardened.

Table 8-3. Generally Available Sucker-rod Couplings

Rod size, in.	OD coupling, in.	For rod-pin size, in.	For min tubing size, in.	Wt rods and couplings lb/100 ft
$\frac{1}{2}$	1*	$\frac{3}{4}$	$1\frac{1}{4}$ nom.	72
$\frac{5}{8}$	$1\frac{1}{4}$*	$1\frac{5}{16}$	$1\frac{1}{2}$ nom.	115
$\frac{5}{8}$	$1\frac{1}{2}$	$1\frac{5}{16}$	$2\frac{1}{16}$ OD	115
$\frac{3}{4}$	$1\frac{1}{2}$	$1\frac{1}{16}$	$2\frac{1}{16}$ OD	164
$\frac{3}{4}$	$1\frac{5}{8}$	$1\frac{1}{16}$	$2\frac{3}{8}$ OD	164
$\frac{3}{4}$	$1\frac{13}{16}$	$1\frac{1}{16}$	$2\frac{7}{8}$ OD	164
$\frac{7}{8}$	$1\frac{5}{8}$*	$1\frac{3}{16}$	$2\frac{3}{8}$ OD	220
$\frac{7}{8}$	$1\frac{13}{16}$	$1\frac{3}{16}$	$2\frac{7}{8}$ OD	220
$\frac{7}{8}$	2	$1\frac{3}{16}$	$2\frac{7}{8}$ OD	220
1	2	$1\frac{3}{8}$	$2\frac{7}{8}$ OD	288
1	$2\frac{3}{16}$	$1\frac{3}{8}$	$3\frac{1}{2}$ OD	288
$1\frac{1}{8}$	$2\frac{3}{8}$	$1\frac{9}{16}$	$3\frac{1}{2}$ OD	368
$\frac{7}{8}$	$1\frac{13}{16}$	$1\frac{3}{16}$	$2\frac{7}{8}$ OD	173
1	$1\frac{13}{16}$	$1\frac{3}{16}$	$2\frac{7}{8}$ OD	209

* Without wrench flats.

AVAILABLE ROD TYPES

Because of dimensional limitations imposed by the tubing and corrosive effects of produced well fluids, a second requirement makes itself apparent: alloy content to provide strength and/or corrosion resistance.

To meet this need, sucker rods are presently manufactured from several different alloy classes. Originally, alloying elements were widely used to combat the severe effect of corrosive fluids, but it is difficult to fit alloying elements to an individual well condition.

It is a known fact that corrosivity of produced well fluids may vary greatly not only from well to well producing from the same formation on the same lease, but from time to time in the same well.

Although alloy content is still considered important in selection of type of rod to be used, a great deal of emphasis has been placed on chemical-inhibitor treatment to protect the rods, tubing, and pump from corrosive attack. Of course, no inhibitor

Table 8-4. Compilation of Published Data on Sucker Rods

General group classification	Manufacturer	Grade of rod	AISI specification	C	Mn	P	S	Si	Ni	Cr	Mo	V	Cu	B
								Chemical properties						
Carbon manganese	Axelson	60	C 1036	.32/.36	1.35/1.50	.03 max	.035 max	.20/.30						
	Bethlehem	X-2	C 1036	.30/.37	1.20/1.50	.04 max	.05 max	.15/.30						
	Continental Emsco	No. 2 CM	C 1036	.30/.37	1.20/1.50	.04 max	.05 max	.15/.30						
	Jones	A	C 1036	.30/.37	1.20/1.50	.025 T	.025 T	.15/.30						
	Liberty (Texasteel)	40	C 1036	.30/.37	1.20/1.50	.04 max	.05 max	.15/.30						
	National	30	C 1036	.30/.37	1.20/1.50	.04 max	.05 max	.15/.30						
	Norris			.30/.37	1.20/1.50	.04 max	.05 max	.15/.30						
	Oilwell	N	C 1036	.30/.37	1.20/1.50	{.04 max / .016 T}	{.05 max / .028 T}	.15/.30						
Intermediate alloys	Bethlehem	X Mayari	Special	.32/.40	.50/.70	.04 max	.05 max	.15/.30	.50/.80	.30/.50	.08/.15			
	Jones	1	Special	.30/.37	.70/1.00	.04 max	.05 max	.20/.35	.70/1.00	.20/.40	.08/.15			
	National	62	Special	.33/.40	.55/.80	.04 max	.04 max	.20/.35	.50/.80	.30/.55	.15/.25			
	Norris	32	8627	.25/.30	.70/.90	.04 max	.04 max	.20/.35	.40/.70	.40/.60				
	Oilwell	L	Special	.31/.38	.60/.90	{.04 max / .015T}	{.04 max / .023T}	.20/.35	1.25/1.75	.60/.90				
Nickel molybdenum	Axelson	59	A 4621	.20/.23	.85/.95	.025 max	.030 max	.20/.30	1.75/1.85		.25/.30			
	Bethlehem	46	A 4621	.18/.23	.70/.90	.04 max	.04 max	.20/.35	1.65/2.00		.20/.30	.05 min		
	Continental-Emsco	5	A 4621 Mod.	.17/.23	.70/.90	.04 max	.04 max	.20/.35	1.65/2.00		.20/.30			
	Jones	7	A 4621	.18/.23	.70/.90	.025 T	.025 T	.20/.35	1.65/2.00		.20/.30			
	Liberty (Texasteel)	NM	A 4621	.18/.25	.70/.90	.04 max	.04 max	.20/.35	1.65/2.00		.20/.30			
	National	81	A 4621 Mod.	.18/.23	.80/1.10	.04 max	.04 max	.20/.35	1.65/2.00		.20/.30	.05		
	Norris	40	A 4621	.18/.23	.70/.90	.04 max	.04 max	.20/.35	1.65/2.00		.20/.30			
	Oilwell	T	A 4615	.13/.18	.45/.65	{.04 max / .016 T}	{.04 max / .020 T}	.20/.35	1.65/2.00		.20/.30			
3½% nickel	Continental-Emsco	Reliance	3310	.08/.13	.45/.60	.025 max	.025 max	.20/.35	3.25/3.75	1.40/1.75				
	National	92	E 3310	.07/.13	.30/.70	.025 max	.025 max	.20/.35	3.20/3.80	1.30/1.80				
High tensile	Axelson	77	Special	.21/.24	1.10/1.20	.025 max	.030 max	.20/.30	1.75/1.85	.70/.90	.25/.30			
	Bethlehem	43	A 4337	.35/.40	.60/.80	.04 max	.04 max	.20/.30	1.65/2.00	.80/1.05	.20/.30			
	Continental-Emsco	Hi-Ten	Special	.13/.18	.90/1.20	.025 max	.025 max	.55/.85	.90/1.20	.70/1.00	.20/.30	.05 min		
	Jones	8	Special	.22/.28	.70/1.00	.04 max	.04 max	.20/.30	1.20/1.50	.80/1.00	.20/.30			
	Liberty (Texasteel)	HT	Special	.39 T	.70 T	.025 T	.025 T	.26 T	1.80 T		.25 T			
	National	85	A 4340	.37/.44	.60/.95	.025 max	.025 max	.20/.35	1.55/2.00	.65/.95	.20/.30		.40/.60	
	Norris	75	A 4340	.38/.43	.60/.80	.04 max	.04 max	.20/.35	1.65/2.00	.70/.90	.20/.30		.40/.70	
	Oilwell	Y	80 B 20	.17/.23	.60/.90	{.04 max / .017 T}	{.04 max / .024 T}	.20/.35	.20/.40	.15/.35	.08/.15			.0005 min

Mod. = modified; max = maximum; min = minimum; avg = average; T = typical.

Table 8-4. Compilation of Published Data on Sucker Rods (Continued)

General group classification	Mechanical properties							Heat-treatment (all heat-treatment operations apply to entire length of rod)	Source of information
	Yield point, psi	Tensile strength, psi	Elong. in 2 in., %	Elong. in 8 in., %	Red. in area, %	Izod impact, ft-lb	Brinell hardness		
Carbon manganese	65,000/72,000	90,000/105,000	30 min	19/24	60/67	70/90	183/207	Normalized	Comp. Data Sheet 4/1/58
	65,000 min 72,000 avg	93,000 min 100,000 avg	37 avg		55 min 60 avg	70 min	192 min 207 avg	Normalized	
	60,000/75,000	90,000/105,000	40/30	25/18	66/55	90/60	180/210	Normalized	Comp. Data Sheet 7/1/58
	60,000/75,000	90,000/105,000	30/45	18/24	60/70	60/90	160/210	Normalized	Comp. Data Sheet 1/1/57
	65,000 min	90,000 min		16 min	55 min	65 min	180 min	Normalized	Data Sheet 11/14/58
	70,000 avg	95,000 avg		19 avg	60 avg	60/85	192 avg	Normalized	Bull 486, Copyright 1959
	60,000/70,000 65,000/75,000	90,000/100,000 95,000/105,000	30/40	15/23 18/23	50/65 50/65	60/90 60/90	180/205 190/205	Normalized	Comp. Data Sheet 4/23/58
	60,000/75,000	90,000/105,000	28/35		53/68	77 T	185 T	Normalized	Booklet ADOWS, 4/58
Intermediate alloys	60,000 min 65,000 avg	88,000 min 95,000 avg	32 min 35 avg		50 min 60 avg	50 min 55/75	174 min 192 avg	Normalized	Comp. Data Sheet 1/1/57
	65,000/75,000]	95,000/105,000	25/40	14/20	50 T	55 T	195/220	Normalized and tempered	Bull 486, Copyright 1959
	60,000 T 60,000/70,000	90,000 T 85,000/95,000	32 T	18/23	55/70	65/90 65 min	173 T 174/202	Normalized and tempered Normalized and tempered	Comp. Data Sheet 4/23/58
	65,000/90,000	95,000/110,000	25/30		55/65	76 T	207 T	Normalized and tempered	Booklet ADOWS, 4/58
Nickel molybdenum	70,000/78,000	87,000/95,000		18.5/22	65/70	90/105	187/207	Normalized and tempered	Comp. Data Sheet 4/1/58
	67,000 min 75,000 avg	82,000 min 90,000 avg	35 min 38 avg		63 avg 68 avg	90 min	170 min 187 avg	Normalized and tempered	
	71,000/92,000	88,000/113,000	45/32	25/16	70/60	105/85	176/220	Normalized and drawn	Comp. Data Sheet 7/1/58
	65,000/80,000	85,000/100,000	30/45	14/22	60/70	90/107	170/210	Normalized and tempered	Comp. Data Sheet 1/1/57
	68,000 min	87,000 min		18 min	60 min	85 min	179 min	Normalized and tempered	Data Sheet 11/14/58
	73,000 min	93,000 min		21 avg	65 avg	85/105	187 avg	Normalized and tempered	Bull 486, Copyright 1959
	75,000/85,000 65,000/75,000	95,000/105,000 82,000/95,000	30/40	15/25 18/25	60/72	90/105	180/205 185/205	Normalized and tempered	Comp. Data Sheet 4/23/58
	73,000/97,000	85,000/105,000	22/32		70/80	100T	196 T	Liquid quenched and tempered	Booklet ADOWS, 4/58
3½% nickel	90,000/105,000	115,000/130,000	35/25	16/12	66/55	100/75	230/260	Normalized and drawn	Comp. Data Sheet 7/1/58
	90,000 T	115,000 T	25 T	12 T	50 T	85 T	230 T	. . . .	Bull 486, Copyright 1959
High tensile	100,000/115,000	120,000/130,000		13/14.5	60/67	70/90	250/275	Normalized and tempered	Comp. Data Sheet 4/1/58
	100,000 min 110,000 min	120,000 min 130,000 min	24 min 30 avg		55 min 60 avg		241 min 262 avg	Normalized and tempered	Comp. Data Sheet 7/1/58
	95,000/110,000	115,000/135,000	36/26	16/12	63/50	90/65	230/260	Normalized and drawn	Comp. Data Sheet 1/1/57
	100,000/115,000	120,000/135,000	20/30	10/15	50/60	65/85	240/260	Normalized and tempered	Data Sheet 11/14/58
	105,000 T 105,000 T	120,000 T 133,000 T	26 T	13 T 13 T	50 T 50 T	75 T 50 T	250 T 277 T	Normalized and tempered Normalized and tempered	Bull 486, Copyright 1959
	105,000/120,000	125,000/140,000		10/15	50/60	65/95 75 min	260/285	Normalized and tempered	Comp. Data Sheet 4/23/58
	95,000/108,000	105,000/115,000	22/29		68/73	83 T	235 T	Liquid quenched and tempered	Booklet ADOWS, 4/58

8-5

provides 100 per cent protection and, in some instances, this necessitates selection of a rod whose alloy content will help to counteract the degree of ineffectiveness of the inhibitor, or to compensate for changes in the nature of the well fluid itself. On the other hand, in many instances the effectiveness of an inhibitor is sufficiently complete to justify the choice of a rod based only on its strength characteristics. There is a growing conviction in some quarters that the use of chemical inhibitors for corrosion control has largely eliminated the need for alloy sucker rods except for certain special cases. The whole problem of corrosion is one of economics, and many volumes have been published covering the subject. Basically, as applied to the sucker rod, it is just this simple. Complete corrosion resistance can be built into a sucker rod by the use of special materials such as K monel but the cost is prohibitive. The oil producer cannot economically justify these materials, and so a more reasonably priced sucker rod must be offered at the sacrifice of built-in corrosion resistance.

Table 8-4 summarizes the general classifications of sucker rods by types as presently manufactured.

Approximately 80 per cent of the rods now sold fall in either the C1036 or A4621 class.

Deeper pumping problems have created a need for higher-strength rods. This has been accomplished by combinations of alloying elements resulting in balanced mechanical properties which provide both strength and good service.

SUCKER-ROD STRING DESIGN

Although the sucker-rod string is an undefined vibratory system, experience and correlation with dynamometer studies have allowed tabulations from which well loads may be calculated and pumping equipment selected.

In the most economical selection of pumping equipment, each component, such as plunger diameter, rod string, unit, and prime mover, should be matched in size. The smallest plunger diameter that will produce the desired volume of fluid at a reasonable pumping speed should be chosen, for the weight of fluid it lifts determines rod-string design, unit-beam strength, gearbox torque rating, and prime-mover horsepower.

PUMP SELECTION

Chapter 7 covers completely the available pump types and factors to consider in selecting the proper type of pump and plunger diameter. Using the various tables

Table 8-5. Pump Constants

Plunger size, in.	Constant K	Plunger size, in.	Constant K
$\frac{5}{8}$	0.046	$1\frac{15}{16}$	0.438
$\frac{3}{4}$	0.066	2	0.466
$\frac{7}{8}$	0.089	$2\frac{1}{4}$	0.590
1	0.117	$2\frac{1}{2}$	0.729
$1\frac{1}{16}$	0.132	$2\frac{3}{4}$	0.881
$1\frac{1}{4}$	0.182	3	1.049
$1\frac{7}{16}$	0.241	$3\frac{1}{4}$	1.231
$1\frac{1}{2}$	0.262	$3\frac{3}{4}$	1.639
$1\frac{3}{4}$	0.357	$4\frac{1}{4}$	2.106
$1\frac{25}{32}$	0.370	$4\frac{3}{4}$	2.630

and formulas starting on page 7–17 which cover rod and tubing stretch, plunger over-travel, and fluid-gravity corrections, the proper plunger diameter to produce the desired volume of fluid may be selected.

In addition to the curves shown in Fig. 7-14 on page 7–18, the pump constants in Table 8-5 are given to allow a more complete coverage of determination of plunger displacement.   The values of D_1 may be calculated by multiplying the calculated net plunger stroke by the pump constant K for the plunger diameter used.

PRACTICAL PUMPING SPEEDS

Maximum sucker-rod life comes from minimum pumping speeds because maximum load, range of load, and pumping speeds are directly proportional.   Choose as long a stroke and slow a speed as the unit and prime mover will allow to make the desired production.

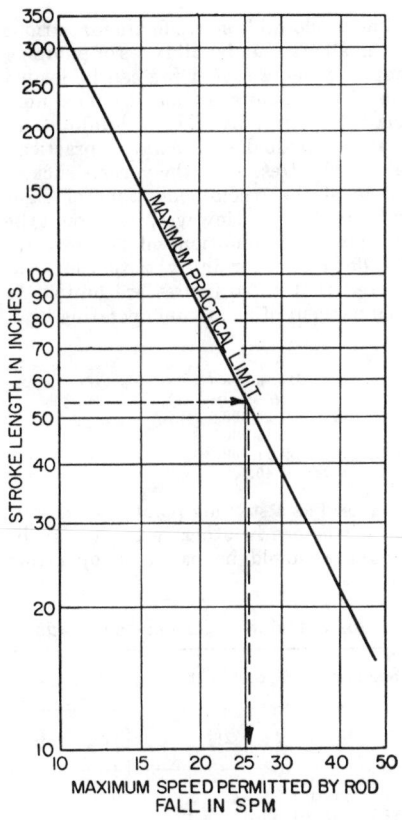

FIG. 8-3. Permissible speed and stroke based on 70 per cent of maximum free fall limit. Example: For a 54-in. stroke 26 spm is a maximum.

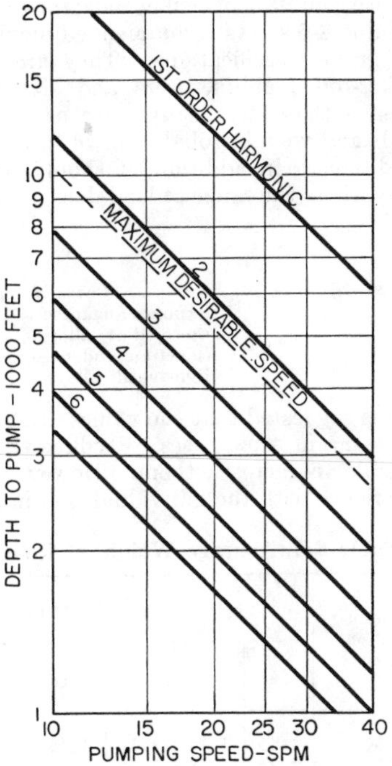

FIG. 8-4. Synchronous-speed curves.

A reasonable speed was previously mentioned.   Always choose a speed below that maximum practical limit permitted by free-rod fall so the polished-rod clamp and hanger bar will not separate on the downstroke.

The product of speed and stroke giving 2,000 in./min is the maximum rate.   Seventy per cent of this is the maximum desirable.   Vibratory problems also place a depth limit on pumping speeds.   Dynamometer studies and experience will check the influence of synchronous pumping speeds.   In the author's experience, it is very difficult to determine any detrimental effect of harmonics, by either experience or dynamometer study. It is recognized that the general shape of the dynamometer card is determined by the order of harmonic near which the pumping motion is operating. Operating on a harmonic speed may improve plunger travel and pump efficiency provided the rod string is not overloaded. Most wells do not exhibit abnormally high loads at harmonic speeds, but there are some exceptions and the effects of harmonic speeds should be checked with a dynamometer if possible. In Fig. 8-4, stay below the maximum limit. Synchronous speeds are the numbered solid lines, in order of harmonic.

ALLOWABLE ROD LOADS

It is difficult to recommend a universal maximum allowable stress figure for various grades of sucker rods which would be applicable in all areas under all types of pumping conditions. Many factors influence the extent to which a sucker rod can be loaded and still give satisfactory service life. Some of the factors influencing maximum allowable loadings are corrosion and its relative control by chemical inhibition; surface condition of sucker rods; range of load; and individual well-operating practices.

Table 8-6 shows recommended maximum allowable stresses for the various sucker-rod grade classifications. They are an average of the recommendations of eight sucker-rod manufacturers and six major oil operators. However, it should be stressed that these figures are based on ideal pumping conditions in noncorrosive fluids and would probably have to be adjusted downward for any variation in these conditions. In addition, it should be considered that these figures are limited to cases where the range of load does not exceed 60 per cent of maximum operating load.

Table 8-6

Grade of rod	Max allowable stress, psi
Carbon manganese (C1036)	28,000
Intermediate alloys	30,000
Nickel molybdenum alloys (A4621)	31,400
High-tensile alloys	40,300

It is suggested that the values in Table 8-6 be used as a starting point. It may be necessary in some cases to reduce these figures, whereas in other cases, it may be possible to increase them. However, any changes should be based on operating experience with the individual well in question.

Table 8-7. Average Weight of Rods per Foot for Calculating Sucker-rod Loads

Combination of rods	Diam plunger, in., and avg wt. of rods, lb/ft											
	5⁄8	3⁄4	1	1 1⁄16	1 1⁄4	1 1⁄2	1 3⁄4	2	2 1⁄4	2 1⁄2	2 3⁄4	3 3⁄4
5⁄8	1.15	1.15	1.15	1.15	1.15	1.15	1.15	1.15				
3⁄4-5⁄8	1.28	1.29	1.30	1.31	1.32	1.34	1.37	1.40				
3⁄4	1.64	1.64	1.64	1.64	1.64	1.64	1.64	1.64	1.64	1.64	1.64	
7⁄8-3⁄4	1.76	1.77	1.78	1.79	1.80	1.81	1.83	1.86	1.88	1.91	1.95	
7⁄8-3⁄4-5⁄8	1.46	1.47	1.50	1.52	1.55	1.61	1.68	1.75				
7⁄8	2.20	2.20	2.20	2.20	2.20	2.20	2.20	2.20	2.20	2.20	2.20	2.20
1-7⁄8-3⁄4	1.96	1.97	2.00	2.00	2.03	2.07	2.12	2.18	2.24	2.32		
1-7⁄8-3⁄4-5⁄8	1.67	1.70	1.76	1.78	1.84	1.93	2.04					
1-7⁄8	2.34	2.34	2.35	2.35	2.36	2.37	2.39	2.41	2.43	2.46	2.48	2.61
1	2.88	2.88	2.88	2.88	2.88	2.88	2.88	2.88	2.88	2.88	2.88	2.88
1 1⁄8-1-7⁄8-3⁄4	2.20	2.21	2.26	2.27	2.32	2.39	2.48	2.58	2.68			

MAXIMUM ROD LOADS

By use of the following formula, a reasonable estimate of the maximum well load may be obtained for average conditions:

$$P = W_r \left(1 + \frac{LN^2}{70,500}\right) + W_o$$

where P = maximum polished-rod load
  W_o = weight of fluid based on net plunger area and 1.0 sp gr
  W_r = weight of rods
  L = polished-rod stroke, in.
  N = strokes/min

By utilizing Tables 8-7, 8-8, and 8-9 and the above formula, the maximum well load may be calculated.

Table 8-8. Impulse Factor for Calculating Sucker-rod Loads

Strokes /min	Length of stroke, in.														
	12	18	24	34	44	54	64	74	84	96	108	120	144	180	240
2															1.014
4					1.010	1.012	1.014	1.016	1.018	1.021	1.024	1.026	1.032	1.040	1.053
6			1.012	1.017	1.022	1.028	1.033	1.038	1.043	1.049	1.055	1.061	1.073	1.092	1.122
8	1.011	1.016	1.022	1.031	1.040	1.049	1.058	1.067	1.076	1.087	1.098	1.109	1.131	1.164	1.218
10	1.017	1.026	1.034	1.048	1.062	1.077	1.091	1.105	1.119	1.136	1.153	1.170	1.204	1.256	1.341
12	1.025	1.037	1.049	1.069	1.090	1.110	1.131	1.151	1.171	1.196	1.220	1.245	1.294	1.367	1.490
14	1.033	1.050	1.067	1.095	1.122	1.150	1.178	1.206	1.234	1.267	1.300	1.334	1.400	1.500	1.667
16	1.044	1.065	1.087	1.123	1.160	1.196	1.232	1.269	1.305	1.348	1.392	1.436	1.523	1.653	
18	1.055	1.083	1.110	1.156	1.202	1.248	1.294	1.340	1.386	1.442	1.497	1.552	1.662		
20	1.068	1.102	1.136	1.193	1.249	1.306	1.363	1.420	1.476	1.544	1.612	1.680			
22	1.082	1.124	1.164	1.234	1.302	1.371	1.440	1.508	1.577	1.660	1.742				
24	1.098	1.147	1.196	1.278	1.359	1.441	1.523	1.605	1.686						
26	1.115	1.173	1.230	1.326	1.422	1.518	1.614	1.710							
28	1.133	1.200	1.266	1.377	1.488	1.599	1.710								
30	1.154	1.230	1.307	1.435	1.563	1.691									
32	1.174	1.261	1.348	1.493	1.638										
34	1.197	1.295	1.394	1.558	1.722										
36	1.221	1.331	1.442	1.626											
38	1.246	1.369	1.492	1.697											
40	1.272	1.409	1.545	1.772											

To find polished-rod load: Multiply weight of rods per foot (Table 8-7) by length of rod string by impulse factor (Table 8-8), and add weight per foot of fluid (Table 8-9) times depth to pump times specific gravity of fluid.

Table 8-9. Weight of Fluid per Foot 0.434 psi/ft, 1.00 sp gr for Calculating Sucker-rod Loads

Combination of rods	Diam plunger, in., and fluid load, lb/ft (sp gr = 1)											
	⅝	¾	1	1¹⁄₁₆	1¼	1½	1¾	2	2¼	2½	2¾	3¾
⅝	0.000	0.059	0.207	0.251	0.399	0.634	0.911	1.230				
¾-⅝	0.000	0.042	0.189	0.233	0.379	0.611	0.884	1.200				
¾	0.000	0.000	0.149	0.193	0.341	0.575	0.852	1.172	1.534	1.939	2.386	
⅞-¾	0.000	0.000	0.131	0.175	0.321	0.553	0.828	1.145	1.504	1.905	2.348	
⅞-¾-⅝	0.000	0.020	0.164	0.207	0.351	0.578	0.847	1.157				
⅞	0.000	0.000	0.080	0.124	0.272	0.506	0.783	1.103	1.465	1.870	2.317	4.533
1-⅞-¾	0.000	0.000	0.105	0.153	0.293	0.523	0.794	1.106	1.460	1.875		
1-⅞-¾-⅝	0.000	0.000	0.134	0.176	0.316	0.540	0.803					
1-⅞	0.000	0.000	0.063	0.106	0.253	0.486	0.760	1.078	1.438	1.840	2.284	4.485
1	0.000	0.000	0.000	0.044	0.192	0.426	0.703	1.023	1.385	1.790	2.230	4.453
1⅛-1-⅞-¾	0.000	0.000	0.075	0.118	0.260	0.485	0.752	1.059	1.409			

TAPERED STRINGS

Generally the smallest rod diameter that meets the load requirement is the most economical. However, should larger rods be indicated, always taper the string. Experience must temper this selection, as it is sometimes undesirable to use small-diameter rods in a long tapered string in large tubing. In some cases, high pumping speeds and abnormal pumping conditions require large-diameter rods all the way for down-hole strength and resistance to flexing. This is particularly true in the case of casing pumps and double-displacement-type pumps.

Table 8-10 for tapered-rod-string design shows the proper proportions of various sizes corresponding to the pump size being used.

Table 8-10. Tapered Sucker-rod Strings

Plunger diam, in.	¾-⅝ in.	⅞-¾ in.	⅞-¾-⅝ in.		1-⅞-¾ in.		1-⅞-¾-⅝ in.		1-⅞ in.		1⅛-1-⅞-¾ in.		
	% ¾ in. needed	% ⅞ in. needed	% ⅞ in. needed	% ¾ in. needed	% 1 in. needed	% ⅞ in. needed	% 1 in. needed	% ⅞ in. needed	% ¾ in. needed	% 1 in. needed	% 1⅛ in. needed	% 1 in. needed	% ⅞ in. needed
⅝	26.4												
¾	27.6	23.6	20.0	22.8	17.5	19.9	15.4	17.4	47.4		13.8	15.4	17.4
1	30.7	25.5	22.2	25.4	19.0	21.5	17.1	19.3	22.0		14.9	16.7	18.8
1 1/16	31.6	26.1	22.9	26.1	19.4	22.0	17.6	19.9	22.6				
1¼	34.6	28.0	25.1	28.6	20.8	23.6	19.3	21.8	24.8		16.3	18.3	20.7
1½	39.4	31.0	28.6	32.6	23.1	26.1	22.0	24.8	28.3		18.1	20.2	22.9
1¾	45.1	34.6	32.7	37.3	25.7	29.2	25.1	28.5	32.3	28.0	20.1	22.6	25.6
2	51.6	38.7	37.5	42.7	28.8	32.6				30.8	22.5	25.3	28.6
2¼		43.4			32.2	36.6				33.9	25.2	28.3	32.1
2½		48.6			36.1	41.0				37.4			
2¾		54.4								41.2			
3¾										60.3			

Blank spaces indicate plunger sizes not recommended.

MINIMUM DOWNSTROKE LOAD

Range of load, being the only undetermined factor of the three controlling sucker-rod life, should now be calculated. Assuming the simple harmonic motion and by subtracting the same acceleration factor that was applied on the upstroke and the buoyant force on the rods, a rough approximation of minimum downstroke load may be made. The formula is as follows:

$$\text{Min downstroke load} = W_r\left(0.8725 - \frac{LN^2}{70{,}500}\right)$$

where $LN^2/70{,}500$ may be calculated or obtained by subtracting 1 from the impulse factor in Table 8-8.

The difference between the maximum well load and the minimum downstroke load is the range of load.

EFFECTS OF MAXIMUM LOADS, MINIMUM LOADS, AND SPEED

The three controlling factors in sucker-rod life, related as they are, must be defined by limits to make all the foregoing calculations worthwhile. Figures 8-3 and 8-4 give maximum pumping speed, and the user is cautioned to select as slow a speed as is consistent with production volumes required and unit and prime-mover capacities.

Maximum load and range of load are inseparable in application although maximum-working-load values are based on average conditions and experience, which take into account an average amount of load range.

GOODMAN'S DIAGRAM

Goodman's diagram, seen in Fig. 8-5, illustrates that the greater the stress range, the lower the allowable maximum load. Many attempts have been made, dating back many years, to fit rod life into the Goodman diagram, with little success. As a guide, it is here offered for consideration but not as a reliable rating criterion, for comparison with calculated maximum loads and range of loads.

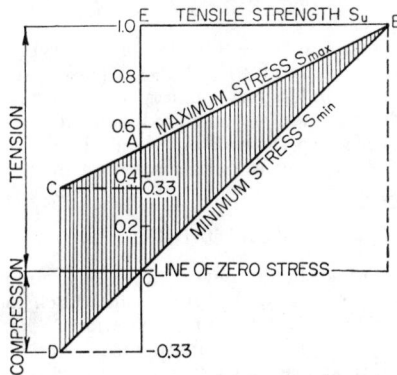

FIG. 8-5. Comparison of experimental results with Goodman's diagram. Tests were made by axial loading. The diagram is meant to show a trend only. As the maximum stress increases, the permissible range of stress must decrease. (*From Summary of Present-day Knowledge of Fatigue Phenomena in Metals, ASTM Fatigue Research Committee, Proc. ASTM, vol. 30, 1930.*)

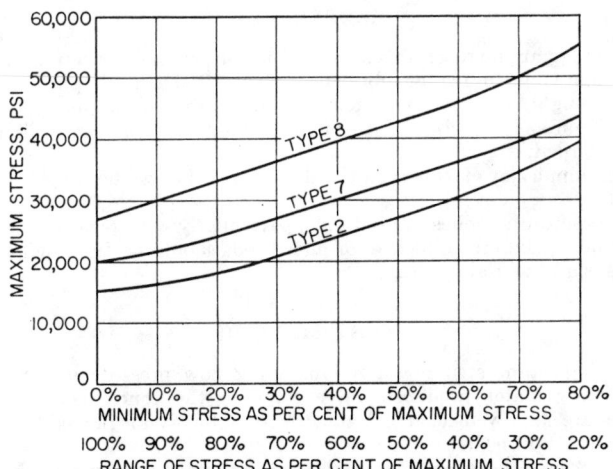

FIG. 8-6. Jones sucker rods. Recommended maximum stress based on range of stress. This chart is the result of a composite study of endurance tests and Goodman diagrams with safety-factor modifiers applied on the basis of field experience. Coordinate points are to be used for reference only and are not to be regarded as limiting or guaranteed.

CARE AND HANDLING

Sucker rods have been defined dimensionally and by composition so that the user may choose the size and type to fit his particular well problem.

Before these rods are run in his well, considerable care must be exercised by all concerned to assure that they reach the well site in the same condition they left the factory.

Many man-hours go into each quality sucker rod in the form of straightening, perfect forging, 100 per cent controlled heat-treatment, shot blasting, precision threading, painting, and complete inspection.

All this can be nullified by improper transportation, unloading, or poor joint-make-up practices.

TRANSPORTATION

Rods should be transported to the well site on a float-type bed at least 24 ft long, with each layer separated by wood strips. With packaged rods, layers should be stacked so that the bottom binders rest squarely on the top binders of the next lower package. The entire load should be anchored down to prevent shifting and the binder chains should never touch the rods but should be placed in such position as to pass over the ends of the extended wooden spacers or, in the case of packaged rods, the wooden binders.

UNLOADING

When unloading, the rods should never under any circumstances be dragged, kicked, shoved, thrown, or rolled off the truck bed. Each rod should be supported by a man on each end during all handing operations. Packaged rods should be unloaded with a properly designed handling device. These rods should be racked either on portable racks or at least on timbers heavy enough to keep them off the ground. The thread protectors may be loosened on the racks at the wellhead just prior to running but should remain in place until the rod is hanging in the derrick or to the mast, being removed just prior to making the connection. This lessens the chance of dirt's getting into the joint.

INSPECTION

Although the manufacturer takes every precaution in lubricating threads, it is possible through long storage for lubricant to dry. If this has happened, pin threads should be thoroughly cleaned and a good zinc-base lubricant applied.

Starting of joints is important. Any joint that binds or galls and will not shoulder should be discarded.

Faulty bell nipples or elevators can kink rods just below the upset. Check these periodically.

The same procedure applies to used rods, particularly with regard to joint cleaning and lubrication. All kinked, nicked, or pitted rods should be discarded at this point, for each one is a potential failure.

JOINT MAKE-UP

The most important step in all rod handling now presents itself: proper joint make-up. Many major producers have come to the conclusion that sucker-rod joint failures are largely mechanical and that practically all pin failures are due to insufficient make-up torque.

Many papers have been written on this subject, but in summary, the problem is to apply enough preload to the joint to prevent separation of pin-shoulder and coupling-shoulder faces by subsequent applied loads. Any separation of pin- and coupling-shoulder faces allows the pin to bend in the notch-sensitive thread areas and fatigue failures will result.

Experimentation and calculations show that even in a joint adequately preloaded to prevent face separation under load, 40 to 50 per cent of the applied load is added on every stroke to the already existing pin load. This indicates that the joint should not be preloaded to yield. By the same token, since the same applied pumping load may exert loosening effects, a minimum value of preload that will prevent face separation should be exceeded.

API recommended practices include the following suggested torque values:

Rod size, in.	35,000 psi rod stress, ft-lb	Over 35,000 psi rod stress
½	110	
⅝	220	
¾	350	Add 10% to the
⅞	520	adjacent values
1	800	
1⅛	1,100	

In most cases where joint failures are being experienced, it is advisable to use power sucker-rod wrenches for joint make-up to assure uniformity of applied torque.

Chalk marking of a spun-in joint is a good alternate procedure. Three or four snaps with a snap rod wrench of proper weight and handle length will usually move the chalk marks approximately ¼ in. apart and will provide adequate joint make-up. High-strength rods require more wrenching to overcome generally higher applied pumping loads.

Hammering of couplings to loosen a tight joint may cause coupling failures. At the very least, it damages the hardened outer case and may distort the coupling enough to carry through to the threads. In this case, the metal is yielded and work-hardened, and a fatigue-prone area is set up. When it becomes absolutely necessary to hammer a coupling in order to loosen a joint, the hammered coupling should be discarded and replaced with a new one.

ALLOWABLE STRETCH

Stressing a sucker rod beyond its yield point results in damage from permanent deformation. In attempting to pull a stuck pump, the chart in Fig. 8-7 will show the

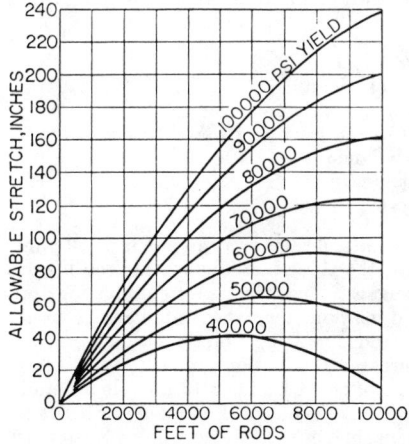

Fig. 8-7. Allowable static rod stretch in pulling stuck pumps.

maximum amount a rod string may be stretched without exceeding the minimum yield point. The graph is applicable to either straight or tapered strings.

Knowing the minimum specified yield point of the particular type of rod and the length of the string, the allowable stretch can be easily obtained from the graph.

The values shown apply only when the load on the top rod before starting the pull does not exceed the dead weight of the rods alone.

The diameter of the rod does not matter, inasmuch as we are dealing with stresses.

DYNAMOMETERS AND WELL STUDIES

Devices for studying the behavior of pumping wells have been used for many years, starting with hydraulic, electrical, and mechanical extensiometer load-measuring instruments, and more recently by the compression-ring type as exemplified by the Johnson-Fagg dynamometer. Subsurface measurements have also been taken with electrical strain gauges and bottom-hole dynagraphs.

Attempts to correlate all the above data have never been too successful, and at present there is further research being done with a mechanical system instrumented to simulate the complete sucker-rod pumping system.

The polished-rod dynamometer measures the summation of all forces acting on the polished rod at any instant during the stroke, coming from either surface or subsurface.

In spite of the difficulty in separating these forces, which makes actual interpretation of the dynamometer card shape a real problem, the dynamometer is an excellent tool for studying the behavior of a pumping well.

It is most impractical to try to catalog dynamometer cards by shape, for the effect of any condition may be masked by the combined effects of all the other factors contributing to the shape of the card. These factors are:

1. Weight of rods and fluid
2. Acceleration factors—up and down stroke
3. Frictional forces—rods, tubing, and fluids
4. Harmonics or vibratory action of rod string
5. Unit geometry—including counterbalance
6. Prime-mover impulses
7. Well conditions—such as fluid pound, gas lock, sanded pump, crooked hole, semiflowing

By careful analysis, however, it is possible to recognize the effects of these various factors and make adjustments for optimum pumping conditions.

The most useful data obtainable from dynamometer cards are the actual measurements that may be made. These measurements are:

1. Maximum upstroke load
2. Minimum downstroke load
3. Card area or polished-rod horsepower
4. Speed and stroke—from card length and timing wave
5. Effective counterbalance
6. Traveling-valve test
7. Standing-valve test

From those measurements, design or adjustment of all pumping equipment may be made, and in particular, the three factors affecting rod life are measured and may be compared with those suggested earlier in this chapter for optimum rod life.

To summarize, the dynamometer, when intelligently used, can pinpoint desirable changes in equipment and operating practices which will result in reduced maintenance costs and/or increased production.

It is beyond the scope of this handbook to include a detailed treatise on the use of the dynamometer or on the analysis of dynamometer cards. However, many papers have been written on this, one of the foremost being Systematic Approach to Problem Pumping Well Testing by C. J. Merryman and D. K. Lawrence, presented at the Southwestern District Production Division Meeting of the API in Fort Worth, Tex., Mar. 12–14, 1958.

Chapter 9

PUMPING UNITS AND PRIME MOVERS FOR PUMPING UNITS

Section Editor

L. A. LITTLE

Vice President, Lufkin Foundry & Machine Company
Lufkin, Texas

Contributors and Co-workers

SAM CURTIS

Engineer, Lufkin Foundry & Machine Company
Lufkin, Texas

F. BEN ELLIOTT, JR.

Experimental Engineer, Lufkin Foundry & Machine Company
Lufkin, Texas

J. TAYLOR HOOD

Manager, Gas Engine Department
Lufkin Foundry & Machine Company

JOHN H. DAY, JR.

Sales Engineer
General Electric Company
Dallas, Texas

INTRODUCTION

When oil wells cease flowing an artificial means of producing the oil is required. About 85 per cent of all secondary or artificial production of oil is accomplished by use of sucker rods lifting the fluid. This oil is pumped by means of a plunger and a traveling valve being moved up and down inside a polished cylinder with a valve at the bottom. The cylinder is called a working barrel. The plunger is actuated by means of a string of sucker rods which extends to the surface. The upper end of the rod string is attached to a polished rod which is moved up and down by a pumping unit. Pumping units will be discussed in this chapter together with prime movers and electric-power-distribution systems required to power the pumping units.

PUMPING UNITS

A pumping unit is a mechanism which imparts reciprocating motion to a polished rod. Several types of pumping units are available today. The component parts of most of the units are basically the same; the arrangement of the parts differ. Selection of the proper size and type of pumping unit for a particular application is important. Similar to most other machinery, pumping units must be installed properly and also must be lubricated and maintained. Built into the majority of pumping units is some method of counterbalance which consists of an adjustable weight or force system opposing the weight of the well. The actual well load on a pumping unit is often measured and analyzed to ensure that the load and torque capacity of the unit has not been exceeded.

Types

Pumping units are generally referred to according to the location or method of counterbalance. This is true for the crank-balanced, air-balanced, and beam-balanced pumping units. The long-stroke hydraulic pumping unit uses air pressure as the counterbalance force.

Crank Balanced

The crank-balanced pumping unit is the type most commonly used today. It adequately serves many field and load demands. Shown in Fig. 9-1 is a crank-

Fig. 9-1. Crank-balanced pumping unit, showing components.

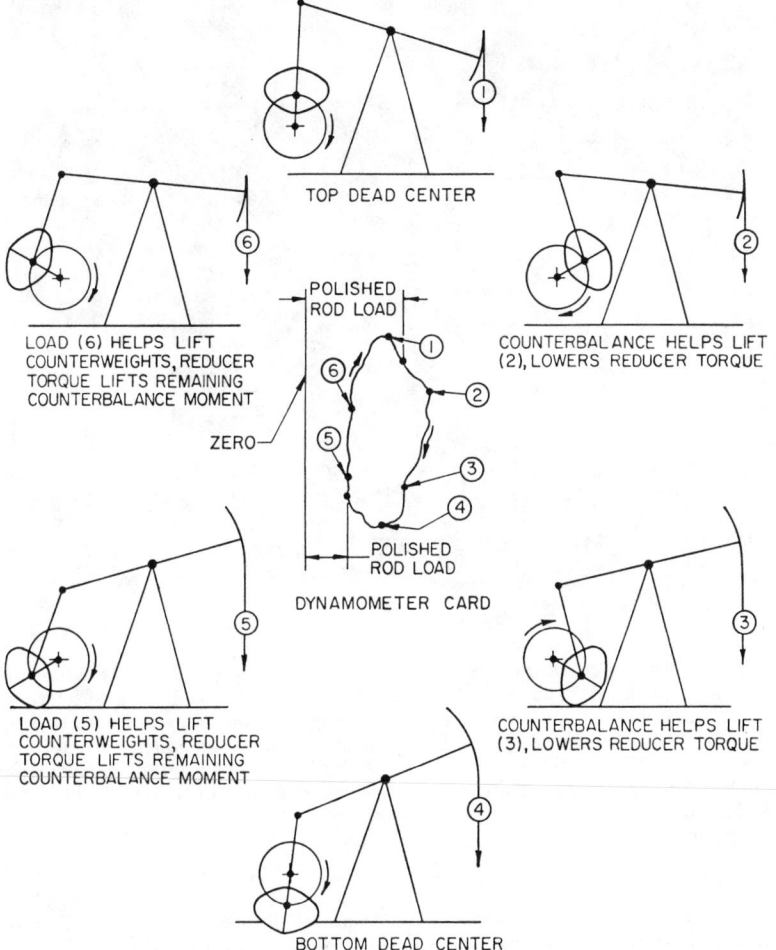

FIG. 9-2. Crank-counterbalanced diagram.

balanced unit with the various parts labeled.   The rotation of the cranks causes the walking beam to pivot about the center bearing, thereby moving the polished rod up and down through its various connections to the horsehead.   The counterweights located on the cranks are heavy metal castings.   Figure 9-2 illustrates the mechanics of counterbalance.   Adjustment and effect of the counterbalance are discussed more thoroughly later in this section.

Air Balanced

The air-balanced pumping unit is basically the same as the crank-balanced unit in that the rotation of the cranks causes the walking beam to pivot and move the polished rod up and down.   Figure 9-3 shows a typical field installation of an air-balanced unit.   The unit is compact and relatively light.   The long cylindrical tank at the front of the unit houses a piston and air cylinder.   Force exerted by compressing air in the cylinder is used to counterbalance the well load.   Special provisions must be made to prevent excessive air leaks between the piston and cylinder.   One

Fig. 9-3. Air-balanced pumping unit.

of the most dependable means found is to utilize a pool of oil on top of the piston as an air seal. Figure 9-4 shows how the counterbalance force works to offset the well load. An auxiliary air compressor is used to build the system pressure up to a working level. The operation of the compressor is normally controlled to maintain air pressure within a manually preset range. An automatic counterbalance device may be employed to adjust the air pressure to the level required for perfect counterbalance even though the well conditions may change from day to day.

Beam Balanced

Figure 9-5 shows a beam-counterbalanced unit. This unit is very similar to the crank-balanced unit except that the counterweights are mounted on an extension of the walking beam. Use of this type of unit has been limited in general to the smaller sizes. One reason for this is that, as the mass of weight mounted on the walking beam increases beyond a certain limit, the inertia forces become excessive and impose undue secondary stresses on the mechanism.

Long-stroke Hydraulic Unit

The long-stroke hydraulic pumping unit consists of a piston and cylinder and a source of hydraulic power. The piston is connected to the polished rod and moved up and down by the action of a hydraulic pump. Figure 9-6 shows one type of long-stroke hydraulic pumping unit. The length of stroke ranges from 20 to 40 ft and the polished-rod capacity is 35,000 lb. The long cylinder located at the front of the unit houses the piston and is positioned directly over the well. The two tanks next to the cylinder are the counterbalance tanks and are interconnected at the top. One of the tanks is filled with air under pressure and the other tank contains hydraulic oil and air. An air compressor is used to supply the air pressure. The air pressure on the hydraulic oil supplies the force necessary to counterbalance the well load. The pump and prime mover are located at the rear of the unit.   The pump supplies the necessary volume of oil under pressure to lift the polished rod.   The fluid-flow-reversing mechanism for the unit shown is built directly into the pump.   A system of gears rotates the pump body in its housing.   The housing has an inlet and an outlet port.   When the pump discharges through the outlet port, fluid is pumped to the cylinder and the polished rod rises.   When the pump discharges through the inlet port, fluid is pumped from the cylinder and the polished rod is lowered.   On the

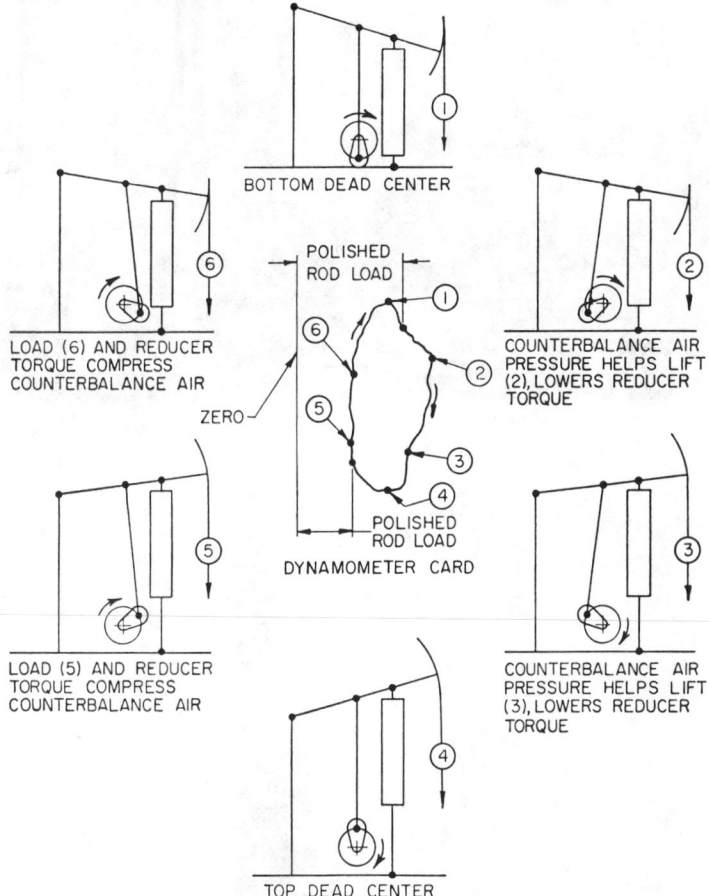

FIG. 9-4. Air-counterbalance diagram.

downstroke, the fluid from the cylinder is pumped into the counterbalance tank. The air in the counterbalance tank is compressed and serves as a source of energy to assist the pump on the next upstroke.

Component Parts

The main parts of a pumping unit consist of structural members, bearings, speed reducer, and drive.   A description and some of the design considerations for the parts are given.   Since the crank-balanced pumping unit is the most common type of unit and consists of parts which are typical for most units, this part of the discussion will be limited to crank-balanced pumping units.

Fig. 9-5. Beam-balanced pumping unit.

Fig. 9-6. Hydraulic pumping unit.

Structure

The main structural part of a crank-balanced pumping unit is the base which is fabricated from rolled-steel shapes. The base serves as a rigid member joining the samson post, gear reducer, and prime mover in proper alignment for attachment of the working mechanism.

The samson post is normally constructed from three or four legs of rolled-steel shapes. The post must have sufficient rigidity and strength to support over twice the maximum polished-rod load.

Centered on top of the samson post is the center bearing which supports the large structural beam called the walking beam. The walking beam must be strong enough to resist bending due to the well load at one end and the actuating force at the other end. The American Petroleum Institute specifies the maximum allowable stresses and other design criteria for walking beams.

The horsehead is attached to the well end of the walking beam and supports the polished rod through a wire line and carrier-bar connections. The center of curvation of the horsehead is the center bearing. Thus the polished rod moves in a straight line tangent to the arc of the horsehead.

On the other end of the walking beam are the equalizer and pitman side members. The motion of the cranks on the speed reducer is transferred to the walking beam by the equalizer and pitman side members. The equalizer is usually mounted on the beam in such a manner that it can move and compensate for some misalignment and manufacturing tolerances. Loading on the pitman side members is tension and loading on the equalizer is bending.

Bearings

Trouble-free operation of a pumping unit depends on the proper functioning of the bearings. Some facts to consider for proper selection or design of bearings are the type and speed of motion and the direction and magnitude of load. On a crank-balanced pumping unit, the center bearing and equalizer bearing support an oscillating load while the crankpin bearing shaft or inner race rotates with respect to the load.

Various types of bearings and bearing materials have been used in these applications. High-lead-bronze bushings have been used successfully for many years at all three bearing points. Bronze bearings suffer little damage even under conditions of borderline lubrication. This is important especially for the oscillating bearing points since complete film lubrication seldom exists.

Tapered and spherical roller bearings are also used especially for crankpin bearings. These bearings are generally considered antifriction and can be packed with a grease type of lubricant.

Pumping unit bearings should be designed or selected very conservatively because they are often subjected to severe shock loads. Provisions must be made for adequate lubrication and for protection from dirt and moisture.

Reducer

A speed reducer is used to convert high-speed low-torque energy of the prime mover into usable low-speed high-torque energy. A reduction ratio of about 30:1 is commonly used. This means that, if the input speed is from 300 to 600 rpm, the output speed or pumping speed will be 10 to 20 spm.

Speed reduction is accomplished by means of herringbone and helical gearing. Spur gearing and chain drives are also used but to a lesser extent. Pumping-unit speed reducers must be sturdy and dependable. Design should include provisions for adequate and proper distribution of lubricant. The bearing capacity and life must meet the requirements of heavy loads and continuous service. The actual gear design is specified by the API. Inspection covers are usually provided; these covers must be close-fitting and not allow the elements to enter the speed reducer.

Drive

V belts are the most universal driving means between the prime mover and the pumping-unit speed reducer. They are a dependable means of transmitting power and provide a certain amount of cushioning effect between the prime mover and speed reducer. This cushioning effect is highly desirable with slow-speed single-cylinder engines. Sheave sizes can be easily changed to adjust unit speeds. Provisions must be made to adjust belt tension. A belt cover or guard is usually provided to protect the belts from the elements and for personnel safety.

Selection

The selection of the proper size and type of pumping unit is based on well conditions and production requirements.

Size

The size of a pumping unit is designated by the peak torque rating of the gear reducer, length of stroke, and polished-rod or beam capacity. The amount of counterbalance available and the maximum strokes per minute often must also be considered in the size selection.

Two methods of selection are discussed. The approximate method is simply a calculated guess. Many factors are neglected, and the results must often be supplanted by experience and a knowledge of well conditions in the particular field.

The engineering analysis of pumping-unit size selection takes into consideration factors such as rod stretch, overtravel, and nonsynchronous pumping speeds. It is an accepted and dependable method of size selection.

Approximate Method. The following empirical formula will permit a rapid approximate evaluation of well conditions without the assistance of lengthy formulas.

Polished-rod Load (PRL)

$$PRL = (W_F + W_R)1.25 \text{ (force} = \text{mass} \times \text{acceleration)}$$

where PRL = polished-rod load, lb
W_F = weight of fluid column, lb
W_R = weight of rod string, lb
1.25 = average acceleration factor (range 1.1 to 1.4)

Counterbalance (CB)

$$CB = W_R + \frac{W_F}{2}$$

Peak Torque (PT), In.-lb

$$PT = (PRL - CB)\frac{S}{2}$$

where S = stroke length, in.

Horsepower Average (hp avg)

$$\text{hp avg} = \frac{D}{600} \times \frac{B/D}{100}$$

where D = well depth, ft
B/D = barrels per day, fluid

Prime-mover Horsepower (hp pm) (Peak Horsepower)

$$\text{hp pm} = \text{hp avg} \times 1.5$$

Engineering Analysis. The engineering analysis of selecting a pumping unit can be divided into two sets of calculations. They are production calculations and pumping-unit load calculations.

First, the production problem must be solved. The proper combination of pump size, unit speed, stroke length, and rod size must be determined to give the desired volume of fluid production. A trial-and-error method will accomplish this.

Second, the pumping-unit load calculations can be made. Here the polished-rod load, counterbalance requirements, and peak-torque requirement must be determined.

The following formulas will serve as a guide in determining both production and pumping-unit size. For the convenience of the reader we have taken as an example a well which has a fluid depth of 4,000 ft. We shall utilize a 2-in. pump, 64-in. stroke, tapered rod string of ¾ and ⅞-in., anchored tubing, and operate at 17 spm. These conditions and their resultants will be used to illustrate our analysis.

Production

B/D at 80 per cent volumetric efficiency = $NPT \times PC \times$ spm $\times$ 80 per cent

where NPT = net plunger travel, in.
= polished-rod stroke, in. − rod-and-tubing* stretch, in. + overtravel, in.

PC = pump constant, which is 0.1484 × area of pump, sq in. (inset, Fig. 9-7).

spm = strokes per minute

Rod stretch for ¾-in. rods is obtained from Fig. 9-7. If rods other than ¾-in. are used, use stretch factors shown on inset in Fig. 9-7. Where tapered rod strings are

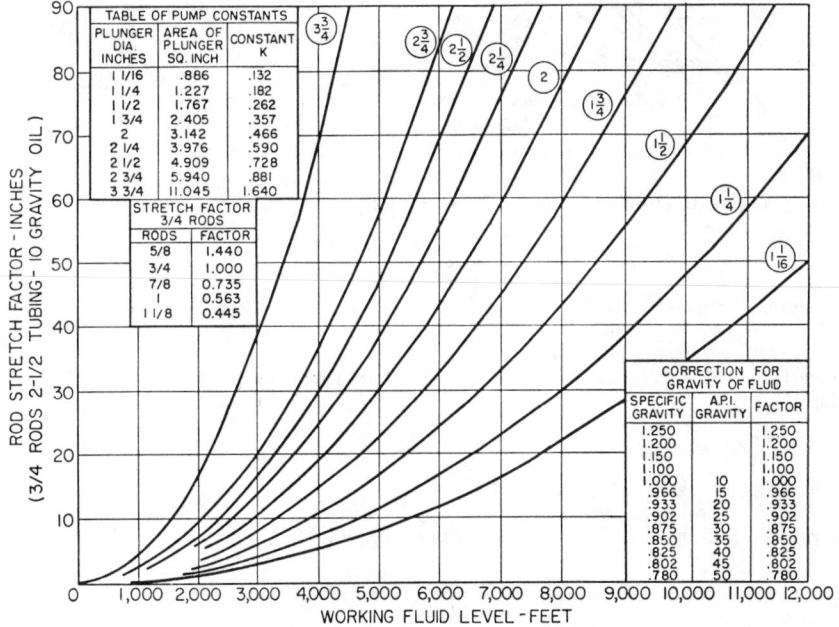

Fig. 9-7. Rod-stretch-factor curves.

used, obtain the per cent of each rod opposite the pump size in Table 9-3. These percentages are then multiplied by the stretch of ¾-in. rods and by the stretch factor. If the tubing is not anchored, the accumulative stretch for ¾-in. rods and 2½-in. tubing can be taken from Fig. 9-8.

Stretch at 4,000 ft of ¾-in. rods for 2-in. pump = 19.5 in.

⅞-in. rods 38.8 per cent × 0.735 stretch factor × 19.5 =   5.56
¾-in. rods 61.2 per cent × 1.0 stretch factor × 19.5 = 11.93
Total stretch of ⅞ by ¾-in. rod string = 17.49

* This is ignored where tubing is anchored.

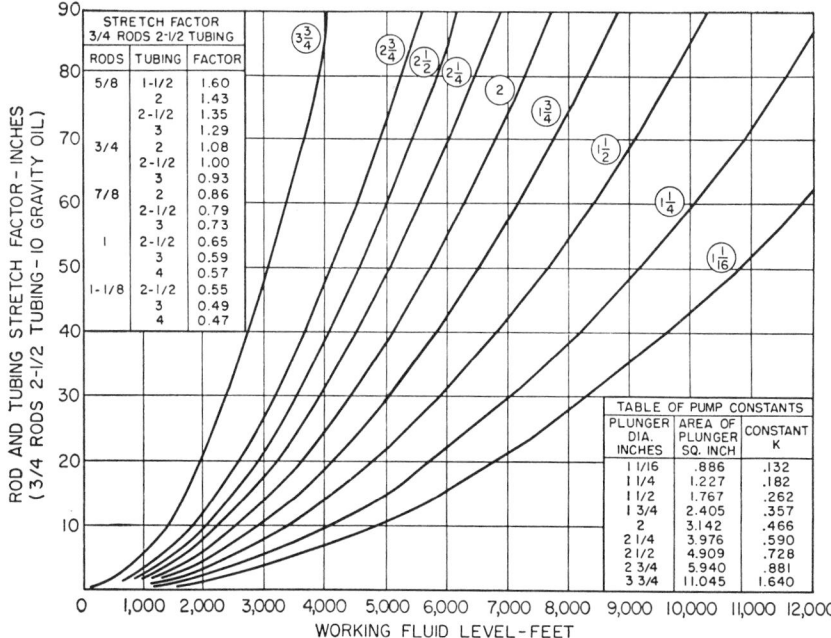

FIG. 9-8. Rod-and-tubing stretch-factor curves.

Overtravel is determined from the following formula:[2]

$$OT = \left(\frac{D}{1,000}\right)^2 OT_F$$

where OT = overtravel, in.
D = pump depth, ft
OT_F = overtravel factor
Overtravel factor can be obtained from Table 9-4 or calculated from the following formula:

$$OT_F = 1.55 \frac{LN^2}{70,500}$$

where L = stroke length, in.
N = strokes per minute
Overtravel for seventeen 64-in. strokes per minute is

$$OT = \left(\frac{4,000}{1,000}\right)^2 \times 0.407 = 6.51 \text{ in.}$$

The maximum recommended pumping speed can be calculated from this formula:

$$\text{spm} = 0.7 \sqrt{\frac{60,000}{\text{stroke length, in.}}}$$

The maximum speed for a 64-in. stroke would be

$$0.7 \sqrt{\frac{60,000}{64 \text{ in.}}} = 21.5 \text{ spm}$$

A nonsynchronous pumping speed should be selected.   This is done by means of the following formulas:[3]

$$\text{Frequency} = \frac{237,000}{\text{depth}}$$

$$\text{Optimum spm} = \frac{\text{frequency}}{1.5, \ 2.5, \ 3.5, \ \text{etc.}}$$

A good pumping rate for 4,000-ft depth is

$$\frac{237,000}{4,000} = 59.25 \text{ frequency}$$

$$\frac{59.25}{3.5} = 17 \text{ spm}$$

Hence the production for our conditions is $NPT \times PC \times$ spm $\times$ 80 per cent

B/D at 80 per cent volumetric efficiency $= (64 - 17.49 = 6.51) \times 0.466 \times 17 \times 0.8$
$$= 336$$

Pumping-unit Loads.   Peak polished-rod load:

$$\text{Peak } PRL = W_F = W_R \ (AF)$$

where W_F = weight of fluid column, lb
$\quad W_R$ = weight of rod string, lb
Weight of fluid and rods per foot for various rod and pump sizes can be obtained from Table 9-5.

$$A_F = \text{acceleration factor}$$

This can be obtained from Table 9-6.   The formula[4] for deriving these values is

$$A_F = 1 = \frac{LN^2}{70,500}$$

where L = stroke length, in.
$\quad N$ = strokes per minute
The peak polished-rod load for the illustrative problem is as follows:

$$\text{Peak } PRL = (4,000 \text{ ft})(1.142 \text{ lb/ft}) = (4,000 \text{ ft}) \ 1.86 \text{ lb} \ (1.262)$$
$$= 13,960 \text{ lb}$$

Rod stress must be kept under the maximum allowable stress for the type used. Hence the rod stress in the top rod is always calculated.

$$\text{Rod stress} = \frac{\text{peak } PRL}{\text{area of top rod, sq in.}}$$

In this case the rod stress is

$$\frac{13,960 \text{ lb}}{0.6 \text{ sq in.}} = 23,260 \text{ psi}$$

Minimum polished-rod load: The minimum polished-rod load is determined to give the load range.

$$\text{Min } PRL = W_R \ (\text{max } A_F - \text{actual } A_F)$$

where W_R = weight of rod string, lb
$\quad$ Max A_F = 1.873
Actual A_F = value obtained from Table 9-6 or $1 = \dfrac{LN^2}{70,500}$

The minimum polished-rod load for the example is

$$\text{Min } PRL = 7,440 \ (1.873 - 1.262)$$
$$= 4,545 \text{ lb}$$

Counterbalance. The effective counterbalance requirements are assumed to be midway between the peak PRL and the min PRL.

$$CB = \frac{\text{peak } PRL + \text{min } PRL}{2}$$

where CB = effective counterbalance, lb
The counterbalance requirement in this hypothetical case is

$$CB = \frac{13,960 \text{ lb} + 4,550 \text{ lb}}{2}$$
$$= 9,250 \text{ lb}$$

Peak Torque. The peak torque is derived by multiplying the unbalanced load by a moment arm which is one-half the stroke length. This assumes a unit with no frictional losses and "perfect" structural dimensions (torque factor = $S/2$):

$$PT + (\text{peak } PRL - CB) \frac{S}{2}$$

where PT = peak torque, in.-lb
$\quad\quad S$ = polished-rod stroke, in.
The peak-torque requirement in the example is

$$PT = (13,960 \text{ lb} - 9,250 \text{ lb}) \frac{64 \text{ in.}}{2}$$
$$= 151,000 \text{ in.-lb}$$

Because of the inherent loss in mechanical advantage shown by torque factor and the frictional loss from the structural bearings some reasonable amount of unit structural efficiency should be applied. As structural efficiency (between the carrier bar and slow-speed shaft) varies with different combinations of torque and counterbalance some compromise amount is needed. An 85 per cent structural efficiency is frequently applied to establish unit size, thus:

$$PT = \frac{151,000 \text{ in.-lb}}{0.85}$$
$$= 178,000 \text{ in.-lb}$$

The unit selected for use in this instance must have 228,000 in.-lb of torque capacity. The next smaller API size unit has a torque capacity of 160,000 in.-lb. In no case should a unit of inadequate capacity be selected. It is always wise to select a unit that has a torque-capacity reserve, as improper counterbalance can cause severe torque overload, which is often unknown to the operator.

Type

The type of pumping unit which is best suited for a particular pumping problem can be fairly well defined. The crank-balanced pumping unit fills the general requirements for sucker-rod pumping. The other types of pumping units not only fill the general requirements but also have some special feature which makes them adaptable to special pumping problems.

The crank-balanced pumping unit may be used where well conditions are stable and counterbalance requirements are fairly constant.

The air-balanced pumping unit is particularly adaptable to pier installations and other unstable substructures. The inertia and shaking forces are very low and the unit is compact and light in weight. Another application for the air-balanced pumping unit is on wells which are unstable and require frequent counterbalance adjustment. The counterbalance on an air-balanced unit can be changed by turning a dial or setscrew. An automatic counterbalance system can also be employed to adjust the counterbalance to offset any change in well loads.

The beam-balanced pumping unit is manufactured only in the smaller sizes. Economics is the prime factor for selecting this type of unit.

The long-stroke hydraulic unit is used for pumping deep wells with heavy fluid loads where rod problems would normally occur. Increasing stroke length and decreasing the number of reversals greatly increases rod life.

Installation

An improperly installed pumping unit can result in early structural and bearing failures and over-all unsatisfactory operation. An adequate foundation must be provided and the unit must be properly erected.

Foundation

A reinforced-concrete block will provide the best type of foundation. Other types of foundations are acceptable under certain circumstances. Foundations of heavy timbers set on alternating layers of sand and gravel have been used successfully in some areas. Close supervision must be provided to correct any settling or shifting of the timbers. This discussion will be limited to the concrete type of foundations.

The manufacturer will provide a certified foundation print showing the location of the foundation bolts or holddowns with respect to the well. The minimum size of outline of the concrete base is usually shown; the actual size and depth of foundation required depend on local soil conditions. Care should be taken to locate the foundation bolts properly since only a small amount of adjustment is built into a pumping unit to compensate for foundation errors. Grouting tubes should be used around foundation bolts.

The foundation must be level and smooth, especially if the pumping-unit base is to be installed without grouting. However, there is no substitute for grouting to ensure complete bearing of the base on the concrete foundation. If the base members do not bear properly, they may deflect with each stroke of the unit. This repeated deflection can result in ultimate failure.

Erection of the Unit

Before placing the base on the foundation, draw a chalk line from the center of the well along the center of the foundation. Place the base on the foundation, lining up the center of the base with the chalk line. The distance from the well to the front of the base should be given on the certified foundation print. Assuming, for this discussion, that the base is to be grouted, place wedges between the base and the foundation at frequent intervals. The base should be about 1 in. above the concrete and leveled.

Follow the manufacturer's instructions and assemble the rest of the unit. Proper alignment of all working parts of the mechanism is essential. This may be checked by use of a level, plumb bob, or a transit. Make necessary adjustment to align the wire-line hanger with the well. Tighten all bolts and nuts. Some pumping-unit manufacturers specify that all structural bolts be hammer-tight.

The base may now be grouted. Grout should be worked under all base members for their full width. Allow the grout to harden before removing the wedges; then grout all areas formerly occupied by wedges. Tighten the foundation bolts securely.

After all other adjustments and inspection have been made and the unit is in operation, visually check alignment of moving parts. This may be done by observing the distance between the cranks and pitman side members on each side of the unit. The distances should be equal.   Check the wire line to see if it is tracking the horse-head properly. Objectionable noises or knocks usually indicate that some part of the unit is out of alignment.   All necessary adjustments should be made at once. Misalignment may result in excessive axial motion of bearings which are designed primarily for a radial load. Oil seals also loose their efficiency when axial motion develops.

Lubrication and Maintenance

Pumping units should be given periodic lubrication and maintenance checks· When they are subjected to heavy variable loads, extreme temperature conditions, or adverse moisture or dust conditions it may be necessary to increase the frequency of the checks.

Bearings

All the structural bearing points, i.e., center bearing, equalizer bearing, and crankpin bearings, require an adequate amount of the proper type of lubricant. A fluid lubricant is more efficient in moving to the areas where the lubricant is most needed; however, good-quality grades of greases are recommended by some manufacturers for their particular bearings.

Reducers[1]

General. This recommended practice covers lubrication procedure for pumping-unit speed reducers using either gears or roller chain and sprockets.

The recommendations apply only when the gears and chain drives are designed and rated in accordance with API standards.   The oil operating-temperature range for which they apply is from -50 to $+155°F$.

It is not possible to describe adequately suitable lubricants by brief specifications or by SAE viscosity number alone. Adequate lubrication instructions cannot be condensed sufficiently to be placed on a nameplate because of the many variables in operating conditions to which pumping units are subjected.

Selection of Oil. The proper oil for pumping-unit speed reducers is best chosen with the advice of a representative of a reputable supplier of lubricants and should be based on the service conditions that are established by the design of the reducer and the service conditions of the particular installation.   For the assistance of the lubricant supplier, these conditions are summarized in ref. 1.

The areas in contact on gear teeth and on chains and sprockets are relatively small, and therefore the unit pressures produced in transmitting peak loads are correspondingly high.   These gears, chains, and sprockets are designed to operate under these high unit pressures provided the lubricant used is also capable of withstanding these unit pressures during the periods of peak loads.

The temperature of the air in the vicinity of the reducer is of considerable importance in selecting oil of the proper viscosity. For high-temperature operations, an oil with a higher SAE viscosity number should be selected.   For low-temperature operation, the oil should have sufficient fluidity to permit a free flow of oil through the lubricating channels.

The operating temperature of oil in pumping-unit reducers normally will be 25° above ambient temperature.   The temperature increase of oil will be negligible in slow-operating lightly loaded reducers but will reach the upper limit in heavily loaded reducers operating at the higher speeds.   Because most pumping units will be stopped at times, the lowest temperature of oil in a reducer usually will be the lowest temperature reached in the locality where the pumping unit is operating.   This is an important consideration when selecting the SAE viscosity number of oil for winter operation.

Either straight-mineral gear oil or automotive-engine oil may be used provided the SAE viscosity number of the oil is suitable for the prevailing operating conditions.

The permissible range of operating-oil temperature for each SAE viscosity number of automotive-engine oil and gear oil is shown for gear and chain reducers in Tables 9-1 and 9-2, respectively.   In each case the minimum temperature is based on the ability of cold oil to flow properly through the lubricating channels, and the maximum temperature is based on the ability of the hot oil to maintain adequate lubrication. The temperature ranges are wide for the purpose of permitting year-long operation with one viscosity grade of oil in localities where seasonal air-temperature range will allow.   The operator should select the grade best meeting his temperature range. If the summer-to-winter range is too great for a single viscosity grade, the oil must be changed accordingly.

It is suggested that nameplates on pumping-unit reducers carry at least a reference to the API Recommended Practice for Lubrication of Pumping Unit Reducers.

Table 9-1. Viscosity Recommendations for Gear Reducers

Temp of oil in gear case, °F*	SAE viscosity No.	
	Automotive-engine oil	Gear oil
− 50 to + 32	5W	75†
− 40 to + 50	10W	
− 20 to + 80	20W	80
0 to +100	30	
+10 to +125	40	90
+20 to +135	50	90
+30 to +155	....	140‡

* Operating temperature of oil in a gear reducer on a pumping unit normally will be from air temperature to 25°F above air temperature.   The temperatures shown in the table are the limiting values between which satisfactory lubrication can be expected.

† SAE 75 gear oil is not usually available.

‡ Pour point for SAE 140 gear oil will not be higher than 25°F.

Table 9-2. Viscosity Recommendations for Chain Reducers

Temp of oil in chain case, °F*	SAE viscosity No.	
	Automotive-engine oil	Gear oil
− 50 to + 50	5W	†
− 20 to + 80	10W	75‡
0 to +100	20W	80
+10 to +125	30	80
+20 to +135	40	
+30 to +155	50	90

* Operating temperature of oil in a chain case on a pumping unit normally will be from ambient temperature to 25°F above ambient temperature.   The temperatures shown in the table are the limiting values between which satisfactory lubrication can be expected.

† SAE gear oils are not recommended for use in chain reducers for this range of temperature.

‡ SAE 75 gear oil is not usually available.

Changing the Oil

The life of a pumping-unit reducer may be increased by using oil of a suitable viscosity and by keeping that oil free from foreign material, sludge, and water.   Oil should be changed in the spring and fall to maintain proper viscosity f the seasonal temperature range exceeds the temperature range of the oil shown in Table 9-1 or 9-2.

The method used to determine how often oil should be changed to maintain the desired condition is a matter of policy with the individual company. Some operators periodically inspect reducers and take samples of oil for laboratory analysis to determine the percentages of water and solid material in the oil. Checks may also be made on viscosity and other properties such as acidity. Oil is then changed whenever the analysis shows that the limit set for any one of the various factors has been exceeded.

Table 9-3. Rod Percentages for Tapered Rod Strings

Plunger diam	¾ and ⅝ % ¾	⅞ and ¾ % ⅞	⅞ %	¾ %	⅝ %	1 and ⅞ % 1	1 %	⅞ %	¾ %
1¹⁄₁₆	31.6	26.0	23.1	26.2	50.7	22.3	19.2	22.1	58.7
1¼	34.8	28.1	25.4	28.8	45.8	23.6	20.8	23.6	55.6
1½	39.6	31.1	28.8	32.8	38.4	25.6	22.9	26.3	50.8
1¾	45.2	34.7	32.9	37.4	29.7	28.0	25.6	29.2	45.2
2	51.8	38.8	37.6	42.8	19.6	30.5	28.7	32.7	38.6
2¼	59.2	43.4	43.0	48.9	8.1	33.9	32.1	36.7	31.2
2½	67.5	48.7	....	....	....	37.5	36.0	41.1	22.9
2¾	76.6	54.4	....	....	....	41.5	40.4	45.8	13.8
3¾	....	83.0	....	....	....	60.5			

Table 9-4. Overtravel Factor

Strokes/min	Length of polished-rod stroke, in.																
	12	18	24	34	44	48	54	64	74	84	96	108	120	144	150	168	192
1	0.000	0.000	0.000	0.001	0.001	0.001	0.001	0.001	0.002	0.002	0.002	0.002	0.002	0.003	0.003	0.004	0.004
2	0.001	0.002	0.002	0.003	0.004	0.004	0.005	0.006	0.007	0.007	0.008	0.009	0.011	0.013	0.013	0.015	0.017
3	0.002	0.004	0.005	0.007	0.009	0.009	0.011	0.003	0.015	0.017	0.019	0.021	0.024	0.028	0.030	0.033	0.038
4	0.004	0.006	0.008	0.012	0.016	0.017	0.019	0.023	0.026	0.029	0.034	0.039	0.042	0.051	0.053	0.059	0.068
5	0.007	0.010	0.013	0.019	0.024	0.026	0.030	0.035	0.041	0.046	0.053	0.059	0.066	0.079	0.082	0.092	0.106
6	0.010	0.014	0.019	0.027	0.035	0.038	0.043	0.051	0.059	0.067	0.076	0.085	0.095	0.114	0.119	0.133	0.152
7	0.013	0.019	0.026	0.037	0.047	0.052	0.058	0.069	0.080	0.090	0.103	0.116	0.129	0.155	0.162	0.181	0.207
8	0.017	0.025	0.034	0.048	0.062	0.068	0.076	0.090	0.104	0.118	0.135	0.152	0.169	0.203	0.211	0.236	0.270
9	0.021	0.032	0.043	0.061	0.078	0.085	0.096	0.114	0.132	0.150	0.171	0.192	0.214	0.256	0.267	0.299	0.342
10	0.026	0.040	0.053	0.075	0.097	0.106	0.119	0.141	0.163	0.185	0.211	0.237	0.264	0.317	0.330	0.369	0.422
11	0.032	0.048	0.064	0.090	0.117	0.128	0.144	0.170	0.197	0.223	0.255	0.287	0.319	0.383	0.399	0.447	0.511
12	0.038	0.057	0.076	0.108	0.139	0.152	0.171	0.203	0.234	0.266	0.304	0.342	0.380	0.456	0.475	0.532	0.608
13	0.045	0.067	0.089	0.126	0.163	0.178	0.201	0.238	0.275	0.312	0.357	0.401	0.453	0.535	0.557	0.624	0.713
14	0.052	0.078	0.103	0.147	0.190	0.207	0.233	0.276	0.319	0.362	0.414	0.465	0.518	0.621	0.646	0.724	0.827
15	0.059	0.089	0.119	0.168	0.218	0.237	0.267	0.317	0.366	0.416	0.475	0.534	0.594	0.712	0.742	0.831	0.950
16	0.068	0.101	0.135	0.191	0.248	0.270	0.304	0.360	0.416	0.473	0.540	0.608	0.675	0.810	0.844	0.946	1.081
17	0.076	0.114	0.152	0.216	0.280	0.305	0.343	0.407	0.470	0.534	0.610	0.686	0.762	0.915	0.953	1.067	
18	0.085	0.128	0.171	0.242	0.313	0.342	0.385	0.456	0.527	0.598	0.684	0.769	0.855	1.026			
19	0.095	0.143	0.190	0.270	0.349	0.381	0.429	0.508	0.587	0.667	0.762	0.857	0.952	1.143			
20	0.106	0.158	0.211	0.299	0.387	0.422	0.475	0.563	0.651	0.739	0.844	0.950	1.055				
21	0.116	0.175	0.233	0.330	0.427	0.465	0.524	0.621	0.717	0.814	0.931	1.047					
22	0.128	0.192	0.255	0.362	0.468	0.511	0.575	0.681	0.787	0.894	1.022	1.149					
23	0.140	0.209	0.279	0.395	0.512	0.558	0.628	0.744	0.861	0.977	1.117						
24	0.152	0.228	0.304	0.431	0.557	0.608	0.684	0.810	0.937	1.064							

Other operators depend upon periodic visual inspection to determine when to change oil. An inspection includes a look inside the reducer case and an examination of a sample of oil that has been drawn off the bottom of the reducer case and allowed to settle. Oil is changed when an inspection shows (1) deposits on the surfaces inside the reducer; (2) emulsification of oil; (3) sludging of oil; (4) contamination of the oil with foreign material such as dirt, sand, or metal particles. Sludging and emulsification of oil are usually found if there has been an excessive accumulation of water in the reducer.

A small amount of water can accumulate in the bottom of the reducer. Such water should be drawn off to prevent accumulation to the point where it will be carried with the oil and cause emulsification or sludging.

The time interval between inspections to determine the condition of the oil depends upon operating conditions. Adverse conditions that may require inspection and change of oil as often as every three or four months include one or more of the following: (1) intermittent operation, (2) excessive dust, (3) sulfur fumes, (4) a combination of high humidity with high variation in daily air temperature. Under the most favorable conditions of minimum daily and seasonal temperature changes, low humidity, and freedom of atmospheric dust, a reducer may operate through one or more years before the oil becomes contaminated or deteriorates to the point that an oil change is required.

If petroleum solvent is used for flushing, all the flushing agent should be removed and the reducer immediately refilled with a suitable oil. If the reducer is not immediately returned to operation, the unit should be operated for at least 10 minutes, or longer if necessary, to ensure that all surfaces are covered with a protective film of oil.

Structure

It is essential to keep all bolted joints tight. Analysis of bolt failures shows the type of failure to be almost invariably fatigue which is caused by a varying load. A properly tightened bolt against solid material such as structural steel or cast iron will not have a varying load and will never fail in fatigue. *Tighten bolts adequately.*

Load Analysis

The actual operating loads on a pumping unit may differ from the loads anticipated and used in selecting the size. When conditions exist that indicate overload, it may be necessary to analyze the load on the unit. The greatest single factor which affects torque loading on a pumping unit is counterbalance. The torque factor of a pumping unit is also important. Torque factor is dependent on the arrangement or geometry of the working parts of a pumping unit.

A dynamometer is an instrument used to measure and record the actual well loads at all points of a pumping cycle. Analysis of a dynamometer card will reveal the accuracy of counterbalance, the maximum or peak torque on the gear reducer, and the maximum polish-rod load. Other information that may be gained from a dynamometer card includes well conditions and bottom-hole pump characteristics.

Counterbalance

Crank-balanced pumping units are counterbalanced by the weight of the cranks and the adjustable counterweights mounted on the cranks. The inset in Fig. 9-1 illustrates how the counterweights can be moved along the crank. Ease of adjustment is very desirable. Figure 9-2 illustrates the effect of counterbalance on reducer torque.

Ideal counterbalance is equal to the weight of the sucker rods plus half the fluid weight supported by the bottom-hole pump. When this condition exists, torque required on the up- and the downstroke is equal—neglecting inertia forces due to acceleration and deceleration of the rods and fluid.

Several simple and reasonably accurate methods are available to determine correct counterbalance. The sound of the prime mover on the up- and on the downstroke is a very good indication of counterbalance. On electric-motor drives an ammeter can be used to compare the current on the up- and downstroke. A vacuum gauge used on a gas engine will give the same type of peak-load comparison. When more accurate counterbalance adjustment is required, a polished-rod dynamometer is used.

Improper counterbalance not only adds to the power that must be supplied by the prime mover but also increases the load on the gear teeth. Abnormal gear-tooth wear can be expected. For efficient operation, correct counterbalance is a must.

Torque Factor

The torque factor of a pumping unit is becoming increasingly more important as more efficient methods or producing oil are demanded. Torque factor is derived from actual unit geometry and depends upon length of walking beam, ratio of working centers, stroke length, samson-post height, pitman length, and relative positions of center bearing, equalizer bearing, and horsehead. It is given as a numerical value for each 15° increment of crank rotation throughout the pumping cycle. Torque factor multiplied by well load equals gross torque. It is often used in this manner to analyze dynamometer cards.

Dynamometer

All oil-field producers desire to obtain the optimum amount of loading and usage from their pumping equipment. The varying polished-rod loads being lifted by the pumping unit cannot adequately be "observed or heard" and preliminary calculations made are sometimes in error because of unknown and unanticipated subsurface conditions. A dynamometer is an instrument used to measure the varying polished-rod loads and relate this load to its location in the stroke. The resulting "dynamometer card" (see Figs. 9-2 and 9-4) can help greatly with analysis of subsurface conditions; however, the card with a nominal amount of calculation can give pertinent surface information such as peak polished-rod load, minimum polished-rod load, peak torques, and reverse torque. An overloaded pumping unit from the standpoint of torque will have greatly reduced gear life in the reducer and potential gear-tooth troubles. The dynamometer gives basic load information which can be used to establish pumping-unit sizes on similar types of wells.

One type of dynamometer, in common use, has two carefully calibrated load rings which are inserted on either side of the polished rod between the carrier bar and rod clamp and support the entire polished-rod load. The deflection of these rings, which is proportional to the load they carry, is then magnified and recorded by a metal stylus on a wax "dynamometer card" showing the varying polished-rod loads. Simultaneously with the recording of the rod load, the card is rotated or moved by means of a drum which relates the vertical position of the card to the actual stroke of the unit through a gearing system in the dynamometer.

Another type of dynamometer utilizes two clamps which are attached firmly to the polished rod at a specified distance apart. When the polished-rod load is induced the distance between the two clamps on the rod will vary depending upon the modulus of elasticity and the resultant "strain," or elongation, in the rod. This minute strain is magnified and recorded by a stylus on the wax "dynamometer card" in similar manner as mentioned above.

Judicious use of a dynamometer in establishing loading of pumping equipment can help in determining if the proper size of pumping unit has been installed which in turn will reduce maintenance problems.

PRIME MOVERS FOR PUMPING UNITS

An internal-combustion engine or an electric motor is normally used as the prime mover for the pumping unit. Internal-combustion engines for oil-well pumping are in two classes, namely:

1. Slow-speed engines
2. High-speed engines

Slow-speed engines are those of one or more cylinders which have a maximum crankshaft speed of 750 rpm or less. High-speed engines are those of one or more (usually multicylinder) which have a maximum crankshaft speed of more than 750 rpm.

Classification of Prime Movers

Prime movers can be classified into six types, viz:

1. Slow-speed single or twin-cylinder two-cycle gas engines
2. Slow-speed single-cylinder four-cycle gas engines

3. High-speed multiple-cylinder four-cycle gas engines
4. Slow-speed diesel or oil-burning engines
5. High-speed diesel engines
6. Electric motors

Advantages and disadvantages of each classification are listed at the end of the engine section (pages 9-26 to 9-28).

Internal-combustion engines are built in two cycles of operation:

1. Two-stroke cycle (two-cycle)
2. Four-stroke cycle (four-cycle)

Two-stroke Cycle

The two-stroke cycle, normally called two-cycle, completes its work cycle in only two strokes of the piston, or one revolution of the crankshaft. The two strokes are (1) compression and (2) power. The process of filling the cylinder with a fresh

Fig. 9-9. Two-cycle gas engine, cross section.

charge and exhausting the burned gases occurs simultaneously at the bottom of the stroke, through ports uncovered by the piston; thus the piston acts as a slide valve. The number of power strokes per revolution is in direct proportion to the number of cylinders. For example, a two-cylinder two-cycle engine has two power strokes per revolution of the crankshaft.

Normally a two-cycle engine, for a given displacement and speed, develops 1.6 times the power of an equivalent four-cycle. It does not develop twice the power because of the loss of effective stroke caused by the ports at the bottom of the stroke which are necessary to scavenge the cylinder.

The slow-speed two-cycle engine is usually built as a crosshead type, as shown in Fig. 9-9, which shows a cross section through a typical two-cycle gas engine. This construction uses a bore in the engine base in which is mounted a crosshead to take the angular thrust of the connecting rod and thus allow a seal to be placed between the cylinder and the crankcase. This prevents the combustion gases from entering the

FIG. 9-10. Slow-speed two-cycle engine, showing large flywheel.

crankcase and contaminating the lubricating oil, thus allowing it to be used for long periods without changing or cleaning.

Slow-speed two-cycle engines are built with large WR^2 flywheels which are not enclosed, as shown in Fig. 9-10. The flywheel absorbs energy from the engine at periods of light load and returns this energy on the pumping peaks, resulting in a small variation of engine speed throughout the pumping cycle. From a safety angle, the flywheel should be provided with suitable guards to protect operating personnel.

High-speed two-cycle engines have not been used to a great extent as pumping engines. They are usually multiple-cylinder type and follow automotive-engine design except that a blower is used to admit the fresh charge through ports at the bottom of the stroke. The exhaust is through an exhaust valve located in the cylinder head. This valve is cam-actuated.

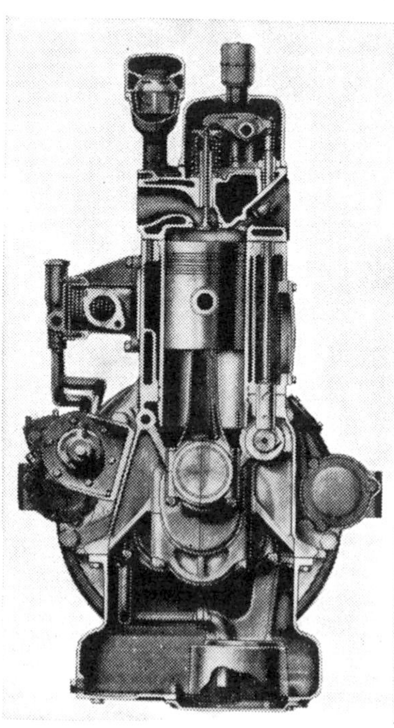

Four-stroke Cycle

The four-stroke cycle, normally called four-cycle, completes its work cycle in four strokes of the piston or once each two revolutions of the crankshaft. The four strokes are (1) suction (intake), (2) compression, (3) power, and (4) exhaust.

The four-stroke engine is built in both slow-speed and high-speed versions. The mechanism of each is essentially the same. Figure 9-11 shows typical four-cycle construction. This type of engine is made with trunk pistons, which means the

FIG. 9-11. Four-cycle cross-section engine, typical construction.

connecting rod is fastened directly to the piston. Intake and exhaust valves are required and are mounted in the cylinder head or the block and are actuated by cams and push rods. The crankcase is connected directly to the cylinders, and thus some of the products of combustion pass the piston rings and contaminate the lubricating oil. Oil changes or cleaning are required frequently.

Slow-speed four-stroke-cycle engines are usually built with a single vertical or horizontal cylinder. Large flywheels, not enclosed, are used to provide steady operating speeds during the pumping cycle.

High-speed four-cycle engines are usually multiple-cylinder, having four or six cylinders, and operate at speeds up to approximately 2,000 rpm. This type of engine is shown in Fig. 9-12. The average pumping speed is usually approximately 1,200 rpm;

Fig. 9-12. High-speed multiple-cylinder four-cycle engine.

however, this type of engine has a wide speed range and is quite flexible and responsive to load changes. It is light in weight for the horsepower available, thus making it especially suitable to portable installations.

Diesel and Oil Engines

Some slow-speed single-cylinder engines burn diesel or fuel oil which is injected into the cylinder under high pressure. The compression is much greater than gas engines and the heat developed by compressing the air in the cylinder ignites the fuel sprayed into the cylinder. Engines of this type are divided into two types:

1. Fuel diesel—cold-starting
2. Semidiesels—require heating to start

The cold-starting diesel uses a compression ratio of 14:1, resulting in compression of approximately 500 psi where the semidiesel uses approximately 250 psi compression and requires a hot tube heated by a torch or electric glow plug to produce enough heat to ignite the charge. Once these engines are started, enough heat is produced in the cylinder to cause ignition of the fuel as it is injected into the cylinder.

High-speed multiple-cylinder diesel engines have been improved until they are quite well adapted for oil-well pumping. Their use is not common where gas is readily available. Diesel engines fill a need where other fuels are not readily available.

Selection of Prime Movers

To make a proper selection of the prime mover requires a knowledge of:

1. Horsepower requirement
2. Possibility of load change
3. Source of power medium
4. Types of prime movers
5. Life expectancy of installation
6. Type of installation
7. Limits of practical application
8. Company policy, etc.

Horsepower Requirements

Horsepower requirements are found from application of standard formulas as found under pumping units. These formulas are based upon peak torque of the gear reducer; however, it must be remembered that the torque peaks are much larger than the average. The average polished-rod horsepower does not indicate these pumping peaks. The size of the prime mover applied depends upon torque, WR^2 of the flywheel, type of prime mover, etc. This requirement must be met by the prime mover with sufficient reserve to allow for peak loads occurring in the pumping cycle, normal reduction of power due to wear, mechanical condition, and other factors which may reduce the prime mover's ability to handle the load.

Engine Rating

Many different ratings are applied to internal-combustion engines. American Petroleum Institute (API) has established standards to obtain uniform peak ratings. These standards should be applied to all engines builders. API Standard 8B is quoted:

The methods of the test stipulated herein are intended to afford the purchaser a uniform basis for comparing similar equipment with respect to capacity, energy requirements, and

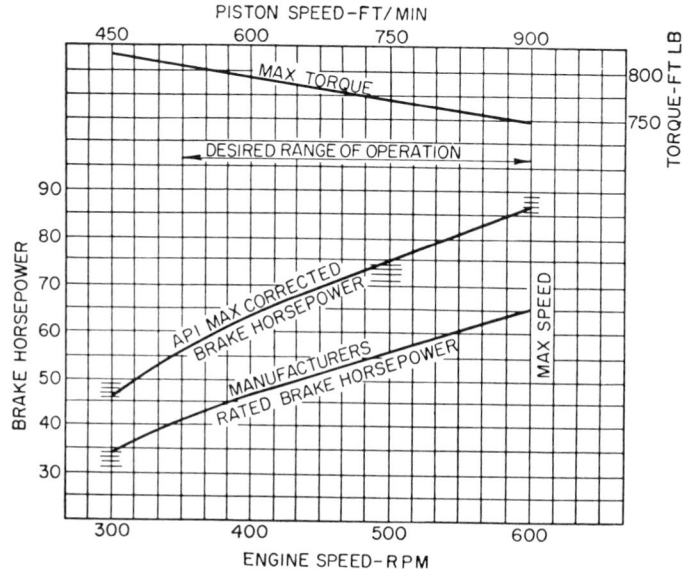

FIG. 9-13. API performance curve.

recommended speed range. Since maintenance and durability factors have not been included in the test procedure, it is assumed that comparison between engines will be made advisedly. A power unit shall be an engine complete with all accessories except muffler, supplied or recommended as standard equipment by the manufacturer.

Maximum Standard Brake Horsepower. At any rotational speed, maximum brake horsepower shall be the greatest horsepower corrected to standard conditions (60°F. and 29.92″ mercury) that can be sustained continuously under the conditions as outlined under test procedure.

A typical API curve is shown in Fig. 9-13. The manufacturer usually shows rating curves below the API curve which are based upon his experience as to the power the engine can produce for various conditions of service. Experience has shown that, for oil-well pumping, high-speed engines must be derated more than slow-speed engines to provided a margin of safety to stand up in continuous service. Normal oil-field ratings for continuous duty, at the speed the engine will be operated, are:

Slow-speed engine—API maximum standard bhp × 0.75
High-speed engine—API maximum standard bhp × 0.65

Altitude and Temperature Corrections

Where engines are to be operated at elevations above 1,500 ft and in hot climates further corrections are necessary for both altitude and temperature. Figure 9-14 gives correction factors to be applied. Normally, an engine is derated 3 per cent for each 1,000 ft of elevation and 1 per cent for each 10° of temperature above 60°F. Add 1 per cent for each 10°F fall in temperature below 60°F.

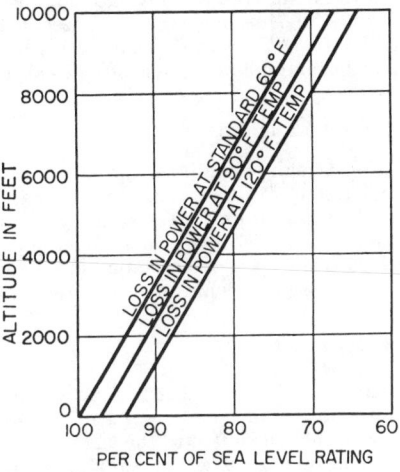

Fig. 9-14. Altitude and temperature corrections.

Fuels

Where natural gas is available and is suitable, it is the logical choice; however, many times this fuel is not suitable or in sufficient quantities; then some other type of power medium must be selected.

Wet Gas

This is the natural gas produced at the casing, or in the oil which is separated by a separator; then it is called separator gas. Gases direct from the well should not be used in any internal-combustion engine. It is necessary that the gas be carried through a scrubber to remove water and oil. Separator gas is a good fuel in that most of the moisture and oil have been removed. Gases which are rich and produce condensation should be run through a scrubber, properly maintained, to prevent condensate from reaching the engine.

Sour Gas

No internal-combustion engine can give good results where the gas contains over 2 per cent sulfur. CO_2 is also a bad factor when combined with sulfur and other minerals. Where the source of the gas is sour, suitable treaters should be installed, or another source of fuel selected. Sour gases cause severe etching and wear of engine parts and cause quick contamination of lubricating oil in four-cycle engines. Many parts are corroded and seize because of the effect of using the contaminated gas.

Two-cycle engines do somewhat better, because the products of combustion do not reach the crankcase, or cause pitting and sticking of valves. Two-cycle engines are subject to cylinder wear and port plugging when used on sour gases. One manufacturer has resorted to the use of chrome-plated cylinder bores with very good results in sour gas. The chrome prevents the fast etching of the cylinder walls. Pistons and rings appear to give normal wear. This is not the answer but only a preventative which protects only until the chrome is etched through.

Residue Gas

Raw gas picked up from the well or separator and carried through a refinery, then piped back to the field, is very good fuel for internal-combustion engines in that the impurities such as sulfur, water, and oil are removed. Such gas is sometimes called dry gas.

LP Gases

Butane and propane, where available, are excellent gases for internal-combustion engines. Such gases must be stored under pressure in suitable pressure tanks to keep them liquefied for transporting. Suitable vaporizers must be provided to turn the liquid into gas form for use in engines. On small engines usually the vapor can be drawn off through a reducing regulator to provide sufficient gas; however, on larger engines the fuel must be vaporized before entering the engine. Butane freezes to liquid at 32°F while propane does not reach this state until −44°F is reached. A blend of butane-propane is often used in mild climates.

Dual-fuel Engines

Most engines can be arranged to run on two or more fuels. For instance, a dual-fuel system can be arranged to use natural gas so long as it is available, but as soon as the pressure drops, the standby fuel is fed automatically to the engine in sufficient quantity to keep the prime mover going continuously. Such systems are primarily designed for gaseous fuels, but similar systems can switch from dry gases to gasoline or vice versa. Dual-fuel installations should not be overlooked in the fuel selection.

Diesel Fuel

Manufacturers of diesel engines supply specifications of diesel fuel. These fuels must be free of moisture and in clean dirt-free containers. Filters must be used to assure only clean fuel to the engine.

Some oil engines which really are semidiesel can burn crude oil of light gravity, but this must be properly cleaned to allow its satisfactory use. The type of crude must meet the standard set by the engine manufacturer.

Installation

The prime mover must be installed correctly to secure good results. Most pumping installations use a V-belt drive from prime mover to pumping unit. Slide rails or some means of adjustment is necessary in order to compensate for belt stretch and to provide proper tension so that the power can be transmitted with minimum loss through slippage. When the prime mover is installed the belts should be aligned and tightened properly, but not overtightened as this will overload the clutch shaft and bearings. Refer to Table 9-5 for allowable side loads as approved by clutch manufacturers.

Slow-speed engines require sturdy foundations such as a steel base set on concrete or set directly on rails embedded in concrete. The slide rails should be set in line with the cylinder because of the horizontal moving forces. Cross rails, sometimes called universal rails, should be used only on small engines.   Most equipment manufacturers provide their units with properly designed slide-rail assemblies for a particular prime mover.

Multiple-cylinder or vertical engines in which the forces are in a vertical plane can be set on much lighter foundations.   Cross rails on such installations are the preferred method.

Provision must be made for exhaust and fuel lines to the engine.   The manufacturer gives specifications for their installation.   Four-cycle engines usually come equipped with a small silencer and short exhaust pipe.   Two-cycle engines are not equipped with such equipment unless specifically ordered by the customer.   The two-cycle engine is very critical to the proper size and length of pipe.   Actually the exhaust system completes the scavenging system.   The pipe of proper size is then fitted to the correct length as recommended by the manufacturer.   This is in effect tuning of the pressure waves in order to allow the engine to develop maximum efficiency and power.   Incorrect exhaust-pipe length has a detrimental effect upon the operation, life, and power developed by the engine.

The gas line is brought to a scrubber and then through a reducing regulator to reduce the gas pressure to a few ounces where it enters the volume tank.   Normally 1-in. pipe is the smallest size recommended from the volume tank to the engine gas connection.   Larger engines require larger lines.   The purpose of the volume tank is to prevent fluctuations of gas pressure, and it should not have a volume of less than five times the cylinder displacement of the engine.

The gas regulator must be fitted with a proper-sized orifice for the pressure being reduced so that proper gas flow is provided.   A regulator with too large an orifice will surge, while a regulator with too small an orifice will not supply enough fuel to produce the power required.

Suitable cutoffs between the field line and the volume tank and between the volume tank and engine should be provided for draining off the scrubber and volume tank and servicing of the reducing regulator.

Many types of starters are used to turn engines over for starting.   Electric starters were put on engines in the automobile, and these were soon used on multiple-cylinder oil-field engines.   Slow-speed engines formerly were started by manually turning the large flywheel; however, now some manufacturers are providing electric and other built-in starters as optional equipment for the slow-speed engines.   Some of these types of starters are as follows:

1. Electric starter motors requiring from 6 to 24 volts direct current, power furnished by batteries.

2. 110- to 440-volt a-c starter motors allowing power and lighting circuits to be used for starting.

3. Air- or gas-motor starters in which a small vane-type air motor turns the engine through reduction gears and a bendix-type engaging mechanism.   This type of starter requires from 20 to 50 lb of gas or air pressure to operate.

4. Friction-wheel starters for slow-speed engines.   These starters use a small gasoline motor or an electric motor to turn a friction wheel which engages the engine flywheel and turns the engine.

5. High-pressure-air starting is usually applied to slow-speed engines, in which a valve admits air compressed to 125 to 200 lb into one or more cylinders to cause the engine to rotate.   Usually a small gasoline-engine-driven compressor is connected to a tank, which is used as a compressed-air storage tank.

6. Diaphragm gas starters in which a rather large rubber diaphragm is expanded by 20 to 50 lb gas pressure.   The expansion of the diaphragm causes a rack to turn a pinion attached to the engine crankshaft.   This rotates the engine for a few revolutions and is repeated until the engine starts.

7. Gasoline-driven engine starters in which a small gasoline engine is mounted on the engine to provide power through reduction gears to turn the engine until it is started.

The electric-motor starter of 6 to 24 volts is probably the most used of all types of starters on the smaller engines.   The battery can be located at the engine and recharged by a generator mounted on the engine. A recent change has been the use of easily attached cables connected to the batteries in trucks or automobiles. In this case, only one battery is required for several engines and the engine can be started while the battery is being recharged by the truck or automobile engine.

Large slow-speed engines are best started by using high-pressure air supplied by a small compressor and storage-tank assembly. This system is simple, foolproof, and reliable but is dependent on an outside source of air. The air compressor can also be used for cleaning or spray painting around the installation. Compressor units mounted in pickup trucks provide easy starting for a large number of engines and thus reduce the installation expense.

Engine Safety Controls

Every oil-field engine should be provided with reliable safety controls as engines in this service are unattended while the pumper is away on other duties. Safety controls are provided by some engine manufacturers as standard equipment. Such controls are available from supply companies for engines not so equipped.

Safety controls usually ground the magneto to cut off the ignition; however, they can be applied to the fuel system, which in case of failure will shut off the fuel to stop the engine. Usually diesel engines are supplied with safety controls to shut off the fuel.

Safety controls desirable for engines are:

1. High water temperature
2. Low oil pressure
3. Overspeed

Other safety controls sometimes used are:

1. Low water
2. Low oil
3. Vibration

Long-interval Maintenance Features

Since the oil operator desires to reduce maintenance and labor several new features have been developed for this purpose for the oil-field engine. These are no longer gadgets but are proved items that do lengthen the intervals of maintenance and reduce operating costs. These are:

1. Low-tension ignition gives better ignition with longer life to magnetos and spark plugs.

2. Extended-service clutches which require lubrication at intervals only once each 6 months.

3. Automatically filled crankcases on engines from drums of oil which assures correct oil level at all times.

4. Water make-up condensers to provide make-up water which is automatically added to the radiator as required.

Development of automatic time cycles for starting and stopping pumping engines for part-time pumping is progressing rapidly and will fill a need of the industry to reduce operating lease costs.

Advantages and Disadvantages of Two-cycle Slow-speed Gas Engines

Advantages

1. Extremely long life due to simple slow-moving parts.
2. Rugged heavy-duty construction with crossheads and packing boxes to seal combustion gases from crankcase.

3. No crankcase contamination from combustion gases.

4. Infrequent crankcase-oil changes.

5. Uniform crankshaft rotation due to a power impulse from each cylinder, each revolution, coupled with large WR^2 flywheels.

6. Engine operates on governor to compensate for load changes without varying speed.

7. Maintenance reduced to minimum because there are no valves or delicate adjustments.

8. Engine can be overhauled without removing from pumping unit.

9. Built-in starting and safety systems.

10. Sizes are available to fit most pumping-unit requirements.

Disadvantages

1. Cost per horsepower is higher than for high-speed engines.

2. Weight per horsepower is higher than for high-speed engines.

3. Can use only natural or LP gases—gasoline cannot be used.

4. Not recommended for portable installations.

5. Requires heavy foundations.

Advantages and Disadvantages of Four-cycle Slow-speed Gas Engines

Advantages

1. Longer life due to fewer and slower-moving parts.

2. Uniform crankshaft speed due to large WR^2 flywheel.

3. Engine operates on governor control of throttle to compensate for load changes.

4. Operation on gasoline, natural gas, or LP gases.

5. Simple construction.

6. Repairs usually made without removing engine from pumping unit.

Disadvantages

1. Cost per horsepower is higher than for high-speed engines.

2. Weight per horsepower is higher than for high-speed engines.

3. Available in sizes up to 30 hp only.

4. Severe shock on power stroke.

5. Requires sturdy foundations.

6. Sludging and contamination of crankcase oil by combustion gases.

7. Frequent oil changes.

8. Starting systems are not standard nor are they built into the engine design.

Advantages and Disadvantages of Four-cycle High-speed Engines

Advantages

1. Low initial cost.

2. Wide speed and power range.

3. Light weight per horsepower.

4. Low installation cost.

5. Ideal for portable installations.

6. Suitable for intermittent service.

7. Built-in starting and safety devices.

8. Small space required for installation.

9. Operation on various available fuels.

Disadvantages

1. Large speed variation in pumping cycle due to small flywheel WR^2 effect.
2. Basic design is not adapted to heavy continuous shock loading of oil-well pumping.
3. Short life because of fast-moving parts and close tolerances required.
4. Sludging and contamination of crankcase by combustion products.
5. Frequent oil changes.
6. Maintenance is frequent and high because of many small parts requiring adjustment.
7. Repairs usually require engine to be removed from pumping unit and placed in hands of expert mechanic.
8. Engine operates on fixed throttle with large speed variations. Governor acts only as overspeed device.

Advantages and Disadvantages of Diesel Engines (Two- or Four-cycle)

Advantages

1. Furnishes power where gas or electricity is not available.
2. Fuel is not explosive and may be transported easily.
3. Low fuel costs.

Disadvantages

1. High initial costs.
2. Maintenance high and must be done by experienced personnel.
3. Fuel storage must be provided.

ELECTRIC MOTORS FOR OIL-WELL PUMPING

Many types of electric motors have been used successfully for oil-well-pumping duty. These vary from a few installations of d-c motors (generally supplied from a small-lease generating plant) to single-phase fractional-horsepower a-c motors, for shallow stripper wells.

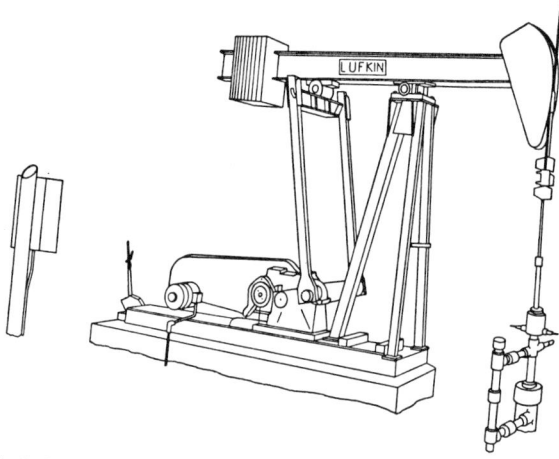

FIG. 9-15. Typical oil-well pumping installation, showing compact arrangement of oil-well-pumping motor, controller, and capacitor at well location.

Today, however, practically all modern electrified oil wells are powered by a-c polyphase squirrel-cage induction motors. These motors are preferred because of their suitability to oil-well load requirements, lower first cost, ready availability from stock, and long record of service dependability in the oil fields.

A-C induction motors for oil-field use are usually operated at 440 volts, three-phase, 60 cycles, a-c power from the secondary of distribution transformers located on the lease, and whose primaries are supplied from high-voltage transmission lines (usually in the range of 9 to 15 kv) from the power company. A few isolated lease generating plants are still in use today.

A modern-day oil-well pumping-unit installation powered by a three-phase induction motor is illustrated in Fig. 9-15.

There are many classifications and standards for squirrel-cage induction motors according to ASA (American Standards Association) and NEMA (National Electrical Manufacturers Association) standards. In general, motors are classified by design characteristics, voltage standards, types of enclosure, insulation, and temperature rise.

Design Standards

According to NEMA and ASA design standards, a-c squirrel-cage motors are classified as follows:

Design B. Normal starting (inrush) current
Normal starting (breakaway) torque—100 to 175 per cent of full-load torque
Normal slip—less than 5 per cent
Design C. Normal starting current
High starting torque—200 to 250 per cent of full-load torque
Normal slip—less than 5 per cent
Design D. Normal starting current
High starting torque—275 per cent or more of full-load torque
High slip—5 per cent or more

The speed-torque characteristics of the three NEMA designs of motors are compared in Fig. 9-16.

The *design B* motor is the most popular general-purpose motor for most industrial applications. However, its comparatively low starting torque makes its use in the oil fields rather limited. This type is seldom used to drive beam pumping units

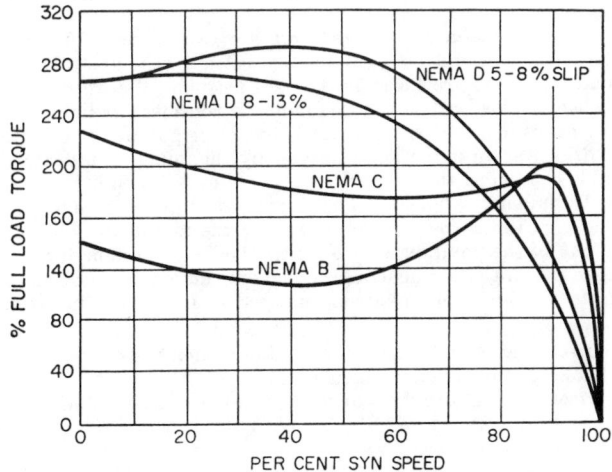

FIG. 9-16. Typical speed-torque characteristic curves for NEMA design B, NEMA design C, and NEMA design D induction motors.

because, generally speaking, it does not possess sufficient starting and accelerating torque characteristics. Therefore, on the lease, the NEMA design B motor is limited to such easy-to-start applications as fans, blowers, small centrifugal pumps, and compressors. The design B motor is also used as the prime mover for surface hydraulic pumping units, as these types of pumps have a low starting-torque requirement.

The *design C* motor has been the most popular type of motor for driving walking-beam pumping units. Its high starting torque and relatively low initial cost have made this type of motor well suited to sucker-rod pumping. Most beam pumping units have double-reduction gearboxes to operate the pump at speeds in the range of 10 to 25 spm. This is accomplished generally by using a 1,200-rpm synchronous-speed motor and a speed reduction of about 3:1 in the V-belt drive between the motor shaft and the gearbox pinion shaft, and a speed reduction of about 30:1 in the double-reduction gear unit between the high-speed pinion shaft and the crankshaft of the pumping unit. Pumping units with single-reduction gearboxes generally require a 900-rpm synchronous-speed motor. If slower-speed pumping is desired, this may be accomplished by means of a jack shaft or double V-belt drive arrangement on the pumping unit.

The high-starting-torque high-slip *design D* motor has recently become a popular choice for oil-well pumping duty, because its performance characteristics are well suited to the peculiar oil-well pumping-duty cycle. A tracing of line current drawn by a motor driving an oil-well pumping unit is shown in

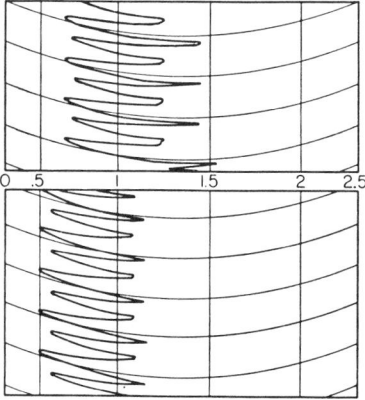

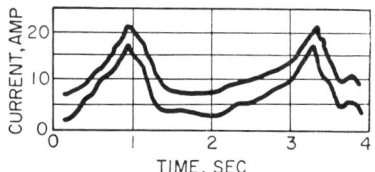

Fig. 9-17. Oscillograph of line current drawn, showing peaking varying load duty on an oil-well-pumping motor.

Fig. 9-18. Comparison of peak currents drawn by NEMA design C motor (top) and NEMA design D motor (bottom) on same oil-well-pumping load.

Fig. 9-17. As indicated on this figure there are two current (or kilowatt) peaks, one when the rod string and fluid column are lifted on the upstroke, and the other when the counterweights are lifted on the downstroke. Between these two peaks are valleys, when the load carried by the motor is considerably lightened, or perhaps even negative peaks if power is regenerated or power pumped back into the line as the motor is driven as an induction generator by the falling counterweights.

The desirable characteristic of the design D motor is its ability to "slip" or slow down on loads suddenly applied. This increased slipping action under overload conditions cushions the current peaks drawn by the motor and allows the WR^2 or "flywheel effect" of the pumping unit to carry the load as the motor gives up speed. Field tests have shown that, in general, the high-slip design D motor has the following desirable effects on oil-well pumping as compared with normal-slip design C motors:

1. Lower current peaks and lower kilowatt billing demands
2. Lower kilowatthour per barrel lifting costs
3. Less thermal loading of motor, or more usable work horsepower per nameplate rating

Typical peak currents drawn by NEMA design C and NEMA design D motors are compared in Fig. 9-18.

Standard Ratings

Integral-horsepower polyphase a-c motors are available in the following standard ratings: 1, 1½, 2, 3, 4, 5, 7½, 10, 15, 20, 25, 30, 40, 50, 60, 75, 100, 125, 150, 200. These motors can be obtained in the following synchronous speeds: 600, 720, 900, 1,200, 1,800 3,600.

Multihorsepower Rated Motors

Multihorsepower rated motors are sometimes used for oil-well pumping. These are either dual-horsepower or triple-horsepower rated motors, usually the latter.

Triple-horsepower rated motors are available in the following standard horsepower ratings:

```
5/3  5/2
10/ 7/4
15/ 9/6
20/14/8
25/14/10
30/21/12
40/28/16
50/35/29
75/52/30
```

Dual- or triple-horsepower-rated motors have been used to gain additional efficiency and power factor when a motor was underloaded initially but when the load was expected to increase—on a waterflood operation, for example, as the water-to-oil ratio built up.   Also, they have been used in the past when it was common practice for the power companies to base their demand billing charge on connected horsepower rather than on maximum power consumption over an integrated period of time as is usually done today.

Because of their higher first cost and the expense involved in reconnecting horsepower ratings, resizing fuses, overload relay heaters, and capacitors, multihorsepower motors are not used to any great extent today by most major oil producers.   With the installation of a capacitor of proper size, a single-rated motor will operate efficiently and with good power factor even when lightly loaded.   In addition, the labor of reconnection and costs of resizing fuses and overload heaters are saved.

Standard Voltage Ratings

Most oil-well pumping motors are rated 200/440 volts, three-phase, 60-cycle nameplate rating, and are usually operated from 480-volt lease-distribution secondary power supply.   Motors up through 10 hp occasionally are operated at 220 volts, three-phase, 60 cycles from 240-volt lease power supply.   There is also a trend toward the use of 762-volt-rated motors, especially where horsepower ratings are large (in excess of 20 hp) and well spacing wide or irregular, necessitating long secondary runs to the motor loads.   For this type of layout, banks of three single-phase transformers are used to step down the high-voltage power supplied to the lease to the motor secondary or motor utilization voltage.   The secondary windings of the distribution transformers are connected in wye with the mid-point connection solidly grounded.   This arrangement results in a balanced three-phase secondary power supply of 480 volts line to ground, and 831 volts line to line.

The advantage of the four-wire 831-volt solidly grounded wye lease-distribution system is that smaller-sized conductor and transformer capacity are required for the same load and spacing, or for the same size of conductor and transformers, power can be submitted about three times as far as 440-volt systems with the same I^2R power losses or system heating losses.   However, the economics of both electrical systems should be carefully compared before making a decision on voltage level to be used.

Standard industrial-type induction motors are dual-voltage-rated with nine leads brought out from the motor winding to the conduit box for reconnection from 220 to 440 volts in either a series-wye or series-delta connection.   The higher voltage rating (440 volts) is the series connection and the lower voltage rating (220 volts) is the multiple or parallel connection.   The 220-volt connection, therefore, has doubled the current rating as the 440-volt connection.   The efficiency, power factor, slip, and torque characteristics are the same for both voltages.

The 762-volt motor has six leads brought out to the motor conduit box for reconnection either wye (762 volts) or delta (440 volts).

Standard a-c induction motors are designed to operate at plus or minus 10 per cent of nameplate voltage, plus or minus 5 per cent of nameplate frequency, or a combination of plus or minus 5 per cent of nameplate voltage and plus or minus 5 per cent of nameplate frequency.

Single-phase Motors

Single-phase a-c motors are also found in the oil field in sizes up through 5 hp, although their use is limited.   In oil-well pumping, their use is confined to shallow stripper wells producing in fields where three-phase power is not available.

Single-phase motors cost more initially than their three-phase counterpart of like rating.   Also, they are less efficient and more costly to operate.   To assure high starting torque and low operating current, single-phase motors of the capacitor-start capacitor-run varieties should be used.

Phase Converters

Occasionally phase converters are used in the oil field to convert single-phase power supply to three-phase power supply to give more motor torque, or where three-phase power is likely to become available to the lease in the near future.   Phase converters are either of the static-component type or of the rotary type.   The static type, in particular, which derives its three-phase power output by splitting one line of the single-phase a-c supply through a capacitive-inductive circuit, must be considerably derated for proper application on oil-well pumping loads.   This is true because of the considerable voltage unbalance that may result under varying peaking load conditions.   Therefore, in general, the use of phase converters is to be discouraged for oil-well pumping applications.

Torque

Torque may be defined as the twisting and turning effort that the driven machine requires to keep it moving at a proper speed.   The motor adjusts its speed over a rather narrow range in accordance with its design to develop the torque required by the driven machine.   The same horsepower can be obtained from either a high-speed low-torque motor or a low-speed high-torque motor.

In (sucker-rod) oil-well-pumping applications, the first and perhaps most important torque consideration for the motor is the *starting* or *breakaway* torque.   The motor should be able to break away and start the load under the worst possible condition of counterbalance and fluid viscosity in the hole.   Slip and torque are closely interrelated in the design of induction motors, and in general the greater the motor slip, the greater the starting torque of the motor up to the point that breakdown torque is obtained at starting.

Breakdown or *pull-out* torque is defined as the maximum torque the motor will develop as load is increased, starting from full-speed no-load until the motor begins to stall.

The torque capability, both breakdown and starting, of an induction motor is drastically affected by changes in the a-c power supply.   The motor torque developed varies directly as the square of the applied voltage.   Therefore, a 10 per cent drop in terminal voltage applied to the motor reduces the maximum starting and breakdown torques to 81 per cent of what they would be at full rated voltage.   Thus it is very important that oil-well pumping motors have rated nameplate voltage applied at the terminals if they are to develop their maximum torque and horsepower ratings.

As mentioned previously, a high-slip NEMA design D motor has a greater starting torque than does the NEMA design C motor.   For this reason, the design D motor is often used where starting is apt to be a problem or where poor voltage regulation exists—on the end of long feeder runs, for example.

Slip

The difference between motor synchronous speed and speed under load is called "slip" and is usually expressed in per cent of synchronous speed.   In a squirrel-cage induction motor, if the rotor could come up to synchronous speed or to the speed of the rotating magnetic field, by the flux produced across the air gap, no current would be induced in the rotor-bar conductors, and no torque would be developed. For this reason, an indication motor, even under no-load operation, does not ever attain synchronous speed.   As more and more load is applied, its speed drops further below its synchronous speed as the motor develops more torque.   Thus, slip increases with load.

Example.   A six-pole 1,200-rpm synchronous-speed induction motor with a full load speed of 1,140 rpm would have a 5 per cent slip.

$$\text{Slip} = \frac{1,200 - 1,140}{1,200} = 5 \text{ per cent}$$

The amount of slip an induction motor will have is controlled to a large measure by the resistance of the rotor winding.   The higher the resistance of the rotor winding, the more slip the motor will have.

Power Factor

Power factor (pf) is a relationship between reactive (magnetizing) power drawn by the motor and load (resistive) power.   Since power-factor angle determines the magnitude of line current drawn by the motor ($I_{\text{line}} = I_{\text{load/pf}}$), high power factor is important in reducing line losses and in minimizing power billing.   Also, since low power factor increases line current, the consideration of power factor is important in the sizing of transformers and conductor to the load.

If average line voltage (phase to phase) is measured in the field (usually by means of a clip-on-type voltammeter), then motor cyclic or average power factor can be determined from

$$\text{pf avg} = \frac{(\text{kw input})(2)}{\sqrt{(3)}(\text{volts avg})(\text{amp}_{\text{rms}})}$$

In general, motors designed with higher torques will have a somewhat lower full-load power factor.   This is true on steady-state loads.   Full-load steady-state power factors for induction motors usually fall in the range of 80 to 88 per cent.   On typical beam-pumping installations with a NEMA design C motor and without capacitors (uncorrected power factor), the power factor will usually measure somewhere between 0.35 and 0.60, depending largely upon the size of the motor compared with its average load and system voltage regulation.   However, the high-torque high-slip NEMA design D motor will generally test out with about 20 points higher average power factor on cyclic load application as compared with normal-slip NEMA design C motors.   Oversized motors inherently have low operating power factors.

Efficiency

An a-c induction motor used for oil-well pumping will have an average power factor and efficiency less than its nameplate full-load steady-state values, even though fully loaded thermally.   This is true because the motor is underloaded mechanically during the major portion of the pumping cycle, despite the fact that the average rms line current drawn may be equal to full-load rated current.

In general, a-c induction motors have flat efficiency curves from about half load to load and a quarter. Motors designed with higher full-load slip will have slightly lower full-load efficiency. The average cyclic load efficiency of a motor on beam-pumping duty is hard to measure and can best be determined from the motor-performance-characteristic curves as follows:

1. From measured rms cyclic load current, determine corresponding "thermal" horsepower load on motor from motor curves. Also, find corresponding motor efficiency and determine motor losses.

2. Measure average electrical load on motor from kilowatthour meter. Subtract motor losses from this measurement of motor horsepower input to obtain actual motor output or mechanical load on motor shaft. This output horsepower divided by input horsepower is cyclic load average efficiency for the motor.

The motor is only one link in the chain of total surface efficiency including losses in the V-belt drive, pumping-unit bearings, and gearbox losses. Therefore, the only time indication of an oil-well pumping motor's efficiency is the change in total surface efficiency with the same polished-rod horsepower load. This can best be determined on a kilowatthour per barrel basis by accurately measuring kilowatt input to the motor over a period of time and accurately measuring total production in barrels for that same period of time. The measurement of kilowatthours per barrel should be taken as accurately as possible over as long a period of time as is practical.

Electric-motor Selection and Application

Various formulas are now in use for determining motor nameplate horsepower required for beam-pumping application. A representative formula is

$$NPHP = \left(\frac{B \times D}{136,000} + \frac{WSL}{1,600,000}\right) K$$

where $NPHP$ = motor nameplate horsepower required
B = max pump capacity at 100 per cent volumetric efficiency, bbl/24 hr
D = depth of fluid level, ft
W = weight of rods, lb
L = length of stroke, in.
S = strokes per minute
K = surface efficiency and motor derating factor

All such formulas for determining motor horsepower rating required revert to the basic formula

$$NPHP = \frac{\text{hyd. hp} + \text{fric. hp}}{\text{surf. eff.}} \times CLF$$

where $NPHP$ = motor nameplate horsepower required
hyd. hp = hydraulic horsepower (pump displacement rates figured at 100 per cent pump volumetric efficiency and 1.0 specific gravity of fluid times fluid lift)
fric. hp = subsurface losses
surf. eff. = surface efficiency of pumping unit (prime-mover shaft to polished rod) usually in range of 0.6 to 0.85
CLF = motor cyclic load factor (inverse of motor derating factor) for beam pumping, usually in the range

Motor type	Motor derating factor	Cyclic load factor
Design C............	0.6–0.7	1.43–1.67
Design D............	0.7–0.8	1.25–1.43

Cyclic Load Factor

A motor applied to cyclic-peaking type of duty, such as oil-well pumping, will be thermally loaded more than it would be for the same average load applied on a steady-state basis. Stated another way, a motor on cyclic-load duty will be thermally heated to a higher equivalent horsepower load than on steady-load duty, when the same average mechanical load is applied. Therefore, for this type of duty, a motor must be derated from its full-load nameplate rating for proper application on cyclic-peaking duty.

The measure of a motor's true performance and rating on cyclic-load application cannot be determined by means of normal indications or recording-type instruments. Since the load is continually fluctuating from a 200 to 275 per cent overload peak to perhaps a negative value, the pointers for indicating instruments are continually swinging in accordance with the load changes. Under these conditions, averaging is impossible or at the best involves extremely tedious and time-consuming work. A simpler, more usable method of determining true motor load or thermal heating is by means of a thermal-type ammeter. This instrument indicates rms current corresponding to the true heating or "thermal" horsepower load on the motor. This current will always be higher than the average input as determined by integrating or graphic methods available, and the corresponding "thermal" horsepower will be higher than the average load horsepower as determined, for example, from kilowatt-input methods. The ratio of the average horsepower output to the "thermal" horsepower output corresponding to rms line current is called motor derating factor and is always less than 1. Its inverse is called cyclic load factor and always is greater than 1.

It is important to select a motor of a horsepower rating closely matched to the load requirements. Obviously a motor too small for the load will overheat and possibly burn out, whereas a motor too large for the load not only represents a greater than necessary initial investment cost but will operate at less desirable power factor and efficiency.

Motor-test Data

If data and information are not available to guide the determination of motor nameplate horsepower rating, the required horsepower can be determined by test using a motor known to be larger than needed and measuring the resulting power consumed. The power measured in watts can be converted to horsepower by the following formula:

$$\text{hp required} = \frac{\text{watts measured} \times \text{estimated efficiency of motor}}{0.746}$$

Note: See discussion on cyclic load factor above for properly rating a-c motors for oil-well pumping duty. On steady-state load or applications, motor derating or cyclic load factors are not used.

The proper sizing of oil-well pumping motors for beam-pumping units can be determined in the field by measuring rms line-current input with a thermal-type ammeter and comparing this value with the full-load nameplate current of the motor. This ratio or comparison of rms line amperes drawn to the full-load nameplate current will give a good indication of the per cent of rated load to which the motor is thermally loaded.

The exact thermal load on the motor may be ascertained by means of the certified operating-performance curves of the motor (furnished by the manufacturer on request). From these performance curves, the "thermal" load or output horsepower of the motor can be found from the measured rms or thermal current during operation.

An indication of motor derating or cyclic load factors can also be determined from the motor-performance-characteristic curves in the following manner:

1. Measure motor rms line current drawn on cyclic-load operation with an rms thermal-type ammeter.

2. Measure kilowatt input to the motor using a stop watch to clock accurately the disk revolutions of a kilowatthour meter connected in the motor line. Then,

$$\text{kw input} = \frac{\text{disk revolutions}}{\text{time, sec}} \times K_h \text{ (meter constant)} \times 60 \text{ sec/min} \times 60 \text{ min/hr}$$

and

$$\text{hp input} = \frac{\text{kw input}}{0.746}$$

NOTE: At least 20 or 30 disk revolutions should be clocked to obtain an accurate indication of actual average kilowatt input to the motor.

3. From the motor-performance-characteristic curves, find the equivalent horsepower output corresponding to the measured rms thermal current drawn. Also find the motor efficiency corresponding to this current on the motor curves.

4. Determine motor losses (in horsepower) from the motor "thermal" horsepower output and efficiency from

$$\text{hp input} = \frac{\text{hp output}}{\text{motor efficiency}}$$

and

$$\text{hp losses} = \text{hp input} - \text{hp output}$$

5. Subtract motor losses from measured motor horsepower input in item 1 above to find the actual motor load or horsepower output.

6. Divide the load horsepower output (5) by the equivalent thermal horsepower output (3) to determine motor derating or cyclic load factor.

A more exact method of determining motor derating or cyclic load factor is by comparing temperature rise (by resistance) at full-load steady-state test with the temperature rise on cyclic load duty with rms current equal to full-load current. This method is not too practical, however, since accurate temperature rise is difficult to measure by thermometer and motors are normally not supplied with thermocouples embedded in the windings for measuring temperature rise by resistance.

Types of Enclosure

There are four basic motor enclosures, as follows:

Dripproof

Allows outside air to move through the motor to cool it but affords adequate protection against most weather conditions. In general, the use of dripproof constructed motors for outdoor oil-well-pumping service has proved entirely satisfactory in most locations. This type of construction is built with closed-front end bell to eliminate the entry of horizontal rain, sleet, or snow into the motor. This fact, coupled with its proved dependability, service-factor rating, and improved insulation system, makes the dripproof motor the first choice for outdoor oil-well-pumping service.

Splashproof

Allows outside air to move through the motor to cool it but affords a somewhat greater degree of protection against splashing liquids entering the motor.

Totally Enclosed

Motor does not have any outside air in contact with windings, and all its heat loss must be conducted away through its frame. This type of construction provides the maximum protection for the windings and should be specified for extremely moist, dirty, or dusty locations, or in corrosive atmospheres, such as sour-gas fields.

Explosion-proof and Dust-explosion-proof

A modification of the totally enclosed construction approved for use in hazardous-gas and hazardous-dust conditions as defined by the National Electric Code.

Temperature Rise

The temperature rise is usually listed on the nameplate of the motor in degrees centigrade and is the limit of maximum temperature increase which any part of the motor winding or magnetic structure, which is accessible for measurement with a thermometer, will have when the motor is developing its full load. Actually these temperature-rise limits are determined by the motor enclosure and class of insulation used, and they do not necessarily mean that these (maximum) temperature increases will occur. Generally, the more the motor enclosure restricts the flow of outside cooling air, the higher will be the temperature-rise limit, and in all probability, the higher will be the temperature of the winding.

Types of Insulation

Atmospheric conditions, ambient temperature, motor design, and application dictate the type of insulation used in motor windings. ASA, NEMA, and AIEE have established the classes of insulation and maximum total temperatures applicable to these classes.

The electrical industry by ASA and NEMA standards presently recognizes four classes of winding insulation. For normal service life, the temperature of the motor windings should not exceed the maximum allowable temperature for that particular type of insulation.

The four classes of motor insulation and maximum internal temperatures follow. Class A and B insulation systems are the most commonly used.

Class A Insulation

Consists basically of organic materials and fibers such as cotton, linen, paper, and varnish, and molded or laminated materials with cellulose filler, phenolic resins, and other cellulose derivatives of similar properties. The maximum total temperature specified is 105°C.

Class B Insulation

Consists mainly of inorganic materials such as glass, mica, asbestos, fiberglass, and similar materials with organic binding substances. A small proportion of class A materials may be used for structural purposes only, but using organic varnishes. The maximum total temperature specified is 130°C.

Class F Insulation

Basically same as inorganic class B materials, but with maximum temperature limit specified as 155°C.

Class H Insulation

Consists only of completely inorganic materials such as glass, mica, asbestos, fiberglass, and other similar inorganic materials composed of silicone compounds or materials with equivalent properties. The maximum total temperature specified is 180°C.

For all insulation classes, the limit of maximum rise for standard motors is based on an ambient temperature of 40°C. Ten degrees centigrade is added to the maximum rise to allow for the "hottest spot" which cannot be reached by thermometer.

The sum of the 40°C ambient base, the rise allowance, plus the 10°C allowance for the hottest spot all add up to the maximum total operating temperature which will exist in a motor operating at its rated load under rated voltage, frequency, and ambient conditions. Any difference between this maximum total operating temperature and the maximum safe total temperature as specified for the particular class of insulation used is marginal and may be retained to permit operation in higher ambient temperatures or operation of the motor in excess of rated load, or it may be retained to afford an insulation life expectancy longer than normal.

NEMA has established the following temperature-rise standards (in degrees centigrade) by thermometer:

Type of enclosure	Class of insulation			
	Class A	Class B	Class F	Class H
Open or dripproof............	40	60*	90†	100‡
Splashproof.................	50	70	95	110
Totally enclosed.............	55	75	100	115

* NEMA has not, up to the present time, established standards for this classification. However, 55 and 60°C limits are now being used by various manufacturers.

† NEMA has not established temperature standards for this classification. However, a limit of 100°C has been set by most manufacturers.

‡ NEMA has not established standards for this classification. However, 100°C rise limits are being used by some manufacturers.

The thermal life of the insulation, hence the motor life, is dependent upon the total temperature of the insulation and its duration in the operation of the motor. Various organizations such as ASA, NEMA, and AIEE have standardized the more common motor-insulation systems into various temperature classes.

The temperature class defines the maximum temperature for a desired insulation life. The two most common temperature classes are the class A system (105°C total temperature) and the class B system (130°C total temperature).

Service Factor

Rated horsepower multiplied by the service-factor rating represents the load which can be carried continuously by the motor, without exceeding standard temperature-insulation limit, provided rated voltage and frequency are maintained. In other words, service factor may be defined as the percentage overload at which a motor may be operated without exceeding safe temperature rise.

NEMA has established the following standards of service factors for class A insulated continuously rated 40°C rise motors, when operated at rated voltage and frequency:

Hp rating	Service factor
½ through 1	1.25
1½ through 2	1.20
3 through 200	1.15

These service factors apply specifically to NEMA designs A, B, and C motors but do not necessarily apply to design D motors. They do not apply to splashproof or totally enclosed motors, unless they are specifically so designed and the service factor is guaranteed on the nameplate.

The result of continuously operating any motor at overloads which produce an excessive temperature rise in the motor will be shortening of the insulation life of the motor. As a general rule, each additional 10°C continuous excess temperature over the maximum safe temperature for class A insulation will shorten the life of the insulation by one-half. For example, since the expected life of class A insulation operated at a total temperature of 105°C is considered to be 10 years, class A insulated motors operated continuously at 125°C would have a life expectancy of only 2½ years.

Class B and class H insulated motors, although capable of operating at much higher temperatures, have similar resulting shortened life when continuously subjected to operating temperatures in excess of their maximum safe total temperature.

Inspection and Maintenance

The service life of an a-c induction motor basically is determined by the bearing life and life of the insulation, since a-c induction motors basically have only two wearing parts, the bearings and the insulation system. With proper care and attention the modern oil-well pumping motor will give many years of trouble-free service on the lease with only a slight amount of maintenance required. If the motor is properly sized to the mechanical and electrical load as previously discussed, and the V-belt drive properly aligned during installation, the motor should require nothing more than a routine inspection every three to six months and periodic regreasing of the bearings every three to five years.

There are two types of ball bearings used on oil-well-pumping motors: the sealed bearing which cannot be regreased; and the regreasable type, which is virtually sealed by the machined fit of the end bell or bearing housing on the outside, and by an inner bearing cap on the inside.

Regreasable-type bearings are normally shipped with pipe plugs in place of grease fittings for oil-field service. Proper regreasing procedure is as follows:

1. Shut the motor down as a safety precaution for men working around the belts and coupling.

2. Replace pipe plug on top of bearing housing with pressure grease fitting and remove purge plug from bottom of housing.

3. Add new ball-bearing grease as recommended by motor manufacturer with pressure gun until new grease is expelled from out the purge opening in the bottom.

4. Start up and run the motor for about five minutes after all grease has been forced out the purge opening.

5. Shut down and replace purge plug in bottom of housing and pipe plug in top of housing.

Note that extreme care should be taken in regreasing and oil-field motor to be certain that the proper grade and type of grease is used (see manufacturers' instructions or recommendations) and that only clean grease in good condition is used. Needless to state, a clean grease gun and grease fittings should be used, and care should be exercised to see that this is done. With this type of care and precaution taken, the motor bearings should last indefinitely.

In the periodic routine inspection of the motor, the pumper or electrician should check for excessive noise, vibration, or heat, any unusual signs of trouble or faults, such as burning insulation, arcing or burned spots, noise, or smoke. In addition, the alignment and condition of the V belts and coupling, debris in air passages, and rigid connection of ground wires should all be carefully checked.

OIL-FIELD-TYPE CONTROL

To use an electric motor as prime mover for oil-field pumping equipment it is necessary to use a control which provides both control of the operation of the motor and protection of the motor and associated control equipment. Since this is an outdoor installation, it is necessary that the components of the control be installed in a weatherproof steel box. Figure 9-19 shows a photograph of a typical oil-field control.

Normally included in the oil-field control are the following components:

1. For control
   Program time switch
   Hand-off-auto selector switch
   Line disconnect switch or air circuit breaker
   Three-pole line contactor

2. For protection
   Three-element thermal-overload relay
   Lightning arrester
   Sequence restart timer
   Undervoltage relay
   Line fuses or thermal-trip air circuit breaker
   The functions of the above components are as follows:

Program Time Switch

This device is essentially an electric clock and is used for automatic unattended operation of oil wells to start and stop the motor on some preselected time-cycle basis.

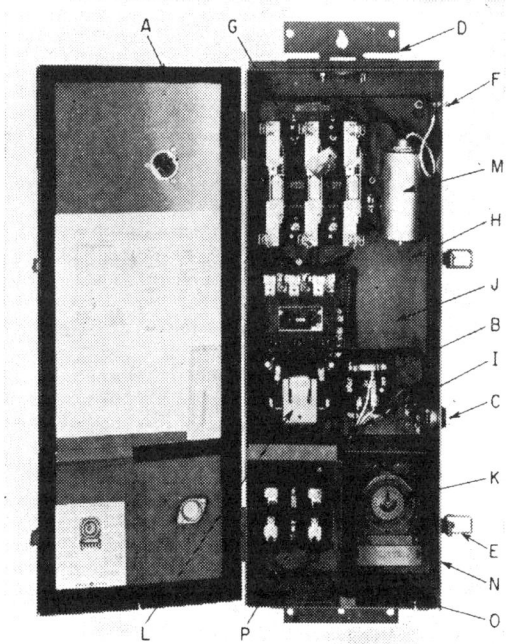

Fig. 9-19. Modern-day oil-well pumping controller showing location of power and control devices within the enclosure. *A*, neoprene gasket on inside of enclosure door seals dust, rain, and snow out of upper compartment. *B*, high drop-out undervoltage relay protects against low voltage and helps to prevent single phasing. *C*, welded conduit hub with pipe plug eliminates possibility of water seepage into enclosure. *D*, winged mounting brackets at top and bottom of enclosure provide easy mounting of controller. *E*, trunk-type latches have provision for padlocking. *F*, pressure-type grounding connector on outside of enclosure gives visual indication of ground. *G*, fusible disconnect switch has interchangeable fuse clips for changing to different ratings; forms are also available with circuit breaker. *H*, space for adding definite sequence restart timer. *I*, neat, laced, harness-type wiring provides extra room; it is color-coded to facilitate trouble shooting. *J*, plenty of room for adding test terminal board or any other special devices that may be required. *K*, reliable, accurate timer functions as both a program and automatic sequence restart timer. *L*, long-life magnetic contractor is easy to service and has dependable strongbox coil construction to protect coil windings against dust, oil, and water. *M*, 3-phase lightning arrester provides secondary protection; it is in separate compartment to minimize component damage in case of direct strike. *N*, louvers in both sides and bottom of overload compartment provide cross and chimney ventilation to assure same ambient for overloads and motor. *O*, 4 combination knockouts in bottom of enclosure provide entrance for power, motor, and control leads and wires from a power-factor capacitor. *P*, bimetallic overload relays in separate ventilated compartment give dependable motor protection.

The time switch is considered standard equipment for the oil-field-type control, except where 24-hour operation is desired. Tabs on this device make it possible to set it to start and stop the motor as desired throughout a 24-hour period.

Hand-off-auto Selector Switch

This switch allows manual operation or automatic control, or allows the operator to stop the motor by placing the switch in off position.

Line Disconnect Switch

The line disconnect switch is a fused disconnect switch which controls the power to the motor and at the same time gives protection by using current-limiting fuses.

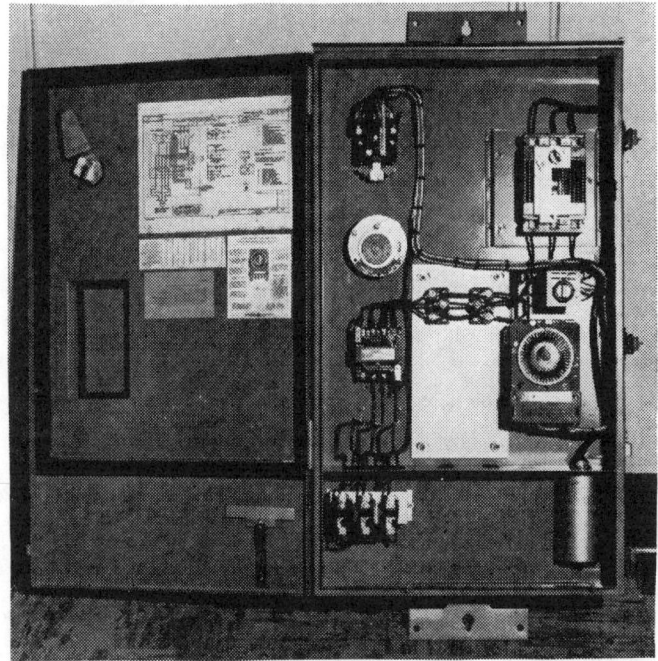

Fig. 9-20. Oil-well-pumping controller with thermal-trip circuit breaker.

A substitute for this switch can be the circuit breaker, which usually has thermal-type trip elements which operate on a thermal or heating principle. Figure 9-20 is a photograph of an oil-field-type control using the circuit breaker.

Three-pole Line Contactor

The line contactor is a power-circuit opening and closing device which starts or stops the motor in accordance with the control-circuit signal.

Three-element Thermal-overload Relay

This device protects the motor on all conditions of sustained overcurrent caused by low-voltage conditions on the line, unbalanced phase voltages, single phasing of power source, or actual overload on the motor itself. This is usually a bimetallic-strip type. This overload relay is tripped by the bending of a bimetallic strip caused by heat, which shuts down the motor.

Lightning Arrester

Lightning is one of the chief causes of motor failures because of the voltage surge sent through all the apparatus connected to the power lines. It should be connected to the incoming line terminals just ahead of the line disconnect switch or circuit breaker. Proper ground for this device should be provided, usually by connection to the well casing.

Sequence Restart Timer

When several wells are connected to a single distribution transformer, it is usually desirable to stagger the restarting of the motors following a shutdown, if the wells are on automatic operation. This may be accomplished by using a definite-sequence restarting device or the random-sequence restarting device. The latter is ordinarily used in oil-well pumping.

Undervoltage Relay

This is a safety device which cuts off the motor if the voltage drops below a pre-determined amount.

Line Fuses or Thermal-trip Air Circuit Breaker

Line fuses burn out under conditions of overload to protect the rest of the system. Thermal-trip air circuit breakers perform the same function by tripping when a certain temperature is reached, disconnecting the rest of the equipment.

How to Select Oil-field-type Control

To select oil-field-type control from manufacturers' bulletins, it is necessary to know the horsepower of the motor involved, the voltage, whether three-phase or single-phase, whether program timer is required, and whether a sequence restart timer is required. The usual components in a control are a fusible disconnect switch, undervoltage relay, three overload relays, a lightning arrester, a selector switch, and a program timer, the latter being optional. The choice can be made between a control with fusible disconnect switch or a control with circuit breaker. To select a control from manufacturers' bulletins determine the catalog number of the control shown for the horsepower and voltage involved and order by that number. The controls are available with program timer and automatic-sequence restart, or with program timer and definite-sequence restart, and the proper catalog number for the voltage involved should be determined after a decision is made as to the type of sequence restart that will be required. Select proper overload relay heaters from the tables given by the manufacturer.

LEASE-DISTRIBUTION SYSTEMS AND EQUIPMENT

General

The basic requirement of the lease electrical-distribution system is to provide an adequate voltage level at the motors during starting and while running. In addition, the lease-distribution system should provide for continuity of service, flexibility in operation, and load growth.

Figure 9-21 depicts a portion of a typical overhead lease-distribution system, showing high-voltage primary lines (crossarm mounted), stepdown distribution transformers (pole-mounted), and low-voltage secondary lines (underbuilt).

FIG. 9-21. Typical lease-distribution system, showing overhead distribution lines and step-down transformers to serve motor loads.

Primary Distribution Voltages

Both primary or high-voltage and secondary or low-voltage service is usually available from electric utilities serving the oil fields. On large leases the purchaser normally chooses primary service and distributes power over the lease from his own distribution system. This choice depends largely on the difference in power rates, the operating economies between high- and low-voltage systems, the size of the connected load, the anticipated growth, the availability and cost of power apparatus, and the cost of erecting and maintaining a power-distribution system to serve the lease.

Usual primary service voltages found in the oil field are 12,000, 13,200, 13,800, and 14,400 volts delta, three-wire; and 12,470 volts wye, four-wire.

Secondary Distribution Voltages

The standard utilization voltage predominantly found in the oil fields is 480 volts delta, three-phase, three-wire, 60 cycles. Other secondary voltages such as 240, 762, 880, and 1,200 volts three-phase and 480 and 240 volts single-phase are also found. In general, three-phase distribution systems better lend themselves to economic design and operation, particularly where large loads and long distribution distances are involved.

Types of Conductor

Overhead open-wire construction is generally used in oil-field distribution systems, both primary and secondary.

Base copper conductor was used predominantly a few years back and is still used quite extensively; however, stranded aluminum-conductor-steel-reinforced (ACSR) is commonly used today.

The motor service drop is usually either a multiconductor cable or single conductors in rigid conduit.

Distribution Transformers

The distribution transformers serve to reduce or transform high-voltage power to a lower utilization voltage, without appreciable loss of power in the transformation.

Distribution transformers are rated in kilovolt-amperes (kva) since they must supply reactive power (kvar) as well as power consumed as useful work (kw).

Single-phase oil-immersed self-cooled transformers are generally used in the oil fields, although three-phase transformers of the self-protected type are also used.

Self-protected transformers offer complete coordinated protection since they have an internally mounted thermal-trip low-voltage breaker, high-voltage bushing-type fuses, and tank-mounted high-voltage lightning arresters.

One advantage of single-phase transformers is that they can be connected two together in an open-delta arrangement. This is sometimes done, to cut down initial expense, when the connected load will be initially low but will build up later—such as when waterflooding. When required, the third transformer can be added to close the delta and permit full loading of the transformer bank. It must be remembered that, on an open-delta connection, the bank will carry only 86.6 per cent of the rating of the two units. Single-phase transformers of the same or different kva ratings may be connected in parallel to give a greater kva capacity, provided the following conditions are met:

1. Voltage ratings are identical.
2. Tap settings are identical.
3. Per cent impedance of one closely matches that of the other.
4. Frequency ratings are identical.

Delta-delta, wye-delta, and delta-wye are the most commonly used three-phase transformation connections. In the case of the wye-delta transformation, the high-voltage neutral of the transformer bank should be isolated and not connected to the power-circuit neutral.

When wye-delta connections are used and the high-voltage neutral of the transformer is not connected to the circuit neutral, an open conductor in the three-phase primary results in a single-phase input and output of the bank. If the transformer supplies a motor, harmful overcurrent may occur, depending on motor load. An equal current flows in two conductors of the motor branch circuit, and the sum of the two currents flows in the third line. Hence, three-phase or three-element thermal-overload protection is indicated for motor protection.

A bank of wye-wye-connected transformers should not be used unless the system is four-wire. The primary neutral of the transformer bank should be tied firmly to the system neutral. If this is not done, excessive voltages may develop on the secondary side of the transformers.

A considerable savings in first cost can sometimes be made by using an autotransformer or one-winding transformer, instead of the conventional two-winding transformer. Autotransformers are economical when it is desired to make a small change in voltage level.

Distribution-system Protection

Lease-distributions systems are normally protected by primary lightning arresters, primary fuse cutouts, and secondary lightning arresters.

For proper protection, the lightning arresters must pass large discharge currents under high-voltage surge or lightning-stroke conditions. Yet they must isolate the ground connection and interrupt the current flow quickly, when voltage levels again are restored to normal.

Lightning arresters should be mounted close to the apparatus being protected. Leads should be short, and the arrester ground lead should provide as direct a path to true ground as is practicable.

Primary fuses perform the following functions:

1. They protect the distribution transformer from secondary short circuits and from damaging overloads.

2. They protect the system from transformer failures and from power outages in adjacent areas by isolating the troubled transformer.

The following methods of supplemental protection have proved effective in reducing motor failures and damage associated with lightning:

1. Install a second low-voltage lightning arrester in parallel with the motor-protective arrester located in the controller. This second arrester is usually located on the line pole at the juncture of the power-service cable to the motor, or one pole span back (at least 100 ft) from the line-service pole—if controller is mounted on line pole.

2. Install low-voltage surge capacitors at motor terminals.

3. Perhaps the most effective method of adequate lightning protection is the use of a good and reliable ground.

The recommended scheme of equipment ground is shown in Fig. 9-22.

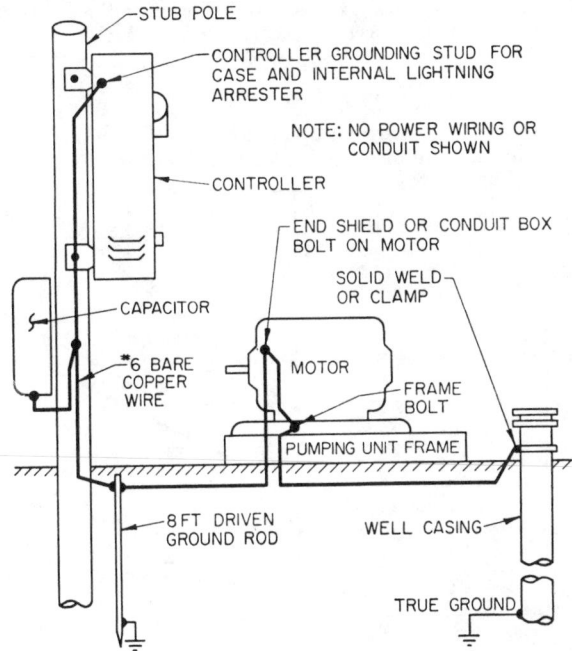

FIG. 9-22. Recommended scheme of equipment grounding, showing common ground connection of motor, controller, capacitor, and pumping-unit frame to well casing.

Ground wires of pole-mounted lightning arresters, transformer tanks, and other pole-mounted equipment should be carried to the nearest well casing and properly terminated. Driven ground rods and butt wraps or plates at the base of poles can be used but may not be sufficient in most oil-producing areas.

Power Factor and the Use of Capacitors

Power factor is the vector relationship between reactive power (kvar) and useful power (kw).

Reactive power can be reduced and low power factor improved simply and most economically by the addition of shunt capacitors at the motor loads, to be switched with the motors. Because they will, in effect, supply the motor magnetizing-current requirements, capacitors will reduce the line current drawn by the motor as shown in Fig. 9-23. This, in turn, will reduce the loading on the transformer and the conductor serving the load, and result in a definite decrease in system I^2R power losses.

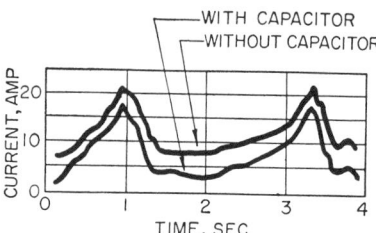

FIG. 9-23. Effect of power-factor correction capacitor in reducing line current drawn by 10-hp motor on oil-well-pumping load.

Typical oil-well-pumping motors have uncorrected power factors of about 0.50. When properly sized to the motor, capacitors will correct the average power factor close to 0.90. The capacitor sizes as recommended by the motor manufacturer should not be exceeded.

Voltage-drop Calculations

Several methods of voltage-drop calculations are used, including the use of voltage-drop charts based on size and distance, and the unit load–unit length method.

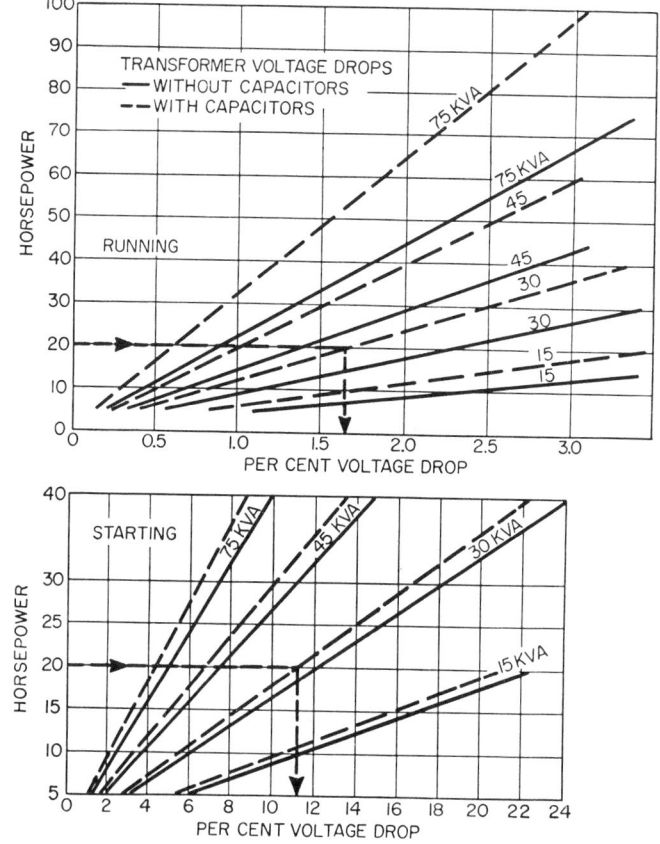

FIG. 9-24. Percentage voltage drop in transformers vs. horsepower load for various kva ratings, both running (a) and starting (b).

One method of voltage-drop calculations is presented in Figs. 9-24 and 9-25. Voltage drops must be calculated for both running and starting conditions. Running voltage drop to the motor farthest from its transformer should not exceed 10 per cent of the motor nameplate voltage rating. Starting voltage drop to the same motor should not exceed 20 per cent of its nameplate voltage rating. Usual procedure is to

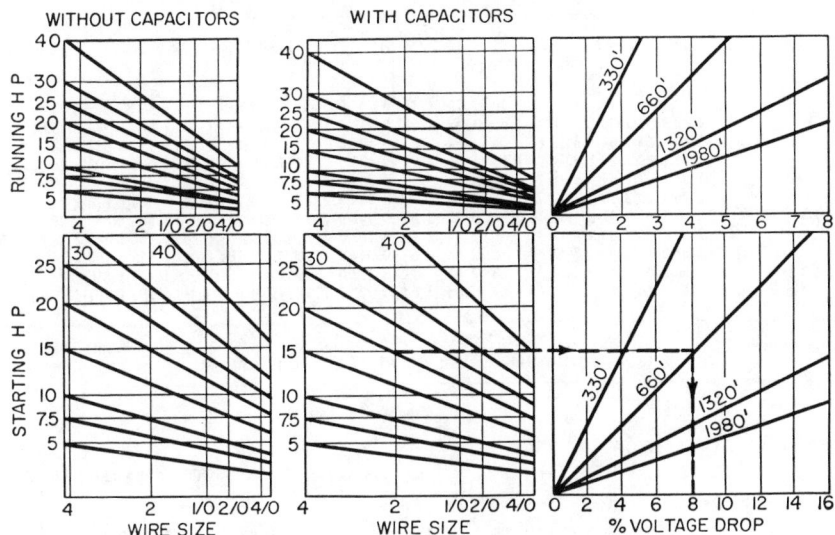

FIG. 9-25. Percentage voltage drop in secondary conductors for various starting and running loads and various wire sizes, both with capacitors and without capacitors.

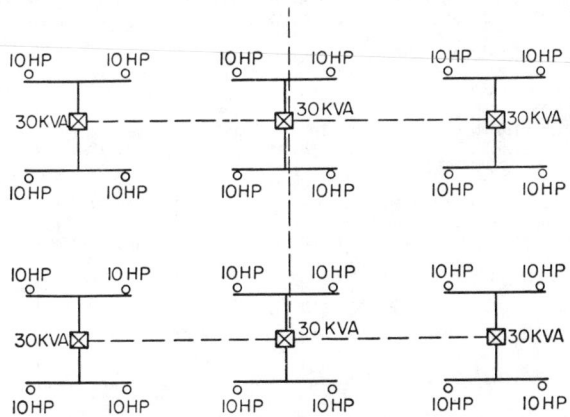

FIG. 9-26. Typical lease-electrification problem, showing symmetrical layout with 40-acre (1,320 ft) uniform spacing of wells, and 10-hp motor at each well location.

assume the far motor on any transformer feeder is to start with the remainder of the motors on this feeder already running.

Voltage drops must be calculated for both the transformer and conductor, and the two added together to give total voltage drop at the motor when starting and running. Primary line-voltage drop can usually be neglected, since it is small. An allowance of 5 per cent should be made for variations in the voltage level of the power-supply system (system-voltage regulation).

Table 9-5

Combination of rods	Rod area, sq in.	Dead wt. of rods/ft — Diam plunger and avg wt. of rods/ft								Dead wt. of fluid/ft, based on net plunger area — Diam plunger and fluid load, lb/ft (sp gr = 1.0)								
		1 1/16	1 1/4	1 1/2	1 3/4	2	2 1/4	2 1/2	2 3/4	1 1/16	1 1/4	1 1/2	1 3/4	2	2 1/4	2 1/2	2 3/4	3 3/4
5/8	0.31	1.18	1.18	1.18	1.18	1.18	1.18	1.18	1.18	0.251	0.399	0.634	0.910	1.230	1.589	1.996	2.443	4.657
3/4-5/8		1.32	1.34	1.36	1.39	1.42	1.452	1.491	1.532	0.233	0.379	0.610	0.885	1.200	1.560	1.958	2.400	
3/4	0.44	1.64	1.64	1.64	1.64	1.64	1.64	1.64	1.64	0.193	0.341	0.575	0.852	1.170	1.535	1.937	2.380	
7/8-3/4		1.78	1.79	1.81	1.83	1.86	1.88	1.91	1.92	0.175	0.322	0.554	0.828	1.142	1.505	1.905	2.345	
7/8-3/4-5/8		1.54	1.57	1.63	1.69	1.76	1.84	....	....	0.204	0.352	0.577	0.851	1.154	1.510			
7/8	0.60	2.20	2.20	2.20	2.20	2.20	2.20	2.20	2.20	0.124	0.272	0.506	0.784	1.105	1.465	1.870	2.310	4.540
1-7/8-3/4		2.00	2.03	2.07	2.12	2.18	2.24	2.32	2.40	0.147	0.296	0.525	0.797	1.107	1.464	1.858	2.295	
1-7/8		2.35	2.36	2.38	2.39	2.41	2.43	2.44	2.48	0.107	0.253	0.485	0.761	1.080	1.437	1.840	2.275	4.480
1	0.78	2.88	2.88	2.88	2.88	2.88	2.88	2.88	2.88	0.044	0.192	0.426	0.704	1.022	1.385	0.790	2.240	4.460
1 1/8-1-7/8-3/4		2.26	2.31	2.39	2.47	2.57	2.68	2.81	....	0.117	0.259	0.484	0.751	1.058	1.410	1.810		
1 1/8	0.99	3.64	3.64	3.64	3.64	3.64	3.64	3.64	3.64	....	0.104	0.339	0.616	0.933	1.298	1.701	2.148	4.362

Table 9-6. Mills Acceleration Factor

Strokes/min	Length of polished-rod stroke, in.																
	12	18	24	34	44	48	54	64	74	84	96	108	120	144	150	168	192
1	1.000	1.000	1.000	1.000	1.000	1.000	1.000	1.001	1.001	1.001	1.001	1.001	1.002	1.002	1.002	1.002	1.003
2	1.001	1.001	1.001	1.002	1.002	1.003	1.003	1.004	1.004	1.005	1.005	1.006	1.007	1.078	1.009	1.010	1.011
3	1.002	1.002	1.003	1.004	1.006	1.006	1.007	1.008	1.009	1.011	1.012	1.014	1.015	1.018	1.019	1.021	1.025
4	1.003	1.004	1.005	1.008	1.010	1.011	1.012	1.015	1.017	1.019	1.022	1.025	1.027	1.033	1.034	1.038	1.044
5	1.004	1.006	1.009	1.012	1.016	1.017	1.019	1.023	1.026	1.030	1.034	1.038	1.043	1.051	1.053	1.060	1.068
6	1.006	1.009	1.012	1.017	1.022	1.025	1.028	1.033	1.038	1.043	1.049	1.055	1.061	1.074	1.077	1.086	1.098
7	1.008	1.013	1.017	1.024	1.031	1.033	1.038	1.044	1.051	1.058	1.067	1.075	1.083	1.100	1.104	1.117	1.133
8	1.011	1.016	1.022	1.031	1.040	1.044	1.049	1.058	1.067	1.076	1.087	1.098	1.109	1.131	1.136	1.153	1.174
9	1.014	1.021	1.028	1.039	1.051	1.055	1.062	1.074	1.085	1.097	1.110	1.124	1.138	1.165	1.172	1.193	1.221
10	1.017	1.026	1.034	1.048	1.062	1.068	1.077	1.091	1.105	1.119	1.136	1.153	1.170	1.204	1.213	1.238	1.272
11	1.021	1.031	1.041	1.058	1.076	1.082	1.093	1.110	1.127	1.144	1.165	1.185	1.206	1.247	1.257	1.288	1.329
12	1.025	1.037	1.049	1.069	1.090	1.098	1.110	1.131	1.151	1.172	1.196	1.221	1.245	1.294	1.306	1.343	1.392
13	1.029	1.043	1.058	1.081	1.105	1.115	1.129	1.153	1.177	1.201	1.230	1.259	1.288	1.345	1.360	1.403	1.460
14	1.034	1.050	1.067	1.095	1.123	1.134	1.151	1.179	1.207	1.235	1.268	1.302	1.335	1.402	1.419	1.469	
15	1.038	1.058	1.077	1.109	1.141	1.154	1.173	1.205	1.237	1.269	1.308	1.346	1.385	1.462	1.481		
16	1.044	1.065	1.087	1.124	1.160	1.174	1.196	1.233	1.269	1.305	1.349	1.392	1.436	1.523			
17	1.049	1.074	1.098	1.139	1.180	1.197	1.221	1.262	1.303	1.344	1.394	1.443	1.492				
18	1.055	1.083	1.110	1.156	1.202	1.221	1.248	1.294	1.340	1.386	1.441	1.497	1.552				
19	1.061	1.092	1.123	1.174	1.225	1.246	1.277	1.328	1.379	1.430	1.492	1.553					
20	1.068	1.102	1.136	1.193	1.250	1.272	1.306	1.363	1.420	1.477	1.545	1.613					
21	1.075	1.113	1.150	1.213	1.275	1.300	1.338	1.400	1.463	1.526	1.601	1.676					
22	1.082	1.124	1.165	1.233	1.302	1.330	1.371	1.440	1.507	1.577	1.659						
23	1.090	1.135	1.180	1.255	1.330	1.360	1.405	1.480	1.555	1.630							
24	1.098	1.147	1.196	1.278	1.360	1.392	1.441	1.523	1.605	1.686							

References

1. Lubrication of Pumping Unit Reducers, part II, secs. 1, 2, and 3, API PR 11G, 1st ed., June, 1956.
2. Overtravel Formula, High Volumetric Efficiency in Oil-well Pumping and Its Practical Results, American Petroleum Division of Production, *Prod. Bull.* 207, June, 1931.
3. Slonneger: Vibration Problems in Oil Wells, *Drill. Prod. Prac.*, *API*, 1937.
4. Mills: Factors Influencing Wells Loads Combined in a New Formula, *Pet. Engr.*, April, 1939.
5. Installation of Beam-type Pumping Units, part 1, secs. 1 and 2, API RP 11G, 1st ed., June, 1956.

Chapter 10

OIL STORAGE

By DON R. BOLING

Division Engineer
National Tank Company, Shreveport, Louisiana

TYPES OF STORAGE TANKS

At the beginning of the first oil production very little oil was stored on the leases in anything except white-pine wooden tanks, which were followed by cypress tanks, and then redwood tanks. The wood tank predominated in the oil fields for many years. Riveted-steel tanks were used very little for lease storage because of the additional cost and difficulties in transportation. The bolted-steel tank was developed next and almost replaced the wooden tank for lease storage.

Early-day roads, to a great degree, controlled hauling in and out of the oil fields. It was not until the hard-surface road became prevalent that the shop-welded-steel tank appeared in any quantity. With today's roads, within a few hours sufficient tankage may be set and connected in many fields to store sizable quantities of oil.[1]

Bolted-steel Tanks. Bolted tanks are available in many capacities, diameters, and heights. Their size is limited to the allowable stress in $\frac{1}{4}$-in. thick steel, which is the heaviest available for bolted-tank use. Because bolted tanks are made of sheet steel bolted together on the location, the transportation of these sheets is no problem. They can be hauled into or out of any location where highway laws would prohibit their movement erected. Should the tank develop a hole from corrosion or be damaged, a single sheet, or more, may be replaced. A whole tank bottom may be replaced, without dismantling the tank, in the field. Also, a section may be removed from the tank at any time, and a new connection installed in the sheet without danger, and the section replaced. This is not true of any other type of steel construction.

No special equipment, such as hoisting machinery, etc., is required for the erection of bolted tanks. These tanks are erected by average-skilled crews using hand tools and usually an air-driven impact wrench run by a small portable compressor. Erection is fast, an average of one and one-half days being required to erect a battery of two high 500-bbl tanks by a crew of four.

Bolted tanks are available with painted or galvanized protective finishes. Painting, on both sides of the sheets, at the time of fabrication gives the inside of the tank some degree of corrosion protection. Galvanizing the sheets and other tank parts by the "hot-dip" process affords high corrosion protection. Galvanized finish is available only on bolted tanks.

Generally bolted tanks are fabricated from 12- or 10-gauge steel, and without a coating for corrosion protection, they do not have the expected life of the welded-steel tanks which are usually constructed of heavier steel. Bolted tanks may leak sometimes with improper erection, but with the proper erection and with present

10–1

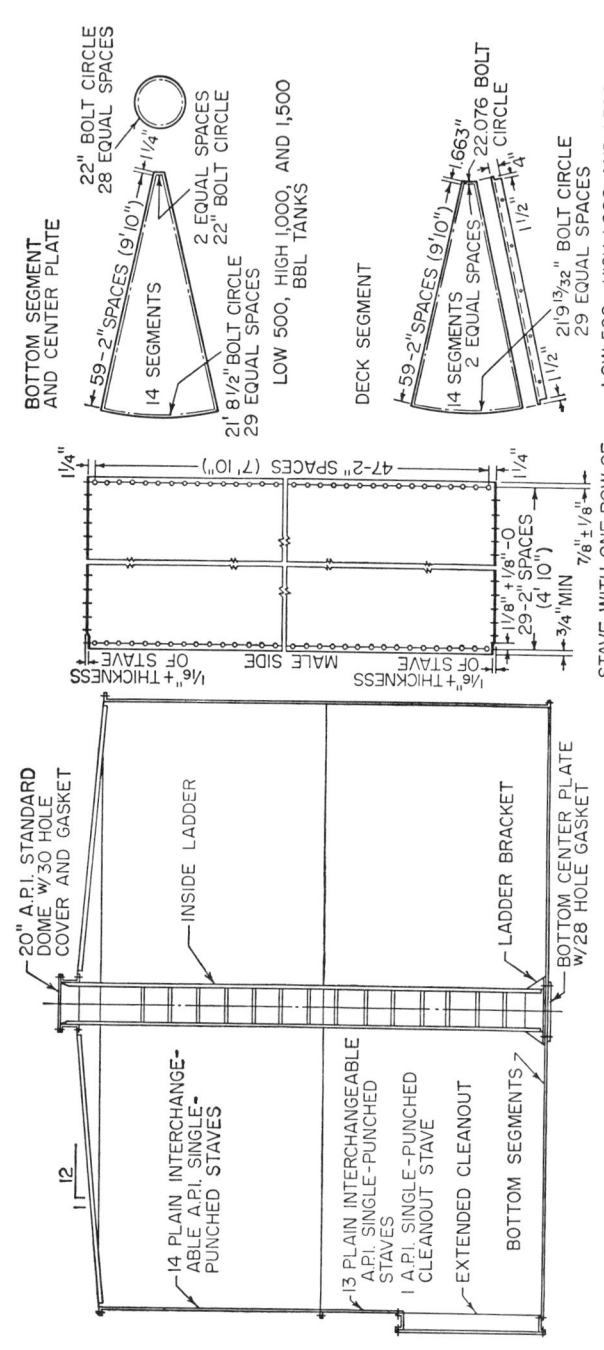

BOTTOM SEGMENT AND CENTER PLATE

22" BOLT CIRCLE
28 EQUAL SPACES

1/4"

59-2" SPACES (9'10")

14 SEGMENTS

2 EQUAL SPACES
22" BOLT CIRCLE

21'8½" BOLT CIRCLE
29 EQUAL SPACES

LOW 500, HIGH 1,000, AND 1,500 BBL TANKS

DECK SEGMENT

.663"
22.076 BOLT CIRCLE
4"
1/2"

59-2" SPACES (9'10")

14 SEGMENTS

2 EQUAL SPACES

1/2"
1/2"
1/4"

21'9 13/32" BOLT CIRCLE
29 EQUAL SPACES

LOW 500, HIGH 1,000, AND 1,500 BBL TANKS

1/4"

47-2" SPACES (7'10")

1/16"+ THICKNESS OF STAVE

MALE SIDE OF STAVE

1/16"+ THICKNESS OF STAVE

1/8"+1/8"—O
29-2" SPACES (4'10")

7/8"±1/8"

3/4" MIN

STAVE WITH ONE ROW OF BOLT HOLES IN VERTICAL SEAMS

20" A.P.I. STANDARD DOME w/30 HOLE COVER AND GASKET

INSIDE LADDER

LADDER BRACKET

BOTTOM CENTER PLATE w/28 HOLE GASKET

12
1

14 PLAIN INTERCHANGE-ABLE A.P.I. SINGLE-PUNCHED STAVES

13 PLAIN INTERCHANGEABLE A.P.I. SINGLE-PUNCHED STAVES

1 A.P.I. SINGLE-PUNCHED CLEANOUT STAVE

EXTENDED CLEANOUT

BOTTOM SEGMENTS

Fig. 10-1. High 1,000-bbl API bolted-steel tank showing stave, deck, and bottom segments.[2] (*Reproduced by permission from API Standard 12B: Specifications for Bolted Production Tanks.*)

gasket materials, they should be tight throughout their life. The use of the bolt-seal washers to prevent seeps past the bolt threads has been very helpful in making good, tight construction.

Table 10-1. API Specifications for Bolted Production Tanks*,2

Capacity		Dimensions		Shell					Bottom		Cone roof		
Nominal capacity, 42-gal bbl	Actual capacity level full, 42-gal bbl	Nominal inside diameter†	Roof and bottom bolt circles, diam	Height	No. staves per ring	M.S. Ga.	No. of rows of bolts	Size of bolts	M.S. Ga.	Size of bolts	M.S. Ga.	Chime	Seam
100	95.80	9'2¾"	9'4¾"	8'0½"	6	12	1	½"	12	½"	12	½"	½"
200	191.64	9'2¾"	9'4¾"	16'1"	6	12 12	1 1	½" ½"	12	½"	12	½"	½"
300	287.46	9'2¾"	9'4¾"	24'1½"	6	12	1	½"	12	½"	12	½"	½"
250	266.28	15'4⅝"	15'6⅝"	8'0½"	10	12	1	½"	12	½"	12	½"	½"
500 high	532.56	15'4⅝"	15'6⅝"	16'1"	10	12 12	1 1	½" ½"	12	½"	12	½"	½"
750	798.84	15'4⅝"	15'6⅝"	24'1½"	10	12 12 10	1 1 1	½" ½" ½"	12	½"	12	½"	½"
500 low	522.01	21'6½"	21'8½"	8'0½"	14	12	1	½"	12	½"	12	½"	½"
1,000 high	1,044.02	21'6½"	21'8½"	16'1"	14	12 12	1 1	½" ½"	12	½"	12	½"	½"
1,500	1,566.03	21'6½"	21'8½"	24'1½"	14	12 12 12‡	1 1 2‡	½" ½" ½"	12 12	½" ½"	12 12	½" ½"	½" ½"
1,000 low	993.53	29'8⅝"	29'10⅝"	8'0½"	20	12	2	½"	12	½"	12	½"	½"
2,000	1,987.06	29'8⅝"	29'10⅝"	16'1"	20	12 12	2 2	½" ½"	12	½"	12	½"	½"
3,000	2,980.59	29'8⅝"	29'10⅝"	24'1½"	20	12 12 10	2 2 2	½" ½" ½"	12	½"	12	½"	½"
5,000	5,037.45	38'7⅝"	38'9⅝"	24'1½"	26	12 10 10	2 2 2	½" ½" ½"	10	½"	12	½"	½"
10,000	10,218.49	54'11¾"	55'1¾"	24'2"	37	10 10 3/16"	2 2 3	½" ½" ½"	10	½"	12	½"	½"

* Reproduced by permission from API Standard 12B: Specifications for Bolted Production Tanks.

† Nominal inside diameter is considered as 2 in. less than bolt-circle diameter and actual capacity figured on that basis.

‡ NOTE: A narrow fill-in stave is issued in conjunction with regular 60-in. wide staves.

If internal gas pressures in excess of 2 oz/sq in. are required, the tank must be equipped with vertical ties which connect the deck and bottom together. Tanks that are larger in diameter than a low 500 bbl should not be subject to more than 1 oz/sq in. of gas pressure without vertical ties. All sizes are satisfactory for 16 oz/sq in. of gas pressure with vertical ties.

Bolted tanks cannot be moved in most areas without dismantling and reerecting at the new location. New gaskets are always used.

Of the three basic types of oil-field tanks—bolted, welded, and wooden—the painted bolted-steel tank is the least expensive.   It averages approximately $7.00 per bbl of storage capacity for the 65-bbl tank to approximately $1.50 per bbl of storage capacity for the 10,000-bbl tank.

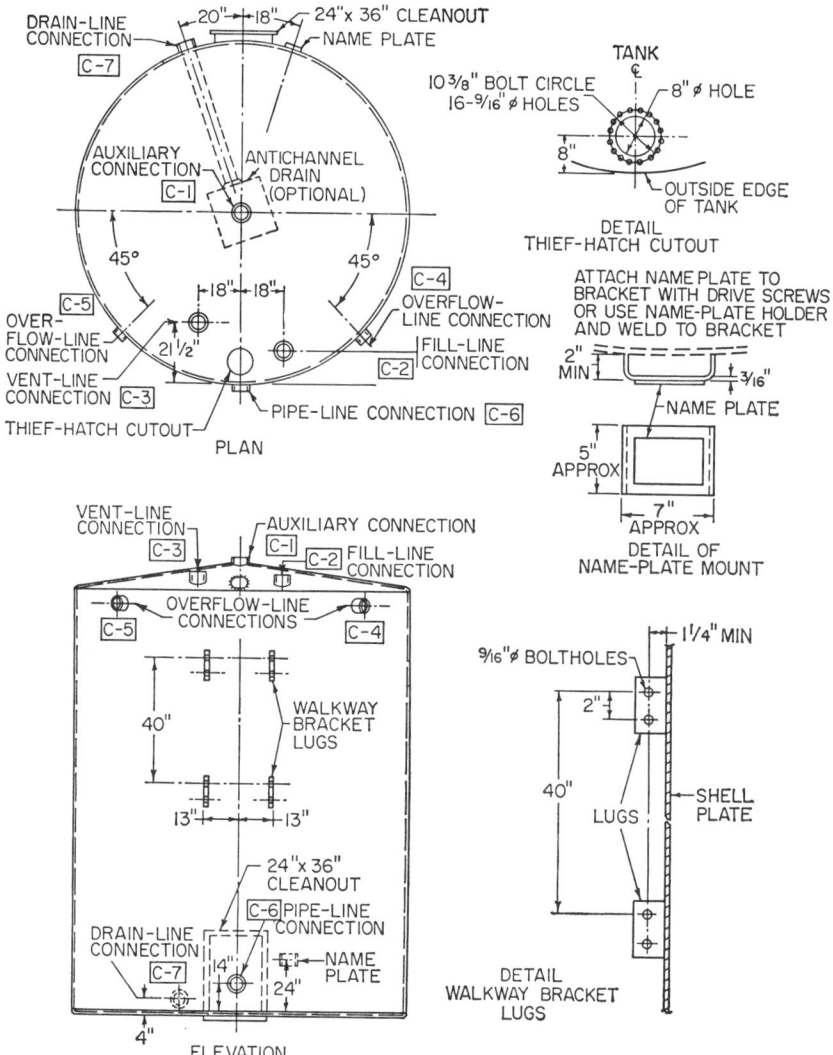

Fig. 10-2. Partial API specifications for welded-steel tanks.[3]   (*Reproduced by permission from API Standard 12F: Specifications for Small Welded Production Tanks.*)

Welded-steel Tanks.   Welded tanks are available in a large variety of sizes as shop-fabricated items.   While the API lists only five sizes, all manufacturers fabricate these and many other popular sizes.   They are usually fabricated from $\frac{3}{16}$ in. or heavier steel and will therefore permit internal gas pressures up to 16 oz.   The heavier steel also affords a corrosion allowance.   Shop fabrication permits testing in the shop for leaks and also provides immediate storage.   The tanks are merely up-ended from a truck on the location.   However, welded tanks are not available in large sizes as a shop-fabricated item. State laws prohibit movement of tanks larger than 400 bbl in most areas (and this size in a few). Welded fabrication prevents replacing sections as with a bolted tank and makes installation of new connections hazardous after initial filling of the tank.

Table 10-2. Specifications for Small Welded Production Tanks*,[3]

Capacity		Dimensions		Connections‡	
Nominal capacity, 42-gal bbl	Working capacity, 42-gal bbl†	Outside diameter	Height	C-1, C-2 C-3, C-7	C-4, C-5 C-6
90§	73.82	8'0''	10'0''	3''	3''
100	79.16	9'6''	8'0''	3''	3''
107	91.54	8'0''	12'0''.	3''	3''
150	129.15	9'6''	12'0''	3''	3''
200§	166.70	12'0''	10'0''	3''	4''
210§	184.96	10'0''	15'0''	3''	4''
224	198.84	10'0''	16'0''	3''	4''
280	254.33	10'0''	20'0''	3''	4''
300§	266.72	12'0''	15'0''	4''	4''
322	286.72	12'0''	16'0''	4''	4''
400§	366.74	12'0''	20'0''	4''	4''

* Reproduced by permission from API Standard 12F: Specifications for Small Welded Tanks.
† Capacities are between center line of pipeline connection and overflow and based on ¼-in. thick steel and connections located as set forth in API Standard 12F.
‡ Nominal pipe size and connections designated as set forth in API Standard 12F.
§ API size as set forth in API Standard 12F.

The cost of welded tanks is higher than that of bolted tanks. Costs run approximately \$9.00 per bbl of storage capacity for a 65-bbl size to \$3.00 per bbl of storage capacity for a 1,000-bbl size.

Wooden Tanks. Wooden tanks also are available in a variety of sizes and dimensions. These tanks are well adapted to situations where corrosion is a problem. Redwood is very stable between a pH of 2 to 11. These tanks are erected in the field and require more skill for erection than a bolted tank, but again only hand tools are required. The wood serves to a degree as a thermal insulator and tends to keep the internal temperature more constant. Wooden tanks should never be painted.

Wooden tanks should be sent to the shop for reworking if they are to be cut down, moved, and reset. With age wooden tanks will usually develop seeps that are unsightly. They give the stored product no fire protection.

The cost of a redwood tank is high when compared to bolted or welded tanks. This is due to the type of wood and its curing. Logs are selected especially for tank lumber, and then only the heart of the log is usable. It must be free of any knot or other defect. After the lumber is received by the tank manufacturer, it must cure in his storage two to five years until excess moisture is gone. The cost will average approximately \$15.00 per bbl of storage capacity for the 65-bbl size to approximately \$4.50 per bbl of storage capacity for the 1,500-bbl size.

Plastic Tanks. Plastic tanks offer excellent corrosion protection. They have been manufactured in the past by several fabricators and are being manufactured today by others. Their cost is high compared to other types of material and their life has not yet been established. Plastic tanks in the past have weakened structurally with age.

Cone-bottom Tanks. The cone bottom in either the bolted or the welded tank offers a means of draining and removing water, or water-cut oil, from only the bottom of the tank, leaving the merchantable oil above. With a flat-bottom tank some of the merchantable oil must be removed if all of the water is removed from the tank. Corrosion on the tank bottom is kept to a minimum by keeping all water removed. The cone-bottom tank can be cleaned without a man entering the tank. A water hose, handled just outside the cleanout opening, is used to flush the solids to the center of the cone and drain connection.

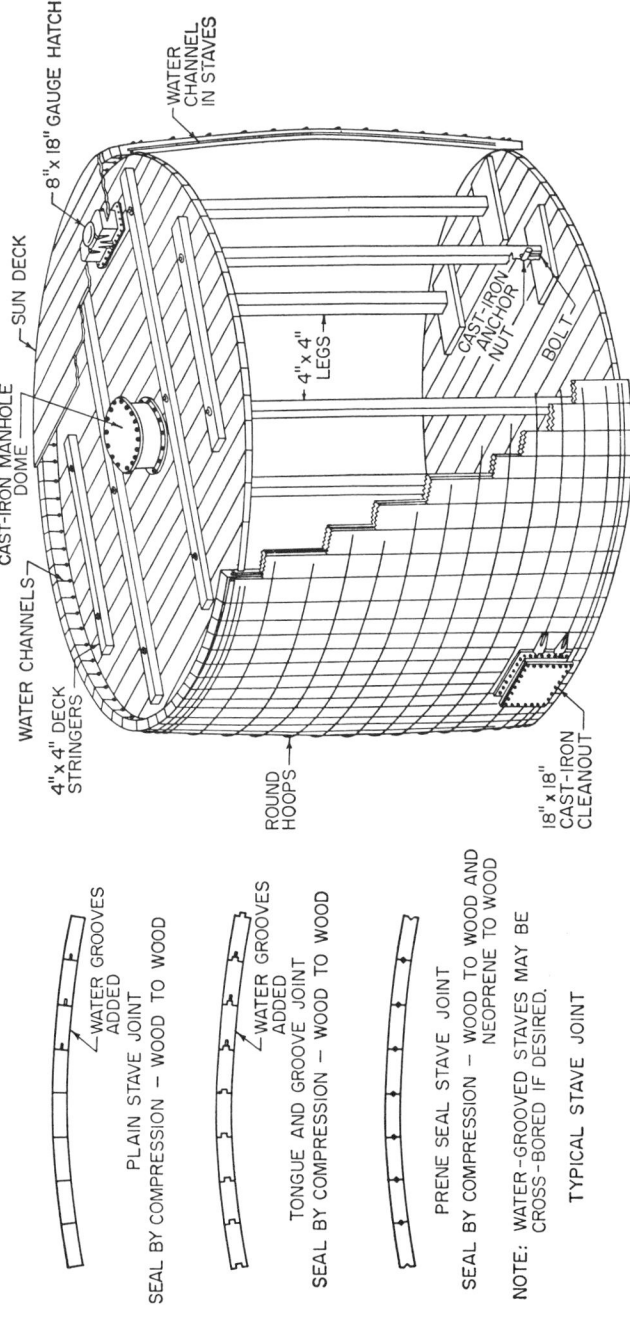

8"×18" GAUGE HATCH

WATER CHANNEL IN STAVES

SUN DECK

CAST-IRON MANHOLE DOME

4"×4" LEGS

CAST-IRON ANCHOR NUT

BOLT

WATER CHANNELS

4"×4" DECK STRINGERS

ROUND HOOPS

18"×18" CAST-IRON CLEANOUT

FIG. 10-3. Wooden storage tank showing water-groove construction.[4]

WATER GROOVES ADDED

PLAIN STAVE JOINT

SEAL BY COMPRESSION – WOOD TO WOOD

WATER GROOVES ADDED

TONGUE AND GROOVE JOINT

SEAL BY COMPRESSION – WOOD TO WOOD

PRENE SEAL STAVE JOINT

SEAL BY COMPRESSION – WOOD TO WOOD AND NEOPRENE TO WOOD

NOTE: WATER-GROOVED STAVES MAY BE CROSS-BORED IF DESIRED.

TYPICAL STAVE JOINT

Table 10-3. API Specifications for Wooden Production Tanks[*,4]

Diameter of bottom and head	Length of staves	Recommended minimum thickness of staves	Inside diameter at bottom and head	Minimum inside diameter at mid-height	Inside height between head and bottom	Capacity 42-gal bbl	
						Nominal	Calculated
8'0"	16'0"	2"	7'11"	8'3"	14'11⅜"	130	137
8'0"	20'0"	2"	7'11"	8'3½"	18'11⅜"	165	174
8'0"	24'0"	2"	7'11"	8'4"	22'11⅜"	200	212
10'0"	16'0"	2"	9'11"	10'3½"	14'11⅜"	200	214
10'0"	20'0"	2"	9'11"	10'4"	18'11⅜"	250	272
10'0"	24'0"	2"	9'11"	10'5"	22'11⅜"	300	331
12'0"	16'0"	2"	11'11"	12'3½"	14'11⅜"	300	308
12'0"	20'0"	2"	11'11"	12'4"	18'11⅜"	375	390
12'0"	24'0"	2"	11'11"	12'5"	22'11⅜"	450	475
16'0"	8'0"	2"	15'11"	16'1½"	6'11⅜"	250	249
16'0"	10'0"	2"	15'11"	16'2"	8'11⅜"	310	322
16'0"	12'0"	2"	15'11"	16'3"	10'11⅜"	375	396
16'0"	16'0"	2"	15'11"	16'4"	14'11⅜"	500	543
16'0"	20'0"	3"	15'10½"	16'5"	18'11⅜"	625	691
16'0"	24'0"	3"	15'10½"	16'6½"	22'11⅜"	750	843
20'0"	8'0"	2"	19'11"	20'2"	6'11⅜"	400	390
20'0"	10'0"	2"	19'11"	20'2½"	8'11⅜"	500	503
20'0"	12'0"	2"	19'11"	20'3½"	10'11⅜"	600	619
20'0"	16'0"	2"	19'11"	20'5"	14'11⅜"	800	850
20'0"	20'0"	3"	19'10½"	20'6"	18'11⅜"	1,100	1,080
22'0"	8'0"	2"	21'11"	22'2"	6'11⅜"	500	472
22'0"	10'0"	2"	21'11"	22'3"	8'11⅜"	625	610
22'0"	12'0"	2"	21'11"	22'4"	10'11⅜"	750	749
22'0"	16'0"	3"	21'10½"	22'5"	14'11⅜"	1,000	1,025
24'0"	8'0"	2"	23'11"	24'2"	6'11⅜"	570	561
24'0"	10'0"	2"	23'11"	24'3"	8'11⅜"	730	726
24'0"	12'0"	2"	23'11"	24'4"	10'11⅜"	890	891
24'0"	16'0"	3"	23'10½"	24'5"	14'11⅜"	1,200	1,219
24'0"	20'0"	3"	23'10½"	24'6"	18'11⅜"	1,500	1,550

* Reproduced by permission from API Standard 12E: Specifications for Wooden Production Tanks.

Welded tanks offer cone bottoms in two basic patterns: (1) the bottom of the tank is cone-shaped and must set on a cone-shaped grade; (2) the cone bottom is placed up in the shell of the tank, leaving a base ring or flat bottom to rest on a flat tank grade. In the latter pattern the producer may select a standard-height tank which will have less capacity than a flat-bottom tank of equal diameter or a tank of equal capacity to a flat-bottom tank but of necessity of slightly greater height.

The cone bottom adds approximately 12 per cent to the cost of a welded tank, depending on which pattern is selected. It adds approximately 3 to 4 per cent to the cost of most popular sizes of bolted tanks.

CORROSION IN TANKS AND STORAGE OF CORROSIVE PRODUCTS

Bolted Tanks. Galvanized bolted tanks offer excellent corrosion resistance. Galvanizing of all parts of the tank is done after all fabrication and by the hot-dip method. By this method the finished piece is dipped in the molten zinc material which applies 2 to 2½ oz spelter per square foot. The cost for a galvanized finish is approximately 25 per cent higher than that for a painted finish. This finish is recommended for storing salt or fresh water or hydrogen sulfide crudes. It is also recommended for all seacoast areas to provide external corrosion resistance.

Aluminum decks are very effective against corrosive hydrogen sulfide crudes.

Along with aluminum decks, some producers use a top ring of staves constructed of aluminum. Aluminum decks add approximately 6 to 10 per cent to the cost of a galvanized tank, depending on the size. All-aluminum tanks are not recommended. Any salt water present will attack the aluminum in the lower part of the tank, causing rapid failure.

Internal coatings of various kinds are being used for corrosion protection in bolted tanks. Holidays, or tiny holes in the coating, may be expected. These holidays allow the corrosion to concentrate on the unprotected steel, and failure by corrosion may be rapid unless some type of cathodic protection is employed. The most successful method of coating has been after erection, demanding field application which is expensive.

Welded Tanks. The usual heavier-steel construction of welded tanks gives them considerable corrosion allowance over bolted tanks. Welded tanks are coated internally against corrosion by the various coatings available. Shop-welded tanks can be coated in the shop and hauled to the location without fear of damaging the coating. This affords a cost advantage over field coating of bolted tanks.

Wooden Tanks. Wooden tanks are recommended for salt and fresh-water storage and hydrogen sulfide crude storage. These tanks should last the life of the lease where corrosive products are stored. The cost of the wood-tank battery is high, however, when compared to other types of storage for corrosive products.

TANK BATTERY FOR HYDROGEN SULFIDE CRUDE STORAGE

For storing sour crude, the first choice is generally galvanized bolted tanks with aluminum decks and probably aluminum top rings. The second choice is usually wooden tanks.

All openings on the tanks should be kept closed. This can be accomplished by equipping the tanks with some type of ground-level gauging and thermometers located in the tank shell. Gauges and temperatures can then be determined from the ground without opening the tank. These gauging devices usually require approval by the crude purchaser. Ground-level sampling can also be accomplished by installation of pipes extending into the tank at any desired level and to any desired distance. Valves are located at a convenient level to permit sampling on the ground without opening the tanks. If available, a small amount of sweet gas should be fed into the top of the tank continually to establish a "gas sweep." This will assure a positive pressure within the tank at all times and will prohibit air from entering the tank, thereby greatly reducing corrosion. It is advisable to extend the tank vent line well beyond the tank battery, and by using a back-pressure valve and flash arrester in the vent line, to burn the vapors. If the crude is very sour, these vapors will be poisonous.

TANK GRADES

Selection of the proper location on the lease for storage tanks is of prime importance. The location should provide good drainage and be on well-packed soil, not a fill, if possible. The tank foundation or grade should be slightly elevated, level, and somewhat larger in diameter than the tank itself. For steel tanks, either bolted or welded, the best grade is one made of small gravel, crushed rock, etc., held in place by steel bands 8 in. high. This type of grade allows no water to stand underneath the tank and provides air circulation. If the tank is to be set directly on the ground, felt tar paper should be applied to the grade first and the tank set on this. If concrete is used for the grade, it should be slightly larger in diameter than the tank and have shallow grooves on the surface to provide air circulation.

For wooden tanks the best grades are made of concrete. The grade should be elevated sufficiently to allow adequate space between the bottom of the staves and the soil, usually 2 in. The concrete should be 6 in. smaller in diameter than the tank bottom. If desired, the concrete may be covered with felt tar paper before the bottom is laid.

Grades for wooden tanks may also be constructed of creosote-treated lumber. These are made by placing a round-shaped mat made from 2-in. lumber on the ground.

Sills of 4- by 4-in. lumber are placed on the mat spaced 8 to 12 in. apart and turned 90° to the mat boards. The tank bottom is then placed on these sills. This provides excellent circulation under the tank.

TANK-BATTERY INSTALLATION AND HOOKUP

A tank battery should contain at least two tanks and usually have a capacity equal to four days' production. All tanks should be level with each other and have a minimum spacing of 3 ft between tanks. If a fire wall is required, it should have a capacity of one and one-half times the total storage and be drained by a pipe placed beneath the fire wall with a valve on the outside. This valve is opened to drain out rain water and then closed again.

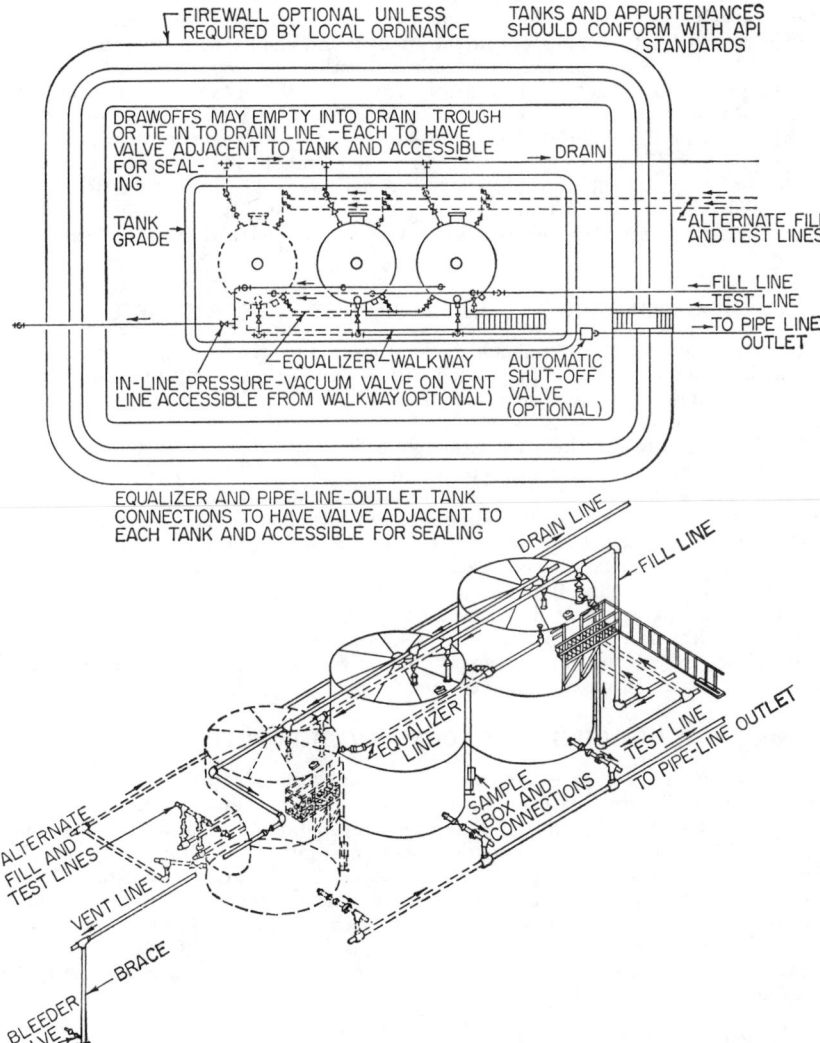

FIG. 10-4. Suggested setting and connection plan for typical tank battery.[5]

Tank-battery Connections. The pipeline connection in the tank should be located directly below the thief hatch and a minimum of 12 in. above the tank bottom. It should be equipped with a valve and sealing device immediately adjacent to the tank.

Inlet connections preferably should be located in the deck of the tank and as far away as practical from the thief hatch. This connection should have a valve located near the inlet capable of closing off against pressure.

Drain connections should be located immediately above the tank bottom in the side of the tank, or in the tank bottom immediately adjacent to the side. They should be equipped with a valve and sealing device located next to the tank. Drains from all tanks in a battery should be connected together and piped well away from the tanks, at least 150 ft if they are connected to a burning pit. The line should have a full-opening check valve installed to prevent flashback from the burning pit.

Equalizer or overflow connections should be installed below the deck in the tank shell. A valve and sealing device should be installed immediately adjacent to the tank if more than two tanks are in the battery and should be connected in such a manner that any two tanks can be equalized together.

Vent connections should be installed in the center of the tank deck and all tanks connected to a common line. This line should have a pressure-vacuum valve installed in the line, or on the end of it. The line should be sloped to prevent accumulation of liquids in it or in the valve and should extend a minimum of 40 ft beyond the last tank.

The use of gas to roll stored products is usually considered poor practice, and its use should be restricted to temporary or emergency use. If a roller line is used, it should enter the tank through the deck and be equipped with a valve next to the tank.[5]

MAINTENANCE AND OPERATION OF TANK BATTERIES

Maintenance. Steel tanks should be kept clean and free from spilled oil or other material. They should be kept painted with a white or reflecting-type paint such as aluminum paint. All water or accumulated dirt should be removed from around the bottom edge of the tanks.

Thief hatches and vent-lines valves should be kept closed and inspected periodically for proper operation and gasket condition.

Should any leaks occur, they may be repaired temporarily with lead sealing plugs or toggle bolts. These leaks should be repaired permanently as soon as possible.

Operation. When a closing gauge is taken, and before the tank is filled again, the pipeline valve should be sealed closed, the drain valve checked to assure that it is closed and the seal removed, and then the seal from the equalizer-line valve removed.

Before the tank is accepted by the crude purchaser, the water should be drained from the tank if necessary, and the valve sealed closed. All other valves should be sealed closed except the vapor-recovery-line valve if such a system is in use. The pipeline valve is then unsealed and opened for delivery to the purchaser.[5]

VAPOR CONTROL AND GRAVITY CONSERVATION WITH STORAGE TANKS

Crude oils and condensates are composed of many different paraffin hydrocarbons. Propane is the lightest hydrocarbon found in any appreciable amount. It is also the hydrocarbon with the greatest tendency to evaporate or vaporize from the liquid stored. When propane and other hydrocarbons pass into the vapor phase by vaporization, the volume of the liquid stored is decreased, and because these lighter hydrocarbons are not now present in their initial amounts, the API gravity of the crude is decreased. There is a definite relationship between API gravity lost and volume lost, depending on the character of the crude. This is shown in Fig. 10-5.

Several factors affect and contribute to vapor and gravity losses in storage tanks. They are:

1. Vapor pressure of the product stored
2. Temperature of the product stored
3. Surface area of the product stored

4. Agitation of the product stored
5. Pressure on the storage tanks
6. Filling losses from the storage tanks
7. Breathing losses from the storage tanks
8. Size of the storage tanks

Several, if not all, of these factors usually contribute to the total loss from any one tank or battery.

Vapor Pressure. The true vapor pressure of a liquid is the actual pressure it exerts on the vapor space in a container at a given temperature. Water, for example, has a TVP of 1 psi at 100°F and a TVP of 14.7 psi at 212°F, yet it must be kept in a closed container to prevent evaporation. The same is true for crude oil if the TVP is below 14.7 psi. Crudes with a TVP of 10 psi and lower are usually relatively stable in closed-atmospheric storage.[6]

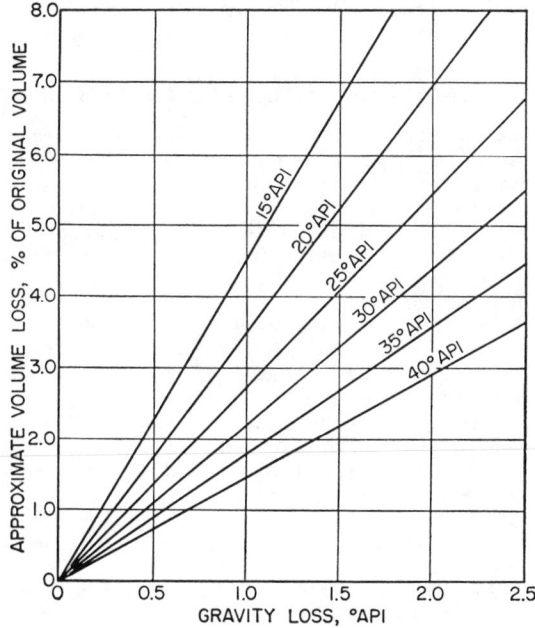

Fig. 10-5. Gravity loss in °API vs. per cent loss by volume.[6]

Temperature. Temperature of the crude, as seen above, is directly related to its vapor pressure. For example, a crude with a TVP of 8 psi at 50°F will have a TVP of 17 psi at 90°F. The vaporization loss is then approximately doubled at the 90° temperature.

Surface Area. Directly related to the rate of evaporation is the surface area of the crude. Take, for example, two tanks with a capacity of 500 bbl each, one a high 500-bbl tank and the other a low 500-bbl tank. If both are filled one-half full, the high 500 has 0.74 sq ft of surface area exposed per barrel stored, while the low 500 has 1.46 sq ft of surface area exposed per barrel stored. The low 500-bbl tank then has twice the evaporation rate of the high 500-bbl tank.[7]

Agitation. Agitation of the stored product is directly related to the vapor pressure. If two crudes under the same conditions receive equal agitation, the one with the higher vapor pressure will show the greatest evaporation loss.

Tank Pressures. The higher the pressure maintained on the storage tank, the less will be the tendency for the crude to evaporate. Pressure storage, considered to be in excess of 1 psi, is required for all stored products with a TVP in excess of 14.7 psi to prevent excessive evaporation losses. High-gravity crudes and distillates or condensates usually require a higher storage pressure than the normal 1 to 4 oz.

Filling Losses. When 475 barrels are run from a 500-bbl tank, crude-oil vapors occupy the displaced oil. Upon filling of the tank again, these vapors are forced from the tank into the atmosphere. These vapors expelled may be equivalent to one or more barrels, depending on the type of crude.[6]

Breathing Losses. Temperature changes between day and night cause vapors to be expelled from the tank and air to be breathed in. These reactions are similar to, but smaller in volume than, the filling and running losses.

Storage Size. A greater vapor space and longer storage time will increase evaporation losses. As an example, consider two tanks with 100 bbl of stored crude each, one a 250-bbl tank and the other a high 500-bbl tank. The 250-bbl tank has 973 cu ft of vapor space while the high 500-bbl tank has 2,469 cu ft, or two and one-half times as much. This added vapor space increases the evaporation losses from the larger tank.[7]

PREVENTING EVAPORATION AND GRAVITY LOSSES

Much can be done by the producer to prevent undue losses of crude oil by evaporation. Products should be introduced into storage as cool as possible and kept that way. Some types of heat-exchange equipment should be employed between an emulsion treater, or other heating equipment, and the tanks to cool the oil before it enters storage. Steel tanks should be painted with a reflecting-type or white paint. Tests show the vapor-space temperature of a tank painted with aluminum paint to average $4\frac{1}{2}°F$ above atmospheric temperature, while a red-painted tank averaged 14°F above atmospheric temperature.[7]

Tanks should be selected with smaller diameters, greater heights, and smaller capacities, all other considerations being equal. These factors will allow the stored product to have relatively smaller surface areas and vapor spaces, as well as a shorter length of storage time before being sold.

Downcomer pipes prevent undue agitation in the tank. They are usually made by installing a line inside the tank from the inlet connection in the tank deck to the center of the tank. The downcomer should be slotted at the top to allow gas to escape and thereby prevent agitation and splashing.

All tank openings should be maintained closed and pressure on the tank should be carried as high as practical. Tanks in a battery should all be connected together into a common vent line to keep breathing and filling losses to a minimum. There are bypass thief hatches manufactured that will do much to prevent evaporation losses when gauging a tank through the thief hatch. These special hatches have the tank-battery vent lines connected to them and will close off or isolate all other tanks except the one being gauged. This allows all other tanks in the battery to maintain their pressure while the tank being gauged is depressured.

The producer may install one of several types of ground-level gauging and sampling devices available that will permit gauging and sampling without opening the tank. The fact that the tank remains closed goes far toward eliminating evaporation losses.

VAPOR-RECOVERY SYSTEM

Vapor-recovery systems are of two basic types. One connects a vacuum line to the tank and transports the tank vapors to a processing or gasoline plant. The other type consists of a small compressor located by the tank battery which compresses the tank vapors to a pressure suitable for lease use or sales.

The vacuum-line system is usually found only in large oil fields where many tank batteries can be connected together into a relatively short gathering system. This system must employ good, dependable control valves to prevent the tanks from collapsing or air from entering the gathering system.

The compressor system is usually electrically driven and all components are skid-mounted. Some of these systems use a vane-type compressor and crude oil to seal the vanes against the compressor walls. In these systems an actual liquid recovery is made by the sealing oil absorbing the condensed hydrocarbons from the compressed vapors and taking them back to storage with the returning sealing oil. Applications for this type system are the compressing of rich stock-tank vapors to send to a gasoline plant and recovering liquids from the rich stock-tank vapors, thus providing a combination of gas sales and liquid recovery. Usually a minimum of 1,000 bbl per day of production is required at a battery before a vapor-recovery unit can be economically considered.

References

1. National Tank Company: Economic Comparison of Wooden, Bolted Steel and Welded Steel Oil Field Stock Tanks, *Bull.* 19, 1935.
2. *API Specifications for Bolted Production Tanks*, 11th ed., American Petroleum Institute, Division of Production, 1958.
3. *API Specifications for Small Welded Production Tanks*, 4th ed., American Petroleum Institute, Division of Production, 1957.
4. *API Specifications for Wooden Production Tanks*, 6th ed., American Petroleum Institute, Division of Production, 1956.
5. *Tentative Bulletin on Recommended Practices in the Setting, Connecting, Maintenance and Operation of Lease Tanks*, 3d ed., American Petroleum Institute, Division of Transportation, 1952.
6. Petroleum Extension Service, University of Texas, Division of Extension: *Vapor and Gravity Control in Crude Oil Production*, 1st ed., 1956.
7. Schmidt, Ludwig: Applied Methods and Equipment for Reducing Evaporation Losses of Petroleum and Gasoline, *U.S. Bur. Mines, Bull.* 379, pp. 27–39, 1934.

Chapter 11

OIL AND GAS SEPARATORS

By H. Vernon Smith

President and General Manager
Oil Metering and Processing Equipment Corp.
Houston, Tex.

The term "oil and gas separator," in oil-field terminology, designates a pressure vessel used for the purpose of separating well fluids into gaseous and liquid components. A separating vessel may be referred to in the following ways:

1. Oil and gas separator
2. Separator
3. Stage separator
4. Trap
5. Knockout (vessel) (drum) (trap)
   Water knockout
   Liquid knockout
6. Flash chamber (trap) (vessel)
7. Expansion vessel (separator)
8. Scrubber (gas scrubber)
   Dry type
   Wet type
9. Filter (gas filter)
   Dry type
   Wet type

The terms oil and gas separator, separator, stage separator, and trap are used interchangeably to refer to a conventional oil and gas separator. These separating vessels are normally used on the producing lease near the wellhead, manifold, or tank battery to separate the fluids produced from oil and gas wells into oil and gas or liquid and gas. They must be capable of handling "slugs" or "heads" of well fluids. Therefore, they are usually sized to handle high instantaneous rates of flow.

A knockout (vessel) (drum) (trap) may be used to remove only water from the well fluid or all liquid, oil plus water, from the gas. In the case of a water knockout the gas and liquid petroleum are discharged together and the water is separated and discharged from the bottom of the vessel.

A liquid knockout is used to remove all liquid, oil plus water, from the gas. The water and liquid hydrocarbons are discharged together from the bottom of the vessel and the gas is discharged from the top.

A flash chamber (trap) (vessel) normally refers to a conventional oil and gas separator operated at low pressure, with the liquid from a higher-pressure separator being "flashed" into it. This flash chamber is quite often the second or third stage of separation, with the liquid being discharged from flash chamber to storage.

An expansion vessel is the first-stage separator vessel on a low-temperature or cold-separation unit. This vessel may be equipped with a heating coil to melt hydrates, or a hydrate-preventative liquid such as alcohol or glycol may be injected into the well fluid just prior to expansion into this vessel.

A gas scrubber may be similar to an oil and gas separator. Usually it is used to handle fluid that contains less liquid than that produced from oil and gas wells. Gas scrubbers are normally used in gas gathering, sales, and distribution lines where they are not required to handle slugs or heads of liquid as is the case with an oil and gas separator.

The dry-type gas scrubber utilizes mist extractors and other internals similar to oil and gas separators, with preference shown to the coalescing-type mist extractor.

The wet-type gas scrubber passes the stream of gas through a bath of oil or other liquid that washes the dust from the gas. The gas is then flowed through mist extractors where all removable liquid is separated from it.

The term scrubber can refer to a vessel used upstream from any gas-processing vessel to protect the downstream vessel from liquid hydrocarbons and/or water.

The term filter (gas filter) can be used to refer to a dry-type gas scrubber, especially if the unit is being used primarily to remove dust from the gas stream. A filtering medium is used in the vessel to remove dust, line scale, rust, and other foreign material from the gas.

A discussion of the design considerations, functions, capacities, operational problems, and other features of conventional oil and gas separators follows.

WELL FLUIDS AND THEIR CHARACTERISTICS

Some of the physical characteristics of well fluids handled by oil and gas separators are briefly outlined here.

Crude Oil

Crude oil is a complex mixture of hydrocarbons produced in liquid form. The API gravity of crude oil may range from 6 to 50°, viscosity from 5.0 to 75,000 cp at standard conditions. Colors vary through shades of green, yellow, brown, and black. (Detailed characteristics of crude oils are listed in Chap. 18.)

Distillate or Condensate

This is a hydrocarbon mixture that may exist in the producing formation either as a liquid or as a condensible vapor. Liquefaction of gaseous components usually occurs with reduction of well-fluid temperature to surface operating conditions. Gravities of the condensed liquids may range from 50 to 120° API and viscosities from 2.0 to 6.0 cp at standard conditions. Color may be water-white, light yellow, or blue.

Natural Gas and Condensible Vapors

A gas may be defined as a substance which has no shape or volume of its own. It will completely fill any container in which it is placed and will take the shape of the container. Hydrocarbon gas associated with crude oil may be found as "free" gas or as "solution" gas. Density (specific gravity) of natural gas may vary from 0.55 to 0.85, viscosity from 0.011 to 0.024 cp at standard conditions.

Free Gas. Free gas is a hydrocarbon that exists in the gaseous phase at reservoir pressure and temperature and remains in the gaseous phase when produced under normal conditions. "Free" gas may refer to any gas at any pressure that is not in solution or mechanically held in the liquid hydrocarbon.

Solution Gas. Solution gas is gas that is homogeneously contained in oil at a given pressure and temperature. A reduction in pressure and/or an increase in temperature may cause the gas to be emitted from the oil, whereupon it assumes the characteristics of free gas.

Condensible Vapors. These hydrocarbons exist as vapor at certain pressures and temperatures and as liquid at other pressures and temperatures. In the vapor form, they assume the general characteristics of natural gas. In the vapor phase, condensible vapors vary in density (specific gravity) from 0.55 to 4.91 (air = 1.0), and in viscosity from 0.006 to 0.011 cp at standard conditions.

Water

Water produced with crude oil and natural gas may be in the form of vapor or liquid. The liquid water may be free or emulsified. Free water reaches the surface separated from the liquid hydrocarbon. Emulsified water is dispersed in the liquid hydrocarbon. Connate water was deposited simultaneously with the hydrocarbons in the reservoir and can exist in both liquid and vapor form.

TWO MAIN FUNCTIONS OF OIL AND GAS SEPARATORS

Removal of Liquid from Gas

Separation of liquid from gas begins as the fluid flows through the formation into the wellbore and progressively increases through the tubing, flow lines, and surface handling equipment. Under certain conditions the fluid may be completely separated into liquid and gas before the oil and gas separator is reached. In such cases, the separator affords only an "enlargement" to permit gas to ascend to one outlet and liquid to descend to another. In other words, the oil and gas separator may perform only the function of providing space in which final separation is accomplished by density difference of the liquid and gas.

Difference in densities of the liquid and gaseous hydrocarbons may accomplish acceptable separation in an oil and gas separator. However, in some instances it may be necessary to use mechanical devices commonly referred to as "mist extractors" to remove liquid mist from the gas before it is discharged from the separator. Also, it may be desirable or necessary to use some means to remove nonsolution gas from the oil before it is discharged from the separator.

Removal of Gas from Liquid

Most crude oils are saturated with natural gas at reservoir pressure and temperature. The physical and chemical characteristics of the oil and its conditions of pressure and temperature determine the amount of gas it will contain in solution. The rate at which the gas is liberated from a given oil is a function of change in pressure and temperature. The volume of gas that an oil and gas separator will remove from crude oil is dependent upon (1) physical and chemical characteristics of the crude, (2) operating pressure, (3) operating temperature, (4) rate of through-put, (5) size and configuration of the separator, and other factors.

Rate of through-put and liquid depth in the separator determine the "retention," or "settling," time of the oil. Retention time of from 1 to 3 minutes is generally adequate to obtain satisfactory separation of crude oil and gas unless foaming oil is being handled. When separating foaming oil, retention time should be increased to 5 to 20 minutes, dependent upon the stability of the foam and on the design of the separator. Improvements in field processing systems and production procedures, such as automatic metering and automatic custody transfer, emphasize the need for complete removal of nonsolution gas from the oil. Agitation, special baffling, coalescing packs, and filtering elements assist in removing nonsolution gas that otherwise may be retained in the oil because of the viscosity and surface tension of the oil.

FIG. 11-1. Low-pressure gas back-pressure valve. (*Courtesy of Kimray Inc., Oklahoma City, Okla.*)

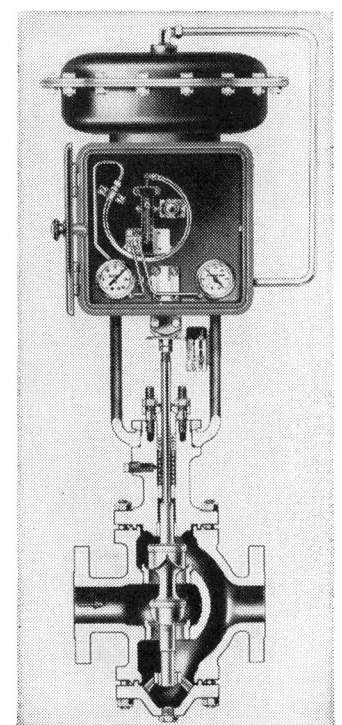

FIG. 11-2. High-pressure gas back-pressure valve. (*Courtesy of Fisher Governor Co., Marshalltown, Iowa.*)

TWO AUXILIARY FUNCTIONS OF OIL AND GAS SEPARATORS

Maintain Optimum Pressure on Separator

For an oil and gas separator to accomplish its functions, pressure must be maintained in the separator so the liquid and gas can be discharged into their respective gathering systems.   Pressure is maintained by use of a gas back-pressure valve on each separator or with a master valve that controls the pressure on a battery of two or more separators.   Figure 11-1 shows a typical low-pressure gas back-pressure valve and Fig. 11-2 shows a typical high-pressure gas back-pressure valve used on oil and gas separators to maintain the desired pressure in the vessel.

The optimum pressure to maintain on a separator is that pressure which will result in the highest economic yield from the sale of the liquid and gaseous hydrocarbons.

Maintain Liquid Seal in Separator

In order to maintain pressure on a separator, a liquid seal must be effected in the lower portion of the vessel.   This liquid seal prevents loss of gas out the liquid line.

FIG. 11-3. Floatless liquid-level controller and diaphragm motor oil control valve on high-pressure oil and gas separator.   (*Courtesy of Kimray Inc., Oklahoma City, Okla.*)

This requires a liquid-level controller and a valve similar to those shown in Fig. 11-3 or 11-4.   A lever-operated valve similar to the one shown in Fig. 11 5 can be used to maintain the liquid seal in a separator when it is operated by a float that is actuated by the oil level in the separator.   The oil discharge control valve shown in Fig. 11-6 can be actuated by a float-operated pilot (not illustrated), by a floatless liquid-level controller similar to the one shown in Fig. 11-3, or by a torque tube (displacement) type liquid-level controller similar to the one shown on the separator in Fig. 11-4.

SPECIAL PROBLEMS IN OIL AND GAS SEPARATION

Removal of Water

In instances where water is produced with oil, conditions may warrant separation of the water from the oil in the separator.   Free water may be removed from well fluids by use of a three-phase (oil-gas-water) separator.   Separation of oil and water in oil and gas separators usually is accomplished by "settling" and use of chemicals.   Separation of emulsified oil and water is sometimes difficult to accomplish, and in such

FIG. 11-4. Horizontal dual-tube three-phase skid-mounted separator with two-torque tube (displacement type) liquid-level controllers, one to control discharge of oil and one for water. (*Courtesy of Oil Metering and Processing Equipment Corp., Houston, Texas.*)

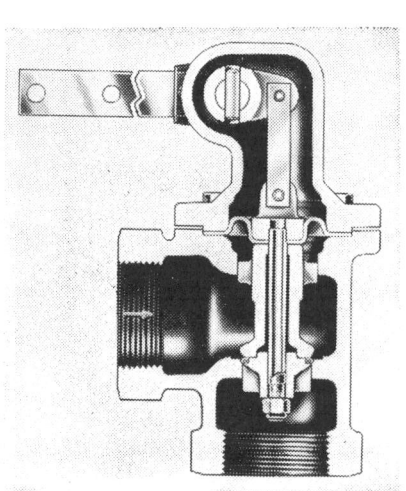

FIG. 11-5. Lever-type valve for controlling oil discharge from oil and gas separators. Valve is float-operated. (*Courtesy of Fisher Governor Co., Marshalltown, Iowa.*)

FIG. 11-6. Diaphragm motor valve for controlling discharge of oil from oil and gas separators, angle body. (*Courtesy of Kimray Inc., Oklahoma City, Okla.*)

instances an emulsion treater or similar equipment is used for this purpose. See Figs. 11-18, 11-19, and 11-20 for illustrations of three-phase separators.

Separating Foaming Crude Oil

If the pressure is reduced on certain types of crude oil, tiny spheres (bubbles) of gas are encased in a thin film of oil when the gas comes out of solution. This results in foam, or froth, being dispersed in the oil and creates what is known as "foaming" oil. In other types of crude oil, the viscosity and surface tension of the oil may mechanically lock gas in the oil and cause an effect similar to foam. Oil foam will not be stable or long-lasting unless a foaming agent is present in the oil.

Foaming greatly reduces the capacity of oil and gas separators since a much longer retention time is required to adequately separate and stabilize a given quantity of oil. Foaming oil cannot be measured accurately with positive-displacement meters or conventional volumetric metering vessels. These problems, combined with the loss of oil and gas due to improper separation, emphasize the need for special procedures in handling foaming oils.

Oil and gas separators of special design are available for handling foaming crude oil. The size and shape of the separator and the size, location, and configuration of the internal parts can be such that the foam will be broken within the separator. Figure 11-10b shows one possible arrangement of special baffling that can be used in oil and gas separators for handling foaming oil.

The main factors that assist in "breaking" foaming oil are

1. Settling
2. Agitation (baffling)
3. Heat (heated salt-water bath)
4. Chemicals

These methods of "reducing" or "breaking" foaming oil are also used to remove entrained gas from oil. They are discussed on pages **11–11** to **11–13**.

Paraffin Deposition

Paraffin deposition in oil and gas separators reduces their efficiency and may render them inoperable by partially filling the vessel and/or blocking the mist extractor and fluid passages. Paraffin can be effectively removed from separators by steaming or by use of solvents. However, the best solution is to prevent initial deposition in the vessel by heating or chemically treating the fluid upstream of the separator. Another deterrent, successful in most instances, involves coating of all internal surfaces of the separator with a plastic for which paraffin has little or no affinity. The weight of the paraffin will cause it to slough off of the plastic-coated surface before it builds up to harmful thickness.

Sand, Mud, Salt, Etc.

If sand and other solids are continuously produced in appreciable quantities with well fluids, they must be removed by settling, centrifuging, or filtering before the liquid enters the pipeline. Medium-grained sand in small quantities can be removed by settling in a vertical separator by using an oversized vessel with a conical bottom and periodically draining the residue from the vessel. Salt may be carried in suspension in the oil. This salt may be removed by means of centrifuging or settling or fresh water may be mixed with the oil and, after the salt is absorbed, the water can be removed by an appropriate means.

MIST EXTRACTORS USED IN REMOVAL OF OIL (LIQUID MIST) FROM GAS

Residual liquid in the form of mist can be effectively removed from the gas stream in an oil and gas separator by a well-designed mist extractor. However, condensible

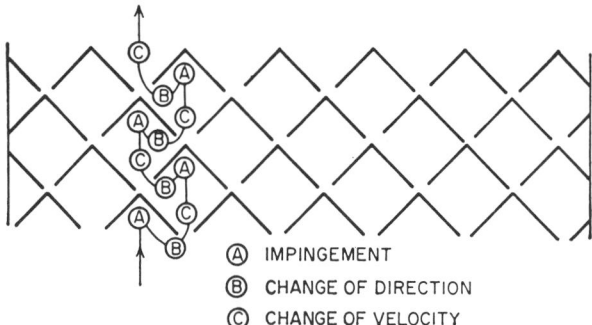

FIG. 11-7a. Illustration of impingement, change of direction of flow, and change of velocity principles of mist extraction.

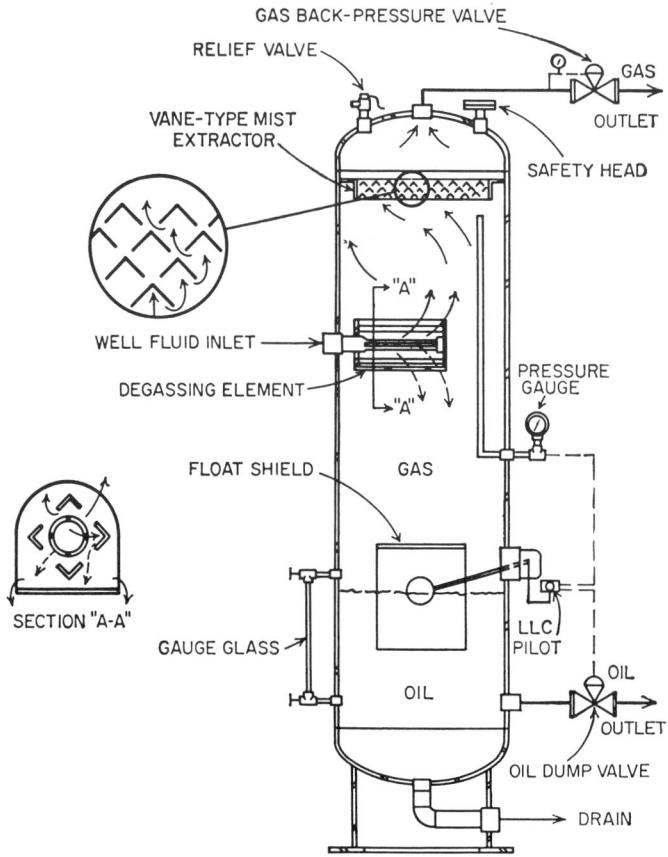

FIG. 11-7b. Vertical two-phase oil and gas separator utilizing a mist extractor of type shown in Fig. 11-7a. Note inlet separating element shown on inlet to separator and shown in detail Section A-A.

vapors in the gas cannot be removed by mist extractors.   Condensation of these vapors, due to reduction of temperature, may occur after the gas has been discharged from the separator.   Thus existence of condensed liquid in the gas effluent from an oil and gas separator, in many instances, does not necessarily reflect upon the efficiency of the separator.   Since condensible vapors may have the characteristics of natural gas when at separator temperature and pressure, condensation of these vapors into liquid may occur immediately after being discharged from the separator.   Density difference between liquid and gas may accomplish separation of liquid droplets from a gas stream where the velocity of the stream is slow enough and sufficient time is allowed to accomplish separation.   Limiting the gas velocity in a separator may obtain satisfactory separation without a mist extractor.   However, mist extractors are generally installed in conventional oil and gas separators to assist in separation and to minimize the amount of liquid (mist) carried out with the gas.

Mist extractors can be of many different designs, utilizing one or more of the principles of (1) impingement, (2) change of flow direction, (3) change of velocity, (4) centrifugal force, (5) coalescing packs, and (6) filters.   See Figs. 11-7a and b, 11-8, and 11-9 for illustrations of various types of mist extractors.   Principles of mist extraction are discussed individually as follows:

Impingement

If a flowing stream of gas containing liquid mist is impinged against a surface, the liquid mist may adhere to, and coalesce on, the surface.   After the mist coalesces into larger droplets, the liquid will gravitate to the liquid section of the vessel.   If the liquid content of the gas is high, or the mist particles extremely fine, several successive impingement surfaces may be required to effect satisfactory removal of the mist.   Refer to Fig. 11-7a.

Change of Flow Direction

When the direction of flow of a gas stream containing liquid mist is changed abruptly, inertia causes the liquid to continue in the original direction of flow.   Separation of liquid mist from the gas is thus effected, since the gas will more readily assume the change of flow direction and continue to flow away from the liquid mist particles.   The liquid thus removed may coalesce on a surface, or it may fall directly to the liquid section below.   Refer to Fig. 11-7a.

Change of Velocity

Separation of liquid and gas is also effected with either a sudden increase or decrease in velocity.   Both conditions utilize the difference in inertia of gas and liquid.   With a decrease in the velocity of gas, the higher inertia of the liquid mist carries it forward and away from the gas.   The liquid may then coalesce upon some surface and gravitate to the liquid section of the separator.   With an increase in gas velocity, the higher inertia of the liquid causes the gas to move away from the liquid, and the liquid may fall to the liquid section of the vessel.   Refer to Fig. 11-7a, which shows one version of a vane-type mist extractor used in oil and gas separators to remove liquid mist from gas.   This mist extractor is shown in a typical vertical oil and gas separator in Fig. 11-7b.

Centrifugal Force

If a gas stream carrying liquid mist flows in a circular motion at sufficiently high velocity, centrifugal force throws the liquid mist outward against the walls of the container or element.   Here it coalesces into progressively larger droplets and finally gravitates to the liquid section below.   Centrifugal force is one of the most effective methods of separating liquid mist from gas. Efficiency of this method increases as the velocity of the gas stream increases.

Figure 11-8 illustrates a centrifugal-type mist extractor used in vertical oil and gas separators. The radial vanes cause a circular motion of the gas, and the resulting centrifugal force throws heavier liquid particles to the wall of the vessel where they coalesce into drops large enough to drain from the mist extractor element.

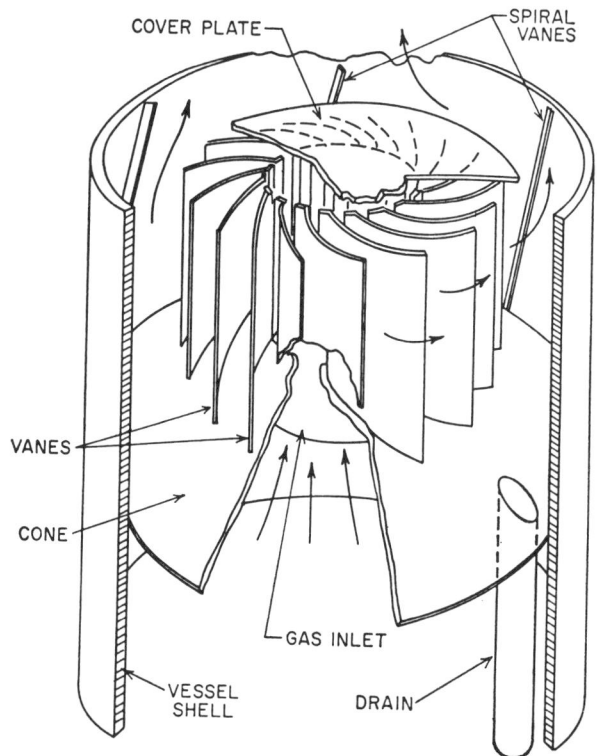

FIG. 11-8. Centrifugal-type mist extractor used in vertical oil and gas separators. (*Courtesy of Parkersburg Rig and Reel Company, Houston, Texas.*)

Small centrifugal-force-type mist extractors have been inserted in small-diameter (4 to 12 in.) vessels, and these "separators" have handled relatively large volumes of gas. This type of separator (or scrubber) is used in scrubbing gas in gas gathering, transmission, and distribution systems. However, a small-diameter vessel usually is not practical for use on oil- and gas-producing wells as the primary separator because of the possibility that the small vessel may be filled with a "slug" or "head" of liquid and cause the liquid to flow out with the gas. Therefore, a larger conventional separator vessel should be used to separate well fluids because miniature vessels may cause trouble by "overloading" with liquid.

Coalescing Packs

Coalescing packs afford an effective means of separating and removing liquid mist from a stream of gas. One of their most appropriate uses is the removal of liquid mist from gas in transmission and distribution systems.

Coalescing packs can be made of Berl saddles, Raschig rings, knitted wire mesh, and other such materials. The packs employ a combination of impingement, change of direction, change of velocity, and centrifugal force in separating and removing liquid mist from gas. These packs provide a large surface area for collection and coalescence of the liquid mist. Figure 11-9 is a schematic illustration of a knitted wire-mesh coalescing-pack-type mist extractor used in some oil and gas separators and gas scrubbers.

A word of caution is appropriate concerning the use of coalescing packs in oil and gas separators for general field use. Coalescing packs may be made of frangible material which can be damaged during transit or installation if they are installed in the manufacturing shop prior to shipment to point of use. Knitted wire mesh may foul or plug from paraffin deposition and other foreign material and thus make a separator which utilizes this material inoperative after a short period of service.

Even though coalescing packs are very effective in removing liquid mist from gas, it is usually preferred to use vane-type mist extractors for oil and gas separators because they may be used under widely varying conditions. The use of coalescing-type mist extractors, because of their "fouling" tendency, is appropriately restricted to gas scrubbers used in gas gathering, transmission, and distribution systems.

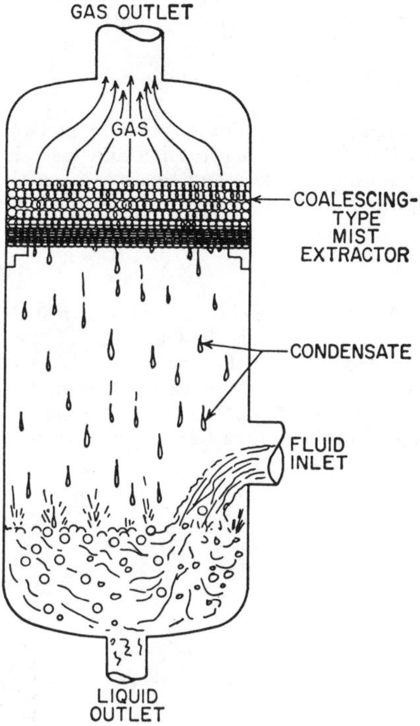

Filters

Porous filters have proved effective in removing liquid mist from gas in certain applications. In effect, the porous material strains or filters the liquid mist from the gas. In addition, the porous material may utilize the principles of impingement, change of flow direction, and change of velocity to accomplish separation of the liquid mist from the gas.

Fig. 11-9. Illustration of coalescing-type mist extractor utilizing knitted wire mesh. Used in gas scrubbers and oil and gas separators. (*Courtesy of Otto H. York Co., West Orange, N.J.*)

Pressure drop through mist extractors used in separators should be as low as possible and still maintain maximum separating efficiency. Generally speaking, filter-type mist extractors will have the highest pressure drop per unit volume of capacity and the coalescing type will have the lowest. Pressure drop through the other types of mist extractors will range between these two extremes.

METHODS USED TO REMOVE GAS FROM OIL (LIQUID)

With a steady demand for natural gas and the widespread reliance on metering of liquid hydrocarbons and for other reasons it is important to remove all nonsolution gas from the oil. Removal of gas from oil can be accomplished in several ways.

Settling

Gas not in solution will separate from oil if the oil is allowed to settle a sufficient length of time. To increase retention time for a fixed liquid through-put requires an increase in the size of the vessel or an increase in liquid depth in the separator. Increasing the depth of oil in the separator may not result in increased emission of nonsolution gas from the oil because "stacking up" of the oil may tend to prevent the nonsolution gas from emerging from the oil.

Agitation

Agitation is helpful in removing nonsolution gas which may be mechanically locked in the oil by surface tension and viscosity of the oil. Agitation may cause the gas bubbles to coalesce and separate from the oil in less time than would be required if agitation were not employed. Agitation is obtained by stirring, vibrating, or baffling.

Baffling

An element similar to that shown in Fig. 11-10a can be installed on the inlet to a separator such as is shown in Fig. 11-10b. This element spreads the oil and disperses it in such manner that gas can readily escape from the oil. This type of element provides additional benefits by eliminating high-velocity impingement of the fluid against the opposite wall of the separator. As illustrated in Fig. 11-10b, baffles placed in the path of the oil spread it into thin layers as it flows from the inlet element

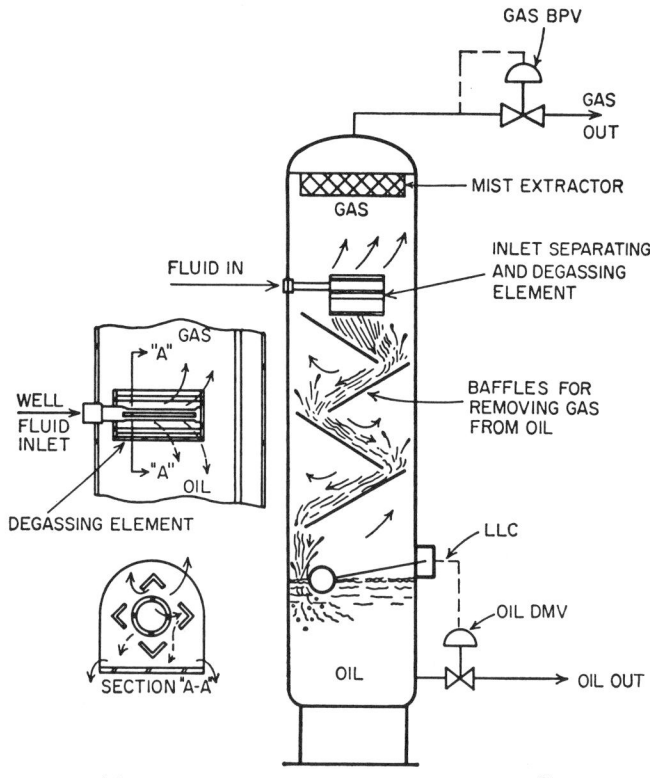

(a)   (b)

FIG. 11-10. (a) Inlet separating element to assist in removing gas from oil. (b) Special baffling to remove gas from oil, especially beneficial in handling foaming oil. (*Courtesy of Oil Metering and Processing Equipment Corp., Houston, Texas.*)

to the oil section of the separator.   The oil is rolled over and over as it cascades down the baffles, and the combination of spreading and rolling is effective in releasing entrained gas bubbles.   This type of baffle is successful in handling foaming oil.

A special type of baffling in the form of coalescing packs can be used to remove non-solution gas from the oil.   This type of element causes the oil to be spread into thin layers, which allows the gas bubbles to break out of the oil film that encases them.

Heat

Heat reduces surface tension of oil and thus assists in releasing gas that is mechanically retained in the oil.   The most effective method of heating crude oil is by passing it through a heated salt-water bath.   A spreader-plate arrangement that disperses the oil into thin layers or streams increases effectiveness of the heated salt-water bath. Flow of the oil in small streams or thin layers upward through the hot salt water affords slight agitation, which is helpful in coalescing the gas bubbles.   A heated salt-water bath is perhaps the most effective method for removing foam bubbles from foaming oil.

Chemicals

Any chemical that reduces the surface tension of crude oil will assist in freeing non-solution gas from the oil.   Chemicals that reduce the surface tension of oil will appreciably reduce the foaming tendency of the oil and thereby increase the capacity of a separator when handling foaming oil.   In one particular case the capacity of an oil and gas separator was increased from 3,800 to 9,600 B/D when a certain chemical was injected into the oil upstream of the separator with no other change being made in the system.

TYPES OF OIL AND GAS SEPARATORS

Oil and gas separators are of two general types, namely, two-phase and three-phase.

1. A two-phase unit separates well fluid into liquid and gas and discharges the gas from the top of the vessel and the liquid from the bottom.

2. A three-phase unit separates well fluids into oil, gas, and water.   Gas is dis-

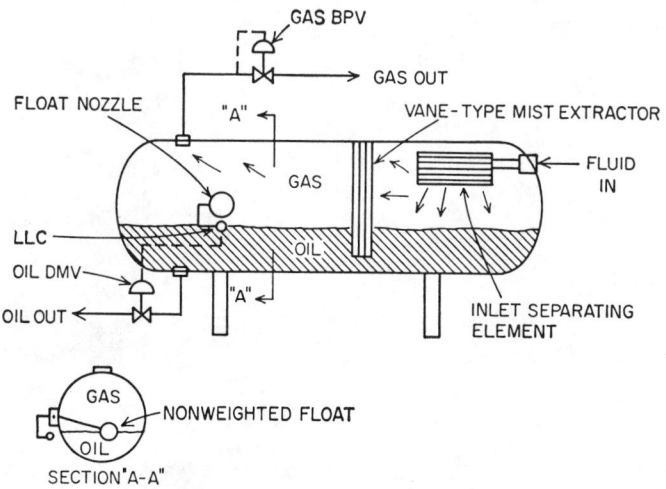

FIG. 11-11. Schematic diagram of typical horizontal two-phase oil and gas separator.

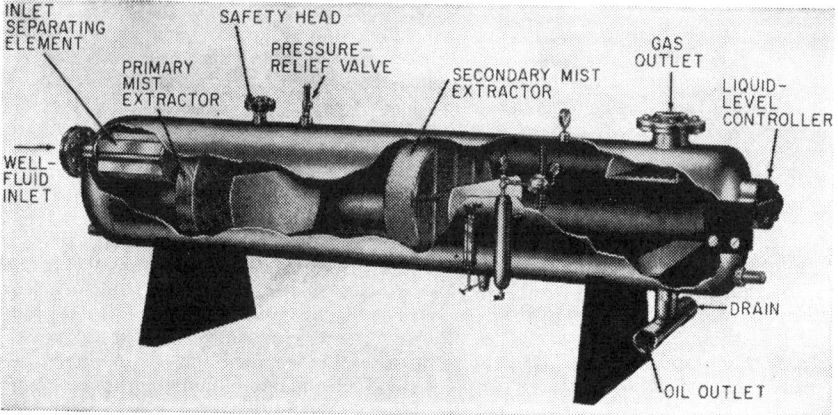

FIG. 11-12. Perspective airbrush sketch of horizontal two-phase oil and gas separator. (*Courtesy of Texas Gulf Tank Co., Houston, Texas.*)

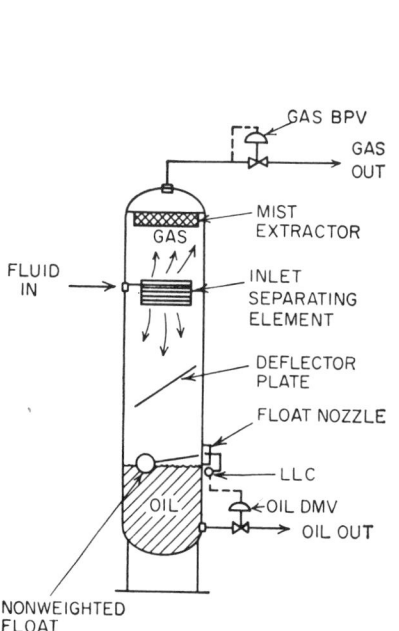

FIG. 11-13. Schematic diagram of typical vertical two-phase oil and gas separator.

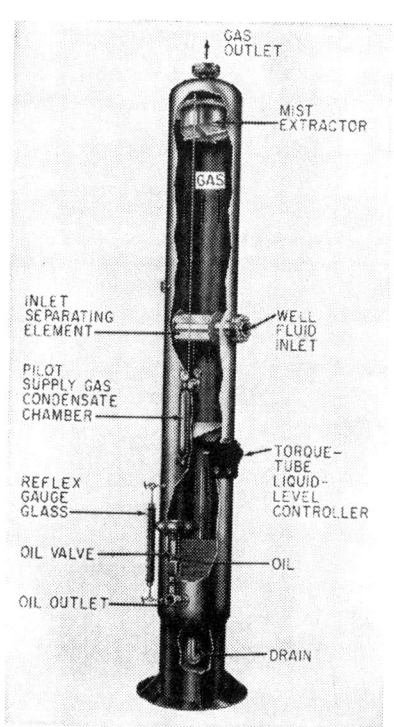

FIG. 11-14. Perspective airbrush sketch of vertical two-phase oil and gas separator. (*Courtesy of Texas Gulf Tank Co., Houston, Texas.*)

charged from the top of the vessel, oil from an intermediate position, and water from the bottom.

Both two-phase and three-phase separators are available in different designs, as follows:

   a. Horizontal
      (1) Monotube
      (2) Dual tube
   b. Vertical
   c. Spherical

Typical examples of these various types of oil and gas separators are illustrated in Figs. 11-11 through 11-20.

Fig. 11-15. Typical field installation of a vertical two-phase oil and gas separator. (*Courtesy of Oil Metering and Processing Equipment Corp., Houston, Texas.*)

Figure 11-11 shows a horizontal two-phase oil and gas separator. Figure 11-12 is an airbrush drawing of a horizontal two-phase oil and gas separator showing the internal components of a typical unit.

Figure 11-13 shows a vertical two-phase oil and gas separator. Figure 11-14 is an airbrush drawing showing one version of such a separator. Figure 11-15 is a photograph of an installation of a vertical two-phase oil and gas separator utilizing a torque tube liquid-level controller and a diaphragm motor valve to control the oil level in the vessel.

Figure 11-16 is a drawing of a spherical two-phase oil and gas separator that utilizes a float-operated lever-type oil valve such as that shown in Fig. 11-5.

Figures 11-17a, b, and c are photographs of spherical two-phase oil and gas separators. Figure 11-17a shows a unit that uses a floatless liquid-level controller to control

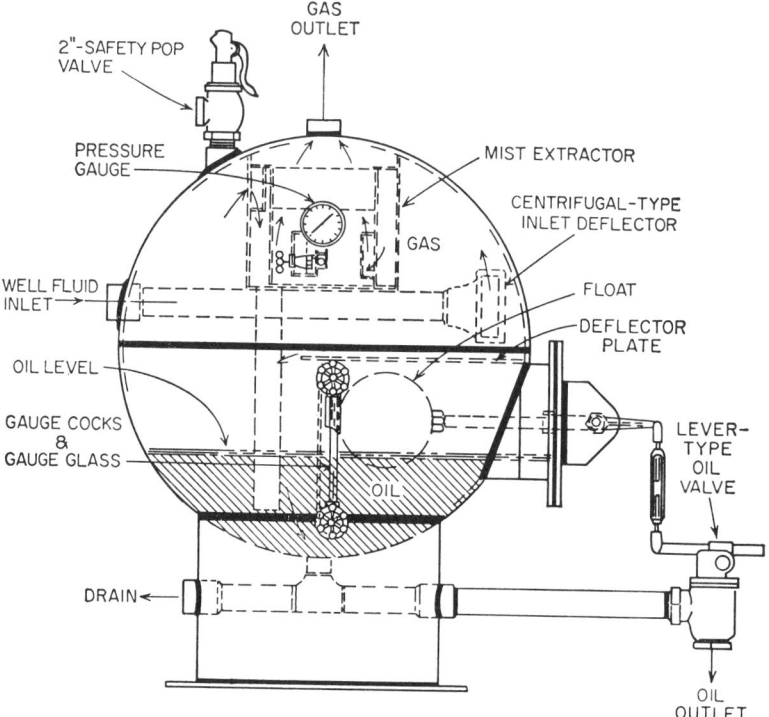

FIG. 11-16. Schematic diagram of typical spherical two-phase oil and gas separator with float-operated lever-type oil control valve.

FIG. 11-17. Photographs of three spherical two-phase oil and gas separators. (*a*) With floatless liquid-level controller. (*b*) With torque tube (displacement) type liquid-level controller. (*c*) With mechanical (float and lever) type oil control valve. (*Courtesy of Delta Tank Company, Baton Rouge, Louisiana.*)

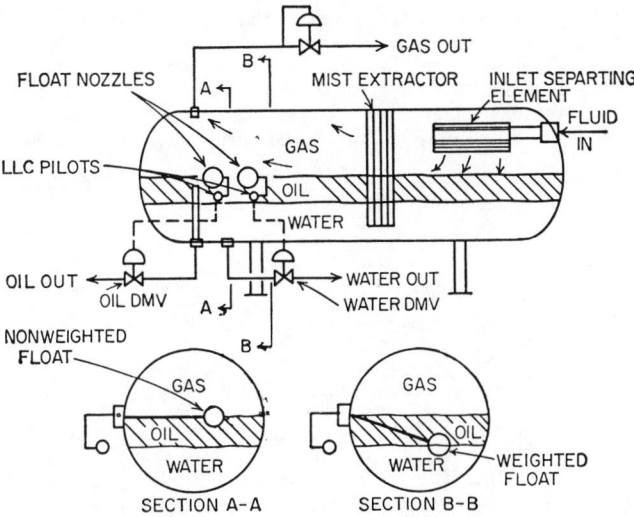

FIG. 11-18. Schematic diagram of typical horizontal three-phase oil-gas-water separator.

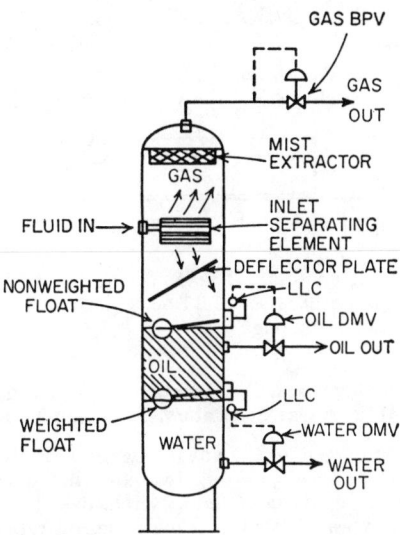

FIG. 11-19. Schematic diagram of a typical vertical three-phase oil-gas-water separator.

the oil valve. Figure 11-17b shows a torque tube (displacement) type liquid-level controller to control the oil valve. Figure 11-17c shows a float-operated lever (mechanical) oil control valve on a spherical separator.

Figure 11-18 is an illustration of a horizontal three-phase oil-gas-water separator. Figure 11-19 is a vertical three-phase oil-gas-water separator. Figure 11-20 is a spherical arrangement of a three-phase separator.

Essential components of oil and gas separators are the separator vessel, liquid-level control, oil discharge valve, and miscellaneous accessories including gauge cocks and glasses, pressure gauges, safety relief valve, gas back-pressure valve, safety head, and ladder. In addition to these, a three-phase separator requires an oil-water interface liquid-level control means and a water-dump valve.

In addition to serving as a means to separate the well fluid into gas and liquids, the separator vessel, in many instances, must also serve as an accumulation or storage vessel. This is particularly true where the wells flow by "heads," where intermittent gas lift is used, and where the tubing and/or flow lines may "unload" liquid into the vessel at high instantaneous flow rates. The separator vessel must be large enough to store these "slugs" of liquid until the gas can be separated from the oil and both com-

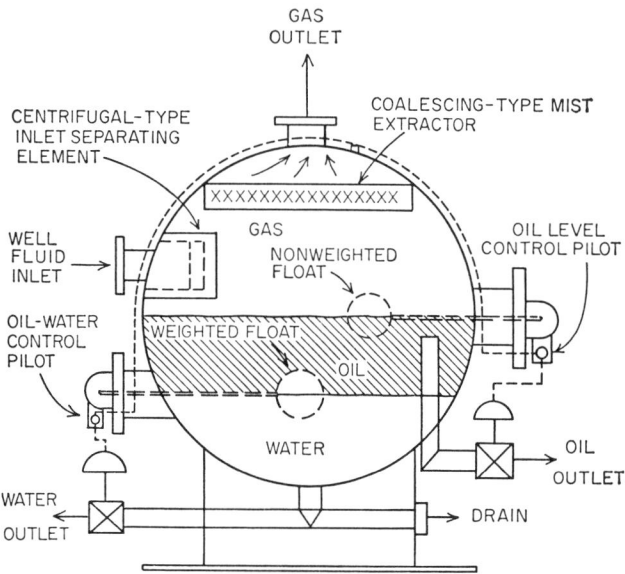

Fig. 11-20. Schematic diagram of a typical spherical three-phase oil-gas-water separator.

ponents discharged from the vessel. This consideration of "storage" quite often dictates a larger vessel than otherwise would be required if the flow of fluid into the separator were steady and continuous.

Comparison of Advantages and Disadvantages of Horizontal, Vertical, and Spherical Oil and Gas Separators, Two- and Three-phase

Table 11-1 shows a comparison of the advantages and disadvantages of horizontal, vertical, and spherical oil and gas separators, two- and three-phase. This table is not intended as an "absolute" guide but affords a relative comparison of the various features of the different types of separators over the full range of types, sizes, and working pressures.

The comparison of oil and gas separators in Table 11-1 assumes that the horizontal oil and gas separators are monotube vessels. Some horizontal oil and gas separators are constructed with two parallel tubes, one above the other, as the separator vessel. These are known as dual-tube separators. A photograph of a horizontal dual-tube oil and gas separator is shown in Fig. 11-4. This is a skid-mounted three-phase oil, gas, and water separator that is used to separate the well stream into these three phases. Gas is discharged from the top of the upper tube, oil is discharged from the bottom of the upper tube, and water is discharged from the bottom of the lower tube.

Dual-tube separators are available for two-phase separation where the well fluid is separated into gas and liquid. The liquid level in such units is carried in the lower tube. Liquid is discharged from the bottom of the lower tube and gas is discharged from the top of the upper tube.

A monotube horizontal oil and gas separator is usually preferred over a dual-tube unit. The monotube unit has a greater area for gas flow as well as a greater interface area than is usually available in a dual-tube separator of comparable price. The monotube separator will usually afford a longer retention time because the larger single-tube vessel retains a larger volume of oil than the dual-tube separator. It is also easier to clean than the dual-tube unit.

Table 11-1. Comparison of Advantages and Disadvantages of Horizontal, Vertical, and Spherical Oil and Gas Separators, Two- and Three-phase

Considerations	Horizontal (monotube)*	Vertical (monotube)*	Spherical (one compartment)*
Efficiency of separation......................	1	2	3
Stabilization of separated fluids...............	1	2	3
Adaptability of varying conditions (such as "heading" flow)...........................	1	2	3
Flexibility of operation (such as adjustment of liquid level)...............................	2	1	3
Capacity (same diameter).....................	1	2	3
Cost per unit capacity........................	1	2	3
Ability to handle foreign material..............	3	1	2
Ability to handle foaming oil..................	1	2	3
Adaptability to portable use..................	1	3	2
Space for installation:			
Vertical plane.............................	1	3	2
Horizontal plane..........................	3	1	2
Ease of installation..........................	2	3	1
Ease of inspection and maintenance...........	1	3	2

* Ratings: (1) most favorable; (2) intermediate; (3) least favorable.

In cold climates freezing will be likely to cause less trouble for the monotube unit because the liquid is usually in close contact with the warm stream of gas flowing through the separator. The monotube design normally has a lower silhouette than the dual-tube unit, and it is easier to stack them for multiple-stage separation units and for platform installations where space is at a premium.

METERING SEPARATORS

The function of separating well fluids into oil, gas, and water and metering the liquids can be accomplished in one vessel. These vessels are commonly referred to as metering separators and are available in "two-phase" and "three-phase" types. Variations of these units that make them suitable for accurately metering foaming oil and heavy viscous oil are classified as "foaming-oil type" and "heavy-viscous-crude type." A two-phase metering separator separates well fluids into liquid and gas and measures the liquid in the lower portion of the vessel. A typical two-phase metering separator is shown in Fig. 11-21. A three-phase metering separator separates the oil, water, and gas and measures either the oil only or both the oil and water. Metering of the liquid is normally accomplished by accumulation, isolation, and discharge of given volumes in a metering compartment in the lower portion of the vessel.

Figure 11-22 illustrates a three-phase metering separator in which the free water is discharged without measuring; Fig. 11-23 shows a similar three-phase unit in which both oil and water are measured.

A "foaming-oil"-type metering separator is shown in Fig. 11-24. This unit utilizes a hydrostatic-head liquid-level controller to accomplish accurate measurement on the basis of weight rather than volume.

The heavy-viscous-oil type of metering separator shown in Fig. 11-25 utilizes pressure flow into and out of the separator and does not rely upon gravity flow. This particular unit is a two-phase vessel with two combination separating and metering

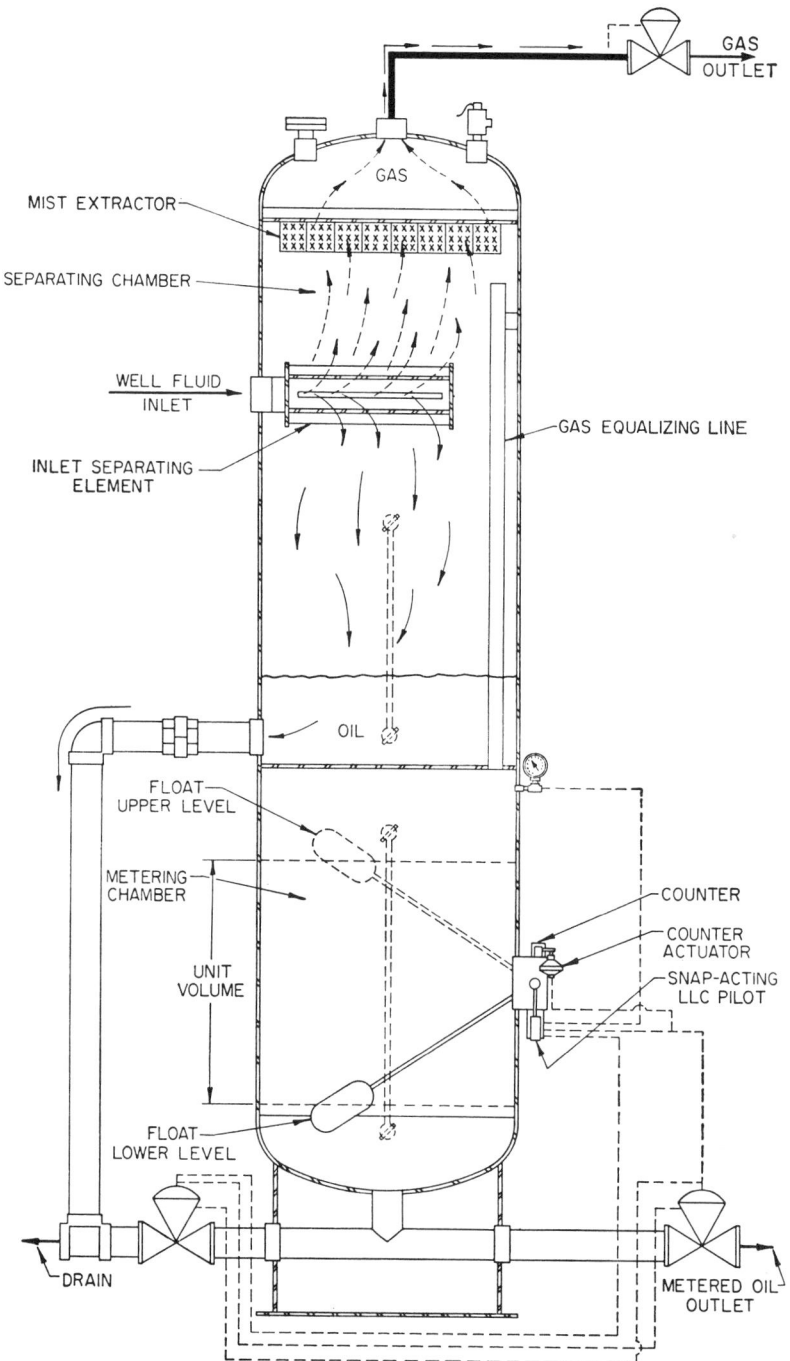

GAS OUTLET

MIST EXTRACTOR

GAS

SEPARATING CHAMBER

WELL FLUID INLET

INLET SEPARATING ELEMENT

GAS EQUALIZING LINE

OIL

FLOAT UPPER LEVEL

METERING CHAMBER

COUNTER

COUNTER ACTUATOR

SNAP-ACTING LLC PILOT

UNIT VOLUME

FLOAT LOWER LEVEL

DRAIN

METERED OIL OUTLET

FIG. 11-21. Schematic diagram of a vertical two-phase metering separator. Liquid is metered in integral metering compartment in lower portion of vessel. (*Control system patented by Oil Metering and Processing Equipment Corp., Houston, Texas.*)

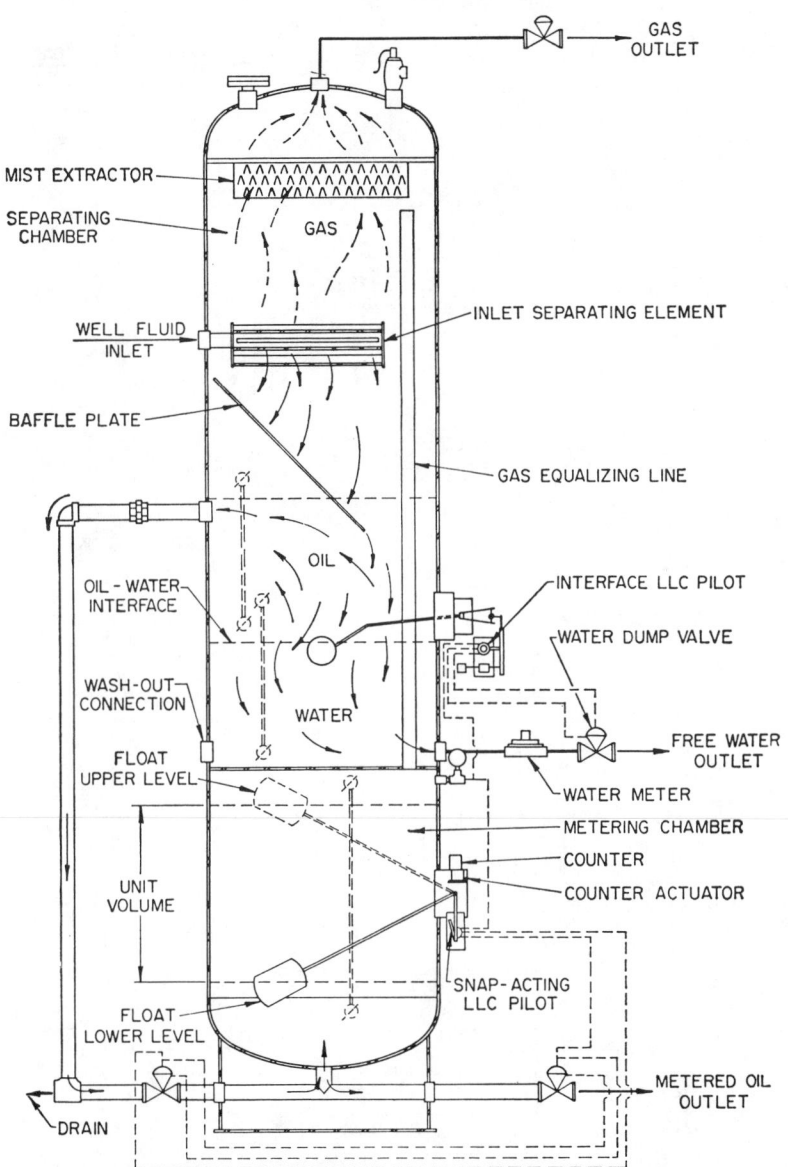

FIG. 11-22. Schematic diagram of a vertical three-phase metering separator with free water not metered. (*Control system patented by Oil Metering and Processing Equipment Corp., Houston, Texas.*)

compartments operating in parallel.   It is equipped with controls and valves that are arranged to permit constant flow of well fluid into the vessel.   With pressure flow into and out of each of the two compartments, it is possible to handle much larger volumes than separators with two compartments that rely on gravity flow from upper to lower compartments.   These units are furnished with hydrostatic-head liquid-level controls for metering foaming oil or float-operated controls for nonfoaming oil.

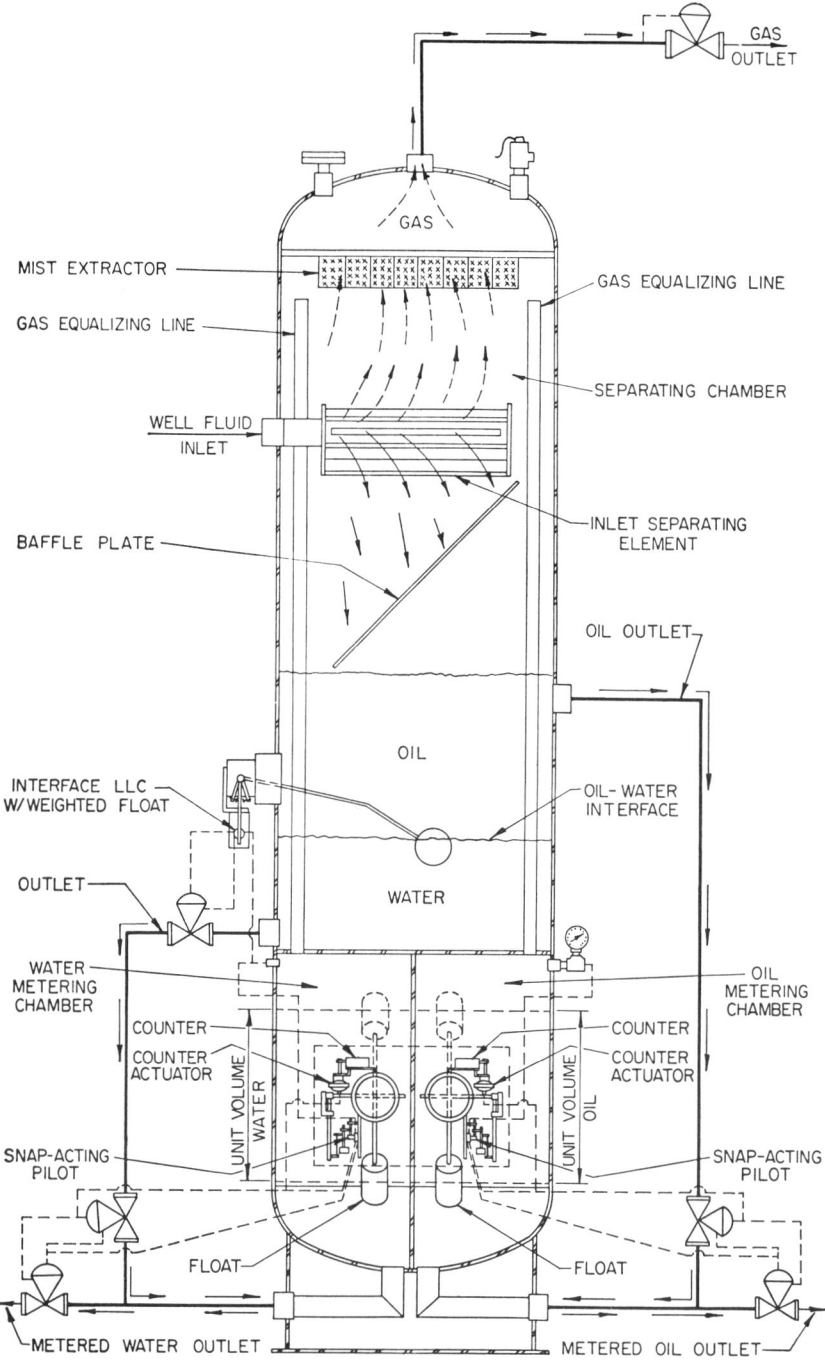

FIG. 11-23. Schematic diagram of a vertical three-phase metering separator in which oil and water are metered in integral compartments. (*Control system patented by Oil Metering and Processing Equipment Corp., Houston, Texas.*)

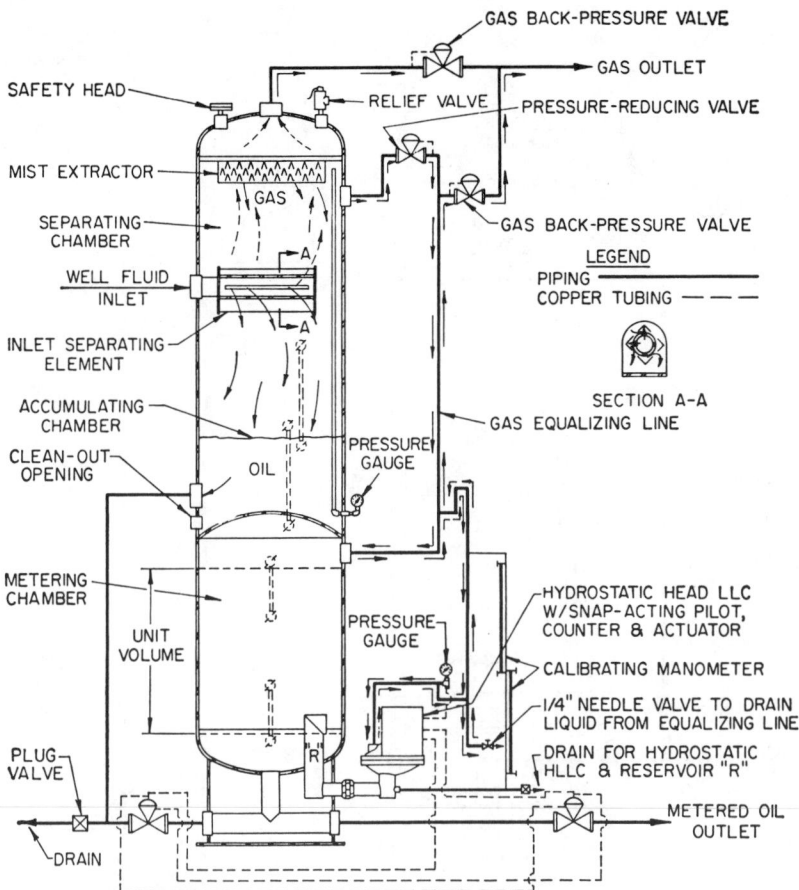

GAS BACK-PRESSURE VALVE

SAFETY HEAD

GAS OUTLET

RELIEF VALVE

PRESSURE-REDUCING VALVE

MIST EXTRACTOR

GAS

SEPARATING
CHAMBER

GAS BACK-PRESSURE VALVE

LEGEND
PIPING ——————
COPPER TUBING — — —

WELL FLUID
INLET

A

A

INLET SEPARATING
ELEMENT

SECTION A-A
GAS EQUALIZING LINE

ACCUMULATING
CHAMBER

CLEAN-OUT
OPENING

OIL

PRESSURE
GAUGE

METERING
CHAMBER

UNIT
VOLUME

PRESSURE
GAUGE

HYDROSTATIC HEAD LLC
W/SNAP-ACTING PILOT,
COUNTER & ACTUATOR

CALIBRATING MANOMETER

1/4" NEEDLE VALVE TO DRAIN
LIQUID FROM EQUALIZING LINE

DRAIN FOR HYDROSTATIC
HLLC & RESERVOIR "R"

PLUG
VALVE

R

METERED OIL
OUTLET

DRAIN

Fig. 11-24. Schematic diagram of vertical two-phase metering separator for metering foaming oil on "weight" basis. (*Control system patented by Oil Metering and Processing Equipment Corp., Houston, Texas.*)

STAGE SEPARATION OF OIL AND GAS

Theoretical Considerations of Stage Separation

Stage separation of oil and gas is accomplished with a series of separators operating at sequentially reduced pressures. Liquid is discharged from a higher-pressure separator into the next lower-pressure separator. The purpose of stage separation is to obtain maximum recovery of liquid hydrocarbons from the well fluid and to provide maximum stabilization of both the liquid and gas effluent.

There are two processes of liberating gas (vapor) from liquid hydrocarbon under pressure. These are flash separation (vaporization) and differential separation (vaporization). Flash separation is accomplished when pressure is reduced on the system with the liquid and vapor (gas) remaining in contact, that is, the vapor (gas) is not removed from contact with the liquid as reduction in pressure allows the vapor (gas) to come out of solution. This process yields the most vapor (gas) and the least liquid. Differential separation is accomplished when the vapor (gas) is removed from

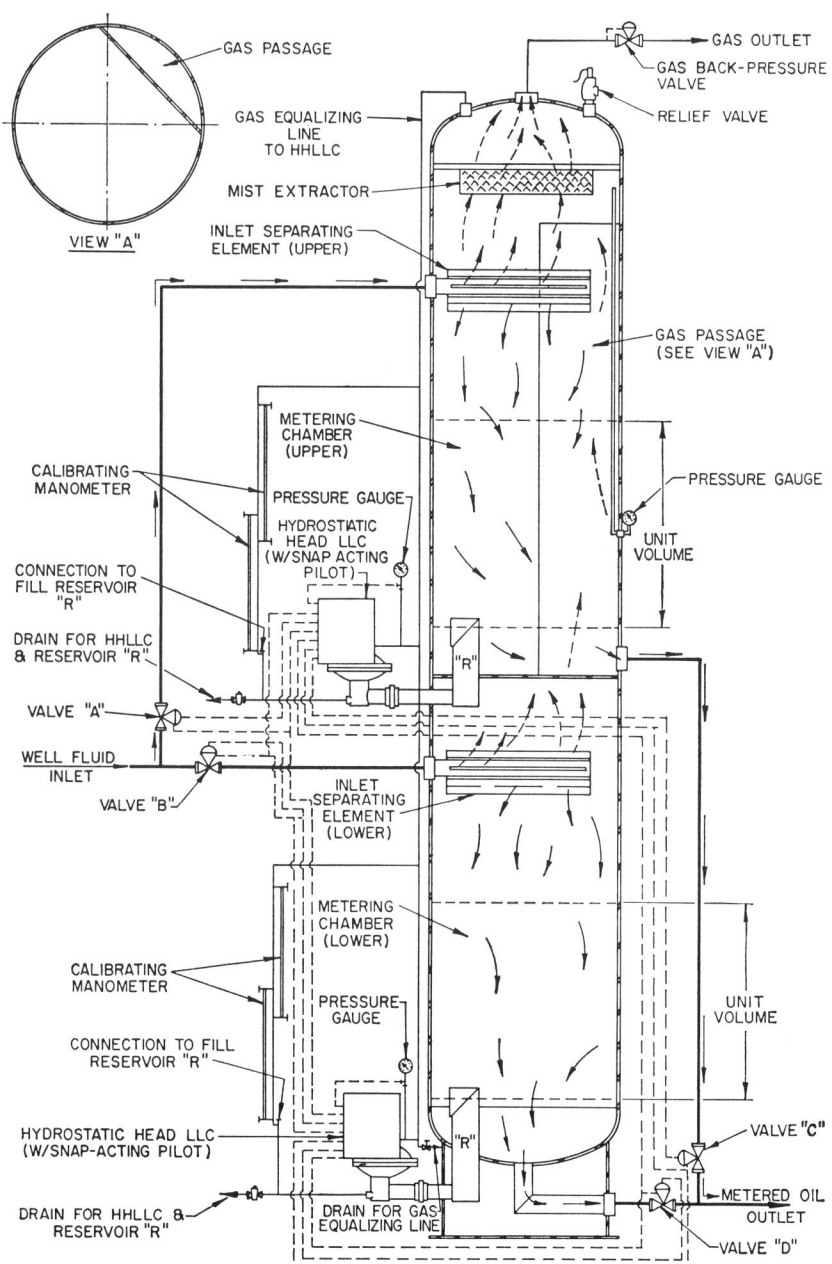

FIG. 11-25. Schematic diagram of vertical two-phase metering separator for metering viscous and/or foaming oil on "weight" basis. Pressure flow into and out of both compartments increases fluid handling capacity. (*Control system patented by Oil Metering and Processing Equipment Corp., Houston, Texas.*)

contact with the liquid as reduction in pressure allows the vapor to come out of solution.   This process yields the most liquid and least vapor (gas).

In a multiple-stage separator installation both processes of gas liberation are obtained.   When the well fluid flows through the formation tubing, chokes, reducing regulators, and surface lines, pressure reduction occurs with the gas in contact with the liquid.   This is flash separation.   When the fluid passes through a separator, pressure reduction is accomplished: also, the oil and gas are separated and discharged separately.   This is differential separation.   The more nearly the separation system approaches true differential separation from producing formation to storage, the higher the yield of liquid will be.

An "ideal" oil and gas separator, from the standpoint of maximum liquid recovery, is one so constructed that it reduces the pressure of the well fluid from the wellhead at the entrance of the separator vessel to, or near, atmospheric pressure at the discharge from the separator.   The gas and/or vapor is removed from the separator continuously as soon as it is separated from the liquid.   This is known as differential vaporization or separation.   However, such an arrangement is not practical.

Some of the benefits of an "ideal" separator may be obtained by use of multiple-stage separation.   The number of stages does not have to be large to obtain an appreciable benefit, as can be seen from the table below:*

Number of stages of separation	Approximate per cent approach to differential vaporization
2	0
3	75
4	90
5	96
6	98½

Economics usually limits the number of stages of separation to three or four, but five or six will pay out under favorable conditions.   Seven stages have been used on large volumes of oil, but such installations are rare.

Ratios of operating pressures between stages in multiple-stage separation can be approximated from the following equation:

$$R = \sqrt[n]{\frac{P1}{Ps}}$$

$$P2 = \frac{P1}{R} = PsR^{n-1}$$

$$P3 = \frac{P2}{R} = PsR^{n-2}$$

where R = stage pressure ratio = $\dfrac{P1}{P2} = \dfrac{P2}{P3} = \cdots \dfrac{Pn}{Ps}$

n = number of interstages (number of stages − 1)
$P1$ = first-stage separator pressure, psia
$P2$ = second-stage separator pressure, psia
$P3$ = third-stage separator pressure, psia
Ps = storage-tank pressure, psia

Equilibrium flash calculations should be made for several assumed conditions of pressures and temperatures to determine the conditions that will yield the most stock-tank liquid.   However, the above equation will give a practical approximation that can be used when no other information is available.

Two-stage separation is normally considered to be obtained when one oil and gas separator is used in conjunction with a storage tank.   Three-stage separation is obtained when two separators are used in series at different pressures, in conjunction

* This table and the equation following it are from Garman O. Kimmel, *ASME Paper* 49-PET-15.

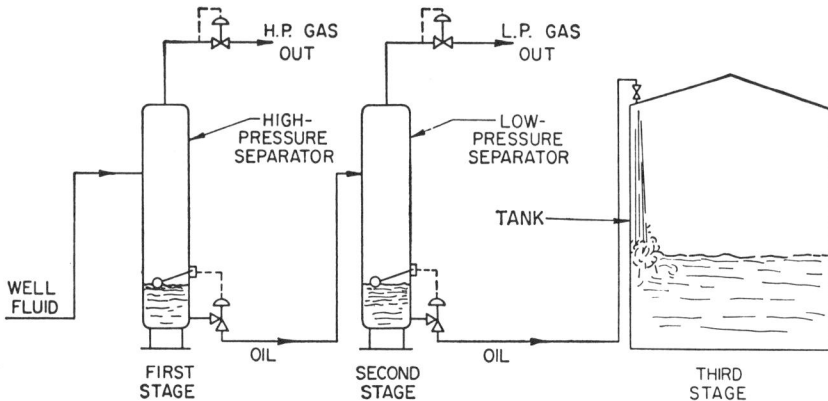

FIG. 11-26. Typical three-stage separator installation (two separators and tank).

with a storage tank. Since gas may continue to separate or "weather" from oil in storage tanks, the storage tank is considered as a "stage" of separation. Figure 11-26 shows schematically a three-stage separator installation.

Economic Considerations of Stage Separation

The extent of application of stage separation will depend upon two principal considerations: (1) the terms of the gas sales contract and (2) the price structure for the gaseous and liquid hydrocarbons.

If gas is sold on volume only, it will usually be desirable to remove all condensible vapors from it. If, on the other hand, gas is sold on GPM content, it may be desirable to permit condensible vapors to remain in the gas depending on conditions, facilities, and location.

If the liquid hydrocarbon is sold on the basis of volume and API gravity, it may be desirable to remove the condensible vapors from the gas and add them to the liquid to increase its sales price. If, on the other hand, the liquid is sold on the basis of volume only, it may be desirable to leave the condensible vapors in the gas.

Table 11-2. Separator Operating at 850 psia and 90°F

Hydro-carbon	Composition of feed		Equilibrium constants		Composition of yield			
					Liquid		Vapor	
	Mole, %	Moles per day	K, 850 psia, 90°F	$KR + 1$	Moles per day	Mole, %	Moles per day	Mole, %
C_1	84.53	26,078	4.0	63.00	414	22.27	25,664	88.50
C_2	5.78	1,784	0.89	14.795	121	6.51	1,663	5.73
C_3	3.56	1,099	0.34	6.270	175	9.41	924	3.19
iC_4	0.96	296	0.185	3.868	77	4.14	219	0.76
nC_4	1.29	398	0.145	3.248	123	6.62	275	0.95
iC_5	0.60	185	0.074	2.147	86	4.63	99	0.34
nC_5	0.42	131	0.059	1.915	68	3.66	63	0.22
C_6	0.81	250	0.025	1.388	180	9.68	70	0.24
C_7^+	2.05	634	0.002	1.031	615	33.08	19	0.07
	100.00	30,855			1,859	100.00	28,996	100.00

$R = (30,855/1,870) - 1 = 15.50$.
Convergence pressure $= CP = 4,000$ psia.

Table 11-3. Separator Operating at 250 psia and 80°F

| Hydro-carbon | Composition of feed | | Equilibrium constants | | Composition of yield | | | |
| | Mole, % | Moles per day | K, 250 psia, 80°F | $KR + 1$ | Liquid | | Vapor | |
					Moles per day	Mole, %	Moles per day	Mole, %
C₁	22.27	414	10.50	3.870	107	7.31	307	77.72
C₂	6.51	121	2.13	1.582	76	5.19	45	11.39
C₃	9.41	175	0.65	1.178	149	10.18	26	6.58
iC₄	4.14	77	0.28	1.077	71	4.85	6	1.52
nC₄	6.62	123	0.206	1.0563	116	7.92	7	1.77
iC₅	4.63	86	0.093	1.0254	84	5.74	2	0.52
nC₅	3.66	68	0.074	1.0202	67	4.58	1	0.25
C₆	9.68	180	0.027	1.0074	179	12.23	1	0.25
C₇⁺	33.08	615	0.0017	1.00046	615	42.00	0	0
	100.00	1,859			1,464	100.00	395	100.00

$R = (1,859/1,460) - 1 = 0.2733$.
Convergence pressure $= CP = 2,000$ psia.

Table 11-4. Tank Maintained at 14.7 psia and 100°F

| Hydro-carbon | Composition of feed | | Equilibrium constants | | Composition of yield | | | |
| | Mole, % | Moles per day | K, 14.7 psia, 100°F | $KR + 1$ | Liquid | | Vapor | |
					Moles per day	Mole, %	Moles per day	Mole, %
C₁	7.31	107	186	107.8	1	0.11	106	20.00
C₂	5.19	76	38	22.816	3	0.32	73	13.77
C₃	10.18	149	10.5	7.0281	21	2.25	128	24.15
iC₄	4.85	71	4.3	3.4686	20	2.14	51	9.62
nC₄	7.92	116	3.25	2.8658	40	4.28	76	14.34
iC₅	5.74	84	1.28	1.7348	48	5.14	36	6.79
nC₅	4.58	67	1.03	1.5913	42	4.50	25	4.73
C₆	12.23	179	0.35	1.2009	149	15.95	30	5.66
C₇⁺	42.00	615	0.0156	1.0090	610	65.31	5	0.94
	100.00	1,464			934	100.00	530	100.00

$R = (1,464/930) - 1 = 0.5741$.
Convergence pressure $= CP = 1,500$ psia.

Other considerations in the application of stage separation are (1) physical and chemical characteristics of the well fluid, (2) flowing wellhead pressure and temperature, (3) operating pressures of available gas-gathering systems, (4) conservation features of liquid-storage facilities, and (5) facilities for transporting liquids.

The point of diminishing returns in stage separation is reached when the cost of additional stages of separation is not justified by increased economic gains. The optimum number of stages of separation can be determined by field testing and/or by equilibrium calculations based on laboratory tests of the well fluid.

Equilibrium flash calculations can indicate accurately the gas and liquid yield from oil and gas separators if the composition of the well fluid is known. Gas produced from seven wells is gathered and separated in three stages as shown in Tables 11-2, 11-3, and 11-4. The first stage operates at 850 psia and 90°F; the second stage operates at 250 psia and 80°F; the third stage (tank) is maintained at atmospheric pressure, 14.7 psia, and is assumed to be at 100°F (summer conditions).

Table 11-2 shows the analysis of the well fluid that flows into the first-stage separator and the liquid and vapor discharged from it. The liquid discharged from the first-stage separator is the liquid that flows into the second-stage separator. Table 11-3 shows the vapor and liquid yield from the second-stage separator. The liquid discharged from the second-stage separator flows into the tank. Table 11-4 shows the amount of liquid that remains in the tank and the vapor that will be vented from the tank.

Stabilization of Liquids

If an oil and gas separator is operated under a vacuum and/or at a temperature higher than ambient, the liquid hydrocarbons flowing through will be stripped of more gas and/or vapors than otherwise would be removed. This tends to stabilize the liquids and results in loss of less gas and condensible vapors from the storage tank.

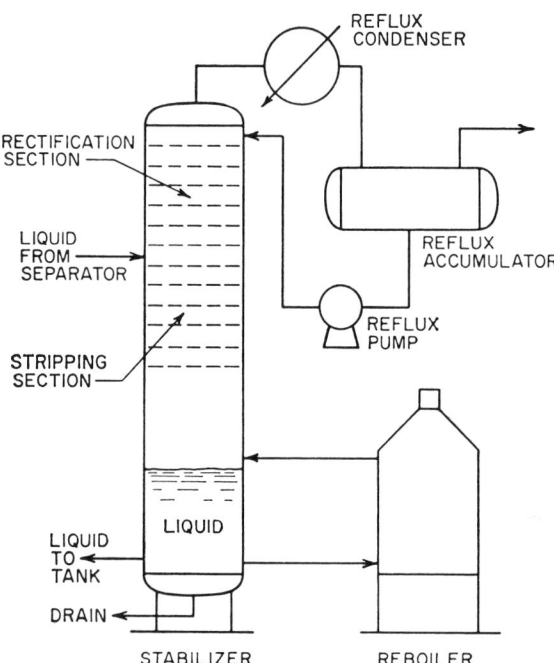

FIG. 11-27. Schematic diagram of typical stabilization unit used for stabilizing and increasing the yield of liquid hydrocarbons.

By the use of a stabilization unit similar to that shown in Fig. 11-27 the yield of stock-tank liquid has been increased by 10 to 15 per cent over that obtainable with standard separators.

When a stabilizer of this type is used, a separator installed upstream of the stabilizer removes gas from the liquid and the liquid is discharged to the stabilizer. The liquid discharged from the stabilizer to the tanks is completely stabilized and has a Reid vapor pressure of 11 to 13 psi, which is less than atmospheric pressure. Therefore there will be no loss of gas or vapor from the tank.

In some installations the initial cost of a stabilizer may be less than the initial cost of multiple-stage oil and gas separators. Use of a stabilization unit has resulted in liquid recovery comparable to that from four to six stages of separation. Each set of conditions should be studied carefully to determine whether or not a stabilizer should be used.   If a highly volatile liquid is being handled, the use of stabilizers may result in increased monetary yield.

CAPACITIES OF OIL AND GAS SEPARATORS

The oil- and gas-capacity ratings of conventional separators are "nominal."   These ratings are determined by calculations and are usually verified by field tests.   Manufacturers of oil and gas separators should provide capacity ratings that are conservative under average operating conditions.   Actual capacities of oil and gas separators will vary with the following factors:

1. Diameter and length of separator vessel
2. Design and arrangement of separator internals
3. Number of stages of separation
4. Physical and chemical characteristics of well fluids (gravity, viscosity, phase equilibrium, etc.)
5. Operating pressure and temperature of separator
6. Liquid level maintained in separator
7. Well-fluid flow pattern, whether steady or surging
8. Foreign-material content of well fluid
9. Foaming tendency of the oil
10. Physical condition of separator and its components

Calculations of the gas capacities (see capacity curves) for oil and gas separators are based on Stokes' law, which can be written as follows:

$$V = K_v D^2 \frac{P_L - P_g}{\mu}$$

where V = relative velocity of falling liquid droplets in gas, ft/sec
K_v = viscous resistance constant
D = diameter of falling droplets, ft
P_L = density of falling droplets, lb/cu ft
P_g = density of gas, lb/cu ft
μ = viscosity of gas, ft-lb sec units

These calculations assume that liquid-gas separation is accomplished by the difference in densities of the liquid and gas and by proper gas velocities within the separator. Net relative gas velocities in the separators were selected which would obtain separation of all liquid mist particles of 100 microns diameter or larger.   It is assumed that mist extractors used in the separators will effect separation of liquid mist particles down to approximately 30 microns in diameter.   Capacities of conventional "gas scrubbers" can be determined from the same curves used for oil and gas separators. If knitted wire mesh is used as the mist extractor in the gas scrubber, the gas capacity of the scrubber will be about 90 per cent of the capacity given in the curves for the corresponding size and type of oil and gas separator.   This reduction in capacity is caused by possible ultimate liquid loading of the wire mesh.

The oil- and gas-capacity curves included herein are arranged so that they may be used reversibly (1) to determine the size of a separator or scrubber required to handle a given volume of fluid and (2) to determine the volume of fluid which a given separator or scrubber will handle.

Capacities of Horizontal Separators

The gas capacity of a horizontal separator (Fig. 11-28) is proportional to the cross-sectional area of the vessel available for gas flow.   Thus the diameter of a horizontal separator and the depth of the liquid determine its gas capacity for a given set of conditions.   Changing the shell length from the conventional 10 ft does not greatly change the gas capacity except under certain circumstances such as handling foaming oil. The liquid capacity of a horizontal separator (Fig. 11-29) depends upon the volumetric

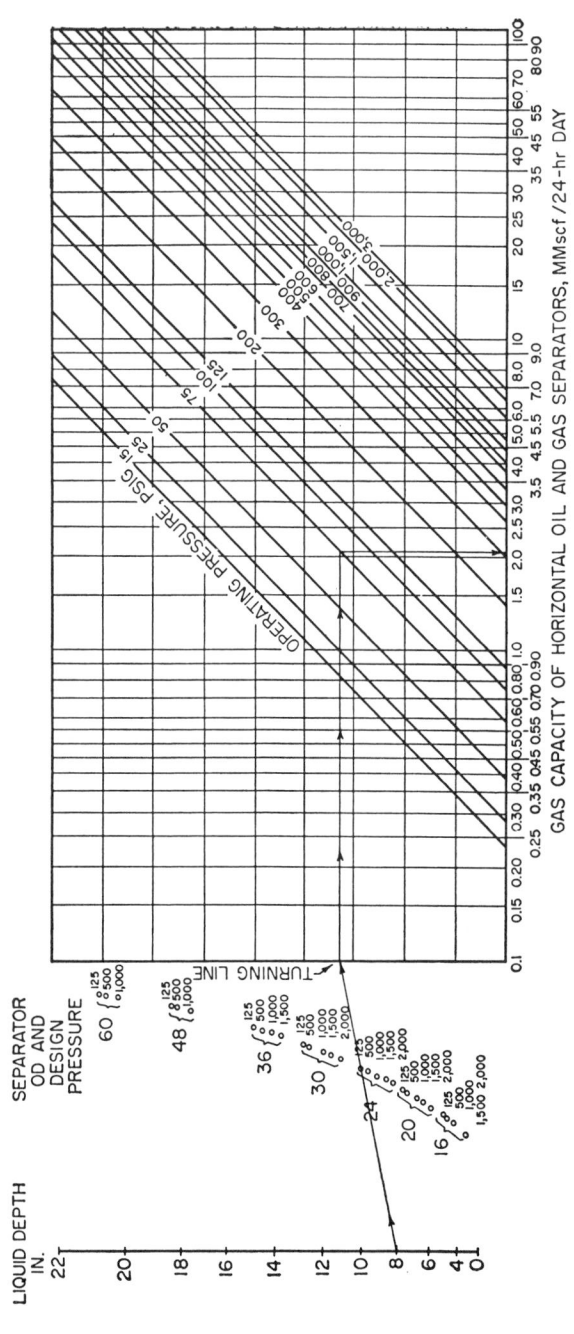

NOTE: THIS CURVE SHOULD NOT BE USED FOR LIQUID DEPTHS GREATER THAN ONE-HALF THE DIAMETER OF THE SEPARATOR VESSEL.

GAS CAPACITY IS BASED ON:
1. VOLUMES MEASURED AT 60°F AND 14.7 PSIA.
2. FLOW RATES ARE STEADY AND NONHEADING.
3. OIL IS NONFOAMING.
4. SHELL LENGTH IS 10 FEET.
5. TEMPERATURE IS ABOVE HYDRATE TEMPERATURE.
6. GAS IS 0.65 SPECIFIC GRAVITY.
7. LIQUID CARRY-OVER WILL BE LESS THAN 1.0 GAL/MMscf.

A 24-IN. BY 10-FT BY 125-PSI HORIZONTAL OIL AND GAS SEPARATOR, WITH A LIQUID DEPTH OF 8 IN. OPERATING AT 75 PSI WILL HANDLE 2.1 MMscf/D. THE PROBLEM CAN BE REVERSED IF THE DAILY VOLUME AND WORKING PRESSURE ARE KNOWN.

FIG. 11-28. Gas capacity of horizontal oil and gas separators. (*Courtesy of Oil Metering and Processing Equipment Corp., Houston, Texas.*)

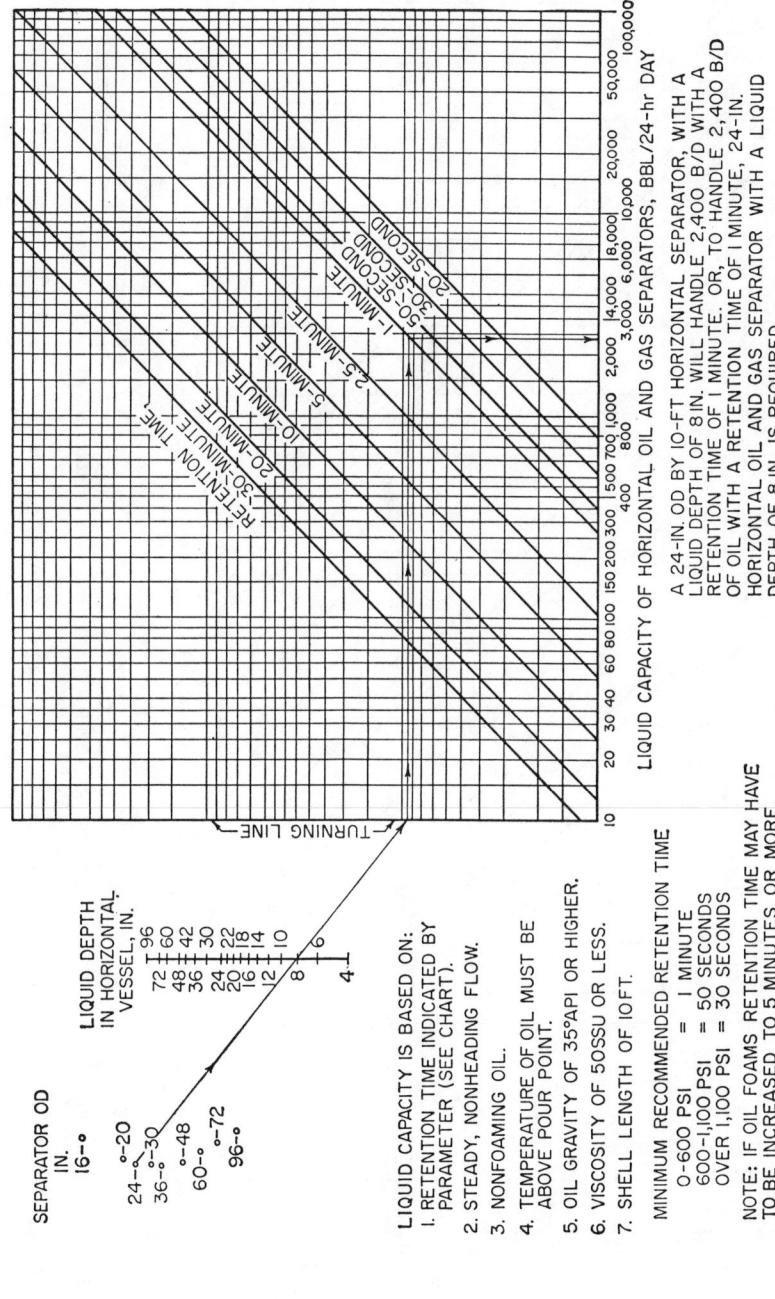

SEPARATOR OD
IN.

16—○

24—○—20
36—○—30
○—48
60—○
○—72
96—○

LIQUID DEPTH
IN HORIZONTAL
VESSEL, IN.

72 ┼ 96
48 ┼ 60
36 ┼ 42
24 ┼ 30
20 ┼ 22
16 ┼ 18
12 ┼ 14
10

8

6

4

LIQUID CAPACITY IS BASED ON:
1. RETENTION TIME INDICATED BY
   PARAMETER (SEE CHART).
2. STEADY, NONHEADING FLOW.
3. NONFOAMING OIL.
4. TEMPERATURE OF OIL MUST BE
   ABOVE POUR POINT.
5. OIL GRAVITY OF 35°API OR HIGHER.
6. VISCOSITY OF 50SSU OR LESS.
7. SHELL LENGTH OF 10FT.

MINIMUM RECOMMENDED RETENTION TIME

0–600 PSI   = 1 MINUTE
600–1,100 PSI   = 50 SECONDS
OVER 1,100 PSI = 30 SECONDS

NOTE: IF OIL FOAMS RETENTION TIME MAY HAVE
TO BE INCREASED TO 5 MINUTES OR MORE.

A 24-IN. OD BY 10-FT HORIZONTAL SEPARATOR, WITH A
LIQUID DEPTH OF 8IN. WILL HANDLE 2,400 B/D WITH A
RETENTION TIME OF 1 MINUTE. OR, TO HANDLE 2,400 B/D
OF OIL WITH A RETENTION TIME OF 1 MINUTE, 24-IN.
HORIZONTAL OIL AND GAS SEPARATOR WITH A LIQUID
DEPTH OF 8 IN. IS REQUIRED.

LIQUID CAPACITY OF HORIZONTAL OIL AND GAS SEPARATORS, BBL/24-hr DAY

FIG. 11-29. Liquid capacity of horizontal oil and gas separators. *(Courtesy of Oil Metering and Processing Equipment Corp., Houston, Texas.)*

11–31

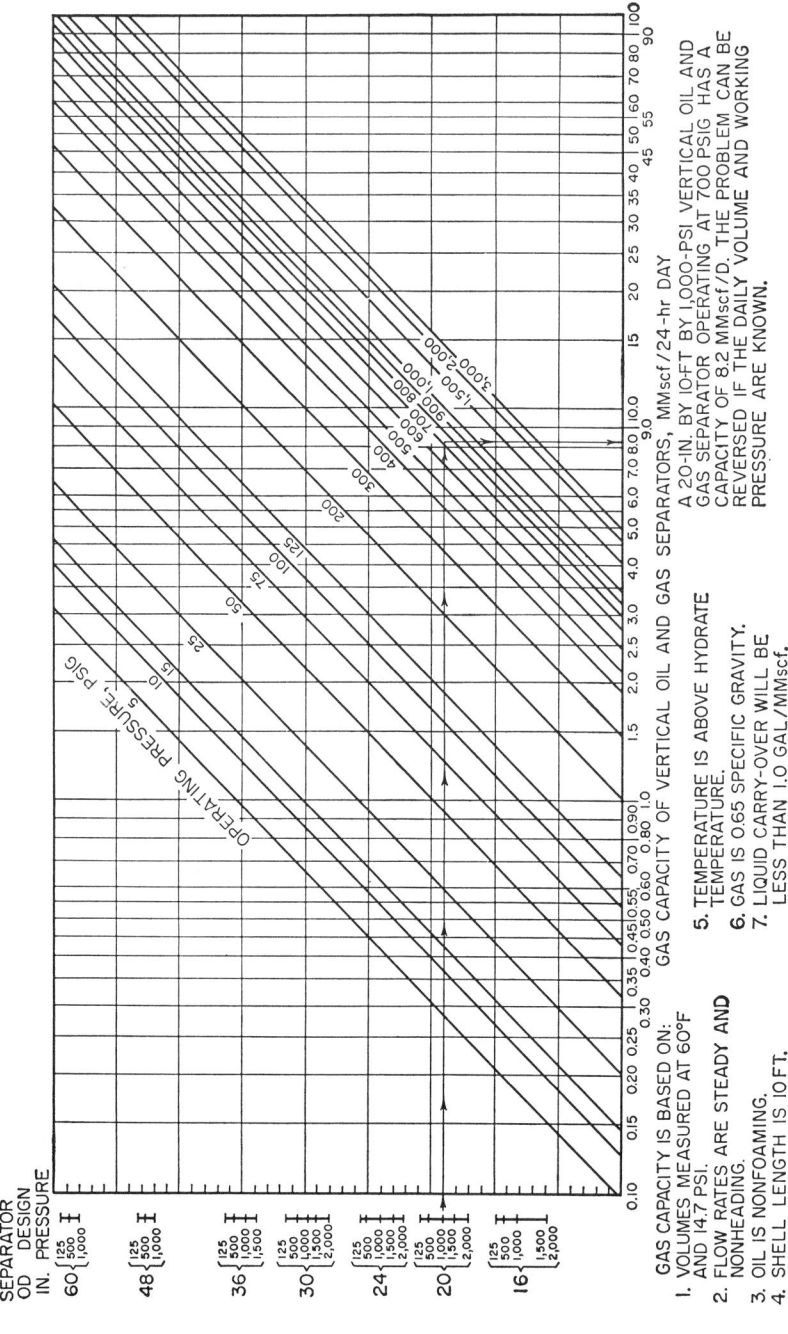

Fig. 11-30. Gas capacity of vertical oil and gas separators. (*Courtesy of Oil Metering and Processing Equipment Corp., Houston, Texas.*)

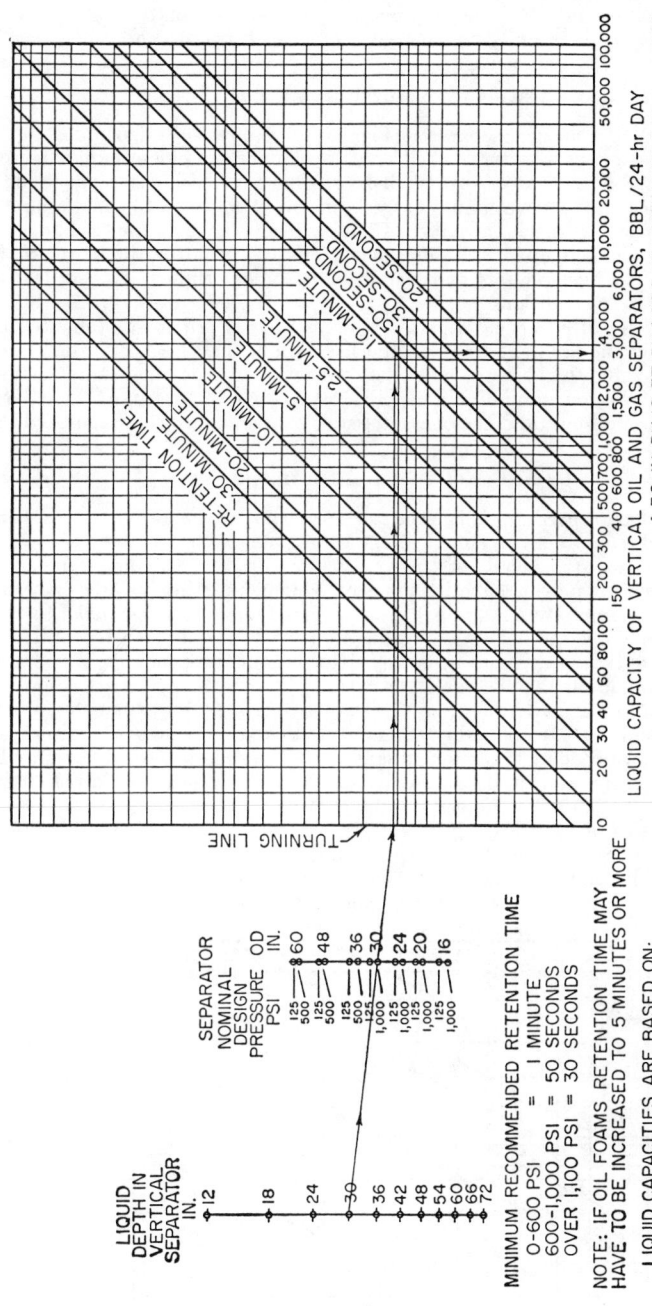

LIQUID DEPTH IN VERTICAL SEPARATOR IN.

12 18 24 30 36 42 48 54 60 66 72

SEPARATOR NOMINAL DESIGN PRESSURE PSI / OD IN.

125/500 60
125/500 48
125/500 36
125/500 30
1,000 30
125 24
1,000 24
125 20
1,000 20
125 16
1,000 16

RETENTION TIME.
30-MINUTE
20-MINUTE
10-MINUTE
5-MINUTE
2.5-MINUTE
1-MINUTE
50-SECOND
30-SECOND
20-SECOND

TURNING LINE

LIQUID CAPACITY OF VERTICAL OIL AND GAS SEPARATORS, BBL/24-hr DAY

A 30-IN. BY 10-FT BY 1,000 PSI SEPARATOR WITH A 30-IN. LIQUID DEPTH WILL HANDLE 2,700 B/D WITH A RETENTION TIME OF 1 MINUTE; OR, IF 2,700 B/D OF OIL REQUIRING A RETENTION TIME OF 1 MINUTE IS TO BE HANDLED IN A SEPARATOR, AND THE WORKING PRESSURE IS 1,000 PSI, A 30-IN. VESSEL WITH A 30-IN. LIQUID DEPTH IS REQUIRED.

MINIMUM RECOMMENDED RETENTION TIME

0-600 PSI = 1 MINUTE
600-1,000 PSI = 50 SECONDS
OVER 1,100 PSI = 30 SECONDS

NOTE: IF OIL FOAMS RETENTION TIME MAY HAVE TO BE INCREASED TO 5 MINUTES OR MORE

LIQUID CAPACITIES ARE BASED ON:

1. RETENTION TIME INDICATED BY PARAMETER (SEE CHART)
2. STEADY NONHEADING FLOW.
3. NONFOAMING OIL.
4. TEMPERATURE OF OIL MUST BE ABOVE POUR POINT.
5. OIL GRAVITY OF 35°API OR HIGHER.
6. VISCOSITY OF 50 SSU OR LESS.
7. LIQUID DEPTH IN SEPARATOR SHOULD NOT EXCEED APPROXIMATELY ONE TO THREE TIMES DIAMETER OF SEPARATOR DEPENDING ON EXACT DESIGN OF SEPARATOR.

Fig. 11-31. Liquid capacity of vertical oil and gas separators. (Courtesy of Oil Metering and Processing Equipment Corp., Houston, Texas.)

liquid-settling capacity of the accumulation (settling) section of the vessel. This volumetric capacity is determined by shell diameter, shell length, and liquid depth.

Capacities of Vertical Separators

The gas capacity of a vertical separator (Fig. 11-30) is directly proportional to the cross-sectional area of the separator. Shell length is a minor and indeterminate factor, for instance, a 50 per cent increase in shell length may increase gas capacity only approximately 5 per cent, while a similar decrease in length may result in only approximately 3 per cent decrease in gas capacity. Changes in gas capacity due to changes in shell length are dependent upon well-fluid characteristics, operating pressure, vessel design, and other pertinent factors and usually must be determined by field testing under actual operating conditions.

The liquid capacity of a vertical separator (Fig. 11-31) is primarily influenced by the volume of oil in the accumulation (settling) section of the vessel. Normal practice is to use a liquid depth above the oil outlet connection of from one to three diameters of the vessel. The optimum liquid depth depends upon the design of the separator, the rate of through-put, and the characteristics of the liquid being separated.

Capacities of Spherical Separators

Spherical oil and gas separators utilize the same principles of separation used in horizontal and vertical separators. A spherical separator can be considered as a truncated vertical separator. As the height of the vessel is reduced, the diameter must be increased to compensate for the reduction in height. In considering the fluid-handling capacity of spherical separators allowance must be made for the reduced height available for separation above the fluid inlet. The same consideration must be applied to spherical separators that is applied to the trays in a fractionating column: the smaller the tray spacing the lower the allowable capacity.

The chief advantage of spherical separators is their relatively low silhouette, which allows all component parts to be readily accessible to operating personnel. However, the horizontal separator offers this same advantage. The spherical separator may be easier and less expensive to install because, on smaller units at least, a gin-pole truck or crane may not be required to unload and place it on location.

The gas capacities of spherical oil and gas separators are shown in Fig. 11-32. These curves for spherical separator capacities were originated by Dave Vondy and were originally published in the Mar. 11, 1957, issue of the *Oil and Gas Journal*. These curves are reproduced here by special permission of Mr. Vondy.

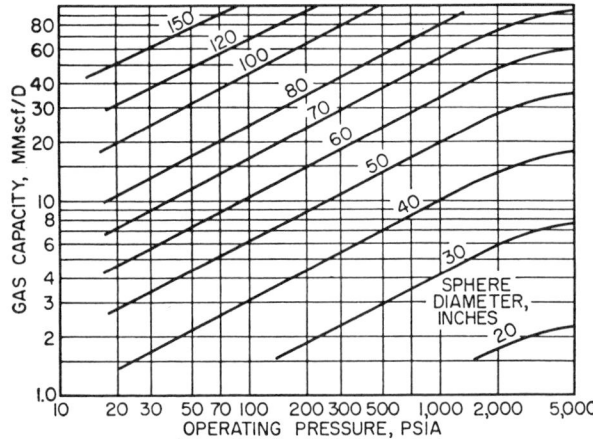

Fig. 11-32. Gas capacity of spherical oil and gas separators. (*Courtesy of Dave Vondy.*)

Table 11-5. Liquid Capacities of Spherical Oil and Gas Separators

ID of sphere, in.	Assumed liquid depth in sphere, in.	Liquid capacity, barrels per 24 hours, 42 U.S. gallons per barrel, steady flow Liquid-retention time							
		20 sec	30 sec	60 sec	2.5 min	5.0 min	10 min	20 min	30 min
16 (1)	5.33	248	165	83	33	17	8	4	3
(2)	8.00	447	318	159	64	32	16	8	5
20 (3)	6.66	483	322	161	64	32	16	8	5
(4)	10.00	932	622	311	124	62	31	16	10
24 (5)	8.00	836	557	278	111	56	28	14	9
(6)	12.00	1,611	1,074	537	215	107	54	27	19
30 (7)	10.00	1,632	1,088	544	218	109	54	27	18
(8)	15.00	3,147	2,098	1,049	420	210	105	52	35
36 (9)	12.00	2,820	1,880	940	376	188	94	47	31
(10)	18.00	5,438	3,625	1,813	725	363	181	91	60
42 (11)	14.00	4,478	2,985	1,493	597	299	149	75	50
(12)	21.00	8,636	5,757	2,879	1,151	576	288	144	96
48 (13)	16.00	6,684	4,456	2,228	891	446	223	111	74
(14)	24.00	12,890	8,594	4,297	1,719	859	430	215	143
60 (15)	20.00	13,056	8,704	4,352	1,741	870	435	216	145
(16)	30.00	25,177	16,785	8,392	3,357	1,678	839	420	280
72 (17)	24.00	22,560	15,040	7,520	3,008	1,502	752	375	250
(18)	36.00	43,505	29,004	14,502	5,801	2,900	1,450	725	483
84 (19)	28.00	35,825	23,880	11,942	4,777	2,388	1,194	597	398
(20)	42.00	69,085	46,057	23,028	9,211	4,606	2,303	1,151	768
96 (21)	32.00	53,477	35,652	17,826	7,130	3,565	1,783	891	594
(22)	48.00	103,125	68,750	34,375	13,750	6,875	3,437	1,719	1,146
100 (23)	33.33	60,444	40,296	20,148	8,059	4,030	2,015	1,007	672
(24)	50.00	116,560	77,707	38,853	15,541	7,771	3,885	1,943	1,295

Odd-number (1, 3, 5, etc.) conditions recommended for two-phase separation.
Even-number (2, 4, 6, etc.) conditions recommended for three-phase separation.

The capacities shown in Fig. 11-32 for various sizes of spheres are conservative and assume the spherical vessel contains no internals. If a properly designed separating element is utilized on the inlet of the spherical vessel, and if an effective mist extractor is used, the capacities shown in Fig. 11-32 can be increased by a multiplier that ranges from 1.0 to 3.0. The following multipliers are recommended:

Service	Vessel design	Multiplier for capacities shown in Fig. 11-32
Foaming crude oil	Average	0.25–0.75
Nonfoaming crude oil	Average	1.0 –1.5
Nonfoaming crude oil	Superior	1.5 –2.0
Distillate or condensate	Average	2.0 –2.5
Distillate or condensate	Superior	2.5 –3.0

The amount of increase in separator capacity that can be obtained by vessel design is dependent upon several factors such as (1) location of inlet connection in vessel with respect to the liquid level in the separator; (2) size, configuration, and location of the inlet separating and spreading element; (3) vertical distance between the inlet separating and spreading element and the mist extractor; (4) size, design, and location of the mist extractor; (5) physical and chemical characteristics of the well fluid being separated; (6) operating pressure and temperature of the separator; (7) flow pattern into the separator (heading or steady); and (8) other pertinent factors.

The oil (liquid hydrocarbon) capacity of spherical oil and gas separators is shown in Table 11-5. The liquid capacity for each size unit is shown for two different liquid depths in the vessel, namely, with the liquid depth equal to one-third the inside diameter of the sphere and with the liquid depth equal to one-half the inside diameter of the sphere. The first condition is appropriate for two-phase (oil-gas) separation and the second condition is appropriate for three-phase (oil-gas-water) separation.

Spherical separators are more appropriately used for two-phase separation than for three-phase separation. This is especially true of sizes smaller than 36-in. diameter.

Field tests should be made on spherical separators to determine and/or confirm their capacity because, of the three shapes of separator vessels available, they are the most difficult to rate properly on oil and gas capacities.

Sizing Oil and Gas Separators

To assure acceptable separation at all times, an oil and gas separator should be sized so that it will never operate above its maximum capacity. A separator must be sized for the maximum *instantaneous* flow rate to which it will be subjected rather than for the total daily production rate. Many wells produce by "heads" or "slugs" as a result of natural causes or intermittent gas lift. Such a well may produce a total of only 200 bbl of liquid in 24 hours. However, if that well "heads" or "intermits" only once each hour it may produce one-twenty-fourth of its total daily production in a matter of 2 or 3 minutes, which would result in an instantaneous flow rate of approximately 2,400 B/D. The separator should be sized to handle the maximum instantaneous rate of fluid produced during these short intervals, or it must be of sufficient size to store a portion of these slugs while it separates and discharges the balance.

Similar sizing procedure should be followed where long flow lines are subject to instantaneous unloading, which is sometimes caused by periodic accumulation and release of gas in the formation, in the tubing, or in the flow line. Under these conditions the separator is subjected to an instantaneous rate of flow much higher than the total daily rate of flow and should be sized accordingly.

Conversely, it is extravagant to install oversize separators under conditions where their additional capacities will never be used. Pumping wells, continuous-flow gas-lift wells, and some flowing wells produce at uniform rates. For these applications separator sizes may be selected based upon total daily production.

Field tests should be made on oil and gas separators to determine their oil- and gas-handling capacities under given conditions. Rated capacities on separators are intended for "general" or "average" conditions, but the only way to determine the exact capacity of a particular separator under a given set of conditions is actually to test the separator under those conditions. Plastic working models of oil and gas separators have been and can be tested to determine the exact effect of design features upon separator capacities.

WORKING PRESSURES OF OIL AND GAS SEPARATOR VESSELS

Design Formulas for Vessel Shell and Head Working Pressures

Most oil and gas separators furnished for field use are designed, constructed, and tested in accordance with the ASME Code for Unfired Pressure Vessels. This is especially true of vessels designed for working pressures above 300 psi. Section VIII of the ASME Boiler and Pressure Vessel Code for Unfired Pressure Vessels is applicable in this design work. Copies of this code may be obtained from the National Headquarters of The American Society of Mechanical Engineers.

Design formulas for shell and head working pressures according to the ASME Code for Unfired Pressure Vessels, Section VIII, are as follows:

1. The thickness and working pressure of cylindrical shells for unfired pressure vessels shall be calculated from the following formulas:

$$t = \frac{PR}{SE - 0.6P} \quad \text{or} \quad P = \frac{SET}{R + 0.6t}$$

where t = minimum required thickness of shell plates, exclusive of corrosion allowance, in.

P = design pressure, psi

R = inside radius of the shell course under consideration, before corrosion allowance is added, in.

S = maximum allowable stress value, psi

E = joint efficiency for appropriate joint in cylindrical shells and any joint in spherical shells or the efficiency of ligaments between openings, whichever is less

2. Thickness and working pressures of ellipsoidal heads shall be calculated from the following formulas:

$$t = \frac{PD}{2SE - 0.2P} \quad \text{or} \quad P = \frac{2SET}{D + 0.2t}$$

3. Thickness and working pressures of torispherical heads are calculated from the following formulas:

$$t = \frac{0.885PL}{SE - 0.1P} \quad \text{or} \quad P = \frac{SET}{.0885L + 0.1t}$$

4. Thickness and working pressures of hemispherical heads are calculated from the following formulas:

$$t = \frac{PL}{2SE - 0.2P} \quad \text{or} \quad P = \frac{2SET}{L + 0.2t}$$

where t = minimum required thickness of head after forming, exclusive of corrosion allowance, in.

P = design pressure, psi

D = inside diameter of head skirt, or inside length of major axes of an ellipsoidal head (measurements to be taken before corrosion allowance is added), in.

S = maximum allowable stress value, psi

E = lowest efficiency of any joint in the head, for hemispherical heads; this includes head to shell joint

L = inside spherical or crown radius, in.

ASME Code for Unfired Pressure Vessels

Use of the ASME Code for fabrication of pressure vessels assures the purchaser that he will obtain vessels that are designed, constructed, and pressure-tested in accordance with established standards, inspected by a disinterested party, and certified safe for use at specified design pressures and temperatures. All vessels labeled with the ASME Code stamp must be constructed in accordance with the ASME Code requirements, and written reports verifying this information must be furnished to the purchaser if so requested.

SAFETY FEATURES FOR OIL AND GAS SEPARATORS

Generally speaking, oil and gas separators are installed at relatively remote distances from other valuable lease equipment. However, where they are installed on offshore platforms or in close proximity to other equipment, it is important that precautions be taken to prevent damage to surrounding equipment and personnel in event of failure of the separator, its controls, or accessories.

The following safety features can be obtained on nearly all standard oil and gas separators.

High- and Low-liquid-level Controls

High- and low-liquid-level controls normally are float-operated pilots that actuate a valve on the inlet to the separator, open a bypass around the separator, sound a warning alarm, or perform some other pertinent function to prevent damage that might result from high or low liquid levels in the separator.

High- and Low-pressure Controls

High- and low-pressure controls are installed on separators to prevent excessively high or low pressures from interfering with normal operations. These high- and low-pressure controls can be mechanical, pneumatic, or electric and can sound a warning, actuate a shut-in valve, open a bypass, or perform other pertinent functions to protect the separator and surrounding equipment.

High- and Low-temperature Controls

Temperature controls may be installed in or on the separator to shut in the unit, open a bypass, or sound a warning should temperature in the separator become too high or too low.

Safety Relief Valves

A spring-loaded safety relief valve is usually furnished with and installed on all oil and gas separators. They normally are set at the design pressure of the vessel. Safety relief valves serve primarily as warning devices and in most instances are too small to handle the full rated capacity of the separator. However, full-capacity safety relief valves can be supplied when requested and are recommended when no safety head (rupture disk) is used on the separator.

Safety Heads or Rupture Disks

The safety head or rupture disk is a device containing a thin membrane that is designed to rupture when pressure in the vessel reaches a predetermined value. This is usually from $1\frac{1}{4}$ to $1\frac{1}{2}$ times the design pressure of the vessel. The safety head is usually selected so that it will not rupture until after the safety relief valve has opened and the safety relief valve is incapable of preventing excessive pressure buildup in the separator.

OPERATING AND MAINTENANCE CONSIDERATIONS FOR SEPARATORS

Periodic Inspection

In refineries and processing plants it is normal practice to inspect all pressure vessels and piping periodically for corrosion and erosion. In the oil fields this practice is not generally followed and equipment is replaced only after actual failure. This policy may create hazardous conditions for operating personnel and surrounding equipment. It is recommended that periodic inspection schedules for all pressure equipment be established and followed to protect against undue failures and hazards.

Installation of Safety Devices

All safety relief devices should be installed as close to the vessel as possible and in such manner that the reaction force from exhausting fluids will not break off, unscrew, or otherwise dislodge the safety device. The discharge from safety devices should not endanger personnel or other equipment.

Safety Heads (Rupture Disks)

The discharge from a safety head should be open and without restriction. The discharge line from a safety device should be parallel to a vertical separator and perpendicular to a horizontal one; otherwise the separator may be blown over by the reaction force from exhausting fluids. A valve should not be used between the safety head and the separator because someone may inadvertently close it. Water should not be allowed to accumulate on top of the rupture diaphragm. It could freeze and alter the rupture characteristics of the diaphragm. Operation of an oil and gas separator without a properly sized and installed safety head or rupture disk is not recommended.

Pressure Relief Valves

Relief valves may corrode and leak or may "freeze" in the closed position. They should be checked periodically and replaced if not in good working condition. Discharge lines, especially those on full-capacity relief valves, should be such that reaction force from discharge will not move the separator. Safety relief valves with "try" handles are recommended for general use.

Mist Extractors

Some mist extractors in oil and gas separators require a drain or "liquid downcomer" to conduct liquid from the mist extractor to the liquid section of the separator. This drain will be a source of trouble when pressure drop through the mist extractor becomes excessive. If the pressure drop across the mist extractor, measured in inches of oil, exceeds the distance from the oil level in the separator to the mist extractor, the oil will flow from the bottom of the separator up through the mist-extractor drain and out with the gas. This condition may be aggravated by partial plugging of the mist extractor with paraffin or other foreign material. This explains why some separators have definite fixed capacities that cannot be exceeded without "liquid carryover" through the gas outlet, and it also explains why the capacities of some separators may be lowered with use. In recent years, separators of advanced design have utilized mist extractors that do not require drains or downcomers. These designs eliminate this source of trouble (see Fig. 11-7b).

Low Temperatures

Separators should be operated above hydrate-formation temperatures. Otherwise hydrates may form in the vessel and partially or completely plug it. This reduces capacity of the separator and, in some instances when the liquid or gas outlet is plugged or restricted, will cause the safety valve to open or the safety head to rupture.

Corrosive Fluid

A separator handling corrosive fluid should be checked periodically to determine if remedial work is required. Extreme cases of corrosion may require a reduction in the rated working pressure of the vessel. Periodic hydrostatic testing is recommended, especially if the fluids being handled are corrosive. Expendable anodes can be used in separators to protect them against electrolytic corrosion.

Paraffin

A separator handling paraffin-base oil may need to be steamed periodically to prevent plugging and a resultant decrease in capacity. This reduction in capacity often results in liquid carry-over in the gas or discharge of gas with the liquid.

High-capacity Operation

Where separators are operating near or at their maximum rated capacity, they should be checked carefully and periodically to determine if acceptable separation is being accomplished.

Pressure Shock Loads

Wells should be switched in and out of the separator slowly. Fast opening and closing of valves cause damaging shock loads on the vessel and its components.

Throttling Discharge of Liquid

Throttling discharge of small volumes of liquid from separators normally should be avoided. Throttling causes erosion or wire drawing of the inner valves and seats of the liquid-dump valves and may erode the dump-valve bodies to the extent that they are in danger of bursting at rated working pressures.

However, throttling discharge may be necessary because of processing units, such as lower-pressure separators or stabilization units, downstream of the separator.

Pressure Gauges

Pressure gauges and other mechanical devices on separators should be checked for accuracy at regular intervals. Isolating valves should be used so gauges can be removed for repairs or replacement.

Gauge Cocks and Glasses

Gauge cocks and gauge glasses should be kept clean so that the liquid level in the gauge glass reflects the true level in the separator at all times. Flushing of the gauge glass or cleaning by use of special swabs is recommended.

Cleaning of Vessels

It is recommended that all separator vessels be equipped with manways, cleanout openings, and/or washout connections so the vessels can be drained and cleaned periodically. Larger vessels can be equipped with manways to facilitate cleaning them. Smaller vessels can be equipped with handholes and/or washout connections so they can be easily cleaned or washed out periodically.

Chapter 12

GAS MEASUREMENT AND REGULATION

By JOHN M. CAMPBELL

Chairman, School of Petroleum Engineering
University of Oklahoma
and Industrial Consultant

Gas measurement and regulation have become an integral part of lease operation as the marketability of gas has continued to increase. Most of the concepts employed —and even the instruments—have been adopted from the transportation and process industries.

The principles governing both measurement and regulation are relatively simple, the mechanical application of these principles being the biggest problem. The first law of thermodynamics, as expressed for a flow system, governs the usual measuring device used—the velocity meter. Although large volumes of gas are metered by positive-displacement meters (PD metering) this is largely confined to residential and industrial sales by gas-distribution companies. Electrical, dilution, and other methods are used but only in special processing applications.

GAS MEASUREMENT

Velocity Meters

A velocity meter is any device which measures the flow of gas by measuring the change in pressure which accompanies a controlled change in velocity. From a mechanical standpoint this change in velocity may be induced in many ways, but regardless of the method the principle is the same.

The Energy Balance. Figure 12-1 illustrates a general flow system on which a general flow equation may be based. Points (1) and (2) represent any two points in a flow system between which an energy balance may be written.

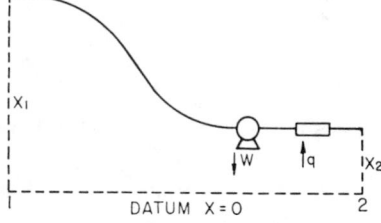

FIG. 12-1. General flow system.

The fluid entering at (1) has an internal energy U_1 which is the result of previous energy obtained. In addition a certain amount of pV work must be done to get the fluid past point (1), i.e., the energy necessary for it to flow. This fluid also possesses potential energy X_1, above the datum plane, and kinetic energy $v_1^2/2g$. The fluid leaving at point (2) possesses the same forms of energy but the amount depends on the work W or heat q gained or lost by the system between the two points. The general equation may then be written

$$U_1 + p_1V_1 + X_1 + \frac{v_1^2}{2g} + q - W = U_2 + p_2V_2 + X_2 + \frac{v_2^2}{2g} \qquad (1)$$

12–1

where U = internal energy, which includes all energy such as heat, electrical, chemical, surface, etc.

p = pressure

V = volume or specific volume

X = height above an arbitrary datum plane

v = velocity in conduit

q = heat gained or lost by system (plus if gained, minus if lost)

W = work done by system (plus if done by system, minus if done on system)

The many ramifications of Eq. (1) are developed in any standard text on thermodynamics.

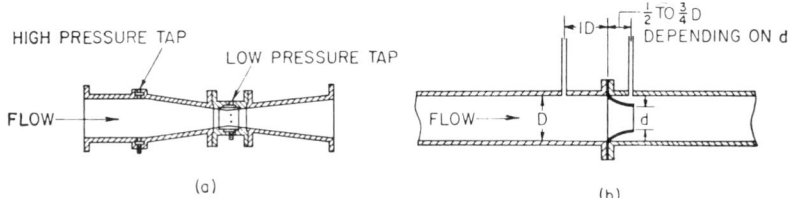

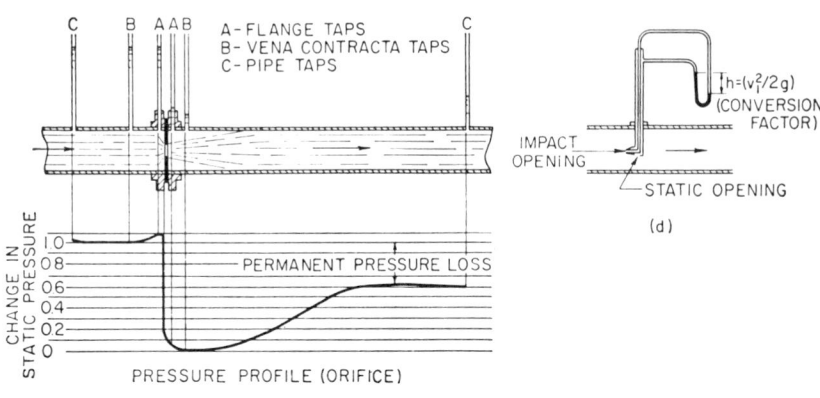

Fig. 12-2. Diagrammatic representation of fluid flow through a flat-plate orifice showing relative positions of the pressure taps in common use and the change in static pressures (flow is from left to right). (a) Venturi tube, cross section; (b) flow nozzle, cross section; (c) location of taps; (d) schematic view of pitot tube. (*Courtesy of The Bristol Co.*)

Equation (1) may be applied to any of the systems shown in Fig. 12-2. When writing it between points (1) and (2) of any of the three systems shown it may be reduced to

$$p_1V_1 - p_2V_2 = \frac{v_2{}^2}{2g} - \frac{v_1{}^2}{2g} \qquad (2)$$

Equation (2) develops on the normally correct premise that q, W, and ΔU are substantially zero between the two points. These two points are furthermore so close together that any change in potential energy is negligible in comparison with the other changes involved. Equation (2) is the basic equation governing velocity or head meters and expresses the general fact that changes in velocity in such a system must be accompanied by a corresponding change in static pressure.

Forms of Meter. Figure 12-2 shows several common ways in which a velocity change may be imposed on the system. In each instance a constriction is supplied for increasing the velocity (decreasing static pressure), following which the velocity returns to normal. The amount of *permanent* pressure loss across the device is small and depends largely on the amount of turbulence and friction loss involved.

The venturi tube shown in part *a* is designed so that a high-pressure differential can be induced and still minimize the permanent pressure loss due to turbulence and eddy currents. In general it will restore at least 90 per cent of the pressure drop at the throat. The sections involved, though, are expensive to manufacture and bulky to handle, especially at elevated pressures. Consequently their use is usually limited to low-pressure applications where high-pressure recovery is essential. The flow nozzle is essentially a cross between the three devices shown and represents an attempt to incorporate the best features of each. General usage is limited.

The flat-plate orifice is used in the majority of all gas-production and transportation facilities. It is simple, inexpensive, handy to change and stock, and gives reproducible results. Although the pressure recovery is seldom higher than 65 per cent this is not a critical fault, for most systems are designed to operate with a low differential pressure. All further discussions will concern this type.

Derivation of an Orifice Equation. Equation (2) may be simplified by assuming that $V_1 = V_2 = V$, an assumption that is approximately true and is later corrected by a term called the expansion factor. Then

$$V_1{}^2 - V_2{}^2 = 2gV(p_1 - p_2) = 2gh \qquad (3)$$

The term h is the pressure drop between points (1) and (2) expressed as "feet of fluid" (that fluid flowing in the system).

The velocities may be expressed in terms of volume rate of flow Q and diameters d_1, and d_2 (internal diameter of pipe and orifice opening, respectively). This substitution yields an intermediate equation

$$Q = A_2 \frac{1}{\sqrt{1 - \beta^4}} \sqrt{2gh} \qquad (4)$$

where A_2 = area of orifice plate opening
$\beta = d_2/d_1$

The second term on the right-hand side of Eq. (4) is often referred to as the approach factor.

Further modification of our theoretical equation is necessary. Part *c* of Fig. 12-1 shows that the diameter of the flowing stream becomes smaller than that of the orifice opening. This point, known as the *vena contracta*, is really the limiting diameter, and some correction must be made when using the orifice-opening diameter in the equation. There is also an energy loss due to turbulence and friction not yet accounted for. Both of these considerations are easily handled by use of an efficiency factor K_o that must be determined experimentally.

For convenience we furthermore like to express h in terms of inches of water h_w. If all these corrections and conversions are superimposed on Eq. (4) the equation reads

$$Q_h = 218.44 \ K_o d_2{}^2 \ \frac{p_f}{p_b} \ \frac{T_b}{T_f} \sqrt{\frac{h_w T_f}{p_f G}} \qquad (5)$$

where Q_h = gas-flow rate, standard cu ft/hr measured at p_b and T_b
d_2 = orifice-opening diameter, in.
p_f = flowing pressure, psia
p_b = base pressure, psia
T_f = flowing temperature, °R
T_b = base temperature, °R
h_w = differential across orifice, in. H_2O
G = specific gravity of gas (air = 1.0)
K_o = efficiency factor, which includes the approach factor

Equation (5) may be modified to a more standard form by

1. Combining terms
2. Writing it for a gas whose specific gravity = 1.0
3. Assuming that $p_b = 14.73$ psia and $T_b = T_f = 520°R$

This yields the two basic orifice equations

$$Q_h = C' \sqrt{h_w p_f} \qquad (6)$$

$$C' = F_b F_{pb} F_{tb} F_g F_{tf} F_r Y F_{pv} F_m \qquad (7)$$

The value C' is known as the orifice constant. It is determined primarily from F_b, the basic orifice flow factor, which is equal to $338.17\ K_o d_2{}^2$. The other multipliers shown in Eq. (7) are correction factors to correct for the basic assumptions necessary to arrive at Eq. (6). Only the first five are usually used in routine lease operations, in measuring gas for proration records and the like. The last four correction factors are relatively small and are used to obtain accurate records in the sale or purchase of gas.

Values for these constants are periodically examined by the Gas Measurement Committee of the American Gas Association (AGA). Those values shown in Table 12-1 are taken from *Gas Measurement Committee Report* 3. The tables shown are specifically taken from Handbook E-2, copyright 1955 by the American Meter Co., which is based on *Report* 3. The results shown are based on empirical equations which in turn depend on past and continuing observation and tests conducted by the gas industry. They therefore reflect the best possible results obtained by fitting curves to the available data. Because of the mass of data already available there has been little change in the values shown with time.

Orifice Constants

The value of the constants in Eq. (7) depends in many cases on the points between which the differential pressure h_w is measured. Two standards are provided in gas measurement—flange taps and pipe taps. With the former the flange or orifice holder is so tapped that the center of the upstream and downstream taps is 1 in. from the respective orifice-plate surfaces. For standard pipe taps, the upstream tap is located $2\frac{1}{2}$ pipe diameters upstream and 8 pipe diameters downstream. The location of the taps makes an obvious difference in the values obtained. Section I of the orifice tables is for *flange taps* and Section III for *pipe taps*. Section II shows the fluid-condition factors common to both types.

Basic Orifice Factor F_b. This factor, as noted above, is based on those assumptions necessary to go from Eq. (5) to (6). These are $T_b = 520°R$, $G = 1.00$, and $T_f = 520°R$. It is a function of the experimental constant K_o, which means that it depends on the location of the differential taps and the internal pipe diameter, in addition to the orifice diameter.

The value of F_b may be found from tables of F_b shown in Table 12-1 if the meter run is of standard internal diameter. For gas-measurement work involving sale and purchase by a gas-transmission or distribution company, corrections are provided for values of F_b not fitting the standard tables. These are not shown here, for they are not normally used in production operations. Sections I and III of the charts show values of F_b for flange and pipe taps, respectively.

Pressure-base Factor F_{pb}. Values of this factor are shown in Section II of the charts. It corrects the value of F_b for the case where the pressure base used is not 14.73 psia. It may be determined by the equation $F_{pb} = 14.73/p_b$.

Temperature-base Factor F_{tb}. This is also shown in Section II and corrects for any contract wherein the base temperature is not 520°R (60°F). This factor may be computed by the formula $F_{tb} = T_b/520$.

Specific-gravity Factor F_g. This factor, shown in Section II, is to correct the basic orifice equation for those cases where the specific gravity of the gas is other than 1.00. The equation is $F_g = (1/G)^{0.5}$.

Flowing-temperature Factor F_{tf}. This factor corrects for those cases where the flowing temperature of the gas is other than 60°F. The equation is $F_{tf} = (520/T_f)^{0.5}$.

Reynolds-number Factor F_r. This takes into account the variation of the discharge coefficient with Reynolds number. In gas measurement the variation is slight and is often ignored in production operations. Values are shown in Sections I and III of the charts. It has been assumed in preparation of these charts that gas viscosity

Table 12-1. Section I*
Flange Taps—Basic Orifice Factors—F_b

Orifice Diam., d, Inches	Internal Diameter of Pipe, D, Inches								
	2			3				4	
	1.689	1.939	2.067	2.300	2.626	2.900	3.068	3.152	3.438
.250	12.695	12.707	12.711	12.714	12.712	12.708	12.705	12.703	12.697
.375	28.474	28.439	28.428	28.411	28.393	28.382	28.376	28.373	28.364
.500	50.777	50.587	50.521	50.435	50.356	50.313	50.292	50.284	50.258
.625	80.090	79.509	79.311	79.052	78.818	78.686	78.625	78.598	78.523
.750	117.09	115.62	115.14	114.52	113.99	113.70	113.56	113.50	113.33
.875	162.95	159.56	158.47	157.12	156.00	155.41	155.14	155.03	154.71
1.000	219.77	212.47	210.22	207.44	205.18	204.04	203.54	203.33	202.75
1.125	230.99	276.20	271.70	266.35	262.06	259.95	259.04	258.65	257.63
1.250	385.78	353.58	345.13	335.12	327.39	323.63	322.03	321.37	319.61
1.375	....	448.57	433.50	415.75	402.18	395.80	393.09	391.97	389.03
1.500	....	....	542.26	510.86	487.98	477.36	472.96	471.14	466.39
1.625	....	....	....	623.91	586.82	569.65	562.58	559.72	552.31
1.750	....	....	....	....	701.27	674.44	663.42	658.96	647.54
1.875	....	....	....	....	834.88	793.88	777.18	770.44	753.17
2.000	....	....	....	....	....	930.65	906.01	896.06	870.59
2.125	....	....	....	....	....	1091.2	1052.5	1038.1	1001.4
2.250	....	....	....	....	....	....	1223.2	1,99.9	1147.7
2.375	....	....	....	....	....	....	....	....	1311.7
2.500	....	....	....	....	....	....	....	....	1498.4

Orifice Diam., d, Inches	Internal Diameter of Pipe, D, Inches								
	4		6				8		
	3.826	4.026	4.897	5.189	5.761	6.065	7.625	7.981	8.071
.250	12.687	12.683	....	....	....	....	....	....	....
.375	28.353	28.348	....	....	....	....	....	....	....
.500	50.234	50.224	50.197	50.191	50.182	50.178	....	....	....
.625	78.450	78.421	78.338	78.321	78.296	78.287	....	....	....
.750	113.15	113.08	112.87	112.82	112.75	112.72	....	....	....
.875	154.40	154.27	153.88	153.78	153.63	153.56	153.34	153.31	153.31
1.000	202.20	201.99	201.34	201.19	200.96	200.85	200.46	200.39	200.38
1.125	256.69	256.33	255.31	255.08	254.72	254.56	253.99	253.89	253.87
1.250	318.03	317.45	315.83	315.48	314.95	314.72	313.91	313.78	313.74
1.375	386.45	385.51	382.99	382.47	381.70	381.37	380.25	380.06	380.02
1.500	462.27	460.79	456.93	456.16	455.03	454.57	453.02	452.78	452.72
1.625	545.89	543.61	537.77	536.64	535.03	534.38	532.27	531.95	531.87
1.750	637.84	634.39	625.73	624.09	621.79	620.88	618.02	617.60	617.50
1.875	738.75	733.68	721.03	718.69	715.44	714.19	710.32	709.77	709.64
2.000	849.41	842.12	823.99	820.68	816.13	814.41	809.22	808.50	808.34
2.125	970.95	960.48	934.97	930.35	924.07	921.71	914.79	913.86	913.64
2.250	1104.7	1089.9	1054.4	1048.1	1039.5	1036.3	1027.1	1025.9	1025.6
2.375	1252.1	1231.7	1182.9	1174.2	1162.6	1158.3	1146.2	1144.7	1144.3
2.500	1415.0	1387.2	1320.9	1309.3	1293.8	1288.2	1272.3	1270.3	1269.8
2.625	1595.6	1558.2	1469.2	1453.9	1433.5	1426.0	1405.4	1402.9	1402.3
2.750	1797.1	1746.7	1628.9	1608.7	1582.1	1572.3	1545.7	1542.5	1541.8
2.875	....	1955.5	1801.0	1774.5	1740.0	1727.5	1693.4	1689.3	1688.4
3.000	....	2194.9	1986.6	1952.4	1907.8	1891.9	1848.6	1843.5	1842.3
3.125	....	....	2187.2	2143.4	2086.4	2066.1	2011.6	2005.2	2003.8
3.250	....	....	2404.2	2348.8	2276.5	2250.8	2182.6	2174.6	2172.9
3.375	....	....	2639.5	2569.8	2479.1	2446.8	2361.8	2352.0	2349.9
3.500	....	....	2895.5	2808.1	2695.1	2654.9	2549.7	2537.7	2535.0
3.625	....	....	3180.8	3065.3	2925.7	2876.0	2746.5	2731.8	2728.6
3.750	....	....	....	3345.8	3172.1	3111.2	2952.6	2934.8	2930.8
3.875	....	....	....	3657.7	3435.7	3361.5	3168.3	3146.9	3142.1
4.000	....	....	....	....	3718.2	3628.2	3394.3	3368.5	3362.9
4.250	....	....	....	....	4354.8	4216.6	3879.4	3842.3	3834.2
4.500	....	....	....	....	....	4900.9	4412.8	4360.5	4349.0
4.750	....	....	....	....	....	....	5000.7	4928.1	4912.2
5.000	....	....	....	....	....	....	5650.0	5551.1	5529.5
5.250	....	....	....	....	....	....	6369.3	6236.4	6207.3
5.500	....	....	....	....	....	....	7170.9	6992.0	6953.6
5.750	....	....	....	....	....	....	....	7830.0	7777.8
6.000	....	....	....	....	....	....	....	....	8706.9

*Courtesy of American Meter Co., Inc.

PRODUCTION EQUIPMENT

Table **12-1**. Section **I** (*Continued*)
Flange Taps—Basic Orifice Factors—F_b

Orifice Diam., d, Inches	Internal Diameter of Pipe, D, Inches								
	10			12			16		
	9.564	10.020	10.136	11.376	11.938	12.090	14.688	15.000	15.250
1.000	200.20	....	....	....	....	....	....	....	....
1.125	253.55	253.48	253.47	....	....	....	....	....	....
1.250	313.31	313.20	313.18	312.94	312.85	312.83	....	....	....
1.375	379.44	379.29	379.26	378.94	378.82	378.79	....	....	....
1.500	451.95	451.76	451.72	451.30	451.14	451.10	450.53	450.48	....
1.625	530.87	530.63	530.57	530.04	529.83	529.78	529.06	528.99	528.94
1.750	616.21	615.90	615.83	615.16	614.90	614.84	613.94	613.85	613.78
1.875	707.99	707.61	707.51	706.68	706.36	706.28	705.18	705.07	704.99
2.000	806.23	805.76	805.65	804.61	804.23	804.13	802.78	802.65	802.55
2.125	910.97	910.38	910.24	908.98	908.51	908.39	906.77	906.61	906.49
2.250	1022.2	1021.5	1021.3	1019.8	1019.2	1019.1	1017.1	1017.0	1016.8
2.375	1140.1	1139.2	1139.0	1137.1	1136.4	1136.2	1133.9	1133.7	1133.5
2.500	1264.5	1263.4	1263.1	1260.8	1260.0	1259.8	1257.1	1256.8	1256.6
2.625	1395.6	1394.2	1393.9	1391.1	1390.1	1389.9	1386.7	1386.4	1386.1
2.750	1533.4	1531.7	1531.3	1528.0	1526.8	1526.5	1522.7	1522.4	1522.1
2.875	1678.0	1675.9	1675.4	1671.4	1670.0	1669.6	1665.2	1664.8	1664.5
3.000	1829.4	1826.9	1826.3	1821.4	1819.7	1819.3	1814.1	1813.7	1813.3
3.125	1987.8	1984.7	1984.0	1978.1	1976.1	1975.6	1969.6	1969.0	1968.6
3.250	2153.2	2149.5	2148.6	2141.5	2139.2	2138.6	2131.5	2130.9	2130.4
3.375	2325.7	2321.2	2320.2	2311.7	2308.9	2308.2	2299.9	2299.2	2298.7
3.500	2505.6	2500.1	2498.9	2488.7	2485.4	2484.6	2474.9	2474.1	2473.5
3.625	2692.8	2686.2	2684.7	2672.6	2668.7	2667.7	2656.4	2655.5	2654.8
3.750	2887.6	2879.7	2877.9	2863.5	2858.8	2857.7	2844.6	2843.5	2842.7
3.875	3090.1	3080.7	3078.5	3061.4	3055.9	3054.6	3039.4	3038.1	3037.2
4.000	3300.6	3289.3	3286.8	3266.4	3260.0	3258.5	3240.8	3239.4	3233.3
4.250	3746.1	3730.2	3726.7	3698.4	3689.6	3687.5	3663.8	3661.9	3660.5
4.500	4226.0	4204.1	4199.2	4160.4	4148.4	4145.5	4113.9	4111.5	4109.7
4.750	4742.7	4712.8	4706.2	4653.4	4637.2	4633.4	4591.5	4588.4	4586.0
5.000	5298.6	5258.5	5249.6	5179.0	5157.4	5152.3	5097.2	5093.1	5090.1
5.250	5897.4	5843.6	5831.8	5738.5	5710.0	5703.3	5631.4	5626.1	5622.3
5.500	6543.1	6471.9	6456.3	6333.8	6296.6	6287.9	6194.8	6188.1	6183.1
5.750	7240.0	7146.9	7126.5	6966.9	6919.0	6907.8	6788.1	6779.6	6773.3
6.000	7993.3	7873.0	7846.6	7640.4	7579.0	7564.7	7412.3	7401.5	7393.6
6.250	8808.9	8654.8	8621.1	8357.3	8278.9	8260.7	8068.4	8054.8	8044.8
6.500	9693.3	9498.1	9455.3	9121.0	9021.7	8998.7	8757.3	8740.3	8727.9
6.750	10654	10409	10355	9935.2	9810.5	9781.6	9480.4	9459.4	9444.0
7.000	11711	11394	11327	10804	10649	10613	10239	10213	10194
7.250	....	12467	12381	11732	11540	11496	11035	11003	10980
7.500	....	13656	13541	12725	12489	12434	11869	11831	11803
7.750	....	....	....	13787	13500	13433	12745	12698	12664
8.000	....	....	....	14927	14578	14498	13664	13607	13566
8.250	....	....	....	16158	15730	15633	14628	14560	14511
8.500	....	....	....	17505	16962	16845	15642	15560	15501
8.750	....	....	....	....	18296	18148	16706	16609	16539
9.000	....	....	....	....	....	19565	17826	17711	17628
9.250	....	....	....	....	....	....	19004	18868	18770
9.500	....	....	....	....	....	....	20245	20085	19969
9.750	....	....	....	....	....	....	21552	21365	21230
10.000	....	....	....	....	....	....	22930	22712	22555
10.250	....	....	....	....	....	....	24385	24132	23948
10.500	....	....	....	....	....	....	25924	25628	25416
10.750	....	....	....	....	....	....	27567	27210	26962
11.000	....	....	....	....	....	....	29331	28899	28600
11.250	....	....	....	....	....	....	....	30710	30348

Table 12-1. Section I (Continued)
"b" Values for Reynolds-number Factor, F_r,—Flange Taps

$$F_r = 1 + \frac{b}{\sqrt{h_w p_f}}$$

Orifice Diam., d, Inches	Internal Diameter of Pipe, D, Inches								
	2			3				4	
	1.689	1.939	2.067	2.300	2.626	2.900	3.068	3.152	3.438
.250	.0879	.0911	.0926	.0950	....	....	....	....	....
.375	.0677	.0709	.0726	.0755	.0792	.0820	.0836	.0844	.0867
.500	.0562	.0576	.0588	.0612	.0648	.0677	.0695	.0703	.0728
.625	.0520	.0505	.0506	.0516	.0541	.0566	.0583	.0591	.0618
.750	.0536	.0485	.0471	.0462	.0470	.0486	.0498	.0504	.0528
.875	.0595	.0506	.0478	.0445	.0429	.0433	.0438	.0442	.0460
1.000	.0677	.0559	.0515	.0458	.0416	.0403	.0402	.0403	.0411
1.125	.0762	.0630	.0574	.0495	.0427	.0396	.0386	.0383	.0380
1.250	.0824	.0707	.0646	.0550	.0456	.0408	.0388	.0381	.0365
1.375	....	.0772	.0715	.0614	.0501	.0435	.0406	.0394	.0365
1.500	....	....	.0773	.0679	.0554	.0474	.0436	.0420	.0378
1.625	....	....	....	.0735	.0613	.0522	.0477	.0457	.0402
1.750	....	....	....	....	.0669	.0575	.0524	.0500	.0434
1.875	....	....	....	....	.0717	.0628	.0574	.0549	.0473
2.000	....	....	....	....	....	.0676	.0624	.0598	.0517
2.125	....	....	....	....	....	.0715	.0669	.0642	.0563
2.250	....	....	....	....	....	....	.0706	.0685	.0607
2.375	....	....	....	....	....	....	....	....	.0648
2.500	....	....	....	....	....	....	....	....	.0683

Orifice Diam., d, Inches	Internal Diameter of Pipe, D, Inches								
	4			6			8		
	3.826	4.026	4.897	5.189	5.761	6.065	7.625	7.981	8.071
.500	.0763	.0779	.0836	....	....	....	....	....	....
.625	.0653	.0670	.0734	.0753	.0785	.0801	....	....	....
.750	.0561	.0578	.0645	.0665	.0701	.0718	....	....	....
.875	.0487	.0502	.0567	.0587	.0625	.0643	.0723	.0738	.0742
1.000	.0430	.0442	.0500	.0520	.0557	.0576	.0660	.0676	.0680
1.125	.0388	.0396	.0444	.0462	.0498	.0517	.0602	.0619	.0623
1.250	.0361	.0364	.0399	.0414	.0447	.0464	.0549	.0566	.0571
1.375	.0347	.0344	.0363	.0375	.0403	.0419	.0501	.0518	.0523
1.500	.0345	.0336	.0336	.0344	.0367	.0381	.0457	.0474	.0479
1.625	.0354	.0338	.0318	.0322	.0337	.0348	.0418	.0435	.0439
1.750	.0372	.0350	.0307	.0306	.0314	.0322	.0383	.0399	.0403
1.875	.0398	.0370	.0305	.0298	.0298	.0303	.0353	.0366	.0371
2.000	.0430	.0395	.0308	.0296	.0287	.0288	.0327	.0340	.0343
2.125	.0467	.0427	.0318	.0300	.0281	.0278	.0304	.0315	.0318
2.250	.0507	.0462	.0334	.0310	.0281	.0274	.0286	.0295	.0297
2.375	.0548	.0501	.0354	.0324	.0286	.0274	.0271	.0278	.0280
2.500	.0589	.0540	.0378	.0342	.0295	.0279	.0259	.0264	.0265
2.625	.0626	.0579	.0406	.0365	.0308	.0287	.0251	.0253	.0254
2.750	.0659	.0615	.0436	.0391	.0324	.0300	.0246	.0245	.0245
2.875	....	.0647	.0468	.0418	.0343	.0314	.0244	.0240	.0240
3.000	....	....	.0500	.0448	.0366	.0332	.0245	.0238	.0237
3.125	....	....	.0533	.0479	.0389	.0353	.0248	.0239	.0237
3.250	....	....	.0564	.0510	.0416	.0375	.0254	.0242	.0240
3.375	....	....	.0594	.0541	.0443	.0400	.0263	.0248	.0244
3.500	....	....	.0620	.0569	.0472	.0426	.0273	.0255	.0251
3.625	....	....	.0643	.0597	.0500	.0452	.0286	.0265	.0260
3.750	....	....	....	.0621	.0527	.0479	.0300	.0274	.0271
3.875	....	....	....	.0640	.0553	.0505	.0316	.0289	.0283
4.000	....	....	....	....	.0578	.0531	.0334	.0304	.0297
4.250	....	....	....	....	.0620	.0579	.0372	.0338	.0330
4.500	....	....	....	....	....	.0618	.0414	.0386	.0366
4.750	....	....	....	....	....	....	.0457	.0416	.0405
5.000	....	....	....	....	....	....	.0500	.0457	.0446
5.250	....	....	....	....	....	....	.0539	.0497	.0487
5.500	....	....	....	....	....	....	.0574	.0535	.0524
5.750	....	....	....	....	....	....	....	.0569	.0559
6.000	....	....	....	....	...	....	....	....	.0588

Table 12-1. Section I (*Continued*)
"b" Values for Reynolds-number Factor, F_r,—Flange Taps

$$F_r = 1 + \frac{b}{\sqrt{h_w p_f}}$$

Orifice Diam., d, Inches	Internal Diameter of Pipe, D, Inches								
	10			12			16		
	9.564	10.020	10.136	11.376	11.938	12.090	14.688	15.000	15.250
1.000	.0738	....	....	....	....	....	....	....	....
1.125	.0685	.0701	....	....	....	....	....	....	....
1.250	.0635	.0652	.0656	.0698	.0714	.0718	....	....	....
1.375	.0588	.0606	.0610	.0654	.0671	.0676	....	....	....
1.500	.0545	.0563	.0568	.0612	.0631	.0635	.0706	.0713	....
1.625	.0504	.0523	.0527	.0573	.0592	.0597	.0670	.0678	.0684
1.750	.0467	.0485	.0490	.0536	.0555	.0560	.0636	.0644	.0650
1.875	.0433	.0451	.0455	.0501	.0521	.0526	.0604	.0612	.0618
2.000	.0401	.0419	.0414	.0469	.0488	.0492	.0572	.0581	.0587
2.125	.0372	.0389	.0383	.0438	.0458	.0463	.0542	.0551	.0558
2.250	.0346	.0362	.0356	.0410	.0429	.0434	.0514	.0523	.0529
2.375	.0322	.0337	.0330	.0383	.0402	.0407	.0487	.0496	.0502
2.500	.0302	.0315	.0308	.0359	.0377	.0382	.0461	.0470	.0476
2.625	.0283	.0296	.0287	.0336	.0354	.0358	.0436	.0445	.0452
2.750	.0267	.0278	.0269	.0316	.0332	.0336	.0413	.0422	.0428
2.875	.0254	.0263	.0253	.0297	.0312	.0317	.0391	.0399	.0406
3.000	.0243	.0250	.0252	.0278	.0294	.0298	.0370	.0378	.0385
3.125	.0234	.0239	.0241	.0264	.0278	.0282	.0350	.0358	.0365
3.250	.0226	.0230	.0231	.0251	.0263	.0266	.0331	.0339	.0346
3.375	.0221	.0223	.0224	.0239	.0250	.0253	.0314	.0321	.0328
3.500	.0219	.0218	.0218	.0229	.0238	.0241	.0298	.0305	.0311
3.625	.0218	.0214	.0214	.0221	.0228	.0230	.0282	.0290	.0295
3.750	.0218	.0213	.0212	.0214	.0219	.0221	.0268	.0275	.0281
3.875	.0221	.0213	.0211	.0208	.0212	.0213	.0255	.0262	.0267
4.000	.0225	.0214	.0212	.0204	.0206	.0207	.0243	.0249	.0254
4.250	.0238	.0222	.0219	.0200	.0198	.0198	.0223	.0228	.0232
4.500	.0256	.0236	.0231	.0201	.0195	.0194	.0206	.0210	.0213
4.750	.0279	.0254	.0249	.0207	.0196	.0194	.0193	.0196	.0198
5.000	.0307	.0277	.0270	.0217	.0202	.0199	.0184	.0185	.0187
5.250	.0337	.0303	.0295	.0231	.0212	.0208	.0178	.0178	.0179
5.500	.0370	.0332	.0323	.0249	.0226	.0221	.0176	.0174	.0174
5.750	.0404	.0363	.0354	.0270	.0243	.0237	.0176	.0174	.0172
6.000	.0438	.0396	.0386	.0294	.0263	.0255	.0180	.0176	.0173
6.250	.0473	.0437	.0418	.0320	.0285	.0277	.0186	.0180	.0177
6.500	.0505	.0462	.0451	.0347	.0309	.0300	.0195	.0188	.0183
6.750	.0536	.0493	.0483	.0376	.0335	.0325	.0206	.0198	.0192
7.000	.0562	.0523	.0513	.0406	.0362	.0351	.0220	.0210	.0202
7.250	....	.0550	.0540	.0435	.0390	.0379	.0235	.0224	.0216
7.500	....	.0572	.0564	.0463	.0418	.0407	.0252	.0240	.0230
7.750	....	....	....	.0491	.0446	.0434	.0271	.0257	.0246
8.000	....	....	....	.0517	.0473	.0461	.0291	.0276	.0264
8.250	....	....	....	.0540	.0498	.0487	.0312	.0296	.0283
8.500	....	....	....	.0560	.0522	.0511	.0334	.0317	.0303
8.750	....	....	....	....	.0543	.0534	.0357	.0338	.0324
9.000	....	....	....	....	....	.0553	.0380	.0361	.0346
9.250	....	....	....	....	....	....	.0402	.0383	.0368
9.500	....	....	....	....	....	....	.0425	.0406	.0390
9.750	....	....	....	....	....	....	.0447	.0428	.0412
10.000	....	....	....	....	....	....	.0469	.0449	.0434
10.250	....	....	....	....	....	....	.0489	.0470	.0455
10.500	....	....	....	....	....	....	.0508	.0490	.0475
10.750	....	....	....	....	....	....	.0526	.0509	.0495
11.000	....	....	....	....	....	....	.0541	.0526	.0513
11.250	....	....	....	....	....	....	....	.0541	.0528

Table **12-1**. Section I (*Continued*)
"*b*" Values for Reynolds-number Factor, F_r,—Flange Taps

$$F_r = 1 + \frac{b}{\sqrt{h_w p_f}}$$

Orifice Diam., d, Inches	Internal Diameter of Pipe, D, Inches								
	20			24			30		
	18.814	19.000	19.250	22.626	23.000	23.250	28.628	29.000	29.250
2.000	.0667	.0671	.0676	....	....	....	....	....	....
2.125	.0640	.0644	.0649	....	....	....	....	....	....
2.250	.0614	.0618	.0622	....	....	....	....	....	....
2.375	.0588	.0592	.0597	.0659	.0665	.0669	....	....	....
2.500	.0563	.0568	.0573	.0636	.0642	.0646	....	....	....
2.625	.0540	.0544	.0549	.0614	.0620	.0624	....	....	....
2.750	.0517	.0521	.0526	.0592	.0599	.0603	....	....	....
2.875	.0494	.0499	.0504	.0571	.0578	.0582	.0662	....	....
3.000	.0473	.0477	.0483	.0551	.0557	.0562	.0644	.0649	.0652
3.125	.0452	.0457	.0462	.0531	.0538	.0542	.0626	.0631	.0634
3.250	.0433	.0437	.0442	.0511	.0520	.0523	.0608	.0613	.0616
3.375	.0414	.0418	.0423	.0493	.0500	.0504	.0590	.0596	.0599
3.500	.0395	.0399	.0405	.0474	.0481	.0486	.0574	.0579	.0582
3.625	.0378	.0382	.0387	.0457	.0464	.0468	.0557	.0562	.0566
3.750	.0361	.0365	.0370	.0440	.0447	.0451	.0541	.0546	.0550
3.875	.0345	.0349	.0354	.0423	.0430	.0435	.0525	.0530	.0534
4.000	.0329	.0333	.0339	.0407	.0414	.0419	.0509	.0515	.0518
4.250	.0301	.0304	.0310	.0376	.0384	.0388	.0479	.0485	.0488
4.500	.0275	.0279	.0283	.0348	.0355	.0360	.0450	.0456	.0460
4.750	.0252	.0256	.0260	.0322	.0328	.0333	.0423	.0429	.0433
5.000	.0232	.0235	.0239	.0297	.0304	.0308	.0397	.0403	.0407
5.250	.0214	.0217	.0220	.0275	.0281	.0285	.0373	.0378	.0382
5.500	.0199	.0201	.0204	.0254	.0260	.0264	.0349	.0355	.0359
5.750	.0186	.0188	.0191	.0236	.0241	.0245	.0327	.0333	.0337
6.000	.0176	.0177	.0179	.0219	.0224	.0228	.0306	.0312	.0316
6.250	.0167	.0168	.0170	.0204	.0208	.0212	.0287	.0292	.0296
6.500	.0161	.0162	.0163	.0191	.0195	.0198	.0269	.0274	.0277
6.750	.0157	.0157	.0157	.0179	.0183	.0185	.0252	.0257	.0260
7.000	.0155	.0155	.0154	.0169	.0172	.0174	.0236	.0240	.0244
7.250	.0155	.0154	.0153	.0161	.0163	.0165	.0221	.0226	.0229
7.500	.0157	.0155	.0154	.0154	.0156	.0157	.0208	.0212	.0215
7.750	.0160	.0158	.0156	.0148	.0150	.0151	.0195	.0199	.0202
8.000	.0166	.0163	.0160	.0144	.0145	.0146	.0184	.0187	.0190
8.250	.0172	.0169	.0165	.0142	.0142	.0142	.0174	.0177	.0179
8.500	.0180	.0177	.0172	.0141	.0140	.0140	.0164	.0168	.0170
8.750	.0190	.0186	.0180	.0141	.0140	.0139	.0156	.0159	.0161
9.000	.0201	.0196	.0190	.0143	.0141	.0140	.0149	.0152	.0153
9.250	.0213	.0208	.0201	.0146	.0143	.0141	.0143	.0145	.0146
9.500	.0226	.0220	.0213	.0150	.0146	.0144	.0138	.0139	.0141
9.750	.0240	.0234	.0226	.0155	.0150	.0147	.0133	.0135	.0136
10.000	.0256	.0249	.0240	.0161	.0155	.0152	.0130	.0131	.0132
10.250	.0271	.0264	.0255	.0168	.0162	.0158	.0128	.0128	.0128
10.500	.0288	.0280	.0270	.0176	.0169	.0164	.0126	.0126	.0126
10.750	.0305	.0297	.0286	.0185	.0176	.0172	.0125	.0125	.0125
11.000	.0322	.0314	.0303	.0194	.0186	.0181	.0125	.0124	.0124
11.250	.0340	.0332	.0320	.0205	.0196	.0190	.0126	.0125	.0124
11.500	.0358	.0349	.0338	.0216	.0207	.0200	.0128	.0126	.0125
11.750	.0376	.0367	.0355	.0228	.0218	.0211	.0130	.0128	.0127
12.000	.0394	.0385	.0373	.0241	.0230	.0223	.0134	.0131	.0129
12.500	.0429	.0420	.0408	.0267	.0255	.0248	.0142	.0138	.0136
13.000	.0463	.0454	.0442	.0296	.0282	.0274	.0153	.0148	.0145
13.500	.0494	.0485	.0474	.0326	.0311	.0302	.0166	.0160	.0157
14.000	.0520	.0512	.0502	.0356	.0341	.0331	.0182	.0175	.0171
14.500	....	....	....	.0386	.0370	.0360	.0199	.0192	.0187
15.000	....	....	....	.0415	.0400	.0390	.0218	.0209	.0204
15.500	....	....	....	.0443	.0428	.0418	.0239	.0230	.0224
16.000	....	....	....	.0470	.0455	.0446	.0260	.0250	.0244
16.500	....	....	....	.0494	.0480	.0471	.0283	.0273	.0266
17.000	....	....	....	....	.0503	.0494	.0307	.0296	.0288
17.500	....	....	....	....	....	....	.0331	.0319	.0312
18.000	....	....	....	....	....	....	.0355	.0343	.0335
18.500	....	....	....	....	....	....	.0379	.0366	.0358
19.000	....	....	....	....	....	....	.0402	.0390	.0382
19.500	....	....	....	....	....	....	.0424	.0412	.0404
20.000	....	....	....	....	....	....	.0446	.0434	.0426
20.500	....	....	....	....	....	....	.0466	.0455	.0448
21.000	....	....	....	....	....	....	.0485	.0475	.0467
21.500	....	....	....	....	....	....	....	.0492	.0485

Table 12-1. Section I (*Continued*)
"*b*" Values for Reynolds-number Factor, F_r,—Flange Taps

$$F_r = 1 + \frac{b}{\sqrt{b_w p_f}}$$

β	Internal Diameter of Pipe, D, inches										
	2			3				4			
	1.689	1.939	2.067	2.300	2.626	2.900	3.068	3.152	3.438	3.826	4.026
0.10	0.1052	0.1027	0.1012	0.0987	0.0958	0.0928	0.0927	0.0921	0.0905	0.0886	0.0877
0.11	0.1020	0.0985	0.0970	0.0945	0.0916	0.0896	0.0885	0.0880	0.0863	0.0844	0.0835
0.12	0.0981	0.0945	0.0930	0.0905	0.0876	0.0856	0.0845	0.0840	0.0823	0.0804	0.0795
0.13	0.0943	0.0907	0.0892	0.0867	0.0838	0.0818	0.0807	0.0802	0.0785	0.0766	0.0757
0.14	0.0906	0.0871	0.0856	0.0831	0.0802	0.0782	0.0771	0.0765	0.0749	0.0730	0.0721
0.15	0.0872	0.0837	0.0822	0.0797	0.0768	0.0748	0.0736	0.0731	0.0715	0.0696	0.0687
0.16	0.0840	0.0805	0.0789	0.0764	0.0736	0.0715	0.0704	0.0699	0.0682	0.0663	0.0654
0.17	0.0809	0.0774	0.0759	0.0734	0.0705	0.0685	0.0673	0.0668	0.0652	0.0633	0.0624
0.18	0.0780	0.0745	0.0730	0.0705	0.0676	0.0656	0.0645	0.0639	0.0623	0.0604	0.0595
0.19	0.0753	0.0718	0.0703	0.0678	0.0649	0.0629	0.0617	0.0612	0.0596	0.0577	0.0568
0.20	0.0728	0.0693	0.0677	0.0653	0.0624	0.0603	0.0592	0.0587	0.0570	0.0551	0.0542
0.21	0.0703	0.0668	0.0652	0.0628	0.0599	0.0579	0.0567	0.0562	0.0546	0.0527	0.0518
0.22	0.0681	0.0646	0.0630	0.0606	0.0577	0.0556	0.0545	0.0540	0.0524	0.0505	0.0496
0.23	0.0660	0.0625	0.0610	0.0585	0.0556	0.0536	0.0525	0.0520	0.0503	0.0484	0.0475
0.24	0.0642	0.0605	0.0591	0.0566	0.0538	0.0517	0.0506	0.0501	0.0484	0.0465	0.0457
0.25	0.0324	0.0589	0.0574	0.0549	0.0520	0.0500	0.0489	0.0483	0.0467	0.0448	0.0439
0.26	0.0307	0.0572	0.0557	0.0532	0.0504	0.0483	0.0472	0.0467	0.0451	0.0431	0.0423
0.27	0.0593	0.0558	0.0543	0.0518	0.0489	0.0469	0.0458	0.0452	0.0436	0.0417	0.0408
0.28	0.0580	0.0545	0.0530	0.0505	0.0476	0.0456	0.0445	0.0440	0.0423	0.0404	0.0395
0.29	0.0559	0.0534	0.0518	0.0494	0.0465	0.0444	0.0433	0.0428	0.0412	0.0393	0.0384
0.30	0.0559	0.0524	0.0508	0.0484	0.0455	0.0434	0.0423	0.0418	0.0402	0.0383	0.0374
0.31	0.0549	0.0514	0.0499	0.0474	0.0445	0.0425	0.0414	0.0409	0.0392	0.0373	0.0364
0.32	0.0541	0.0506	0.0491	0.0467	0.0438	0.0417	0.0406	0.0401	0.0385	0.0366	0.0357
0.33	0.0534	0.0499	0.0484	0.0460	0.0431	0.0411	0.0399	0.0394	0.0378	0.0359	0.0350
0.34	0.0529	0.0495	0.0479	0.0455	0.0426	0.0406	0.0395	0.0389	0.0373	0.0354	0.0345
0.35	0.0525	0.0490	0.0475	0.0450	0.0422	0.0401	0.0390	0.0385	0.0369	0.0350	0.0341
0.36	0.0521	0.0487	0.0471	0.0447	0.0418	0.0398	0.0387	0.0382	0.0366	0.0347	0.0338
0.37	0.0520	0.0485	0.0470	0.0446	0.0417	0.0397	0.0386	0.0380	0.0364	0.0345	0.0337
0.38	0.0519	0.0484	0.0469	0.0445	0.0416	0.0396	0.0385	0.0380	0.0363	0.0344	3.0336
0.39	0.0520	0.0485	0.0470	0.0445	0.0417	0.0397	0.0386	0.0380	0.0364	0.0345	0.0337
0.40	0.0521	0.0486	0.0471	0.0446	0.0418	0.0398	0.0387	0.0382	0.0365	0.0346	0.0338
0.41	0.0523	0.0488	0.0473	0.0449	0.0420	0.0400	0.0389	0.0384	0.0368	0.0349	0.0340
0.42	0.0526	0.0491	0.0476	0.0452	0.0423	0.0403	0.0392	0.0387	0.0371	0.0352	0.0343
0.43	0.0530	0.0495	0.0480	0.0456	0.0427	0.0407	0.0396	0.0391	0.0375	0.0356	0.0348
0.44	0.0534	0.0500	0.0485	0.0461	0.0432	0.0412	0.0401	0.0396	0.0380	0.0361	0.0353
0.45	0.0540	0.0506	0.0490	0.0466	0.0438	0.0418	0.0407	0.0402	0.0386	0.0367	0.0359
0.46	0.0546	0.0512	0.0497	0.0473	0.0445	0.0425	0.0414	0.0409	0.0393	0.0374	0.0365
0.47	0.0553	0.0519	0.0504	0.0479	0.0451	0.0431	0.0421	0.0415	0.0400	0.0381	0.0372
0.48	0.0561	0.0527	0.0512	0.0488	0.0459	0.0440	0.0423	0.0424	0.0408	0.0389	0.0380
0.49	0.0569	0.0535	0.0520	0.0496	0.0468	0.0448	0.0437	0.0432	0.0416	0.0397	0.0389
0.50	0.0578	0.0544	0.0529	0.0505	0.0477	0.0457	0.0446	0.0441	0.0426	0.0407	0.0398
0.51	0.0587	0.0553	0.0538	0.0514	0.0486	0.0467	0.0456	0.0451	0.0435	0.0417	0.0408
0.52	0.0598	0.0564	0.0549	0.0525	0.0497	0.0478	0.0467	0.0462	0.0446	0.0427	0.0419
0.53	0.0608	0.0574	0.0559	0.0535	0.0508	0.0488	0.0477	0.0472	0.0457	0.0438	0.0430
0.54	0.0617	0.0584	0.0569	0.0546	0.0518	0.0498	0.0488	0.0483	0.0467	0.0449	0.0440
0.55	0.0629	0.0595	0.0580	0.0557	0.0529	0.0510	0.0499	0.0494	0.0479	0.0460	0.0452
0.56	0.0639	0.0606	0.0591	0.0568	0.0540	0.0521	0.0511	0.0506	0.0490	0.0472	0.0464
0.57	0.0651	0.0618	0.0603	0.0580	0.0553	0.0534	0.0523	0.0518	0.0503	0.0484	0.0476
0.58	0.0663	0.0630	0.0615	0.0592	0.0565	0.0545	0.0535	0.0530	0.0515	0.0496	0.0488
0.59	0.0675	0.0642	0.0628	0.0605	0.0578	0.0558	0.0548	0.0543	0.0528	0.0510	0.0501
0.60	0.0687	0.0654	0.0640	0.0617	0.0590	0.0571	0.0560	0.0556	0.0540	0.0522	0.0514
0.61	0.0698	0.0666	0.0651	0.0628	0.0602	0.0583	0.0572	0.0567	0.0552	0.0534	0.0526
0.62	0.0711	0.0678	0.0664	0.0641	0.0614	0.0595	0.0585	0.0580	0.0565	0.0548	0.0539
0.63	0.0722	0.0690	0.0676	0.0653	0.0626	0.0608	0.0597	0.0593	0.0578	0.0560	0.0552
0.64	0.0733	0.0701	0.0687	0.0665	0.0638	0.0620	0.0610	0.0605	0.0590	0.0572	0.0564
0.65	0.0745	0.0713	0.0699	0.0677	0.0651	0.0632	0.0622	0.0617	0.0602	0.0585	0.0577
0.66	0.0756	0.0724	0.0710	0.0688	0.0662	0.0643	0.0633	0.0629	0.0614	0.0597	0.0589
0.67	0.0766	0.0735	0.0721	0.0699	0.0673	0.0655	0.0645	0.0640	0.0626	0.0608	0.0601
0.68	0.0777	0.0745	0.0732	0.0710	0.0684	0.0666	0.0656	0.0652	0.0637	0.0620	0.0612
0.69	0.0786	0.0755	0.0741	0.0720	0.0694	0.0676	0.0667	0.0662	0.0648	0.0631	0.0623
0.70	0.0795	0.0765	0.0751	0.0730	0.0704	0.0687	0.0677	0.0672	0.0658	0.0641	0.0634
0.71	0.0803	0.0773	0.0759	0.0738	0.0713	0.0695	0.0686	0.0681	0.0667	0.0651	0.0643
0.72	0.0811	0.0781	0.0768	0.0747	0.0722	0.0704	0.0695	0.0690	0.0676	0.0660	0.0652
0.73	0.0818	0.0789	0.0776	0.0755	0.0730	0.0713	0.0704	0.0699	0.0685	0.0669	0.0662
0.74	0.0825	0.0795	0.0782	0.0762	0.0738	0.0721	0.0711	0.0707	0.0693	0.0677	0.0670
0.75	0.0829	0.0800	0.0788	0.0767	0.0743	0.0726	0.0718	0.0713	0.0699	0.0683	0.0677

Table 12-1. Section I (*Continued*)
"b" Values for Reynolds-number Factor, F_r,—Flange Taps

$$F_r = 1 + \frac{b}{\sqrt{h_w p_f}}$$

	Internal Diameter of Pipe, D, inches												
β	6				8			10			12		
	4.897	5.189	5.761	6.065	7.625	7.981	8.071	9.564	10.020	10.136	11.376	11.938	12.090
0.10	0.0859	0.0846	0.0825	0.0815	0.0777	0.0771	0.0769	0.0747	0.0742	0.0741	0.0729	0.0724	0.0725
0.11	0.0818	0.0805	0.0783	0.0773	0.0736	0.0729	0.0727	0.0706	0.0700	0.0699	0.0687	0.0682	0.0681
0.12	0.0777	0.0764	0.0742	0.0732	0.0695	0.0688	0.0687	0.0665	0.0660	0.0658	0.0646	0.0642	0.0640
0.13	0.0738	0.0725	0.0703	0.0694	0.0656	0.0649	0.0648	0.0626	0.0621	0.0619	0.0607	0.0603	0.0602
0.14	0.0701	0.0688	0.0666	0.0657	0.0619	0.0612	0.0611	0.0589	0.0584	0.0583	0.0571	0.0566	0.0565
0.15	0.0666	0.0653	0.0631	0.0622	0.0584	0.0578	0.0576	0.0554	0.0549	0.0548	0.0536	0.0531	0.0530
0.16	0.0633	0.0620	0.0598	0.0589	0.0551	0.0545	0.0543	0.0522	0.0516	0.0515	0.0503	0.0498	0.0497
0.17	0.0601	0.0589	0.0567	0.0558	0.0520	0.0514	0.0512	0.0491	0.0485	0.0484	0.0472	0.0467	0.0466
0.18	0.0571	0.0558	0.0537	0.0527	0.0490	0.0484	0.0482	0.0461	0.0455	0.0454	0.0442	0.0438	0.0436
0.19	0.0544	0.0531	0.0510	0.0500	0.0463	0.0456	0.0455	0.0433	0.0428	0.0427	0.0415	0.0410	0.0409
0.20	0.0517	0.0504	0.0483	0.0474	0.0436	0.0430	0.0428	0.0407	0.0402	0.0401	0.0389	0.0384	0.0383
0.21	0.0492	0.0480	0.0459	0.0449	0.0412	0.0405	0.0404	0.0383	0.0377	0.0376	0.0364	0.0360	0.0359
0.22	0.0469	0.0457	0.0436	0.0426	0.0389	0.0383	0.0381	0.0360	0.0355	0.0353	0.0342	0.0337	0.0336
0.23	0.0448	0.0435	0.0414	0.0405	0.0368	0.0362	0.0360	0.0339	0.0334	0.0333	0.0321	0.0316	0.0315
0.24	0.0428	0.0416	0.0395	0.0385	0.0349	0.0342	0.0341	0.0320	0.0314	0.0313	0.0302	0.0297	0.0296
0.25	0.0410	0.0398	0.0377	0.0367	0.0331	0.0324	0.0323	0.0302	0.0297	0.0296	0.0284	0.0279	0.0278
0.26	0.0393	0.0381	0.0360	0.0350	0.0314	0.0308	0.0306	0.0285	0.0280	0.0279	0.0267	0.0263	0.0262
0.27	0.0378	0.0366	0.0345	0.0336	0.0299	0.0293	0.0292	0.0271	0.0266	0.0264	0.0253	0.0248	0.0247
0.28	0.0365	0.0352	0.0332	0.0322	0.0286	0.0280	0.0278	0.0258	0.0252	0.0251	0.0240	0.0235	0.0234
0.29	0.0352	0.0340	0.0319	0.0310	0.0274	0.0268	0.0266	0.0245	0.0240	0.0239	0.0228	0.0223	0.0222
0.30	0.0341	0.0328	0.0308	0.0299	0.0263	0.0257	0.0255	0.0235	0.0230	0.0228	0.0217	0.0213	0.0211
0.31	0.0331	0.0319	0.0298	0.0289	0.0254	0.0247	0.0246	0.0225	0.0220	0.0219	0.0208	0.0203	0.0202
0.32	0.0322	0.0310	0.0290	0.0280	0.0245	0.0239	0.0237	0.0217	0.0212	0.0211	0.0199	0.0195	0.0194
0.33	0.0314	0.0302	0.0282	0.0273	0.0238	0.0232	0.0230	0.0210	0.0205	0.0204	0.0192	0.0188	0.0187
0.34	0.0308	0.0296	0.0276	0.0267	0.0232	0.0226	0.0225	0.0204	0.0199	0.0198	0.0187	0.0183	0.0182
0.35	0.0303	0.0291	0.0272	0.0263	0.0228	0.0221	0.0220	0.0200	0.0195	0.0194	0.0183	0.0178	0.0177
0.36	0.0299	0.0287	0.0268	0.0259	0.0224	0.0218	0.0216	0.0196	0.0192	0.0190	0.0179	0.0175	0.0174
0.37	0.0296	0.0284	0.0265	0.0256	0.0221	0.0215	0.0214	0.0194	0.0189	0.0188	0.0177	0.0173	0.0172
0.38	0.0294	0.0282	0.0263	0.0254	0.0220	0.0214	0.0212	0.0193	0.0188	0.0187	0.0176	0.0171	0.0170
0.39	0.0293	0.0281	0.0262	0.0253	0.0219	0.0213	0.0211	0.0192	0.0187	0.0186	0.0175	0.0171	0.0170
0.40	0.0292	0.0281	0.0261	0.0253	0.0219	0.0213	0.0212	0.0192	0.0187	0.0186	0.0175	0.0171	0.0170
0.41	0.0292	0.0281	0.0262	0.0253	0.0220	0.0214	0.0213	0.0193	0.0189	0.0187	0.0177	0.0173	0.0172
0.42	0.0294	0.0282	0.0263	0.0255	0.0222	0.0216	0.0214	0.0195	0.0191	0.0189	0.0179	0.0175	0.0174
0.43	0.0296	0.0285	0.0266	0.0257	0.0224	0.0218	0.0217	0.0198	0.0193	0.0192	0.0182	0.0178	0.0177
0.44	0.0298	0.0287	0.0268	0.0260	0.0227	0.0221	0.0220	0.0201	0.0197	0.0196	0.0185	0.0181	0.0180
0.45	0.0301	0.0290	0.0272	0.0263	0.0231	0.0225	0.0224	0.0205	0.0201	0.0200	0.0189	0.0185	0.0184
0.46	0.0305	0.0294	0.0276	0.0268	0.0235	0.0230	0.0228	0.0210	0.0205	0.0204	0.0194	0.0190	0.0189
0.47	0.0309	0.0298	0.0280	0.0272	0.0240	0.0235	0.0233	0.0215	0.0210	0.0209	0.0199	0.0195	0.0194
0.43	0.0314	0.0303	0.0285	0.0277	0.0245	0.0240	0.0238	0.0220	0.0216	0.0215	0.0205	0.0201	0.0200
0.49	0.0319	0.0308	0.0290	0.0282	0.0251	0.0245	0.0244	0.0226	0.0222	0.0221	0.0211	0.0207	0.0206
0.50	0.0324	0.0314	0.0296	0.0288	0.0257	0.0252	0.0250	0.0233	0.0228	0.0227	0.0217	0.0213	0.0212
0.51	0.0330	0.0319	0.0302	0.0294	0.0263	0.0258	0.0257	0.0239	0.0235	0.0234	0.0224	0.0220	0.0219
0.52	0.0335	0.0325	0.0308	0.0300	0.0270	0.0265	0.0263	0.0246	0.0242	0.0241	0.0231	0.0227	0.0226
0.53	0.0342	0.0332	0.0315	0.0307	0.0277	0.0272	0.0270	0.0253	0.0249	0.0248	0.0238	0.0235	0.0234
0.54	0.0348	0.0338	0.0321	0.0314	0.0284	0.0279	0.0278	0.0261	0.0256	0.0255	0.0246	0.0242	0.0241
0.55	0.0355	0.0345	0.0328	0.0321	0.0291	0.0286	0.0285	0.0268	0.0264	0.0263	0.0254	0.0250	0.0249
0.56	0.0361	0.0351	0.0335	0.0327	0.0298	0.0293	0.0292	0.0276	0.0272	0.0271	0.0261	0.0258	0.0257
0.57	0.0368	0.0358	0.0342	0.0335	0.0306	0.0301	0.0300	0.0283	0.0279	0.0278	0.0269	0.0266	0.0265
0.58	0.0375	0.0365	0.0349	0.0342	0.0313	0.0309	0.0307	0.0291	0.0287	0.0286	0.0277	0.0274	0.0273
0.59	0.0381	0.0372	0.0356	0.0349	0.0321	0.0316	0.0315	0.0299	0.0295	0.0294	0.0285	0.0282	0.0281
0.60	0.0388	0.0378	0.0363	0.0356	0.0328	0.0323	0.0322	0.0307	0.0303	0.0302	0.0293	0.0290	0.0289
0.61	0.0393	0.0384	0.0369	0.0362	0.0335	0.0330	0.0329	0.0314	0.0310	0.0309	0.0300	0.0297	0.0296
0.62	0.0399	0.0390	0.0375	0.0368	0.0342	0.0337	0.0336	0.0321	0.0317	0.0316	0.0307	0.0304	0.0303
0.63	0.0405	0.0396	0.0381	0.0375	0.0348	0.0344	0.0343	0.0328	0.0324	0.0323	0.0315	0.0311	0.0311
0.64	0.0411	0.0402	0.0387	0.0381	0.0355	0.0350	0.0349	0.0334	0.0331	0.0330	0.0322	0.0318	0.0318
0.65	0.0416	0.0407	0.0393	0.0386	0.0361	0.0357	0.0355	0.0341	0.0337	0.0336	0.0328	0.0325	0.0324
0.66	0.0421	0.0412	0.0398	0.0391	0.0366	0.0362	0.0361	0.0347	0.0343	0.0342	0.0334	0.0331	0.0331
0.67	0.0425	0.0417	0.0403	0.0397	0.0372	0.0368	0.0367	0.0352	0.0349	0.0349	0.0341	0.0338	0.0337
0.68	0.0430	0.0422	0.0408	0.0402	0.0377	0.0373	0.0372	0.0358	0.0355	0.0354	0.0346	0.0344	0.0343
0.69	0.0433	0.0425	0.0411	0.0405	0.0381	0.0377	0.0376	0.0363	0.0359	0.0359	0.0351	0.0348	0.0347
0.70	0.0436	0.0428	0.0415	0.0409	0.0386	0.0382	0.0381	0.0367	0.0364	0.0363	0.0356	0.0353	0.0352

Table 12-1. Section I (*Continued*)
Expansion Factors—Flange Taps—Y_1
Static Pressure Taken from Upstream Taps

$\frac{h_w}{p_{f1}}$ Ratio	$\beta = \frac{d}{D}$ Ratio												
	.1	.2	.3	.4	.45	.50	.52	.54	.56	.58	.60	.61	.62
0.0	1.0000	1.0000	1.0000	1.0000	1.0000	1.0000	1.0000	1.0000	1.0000	1.0000	1.0000	1.0000	1.0000
0.1	.9989	.9989	.9989	.9988	.9988	.9988	.9988	.9988	.9988	.9988	.9987	.9987	.9987
0.2	.9977	.9977	.9977	.9977	.9976	.9976	.9976	.9976	.9975	.9975	.9975	.9975	.9974
0.3	.9956	.9956	.9956	.9965	.9965	.9964	.9964	.9963	.9963	.9963	.9962	.9962	.9952
0.4	.9954	.9954	.9954	.9953	.9953	.9952	.9952	.9951	.9951	.9950	.9949	.9949	.9949
0.5	.9943	.9943	.9943	.9942	.9941	.9940	.9940	.9939	.9938	.9938	.9937	.9936	.9936
0.6	.9932	.9932	.9931	.9930	.9929	.9928	.9927	.9927	.9926	.9925	.9924	.9924	.9923
0.7	.9920	.9920	.9920	.9919	.9918	.9916	.9915	.9915	.9914	.9913	.9912	.9911	.9910
0.8	.9909	.9909	.9908	.9907	.9906	.9904	.9903	.9902	.9901	.9900	.9899	.9898	.9897
0.9	.9898	.9897	.9897	.9895	.9894	.9892	.9891	.9890	.9889	.9888	.9886	.9885	.9885
1.0	.9886	.9886	.9885	.9884	.9882	.9880	.9879	.9878	.9877	.9875	.9874	.9873	.9872
1.1	.9875	.9875	.9874	.9872	.9870	.9868	.9867	.9866	.9864	.9863	.9861	.9860	.9859
1.2	.9863	9863	.9862	.9860	.9859	.9856	.9855	.9853	.9852	.9850	.9848	.9847	.9846
1.3	.9852	.9852	.9851	.9849	.9847	.9844	.9843	.9841	.9840	.9838	.9836	.9835	.9833
1.4	.9841	.9840	.9840	.9837	.9835	.9832	.9831	.9829	.9827	.9825	.9823	.9822	.9821
1.5	.9829	.9829	.9828	.9826	.9823	.9820	.9819	.9817	.9815	.9813	.9810	.9809	.9808
1.6	.9818	.9818	.9817	.9814	.9811	.9808	.9806	.9805	.9803	.9800	.9798	.9796	.9795
1.7	.9806	.9806	.9805	.9802	.9800	.9796	.9794	.9792	.9790	.9788	.9785	.9784	.9782
1.8	.9795	.9795	.9794	.9791	.9788	.9784	.9782	.9780	.9778	.9775	.9772	.9771	.9769
1.9	.9784	.9783	.9782	.9779	.9776	.9772	.9770	.9768	.9766	.9763	.9760	.9758	.9756
2.0	.9772	.9772	.9771	.9767	.9764	.9760	.9758	.9756	.9753	.9750	.9747	.9745	.9744
2.1	.9761	.9761	.9759	.9756	.9753	.9748	.9746	.9744	.9741	.9738	.9734	.9733	.9731
2.2	.9750	.9749	.9748	.9744	.9741	.9736	.9734	.9731	.9729	.9725	.9722	.9720	.9718
2.3	.9738	.9738	.9736	.9732	.9729	.9724	.9722	.9719	.9716	.9713	.9709	.9707	.9705
2.4	.9727	.9726	.9725	.9721	.9717	.9712	.9710	.9707	.9704	.9700	.9697	.9694	.9692
2.5	.9715	.9715	.9713	.9709	.9705	.9700	.9698	.9695	.9692	.9688	.9684	.9682	.9680
2.6	.9704	.9704	.9702	.9698	.9694	.9688	.9686	.9683	.9679	.9675	.9671	.9669	.9667
2.7	.9693	.9692	.9591	.9686	.9582	.9676	.9673	.9670	.9667	.9663	.9659	.9655	.9654
2.8	.9581	.9681	.9679	.9674	.9570	.9664	.9661	.9658	.9654	.9650	.9646	.9644	.9641
2.9	.9670	.9669	.9668	.9663	.9658	.9652	.9649	.9646	.9642	.9638	.9633	.9631	.9628
3.0	.9658	.9558	.9656	.9651	.9547	.9640	.9637	.9634	.9630	.9626	.9621	.9618	.9615
3.1	.9647	.9647	.9645	.9639	.9635	.9628	.9625	.9622	.9617	.9613	.9608	.9605	.9603
3.2	.9635	.9635	.9633	.9628	.9623	.9616	.9613	.9609	.9605	.9601	.9595	.9593	.9590
3.3	.9624	.9624	.9522	.9616	.9611	.9504	.9501	.9597	.9593	.9588	.9583	.9580	.9577
3.4	.9613	.9512	.9610	.9604	.9599	.9592	.9589	.9585	.9580	.9576	.9570	.9567	.9564
3.5	.9502	.9501	.9599	.9593	.9588	.9580	.9577	.9573	.9568	.9563	.9558	.9554	.9551
3.6	.9590	.9590	.9587	.9581	.9576	.9568	.9555	.9560	.9556	.9551	.9545	.9542	.9538
3.7	.9579	.9578	.9576	.9570	.9554	.9556	.9553	.9548	.9543	.9538	.9532	.9529	.9525
3.8	.9567	.9567	.9554	.9558	.9552	.9544	.9540	.9536	.9531	.9526	.9520	.9516	.9513
3.9	.9556	.9555	.9553	.9546	.9540	.9532	.9528	.9524	.9519	.9513	.9507	.9504	.9500
4.0	.9545	.9544	.9542	.9535	.9529	.9520	.9516	.9512	.9506	.9501	.9494	.9491	.9487

Table 12-1. Section I (*Continued*)
Expansion Factors—Flange Taps—Y_1
Static Pressure Taken from Upstream Taps

$\dfrac{h_w}{P_{f1}}$ Ratio	.63	.64	.65	.66	.67	.68	.69	.70	.71	.72	.73	.74	.75
0.0	1.0000	1.0000	1.0000	1.0000	1.0000	1.0000	1.0000	1.0000	1.0000	1.0000	1.0000	1.0000	.10000
0.1	.9987	.9987	.9987	.9987	.9987	.9987	.9986	.9986	.9986	.9986	.9986	.9986	.9986
0.2	.9974	.9974	.9974	.9974	.9973	.9973	.9973	.9973	.9972	.9972	.9972	.9971	.9971
0.3	.9961	.9961	.9961	.9960	.9960	.9960	.9959	.9959	.9958	.9958	.9958	.9957	.9957
0.4	.9948	.9948	.9948	.9947	.9947	.9946	.9946	.9945	.9945	.9944	.9943	.9943	.9942
0.5	.9935	.9935	.9934	.9934	.9933	.9933	.9932	.9931	.9931	.9930	.9929	.9929	.9928
0.6	.9923	.9922	.9921	.9921	.9920	.9919	.9918	.9918	.9917	.9916	.9915	.9914	.9913
0.7	.9910	.9909	.9908	.9907	.9907	.9906	.9905	.9904	.9903	.9902	.9901	.9900	.9899
0.8	.9897	.9896	.9895	.9894	.9893	.9892	.9891	.9890	.9889	.9888	.9887	.9886	.9884
0.9	.9884	.9883	.9882	.9881	.9880	.9879	.9878	.9877	.9875	.9874	.9873	.9871	.9870
1.0	.9871	.9870	.9869	.9868	.9867	.9865	.9864	.9863	.9861	.9860	.9859	.9857	.9855
1.1	.9858	.9857	.9856	.9854	.9853	.9852	.9851	.9849	.9848	.9846	.9844	.9843	.9841
1.2	.9845	.9844	.9843	.9841	.9840	.9838	.9837	.9835	.9834	.9832	.9830	.9828	.9826
1.3	.9832	.9831	.9829	.9828	.9827	.9825	.9823	.9822	.9820	.9818	.9816	.9814	.9812
1.4	.9819	.9818	.9816	.9815	.9813	.9812	.9810	.9808	.9806	.9804	.9802	.9800	.9798
1.5	.9806	.9805	.9803	.9802	.9800	.9798	.9796	.9794	.9792	.9790	.9788	.9786	.9783
1.6	.9793	.9792	.9790	.9788	.9787	.9785	.9783	.9781	.9778	.9776	.9774	.9771	.9769
1.7	.9780	.9779	.9777	.9775	.9773	.9771	.9769	.9767	.9764	.9762	.9760	.9757	.9754
1.8	.9768	.9766	.9764	.9762	.9760	.9758	.9755	.9753	.9751	.9748	.9745	.9743	.9740
1.9	.9755	.9753	.9751	.9749	.9747	.9744	.9742	.9739	.9737	.9734	.9731	.9728	.9725
2.0	.9742	.9740	.9738	.9735	.9733	.9731	.9728	.9726	.9723	.9720	.9717	.9714	.9711
2.1	.9729	.9727	.9725	.9722	.9720	.9717	.9715	.9712	.9709	.9706	.9703	.9700	.9696
2.2	.9716	.9714	.9711	.9709	.9706	.9704	.9701	.9698	.9695	.9692	.9689	.9685	.9682
2.3	.9703	.9701	.9698	.9696	.9693	.9690	.9688	.9685	.9681	.9678	.9675	.9671	.9667
2.4	.9690	.9688	.9685	.9683	.9680	.9677	.9674	9671	.9668	.9664	.9661	.9657	.9653
2.5	.9677	.9675	.9672	.9669	.9666	.9663	.9660	.9657	.9654	.9650	.9646	.9643	.9639
2.6	.9664	.9662	.9659	.9656	.9653	.9650	.9647	.9643	.9640	.9636	.9632	.9628	.9624
2.7	.9651	.9649	.9646	.9643	.9640	.9637	.9633	.9630	.9626	.9622	.9618	.9614	.9610
2.8	.9638	.9636	.9633	.9630	.9626	.9623	.9620	.9616	.9612	.9608	.9604	.9600	.9595
2.9	.9625	.9623	.9620	.9616	.9613	.9610	.9606	.9602	.9598	.9594	.9590	.9585	.9581
3.0	.9613	.9610	.9606	.9603	.9600	.9596	.9592	.9588	.9584	.9580	.9576	.9571	.9566
3.1	.9600	.9597	.9593	.9590	.9586	.9583	.9579	.9575	.9571	.9566	.9562	.9557	.9552
3.2	.9587	.9584	.9580	.9577	.9573	.9569	.9565	.9561	.9557	.9552	.9547	.9542	.9537
3.3	.9574	.9571	.9567	.9564	.9560	.9556	.9552	.9547	.9543	.9538	.9533	.9528	.9523
3.4	.9561	.9558	.9554	.9550	.9546	.9542	.9538	.9534	.9529	.9524	.9519	.9514	.9508
3.5	.9548	.9545	.9541	.9537	.9533	.9529	.9524	.9520	.9515	.9510	.9505	.9500	.9494
3.6	.9535	.9532	.9528	.9524	.9520	.9515	.9511	.9506	.9501	.9496	.9491	.9485	.9480
3.7	.9522	.9518	.9515	.9511	.9506	.9502	.9497	.9492	.9487	.9482	.9477	.9471	.9465
3.8	.9509	.9505	.9502	.9497	.9493	.9488	.9484	.9479	.9474	.9468	.9463	.9457	.9451
3.9	.9496	.9492	.9488	.9484	.9480	.9475	.9470	.9465	.9460	.9454	.9448	.9442	.9436
4.0	.9483	.9479	.9475	.9471	.9466	.9462	.9457	.9451	.9446	.9440	.9434	.9428	.9422

PRODUCTION EQUIPMENT

Table 12-1. Section I (*Continued*)
Expansion Factors—Flange Taps—Y_m
Static Pressure, Mean of Upstream and Downstream

$\dfrac{h_w}{pfm}$ Ratio	$\beta = \dfrac{d}{D}$ Ratio												
	.63	.64	.65	.66	.67	.68	.69	.70	.71	.72	.73	.74	.75
0.0	1.0000	1.0000	1.0000	1.0000	1.0000	1.0000	1.0000	1.0000	1.0000	1.0000	1.0000	1.0000	1.0000
0.1	.9996	.9996	.9996	.9996	.9996	.9996	.9995	.9995	.9995	.9995	.9995	.9995	.9995
0.2	.9992	.9992	.9992	.9992	.9991	.9991	.9991	.9991	.9990	.9990	.9990	.9989	.9989
0.3	.9988	.9988	.9988	.9987	.9987	.9987	.9986	.9986	.9986	.9985	.9985	.9984	.9984
0.4	.9984	.9984	.9984	.9983	.9983	.9982	.9982	.9981	.9981	.9980	.9980	.9979	.9978
0.5	.9981	.9980	.9980	.9979	.9978	.9978	.9977	.9977	.9976	.9975	.9974	.9974	.9973
0.6	.9977	.9976	.9975	.9975	.9974	.9973	.9973	.9972	.9971	.9970	.9969	.9968	.9967
0.7	.9973	.9972	.9971	.9971	.9970	.9969	.9968	.9967	.9966	.9965	.9964	.9963	.9962
0.8	.9969	.9968	.9967	.9967	.9965	.9965	.9964	.9963	.9962	.9961	.9960	.9959	.9957
0.9	.9966	.9965	.9964	.9963	.9962	.9961	.9960	.9959	.9957	.9956	.9955	.9953	.9952
1.0	.9962	.9961	.9960	.9959	.9958	.9957	.9955	.9954	.9953	.9951	.9950	.9948	.9947
1.1	.9958	.9957	.9956	.9955	.9953	.9952	.9951	.9949	.9948	.9946	.9945	.9943	.9941
1.2	.9954	.9953	.9952	.9951	.9949	.9948	.9946	.9945	.9943	.9941	.9940	.9938	.9936
1.3	.9951	.9949	.9948	.9946	.9945	.9943	.9942	.9940	.9938	.9936	.9934	.9933	.9931
1.4	.9947	.9945	.9944	.9942	.9941	.9939	.9938	.9936	.9934	.9932	.9930	.9928	.9926
1.5	.9944	.9942	.9941	.9939	.9937	.9935	.9933	.9932	.9929	.9927	.9925	.9923	.9920
1.6	.9940	.9938	.9937	.9935	.9933	.9931	.9929	.9927	.9925	.9922	.9920	.9918	.9915
1.7	.9936	.9934	.9933	.9931	.9929	.9927	.9925	.9923	.9921	.9918	.9916	.9913	.9910
1.8	.9932	.9930	.9928	.9927	.9925	.9923	.9920	.9918	.9916	.9913	.9911	.9908	.9905
1.9	.9929	.9927	.9925	.9923	.9921	.9919	.9916	.9914	.9911	.9908	.9906	.9903	.9900
2.0	.9923	.9921	.9919	.9917	.9915	.9912	.9910	.9907	.9904	.9901	.9899	.9896	.9892
2.1	.9921	.9919	.9917	.9915	.9913	.9910	.9908	.9905	.9902	.9899	.9896	.9893	.9890
2.2	.9918	.9916	.9913	.9911	.9908	.9906	.9903	.9900	.9897	.9894	.9892	.9888	.9884
2.3	.9915	.9913	.9910	.9908	.9905	.9902	.9900	.9897	.9894	.9891	.9887	.9884	.9880
2.4	.9911	.9909	.9906	.9904	.9901	.9898	.9895	.9892	.9889	.9886	.9882	.9878	.9875
2.5	.9907	.9905	.9902	.9900	.9897	.9894	.9891	.9888	.9885	.9881	.9878	.9874	.9870
2.6	.9904	.9902	.9899	.9896	.9893	.9890	.9887	.9884	.9880	.9876	.9873	.9869	.9865
2.7	.9900	.9898	.9895	.9692	.9889	.9886	.9883	.9880	.9876	.9872	.9869	.9864	.9860
2.8	.9897	.9895	.9892	.9889	.9886	.9882	.9879	.9875	.9871	.9867	.9864	.9859	.9855
2.9	.9893	.9891	.9888	.9885	.9882	.9878	.9874	.9871	.9867	.9863	.9859	.9855	.9850
3.0	.9890	.9887	.9884	.9881	.9877	.9874	.9870	.9867	.9863	.9859	.9854	.9850	.9845
3.1	.9887	.9884	.9881	.9877	.9874	.9870	.9867	.9863	.9859	.9854	.9850	.9845	.9840
3.2	.9883	.9880	.9877	.9873	.9870	.9866	.9862	.9858	.9854	.9850	.9845	.9840	.9835
3.3	.9880	.9877	.9873	.9870	.9866	.9863	.9859	.9854	.9850	.9845	.9841	.9836	.9831
3.4	.9876	.9873	.9869	.9866	.9862	.9858	.9854	.9850	.9845	.9841	.9836	.9831	.9825
3.5	.9873	.9870	.9866	.9863	.9859	.9855	.9850	.9846	.9841	.9837	.9832	.9826	.9821
3.6	.9869	.9866	.9862	.9859	.9855	.9851	.9846	.9842	.9837	.9833	.9827	.9822	.9816
3.7	.9866	.9863	.9859	.9855	.9851	.9847	.9842	.9838	.9833	.9828	.9822	.9817	.9811
3.8	.9863	.9859	.9855	.9851	.9847	.9843	.9838	.9834	.9829	.9824	.9818	.9813	.9807
3.9	.9860	.9856	.9852	.9848	.9844	.9839	.9835	.9830	.9825	.9820	.9814	.9808	.9802
4.0	.9857	.9853	.9849	.9845	.9840	.9836	.9831	.9826	.9820	.9815	.9809	.9803	.9797

Table 12-1. Section I (*Continued*)
Expansion Factors—Flange Taps—Y_m
Static Pressure, Mean of Upstream and Downstream

h_w / P_{fm} Ratio	$\beta = \dfrac{d}{D}$ Ratio												
	.1	.2	.3	.4	.45	.50	.52	.54	.56	.58	.60	.61	.62
0.0	1.0000	1.0000	1.0000	1.0000	1.0000	1.0000	1.0000	1.0000	1.0000	1.0000	1.0000	1.0000	1.0000
0.1	.9998	.9998	.9998	.9997	.9997	.9997	.9997	.9997	.9997	.9997	.9996	.9996	.9996
0.2	.9995	.9995	.9995	.9995	.9994	.9994	.9994	.9994	.9993	.9993	.9993	.9993	.9992
0.3	.9993	.9993	.9993	.9992	.9992	.9991	.9991	.9990	.9990	.9990	.9989	.9989	.9989
0.4	.9991	.9991	.9990	.9990	.9989	.9988	.9988	.9987	.9987	.9986	.9986	.9985	.9985
0.5	.9988	.9988	.9988	.9987	.9986	.9985	.9985	.9984	.9983	.9983	.9982	.9981	.9981
0.6	.9986	.9986	.9985	.9984	.9984	.9982	.9982	.9981	.9980	.9979	.9978	.9978	.9977
0.7	.9984	.9984	.9983	.9982	.9981	.9979	.9979	.9978	.9977	.9976	.9975	.9974	.9973
0.8	.9981	.9981	.9981	.9979	.9978	.9976	.9976	.9975	.9974	.9972	.9971	.9970	.9970
0.9	.9979	.9979	.9978	.9977	.9975	.9973	.9973	.9972	.9971	.9969	.9968	.9967	.9967
1.0	.9977	.9977	.9976	.9975	.9973	.9971	.9970	.9969	.9968	.9967	.9965	.9964	.9963
1.1	.9975	.9974	.9974	.9972	.9971	.9968	.9967	.9966	.9965	.9963	.9961	.9960	.9959
1.2	.9973	.9973	.9972	.9970	.9968	.9966	.9964	.9963	.9961	.9960	.9958	.9957	.9955
1.3	.9971	.9970	.9970	.9967	.9965	.9963	.9961	.9960	.9958	.9956	.9954	.9953	.9952
1.4	.9968	.9968	.9967	.9965	.9963	.9960	.9958	.9957	.9955	.9953	.9951	.9949	.9948
1.5	.9966	.9966	.9965	.9962	.9960	.9957	.9955	.9954	.9952	.9950	.9948	.9946	.9945
1.6	.9964	.9964	.9962	.9960	.9957	.9954	.9952	.9950	.9948	.9946	.9944	.9943	.9941
1.7	.9962	.9962	.9960	.9958	.9955	.9952	.9950	.9948	.9946	.9943	.9941	.9939	.9938
1.8	.9959	.9959	.9958	.9955	.9953	.9949	.9947	.9945	.9943	.9940	.9937	.9936	.9934
1.9	.9957	.9957	.9956	.9953	.9950	.9948	.9944	.9942	.9940	.9937	.9934	.9933	.9931
2.0	.9955	.9954	.9953	.9950	.9946	.9942	.9940	.9938	.9935	.9932	.9929	.9927	.9925
2.1	.9953	.9953	.9952	.9948	.9945	.9940	.9938	.9936	.9933	.9930	.9927	.9925	.9923
2.2	.9951	.9951	.9950	.9947	.9943	.9938	.9936	.9934	.9931	.9927	.9924	.9922	.9920
2.3	.9949	.9949	.9947	.9944	.9940	.9936	.9933	.9931	.9928	.9924	.9921	.9919	.9917
2.4	.9947	.9947	.9945	.9941	.9938	.9933	.9930	.9927	.9924	.9921	.9917	.9915	.9913
2.5	.9945	.9944	.9943	.9938	.9935	.9930	.9927	.9924	.9921	.9918	.9914	.9912	.9909
2.6	.9943	.9942	.9941	.9936	.9933	.9928	.9925	.9922	.9919	.9915	.9911	.9909	.9907
2.7	.9941	.9941	.9939	.9934	.9930	.9925	.9922	.9919	.9916	.9912	.9907	.9905	.9903
2.8	.9939	.9938	.9937	.9932	.9928	.9922	.9919	.9916	.9913	.9909	.9904	.9902	.9900
2.9	.9937	.9936	.9934	.9929	.9925	.9919	.9916	.9913	.9909	.9905	.9901	.9899	.9896
3.0	.9935	.9934	.9932	.9927	.9923	.9917	.9914	.9911	.9907	.9903	.9898	.9895	.9892
3.1	.9932	.9932	.9930	.9925	.9920	.9914	.9911	.9908	.9904	.9900	.9895	.9892	.9890
3.2	.9931	.9931	.9929	.9923	.9919	.9912	.9909	.9905	.9901	.9897	.9892	.9889	.9886
3.3	.9929	.9928	.9926	.9921	.9916	.9909	.9906	.9902	.9898	.9894	.9889	.9886	.9883
3.4	.9927	.9926	.9924	.9918	.9913	.9907	.9903	.9899	.9895	.9890	.9885	.9882	.9879
3.5	.9925	.9924	.9922	.9916	.9911	.9905	.9901	.9897	.9893	.9888	.9883	.9880	.9877
3.6	.9923	.9923	.9920	.9914	.9909	.9902	.9898	.9894	.9890	.9885	.9878	.9876	.9873
3.7	.9921	.9920	.9918	.9912	.9907	.9899	.9895	.9891	.9887	.9882	.9876	.9873	.9870
3.8	.9919	.9918	.9916	.9910	.9905	.9897	.9893	.9889	.9884	.9879	.9873	.9870	.9866
3.9	.9918	.9917	.9915	.9908	.9902	.9894	.9890	.9886	.9881	.9876	.9870	.9867	.9863
4.0	.9916	.9915	.9913	.9906	.9900	.9892	.9888	.9884	.9879	.9873	.9867	.9864	.9861

Table 12-1. Section I (*Continued*)
Expansion Factors—Flange Taps—Y_2
Static Pressure Taken from Downstream Taps

$\dfrac{h_w}{p_{f2}}$ Ratio							$\beta = \dfrac{d}{D}$ Ratio						
	.1	.2	.3	.4	.45	.50	.52	.54	.56	.58	.60	.61	.62
0.0	1.0000	1.0000	1.0000	1.0000	1.0000	1.0000	1.0000	1.0000	1.0000	1.0000	1.0000	1.0000	1.0000
0.1	1.0007	1.0007	1.0007	1.0006	1.0006	1.0006	1.0006	1.0006	1.0006	1.0006	1.0006	1.0005	1.0005
0.2	1.0013	1.0013	1.0013	1.0013	1.0013	1.0012	1.0012	1.0012	1.0012	1.0012	1.0011	1.0011	1.0011
0.3	1.0020	1.0020	1.0020	1.0020	1.0019	1.0018	1.0018	1.0018	1.0017	1.0017	1.0016	1.0016	1.0016
0.4	1.0027	1.0027	1.0027	1.0026	1.0026	1.0025	1.0024	1.0024	1.0023	1.0023	1.0022	1.0022	1.0021
0.5	1.0033	1.0033	1.0033	1.0032	1.0031	1.0030	1.0029	1.0029	1.0028	1.0028	1.0027	1.0027	1.0027
0.6	1.0040	1.0040	1.0040	1.0039	1.0038	1.0036	1.0036	1.0035	1.0034	1.0033	1.0032	1.0032	1.0031
0.7	1.0047	1.0047	1.0047	1.0045	1.0044	1.0043	1.0042	1.0041	1.0040	1.0039	1.0038	1.0038	1.0037
0.8	1.0053	1.0053	1.0053	1.0051	1.0050	1.0049	1.0048	1.0047	1.0046	1.0045	1.0044	1.0043	1.0043
0.9	1.0060	1.0060	1.0060	1.0058	1.0057	1.0055	1.0054	1.0053	1.0052	1.0050	1.0049	1.0048	1.0048
1.0	1.0067	1.0066	1.0066	1.0064	1.0063	1.0061	1.0060	1.0059	1.0058	1.0056	1.0055	1.0054	1.0053
1.1	1.0074	1.0073	1.0073	1.0071	1.0069	1.0067	1.0066	1.0065	1.0063	1.0061	1.0060	1.0059	1.0058
1.2	1.0080	1.0080	1.0079	1.0077	1.0075	1.0073	1.0072	1.0071	1.0069	1.0067	1.0066	1.0065	1.0064
1.3	1.0087	1.0087	1.0086	1.0084	1.0082	1.0080	1.0078	1.0077	1.0075	1.0073	1.0071	1.0070	1.0069
1.4	1.0094	1.0093	1.0093	1.0090	1.0088	1.0086	1.0084	1.0083	1.0081	1.0079	1.0077	1.0076	1.0074
1.5	1.0100	1.0100	1.0099	1.0097	1.0094	1.0091	1.0090	1.0088	1.0086	1.0084	1.0082	1.0081	1.0080
1.6	1.0108	1.0107	1.0106	1.0104	1.0101	1.0097	1.0097	1.0095	1.0093	1.0090	1.0088	1.0086	1.0085
1.7	1.0114	1.0114	1.0113	1.0110	1.0108	1.0104	1.0103	1.0101	1.0099	1.0096	1.0094	1.0092	1.0091
1.8	1.0121	1.0120	1.0120	1.0117	1.0114	1.0110	1.0108	1.0106	1.0104	1.0102	1.0100	1.0097	1.0096
1.9	1.0128	1.0127	1.0126	1.0123	1.0120	1.0116	1.0115	1.0112	1.0110	1.0107	1.0104	1.0103	1.0101
2.0	1.0134	1.0133	1.0132	1.0129	1.0126	1.0122	1.0121	1.0118	1.0116	1.0113	1.0110	1.0108	1.0106
2.1	1.0140	1.0140	1.0139	1.0136	1.0133	1.0129	1.0127	1.0124	1.0122	1.0119	1.0115	1.0114	1.0111
2.2	1.0147	1.0147	1.0146	1.0142	1.0139	1.0135	1.0133	1.0130	1.0128	1.0125	1.0121	1.0120	1.0118
2.3	1.0154	1.0154	1.0153	1.0149	1.0146	1.0141	1.0139	1.0136	1.0133	1.0130	1.0127	1.0125	1.0123
2.4	1.0160	1.0160	1.0159	1.0154	1.0151	1.0146	1.0144	1.0141	1.0138	1.0135	1.0133	1.0130	1.0128
2.5	1.0167	1.0167	1.0166	1.0162	1.0158	1.0153	1.0150	1.0148	1.0145	1.0141	1.0137	1.0135	1.0133
2.6	1.0174	1.0173	1.0172	1.0168	1.0164	1.0159	1.0156	1.0154	1.0151	1.0147	1.0143	1.0141	1.0139
2.7	1.0183	1.0182	1.0181	1.0176	1.0172	1.0167	1.0164	1.0161	1.0158	1.0154	1.0150	1.0148	1.0146
2.8	1.0187	1.0186	1.0185	1.0180	1.0176	1.0171	1.0168	1.0165	1.0162	1.0158	1.0154	1.0152	1.0149
2.9	1.0194	1.0194	1.0192	1.0187	1.0183	1.0177	1.0175	1.0172	1.0168	1.0164	1.0160	1.0157	1.0155
3.0	1.0200	1.0200	1.0198	1.0193	1.0189	1.0183	1.0180	1.0177	1.0173	1.0169	1.0165	1.0162	1.0160
3.1	1.0207	1.0206	1.0205	1.0200	1.0195	1.0189	1.0186	1.0183	1.0179	1.0175	1.0171	1.0168	1.0166
3.2	1.0213	1.0213	1.0211	1.0206	1.0201	1.0195	1.0192	1.0189	1.0185	1.0180	1.0176	1.0173	1.0171
3.3	1.0220	1.0220	1.0218	1.0213	1.0208	1.0202	1.0199	1.0195	1.0191	1.0186	1.0181	1.0178	1.0176
3.4	1.0227	1.0227	1.0225	1.0219	1.0214	1.0208	1.0205	1.0201	1.0197	1.0192	1.0187	1.0184	1.0182
3.5	1.0233	1.0233	1.0231	1.0225	1.0220	1.0214	1.0210	1.0207	1.0202	1.0198	1.0192	1.0190	1.0187
3.6	1.0240	1.0239	1.0237	1.0232	1.0227	1.0220	1.0216	1.0212	1.0208	1.0203	1.0198	1.0195	1.0192
3.7	1.0246	1.0246	1.0244	1.0238	1.0232	1.0225	1.0221	1.0217	1.0213	1.0208	1.0203	1.0200	1.0197
3.8	1.0252	1.0252	1.0250	1.0244	1.0238	1.0231	1.0227	1.0223	1.0219	1.0214	1.0209	1.0206	1.0203
3.9	1.0259	1.0259	1.0257	1.0250	1.0245	1.0237	1.0234	1.0229	1.0225	1.0220	1.0214	1.0211	1.0208
4.0	1.0265	1.0265	1.0263	1.0256	1.0251	1.0243	1.0240	1.0235	1.0231	1.0225	1.0220	1.0217	1.0213

Table 12-1. Section I (*Continued*)
Expansion Factors—Flange Taps—Y_2
Static Pressure Taken from Downstream Tap

$\dfrac{h_w}{p_{f2}}$ Ratio	$\beta = \dfrac{d}{D}$ Ratio												
	.63	.64	.65	.66	.67	.68	.69	.70	.71	.72	.73	.74	.75
0.0	1.0000	1.0000	1.0000	1.0000	1.0000	1.0000	1.0000	1.0000	1.0000	1.0000	1.0000	1.0000	1.0000
0.1	1.0005	1.0005	1.0005	1.0005	1.0005	1.0005	1.0004	1.0004	1.0004	1.0004	1.0004	1.0004	1.0004
0.2	1.0010	1.0010	1.0010	1.0010	1.0010	1.0009	1.0009	1.0009	1.0008	1.0008	1.0008	1.0008	1.0007
0.3	1.0016	1.0015	1.0015	1.0015	1.0014	1.0014	1.0014	1.0013	1.0013	1.0012	1.0012	1.0011	1.0011
0.4	1.0021	1.0021	1.0020	1.0020	1.0019	1.0019	1.0018	1.0018	1.0017	1.0017	1.0016	1.0015	1.0015
0.5	1.0026	1.0026	1.0025	1.0025	1.0024	1.0024	1.0023	1.0022	1.0022	1.0021	1.0020	1.0019	1.0019
0.6	1.0031	1.0030	1.0030	1.0029	1.0028	1.0027	1.0027	1.0026	1.0025	1.0024	1.0023	1.0022	1.0022
0.7	1.0036	1.0036	1.0035	1.0034	1.0033	1.0032	1.0031	1.0031	1.0030	1.0029	1.0028	1.0026	1.0025
0.8	1.0042	1.0041	1.0040	1.0039	1.0038	1.0037	1.0036	1.0035	1.0034	1.0033	1.0032	1.0031	1.0029
0.9	1.0047	1.0046	1.0045	1.0043	1.0042	1.0041	1.0040	1.0039	1.0039	1.0037	1.0036	1.0035	1.0033
1.0	1.0052	1.0051	1.0050	1.0049	1.0048	1.0046	1.0045	1.0044	1.0043	1.0041	1.0040	1.0039	1.0037
1.1	1.0057	1.0056	1.0055	1.0054	1.0053	1.0051	1.0050	1.0049	1.0047	1.0046	1.0044	1.0042	1.0040
1.2	1.0062	1.0061	1.0060	1.0059	1.0057	1.0056	1.0054	1.0053	1.0051	1.0050	1.0048	1.0046	1.0044
1.3	1.0067	1.0066	1.0065	1.0064	1.0062	1.0061	1.0059	1.0058	1.0056	1.0054	1.0052	1.0050	1.0048
1.4	1.0073	1.0072	1.0070	1.0069	1.0067	1.0065	1.0063	1.0062	1.0060	1.0058	1.0056	1.0054	1.0052
1.5	1.0078	1.0077	1.0075	1.0074	1.0072	1.0070	1.0068	1.0067	1.0065	1.0063	1.0060	1.0058	1.0056
1.6	1.0083	1.0081	1.0080	1.0078	1.0076	1.0075	1.0073	1.0071	1.0069	1.0066	1.0064	1.0062	1.0059
1.7	1.0089	1.0087	1.0086	1.0084	1.0082	1.0080	1.0078	1.0076	1.0074	1.0071	1.0069	1.0066	1.0064
1.8	1.0094	1.0092	1.0091	1.0089	1.0087	1.0084	1.0082	1.0080	1.0078	1.0075	1.0073	1.0070	1.0067
1.9	1.0099	1.0097	1.0095	1.0093	1.0091	1.0089	1.0087	1.0084	1.0082	1.0079	1.0077	1.0074	1.0071
2.0	1.0104	1.0102	1.0100	1.0098	1.0096	1.0094	1.0092	1.0089	1.0087	1.0084	1.0081	1.0078	1.0075
2.1	1.0110	1.0108	1.0105	1.0103	1.0101	1.0099	1.0096	1.0094	1.0091	1.0088	1.0085	1.0082	1.0079
2.2	1.0116	1.0114	1.0111	1.0109	1.0107	1.0104	1.0101	1.0098	1.0095	1.0094	1.0089	1.0086	1.0083
2.3	1.0121	1.0119	1.0116	1.0114	1.0111	1.0109	1.0106	1.0103	1.0100	1.0097	1.0093	1.0090	1.0086
2.4	1.0126	1.0124	1.0121	1.0119	1.0116	1.0114	1.0111	1.0108	1.0105	1.0102	1.0098	1.0095	1.0091
2.5	1.0131	1.0128	1.0126	1.0123	1.0120	1.0118	1.0115	1.0112	1.0109	1.0106	1.0102	1.0098	1.0094
2.6	1.0136	1.0134	1.0131	1.0128	1.0125	1.0123	1.0120	1.0116	1.0113	1.0110	1.0106	1.0102	1.0099
2.7	1.0143	1.0141	1.0138	1.0135	1.0132	1.0129	1.0126	1.0123	1.0119	1.0115	1.0111	1.0107	1.0103
2.8	1.0147	1.0144	1.0141	1.0139	1.0136	1.0132	1.0129	1.0126	1.0122	1.0118	1.0114	1.0110	1.0106
2.9	1.0152	1.0150	1.0147	1.0144	1.0141	1.0137	1.0134	1.0130	1.0127	1.0123	1.0119	1.0114	1.0110
3.0	1.0157	1.0155	1.0152	1.0149	1.0146	1.0142	1.0139	1.0135	1.0131	1.0127	1.0123	1.0119	1.0114
3.1	1.0163	1.0160	1.0157	1.0153	1.0150	1.0147	1.0143	1.0139	1.0135	1.0131	1.0127	1.0123	1.0118
3.2	1.0168	1.0165	1.0162	1.0158	1.0155	1.0152	1.0148	1.0144	1.0140	1.0136	1.0131	1.0127	1.0122
3.3	1.0173	1.0170	1.0166	1.0163	1.0159	1.0156	1.0152	1.0148	1.0144	1.0139	1.0135	1.0130	1.0125
3.4	1.0179	1.0175	1.0172	1.0169	1.0165	1.0161	1.0157	1.0153	1.0149	1.0144	1.0139	1.0135	1.0129
3.5	1.0183	1.0180	1.0177	1.0173	1.0169	1.0165	1.0161	1.0157	1.0153	1.0148	1.0143	1.0139	1.0133
3.6	1.0188	1.0185	1.0182	1.0178	1.0174	1.0170	1.0166	1.0162	1.0158	1.0153	1.0148	1.0143	1.0138
3.7	1.0193	1.0190	1.0187	1.0183	1.0179	1.0175	1.0171	1.0166	1.0162	1.0157	1.0152	1.0146	1.0141
3.8	1.0199	1.0196	1.0192	1.0189	1.0185	1.0180	1.0176	1.0171	1.0167	1.0162	1.0156	1.0151	1.0145
3.9	1.0205	1.0201	1.0197	1.0193	1.0189	1.0185	1.0180	1.0176	1.0171	1.0166	1.0160	1.0155	1.0149
4.0	1.0210	1.0206	1.0202	1.0198	1.0194	1.0190	1.0185	1.0180	1.0175	1.0170	1.0164	1.0159	1.0153

Table 12-1. Section II
Pressure-base Factors—F_{pb}

$$F_{pb} = 14.73 \div \text{base pressure, psia}$$

Pressure base, psia	Factor Fpb	Pressure base, psia	Factor Fpb
14.4.....................	1.0229	15.2 (8 oz. above 14.7).....	0.9691
14.65 (4 oz. above 14.4)....	1.0055	15.325 (10 oz. above 14.7)..	0.9612
14.73.....................	1.0000	15.4 (1 psi above 14.4).....	0.9565
14.9 (8 oz. above 14.4).....	0.9886	15.7 (1 psi above 14.7).....	0.9382
14.95 (4 oz. above 14.7)....	0.9853	16.4 (2 psi above 14.4).....	0.8982
15.025 (10 oz. above 14.4)..	0.9804	16.7 (2 psi above 14.7).....	0.8820

Temperature-base Factors—F_{tb}

$$F_{tb} = \frac{460 + \text{temperature base } °F}{520}$$

Temperature base °F	Factor F_{tb}	Temperature base °F	Factor F_{tb}	Temperature base °F	Factor F_{tb}
45	0.9712	65	1.0096	85	1.0481
50	0.9808	70	1.0192	90	1.0577
55	0.9904	75	1.0288	95	1.0673
60	1.0000	80	1.0385	100	1.0769

Specific-gravity Factors—F_g

$$F_g = \sqrt{\frac{1.0000}{G}}$$

Specific gravity G	Factor F_g	Specific gravity G	Factor F_g	Specific gravity G	Factor F_g	Specific gravity G	Factor F_g
0.500	1.4142	0.675	1.2172	0.850	1.0847	1.05	0.9759
0.505	1.4072	0.680	1.2127	0.855	1.0815	1.06	0.9713
0.510	1.4003	0.685	1.2082	0.860	1.0783	1.07	0.9667
0.515	1.3935	0.690	1.2039	0.865	1.0752	1.08	0.9623
0.520	1.3868	0.695	1.1995	0.870	1.0721	1.09	0.9578
0.525	1.3801	0.700	1.1952	0.875	1.0690	1.10	0.9535
0.530	1.3736	0.705	1.1910	0.880	1.0660	1.11	0.9492
0.535	1.3672	0.710	1.1868	0.885	1.0630	1.12	0.9449
0.540	1.3608	0.715	1.1826	0.890	1.0600	1.13	0.9407
0.545	1.3546	0.720	1.1785	0.895	1.0570	1.14	0.9366
0.550	1.3484	0.725	1.1744	0.900	1.0541	1.15	0.9325
0.555	1.3423	0.730	1.1704	0.905	1.0512	1.16	0.9285
0.560	1.3363	0.735	1.1664	0.910	1.0483	1.17	0.9245
0.565	1.3304	0.740	1.1625	0.915	1.0454	1.18	0.9206
0.570	1.3245	0.745	1.1586	0.920	1.0426	1.19	0.9167
0.575	1.3188	0.750	1.1547	0.925	1.0398	1.20	0.9129
0.580	1.3131	0.755	1.1509	0.930	1.0370	1.21	0.9091
0.585	1.3074	0.760	1.1471	0.935	1.0342	1.22	0.9054
0.590	1.3019	0.765	1.1433	0.940	1.0314	1.23	0.9017
0.595	1.2964	0.770	1.1396	0.945	1.0287	1.24	0.8980
0.600	1.2910	0.775	1.1359	0.950	1.0260	1.25	0.8944
0.605	1.2856	0.780	1.1323	0.955	1.0233	1.26	0.8909
0.610	1.2804	0.785	1.1287	0.960	1.0206	1.27	0.8874
0.615	1.2752	0.790	1.1251	0.965	1.0180	1.28	0.8839
0.620	1.2700	0.795	1.1215	0.970	1.0153	1.29	0.8805
0.625	1.2649	0.800	1.1180	0.975	1.0127	1.30	0.8771
0.630	1.2599	0.805	1.1146	0.980	1.0102	1.31	0.8737
0.635	1.2549	0.810	1.1111	0.985	1.0076	1.32	0.8704
0.640	1.2500	0.815	1.1077	0.990	1.0050	1.33	0.8671
0.645	1.2451	0.820	1.1043	0.995	1.0025	1.34	0.8639
0.650	1.2403	0.825	1.1010	1.00	1.0000	1.35	0.8607
0.655	1.2356	0.830	1.0976	1.01	0.9950	1.36	0.8575
0.660	1.2309	0.835	1.0944	1.02	0.9901	1.37	0.8544
0.665	1.2263	0.840	1.0911	1.03	0.9853	1.38	0.8513
0.670	1.2217	0.845	1.0879	1.04	0.9806	1.39	0.8482

Table 12-1. Section II (*Continued*)
Flowing-temperature Factors—F_{tf}

$$F_{tf} = \sqrt{\frac{520}{460 + \text{actual flowing temperature}}}$$

°F.	Factor	°F.	Factor	°F.	Factor	°F.	Factor	°F.	Factor	°F.	Factor
1	1.0621	21	1.0398	41	1.0188	61	0.9990	81	0.9804	110	0.9551
2	1.0609	22	1.0387	42	1.0178	62	0.9981	82	0.9795	120	0.9469
3	1.0598	23	1.0376	43	1.0168	63	0.9971	83	0.9786	130	0.9388
4	1.0586	24	1.0365	44	1.0157	64	0.9962	84	0.9777	140	0.9309
5	1.0575	25	1.0355	45	1.0147	65	0.9952	85	0.9768	150	0.9233
6	1.0564	26	1.0344	46	1.0137	66	0.9943	86	0.9759	160	0.9158
7	1.0552	27	1.0333	47	1.0127	67	0.9933	87	0.9750	170	0.9085
8	1.0541	28	1.0323	48	1.0117	68	0.9924	88	0.9741	180	0.9014
9	1.0530	29	1.0312	49	1.0107	69	0.9915	89	0.9732	190	0.8944
10	1.0518	30	1.0302	50	1.0098	70	0.9905	90	0.9723	200	0.8876
11	1.0507	31	1.0291	51	1.0088	71	0.9896	91	0.9715	210	0.8810
12	1.0496	32	1.0281	52	1.0078	72	0.9887	92	0.9706	220	0.8745
13	1.0485	33	1.0270	53	1.0068	73	0.9877	93	0.9697	230	0.8681
14	1.0474	34	1.0260	54	1.0058	74	0.9868	94	0.9688	240	0.8619
15	1.0463	35	1.0249	55	1.0048	75	0.9859	95	0.9680	250	0.8558
16	1.0452	36	1.0239	56	1.0039	76	0.9850	96	0.9671	260	0.8498
17	1.0441	37	1.0229	57	1.0029	77	0.9840	97	0.9662	270	0.8440
18	1.0430	38	1.0219	58	1.0019	78	0.9831	98	0.9653	280	0.8383
19	1.0419	39	1.0208	59	1.0010	79	0.9822	99	0.9645	290	0.8327
20	1.0408	40	1.0198	60	1.0000	80	0.9813	100	0.9636	300	0.8272

Manometer Factors (Mercury Meters)—F_m

Specific Gravity, G	Flowing Pressure, psig						
	0	500	1000	1500	2000	2500	3000
	Ambient Temperature = 0°F						
.55	1.0000	.9989	.9976	.9960	.9943	.9930	.9921
.60	1.0000	.9988	.9972	.9952	.9932	.9919	.9910
.65	1.0000	.9987	.9967	.9941	.9920	.9908	.9900
.70	1.0000	.9985	.9961	.9927	.9907	.9896	.9890
.75	1.0000	....	....	....	....	....	....
	Ambient Temperature = 40°F						
.55	1.0000	.9990	.9979	.9967	.9954	.9942	.9932
.60	1.0000	.9989	.9976	.9962	.9946	.9933	.9923
.65	1.0000	.9988	.9973	.9955	.9937	.9923	.9913
.70	1.0000	.9987	.9970	.9947	.9926	.9912	.9903
.75	1.0000	.9986	.9965	.9937	.9915	.9902	.9893
	Ambient Temperature = 80°F						
.55	1.0000	.9991	.9981	.9971	.9960	.9950	.9941
.60	1.0000	.9990	.9979	.9967	.9955	.9943	.9933
.65	1.0000	.9989	.9977	.9963	.9948	.9935	.9925
.70	1.0000	.9988	.9974	.9958	.9940	.9926	.9915
.75	1.0000	.9987	.9971	.9951	.9931	.9916	.9906
	Ambient Temperature = 120°F						
.55	1.0000	.9992	.9983	.9974	.9965	.9956	.9948
.60	1.0000	.9991	.9981	.9971	.9960	.9950	.9941
.65	1.0000	.9990	.9979	.9967	.9955	.9944	.9934
.70	1.0000	.9989	.9977	.9963	.9950	.9937	.9926
.75	1.0000	.9988	.9975	.9959	.9943	.9929	.9918

Table 12-1. Section III
Pipe Taps—Basic Orifice Factors—F_b

Orifice Diam., d, Inches	Internal Diameter of Pipe, D, Inches								
	2			3				4	
	1.689	1.939	2.067	2.300	2.626	2.900	3.068	3.152	3.438
.250	12.850	12.813	12.800	12.782	12.765	12.753	12.748	12.745	12.737
.375	29.359	29.097	29.005	28.882	28.771	28.710	28.682	28.669	28.634
.500	53.703	52.816	52.481	52.019	51.591	51.353	51.243	51.196	51.064
.625	87.212	84.919	84.083	82.922	81.795	81.142	80.835	80.703	80.332
.750	132.23	126.86	124.99	122.45	120.06	118.67	118.00	117.70	116.86
.875	192.74	181.02	177.08	171.92	167.23	164.58	163.31	162.76	161.17
1.000	275.45	251.10	243.27	233.30	224.56	219.76	217.52	216.55	213.79
1.125	391.93	342.98	327.98	309.43	293.79	285.48	281.66	280.02	275.42
1.250	....	465.99	437.99	404.52	377.36	363.41	357.12	354.45	347.03
1.375	....	....	583.96	524.68	478.68	455.82	445.74	441.48	429.83
1.500	....	....	....	679.10	602.45	565.79	549.94	543.31	525.40
1.625	....	....	....	....	755.34	697.43	672.95	662.81	635.76
1.750	....	....	....	....	946.99	856.37	819.05	803.77	763.51
1.875	....	....	....	....	....	1050.4	993.98	971.19	911.98
2.000	....	....	....	....	....	1290.7	1205.6	1171.8	1085.5
2.125	....	....	....	....	....	....	1465.1	1415.0	1289.7
2.250	....	....	....	....	....	....	....	....	1532.0
2.375	....	....	....	....	....	....	....	....	1822.8

Orifice Diam., d, Inches	Internal Diameter of Pipe, D, Inches								
	4		6				8		
	3.826	4.026	4.897	5.189	5.761	6.065	7.625	7.981	8.071
.250	12.727	12.722	·....	....	....	....	....	....	....
.375	28.598	28.584	·....	....	....	....	....	....	....
.500	50.936	50.886	50.739	50.705	50.652	50.628	....	....	....
.625	79.974	79.835	79.436	79.349	79.217	79.162	....	....	....
.750	116.05	115.73	114.81	114.61	114.32	114.20	....	....	....
.875	159.57	158.94	157.11	156.71	156.13	155.89	155.10	154.99	154.96
1.000	211.03	209.91	206.62	205.91	204.84	204.41	203.00	202.80	202.75
1.125	270.90	269.10	263.71	262.51	260.71	259.98	257.62	257.28	257.20
1.250	339.87	337.05	328.73	326.85	324.02	322.86	319.10	318.56	318.44
1.375	418.79	414.51	402.06	399.30	395.08	393.33	387.62	386.81	386.62
1.500	508.76	502.38	484.20	480.23	474.20	471.69	463.39	462.19	461.92
1.625	611.11	601.80	575.73	570.14	561.73	558.24	546.61	544.92	544.53
1.750	727.54	714.16	677.38	669.63	658.08	653.33	637.51	.635.19	634.65
1.875	860.17	841.19	789.99	779.40	763.77	757.39	736.34	733.23	732.52
2.000	1011.7	985.04	914.57	900.28	879.38	870.93	843.34	839.29	838.35
2.125	1185.3	1148.4	1052.3	1033.2	1005.6	994.52	958.78	953.58	952.38
2.250	1385.4	1334.4	1204.7	1179.4	1143.2	1128.8	1083.0	1076.4	1074.9
2.375	1617.2	1547.3	1373.4	1340.2	1293.1	1274.6	1216.3	1208.0	1206.1
2.500	1887.6	1792.3	1560.5	1517.2	1456.4	1432.7	1359.2	1348.8	1346.5
2.625	2206.0	2075.9	1768.3	1712.3	1634.3	1604.3	1512.0	1499.2	1496.3
2.750	....	2407.0	1999.8	1927.6	1828.3	1790.3	1675.4	1659.7	1656.1
2.875	....	....	2258.5	2165.9	2039.9	1992.2	1849.9	1830.6	1826.3
3.000	....	....	2548.6	2430.2	2271.2	2211.6	2036.0	2012.7	2007.3
3.125	....	....	2875.2	2724.4	2524.3	2450.1	2234.7	2206.4	2199.9
3.250	....	....	3244.8	3052.8	2801.8	2709.9	2446.5	2412.4	2404.7
3.375	....	....	3665.6	3420.9	3106.9	2993.3	2672.5	2631.6	2622.3
3.500	....	....	....	3835.7	3443.0	3303.0	2913.7	2864.7	2853.7
3.625	....	....	....	4305.7	3814.4	3642.3	3171.1	3112.7	3099.6
3.750	....	....	....	....	4226.3	4014.8	3446.0	3376.6	3361.0
3.875	....	....	....	....	4684.9	4425.1	3739.9	3657.6	3639.2
4.000	....	....	....	....	5197.7	4878.4	4054.2	3957.0	3935.2
4.250	....	....	....	....	....	....	4751.4	4616.6	4586.6
4.500	....	....	....	....	....	....	5554.7	5369.0	5327.9
4.750	....	....	....	....	....	....	6485.3	6231.1	6175.2
5.000	....	....	....	....	....	....	7571.4	7224.3	7148.7
5.250	....	....	....	....	....	....	8850.3	8376.3	8274.0
5.500	....	....	....	....	....	....	....	9723.8	9585.1

Table 12-1. Section III (*Continued*)
Pipe Taps—Basic Orifice Factors—F_b

Orifice Diam., d, Inches	Internal Diameter of Pipe, D, Inches								
	10			12			16		
	9.564	10.020	10.136	11.376	11.938	12.090	14.688	15.000	15.250
1.000	202.16	....	....	....	....	....	....	....	....
1.125	256.22	256.01	255.96	....	....	....	....	....	....
1.250	316.90	316.56	316.49	315.84	315.57	315.51	....	....	....
1.375	384.29	383.79	383.68	382.66	382.30	382.22	....	....	....
1.500	458.52	457.79	457.63	456.16	455.64	455.52	453.92	453.78	....
1.625	539.72	538.69	538.45	536.38	535.66	535.48	533.27	533.07	532.93
1.750	628.03	626.61	626.29	623.44	622.45	622.20	619.18	618.92	618.73
1.875	723.61	721.70	721.27	717.43	716.10	715.78	711.73	711.39	711.13
2.000	826.63	824.12	823.54	818.48	816.73	816.30	810.99	810.53	810.19
2.125	937.28	934.02	933.27	926.72	924.44	923.88	917.01	916.43	915.99
2.250	1055.7	1051.6	1050.6	1042.3	1039.4	1038.7	1029.9	1092.6	1028.6
2.375	1182.2	1177.0	1175.8	1165.3	1161.6	1160.7	1149.7	1148.8	1148.1
2.500	1316.9	1310.5	1309.0	1295.9	1291.4	1290.2	1276.5	1275.4	1274.5
2.625	1460.0	1452.1	1450.3	1434.3	1428.7	1427.4	1410.5	1409.1	1408.0
2.750	1611.8	1602.3	1600.1	1580.7	1573.9	1572.2	1551.7	1549.9	1548.6
2.875	1772.5	1761.0	1758.4	1735.1	1726.9	1724.9	1700.1	1698.1	1696.5
3.000	1942.5	1928.8	1925.6	1897.8	1888.1	1885.7	1856.1	1853.6	1851.7
3.125	2122.1	2105.7	2102.0	2069.0	2057.5	2054.7	2019.5	2016.6	2014.3
3.250	2311.6	2292.2	2287.8	2248.9	2235.4	2232.1	2190.7	2187.2	2184.5
3.375	2511.5	2488.6	2483.4	2437.7	2421.8	2418.0	2369.6	2365.5	2362.4
3.500	2722.3	2695.3	2689.1	2635.6	2617.2	2612.6	2556.5	2551.7	2548.1
3.625	2944.3	2912.7	2905.5	2843.0	2821.6	2816.3	2751.4	2745.9	2741.7
3.750	3178.1	3141.2	3132.7	3060.2	3035.3	3029.3	2954.5	2948.1	2943.3
3.875	3424.3	3381.3	3371.5	3287.4	3258.7	3251.7	3165.9	3158.6	3153.1
4.000	3683.5	3633.5	3622.1	3524.9	3492.0	3483.9	3385.8	3377.5	3371.2
4.250	4243.8	4176.8	4161.6	4032.8	3989.5	3979.0	3851.6	3840.9	3832.8
4.500	4865.1	4776.2	4756.1	4587.1	4530.8	4517.2	4353.4	4339.8	4329.6
4.750	5554.9	5437.9	5411.5	5191.5	5119.0	5101.5	4892.9	4875.8	4862.9
5.000	6322.2	6169.2	6134.9	5850.6	5757.8	5735.4	5471.9	5450.5	5434.3
5.250	7177.7	6978.9	6934.4	6569.4	6451.5	6423.2	6092.5	6065.9	6045.9
5.500	8134.1	7877.2	7820.0	7354.1	7205.1	7169.5	6757.0	6724.1	6699.4
5.750	9207.0	8876.3	8803.1	8211.4	8024.2	7979.6	7468.0	7427.6	7397.4
6.000	10415	9991.2	9897.8	9149.5	8915.4	8859.8	8228.5	8179.2	8142.3
6.250	11783	11240	11121	10178	9886.1	9817.2	9041.6	8981.7	8937.0
6.500	13340	12644	12492	11307	10945	10860	9911.2	9838.7	9784.7
6.750	....	14230	14038	12550	12103	11998	10841	10754	10689
7.000	....	16035	15790	13923	13371	13242	11837	11732	11654
7.250	....	....	....	15442	14762	14604	12902	12777	12684
7.500	....	....	....	17131	16294	16101	14044	13894	13783
7.750	....	....	....	19017	17986	17750	15268	15090	14959
8.000	....	....	....	....	19861	19572	16583	16371	16216
8.250	....	....	....	....	21947	21593	17996	17746	17561
8.500	....	....	....	....	....	....	19517	19221	19003
8.750	....	....	....	....	....	....	21156	20807	20551
9.000	....	....	....	....	....	....	22926	22515	22214
9.250	....	....	....	....	....	....	24841	24356	24003
9.500	....	....	....	....	....	....	26917	26346	25932
9.750	....	....	....	....	....	....	29172	28501	28014
10.000	....	....	....	....	....	....	31629	30839	30268
10.250	....	....	....	....	....	....	34315	33383	32713
10.500	....	....	....	....	....	....	....	36160	35372

Table 12-1. Section III *(Continued)*
Pipe Taps—Basic Orifice Factors—F_b

Orifice Diam., d, Inches	Internal Diameter of Pipe, D, Inches								
	20			24			30		
	18.814	19.000	19.250	22.626	23.000	23.250	28.628	29.000	29.250
2.000	806.71	806.57	806.40	....	....	....	....	....	....
2.125	911.51	911.35	911.13	....	....	....	....	....	....
2.250	1022.9	1022.7	1022.4	....	....	....	....	....	....
2.375	1141.0	1140.7	1140.4	1136.8	1136.5	1136.3	....	....	....
2.500	1265.7	1265.4	1265.0	1260.6	1260.2	1259.9	....	....	....
2.625	1397.2	1396.8	1396.3	1390.9	1390.5	1390.2	....	....	....
2.750	1535.5	1535.0	1534.4	1527.9	1527.3	1527.0	....	....	....
2.875	1680.7	1680.1	1679.3	1671.5	1670.9	1670.4	1663.8	....	....
3.000	1832.7	1832.1	1831.2	1821.9	1821.1	1820.6	1812.7	1812.3	1812.0
3.125	1991.8	1991.0	1990.0	1978.9	1978.0	1977.4	1968.1	1967.7	1967.4
3.250	2158.0	2157.0	2155.8	2142.8	2141.7	2141.0	2130.2	2129.6	2129.3
3.375	2331.3	2330.2	2328.7	2313.5	2312.3	2311.5	2298.8	2298.2	2297.7
3.500	2511.9	2510.6	2508.8	2491.2	2489.7	2488.8	2474.1	2473.3	2472.9
3.625	2699.7	2698.2	2696.2	2675.8	2674.0	2673.0	2656.0	2655.2	2654.6
3.750	2895.0	2893.2	2890.9	2867.4	2865.4	2864.1	2844.6	2843.7	2843.0
3.875	3097.7	3095.7	3093.0	3066.0	3063.8	3062.3	3040.0	3038.9	3038.2
4.000	3308.0	3305.7	3302.7	3271.8	3269.2	3267.6	3242.2	3240.9	3240.1
4.250	3751.6	3748.7	3744.8	3705.0	3701.7	3699.6	3666.9	3665.3	3664.3
4.500	4226.8	4223.0	4218.1	4167.6	4163.4	4160.7	4119.3	4117.3	4116.0
4.750	4734.1	4729.4	4723.3	4660.0	4654.8	4651.4	4599.6	4597.1	4595.4
5.000	5274.6	5268.7	5261.1	5183.0	5176.4	5172.3	5108.2	5105.0	5103.0
5.250	5849.0	5841.9	5832.6	5737.1	5729.1	5723.9	5645.4	5641.6	5639.1
5.500	6458.6	6449.9	6438.7	6322.9	6313.2	6307.0	6211.8	6207.2	6204.2
5.750	7104.4	7094.0	7080.4	6941.3	6929.7	6922.2	6807.7	6802.1	6798.5
6.000	7787.9	7775.4	7759.1	7592.8	7579.0	7570.1	7433.6	7426.9	7422.6
6.250	8510.4	8495.4	8476.0	8278.3	8262.0	8251.5	8089.9	8082.0	8076.9
6.500	9273.4	9255.6	9232.5	8998.8	8979.5	8967.1	8777.2	8768.0	8761.9
6.750	10079	10058	10030	9755.0	9732.4	9717.9	9496.0	9485.2	9478.1
7.000	10928	10903	10871	10548	10522	10505	10247	10234	10226
7.250	11823	11794	11756	11379	11348	11329	11030	11016	11006
7.500	12767	12733	12689	12249	12214	12191	11847	11830	11819
7.750	13762	13722	13670	13160	13119	13093	12697	12678	12665
8.000	14810	14763	14703	14113	14065	14035	13582	13560	13546
8.250	15914	15860	15791	15109	15054	15020	14501	14477	14461
8.500	17073	17015	16935	16150	16087	16048	15457	15429	15411
8.750	18305	18232	18139	17237	17166	17121	16450	16418	16397
9.000	19598	19515	19408	18373	18292	18241	17480	17444	17421
9.250	20963	20866	20743	19560	19468	19409	18548	18508	18482
9.500	22402	22292	22151	20800	20695	20628	19656	19611	19582
9.750	23923	23796	23634	22094	21976	21900	20805	20754	20721
10.000	25529	25384	25198	23447	23312	23227	21995	21938	21901
10.250	27227	27061	26849	24859	24708	24612	23228	23165	23124
10.500	29023	28834	28592	26335	26164	26056	24505	24434	24388
10.750	30925	30709	30434	27878	27685	27563	25827	25749	25698
11.000	32940	32694	32381	29490	29273	29136	27196	27109	27052
11.250	35078	34798	34443	31175	30932	30779	28613	28516	28453
11.500	37348	37030	36626	32938	32666	32494	30080	29972	29903
11.750	39761	39400	38941	34783	34478	34285	31598	31479	31402
12.000	42330	41920	41399	36714	36373	36158	33169	33038	32953
12.500	47991	47461	46790	40855	40429	40161	36478	36318	36215
13.000	54463	53778	52914	45406	44877	44544	40024	39829	39704
13.500	....	....	....	50420	49763	49352	43823	43589	43437
14.000	....	....	....	55959	55147	54638	47898	47615	47433
14.500	....	....	....	62099	61094	60468	52271	51932	51714
15.000	....	....	....	68929	67687	66915	56967	56562	56301
15.500	....	....	....	76562	75025	74074	62017	61593	61223
16.000	....	....	....	....	83231	82055	67453	66878	66509
16.500	....	....	....	....	....	....	73314	72630	72193
17.000	....	....	....	....	....	....	79641	78831	78313
17.500	....	....	....	....	....	....	86485	85525	84913
18.000	....	....	....	....	....	....	93900	92765	92042
18.500	....	....	....	....	....	....	101950	100610	99758
19.000	....	....	....	....	....	....	110720	109130	108130
19.500	....	....	....	....	....	....	120300	118420	117230
20.000	....	....	....	....	....	....	130780	128560	127150

Table 12-1. Section III (Continued)
"b" Values for Reynolds-number Factor, F_r,—Pipe Taps

$$F_r = 1 + \frac{b}{\sqrt{h_w p_f}}$$

Orifice Diam., d, Inches	Internal Diameter of Pipe, D, Inches								
	2			3				4	
	1.689	1.939	2.067	2.300	2.626	2.900	3.068	3.152	3.438
.250	.1105	.1091	.1087	.1081	....	....	....	....	....
.375	.0890	.0878	.0877	.0879	.0888	.0898	.0905	.0908	.0918
.500	.0758	.0734	.0729	.0728	.0737	.0750	.0758	.0763	.0778
.625	.0693	.0647	:0635	.0624	.0624	.0634	.0642	.0646	.0662
.750	.0675	.0608	.0586	.0559	.0546	.0548	.0552	.0555	.0568
.875	.0684	.0602	.0570	.0528	.0497	.0488	.0488	.0489	.0496
1.000	.0702	.0614	.0576	.0522	.0473	.0452	.0445	.0443	.0443
1.125	.0708	.0635	.0595	.0532	.0469	.0435	.0422	.0417	.0407
1.250	....	.0650	.0616	.0552	.0478	.0434	.0414	.0406	.0387
1.375	....	....	.0629	.0574	.0496	.0443	.0418	.0408	.0379
1.500	....	....	....	.0590	.0518	.0460	.0431	.0418	.0382
1.625	....	....	....	....	.0539	.0482	.0450	.0435	.0392
1.750	....	....	....	....	.0553	.0504	.0471	.0456	.0408
1.875	....	....	....	....	....	.0521	.0492	.0477	.0427
2.000	....	....	....	....	....	.0532	.0508	.0495	.0448
2.125	....	....	....	....	....	....	.0519	.0509	.0467
2.250	....	....	....	....	....	....	....	....	.0483
2.375	....	....	....	....	....	....	....	....	.0494

Orifice Diam., d, Inches	Internal Diameter of Pipe, D, Inches								
	4		6				8		
	3.826	4.026	4.897	5.189	5.761	6.065	7.625	7.981	8.071
.500	.0799	.0810	.0850	....	....	....	....	....	....
.625	.0685	.0697	.0747	.0762	.0789	.0802	....	....	....
.750	.0590	.0602	.0655	.0672	.0703	.0718	....	....	....
.875	.0513	.0524	.0575	.0592	.0625	.0642	.0716	.0730	.0733
1.000	.0453	.0461	.0506	.0523	.0556	.0573	.0652	.0668	.0662
1.125	.0408	.0412	.0448	.0464	.0495	.0512	.0592	.0609	.0613
1.250	.0376	.0377	.0401	.0413	.0442	.0458	.0538	.0555	.0560
1.375	.0358	.0353	.0363	.0373	.0397	.0412	.0489	.0506	.0510
1.500	.0350	.0340	.0334	.0340	.0360	.0372	.0445	.0462	.0466
1.625	.0351	.0336	:0313	.0315	.0329	.0339	.0404	.0421	.0425
1.750	.0358	.0340	.0300	.0298	.0304	.0311	.0369	.0384	.0388
1.875	.0371	.0349	.0293	.0287	.0285	.0290	.0338	.0352	.0355
2.000	.0388	.0363	.0292	.0281	.0273	.0273	.0311	.0323	.0327
2.125	.0407	.0380	.0297	.0281	.0265	.0262	.0288	.0298	.0301
2.250	.0427	.0398	.0305	.0285	.0261	.0258	.0268	.0277	.0280
2.375	.0445	.0417	.0316	.0293	.0262	.0253	.0252	.0259	.0261
2.500	.0460	.0435	.0330	.0304	.0267	.0254	.0239	.0244	.0246
2.625	.0472	.0450	.0345	.0317	.0274	.0258	.0230	.0232	.0233
2.750	....	.0462	.0362	.0331	.0284	.0265	.0224	.0224	.0224
2.875	....	....	.0379	.0347	.0295	.0274	.0220	.0218	.0218
3.000	....	....	.0395	.0364	.0308	.0285	.0219	.0214	.0213
3.125	....	....	.0410	.0380	.0323	.0297	.0220	.0213	.0211
3.250	....	....	.0422	.0394	.0338	.0311	.0223	.0214	.0212
3.375	....	....	.0432	.0408	.0353	.0325	.0228	.0216	.0214
3.500	....	....	....	.0419	.0367	.0339	.0235	.0221	.0218
3.625	....	....	....	.0428	.0381	.0354	.0243	.0227	.0224
3.750	....	....	....	....	.0393	.0367	.0252	.0234	.0230
3.875	....	....	....	....	.0404	.0380	.0262	.0243	.0238
4.000	....	....	....	....	.0413	.0391	.0273	.0252	.0246
4.250	....	....	....	....	....	....	.0296	.0273	.0268
4.500	....	....	....	....	....	....	.0321	.0296	.0290
4.750	....	....	....	....	....	....	.0344	.0320	.0314
5.000	....	....	....	....	....	....	.0364	.0342	.0336
5.250	....	....	....	....	....	....	.0381	.0361	.0356
5.500	....	....	....	....	....	....	....	.0377	.0372

Table 12-1. Section III *(Continued)*
"b" Values for Reynolds-number Factor, F_r,—Pipe Taps

$$F_r = 1 + \frac{b}{\sqrt{h_w p_f}}$$

Orifice Diam., d, Inches	Internal Diameter of Pipe, D, Inches								
	10			12			16		
	9.564	10.020	10.136	11.376	11.938	12.090	14.688	15.000	15.250
1.000	.0728	....	....	....	....	....	....	....	....
1.125	.0674	.0690	.0694	....	....	....	....	....	....
1.250	.0624	.0641	.0646	.0687	.0704	.0708	....	....	....
1.375	.0576	.0594	.0599	.0643	.0661	.0666	....	....	....
1.500	.0532	.0550	.0555	.0601	.0620	.0625	.0697	.0705	....
1.625	.0490	.0509	.0514	.0561	.0580	.0585	.0662	.0670	.0676
1.750	.0452	.0471	.0476	.0523	.0543	.0548	.0628	.0636	.0642
1.875	.0417	.0436	.0440	.0488	.0508	.0513	.0594	.0603	.0610
2.000	.0385	.0403	.0407	.0454	.0475	.0480	.0563	.0572	.0578
2.125	.0355	.0372	.0377	.0423	.0443	.0449	.0532	.0541	.0548
2.250	.0329	.0345	.0349	.0394	.0414	.0419	.0503	.0512	.0519
2.375	.0305	.0320	.0324	.0367	.0387	.0392	.0475	.0484	.0492
2.500	.0283	.0298	.0301	.0342	.0361	.0366	.0449	.0458	.0466
2.625	.0265	.0277	.0281	.0319	.0337	.0342	.0424	.0433	.0440
2.750	.0248	.0260	.0262	.0298	.0316	.0320	.0400	.0409	.0417
2.875	.0234	.0244	.0246	.0279	.0295	.0300	.0378	.0387	.0394
3.000	.0222	.0230	.0232	.0262	.0277	.0281	.0356	.0365	.0372
3.125	.0212	.0218	.0220	.0244	.0260	.0264	.0336	.0345	.0352
3.250	.0204	.0209	.0210	.0232	.0245	.0249	.0317	.0326	.0332
3.375	.0199	.0201	.0202	.0220	.0232	.0235	.0300	.0308	.0314
3.500	.0195	.0195	.0196	.0210	.0220	.0222	.0283	.0291	.0297
3.625	.0193	.0191	.0191	.0200	.0209	.0212	.0268	.0275	.0281
3.750	.0192	.0188	.0188	.0193	.0200	.0202	.0254	.0261	.0267
3.875	.0193	.0187	.0186	.0187	.0192	.0194	.0240	.0247	.0253
4.000	.0195	.0187	.0186	.0182	.0185	.0187	.0228	.0235	.0240
4.250	.0203	.0192	.0189	.0176	.0176	.0177	.0207	.0213	.0217
4.500	.0215	.0200	.0197	.0175	.0172	.0171	.0190	.0194	.0198
4.750	.0230	.0212	.0208	.0178	.0171	.0170	.0176	.0180	.0182
5.000	.0248	.0228	.0223	.0185	.0174	.0173	.0166	.0168	.0170
5.250	.0267	.0244	.0239	.0194	.0181	.0178	.0160	.0161	.0162
5.500	.0287	.0263	.0257	.0207	.0190	.0186	.0156	.0156	.0156
5.750	.0307	.0282	.0276	.0221	.0202	.0197	.0155	.0154	.0153
6.000	.0326	.0302	.0295	.0231	.0215	.0210	.0157	.0154	.0153
6.250	.0343	.0320	.0316	.0253	.0230	.0224	.0161	.0157	.0154
6.500	.0358	.0336	.0331	.0270	.0246	.0239	.0167	.0162	.0159
6.750	....	.0351	.0346	.0288	.0262	.0256	.0174	.0169	.0164
7.000	....	.0363	.0359	.0304	.0279	.0272	.0184	.0177	.0172
7.250	....	....	....	.0320	.0295	.0288	.0195	.0187	.0181
7.500	....	....	....	.0334	.0310	.0304	.0206	.0198	.0191
7.750	....	....	....	.0347	.0325	.0318	.0219	.0209	.0202
8.000	....	....	....	....	.0338	.0332	.0232	.0222	.0214
8.250	....	....	....	....	.0349	.0344	.0246	.0235	.0227
8.500	....	....	....	....	....	....	.0259	.0248	.0240
8.750	....	....	....	....	....	....	.0273	.0262	.0253
9.000	....	....	....	....	....	....	.0286	.0276	.0267
9.250	....	....	....	....	....	....	.0299	.0288	.0280
9.500	....	....	....	....	....	....	.0311	.0300	.0292
9.750	....	....	....	....	....	....	.0322	.0312	.0304
10.000	....	....	....	....	....	....	.0332	.0323	.0315
10.250	....	....	....	....	....	....	.0341	.0333	.0326
10.500	....	....	....	....	....	....	....	.0341	.0335

Table 12-1. Section III (Continued)
"b" Values for Reynolds-number Factor, F_r,—Pipe Taps

$$F_r = 1 + \frac{b}{\sqrt{h_w\, p_f}}$$

Orifice Diam., d, Inches	Internal Diameter of Pipe, D, Inches								
	20			24			30		
	18.814	19.000	19.250	22.626	23.000	23.250	28.628	29.000	29.250
2.000	.0663	.0667	.0672	....	....	....	....	....	....
2.125	.0635	.0639	.0644	....	....	....	....	....	....
2.250	.0609	.0613	.0618	....	....	....	....	....	....
2.375	.0583	.0588	.0593	.0658	.0665	.0669	....	....	....
2.500	.0558	.0562	.0568	.0635	.0642	.0646	....	....	....
2.625	.0534	.0539	.0544	.0613	.0620	.0624	....	....	....
2.750	.0510	.0515	.0520	.0591	.0598	.0603	....	....	....
2.875	.0488	.0492	.0498	.0570	.0577	.0582	.0667	....	....
3.000	.0466	.0470	.0476	.0549	.0556	.0561	.0649	.0654	.0657
3.125	.0445	.0449	.0455	.0529	.0536	.0541	.0630	.0636	.0639
3.250	.0425	.0429	.0435	.0509	.0516	.0521	.0613	.0616	.0622
3.375	.0406	.0410	.0416	.0490	.0497	.0502	.0595	.0601	.0604
3.500	.0387	.0391	.0397	.0471	.0479	.0484	.0578	.0584	.0587
3.625	.0369	.0373	.0379	.0454	.0461	.0466	.0561	.0567	.0571
3.750	.0352	.0356	.0362	.0436	.0444	.0449	.0545	.0550	.0554
3.875	.0336	.0340	.0346	.0419	.0427	.0432	.0528	.0534	.0538
4.000	.0320	.0324	.0330	.0403	.0411	.0416	.0513	.0518	.0522
4.250	.0291	.0295	.0301	.0372	.0380	.0385	.0482	.0488	.0492
4.500	.0265	.0269	.0274	.0343	.0351	.0356	.0453	.0459	.0463
4.750	.0242	.0246	.0250	.0316	.0324	.0328	.0425	.0431	.0435
5.000	.0221	.0225	.0229	.0292	.0299	.0303	.0399	.0405	.0409
5.250	.0203	.0206	.0210	.0269	.0276	.0280	.0374	.0380	.0384
5.500	.0188	.0190	.0194	.0248	.0255	.0259	.0350	.0356	.0360
5.750	.0175	.0177	.0180	.0230	.0236	.0240	.0328	.0334	.0338
6.000	.0164	.0165	.0168	.0212	.0218	.0222	.0307	.0313	.0317
6.250	.0155	.0156	.0158	.0197	.0202	.0206	.0287	.0293	.0297
6.500	.0148	.0149	.0150	.0184	.0189	.0192	.0269	.0274	.0278
6.750	.0143	.0144	.0145	.0172	.0176	.0179	.0252	.0257	.0260
7.000	.0141	.0141	.0141	.0162	.0166	.0168	.0236	.0241	.0244
7.250	.0140	.0140	.0139	.0153	.0156	.0158	.0221	.0226	.0229
7.500	.0140	.0140	.0139	.0146	.0148	.0150	.0207	.0212	.0215
7.750	.0142	.0141	.0140	.0140	.0142	.0144	.0195	.0199	.0202
8.000	.0146	.0144	.0142	.0136	.0138	.0138	.0183	.0187	.0190
8.250	.0151	.0148	.0146	.0133	.0134	.0132	.0173	.0177	.0179
8.500	.0156	.0154	.0151	.0132	.0132	.0130	.0164	.0167	.0169
8.750	.0163	.0160	.0157	.0131	.0130	.0130	.0155	.0158	.0161
9.000	.0171	.0168	.0163	.0131	.0130	.0130	.0148	.0151	.0153
9.250	.0180	.0176	.0171	.0133	.0131	.0130	.0142	.0144	.0146
9.500	.0189	.0185	.0180	.0136	.0133	.0132	.0136	.0138	.0140
9.750	.0198	.0194	.0189	.0139	.0136	.0134	.0132	.0133	.0134
10.000	.0209	.0204	.0198	.0143	.0140	.0138	.0128	.0129	.0130
10.250	.0219	.0214	.0208	.0148	.0144	.0142	.0125	.0126	.0127
10.500	.0230	.0225	.0219	.0154	.0150	.0147	.0123	.0124	.0124
10.750	.0241	.0236	.0229	.0160	.0155	.0152	.0122	.0122	.0122
11.000	.0252	.0247	.0240	.0168	.0162	.0158	.0121	.0121	.0121
11.250	.0263	.0261	.0251	.0175	.0169	.0165	.0122	.0121	.0121
11.500	.0273	.0268	.0262	.0183	.0176	.0172	.0122	.0121	.0122
11.750	.0284	.0278	.0272	.0191	.0184	.0180	.0124	.0123	.0122
12.000	.0293	.0288	.0282	.0200	.0192	.0190	.0126	.0124	.0123
12.500	.0312	.0307	.0301	.0218	.0210	.0204	.0132	.0130	.0128
13.000	.0327	.0323	.0318	.0236	.0228	.0222	.0140	.0137	.0135
13.500	....	....	....	.0254	.0246	.0240	.0150	.0146	.0143
14.000	....	....	....	.0272	.0264	.0258	.0161	.0156	.0153
14.500	....	....	....	.0289	.0280	.0275	.0173	.0168	.0165
15.000	....	....	....	.0304	.0296	.0291	.0186	.0181	.0177
15.500	....	....	....	.0318	.0311	.0306	.0200	.0194	.0190
16.000	....	....	....	....	.0323	.0318	.0215	.0209	.0204
16.500	....	....	....	....	....	....	.0230	.0223	.0219
17.000	....	....	....	....	....	....	.0244	.0238	.0233
17.500	....	....	....	....	....	....	.0259	.0252	.0248
18.000	....	....	....	....	....	....	.0272	.0266	.0261
18.500	....	....	....	....	....	....	.0286	.0279	.0275
19.000	....	....	....	....	....	....	.0298	.0292	.0288
19.500	....	....	....	....	....	....	.0309	.0303	.0299
20.000	....	....	....	....	....	....	.0318	.0313	.0310

PRODUCTION EQUIPMENT

Table 12-1. Section III (Continued)
"b" Values for Reynolds-number Factor, F_r,—Pipe Taps

$$F_r = 1 + \frac{b}{\sqrt{h_w p_f}}$$

β	Internal Diameter of Pipe, D, inches										
	2			3				4			
	1.689	1.939	2.067	2.300	2.626	2.900	3.068	3.152	3.438	3.826	4.026
0.10	0.1295	0.1209	0.1173	0.1118	0.1058	0.1017	0.0996	0.0986	0.0957	0.0924	0.0909
0.11	0.1253	0.1167	0.1132	0.1077	0.1016	0.0976	0.0954	0.0945	0.0915	0.0882	0.0867
0.12	0.1212	0.1126	0.1090	0.1035	0.0975	0.0934	0.0913	0.0903	0.0874	0.0841	0.0826
0.13	0.1172	0.1086	0.1051	0.0996	0.0935	0.0895	0.0874	0.0864	0.0835	0.0802	0.0787
0.14	0.1134	0.1049	0.1013	0.0958	0.0898	0.0858	0.0837	0.0827	0.0797	0.0765	0.0750
0.15	0.1098	0.1013	0.0978	0.0923	0.0863	0.0823	0.0801	0.0792	0.0762	0.0729	0.0715
0.16	0.1065	0.0980	0.0944	0.0889	0.0829	0.0789	0.0768	0.0758	0.0729	0.0696	0.0682
0.17	0.1033	0.0948	0.0912	0.0856	0.0798	0.0758	0.0737	0.0727	0.0698	0.0665	0.0650
0.18	0.1001	0.0916	0.0881	0.0827	0.0767	0.0727	0.0706	0.0696	0.0667	0.0634	0.0620
0.19	0.0973	0.0888	0.0853	0.0799	0.0739	0.0699	0.0678	0.0669	0.0639	0.0607	0.0592
0.20	0.0945	0.0861	0.0825	0.0771	0.0712	0.0672	0.0651	0.0642	0.0613	0.0580	0.0566
0.21	0.0919	0.0835	0.0800	0.0746	0.0687	0.0647	0.0626	0.0617	0.0588	0.0555	0.0541
0.22	0.0894	0.0811	0.0776	0.0722	0.0663	0.0623	0.0603	0.0593	0.0564	0.0532	0.0518
0.23	0.0872	0.0788	0.0753	0.0700	0.0641	0.0602	0.0581	0.0571	0.0543	0.0510	0.0496
0.24	0.0851	0.0767	0.0733	0.0679	0.0621	0.0581	0.0561	0.0551	0.0523	0.0490	0.0476
0.25	0.0831	0.0748	0.0714	0.0660	0.0602	0.0563	0.0542	0.0533	0.0504	0.0472	0.0458
0.26	0.0812	0.0730	0.0695	0.0642	0.0584	0.0545	0.0524	0.0515	0.0487	0.0455	0.0441
0.27	0.0796	0.0713	0.0679	0.0626	0.0568	0.0530	0.0509	0.0500	0.0471	0.0440	0.0426
0.28	0.0781	0.0699	0.0665	0.0612	0.0554	0.0516	0.0495	0.0486	0.0458	0.0426	0.0412
0.29	0.0766	0.0685	0.0651	0.0598	0.0541	0.0502	0.0482	0.0473	0.0445	0.0413	0.0399
0.30	0.0753	0.0672	0.0638	0.0586	0.0529	0.0490	0.0470	0.0461	0.0433	0.0401	0.0388
0.31	0.0741	0.0661	0.0627	0.0575	0.0518	0.0480	0.0460	0.0451	0.0423	0.0391	0.0378
0.32	0.0730	0.0650	0.0616	0.0564	0.0508	0.0470	0.0450	0.0441	0.0413	0.0382	0.0368
0.33	0.0720	0.0640	0.0606	0.0555	0.0499	0.0461	0.0441	0.0432	0.0405	0.0374	0.0360
0.34	0.0712	0.0632	0.0599	0.0548	0.0492	0.0455	0.0435	0.0426	0.0398	0.0368	0.0354
0.35	0.0705	0.0626	0.0593	0.0542	0.0486	0.0449	0.0429	0.0420	0.0393	0.0362	0.0349
0.36	0.0699	0.0620	0.0587	0.0537	0.0481	0.0444	0.0424	0.0416	0.0388	0.0358	0.0345
0.37	0.0693	0.0615	0.0582	0.0532	0.0477	0.0440	0.0421	0.0412	0.0385	0.0355	0.0341
0.38	0.0689	0.0611	0.0578	0.0529	0.0474	0.0437	0.0418	0.0409	0.0382	0.0352	0.0339
0.39	0.0684	0.0607	0.0575	0.0525	0.0471	0.0435	0.0415	0.0407	0.0380	0.0350	0.0337
0.40	0.0681	0.0604	0.0572	0.0523	0.0469	0.0433	0.0414	0.0405	0.0379	0.0349	0.0336
0.41	0.0678	0.0603	0.0571	0.0522	0.0468	0.0432	0.0414	0.0405	0.0379	0.0349	0.0336
0.42	0.0677	0.0602	0.0570	0.0521	0.0468	0.0433	0.0414	0.0405	0.0379	0.0350	0.0337
0.43	0.0676	0.0601	0.0570	0.0522	0.0469	0.0434	0.0415	0.0402	0.0381	0.0352	0.0339
0.44	0.0675	0.0601	0.0570	0.0522	0.0470	0.0435	0.0417	0.0408	0.0382	0.0354	0.0341
0.45	0.0675	0.0602	0.0571	0.0524	0.0472	0.0437	0.0419	0.0410	0.0385	0.0357	0.0344
0.46	0.0676	0.0603	0.0572	0.0526	0.0474	0.0440	0.0422	0.0413	0.0388	0.0360	0.0347
0.47	0.0676	0.0605	0.0574	0.0528	0.0476	0.0442	0.0424	0.0416	0.0391	0.0363	0.0351
0.48	0.0677	0.0606	0.0576	0.0530	0.0479	0.0446	0.0428	0.0420	0.0395	0.0367	0.0355
0.49	0.0678	0.0608	0.0578	0.0532	0.0482	0.0449	0.0431	0.0423	0.0399	0.0372	0.0359
0.50	0.0680	0.0611	0.0581	0.0536	0.0486	0.0453	0.0436	0.0428	0.0404	0.0377	0.0365
0.51	0.0682	0.0613	0.0584	0.0539	0.0490	0.0458	0.0440	0.0433	0.0409	0.0382	0.0370
0.52	0.0684	0.0615	0.0587	0.0543	0.0494	0.0462	0.0445	0.0437	0.0413	0.0387	0.0375
0.53	0.0687	0.0619	0.0590	0.0547	0.0499	0.0467	0.0450	0.0442	0.0419	0.0393	0.0381
0.54	0.0689	0.0622	0.0594	0.0551	0.0503	0.0472	0.0455	0.0448	0.0424	0.0398	0.0387
0.55	0.0692	0.0625	0.0598	0.0555	0.0508	0.0477	0.0460	0.0453	0.0430	0.0404	0.0393
0.56	0.0694	0.0628	0.0601	0.0559	0.0513	0.0482	0.0466	0.0458	0.0435	0.0410	0.0399
0.57	0.0696	0.0632	0.0505	0.0563	0.0517	0.0487	0.0471	0.0464	0.0441	0.0416	0.0405
0.58	0.0699	0.0635	0.0608	0.0567	0.0522	0.0492	0.0476	0.0469	0.0447	0.0422	0.0412
0.59	0.0701	0.0638	0.0612	0.0571	0.0527	0.0497	0.0482	0.0474	0.0453	0.0428	0.0418
0.60	0.0704	0.0641	0.0615	0.0575	0.0532	0.0502	0.0487	0.0480	0.0458	0.0434	0.0424
0.61	0.0705	0.0643	0.0618	0.0578	0.0535	0.0506	0.0491	0.0484	0.0463	0.0439	0.0429
0.62	0.0706	0.0645	0.0620	0.0581	0.0539	0.0510	0.0495	0.0489	0.0468	0.0444	0.0434
0.63	0.0707	0.0648	0.0623	0.0585	0.0543	0.0515	0.0500	0.0493	0.0473	0.0450	0.0440
0.64	0.0708	0.0649	0.0625	0.0587	0.0546	0.0518	0.0504	0.0497	0.0477	0.0454	0.0444
0.65	0.0709	0.0651	0.0627	0.0590	0.0549	0.0522	0.0508	0.0501	0.0481	0.0459	0.0449
0.66	0.0708	0.0651	0.0628	0.0591	0.0551	0.0525	0.0511	0.0504	0.0485	0.0463	0.0453
0.67	0.0708	0.0653	0.0629	0.0594	0.0554	0.0528	0.0514	0.0508	0.0489	0.0467	0.0458
0.68	0.0708	0.0653	0.0630	0.0595	0.0556	0.0531	0.0517	0.0511	0.0492	0.0471	0.0462
0.69	0.0705	0.0652	0.0629	0.0595	0.0557	0.0532	0.0518	0.0512	0.0494	0.0473	0.0464
0.70	0.0704	0.0651	0.0629	0.0595	0.0558	0.0533	0.0520	0.0514	0.0496	0.0476	0.0467

Table 12-1. Section III (*Continued*)
"*b*" Values for Reynolds-number Factor, F_r,—Pipe Taps

$$F_r = 1 + \frac{b}{\sqrt{h_w p_f}}$$

β		Internal Diameter of Pipe, D, inches											
	6				8			10			12		
	4.897	5.189	5.761	6.065	7.625	7.981	8.071	9.564	10.020	10.136	11.376	11.938	12.090
0.10	0.0845	0.0836	0.0821	0.0814	0.0784	0.0778	0.0777	0.0757	0.0752	0.0751	0.0739	0.0734	0.0733
0.11	0.0803	0.0795	0.0779	0.0772	0.0742	0.0736	0.0735	0.0716	0.0710	0.0709	0.0697	0.0692	0.0691
0.12	0.0763	0.0755	0.0739	0.0732	0.0702	0.0696	0.0695	0.0676	0.0670	0.0669	0.0657	0.0652	0.0651
0.13	0.0725	0.0717	0.0701	0.0694	0.0664	0.0658	0.0657	0.0538	0.0632	0.0631	0.0619	0.0614	0.0613
0.14	0.0689	0.0680	0.0665	0.0658	0.0628	0.0622	0.0621	0.0601	0.0596	0.0595	0.0583	0.0578	0.0577
0.15	0.0655	0.0646	0.0631	0.0624	0.0594	0.0588	0.0587	0.0567	0.0562	0.0561	0.0549	0.0544	0.0543
0.16	0.0623	0.0614	0.0599	0.0591	0.0561	0.0556	0.0554	0.0535	0.0530	0.0528	0.0516	0.0512	0.0510
0.17	0.0592	0.0583	0.0568	0.0561	0.0531	0.0525	0.0524	0.0504	0.0499	0.0498	0.0486	0.0481	0.0480
0.18	0.0553	0.0554	0.0539	0.0532	0.0502	0.0496	0.0495	0.0475	0.0470	0.0469	0.0457	0.0452	0.0451
0.19	0.0536	0.0527	0.0512	0.0505	0.0475	0.0469	0.0468	0.0448	0.0443	0.0442	0.0430	0.0425	0.0424
0.20	0.0511	0.0502	0.0487	0.0479	0.0449	0.0444	0.0442	0.0423	0.0418	0.0416	0.0404	0.0400	0.0398
0.21	0.0486	0.0477	0.0462	0.0455	0.0425	0.0419	0.0418	0.0398	0.0393	0.0392	0.0380	0.0375	0.0374
0.22	0.0464	0.0455	0.0440	0.0433	0.0403	0.0397	0.0396	0.0376	0.0371	0.0370	0.0358	0.0353	0.0352
0.23	0.0444	0.0435	0.0420	0.0412	0.0382	0.0377	0.0375	0.0356	0.0351	0.0350	0.0338	0.0333	0.0332
0.24	0.0425	0.0416	0.0401	0.0393	0.0364	0.0358	0.0357	0.0337	0.0332	0.0331	0.0319	0.0314	0.0313
0.25	0.0407	0.0399	0.0383	0.0376	0.0346	0.0341	0.0339	0.0320	0.0315	0.0313	0.0301	0.0297	0.0295
0.26	0.0391	0.0382	0.0367	0.0360	0.0330	0.0324	0.0323	0.0303	0.0298	0.0297	0.0285	0.0280	0.0279
0.27	0.0377	0.0368	0.0353	0.0345	0.0315	0.0310	0.0309	0.0289	0.0284	0.0283	0.0271	0.0266	0.0265
0.28	0.0364	0.0355	0.0340	0.0332	0.0303	0.0297	0.0296	0.0276	0.0271	0.0270	0.0258	0.0253	0.0252
0.29	0.0352	0.0343	0.0328	0.0321	0.0291	0.0286	0.0284	0.0265	0.0260	0.0258	0.0246	0.0242	0.0240
0.30	0.0342	0.0333	0.0318	0.0311	0.0281	0.0275	0.0274	0.0255	0.0249	0.0248	0.0236	0.0231	0.0230
0.31	0.0333	0.0324	0.0309	0.0302	0.0272	0.0266	0.0265	0.0245	0.0240	0.0239	0.0227	0.0222	0.0221
0.32	0.0325	0.0317	0.0301	0.0294	0.0264	0.0259	0.0257	0.0238	0.0233	0.0232	0.0220	0.0215	0.0214
0.33	0.0319	0.0310	0.0295	0.0288	0.0258	0.0252	0.0251	0.0231	0.0226	0.0225	0.0213	0.0208	0.0207
0.34	0.0314	0.0305	0.0290	0.0283	0.0253	0.0247	0.0246	0.0226	0.0221	0.0220	0.0208	0.0203	0.0202
0.35	0.0310	0.0301	0.0286	0.0278	0.0249	0.0243	0.0242	0.0222	0.0217	0.0216	0.0204	0.0199	0.0198
0.36	0.0306	0.0298	0.0283	0.0275	0.0246	0.0240	0.0239	0.0219	0.0214	0.0213	0.0201	0.0196	0.0195
0.37	0.0305	0.0296	0.0281	0.0274	0.0244	0.0239	0.0237	0.0218	0.0213	0.0212	0.0200	0.0195	0.0194
0.38	0.0304	0.0285	0.0280	0.0273	0.0244	0.0238	0.0237	0.0217	0.0212	0.0211	0.0199	0.0195	0.0193
0.39	0.0305	0.0296	0.0281	0.0274	0.0244	0.0239	0.0238	0.0218	0.0213	0.0212	0.0200	0.0195	0.0194
0.40	0.0306	0.0296	0.0283	0.0276	0.0246	0.0240	0.0239	0.0220	0.0215	0.0213	0.0202	0.0197	0.0196
0.41	0.0309	0.0300	0.0285	0.0278	0.0248	0.0243	0.0241	0.0222	0.0217	0.0216	0.0204	0.0199	0.0198
0.42	0.0312	0.0303	0.0288	0.0281	0.0252	0.0246	0.0245	0.0226	0.0221	0.0219	0.0208	0.0203	0.0202
0.43	0.0316	0.0308	0.0293	0.0286	0.0256	0.0251	0.0249	0.0230	0.0225	0.0224	0.0212	0.0207	0.0206
0.44	0.0321	0.0313	0.0298	0.0291	0.0261	0.0256	0.0254	0.0235	0.0230	0.0229	0.0217	0.0213	0.0211
0.45	0.0327	0.0319	0.0304	0.0297	0.0267	0.0262	0.0261	0.0241	0.0236	0.0235	0.0223	0.0219	0.0217
0.46	0.0334	0.0326	0.0311	0.0304	0.0274	0.0269	0.0267	0.0248	0.0243	0.0242	0.0230	0.0226	0.0224
0.47	0.0341	0.0333	0.0318	0.0311	0.0282	0.0276	0.0275	0.0256	0.0251	0.0249	0.0238	0.0233	0.0232
0.48	0.0350	0.0341	0.0326	0.0319	0.0290	0.0284	0.0283	0.0264	0.0259	0.0258	0.0246	0.0242	0.0240
0.49	0.0358	0.0349	0.0335	0.0328	0.0299	0.0293	0.0292	0.0273	0.0268	0.0267	0.0255	0.0250	0.0249
0.50	0.0368	0.0359	0.0344	0.0337	0.0308	0.0303	0.0302	0.0283	0.0278	0.0276	0.0265	0.0260	0.0259
0.51	0.0378	0.0369	0.0354	0.0347	0.0318	0.0313	0.0312	0.0293	0.0288	0.0287	0.0275	0.0270	0.0269
0.52	0.0388	0.0380	0.0365	0.0358	0.0329	0.0324	0.0323	0.0304	0.0299	0.0298	0.0286	0.0281	0.0280
0.53	0.0399	0.0391	0.0376	0.0369	0.0340	0.0335	0.0334	0.0315	0.0310	0.0309	0.0297	0.0293	0.0291
0.54	0.0410	0.0402	0.0387	0.0380	0.0351	0.0346	0.0345	0.0326	0.0321	0.0320	0.0308	0.0304	0.0303
0.55	0.0422	0.0413	0.0399	0.0392	0.0363	0.0358	0.0357	0.0338	0.0333	0.0332	0.0321	0.0316	0.0315
0.56	0.0433	0.0425	0.0411	0.0404	0.0375	0.0370	0.0369	0.0350	0.0345	0.0344	0.0333	0.0328	0.0327
0.57	0.0446	0.0438	0.0423	0.0416	0.0388	0.0383	0.0381	0.0363	0.0358	0.0357	0.0346	0.0341	0.0340
0.58	0.0458	0.0450	0.0436	0.0429	0.0401	0.0395	0.0394	0.0376	0.0371	0.0370	0.0358	0.0354	0.0353
0.59	0.0472	0.0463	0.0449	0.0442	0.0414	0.0409	0.0408	0.0389	0.0384	0.0383	0.0372	0.0367	0.0366
0.60	0.0484	0.0476	0.0462	0.0455	0.0427	0.0422	0.0421	0.0402	0.0398	0.0397	0.0385	0.0381	0.0380
0.61	0.0497	0.0489	0.0474	0.0468	0.0440	0.0435	0.0433	0.0415	0.0411	0.0409	0.0398	0.0394	0.0393
0.62	0.0510	0.0502	0.0488	0.0481	0.0402	0.0448	0.0447	0.0429	0.0424	0.0423	0.0412	0.0407	0.0406
0.63	0.0523	0.0515	0.0501	0.0494	0.0466	0.0461	0.0460	0.0442	0.0437	0.0436	0.0425	0.0421	0.0420
0.64	0.0535	0.0527	0.0513	0.0507	0.0479	0.0474	0.0473	0.0455	0.0451	0.0449	0.0438	0.0434	0.0433
0.65	0.0548	0.0540	0.0526	0.0520	0.0492	0.0487	0.0486	0.0468	0.0464	0.0463	0.0452	0.0447	0.0446
0.66	0.0560	0.0552	0.0538	0.0532	0.0505	0.0500	0.0499	0.0481	0.0476	0.0475	0.0465	0.0460	0.0459
0.67	0.0572	0.0564	0.0551	0.0544	0.0517	0.0512	0.0511	0.0494	0.0489	0.0488	0.0477	0.0473	0.0472
0.68	0.0584	0.0576	0.0563	0.0556	0.0530	0.0525	0.0523	0.0506	0.0502	0.0500	0.0490	0.0486	0.0484
0.69	0.0595	0.0587	0.0574	0.0567	0.0541	0.0536	0.0535	0.0518	0.0513	0.0512	0.0502	0.0497	0.0496
0.70	0.0606	0.0598	0.0585	0.0579	0.0552	0.0548	0.0546	0.0529	0.0525	0.0524	0.0513	0.0509	0.0508
0.71	0.0616	0.0608	0.0595	0.0589	0.0563	0.0558	0.0557	0.0540	0.0535	0.0534	0.0524	0.0520	0.0519
0.72	0.0625	0.0618	0.0605	0.0599	0.0573	0.0568	0.0567	0.0550	0.0546	0.0545	0.0535	0.0530	0.0529
0.73	0.0635	0.0627	0.0614	0.0608	0.0583	0.0578	0.0577	0.0560	0.0556	0.0555	0.0545	0.0541	0.0540
0.74	0.0643	0.0636	0.0623	0.0617	0.0592	0.0587	0.0586	0.0570	0.0565	0.0564	0.0554	0.0550	0.0549
0.75	0.0650	0.0643	0.0630	0.0624	0.0599	0.0594	0.0594	0.0577	0.0573	0.0572	0.0562	0.0558	0.0557

PRODUCTION EQUIPMENT

Table 12-1. Section III (Continued)
"b" Values for Reynolds-number Factor, F_r,—Pipe Taps

$$F_r = 1 + \frac{b}{\sqrt{h_w p_f}}$$

	Internal Diameter of Pipe, D, inches											
β	16			20			24			30		
	14.688	15.000	15.250	18.814	19.000	19.250	22.626	23.000	23.250	28.628	29.000	29.250
0.10	0.0706	0.0705	0.0704	0.0690	0.0689	0.0688	0.0680	0.0679	0.0678	0.0669	0.0669	0.0668
0.11	0.0665	0.0663	0.0662	0.0648	0.0647	0.0647	0.0638	0.0637	0.0637	0.0628	0.0627	0.0627
0.12	0.0624	0.0622	0.0621	0.0607	0.0607	0.0606	0.0597	0.0596	0.0596	0.0587	0.0586	0.0586
0.13	0.0585	0.0584	0.0582	0.0569	0.0568	0.0567	0.0558	0.0558	0.0557	0.0548	0.0548	0.0547
0.14	0.0549	0.0548	0.0546	0.0532	0.0531	0.0530	0.0522	0.0521	0.0520	0.0511	0.0511	0.0511
0.15	0.0514	0.0512	0.0511	0.0497	0.0497	0.0496	0.0487	0.0486	0.0486	0.0477	0.0476	0.0476
0.16	0.0481	0.0479	0.0478	0.0464	0.0464	0.0463	0.0454	0.0453	0.0453	0.0444	0.0443	0.0443
0.17	0.0450	0.0448	0.0447	0.0433	0.0433	0.0432	0.0423	0.0423	0.0422	0.0413	0.0413	0.0412
0.18	0.0420	0.0419	0.0417	0.0404	0.0403	0.0402	0.0394	0.0393	0.0392	0.0383	0.0383	0.0383
0.19	0.0393	0.0391	0.0390	0.0376	0.0376	0.0375	0.0366	0.0366	0.0365	0.0356	0.0356	0.0355
0.20	0.0367	0.0365	0.0364	0.0350	0.0350	0.0349	0.0340	0.0340	0.0339	0.0330	0.0330	0.0329
0.21	0.0343	0.0341	0.0340	0.0326	0.0326	0.0325	0.0316	0.0316	0.0315	0.0306	0.0306	0.0305
0.22	0.0320	0.0318	0.0317	0.0304	0.0303	0.0302	0.0294	0.0293	0.0293	0.0284	0.0283	0.0283
0.23	0.0299	0.0298	0.0296	0.0283	0.0282	0.0281	0.0273	0.0272	0.0272	0.0263	0.0262	0.0262
0.24	0.0280	0.0278	0.0277	0.0264	0.0263	0.0262	0.0254	0.0253	0.0253	0.0244	0.0243	0.0243
0.25	0.0262	0.0261	0.0260	0.0246	0.0246	0.0245	0.0236	0.0236	0.0235	0.0226	0.0226	0.0226
0.26	0.0246	0.0244	0.0243	0.0230	0.0229	0.0228	0.0220	0.0219	0.0219	0.0210	0.0210	0.0209
0.27	0.0231	0.0230	0.0229	0.0215	0.0215	0.0214	0.0206	0.0205	0.0204	0.0196	0.0195	0.0195
0.28	0.0218	0.0217	0.0216	0.0202	0.0202	0.0201	0.0193	0.0192	0.0191	0.0183	0.0182	0.0182
0.29	0.0206	0.0205	0.0204	0.0191	0.0190	0.0189	0.0181	0.0180	0.0180	0.0171	0.0171	0.0170
0.30	0.0196	0.0194	0.0193	0.0180	0.0179	0.0179	0.0170	0.0170	0.0169	0.0161	0.0160	0.0160
0.31	0.0187	0.0185	0.0184	0.0171	0.0170	0.0170	0.0161	0.0161	0.0160	0.0152	0.0151	0.0151
0.32	0.0179	0.0177	0.0176	0.0163	0.0162	0.0162	0.0153	0.0153	0.0152	0.0144	0.0143	0.0143
0.33	0.0172	0.0170	0.0169	0.0156	0.0156	0.0155	0.0147	0.0146	0.0146	0.0137	0.0137	0.0136
0.34	0.0166	0.0165	0.0164	0.0151	0.0150	0.0150	0.0142	0.0141	0.0140	0.0132	0.0131	0.0131
0.35	0.0162	0.0161	0.0160	0.0147	0.0146	0.0145	0.0137	0.0137	0.0136	0.0128	0.0127	0.0127
0.36	0.0159	0.0157	0.0156	0.0144	0.0143	0.0142	0.0134	0.0134	0.0133	0.0125	0.0124	0.0124
0.37	0.0157	0.0155	0.0154	0.0141	0.0141	0.0140	0.0132	0.0132	0.0131	0.0123	0.0122	0.0122
0.38	0.0155	0.0154	0.0153	0.0140	0.0140	0.0139	0.0131	0.0130	0.0130	0.0122	0.0121	0.0121
0.39	0.0155	0.0154	0.0153	0.0140	0.0139	0.0139	0.0131	0.0130	0.0130	0.0122	0.0121	0.0121
0.40	0.0156	0.0154	0.0153	0.0141	0.0140	0.0139	0.0132	0.0131	0.0130	0.0122	0.0122	0.0122
0.41	0.0157	0.0155	0.0154	0.0142	0.0142	0.0141	0.0133	0.0132	0.0132	0.0124	0.0124	0.0123
0.42	0.0159	0.0158	0.0157	0.0144	0.0144	0.0143	0.0136	0.0135	0.0134	0.0126	0.0126	0.0126
0.43	0.0162	0.0161	0.0160	0.0148	0.0147	0.0146	0.0139	0.0138	0.0138	0.0130	0.0129	0.0129
0.44	0.0166	0.0164	0.0163	0.0151	0.0151	0.0150	0.0143	0.0142	0.0141	0.0134	0.0133	0.0133
0.45	0.0170	0.0169	0.0168	0.0156	0.0155	0.0155	0.0147	0.0146	0.0146	0.0138	0.0138	0.0137
0.46	0.0175	0.0174	0.0173	0.0161	0.0160	0.0160	0.0152	0.0151	0.0151	0.0143	0.0143	0.0143
0.47	0.0180	0.0179	0.0178	0.0166	0.0166	0.0165	0.0158	0.0157	0.0157	0.0149	0.0149	0.0148
0.48	0.0186	0.0185	0.0184	0.0172	0.0172	0.0171	0.0164	0.0163	0.0163	0.0155	0.0155	0.0154
0.49	0.0192	0.0191	0.0190	0.0178	0.0178	0.0177	0.0170	0.0169	0.0169	0.0162	0.0161	0.0161
0.50	0.0199	0.0198	0.0197	0.0185	0.0185	0.0184	0.0177	0.0176	0.0176	0.0169	0.0168	0.0168
0.51	0.0206	0.0205	0.0204	0.0193	0.0192	0.0191	0.0184	0.0184	0.0183	0.0176	0.0176	0.0175
0.52	0.0213	0.0212	0.0211	0.0200	0.0199	0.0199	0.0192	0.0191	0.0191	0.0183	0.0183	0.0183
0.53	0.0221	0.0220	0.0219	0.0208	0.0207	0.0207	0.0200	0.0199	0.0199	0.0191	0.0191	0.0191
0.54	0.0229	0.0227	0.0226	0.0215	0.0215	0.0214	0.0208	0.0207	0.0207	0.0199	0.0199	0.0199
0.55	0.0237	0.0235	0.0234	0.0224	0.0223	0.0223	0.0216	0.0215	0.0215	0.0208	0.0207	0.0207
0.56	0.0244	0.0243	0.0242	0.0232	0.0231	0.0231	0.0224	0.0223	0.0223	0.0216	0.0216	0.0215
0.57	0.0253	0.0251	0.0250	0.0240	0.0239	0.0239	0.0232	0.0232	0.0231	0.0224	0.0224	0.0224
0.58	0.0261	0.0260	0.0259	0.0248	0.0248	0.0247	0.0241	0.0240	0.0240	0.0233	0.0233	0.0232
0.59	0.0269	0.0268	0.0267	0.0256	0.0256	0.0255	0.0249	0.0248	0.0248	0.0241	0.0241	0.0241
0.60	0.0277	0.0276	0.0275	0.0265	0.0264	0.0264	0.0257	0.0257	0.0256	0.0250	0.0249	0.0249
0.61	0.0284	0.0283	0.0282	0.0272	0.0272	0.0271	0.0265	0.0265	0.0264	0.0258	0.0257	0.0257
0.62	0.0292	0.0291	0.0290	0.0280	0.0280	0.0279	0.0273	0.0272	0.0272	0.0266	0.0265	0.0265
0.63	0.0299	0.0298	0.0297	0.0288	0.0287	0.0287	0.0281	0.0280	0.0280	0.0273	0.0273	0.0273
0.64	0.0306	0.0305	0.0304	0.0295	0.0295	0.0294	0.0288	0.0288	0.0287	0.0281	0.0281	0.0280
0.65	0.0313	0.0312	0.0312	0.0302	0.0302	0.0301	0.0295	0.0295	0.0294	0.0288	0.0288	0.0288
0.66	0.0320	0.0319	0.0318	0.0309	0.0308	0.0308	0.0302	0.0301	0.0301	0.0295	0.0295	0.0295
0.67	0.0326	0.0325	0.0324	0.0315	0.0315	0.0314	0.0309	0.0308	0.0308	0.0302	0.0302	0.0302
0.68	0.0332	0.0331	0.0330	0.0322	0.0321	0.0321	0.0315	0.0315	0.0314	0.0308	0.0308	0.0308
0.69	0.0337	0.0336	0.0335	0.0327	0.0326	0.0326	0.0320	0.0320	0.0320	0.0314	0.0314	0.0313
0.70	0.0342	0.0341	0.0340	0.0332	0.0332	0.0331	0.0326	0.0325	0.0325	0.0319	0.0319	0.0319

Table 12-1. Section III (*Continued*)
Expansion Factors—Pipe Taps—Y_1
Static Pressure Taken from Upstream Taps

$\dfrac{h_w}{p_{f_1}}$ Ratio	$\beta = \dfrac{d}{D}$ Ratio										
	.1	.2	.3	.4	.45	.50	.52	.54	.56	.58	.60
0.0	1.0000	1.0000	1.0000	1.0000	1.0000	1.0000	1.0000	1.0000	1.0000	1.0000	1.0000
0.1	.9990	.9989	.9988	.9985	.9984	.9982	.9981	.9980	.9979	.9978	.9977
0.2	.9981	.9979	.9976	.9971	.9968	.9964	.9962	.9961	.9959	.9957	.9954
0.3	.9971	.9968	.9964	.9956	.9952	.9946	.9944	.9941	.9938	.9935	.9931
0.4	.9962	.9958	.9951	.9942	.9936	.9928	.9925	.9921	.9917	.9913	.9908
0.5	.9952	.9947	.9939	.9927	.9919	.9910	.9906	.9902	.9897	.9891	.9885
0.6	.9943	.9937	.9927	.9913	.9903	.9892	.9887	.9882	.9876	.9870	.9862
0.7	.9933	.9926	.9915	.9898	.9887	.9874	.9869	.9862	.9856	.9848	.9840
0.8	.9923	.9916	.9903	.9883	.9871	.9857	.9850	.9843	.9835	.9826	.9817
0.9	.9914	.9905	.9891	.9869	.9855	.9839	.9831	.9823	.9814	.9805	.9794
1.0	.9904	.9895	.9878	.9854	.9839	.9821	.9812	.9803	.9794	.9783	.9771
1.1	.9895	.9884	.9866	.9840	.9823	.9803	.9794	.9784	.9773	.9761	.9748
1.2	.9885	.9874	.9854	.9825	.9807	.9785	.9775	.9764	.9752	.9739	.9725
1.3	.9876	.9863	.9842	.9811	.9791	.9767	.9756	.9744	.9732	.9718	.9702
1.4	.9866	.9853	.9830	.9796	.9775	.9749	.9737	.9725	.9711	.9696	.9679
1.5	.9857	.9842	.9818	.9782	.9758	.9731	.9719	.9705	.9690	.9674	.9656
1.6	.9847	.9832	.9805	.9767	.9742	.9713	.9700	.9685	.9670	.9652	.9633
1.7	.9837	.9821	.9793	.9752	.9726	.9695	.9681	.9666	.9649	.9631	.9610
1.8	.9828	.9811	.9781	.9738	.9710	.9677	.9662	.9646	.9628	.9609	.9587
1.9	.9818	.9800	.9769	.9723	.9694	.9659	.9643	.9626	.9608	.9587	.9565
2.0	.9809	.9790	.9757	.9709	.9678	.9641	.9625	.9607	.9587	.9566	.9542
2.1	.9799	.9779	.9745	.9694	.9662	.9623	.9606	.9587	.9566	.9544	.9519
2.2	.9790	.9768	.9732	.9680	.9646	.9605	.9587	.9567	.9546	.9522	.9496
2.3	.9780	.9758	.9720	.9665	.9630	.9587	.9568	.9548	.9525	.9500	.9473
2.4	.9770	.9747	.9708	.9650	.9613	.9570	.9550	.9528	.9505	.9479	.9450
2.5	.9761	.9737	.9696	.9636	.9597	.9552	.9531	.9508	.9484	.9457	.9427
2.6	.9751	.9726	.9684	.9621	.9581	.9534	.9512	.9489	.9463	.9435	.9404
2.7	.9742	.9716	.9672	.9607	.9565	.9516	.9493	.9469	.9443	.9414	.9381
2.8	.9732	.9705	.9659	.9592	.9549	.9498	.9475	.9449	.9422	.9392	.9358
2.9	.9723	.9695	.9647	.9578	.9533	.9480	.9456	.9430	.9401	.9370	.9335
3.0	.9713	.9684	.9635	.9563	.9517	.9462	.9437	.9410	.9381	.9348	.9312
3.1	.9704	.9674	.9623	.9549	.9501	.9444	.9418	.9390	.9360	.9327	.9290
3.2	.9694	.9663	.9611	.9534	.9485	.9426	.9400	.9371	.9339	.9305	.9267
3.3	.9684	.9653	.9599	.9519	.9469	.9408	.9381	.9351	.9319	.9283	.9244
3.4	.9675	.9642	.9587	.9505	.9452	.9390	.9362	.9331	.9298	.9261	.9221
3.5	.9665	.9632	.9574	.9490	.9436	.9372	.9343	.9312	.9277	.9240	.9198
3.6	.9656	.9621	.9562	.9476	.9420	.9354	.9324	.9292	.9257	.9218	.9175
3.7	.9646	.9611	.9550	.9461	.9404	.9336	.9306	.9272	.9236	.9196	.9152
3.8	.9637	.9600	.9538	.9447	.9388	.9318	.9287	.9253	.9216	.9175	.9129
3.9	.9627	.9590	.9526	.9432	.9372	.9301	.9268	.9233	.9195	.9153	.9106
4.0	.9617	.9579	.9514	.9417	.9356	.9283	.9249	.9213	.9174	.9131	.9083

Table 12-1. Section III (*Continued*)
Expansion Factors—Pipe Taps—Y_1
Static Pressure Taken from Upstream Taps

$\dfrac{h_w}{p_{f1}}$ Ratio	$\beta = \dfrac{d}{D}$ Ratio									
	.61	.62	.63	.64	.65	.66	.67	.68	.69	.70
0.0	1.0000	1.0000	1.0000	1.0000	1.0000	1.0000	1.0000	1.0000	1.0000	1.0000
0.1	.9976	.9976	.9975	.9974	.9973	.9972	.9971	.9970	.9969	.9968
0.2	.9953	.9951	.9950	.9948	.9947	.9945	.9943	.9941	.9938	.9935
0.3	.9929	.9927	.9925	.9923	.9920	.9917	.9914	.9911	.9907	.9903
0.4	.9906	.9903	.9900	.9897	.9893	.9890	.9886	.9881	.9876	.9871
0.5	.9882	.9879	.9875	.9871	.9867	.9862	.9857	.9851	.9845	.9839
0.6	.9859	.9854	.9850	.9845	.9840	.9834	.9828	.9822	.9814	.9806
0.7	.9835	.9830	.9825	.9819	.9813	.9807	.9800	.9792	.9784	.9774
0.8	.9811	.9806	.9800	.9794	.9787	.9779	.9771	.9762	.9753	.9742
0.9	.9788	.9782	.9775	.9768	.9760	.9752	.9742	.9733	.9722	.9710
1.0	.9764	.9757	.9750	.9742	.9733	.9724	.9714*	.9703	.9691	.9677
1.1	.9741	.9733	.9725	.9716	.9707	.9696	.9685	.9673	.9660	.9645
1.2	.9717	.9709	.9700	.9690	.9680	.9669	.9657	.9643	.9629	.9613
1.3	.9694	.9685	.9675	.9664	.9653	.9641	.9628	.9614	.9598	.9581
1.4	.9670	.9660	.9650	.9639	.9627	.9614	.9599	.9584	.9567	.9548
1.5	.9646	.9636	.9625	.9613	.9600	.9586	.9571	.9554	.9536	.9516
1.6	.9623	.9612	.9600	.9587	.9573	.9558	.9542	.9525	.9505	.9484
1.7	.9599	.9587	.9575	.9561	.9547	.9531	.9514	.9495	.9474	.9452
1.8	.9576	.9563	.9550	.9535	.9520	.9503	.9485	.9465	.9443	.9419
1.9	.9552	.9539	.9525	.9510	.9493	.9476	.9456	.9435	.9412	.9387
2.0	.9529	.9515	.9500	.9484	.9467	.9448	.9428	.9406	.9381	.9355
2.1	.9505	.9490	.9475	.9458	.9440	.9420	.9399	.9376	.9351	.9323
2.2	.9481	.9466	.9450	.9432	.9413	.9393	.9371	.9346	.9320	.9290
2.3	.9458	.9442	.9425	.9406	.9387	.9365	.9342	.9317	.9289	.9258
2.4	.9434	.9418	.9400	.9381	.9360	.9338	.9313	.9287	.9258	.9226
2.5	.9411	.9393	.9375	.9355	.9333	.9310	.9285	.9257	.9227	.9194
2.6	.9387	.9369	.9350	.9329	.9307	.9282	.9256	.9227	.9196	.9161
2.7	.9364	.9345	.9325	.9303	.9280	.9255	.9227	.9198	.9165	.9129
2.8	.9340	.9321	.9300	.9277	.9253	.9227	.9199	.9168	.9134	.9097
2.9	.9316	.9296	.9275	.9252	.9227	.9200	.9170	.9138	.9103	.9064
3.0	.9293	.9272	.9250	.9226	.9200	.9172	.9142	.9108	.9072	.9032
3.1	.9269	.9248	.9225	.9200	.9173	.9144	.9113	.9079	.9041	.9000
3.2	.9246	.9223	.9200	.9174	.9147	.9117	.9084	.9049	.9010	.8968
3.3	.9222	.9199	.9175	.9148	.9120	.9089	.9056	.9019	.8979	.8935
3.4	.9199	.9175	.9150	.9122	.9093	.9062	.9027	.8990	.8948	.8903
3.5	.9175	.9151	.9125	.9097	.9067	.9034	.8999	.8960	.8918	.8871
3.6	.9151	.9126	.9100	.9071	.9040	.9006	.8970	.8930	.8887	.8839
3.7	.9128	.9102	.9075	.9045	.9013	.8979	.8941	.8900	.8856	.8806
3.8	.9104	.9078	.9050	.9019	.8987	.8951	.8913	.8871	.8825	.8774
3.9	.9081	.9054	.9025	.8993	.8960	.8924	.8884	.8841	.8794	.8742
4.0	.9057	.9029	.9000	.8968	.8933	.8896	.8856	.8811	.8763	.8710

Table 12-1. Section III (*Continued*)
Expansion Factors—Pipe Taps—Y_2
Static Pressure Taken from Downstream Taps

$\dfrac{h_w}{P_{f2}}$ Ratio	$\beta = \dfrac{d}{D}$ Ratio										
	.1	.2	.3	.4	.45	.50	.52	.54	.56	.58	.60
0.0	1.0000	1.0000	1.0000	1.0000	1.0000	1.0000	1.0000	1.0000	1.0000	1.0000	1.0000
0.1	1.0008	1.0007	1.0006	1.0003	1.0002	1.0000	.9999	.9998	.9997	.9996	.9995
0.2	1.0017	1.0015	1.0012	1.0007	1.0004	1.0000	.9998	.9997	.9995	.9993	.9990
0.3	1.0025	1.0023	1.0018	1.0010	1.0006	1.0000	.9998	.9995	.9992	.9989	.9985
0.4	1.0033	1.0031	1.0024	1.0014	1.0008	1.0000	.9997	.9994	.9989	.9985	.9980
0.5	1.0042	1.0037	1.0029	1.0018	1.0010	1.0001	.9997	.9993	.9987	.9982	.9975
0.6	1.0051	1.0045	1.0035	1.0021	1.0012	1.0001	.9996	.9991	.9985	.9979	.9972
0.7	1.0059	1.0053	1.0042	1.0024	1.0014	1.0001	.9996	.9989	.9983	.9976	.9968
0.8	1.0068	1.0060	1.0048	1.0028	1.0016	1.0002	.9995	.9988	.9981	.9972	.9963
0.9	1.0076	1.0068	1.0053	1.0032	1.0018	1.0003	.9995	.9987	.9978	.9969	.9958
1.0	1.0084	1.0075	1.0059	1.0036	1.0021	1.0003	.9994	.9986	.9976	.9965	.9954
1.1	1.0093	1.0082	1.0065	1.0039	1.0023	1.0004	.9994	.9984	.9974	.9962	.9949
1.2	1.0101	1.0090	1.0071	1.0043	1.0025	1.0004	.9994	.9984	.9972	.9959	.9945
1.3	1.0110	1.0098	1.0077	1.0047	1.0027	1.0004	.9994	.9982	.9969	.9956	.9941
1.4	1.0119	1.0106	1.0083	1.0050	1.0030	1.0005	.9993	.9981	.9967	.9953	.9937
1.5	1.0127	1.0113	1.0089	1.0054	1.0032	1.0005	.9993	.9980	.9965	.9950	.9932
1.6	1.0136	1.0121	1.0095	1.0058	1.0034	1.0006	.9993	.9979	.9964	.9947	.9928
1.7	1.0143	1.0128	1.0101	1.0062	1.0036	1.0006	.9993	.9978	.9962	.9944	.9924
1.8	1.0152	1.0136	1.0107	1.0065	1.0038	1.0007	.9992	.9977	.9960	.9942	.9920
1.9	1.0161	1.0143	1.0113	1.0069	1.0041	1.0008	.9992	.9976	.9958	.9938	.9916
2.0	1.0169	1.0150	1.0119	1.0073	1.0044	1.0008	.9992	.9975	.9956	.9935	.9912
2.1	1.0177	1.0158	1.0125	1.0077	1.0046	1.0008	.9992	.9974	.9954	.9933	.9908
2.2	1.0185	1.0165	1.0131	1.0081	1.0048	1.0009	.9992	.9973	.9953	.9930	.9905
2.3	1.0194	1.0173	1.0137	1.0084	1.0050	1.0010	.9992	.9972	.9951	.9928	.9902
2.4	1.0202	1.0180	1.0142	1.0089	1.0053	1.0011	.9992	.9971	.9949	.9924	.9897
2.5	1.0210	1.0188	1.0148	1.0092	1.0056	1.0012	.9992	.9971	.9948	.9922	.9894
2.6	1.0219	1.0195	1.0154	1.0096	1.0058	1.0013	.9992	.9970	.9946	.9919	.9890
2.7	1.0230	1.0205	1.0162	1.0101	1.0061	1.0014	.9992	.9969	.9944	.9916	.9885
2.8	1.0236	1.0210	1.0166	1.0104	1.0063	1.0014	.9992	.9969	.9943	.9914	.9882
2.9	1.0244	1.0217	1.0173	1.0107	1.0065	1.0015	.9992	.9968	.9941	.9912	.9879
3.0	1.0251	1.0224	1.0179	1.0111	1.0067	1.0017	.9992	.9967	.9939	.9910	.9875
3.1	1.0259	1.0232	1.0185	1.0115	1.0070	1.0018	.9993	.9966	.9938	.9907	.9872
3.2	1.0267	1.0239	1.0190	1.0119	1.0072	1.0018	.9993	.9966	.9936	.9905	.9869
3.3	1.0276	1.0247	1.0196	1.0122	1.0075	1.0019	.9993	.9966	.9935	.9903	.9866
3.4	1.0284	1.0253	1.0202	1.0126	1.0077	1.0020	.9994	.9965	.9934	.9901	.9863
3.5	1.0291	1.0261	1.0208	1.0130	1.0080	1.0021	.9994	.9964	.9933	.9898	.9860
3.6	1.0301	1.0238	1.0214	1.0134	1.0083	1.0022	.9994	.9964	.9931	.9896	.9857
3.7	1.0309	1.0276	1.0219	1.0137	1.0085	1.0023	.9995	.9964	.9930	.9894	.9854
3.8	1.0316	1.0287	1.0225	1.0141	1.0088	1.0024	.9995	.9963	.9929	.9892	.9850
3.9	1.0324	1.0290	1.0231	1.0145	1.0091	1.0025	.9995	.9963	.9928	.9889	.9847
4.0	1.0332	1.0297	1.0237	1.0149	1.0093	1.0025	.9995	.9963	.9927	.9887	.9844

Table 12-1. Section III (*Continued*)
Expansion Factors—Pipe Taps—Y_2
Static Pressure Taken from Downstream Taps

$\dfrac{h_w}{p_{f2}}$ Ratio	$\beta = \dfrac{d}{D}$ Ratio									
	.61	.62	.63	.64	.65	.66	.67	.68	.69	.70
0.0	1.0000	1.0000	1.0000	1.0000	1.0000	1.0000	1.0000	1.0000	1.0000	1 0000
0.1	.9994	.9994	.9993	.9992	.9991	.9990	.9989	.9988	.9987	.9986
0.2	.9989	.9987	.9986	.9984	.9983	.9981	.9979	.9977	.9974	.9971
0.3	.9983	.9981	.9979	.9977	.9974	.9971	.9968	.9965	.9962	.9958
0.4	.9978	.9975	.9972	.9969	.9966	.9963	.9959	.9954	.9949	.9944
0.5	.9973	.9970	.9966	.9962	.9958	.9953	.9948	.9942	.9936	.9930
0.6	.9969	.9964	.9959	.9954	.9949	.9943	.9937	.9931	.9924	.9916
0.7	.9963	.9958	.9953	.9947	.9940	.9932	.9928	.9920	.9912	.9903
0.8	.9957	.9952	.9947	.9941	.9933	.9925	.9918	.9909	.9900	.9889
0.9	.9952	.9947	.9940	.9933	.9925	.9917	.9907	.9898	.9888	.9876
1.0	.9947	.9941	.9934	.9926	.9917	.9908	.9898	.9887	.9876	.9863
1.1	.9942	.9935	.9927	.9919	.9910	.9899	.9889	.9877	.9865	.9849
1.2	.9938	.9929	.9921	.9911	.9902	.9890	.9878	.9865	.9851	.9835
1 3	.9933	.9924	.9914	.9904	.9893	.9881	.9869	.9855	.9839	.9823
1.4	.9928	.9918	.9908	.9897	.9886	.9873	.9859	.9845	.9827	.9810
1.5	.9923	.9913	.9903	.9891	.9878	.9865	.9849	.9834	.9815	.9796
1.6	.9919	.9908	.9897	.9883	.9870	.9856	.9840	.9823	.9804	.9784
1.7	.9914	.9902	.9890	.9876	.9863	.9848	.9831	.9813	.9793	.9771
1.8	.9909	.9897	.9884	.9870	.9855	.9840	.9822	.9802	.9781	.9758
1 9	.9905	.9892	.9878	.9863	.9848	.9831	.9812	.9792	.9770	.9746
2.0	.9900	.9887	.9872	.9857	.9840	.9823	.9803	.9782	.9759	.9733
2 1	.9895	.9882	.9867	.9851	.9833	.9815	.9794	.9771	.9748	.9720
2.2	.9891	.9876	.9861	.9844	.9826	.9807	.9785	.9762	.9737	.9708
2.3	.9887	..9871	.9855	.9837	.9818	.9798	.9776	.9752	.9726	.9696
2.4	.9882	.9866	.9850	.9831	.9812	.9791	.9768	.9742	.9715	.9683
2.5	.9878	.9861	.9844	.9825	.9805	.9783	.9759	.9732	.9704	.9672
2.6	.9874	.9857	.9839	.9819	.9798	.9775	.9750	.9722	.9693	.9660
2.7	.9869	.9850	.9832	.9811	.9788	.9765	.9738	.9709	.9679	.9644
2.8	.9866	.9847	.9828	.9807	.9784	.9759	.9732	.9703	.9672	.9636
2.9	.9861	.9842	.9822	.9800	.9777	.9751	.9723	.9693	.9660	.9624
3.0	.9857	.9838	.9817	.9794	.9770	.9744	.9715	.9685	.9650	.9613
3.1	.9853	.9834	.9812	.9788	.9763	.9737	.9707	.9676	.9640	.9602
3.2	.9849	.9829	.9807	.9783	.9757	.9729	.9699	.9666	.9630	.9590
3.3	.9846	.9825	.9802	.9777	.9750	.9722	.9690	.9657	.9619	.9579
3.4	.9842	.9820	.9797	.9771	.9744	.9715	.9683	.9648	.9609	.9568
3.5	.9838	.9816	.9792	.9765	.9738	.9707	.9675	.9639	.9600	.9556
3.6	.9834	.9811	.9787	.9760	.9731	.9700	.9666	.9630	.9590	.9545
3.7	.9831	.9807	.9782	.9755	.9725	.9693	.9658	.9621	.9579	.9534
3.8	.9827	.9802	.9777	.9749	.9719	.9686	.9651	.9613	.9570	.9523
3.9	.9823	.9798	.9773	.9743	.9712	.9679	.9643	.9604	.9560	.9512
4.0	.9820	.9795	.9769	.9738	.9706	.9673	.9636	.9595	.9551	.9502

is substantially constant. The constant b shown in the charts is then primarily a function of pipe diameter, orifice diameter, and the location of the differential-pressure taps.

Expansion Factor Y. This factor accounts for the change in gas density as the pressure changes across the orifice. Inasmuch as the differential involved is usually small, this correction is small and often ignored. The value used depends on which one of the differential-pressure taps is used to measure static pressure and the location of the tap. The additional primary variables involved are (1) β, (2) ratio of differential pressure to absolute pressure, and (3) the specific-heat ratio C_p/C_v. In the standard chart the last variable is taken as constant and equal to 1.3. Tables of this factor are shown in Sections I and III of the charts.

Supercompressibility Factor F_{pv}. The variation from the ideal-gas laws by an actual gas is the function of this factor. The factor may be measured experimentally or determined by detailed methods outlined in *AGA Committee Report* 3. The correction is usually small and is often ignored. It may be estimated from the equation $F_{pv} = (1/Z)^{0.5}$ where Z is equal to the compressibility factor obtained from standard correlations.

Manometer Factor F_m. This is used only with mercury-type meters to correct for the slight error in measurement caused by having different heads of gas above the two legs of the manometer. For all practical purposes it is insignificant.

Example Problem. A 0.7 sp gr natural gas is measured in an orifice meter having flange taps. Determine the flow rate in scf/hr at 14.4 psia and 60°F if the following data apply:

Avg h_w = 40 in. H_2O
Avg p_f = 143 psig (measured downstream)
Avg flowing temp = 84°F
Line size = 4.026 in.
Orifice-plate opening = 1.50 in.

The respective coefficients are

$$F_b = 460.79$$
$$F_{pb} = 1.0229$$
$$F_{tb} = 1.0000$$
$$F_g = 1.1952$$
$$F_{tf} = 0.9777$$

C', the product of the above numbers = 551

Then Q_h = 551 (40)(143 + 14.73)$^{\frac{1}{2}}$
= 43,800 scf/hr

The above computation was performed on the slide rule. F_r, Y, F_{pv}, and F_m were therefore ignored because of their closeness to unity. As a practical matter, the accuracy of the meter device itself does not justify the number of significant figures shown in the charts. Consequently in most production operations and engineering calculations the values of the coefficients may be rounded off and sometimes ignored, with no practical loss of accuracy.

Physical Setup of System

Inasmuch as standard tables are used, careful attention must be paid to the physical setup of the metering system. Otherwise the results would vary with the installation.

Straightening Vanes. The purpose of these vanes is to minimize the effect of swirls, eddy currents, or irregular velocity distribution on meter accuracy. These vanes are built into a nipple and consist of a bundle of small pipe or tubing as shown in Fig. 12-3. The dimension of each tube d should not exceed $\frac{1}{4}$ the inside pipe diameter D. The length should be at least 10d.

Unless necessary, vanes should not be used for they are susceptible to erosion, introduce additional pressure loss, and clog easily.

Orifice Location. Figure 12-3 shows the minimum distance the orifice should be from valves and fittings in order that proper metering might result.

Size of Orifice and Meter Run. The meter run should be sized so that the anticipated maximum and minimum flow rates may be handled within the satisfactory ratio of orifice to pipe diameter. In doing this it should be kept in mind that

1. The differential h_w should not exceed the static pressure p_f (based on numerical values only, not units).

2. The meter run ID should be at least one-third larger than the orifice opening.

3. Both the differential- and static-pressure pens should preferably operate within the middle 60 per cent of the recording-chart range.

As a practical matter, the meter run ID should not be less than 3 in. in nominal diameter regardless of the small quantity of gas flowing. As a first approximation Eq. (6) should be solved for C' at the flow rate h_w and p_f desired. Then

$$\text{Orifice ID (in.)} = \left(\frac{C'}{250}\right)^{0.5} \tag{8}$$

If the maximum anticipated flow rate is used to find C', multiplying the orifice size found in Eq. (8) by 1.5 gives the approximate minimum pipe diameter needed. Once this has been established it is a relatively simple matter to change orifice plates as the flow varies to keep the values of h_w and p_f in the desired range.

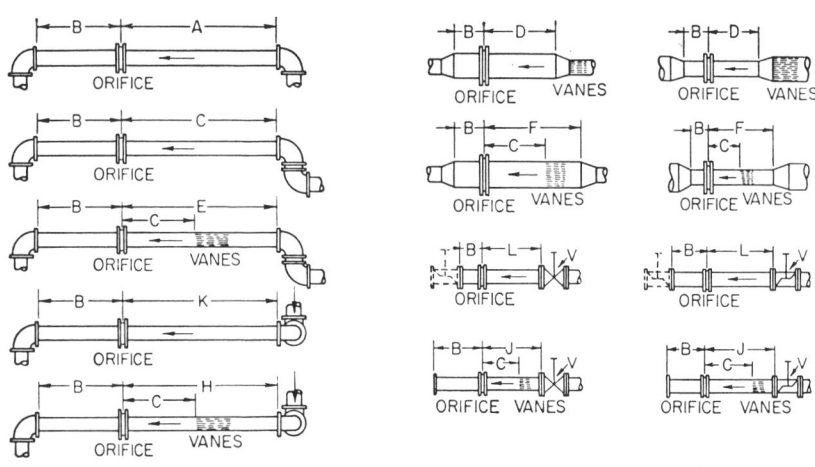

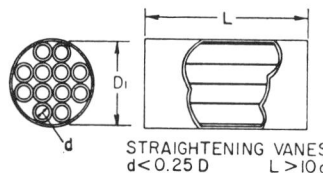

STRAIGHTENING VANES
d < 0.25 D   L > 10 d

MINIMUM LENGTHS OF STRAIGHT PIPE

β	A	B	C	D	E	F	G	H	J	K	L
0.10	6.0	2.4	5.0	6.0	8.5	8.5	8.5	9.5	9.5	14.0	16.0
0.20	6.0	2.7	5.0	6.0	8.5	8.5	8.5	9.5	9.5	14.5	17.5
0.30	6.0	3.0	5.0	6.0	8.5	8.5	8.5	9.6	9.5	16.0	19.5
0.40	6.0	3.3	5.0	6.0	8.5	8.5	8.5	9.6	9.5	17.8	21.6
0.50	6.8	3.6	5.3	7.4	9.2	9.3	10.0	10.0	10.3	20.2	25.0
0.60	9.0	3.9	5.7	9.4	10.4	10.4	13.4	11.3	12.0	24.7	30.0
0.70	14.0	4.2	6.6	12.0	12.2	12.0	18.5	13.0	15.0	30.5	38.0
0.80	20.0	4.5	8.0	15.0	15.5	15.0	25.0	16.5	19.5	40.0	50.0

β = ratio diameter of orifice to inside diameter of pipe.

FIG. 12-3. Proper installation of a meter run for an orifice meter. (*Courtesy of National Gasoline Supply Men's Assoc.*)

Standard sharp-edged orifice plates should be used, the thickness of which is at least $\frac{1}{16}$ in. For pipes larger than 4 in. it is at least $\frac{1}{8}$ in. The thickness should not exceed one-eighth the orifice opening.

Other Forms of Metering Systems

For well-test purposes other forms of velocity meters are used—orifice well testers, critical-flow provers, pilot tubes, and side-static methods. These methods are not so accurate as the meters discussed above but are convenient and often yield results accurate enough for the purpose.

Orifice Well Tester. This consists of a 2-in. nipple with provision for attaching different sharp-edged orifice plates on the end. The static pressure just upstream from this plate may then be measured. Table 12-2 shows various applicable charts for measuring flow.

Table 12-2a. Capacities of Orifice Well Testers*†

Values are cubic feet in 24 hours at a base pressure of 14.65 psia; base and flowing temperature, 60°F

Pressure, in. of water	Specific gravity								
	0.60	0.70	0.80	0.90	1.00	1.10	1.20	1.30	1.50
⅛-in. Orifice in ⅛-in. Plate									
1.0	528	489	458	432	409	390	374	359	334
1.2	578	536	501	473	448	427	409	393	366
1.4	625	579	541	511	484	462	442	425	395
1.6	669	619	579	546	518	494	473	454	423
1.8	709	657	614	579	549	524	502	482	449
2.0	747	692	647	610	579	552	528	508	473
2.2	784	726	679	640	607	579	554	532	496
2.4	818	758	709	669	634	605	579	556	518
2.6	852	789	738	696	660	629	603	579	539
2.8	884	819	766	722	685	653	625	601	559
3.0	915	848	793	747	709	676	647	622	579
3.2	945	875	819	772	732	698	669	642	598
3.4	975	902	844	796	755	720	689	662	616
3.6	1000	928	868	819	777	740	709	681	634
3.8	1030	954	892	841	798	761	728	700	651
4.0	1060	979	915	863	819	781	747	718	669
4.5	1120	1040	971	915	868	823	793	762	709
5.0	1180	1090	1020	965	915	873	836	803	747
5.5	1240	1150	1070	1010	960	915	876	842	784
6.0	1290	1200	1120	1060	1000	956	915	879	819
6.5	1340	1250	1170	1100	1040	995	953	916	852
7.0	1390	1290	1210	1140	1080	1030	989	950	885
8.0	1500	1380	1290	1220	1160	1100	1060	1020	945
9.0	1590	1470	1370	1290	1230	1170	1120	1080	1000
10.0	1670	1550	1450	1360	1290	1230	1180	1140	1060
11.0	1750	1620	1520	1430	1360	1300	1240	1190	1110
12.0	1830	1700	1590	1500	1420	1350	1300	1250	1160
13.0	1910	1770	1650	1560	1480	1410	1350	1300	1200
14.0	1980	1830	1720	1620	1540	1460	1400	1350	1250
15.0	2050	1900	1780	1680	1590	1520	1450	1390	1300
¼-in. Orifice in ⅛-in. Plate									
1.0	1680	1560	1460	1370	1300	1240	1190	1140	1060
1.2	1850	1710	1600	1510	1430	1360	1300	1250	1170
1.4	1990	1840	1730	1630	1540	1470	1410	1350	1260
1.6	2130	1970	1840	1740	1650	1570	1510	1450	1350
1.8	2260	2090	1960	1840	1750	1670	1660	1530	1430
2.0	2370	2200	2060	1940	1840	1760	1680	1620	1510
2.2	2490	2310	2160	2040	1930	1840	1770	1700	1580
2.4	2610	2410	2260	2130	2020	1930	1840	1770	1650
2.6	2710	2510	2350	2220	2100	2000	1920	1840	1720
2.8	2810	2610	2440	2300	2180	2080	1990	1910	1780
3.0	2920	2700	2530	2380	2260	2150	2060	1980	1840
3.2	3010	2790	2610	2460	2330	2220	2130	2050	1900
3.4	3110	2870	2690	2540	2410	2290	2200	2110	1960
3.6	3190	2960	2770	2610	2470	2360	2260	2170	2020
3.8	3280	3040	2840	2680	2540	2420	2320	2230	2070
4.0	3370	3120	2920	2750	2610	2490	2380	2290	2130
4.5	3580	3310	3090	2920	2770	2640	2530	2430	2260
5.0	3710	3490	3260	3070	2920	2780	2660	2560	2380
5.5	3950	3650	3420	3220	3060	2920	2790	2680	2500
6.0	4120	3820	3570	3370	3190	3040	2910	2800	2610
6.5	4300	3970	3720	3500	3330	3170	3040	2920	2710
7.0	4450	4120	3860	3640	3450	3290	3150	3030	2820
8.0	4760	4410	4120	3890	3690	3520	3370	3230	3010
9.0	5050	4680	4370	4120	3910	3730	3570	3430	3190
10.0	5320	4930	4610	4350	4120	3930	3760	3620	3370
11.0	5600	5180	4850	4570	4340	4140	3960	3810	3540
12.0	5860	5420	5070	4780	4540	4325	4150	3980	3700
13.0	6100	5650	5280	4980	4730	4510	4320	4140	3860
14.0	6330	5860	5480	5170	4900	4670	4480	4300	4000
15.0	6550	6070	5670	5350	5080	4840	4640	4450	4140

Table 12-2a. Capacities of Orifice Well Testers*† (*Continued*)

Pressure, in. of water	Specific gravity								
	0.60	0.70	0.80	0.90	1.00	1.10	1.20	1.30	1.50
⅜-in. Orifice in ⅛-in. Plate									
1.0	3560	3300	3090	2910	2760	2640	2520	2430	2260
1.2	3910	3620	3390	3190	3030	2890	2760	2660	2470
1.4	4220	3910	3360	3450	3270	3120	2990	2870	2670
1.6	4520	4180	3910	3690	3500	3340	3190	3070	2860
1.8	4790	4440	4150	3910	3710	3540	3390	3250	3030
2.0	5050	4670	4370	4120	3910	3780	3570	3430	3190
2.2	5290	4900	4580	4320	4100	3910	3740	3600	3350
2.4	5520	5120	4790	4510	4280	4080	3910	3760	3500
2.6	5760	5330	4980	4700	4460	4250	4070	3910	3640
2.8	5980	5530	5170	4880	4630	4410	4220	4060	3780
3.0	6180	5720	5350	5050	4790	4570	4370	4200	3910
3.2	6390	5910	5530	5210	4950	4720	4520	4340	4040
3.4	6580	6090	5700	5370	5100	4860	4650	4470	4160
3.6	6780	6270	5860	5530	5250	5000	4790	4600	4280
3.8	6960	6440	6020	5680	5390	5140	4920	4730	4400
4.0	7140	6610	6180	5830	5530	5270	5050	4850	4520
4.5	7580	7010	6560	6180	5870	5590	5350	5410	4790
5.0	7980	7390	6910	6520	6180	5890	5640	5420	5050
5.5	8370	7750	7250	6830	6480	6180	5920	5690	5290
6.0	8740	8090	7570	7140	6770	6460	6180	5940	5530
6.5	9100	8430	7880	7430	7050	6720	6440	6180	5760
7.0	8450	8740	8180	7710	7320	6980	6680	6420	5970
8.0	10100	9350	8740	8240	7820	7460	7140	6860	6380
9.0	10700	9910	9270	8740	8300	7910	7570	7280	6770
10.0	11300	10400	9770	9200	8740	8340	7980	7670	7140
11.0	11900	11000	10300	9700	9200	8780	8410	8070	7510
12.0	12400	11500	10800	10100	9620	9180	8790	8440	7860
13.0	12900	12000	11200	10600	10000	9560	9160	8790	8190
14.0	13400	12400	11600	11000	10400	9920	9510	9120	8490
15.0	13900	12900	12000	11300	10800	10300	9840	9440	8790
½-in. Orifice in ⅛-in. Plate									
1.0	6270	5810	5430	5120	4860	4630	4440	4260	3970
1.2	6870	6360	5950	5610	5320	5070	4860	4670	4350
1.4	7420	6870	6430	6060	5750	5480	5250	5040	4690
1.6	7940	7350	6870	6480	6150	5860	5610	5390	5020
1.8	8430	7880	7290	6870	6520	6220	5950	5720	5330
2.0	8870	8210	7680	7240	6870	6550	6270	6330	5610
2.2	9310	8610	8060	7600	7210	6870	6580	6320	5880
2.4	9720	9000	8420	7940	7530	7180	6870	6600	6150
2.6	10100	9360	8760	8260	7830	7470	7150	6870	6400
2.8	10500	9720	9090	8570	8130	7750	7420	7130	6640
3.0	10900	10100	9410	8870	8420	8030	7680	7380	6870
3.2	11200	10400	9720	9170	8700	8290	7940	7630	7100
3.4	11600	10700	10000	9450	8960	8550	8180	7860	7320
3.6	11900	11000	10300	9720	9220	8790	8420	8090	7530
3.8	12200	11300	10600	9980	9470	9030	8650	8310	7730
4.0	12500	11600	10900	10200	9720	9270	8870	8530	7940
4.5	13300	12300	11500	10900	10300	9830	8410	9040	8420
5.0	14100	13000	12100	11500	10900	10400	9920	9530	8870
5.5	14700	13600	12700	12000	11400	10900	10400	10000	9310
6.0	15400	14200	13300	12500	11900	11300	10900	10400	9720
6.5	16000	14800	13900	13100	12400	11800	11300	10900	10100
7.0	16700	15400	14400	13600	12900	12300	11700	11300	10500
8.0	17200	16400	15400	14500	13700	13100	12500	12100	11200
9.0	18800	17400	16300	15400	14600	13900	13300	12800	11900
10.0	19900	18400	17200	16200	15400	14700	14000	13500	12500
11.0	20900	19400	18100	17100	16200	15500	14800	14200	13200
12.0	21900	20300	19000	17900	17000	16200	15500	14900	13800
13.0	22800	21100	19700	18600	17700	16800	16100	15500	14400
14.0	23700	21900	20500	19300	18300	17500	16700	16100	15000
15.0	24500	22700	21200	20000	19000	18100	17300	16600	15500

Table 12-2a. Capacities of Orifice Well Testers*† (Continued)

Pressure, in. of water	Specific gravity								
	0.60	0.70	0.80	0.90	1.00	1.10	1.20	1.30	1.50

¾-in. Orifice in ⅛-in. Plate

Pressure, in. of water	0.60	0.70	0.80	0.90	1.00	1.10	1.20	1.30	1.50
1.0	14200	13100	12300	11600	11000	10500	10000	9260	8960
1.2	15500	14400	13400	12700	12000	11500	11000	10500	9810
1.5	16800	15500	14500	13700	13000	12400	11800	11400	10600
1.6	17900	16600	15500	14600	13900	13200	12700	12200	11300
1.8	19000	17600	16500	15500	14700	14000	13400	12900	12000
2.0	20000	18500	17300	16400	15500	14800	14200	13600	12700
2.2	21000	19400	18200	17100	16300	15500	14900	14300	13300
2.4	21900	20300	19000	17900	17000	16200	15500	14900	13900
2.6	22900	21100	19800	18600	17700	16800	16100	15500	14400
2.8	23800	21900	20500	19300	18400	17500	16800	16100	15000
3.0	24500	22700	21200	20000	19000	18100	17300	16700	15500
3.2	25300	23500	21900	20700	19600	18700	17900	17200	16000
3.4	26100	24200	22600	21300	20200	19300	18500	17770	16500
3.6	26900	24900	23300	21900	20800	19800	19000	18300	17000
3.8	27600	25600	23900	22500	21400	20400	19500	18800	17500
4.0	28300	26200	24500	23100	21900	20900	20000	19200	17900
4.5	30100	27800	26000	24500	23300	22200	21200	20400	19000
5.0	31600	29300	27400	25900	24500	23400	22400	21500	20000
5.5	33200	30700	28800	27100	25700	24500	23500	22600	21000
6.0	34700	32100	30000	28300	26900	25600	24500	23600	21900
6.5	36100	33400	31300	29500	28000	26700	25500	24500	22800
7.0	37400	34700	32500	30600	29000	27700	26500	25500	23700
8.0	40000	37100	34700	32700	31000	29600	28300	27200	25300
9.0	42500	39300	36800	34700	32900	31400	30000	28900	26900
10.0	44800	41500	38800	36600	34700	33100	31700	30400	28300
11.0	47200	43700	40900	38500	36500	34800	33400	32000	29800
12.0	49300	45700	42700	40300	38200	36400	34900	33500	31200
13.0	51400	47600	44500	42000	39800	38000	36400	34900	32500
14.0	53300	49300	46200	43500	41300	39400	37700	36200	33700
15.0	55200	51100	47800	45100	42800	40800	39100	37500	34900

1-in. Orifice in ⅛-in. Plate

Pressure, in. of water	0.60	0.70	0.80	0.90	1.00	1.10	1.20	1.30	1.50
1.0	25800	23900	22400	21100	20000	19100	18300	17500	16300
1.2	28300	26200	24500	23100	21900	20900	20000	19200	17900
1.4	30600	28300	26500	24900	23700	22600	21600	20800	19300
1.6	32700	30200	28300	26700	25300	24100	23100	22200	20700
1.8	34600	32100	30000	28300	26800	25600	24500	23500	21900
2.0	36500	33800	31600	29800	28300	27000	25800	24800	23100
2.2	38300	35400	33200	31300	29700	28300	27100	26000	24200
2.4	40000	37000	34600	32700	31000	29500	28300	27200	25300
2.6	41600	38500	36000	34000	32200	30700	29400	28300	26300
2.8	43200	40000	37400	35300	33500	31900	30500	29300	27300
3.0	44700	41400	38700	36500	34600	33000	31600	30400	28300
3.2	46200	42800	40000	37700	35800	34100	32700	31400	29200
3.4	47600	44100	41200	38900	36900	35200	33700	32300	30100
3.6	48900	45300	42400	40000	37900	36200	34600	33300	31000
3.8	50300	46600	43600	41100	39000	37200	35600	34200	31800
4.0	51600	47800	44700	42200	40000	38100	36500	35100	32700
4.5	54700	50700	47400	44700	42400	40400	38700	37200	34600
5.0	57700	53400	50000	47100	44700	42600	40800	39200	36500
5.5	60500	56100	52400	49400	46900	44700	42800	41100	38300
6.0	63300	58500	54800	51600	49000	46700	44700	43000	40000
6.5	65800	61000	57000	53800	51000	48600	46600	44700	41600
7.0	68300	63200	59200	55800	52900	50500	48300	46400	43200
8.0	73100	67600	63200	59600	56600	53900	51600	49600	46200
9.0	77500	71700	67100	63200	60000	57200	54800	52600	49000
10.0	81600	75600	70700	66700	63200	60300	57700	55500	51600
11.0	85900	79500	74400	70100	66500	63500	60800	58400	54300
12.0	89800	83200	77800	73300	69600	66400	63600	61000	56800
13.0	93600	86600	81000	76400	72500	69100	66200	63600	59200
14.0	97300	89900	84100	79300	75200	71700	68700	66000	61400
15.0	101000	93000	87100	82100	77900	74200	71200	68300	63600

Table 12-2a. Capacities of Orifice Well Testers*† *(Continued)*

Pressure, in. of water	Specific gravity								
	0.60	0.70	0.80	0.90	1.00	1.10	1.20	1.30	1.50
1¼-in. Orifice in ⅛-in. Plate									
1.0	43900	40600	38000	35800	34000	32400	31000	29800	27700
1.2	48000	44500	41600	39200	37200	35500	34000	32600	30400
1.4	51900	48000	44900	42400	40200	38300	36700	35300	32800
1.6	55500	51400	48100	45300	43000	41000	39200	37700	35100
1.8	58900	54500	51000	48100	45600	43500	41600	40000	37200
2.0	62000	57400	53700	50600	40800	45800	43900	42100	39200
2.2	65100	60200	56300	53100	50400	48000	46000	44200	41100
2.4	67900	62900	58800	55500	52600	50200	48100	46200	43000
2.6	70700	65500	61200	57700	54800	52200	50000	48000	44700
2.8	73300	67900	63600	59900	56800	54200	51900	49900	46400
3.0	76000	70300	65800	62000	58900	56100	53700	51600	48100
3.2	78500	72700	68000	64100	60800	58000	55500	53300	49600
3.4	80900	74900	70100	66000	62700	59700	57200	55000	51200
3.6	83300	77000	72100	67900	64500	61500	58800	56500	52600
3.8	85500	79200	74000	69800	66200	63100	60500	58100	54100
4.0	87800	81200	76000	71600	68000	64800	62000	59600	55500
4.5	93100	86100	80600	76000	72100	68700	65800	63200	58800
5.0	98100	90800	84900	80100	76000	72400	69400	66600	62000
5.5	103000	95200	89100	84000	79700	76000	72700	69900	65100
6.0	107000	99500	93000	87700	83200	79300	76000	73000	67900
6.5	112000	104000	96900	91300	86600	82600	79100	76000	70700
7.0	116000	107000	101000	98400	89900	85700	82100	78900	73400
8.0	124000	115000	107000	101000	96100	91600	87700	84300	78500
9.0	132000	122000	114000	107000	102000	97200	93100	89400	83200
10.0	138000	128000	120000	113000	107000	102000	98100	94200	87700
11.0	145000	135000	126000	119000	113000	107000	103000	98800	92000
12.0	152000	141000	132000	124000	118000	112000	108000	103000	96200
13.0	158000	147000	137000	129000	123000	117000	112000	108000	100000
14.0	164000	152000	142000	134000	127000	121000	116000	112000	104000
15.0	170000	158000	147000	139000	132000	126000	120000	116000	108000

* Courtesy of NGSMA Handbook.

† The volumes obtained from these tables apply only to Orifice Well Testers manufactured by American Meter Company.   For other testers, use the tables recommended by the manufacturer.

The rates given in the tables for water are based on the following formula:

$$Q = C \sqrt{h}$$

where Q = rate in cubic feet in 24 hours
   C = rate for 1 in. given in the tables
   h = pressure in inches of water

The rates given in the tables for mercury are based on the following equation which was determined from a series of 100 tests covering the limits of the tables:

$$Q = C \sqrt{H(29.32 + 0.3H) \div G}$$

where Q = rate in thousands of cubic feet in 24 hours
   C = 7.464 for ¾-in. orifice
     = 13.61 for 1-in. orifice
     = 23.10 for 1¼-in. orifice
   H = pressure in inches of mercury
   29.32 = assumed atmospheric pressure in inches of mercury
     = 14.4 psi
   0.3 = factor determined by tests
   G = specific gravity of gas

Table 12-2b. Capacities of Orifice Well Testers

Values are thousands of cubic feet in 24 hours at a base pressure of 14.65 psia; base and flowing temperature, 60°F

Pressure, in. of mercury	Specific gravity								
	0.60	0.70	0.80	0.90	1.00	1.10	1.20	1.30	1.50
¾-in. Orifice in ⅛-in. Plate									
1.0	52	49	45	43	41	39	37	36	33
1.1	55	51	48	45	43	41	39	37	35
1.2	58	53	50	47	45	43	41	39	36
1.3	60	55	52	49	46	44	42	41	38
1.4	62	58	54	51	48	46	44	42	39
1.5	64	60	56	53	50	48	45	44	41
1.6	67	62	58	54	52	49	47	45	42
1.7	69	64	59	56	53	51	48	47	43
1.8	71	65	61	58	55	52	50	48	45
1.9	73	67	63	59	56	54	51	49	46
2.0	75	69	65	61	58	55	53	51	47
2.2	78	72	68	64	61	58	55	53	49
2.4	82	76	71	67	63	60	58	56	52
2.6	85	79	74	70	66	63	60	58	54
2.8	89	82	77	72	69	65	63	60	56
3.0	92	85	79	75	71	68	65	62	58
3.2	95	88	82	77	73	70	67	64	60
3.4	98	91	85	80	76	72	69	67	62
3.6	101	93	87	82	78	74	71	69	64
3.8	104	96	90	85	80	77	73	70	66
4.0	107	99	92	87	82	79	75	72	67
4.5	113	105	98	92	88	84	80	77	72
5.0	120	111	103	98	93	88	85	81	76
5.5	126	116	109	103	97	93	89	85	79
6.0	132	122	114	108	102	97	93	89	83
6.5	137	127	119	112	106	102	97	93	87
7.0	143	132	124	117	111	106	101	97	90
8.0	154	142	133	125	119	113	108	104	97
9.0	164	151	142	134	127	121	116	111	103
10.0	173	160	150	142	134	128	122	118	109
11.0	183	169	158	149	141	135	129	124	115
12.0	192	177	166	156	148	142	135	130	121
13.0	200	185	173	164	155	148	142	136	127
14.0	209	193	181	170	162	154	148	142	132
15.0	217	210	188	177	168	160	153	148	137
16.0	225	208	195	184	174	166	159	153	142
17.0	233	216	202	190	180	172	165	158	147
18.0	241	223	209	197	187	178	170	164	152
19.0	249	230	215	203	192	184	176	169	157
20.0	256	237	222	209	198	189	181	174	162
21.0	264	244	228	215	204	195	186	179	167
22.0	271	251	234	221	210	200	191	184	171
23.0	278	257	241	227	215	205	197	189	176
24.0	285	264	247	233	221	211	202	194	180
25.0	292	271	253	239	226	216	207	199	185
26.0	300	277	259	245	232	221	212	204	189
27.0	306	284	265	250	237	226	216	208	194
28.0	313	290	271	256	242	231	221	213	198
29.0	320	296	277	261	248	236	226	218	202
30.0	327	302	283	267	253	241	231	222	207
31.0	334	309	289	272	258	246	236	227	211
32.0	340	315	294	278	263	251	240	231	215
33.0	347	321	300	283	268	256	245	236	219
34.0	353	327	306	289	273	261	250	240	223
35.0	360	333	311	294	278	266	254	245	227
36.0	336	339	317	299	283	271	259	249	231
37.0	373	345	323	304	288	275	263	253	236
38.0	379	351	328	310	293	280	268	258	240
39.0	386	357	334	315	298	285	272	262	244
40.0	392	363	339	320	303	289	277	266	248

Table 12-2b. Capacities of Orifice Well Testers (Continued)

Pressure, in. of mercury	Specific gravity								
	0.60	0.70	0.80	0.90	1.00	1.10	1.20	1.30	1.50
1-in. Orifice in ⅛-in. Plate									
1.0	96	89	83	78	74	71	68	65	60
1.1	100	93	87	82	78	74	71	68	63
1.2	105	97	91	86	81	77	74	71	66
1.3	109	101	95	89	85	81	77	74	69
1.4	113	105	98	93	88	84	80	77	72
1.5	117	109	102	96	91	87	83	80	74
1.6	121	112	105	99	94	90	86	83	77
1.7	125	116	108	102	97	92	88	85	79
1.8	129	119	112	105	100	95	91	88	81
1.9	132	123	115	108	103	98	94	90	84
2.0	136	126	118	111	105	100	96	92	86
2.2	143	132	124	117	111	105	101	97	90
2.4	149	138	129	122	116	110	105	101	94
2.6	155	144	135	127	120	115	110	106	98
2.8	161	150	140	132	125	119	114	110	102
3.0	167	155	145	137	130	124	118	114	106
3.2	173	160	150	141	134	128	122	117	109
3.4	179	165	155	146	138	132	126	121	113
3.6	184	170	159	150	142	136	130	125	116
3.8	189	175	164	154	146	140	134	128	120
4.0	194	180	168	159	150	143	137	132	123
4.5	206	191	179	169	160	153	146	140	131
5.0	218	202	189	178	169	161	154	148	138
5.5	229	212	199	187	178	169	162	156	145
6.0	240	222	208	196	186	177	170	163	152
6.5	251	232	217	205	194	185	177	170	158
7.0	261	241	226	213	202	192	184	177	165
8.0	280	259	242	229	217	207	198	190	177
9.0	298	278	258	244	231	220	211	203	189
10.0	316	293	274	258	245	233	223	215	200
11.0	333	308	288	272	258	246	235	226	210
12.0	349	323	303	285	271	258	247	237	221
13.0	365	338	316	298	283	270	258	248	231
14.0	381	352	330	311	295	281	269	259	241
15.0	396	366	343	323	306	292	280	269	250
16.0	411	380	356	335	318	303	290	279	260
17.0	425	394	368	347	329	314	300	289	269
18.0	439	407	381	359	340	325	311	299	278
19.0	453	420	393	370	351	335	320	308	287
20.0	467	432	405	381	362	345	330	317	295
21.0	481	445	416	392	372	355	340	327	304
22.0	494	457	428	403	383	365	349	336	312
23.0	507	470	439	414	393	375	358	345	321
24.0	520	482	451	425	403	384	368	354	329
25.0	533	494	462	435	413	394	377	362	337
26.0	546	506	473	446	423	403	386	371	345
27.0	559	517	484	456	433	413	395	380	353
28.0	571	529	495	466	442	422	404	388	361
29.0	583	540	505	477	452	431	412	397	369
30.0	596	552	516	487	462	440	421	405	377
31.0	608	563	527	496	471	449	430	413	384
32.0	620	574	539	506	480	458	438	421	392
33.0	632	585	548	516	490	467	447	430	400
34.0	644	596	558	526	499	476	455	438	407
35.0	656	607	568	536	508	485	464	446	415
36.0	668	618	578	545	517	493	472	454	422
37.0	679	629	589	555	526	502	480	462	430
38.0	691	640	599	565	535	511	489	470	437
39.0	703	651	609	574	544	519	497	478	444
40.0	714	661	619	583	553	528	505	485	452

Table 12-2b. Capacities of Orifice Well Testers (*Continued*)

Pressure, in. of mercury	Specific gravity								
	0.60	0.70	0.80	0.90	1.00	1.10	1.20	1.30	1.50
1¼-in. Orifice in ⅛-in. Plate									
1.0	162	150	141	132	126	120	115	110	103
1.1	170	158	147	139	132	126	120	116	108
1.2	178	165	154	145	138	132	126	121	113
1.3	185	171	160	151	143	137	131	126	117
1.4	192	178	167	157	149	142	136	131	122
1.5	199	184	173	163	154	147	141	135	126
1.6	206	191	178	168	160	152	146	140	130
1.7	212	197	184	173	164	157	150	144	134
1.8	219	202	189	178	169	161	155	149	138
1.9	225	208	195	184	174	166	159	153	142
2.0	231	214	200	188	179	171	163	157	146
2.2	242	224	210	198	188	179	171	165	153
2.4	253	234	219	206	196	187	179	172	160
2.6	264	244	229	215	204	195	187	179	167
2.8	274	254	237	224	212	202	194	186	173
3.0	284	263	246	232	220	210	201	193	180
3.2	293	272	254	240	227	217	208	199	186
3.4	303	281	262	247	235	224	214	206	192
3.6	312	289	270	255	242	230	221	212	197
3.8	321	297	278	262	249	237	227	218	203
4.0	330	305	285	269	255	243	233	224	208
4.5	350	324	304	286	271	259	248	238	222
5.0	370	343	321	302	287	273	262	251	234
5.5	389	360	337	318	301	287	275	264	246
6.0	407	377	353	333	316	301	288	277	258
6.5	425	394	368	347	329	314	301	289	269
7.0	442	409	383	361	343	327	313	300	280
8.0	475	440	411	388	368	351	336	323	300
9.0	506	469	439	413	392	374	358	344	320
10.0	536	496	464	438	415	396	379	364	339
11.0	565	523	489	461	438	417	399	384	357
12.0	593	549	514	484	459	438	419	403	375
13.0	620	574	537	506	480	458	438	421	392
14.0	646	598	559	527	500	477	457	439	409
15.0	672	622	582	548	520	496	475	456	425
16.0	697	645	604	569	540	515	493	473	441
17.0	721	668	625	589	559	533	510	490	456
18.0	746	690	646	609	578	551	527	507	472
19.0	769	712	666	628	596	568	544	523	487
20.0	793	734	687	647	614	586	561	539	501
21.0	816	755	706	666	632	603	577	554	516
22.0	838	776	726	684	649	619	593	570	530
23.0	861	797	745	703	667	636	609	585	544
24.0	883	818	765	721	684	652	624	600	558
25.0	905	838	784	739	701	668	640	615	572
26.0	927	858	803	757	718	684	655	629	586
27.0	948	878	821	774	734	700	670	644	600
28.0	969	897	839	789	751	716	685	658	613
29.0	990	917	858	809	761	732	700	673	626
30.0	1011	936	876	826	783	747	715	687	640
31.0	1032	955	894	843	799	762	730	701	653
32.0	1052	974	912	859	815	777	744	715	666
33.0	1073	993	929	876	831	793	759	729	679
34.0	1093	1012	947	893	847	808	773	743	691
35.0	1113	1031	964	909	862	822	787	756	704
36.0	1133	1049	982	925	878	837	801	770	717
37.0	1153	1068	999	942	893	852	816	783	729
38.0	1173	1086	1016	958	909	867	830	797	742
39.0	1193	1104	1033	974	924	881	844	810	754
40.0	1212	1122	1050	990	939	896	857	824	767

The accuracy of this device is limited but it is suitable for measuring the amount of gas being produced where the pressures are relatively low and the production is to the atmosphere.

Critical-flow Prover. The critical-flow prover is a similar device that exhausts the gas to the atmosphere. It is also a special pipe nipple with a flange for holding special plates to the end. It is based on the principle that the velocity of sound represents the maximum speed at which a pressure effect may be propagated through a gas; i.e., once this velocity is reached further increase in the pressure differential will not increase the pressure at the throat. This means that the mass rate of flow would not increase as the pressure differential p_2/p_1 was decreased below this critical value. With ideal gases the critical ratio is 0.49 for monatomic gases and 0.53 for diatomic gases, with slightly higher values for complex gases. Saturated steam, for example, shows a critical pressure ratio of 0.55. The range of these values is the source of the common rule of thumb that, once the pressure reduction is twofold, critical-flow phenomena limit the *mass* rate of flow.

When metering gas under such conditions the *volume* rate of flow will be a function of upstream pressure, gas gravity, and gas temperature since it is a compressible fluid.

The orifice used differs from that in the orifice meter. This one is thicker and has a rounded edge. This edge is placed toward the flow, for experience has shown that a sharp-edged orifice does not give reproducible results under critical-flow conditions. In fact sharp-edged orifices do not conform to existing theories and correlations.

The general equation for a critical-flow prover is

$$Q = \frac{Cp}{(GT)^{0.5}} \tag{9}$$

where p = pressure on prover, psia
    C = orifice coefficient for prover
    Q = rate of flow, thousands of standard cu ft/24 hr (Mcf/D), measured at 14.4 psia and 60°F
    G = specific gravity of gas (air = 1.00)
    T = absolute temperature, °R

The critical-flow prover is one of the basic devices used for determining the gas-flow rate in the open-flow testing of gas wells. Values of the coefficient C may be found in Table 12-3.

Table 12-3. Orifice Coefficients for Critical-flow Provers

Size of orifice, in.	Orifice coefficient	
	2-in. prover	4-in. prover
$\frac{1}{16}$	1.524	
$\frac{3}{32}$	3.355	
$\frac{1}{8}$	6.301	
$\frac{5}{16}$	14.47	
$\frac{7}{32}$	19.97	
$\frac{1}{4}$	25.86	24.92
$\frac{5}{16}$	39.77	
$\frac{3}{8}$	56.68	56.01
$\frac{7}{16}$	81.09	
$\frac{1}{2}$	101.8	100.2
$\frac{5}{8}$	154.0	156.1
$\frac{3}{4}$	224.9	223.7
$\frac{7}{8}$	309.3	304.2
1	406.7	396.3
$1\frac{1}{8}$	520.8	499.2
$1\frac{1}{4}$	657.5	616.4
$1\frac{3}{8}$	807.8	742.1
$1\frac{1}{2}$	1,002	884.3
$1\frac{3}{4}$		1,208
2		1,596
$2\frac{1}{2}$		2,566
3		3,904

Pitot Tube. The pitot tube is another measuring device used extensively for testing flow rates during tests. It works by measuring the difference between the impact pressure at the tip and the static pressure in the flowing stream. This impact pressure results from conversion of the kinetic energy of the flowing gas to pressure. If the conversion efficiency is relatively constant a conversion between pressure and flow rate is possible. The pitot tube is normally made of ⅛-in.-ID pipe and is inserted in the center of a nipple at least 8 diameters long.

Table 12-4 gives the flow rate in thousands of cubic feet per day for a pitot tube inserted in different-diameter nipples. Figure 12-2d shows the general schematic arrangement.

A pitot tube is used largely for temporary flow measurement since it is small and easy to handle. Very few permanent installations are made, for it produces low-pressure differentials, is difficult to calibrate, and often clogs.

A pitot tube measures a point velocity, i.e., the velocity at only one point across the cross section of the pipe. Inasmuch as the velocity varies throughout this cross section, the problem of proper location presents itself. In the absence of unknown disturbing elements such as pipe burrs or undue roughness, the velocity at the center is theoretically 20 per cent greater than the mean velocity. For approximate measurement, the standard tables use this factor to convert readings taken at the center of the pipe to a volume flow rate. For exact work the mean velocity would be found by taking a series of experimental velocity measurements across the pipe diameter.

A similar method is used for large gas-flow rates and/or where debris produced with the gas makes other methods unfeasible. This consists simply of measuring the static pressure through a side opening 4 diameters from the end of a nipple at least 8 diameters long. Values for this system are also shown in Table 12-4. This is the least desirable of the methods discussed because of the potential error involved.

Further data on the use of these four devices for the measurement of gas flow may be found in U.S. Bureau of Mines Monograph 7.

Recorder. The normal orifice meter is equipped with a two-pen recorder for measuring both static and differential pressure. The differential pen is normally actuated through a mechanical system using either a mercury manometer or a bellows. Both types are shown in Fig. 12-4.

With the former a slight change in flow rate changes the level in the mercury manometer. A large float resting on the mercury changes level correspondingly and transmits this movement to the chart pen through a system of levers.

The bellows-type or mercuryless meter consists of two bellows filled with some fluid such as glycol. As the pressure differential changes this fluid moves between the bellows through a damping device, causing the bellows to expand or contract. The pen is actuated by a center rod which is connected to the free ends of the bellows. The small liquid-filled bellows located on the high-pressure side serves as an expansion device to correct for changes in ambient temperature.

Both types of instruments are equipped with check valves to protect them from differential pressures that exceed the range of the instrument. This is more of a problem with the mercury meter, for excessive differential pressure can blow mercury out of the meter, which destroys its calibration. In the bellows meter, soft-seated check valves prevent the flow of fluid between the bellows. The bellows are then not likely to rupture for they are supported internally by the fluid contained within them.

The bellows meter has gained increasing popularity, particularly in field operations. Even though the initial cost is higher many operators feel that this is compensated for by decreased maintenance. It also offers the advantage of operating either properly or not at all, with little range in between. Eliminated are the problems of mercury loss, worrying about the change in calibration with the amount of mercury, and the like. Until it fails, experience has shown that this meter needs little routine calibration.

With both types the static pressure is read from a pen actuated by a bourdon tube. The lead for this may come off either the upstream or downstream tap. In most installations it is good practice to order a bourdon tube having about twice the

PRODUCTION EQUIPMENT

Table 12-4. Pitot-tube Table*

In. of water	In. of mercury	Psi	1 in.	2 in.	3 in.	4 in.	5 in.	6 in.	8 in.	10 in.	12 in.
Impact pressure			Open flow, Mcf/D								
0.1	....	...	10.97	44	99	176	274	395	702	1,100	1,580
0.2	....	...	15.52	62	140	248	388	559	944	1,550	2,240
0.3	....	...	19.00	76	171	304	475	684	1,220	1,900	2,740
0.4	....	...	21.95	88	198	351	549	790	1,410	2,200	3,160
0.5	....	...	24.53	98	221	392	613	882	1,570	2,450	3,530
0.6	....	...	26.89	108	242	430	672	968	1,720	2,690	3,870
0.7	....	...	29.03	116	261	464	726	1,050	1,860	2,900	4,180
0.8	....	...	31.02	124	279	497	776	1,120	1,990	3,100	4,470
0.9	....	...	32.92	132	296	526	823	1,180	2,110	3,290	4,740
1.0	....	...	34.69	139	312	555	867	1,250	2,200	3,470	5,000
1.25	....	...	38.78	155	349	620	969	1,400	2,480	3,880	5,580
1.36	0.10	...	40.45	162	364	648	1,010	1,460	2,590	4,050	5,820
1.6	0.12	...	43.89	175	395	702	1,100	1,580	2,810	4,390	6,320
1.8	0.13	...	46.56	186	419	744	1,160	1,680	2,980	4,660	6,700
2.0	0.15	...	49.00	196	441	784	1,230	1,760	3,140	4,900	7,060
2.2	0.16	...	51.45	206	463	823	1,290	1,850	3,290	5,150	7,410
2.4	0.18	...	53.74	214	483	860	1,340	1,930	3,440	5,370	7,740
2.7	0.20	...	57.20	228	515	915	1,430	2,060	3,660	5,720	8,230
3.0	0.22	...	60.02	240	540	961	1,500	2,160	3,840	6,000	8,640
3.5	0.26	...	64.91	260	584	1,040	1,620	2,340	4,160	6,490	9,340
4.1	0.30	...	70.01	280	630	1,120	1,750	2,520	4,480	7,000	10,100
4.5	0.33	...	73.60	295	662	1,180	1,840	2,650	4,710	7,360	10,600
5.0	0.37	...	77.57	310	698	1,240	1,940	2,790	4,960	7,760	11,200
5.4	0.40	...	80.90	324	728	1,300	2,020	2,910	5,180	8,090	11,700
6.0	0.44	...	84.91	340	764	1,360	2,120	3,060	5,430	8,490	12,200
6.8	0.50	...	90.48	362	814	1,450	2,260	3,260	5,790	9,050	13,000
8.2	0.60	...	99.20	396	892	1,590	2,480	3,570	6,350	9,920	14,300
9.0	0.66	...	104.0	416	936	1,670	2,600	3,750	6,660	10,400	15,000
9.5	0.70	...	107.0	428	962	1,710	2,680	3,850	6,850	10,700	15,400
10.0	0.74	...	109.7	439	987	1,760	2,740	3,950	7,020	11,000	15,800
10.9	0.80	...	114.5	458	1,030	1,830	2,860	4,120	7,330	11,500	16,500
12.0	0.88	...	120.1	481	1,080	1,920	3,000	4,300	7,690	12,000	17,300
12.2	0.90	...	121.4	486	1,090	1,940	3,040	4,370	7,770	12,100	17,500
13.9	1.02	0.5	129.2	517	1,160	2,070	3,230	4,650	8,270	12,900	18,600
15.0	1.1	...	134.2	537	1,210	2,150	3,360	4,830	8,590	13,400	19,300
16.3	1.2	...	140.1	560	1,260	2,240	3,500	5,040	8,960	14,000	20,200
17.7	1.3	...	145.8	584	1,310	2,330	3,650	5,250	9,330	14,600	21,000
19.0	1.4	...	151.4	606	1,360	2,420	3,790	5,450	9,680	15,100	21,900
20.4	1.5	...	156.7	627	1,410	2,510	3,920	5,640	10,000	15,700	22,600
21.8	1.6	...	161.8	648	1,460	2,590	4,050	5,820	10,400	16,200	23,300
24.5	1.8	...	171.7	686	1,550	2,750	4,290	6,180	11,100	17,200	24,700
27.2	2.0	1.0	180.9	734	1,630	2,890	4,520	6,510	11,600	18,100	26,000
29.9	2.2	...	189.7	768	1,710	3,040	4,740	6,830	12,100	19,000	27,300
32.6	2.4	...	198.0	802	1,780	3,170	4,950	7,130	12,700	19,800	28,500
.....	2.6	...	206.1	824	1,860	3,300	5,150	7,420	13,200	20,600	29,700
	2.8	...	214.0	857	1,930	3,420	5,350	7,700	13,700	21,400	30,800
	3.0	1.5	221.6	887	2,000	3,500	5,540	7,980	14,200	22,600	31,900
	3.2	...	228.9	917	2,060	3,660	5,720	8,240	14,600	22,900	32,000
	3.4	...	235.8	943	2,120	3,770	5,900	8,480	15,100	23,600	34,000
	3.6	...	242.8	971	2,180	3,880	6,070	8,740	15,500	24,300	35,000

Table 12-4. Pitot-tube Table* *(Continued)*

Impact pressure			Open flow, Mcf/D								
In. of water	In. of mercury	Psi	1 in.	2 in.	3 in.	4 in.	5 in.	6 in.	8 in.	10 in.	12 in.
	3.8	....	249.4	998	2,240	3,990	6,230	8,980	16,000	24,900	35,900
	4.0	2.0	255.9	1,020	2,300	4,090	6,400	9,210	16,400	25,600	36,800
	4.2	....	262.0	1,050	2,360	4,190	6,550	9,430	16,800	26,200	37,700
	4.4	....	268.4	1,070	2,410	4,290	6,710	9,650	17,200	26,800	38,600
	4.6	....	274.5	1,100	2,470	4,390	6,860	9,880	17,600	27,500	39,500
	4.8	....	280.3	1,120	2,520	4,490	7,010	10,100	18,000	28,000	40,400
	5.0	2.5	286.1	1,140	2,570	4,580	7,150	10,300	18,300	28,600	41,200
	5.2	....	291.8	1,170	2,630	4,670	7,300	10,500	18,700	29,200	42,000
	5.4	...	297.4	1,190	2,680	4,760	7,440	10,700	19,000	29,700	42,800
	5.6	....	302.7	1,210	2,720	4,840	7,560	10,900	19,400	30,300	43,600
	5.8	....	308.1	1,230	2,770	4,920	7,700	11,100	19,700	30,800	44,300
	6.0	3.0	313.4	1,250	2,820	5,010	7,830	11,300	20,000	31,300	45,100
	6.5	....	326.0	1,300	2,930	5,220	8,150	11,700	20,900	32,600	47,000
	7.0	3.5	338.6	1,350	3,050	5,420	8,460	12,200	21,700	33,900	48,800
	7.5	....	350.0	1,400	3,150	5,600	8,760	12,600	22,400	35,000	50,400
	8.0	4.0	361.5	1,450	3,250	5,780	9,040	13,000	23,100	36,200	52,100
	8.5	....	373.9	1,500	3,370	5,980	9,340	13,400	23,900	37,400	53,700
	9.0	4.5	383.9	1,540	3,460	6,140	9,600	13,800	24,600	38,400	55,300
	9.5	....	394.2	1,580	3,550	6,310	9,860	14,200	25,200	39,400	56,800
	10.0	....	404.6	1,620	3,640	6,470	10,100	14,600	25,900	40,500	58,200
	10.2	5.0	408.1	1,630	3,690	6,540	10,200	14,700	26,100	40,800	58,800
	11.2	5.5	428.0	1,710	3,850	6,850	10,700	15,400	27,400	42,800	61,600
	12.2	6.0	447.0	1,790	4,030	7,150	11,200	16,100	28,600	44,700	64,400
	13.2	6.5	465.5	1,860	4,190	7,450	11,600	16,800	29,800	46,600	67,000
	14.3	7.0	483.0	1,930	4,350	7,730	12,100	17,400	30,900	48,300	69,600
	15.3	7.5	500.0	2,000	4,500	8,000	12,500	18,000	32,000	50,000	72,000
	16.3	8.0	516.0	2,060	4,650	8,260	12,900	18,600	33,000	51,600	74,300
	17.3	8.5	532.1	2,130	4,790	8,520	13,300	19,200	34,100	53,200	76,600
	18.3	9.0	548.0	2,190	4,930	8,770	13,700	19,700	35,100	54,800	78,900
	19.3	9.5	563.0	2,250	5,070	9,000	14,100	20,300	36,000	56,300	81,100
	20.4	10.0	577.6	2,310	5,200	9,240	14,400	20,800	37,000	57,800	83,200
	22.4	11.0	605.6	2,420	5,450	9,680	15,100	21,800	38,800	60,600	87,200
	24.4	12.0	632.5	2,530	5,700	10,100	15,800	22,800	40,500	63,300	91,200
	26.5	13.0	658.0	2,630	5,920	10,500	16,500	23,700	42,100	65,800	94,800
	28.5	14.0	683.8	2,740	6,150	10,900	17,100	24,600	43,800	68,400	98,600
		15.0	707	2,830	6,360	11,300	17,700	25,500	45,200	70,700	102,000
		16.0	731	2,930	6,580	11,700	18,300	26,300	46,800	73,100	105,000
		17.0	755	3,020	6,800	12,100	18,900	27,200	48,300	75,500	109,000
		18.0	779	3,120	7,010	12,500	19,500	28,000	49,900	77,900	112,000
		19.0	802	3,210	7,220	12,800	20,100	28,900	51,300	80,200	115,000
		20.0	826	3,310	7,440	13,200	20,700	29,700	52,900	82,600	119,000
		21.0	850	3,400	7,650	13,600	21,300	30,600	54,400	85,000	122,000
		22.0	874	3,500	7,870	14,000	21,900	31,500	55,900	87,400	126,000
		23.0	898	3,590	8,080	14,400	22,500	32,300	57,500	89,800	129,000
		24.0	922	3,690	8,300	14,800	23,100	33,200	59,000	92,200	133,000
		25.0	946	3,780	8,520	15,100	23,700	34,100	60,500	94,600	136,000
		26.0	969	3,880	8,720	15,500	24,200	34,900	62,000	96,900	140,000
		27.0	993	3,970	8,940	15,900	24,800	35,700	63,500	93,300	143,000
		28.0	1,017	4,070	9,150	16,300	25,400	36,600	65,100	102,000	146,000
		29.0	1,040	4,160	9,360	16,600	26,200	37,400	66,600	104,000	150,000

Table 12-4. Pitot-tube Table* *(Continued)*

In. of water	In. of mercury	Psi	1 in.	2 in.	3 in.	4 in.	5 in.	6 in.	8 in.	10 in.	12 in.
		30.0	1,064	4,260	9,580	17,000	26,600	38,300	68,100	106,000	153,000
		32.0	1,112	4,450	10,000	17,800	27,800	40,100	71,200	111,000	160,000
		34.0	1,159	4,640	10,400	18,600	29,000	41,700	74,200	116,000	167,000
		36.0	1,207	4,830	10,900	19,300	30,200	43,500	77,300	121 000	174,000
		38.0	1,255	5,020	11,300	20,100	31,400	45,200	80,300	126,000	181,000
		40.0	1,302	5,210	11,700	20,800	32,600	46,900	83,400	130,000	188,000
		45.0	1,421	5,690	12,800	22,800	35,500	51,200	91,000	142,000	205,000
		50.0	1,540	6,160	13,900	24,700	38,500	55,400	98,600	154,000	222,000
		55.0	1,660	6,640	15,000	26,600	41,500	59,800	106,000	166,000	239,000
		60.0	1,778	7,120	16,000	28,500	44,500	64,000	114,000	178,000	256,000
		65.0	1,898	7,600	17,100	30,400	47,500	68,400	122,000	190,000	273,000
		70.0	2,017	8,060	18,200	32,300	50,400	72,600	129,000	202,000	290,000
		75.0	2,136	8,840	19,200	34,200	53,400	76,800	137,000	214,000	308,000
		80.0	2,252	9,010	20,300	36,000	56,400	81,100	144,000	225,000	324,000
		90.0	2,492	9,980	22,400	39,900	62,400	89,800	160,000	249,000	359,000
		100.0	2,732	10,900	24,600	43,700	68,400	98,400	175,000	273,000	394,000
		110.0	2,970	11,900	26,700	47,500	74,200	107,000	190,000	297,000	428,000
		120.0	3,208	12,800	28,900	51,300	80,200	116,000	205,000	321,000	462,000
		130.0	3,445	13,800	31,000	55,100	86,200	124,000	221,000	345,000	496,000
		140.0	3,681	14,700	33,100	58,900	92,000	133,000	236,000	368,000	530,000
		150.0	3,921	15,700	35,300	62,800	98,000	141,000	251,000	392,000	565,000
		160.0	4,160	16,700	37,500	66,600	104,000	150,000	266,000	416,000	599,000
		170.0	4,399	17,600	39,600	70,400	110,000	158,000	282,000	440,000	634,000
		180.0	4,635	18,600	41,700	74,200	116,000	167,000	297,000	464,000	668,000
		190.0	4,870	19,500	43,900	78,000	122,000	175,000	312,000	847,000	702,000
		200 0	5,108	20,500	46,000	81,800	128,000	185,000	327,000	511,000	736,000

*Courtesy of NGSMA Handbook.

Table 12-4. Pitot-tube Table* (*Continued*)

For Determining Open Flow of Gas Wells from Side Static Pressure Four Diameters from Opening

Side static pressure		Open flow, Mcf/D								
In. of mercury	Psi	1 in.	2 in.	3 in.	4 in.	5 in.	6 in.	8 in.	10 in.	12 in.
5.0	...	704	2,820	6,340	11,300	17,600	25,300	45,100	70,400	101,300
5.5	...	714	2,860	6,430	11,400	17,900	25,700	45,700	71,400	103,000
6.0	3	725	2,900	6,530	11,600	18,100	26,100	46,400	72,500	104,000
6.5	...	735	2,940	6,620	11,800	18,400	26,500	47,000	73,500	106,000
7.0	...	745	2,980	6,710	11,900	18,600	26,800	47,700	74,500	107,000
7.5	...	754	3,020	6,790	12,100	18,900	27,100	48,300	75,400	109,000
8.0	4	764	3,060	6,880	12,200	19,100	27,500	48,900	76,400	110,000
8.5	...	775	3,100	6,980	12,400	19,400	27,900	49,600	77,500	112,000
9.0	...	784	3,140	7,060	12,500	19,600	28,200	50,200	78,400	113,000
9.5	...	795	3,180	7,160	12,700	19,900	28,600	50,900	79,500	114,000
10.0	5	805	3,220	7,250	12,900	20,100	29,000	51,500	80,500	116,000
11.0	...	825	3,300	7,430	13,200	20,600	29,700	52,800	82,500	119,000
12.0	6	845	3,380	7,610	13,500	21,100	30,400	54,100	84,500	122,000
13.0	...	865	3,460	7,790	13,800	21,600	31,100	55,400	86,500	125,000
14.0	7	885	3,540	7,970	14,200	22,100	31,900	56,600	88,500	127,000
15.0	...	906	3,630	8,160	14,500	22,700	32,600	58,000	90,600	130,000
16.0	8	926	3,710	8,340	14,800	23,200	33,300	59,300	92,600	133,000
17.0	...	945	3,780	8,510	15,100	23,600	34,000	60,500	94,500	136,000
18.0	9	966	3,870	8,700	15,500	24,200	34,800	61,800	96,600	139,000
19.0	...	986	3,950	8,880	15,800	24,700	35,500	63,100	98,600	142,000
20.0	10	1,013	4,050	9,120	16,200	25,300	36,500	64,800	101,000	146,000
22.0	11	1,055	4,220	9,500	16,900	26,400	38,000	67,500	106,000	152,000
24.0	12	1,095	4,380	9,860	17,500	27,400	39,400	70,100	110,000	158,000
26.0	13	1,137	4,550	10,200	18,200	28,400	40,900	72,800	114,000	164,000
28.0	14	1,178	4,710	10,600	18,800	29,500	42,400	75,400	118,000	170,000
30.0	15	1,218	4,870	11,000	19,500	30,500	43,800	78,000	123,000	175,000
	16	1,260	5,040	11,300	20,200	31,500	45,400	80,600	126,000	181,000
	18	1,343	5,370	12,100	21,500	33,600	48,300	86,000	134,000	193,000
	20	1,424	5,700	12,800	22,800	35,600	51,300	91,100	142,000	205,000
	25	1,629	6,520	14,700	26,100	40,700	58,600	104,000	163,000	235,000
	30	1,834	7,340	16,500	29,300	45,900	66,000	117,000	183,000	
	35	2,041	8,170	18,400	32,700	51,000	73,500	131,000	204,000	
	40	2,245	8,980	20,200	35,900	56,100	80,800	144,000	225,000	
	45	2,450	9,800	22,100	39,200	61,300	88,200	157,000	245,000	
	50	2,657	10,600	23,900	42,500	66,400	95,700	170,000		
	60	3,067	12,300	27,600	49,100	76,700	110,000	196,000		
	70	3,476	13,900	31,300	55,600	86,900	125,000	222,000		
	80	3,887	15,500	35,000	62,200	97,200	140,000	249,000		
	90	4,298	17,200	38,700	68,800	107,000	155,000			
	100	4,708	18,800	42,400	75,300	118,000	169,000			
	120	5,531	22,100	49,800	88,500	138,000	199,000			
	150	6,762	27,000	60,900	108,000	169,000				
	200	8,810	35,200	79,300	141,000	220,000				

maximum pressure anticipated. This minimizes the problem of distortion, which destroys the original calibration of the tube. These tubes are available in many materials, the type depending on the service and the pressure rating desired.

Most meters are hooked up using a standard five-valve manifold of the type shown just above the bellows meter in Fig. 12-4. One valve is placed on each of the leads to the pressure taps, two valves on the bypass, plus a vent valve. When the meter is placed in operation the bypass valves would be open, as would the two main valves, with the vent valve closed. The meter is then placed in service by slowly closing

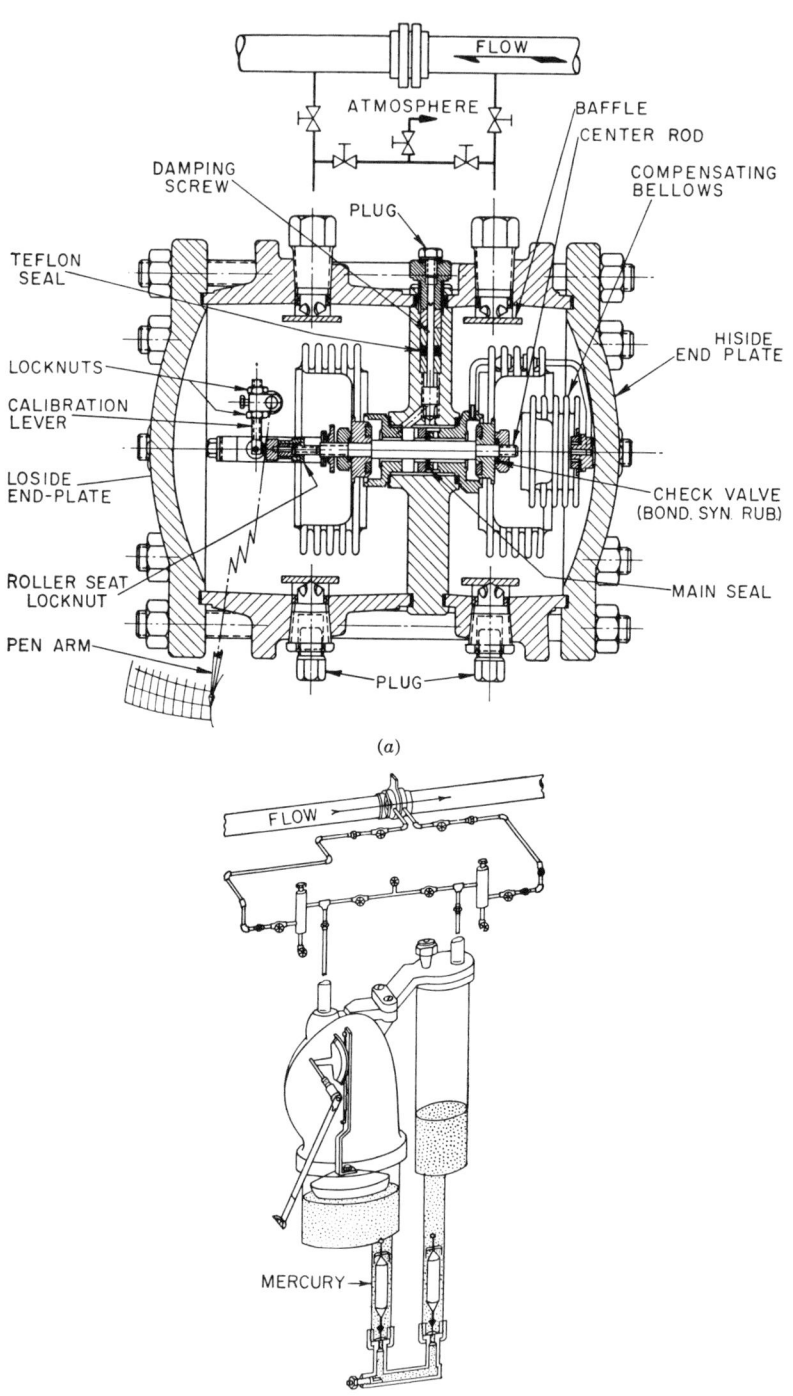

FIG. 12-4. Views showing construction of meters. [(*a*) *Courtesy of American Meter Co.;* (*b*) *courtesy of The Foxboro Co.*)]

the bypass valves, followed by opening of the vent valve. This procedure prevents momentary pressure surges which might damage the meter or upset the calibration. The reverse procedure would then be used in taking the meter out of service. When the leads are bypassed the vent valve is an excellent place to obtain a gas sample. A slightly more complex manifold is shown above the mercury meter, with drip pots for removing any liquid entrained in the gas.

Standard calibration procedure on the differential pen calls for connecting one side of a water manometer into the high-pressure side of the meter. The low-pressure side of the meter is then opened to the atmosphere. This gives two manometers in parallel. By superimposing pressure on the high-pressure cell with a hand pump or similar device one may compare the meter reading with that of the manometer. If they are different the meter must be adjusted accordingly.

The bourdon tube may be calibrated simply by placing a dead-weight tester (preferred) or a calibrated pressure gauge in the lead line to the bourdon tube. By proper manipulation of the valves, the vent valve may be used to make this connection.

The circular charts used usually cover a time period of 24 hours or 7 days. Many meters have clocks which may be easily adjusted for either time period. In most production operations 7-day periods are preferred, for this minimizes the cost of changing charts and the number of charts to be handled.

GAS REGULATION*

Principles of Control

A large percentage of the routine problems encountered with lease equipment stem from failure or misapplication of controls. This has become even more pronounced in recent years as this equipment has become more complex.

Oil-field instrumentation is less complex than that in plants and refineries but imposes severe service conditions. In such service the instruments often have only wet supply gas and rare adjustment by expert servicemen and are exposed to the elements, yet must give continuous and trouble-free service. Even with these severe conditions it must be concluded that many troubles stem from improper application rather than inadequacy of the controls themselves, although many types are not suitable for oil-field use.

Nomenclature. In order to choose controls properly it is necessary to know not only the requirements of the process but also the corresponding characteristics of the controls available. No understanding of controls may be complete without a familiarity with applicable nomenclature.

Pneumatic controls—those which are actuated by air or gas (the most common type used in the field)

Diaphragm motor valve—the term applied to a complete valve that uses pressure to open and close it

Topworks (motor)—that portion of the motor valve which contains the mechanism to open and close the valve

Inner-valve assembly (trim)—includes the stem and seat within the valve body that actually controls the flow of fluid

Fluid—any liquid or gas being controlled

Proportional control—the system whereby the valve opening is proportional to the degree of change in the controlled variable

Snap action—a mode of control whereby the valve is either wide open or closed

Reset—an addition to a proportional-control system to enable the instrument to hold itself at the control point as the process load varies

Derivative response—a further addition that provides corrective action based on the time rate of change of the deviation from the control point

Self-operated controller—a valve which is actuated directly by the controlled variable

* The majority of the material in this section is from Elements of Field Processing, a series of articles by the author in the *Oil and Gas Journal*.

Pilot—a relay that transforms the controlled variable into an equivalent signal to the control valve, such signal controlling the action of that valve

Supply gas—that gas necessary in a pneumatic pilot to operate it

Controlled variable—the pressure, liquid level, temperature, or flow rate being controlled

Measuring means—the means used to detect any change in the controlled variable

Sensitivity—the ability to detect small deviations in the controlled variable

Reproducibility—the ability of an instrument to repeat and measure consistently the values of a static condition over a period of time

Static error—the difference between the absolute value of the controlled variable and the measured value

Lag—the period of time by which the measured value follows the change in the absolute value of the controlled variable

Static conditions—where all changes in the controlled variable are instantaneous

Dynamic conditions—where the controlled variable is continually changing

Normally closed valve—a valve that is held closed by a spring or some similar device and is opened by the action of pilot and/or the controlled variable

Normally open valve—reverse of the above; one that is closed by the action of the pilot and/or the controlled variable

Drift—includes reproducibility and the inability to repeat a measurement because of changes in the measured variable

Process Characteristics. In that it is the purpose of an automatic controller to regulate a process, it is fundamental that the properties and characteristics of a process be understood. A process is defined as the collective functions performed in and by equipment in which a variable is controlled. As an example, a field heater which heats well effluent by hot circulating water is a unit of equipment in which the process of heating the wellstream is accomplished. The process consists of a controlled variable (the temperature) and a controlled medium (the wellstream). Other controlled variables could be rate of flow, liquid level, or pressure. A control agent (circulating water) is the medium for effecting the temperature change, and thus regulation of the control agent regulates the controlled variable. The total requirements of the process for the control agent at any one time are defined as the process load. If the rate of flow of the wellstream increases, then more or hotter water is required to maintain the same temperature, and a change in process load has taken place. By the same token a drop in inlet temperature at the original rate of flow would also constitute a process-load change.

The properties of an entire process include its potential, capacitance, resistance, and dead time. Capacitance, not to be confused with capacity, is the change in the quantity of energy or material per unit change in some variable, usually the controlled variable.

Resistance, or opposition to the flow of energy or material, is another process characteristic. The most familiar concept of resistance is in electricity when it is expressed as the ohm.

Potential is most generally recognized in the concept of electricity where it is expressed as a volt. The table below summarizes the characteristics of a process.

Characteristic	Thermal	Pressure	Liquid level	Electrical
Capacity...............	Btu	Cu ft	Cu ft	Coulomb
Potential..............	Degree	Psi	Ft	Volt
Capacitance..........	$\dfrac{\text{Btu}}{\text{Degree}}$	$\dfrac{\text{Cu ft}}{\text{Psi}}$	$\dfrac{\text{Cu ft}}{\text{Ft}}$	Farad
Resistance............	$\dfrac{\text{Degree}}{\text{Btu/sec}}$	$\dfrac{\text{Psi}}{\text{Cu ft/sec}}$	$\dfrac{\text{Ft}}{\text{Cu ft/sec}}$	Ohm

Dead time is that time lag which occurs when energy is being transferred at a constant rate of flow through a given distance. It is equal to the time it takes the energy to move the distance. The dead time is a characteristic of the process, and it is not to be confused with the time lag inherent in the automatic controller itself.

The purpose of the automatic controller is to prevent deviation of a process from a desired standard. This may be accomplished by various modes of control action, each of which incorporates a distinct limit, range, and speed of correction.

Proportional Control. The modes used depend on the frequency and magnitude of the process load changes, the degree of control needed, and the dynamic lag inherent in the process and controls used.

Proportional control is the basic action that is employed in all controllers not using snap (on-off) action. Since it is defined as control action in which a continuous linear relation exists between the value of the controlled variable and the position of the valve, the following equation may be written:

$$\frac{dP}{dt} = S \frac{dy}{dt} \tag{10}$$

where $\frac{dy}{dt}$ = rate of change of the controlled variable with time (level, pressure, etc.)

$\frac{dp}{dt}$ = rate of change of pilot output pressure or current signal with time

S = characteristic constant of the pilot relating output to input

This characteristic is represented by the sensitivity usually expressed as a percentage. The proportional band or range, expressed as a percentage, relates the percentage of the full range of the measuring means that the controlled variable has to traverse to stroke the valve fully. This may be illustrated in Fig. 12-5.

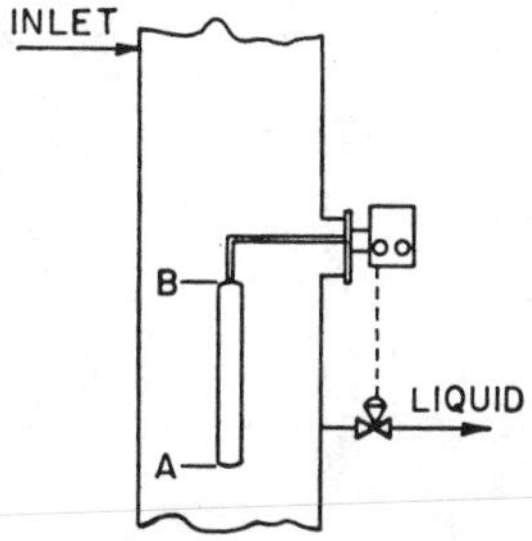

This figure represents a typical level-control application utilizing a displacement-type controller, i.e., one which does not float on top of the liquid but depends on the varying buoyancy of the liquid as the level changes. Consequently, the control range is represented by the distance between points A and B, for below A or above B a change in level has no effect on the buoyancy of the float.

Therefore, at 100 per cent proportional control the level would have to move from A to B, or vice versa, to stroke the valve fully from full open to closed. At 25 per cent, a level change of 0.25 × distance AB would fully stroke the valve, etc. The same principles apply with all other modes of control, including gas regulation.

Fig. 12-5. Liquid-level control using displacement-type float.

Example. A back-pressure controller with a range of 0 to 100 psig is set at 50 per cent proportional control, using a normally open valve. If the valve is open at 100 psig, (a) at what pressure will it be fully closed? (b) what is the opening at 75 psig?

Solution. The control range is 100 psig, which at 50 per cent proportional control means that a 0.50 × 100 = 50 psig change will fully stroke the valve; therefore it is fully closed at 50 psig. At 75 psig it would be half open.

The amount of fluid that a valve will pass at a given position depends on the size and characteristic of the inner-valve assembly. Ideally the amount of fluid passed under given conditions, with a given valve, should be directly proportional to the valve opening. Often it is not, however; so that the type of inner valve has a definite effect on the proper proportional setting. Also ideally, the diameter of the inner valve should be such that the range of anticipated process loads may be handled when the valve is between 25 and 75 per cent open. In the final analysis the choice of the proportional band to use in a given installation must be governed by experience and adjustment on the job.

· This is illustrated in Fig. 12-6. The slope of the lines depends on the proportional band used, each line representing a valve of given size. Under these conditions each valve may operate only along a single line, in accordance with Eq. (1).

If the instrument were set to control at 60 per cent of the range, valve A would be 50 per cent open, valve B 25 per cent open, and valve C 75 per cent open.

Suppose, however, that an instrument set to operate along line A is in gas-regulation service and the flow rate increases such that a valve opening of 75 per cent is needed to maintain the pressure. According to line A the only way the proportional controller can provide this opening is for the pressure to be at 70 per cent of the range, or 10 per cent above the set point. This 10 per cent is called offset.

Consequently, with proportional control alone a change in process load brings a change in the valve position and some change in the liquid level. The proper proportional setting is therefore one which makes the lines in Fig. 12-6 as perpendicular as possible.

Zero per cent proportional control represents a special case. It is the upper limit of a range where the pressure is controlled by the valve alternately opening and closing. This is normally called snap action or on-off control. At a given snap setting the valve will stay closed until the liquid level reaches a certain point between A and B and then remain full open until the liquid level drops to the control point. Where rapid process load changes are encountered, such as surging flow through separators, snap action is normally recommended.

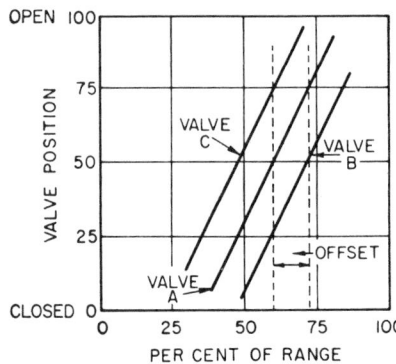

FIG. 12-6. Characteristics of proportional control.

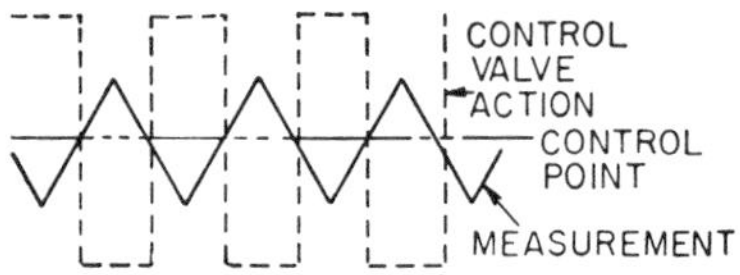

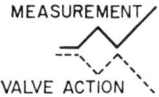

FIG. 12-7. On-off action of a controller.

FIG. 12-8. Proportional action of a controller.

Reset. The "offset" obtained with proportional control is sometimes too great to be tolerated and it is necessary to add other modes of control. One such addition is known as *reset*.

Figures 12-7 and 12-8 show on-off action and proportional action, respectively. In the latter it is seen that the amount of valve movement is proportional to the deviation of the measured variable. By contrast the amount of correction applied with reset action depends on both the magnitude and duration of the deviation away from the control point. The prime purpose of reset is therefore to prevent "offset" and keep the controlled variable at the control point even as the process load changes.

The differential equation of a controller with proportional plus reset action is

$$\frac{dP}{dt} = S\frac{dy}{dt} + SR(y - y_o) \tag{11}$$

where $\dfrac{dP}{dt}$, S, and $\dfrac{dy}{dt}$ have been previously defined

     R = controller reset constant

     $y - y_o$ = duration of the controlled variable from the control point

In this type of controller the two corrections occur simultaneously as shown in Fig. 12-9 Figure 12-9 also shows the action if they took place separately.

Figure 12-10 shows typical curves in a process being controlled by this combination action. When a change in process load takes place the valve returns the measurement to the control point with a minimum of cycling. The original motion of the valve corresponding to the measurement change is due to proportional action, but the change of the valve to its new position is due entirely to reset. In other words, the valve has moved to a new position to maintain the controlled condition. With only proportional control both the valve and controller would have changed.

Derivative Response. Proportional control plus reset does not provide correction that is rapid enough for certain processes. Derivative response may therefore be added to anticipate a change in process load and transmit a corrective signal to minimize the lag. This action corrects on the basis of the rate of change of the deviation from the desired standard. This term stems from the fact that the first

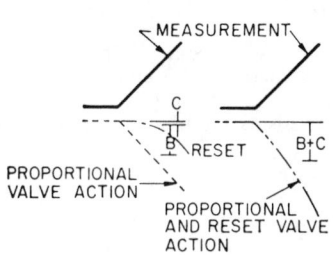

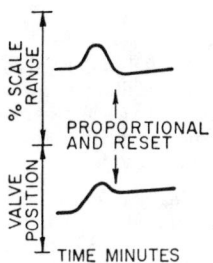

Fig. 12-9. Valve action for reset and proportional controllers (at left); valve action for combined proportional-reset controller (at right).

Fig. 12-10. Typical control curves when using a proportional-reset controller.

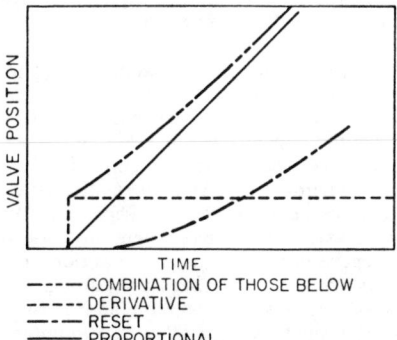

Fig. 12-11. Typical control curves for proportional, reset, and derivative-action controllers.

derivative of the change from the desired standard is incorporated into the control mechanism. The equation for an instrument with proportional plus reset plus derivative response is therefore

$$\frac{dP}{dt} = SR(y - y_o) + S\frac{dy}{dt} + ST\frac{d^2y}{dt^2} \tag{12}$$

where T is an instrument-adjustment factor. The action of a controller with this response is shown in Fig. 12-11.

The general applications of the various combinations of control action may be summarized as follows:

Proportional. Where process time lag is small in comparison with the apparatus capacity such as tank heating or large surge vessels, or where "offset" may be tolerated.

Proportional plus Reset. Where it is necessary to use a narrow band to prevent "hunting" or overcontrol, and as the frequency and magnitude of the process load changes become greater.

Proportional plus Derivative Response. In processes involving long time lags and large capacities when small and frequent load changes occur. Does not provide compensation for process load changes.

Proportional plus Reset plus Derivative Response. Where long time lags and large capacities are combined with large and sudden load changes.

Inasmuch as the addition of reset and derivative response increases the investment cost, they should not be utilized unless their action is needed for proper control.

Liquid-level Control

The control of liquid level is an integral part of gas processing. It furthermore affords a means of illustrating the general problem of instrumentation and gas regulation. In view of the widespread applications and the variety of conditions encountered, it is not surprising that a number of mechanisms are used. These may be conveniently subdivided as

1. Mechanically operated valve actuated by a float
2. Pilot-operated valve actuated by a float
3. Diaphragm motor valve actuated by
    a. Displacement-type controller
    b. "Floatless" level controller
4. External devices, including inverted bucket traps, float traps, etc.

Either snap action or proportional control is normally employed on most lease equipment. Most applications do not justify the cost of reset and/or derivative response since small changes in level with flow rate and time lag are usually not critical problems.

Separator controls, in fact, are usually set on snap action because this enables the controller to handle a surging condition better. The degree of snap action will depend on the conditions encountered. However, it should be set so that not over 25 per cent of the vessel's liquid capacity is filled, above the control point, before the valve opens. The inner-valve size should be determined on the basis of 110 per cent of the maximum flow to be encountered. This means that during a surging condition the valve can handle the volume and prevent the separator from filling up.

Some uncertainty always exists, of course, when one tries to estimate future flow rates. On low-pressure separators, sizing is not a serious problem because of the low-pressure drop across the valve. On high-pressure gas-condensate separators, however, where the liquid flow rate is low, too large an inner valve on snap action can blow all the liquid out of the separator and allow gas to enter the stock tank before the valve can close. The author observed one such installation when 1,000-psig gas hit a 100-bbl tank, knocked the cover off the vent valve, sprayed oil over the countryside, and lifted the tank off the ground.

The manufacturers of control valves furnish sizing curves, and these should be consulted. In using these it should be remembered that critical-flow conditions occur when the upstream pressure is approximately twice the valves' downstream pressure. Consequently, only twice the downstream pressure should be used with these sizing curves if the actual pressure ratio exceeds 2.

When handling very small volumes of liquid, the use of such curves often indicates the use of so-called "metering trim." Its use is not recommended in field applications, for the small quantities of solid materials often present may clog the valve. For this reason nothing smaller than $\frac{3}{16}$-in. needle trim is usually recommended in field service.

Float-operated mechanical oil valves are satisfactory at pressures up to 125 psig. Such valves are directly actuated by movement of the float on top of the liquid, through an adjustable linkage. At higher pressure the leverage supplied by the float is insufficient to provide satisfactory valve action because of the pressure acting on the valve seat.   On separators with greater than 125 psig working pressure, the use of a pilot-operated valve is advisable.   Whenever applicable this type of control is very dependable and simple to adjust and repair.

Float-actuated pilot-operated valves are particularly applicable at pressure to 1,000 psig on vertical vessels.   Such control has been "standard" on separators for years because the pilot is rugged and simple and will operate satisfactorily with the "wet" supply gas from the separator overhead.

This overhead gas contains entrained liquid so that a drip pot ahead of the pilot is advisable.   With high-pressure separators the expansion of gas from separator to instrument pressure may cause sufficient temperature drop to condense some water. This in turn presents hydrate or freezing problems, particularly in cold weather.   A variety of solutions have been used, including tracing with warm separator gas, use of dehydrator pots, running such gas through a heater or treater if available, and insulation of the lines.

Displacement-type liquid-level controls utilize the buoyant effect of liquid on the float.   The average float movement does not exceed $3/16$ in.   As the level varies on the float, the weight changes correspondingly and this change in torque is transmitted to the pilot which, in turn, controls the valve movement.   This type of control is applicable in all pressure ranges but is used primarily at high pressures and/or in horizontal vessels.   Because of the small movement and small float diameter, the vessel opening may therefore be decreased.   This advantage becomes pronounced at high pressure or on small-diameter horizontal vessels.

The pilots on such controls are more sensitive than those discussed above, which allows one to control the level closer.   Most such pilots also allow the valve action to be changed from snap to varying degrees of proportional control by a simple adjustment.

They are necessarily more complex and expensive.   Consequently their use must be justified by process requirements.   The instrument gas requirements are also more critical, for as little as one drop of water may plug the small orifice in some pilots.

Floatless level controls are a relatively new development.   With these the pilot is actuated by the varying liquid head in the vessel.   As the liquid rises in the separator it overcomes the pilot spring and forces the pilot assembly upward, closing the upper seat and opening the lower separator seat which vents the diaphragm pressure to atmosphere.   The separator fluid pressure then opens the valve.   When the valve is throttling, the nonbleed three-way valve action of the pilot plug against its seat adjusts the motor-valve diaphragm pressure.   This type of control has the obvious advantage of eliminating large vessel openings and offering application on very small vessels.

External devices such as float cages and traps find application particularly on vessels with small and/or infrequent liquid loads.   Some types of float cages offer no particular economic advantage at high pressure.   They are most commonly used on low-pressure plant suction and instrument systems.   Inverted bucket traps have been successfully used on small glycol absorbers for economic reasons but regular level controls certainly offer advantage.

At high pressures a choke nipple downstream from the control valve is advisable, for it

1. Provides a factor of safety if the valve "cuts out" or fails to close for any reason
2. Reduces the pressure differential across the valve, which improves the valve action and enables it to shut off tighter
3. Prevents damage to low-pressure equipment downstream if the instrument supply gas fails on a normally open valve

The control range with a float-operated controller is limited by the flange diameter and the float-arm length.   With a displacement element, control is possible only throughout the float length, for a change in level above or below the float does not affect the buoyancy.   Therefore, the desired change in level should not exceed the float length.

The choice of a liquid-level control is somewhat arbitrary but it is good policy to choose the simplest control that will meet process requirements. Average lease-operating conditions impose severe service on the control, and the ability to make repairs with field personnel will generally reduce down time.

Types of Regulators

The regulation of back pressure and pressure reduction in a system may be conveniently divided into three categories when considering the type system needed. The low-pressure range is usually 0 to 125 psig, the intermediate pressure 125 to 500 psig, and the high pressure greater than 500 psig. The use of these ranges is primarily for convenience since some types of valves can operate satisfactorily in all of them.

All pressure regulators are similar in principle, the specification of type being dependent on the process requirements, pressure drop, variation in flow rate, limitations of the loading device, and the maximum pressure. In either of these services pressure is regulated by the control of flow rate.

This flow is controlled through movement of the regulator inner valve which is held either open or closed by some means of preloading. The amount of preloading and the size of the diaphragm used, if any, are such that the inner valve will move to the opposite extreme of travel shortly after the diaphragm pressure passes the desired working pressure. The control pressure is therefore varied by changing the amount of preload, thus upsetting the equilibrium between it and the diaphragm pressure. With most valves increasing preload increases pressure.

The preloading may be accomplished through the use of spring compression, dead weight, or fluid pressure. Valves *a* and *b* in Fig. 12-12 are examples of weight-loaded and spring-loaded valves, respectively. Valve *c* is a spring-loaded valve incorporating a pilot.

In back-pressure service the preloading normally closes the valve, while in pressure reduction the valve is normally open. With the former the upstream pressure is introduced under the diaphragm and works against the loading device to position the valve properly. In pressure-reduction service, the downstream pressure is introduced under the diaphragm and tends to close the valve until the inner valve is properly positioned. Many valves may be changed from one service to the other by simply reversing the valve body and the stem, while still others have provision for reversing the diaphragm action.

Some applications require that a certain differential pressure be maintained across the valve regardless of how much the upstream or downstream pressures vary. The chief application of this is with positive-displacement pumps where the maximum pressure ratio is controlled by a valve located on a bypass.

In this service the valve is normally closed with the downstream (higher) pressure under the diaphragm and the upstream (lower) pressure on top of the diaphragm. The desired differential is then established with the loading device.

Each of the types of preloading has its distinct applications and limitations. The weight-loaded regulator is very sensitive within its pressure range if the flow rate does not vary widely. This is primarily true because the inner valve may move through a greater change of position than with a spring-loaded valve. The greater sensitivity is particularly pronounced when the diaphragm is in direct communication with the valve body, which eliminates friction in the stuffing box.

Very few weight-loaded regulators are recommended above 50 psig because at greater pressures heavy weights are necessary. As a result a small change in controlled pressure is only a small portion of the loading weight and there is less subsequent movement of the inner valve, which in turn renders control more difficult.

A spring-loaded regulator is generally slightly less sensitive than a comparable weight-loaded regulator under constant-flow conditions. In low-pressure service (particularly between 0 and 20 psig) it is an ideal type of loading, for the springs used tend to compress in direct proportion to the load, with constant load increase being required for each increment of compression. Consequently, spring loading is excellent in low-pressure systems and where the diaphragm is loaded with a pilot. As each compression increment is a valve-travel increment, the valve travel is always in proportion to the relationship of the controlled pressure to the preloading. At high pressure this characteristic does not exist because of the heavy springs required. Therefore, non-pilot-operated spring-loaded regulators are not normally recommended above 125 psig because of this loss in sensitivity and their closer approach to the price of pilot-loaded regulators.

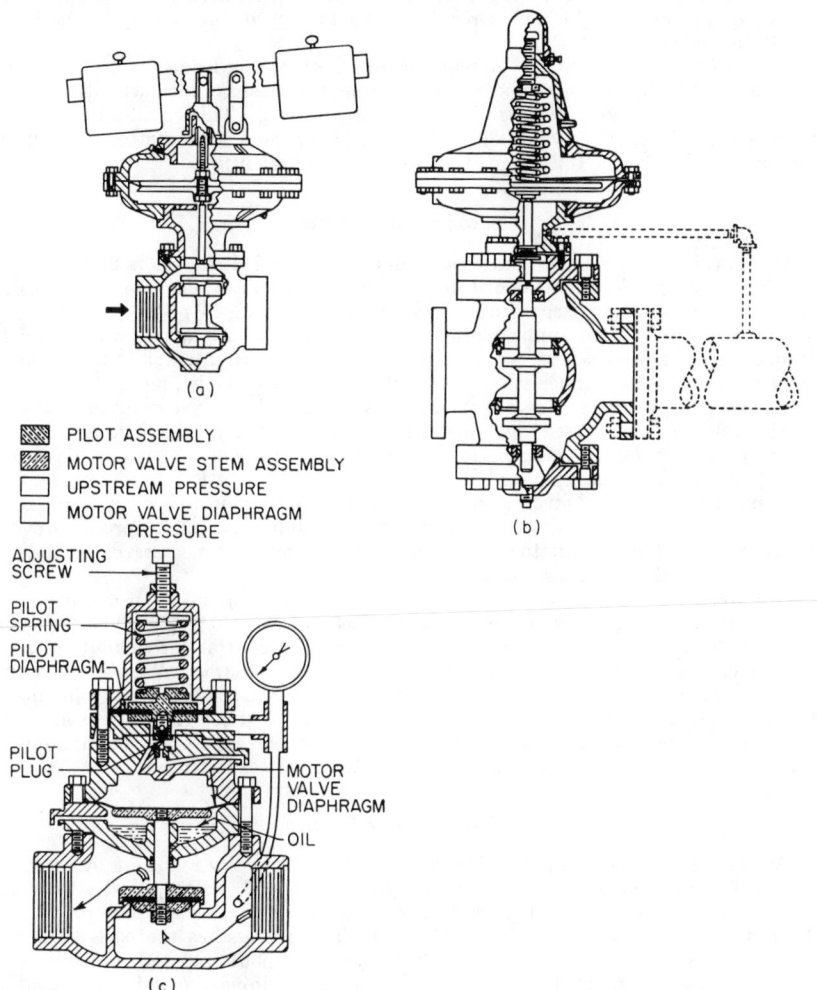

FIG. 12-12. (a) Weight-loaded back-pressure regulator. (b) Pressure-reducing valve. (c) Back-pressure valve with self-contained pilot.

With either a direct-acting weight or spring-loaded regulator a change in the uncontrolled pressure will cause a corresponding change in the controlled pressure if the pressure drop is low. This is true especially if the pressure drop is less than 25 per cent of the inlet pressure. Therefore, when accurate control is necessary under these circumstances, pressure-loaded or pilot-operated valves are recommended.

Both the regulation of flow and tight shut-off should not normally be attempted with the same valve unless absolutely necessary. If this is required by operating conditions, a single-seated valve should be used.   Double-ported valves are seldom operated under the actual conditions at which they were manufactured and tested. Consequently, as temperature changes the distance between the two seats only one of the two will seal off tight.

Single-ported valves will seal off tight but the unbalancing force on the inner valve increases with the square of diameter.   Inasmuch as the diaphragm-spring combination must overcome this force and still control travel, it is logical that the inner-valve size is limited by practical diaphragm size.   As a general rule of thumb, direct-acting spring- and weight-loaded regulators up to 2-in. diameter may be used with single-port construction.

Pilot-loaded valves, either pressure-balanced or spring-loaded, offer particular advantage at higher pressure since the pilot presents a means of increasing the control-valve travel with a given change in controlled pressure.   This enables one to use a more accurately sized valve.   The resultant smaller valve gives better shut-off and closer control since the full range of valve travel may be utilized.

Low-pressure Service

It is in this pressure range that weight- and spring-loaded regulators find particular application on the lease.   One of the most common applications is in back-pressure service on low-pressure separators operating at less than 40 psig.   All the valves shown in Fig. 12-12 are applicable.   One modification of a diaphragm-type weight-loaded valve is used where the weight simply acts to counteract the unbalanced force acting under the inner valve.   The choice of this valve is predicated primarily from cost considerations since it is the cheapest of the valves.   No diaphragm is used.

The simple weight-loaded valve has the advantage of being cheap and simple.   Its primary disadvantage stems not from its operation but from the circumstances surrounding its use.   The weights become loose and shift, are lost or are hindered in movement by outside obstructions.   It is not too uncommon to see rocks and other miscellaneous objects used as substitutes for, or additions to, the proper weights. Consequently, these regulators serve as a proper but not necessarily completely satisfactory back-pressure control.

Not too many spring-loaded regulators are used on separators because of their higher price, although they are generally satisfactory below 40 psig.   The best regulator in this range is valve c, Fig. 12-12.   It gives fine control throughout the range with widely fluctuating flow rates and uncontrolled pressures.   Where fine control is necessary, particularly above 40 psig, the extra investment is normally justifiable.

Because of the almost infinite number of different field conditions that arise, the above considerations can at best serve only as a general guide.   Unfortunately the actual choice of type must often stem largely from past experience.

High-pressure Service

At pressures above 125 psig it is usually difficult to justify anything other than a pilot-operated diaphragm motor valve for pressure control.   Non-pilot-loaded valves are sometimes applicable but usually only in those circumstances where pronounced load changes are not encountered.   At these higher pressures the cost differential also becomes less, which further encourages the use of pilot-operated controls.

Most pilots now in use in the oil field are pneumatic in nature and use natural gas as the actuating fluid.   Any natural gas that is free of fluids and at a pressure greater than 15 psig is suitable in this service.

Figure 12-13 is a schematic view of a pressure pilot that will give both proportional and on-off control   As the controlled pressure varies the bourdon tube will change shape and in turn raise or lower the curved bar.

The supply pressure is held constant between 15 and 20 psig by the pressure regulator.   The vent nozzle is so sized that when wide open (curved bar away from it) it will pass more gas than the orifice.   Consequently the pressure on the valve diaphragm and the valve position depends on the opening of the vent, which in turn depends on the position of the curved bar, as fixed by the bourdon tube. If the vent is wide open the pressure on the diaphragm is zero while if it is fully closed the diaphragm pressure equals the controlled supply pressure.

It is necessary that both the vent and orifice be very small in order to minimize the amount of gas vented. If the curved bar had a fixed pivot rather than a bellows only on-off (snap) action would be possible because of these small openings. From a purely mechanical standpoint any small movement of the curved bar would in effect make the vent wide open.

The bellows is used to impart a rotating motion to the curved bar around the end of the vent. When the bar begins to rise off the vent the bellows contracts, which tends to keep part of the vent opening covered. As a result more vertical movement of the bar is necessary to open (or close) the valve fully. All in-between points then represent some degree of proportional control.

The vertical distance that the bourdon tube has to lift the bar to stroke the valve completely increases as the lever arm decreases. This then allows for adjustment of the proportional band.

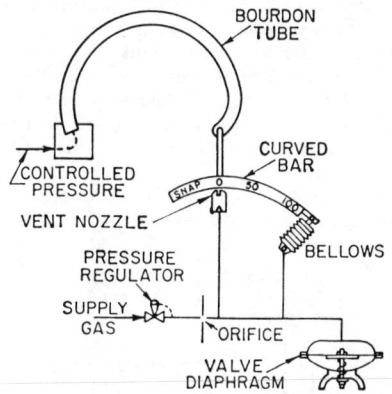

FIG. 12-13. Proportional pilot for pneumatic service.

If the vent is close to the left end of the curved bar the movement of the bellows imparts little rotation to the bar and on-off action results.

Most pressure pilots have the bar marked to show various percentages of proportional control. The percentage shown indicates that the controlled variable must vary through that percentage of the instrument's range to open or close the valve fully

Example. If a pressure pilot has a bourdon tube with a range of 0 to 200 psig and it is set on 50 per cent proportional control how much must the pressure vary to make the valve be fully stroked?

Answer. It must vary $(0.50)(200 - 0) = 100$ psig to stroke the valve fully.

From the discussion above it therefore follows that the closer the vent is to the bellows the higher the percentage of proportional control obtained.

Most pressure pilots are slightly more complex than the schematic presentation in Fig. 12-13, in order to improve the mechanical action and the sensitivity. However, the basic mechanism and principle of operation shown is common to all pneumatic pilots.

In most applications the valve is spring-loaded but there are some where a large quantity of high-pressure gas must be controlled with a low-pressure drop. Such an application is encountered with the switching valves of a dry-desiccant dehydrator. A large inner-valve assembly is required which increases the unbalanced forces on the diaphragm, which in turn necessitates a heavy spring. In such cases the use of a pressure-loaded balanced diaphragm valve is indicated. With this type greater valve travel may be obtained, with less change of controlled pressure than with any other type. With a constant loading pressure on a larger balanced diaphragm the available force to travel the valve with incremental change of control pressure is greater than with a spring-loaded valve because of spring characteristics. However, spring loading is simpler wherever applicable.

The greater the pressure drop across a valve the greater the unbalanced force that exists. Where this pressure drop is greater than several hundred psi it is good practice to install a choke nipple downstream from the valve. This choke nipple should

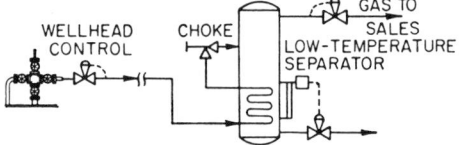

FIG. 12-14. Typical pressure control for a high-pressure well.

preferably be about 10 to 25 per cent larger than the inner valve so that the latter is the controlling element. The nipple serves two purposes: (1) it reduces the pressure drop across the valve and increases sensitivity, and (2) it acts as a secondary control in the event the valve fails to close or cuts out.

The pilot shown in Fig. 12-13 may be modified to give what is known as high-low shut-off. A pilot so modified will cause the valve to close if the controlled pressure becomes higher (or lower) than the preset condition. This modification has particular application in high-pressure wells to

1. Shut in the well in the event a line break is encountered.

2. Prevent overpressuring of a separator or other piece of equipment downstream from a choke or valve.

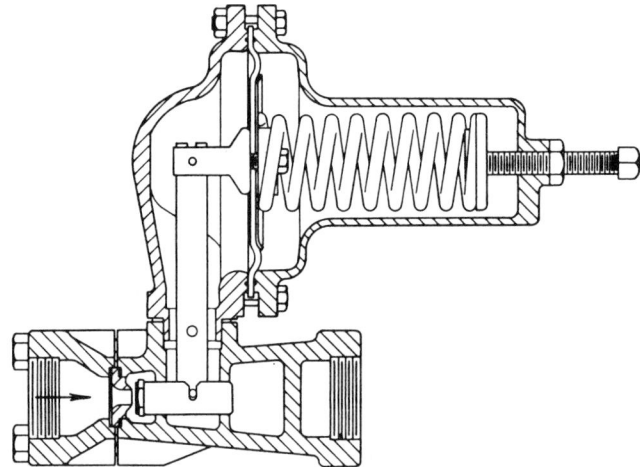

FIG. 12-15. Small high-pressure spring-loaded pressure regulator. (*Courtesy of Fisher Governor Co.*)

In some instances it is desirable to use an automatic rather than a manual adjustable positive choke. A regular diaphragm-motor-valve topworks may then be combined with the choke body to give a control valve and choke combined. Although it costs more there is some advantage to using the positive choke as a rough control with a separate valve at the wellhead for safety. Figure 12-14 illustrates such a scheme where several wells are being flowed to a central low-temperature separation unit, the pressure drop being taken at the unit. The valve at the well protects against line break while the back-pressure valve at the separator holds the separation pres-

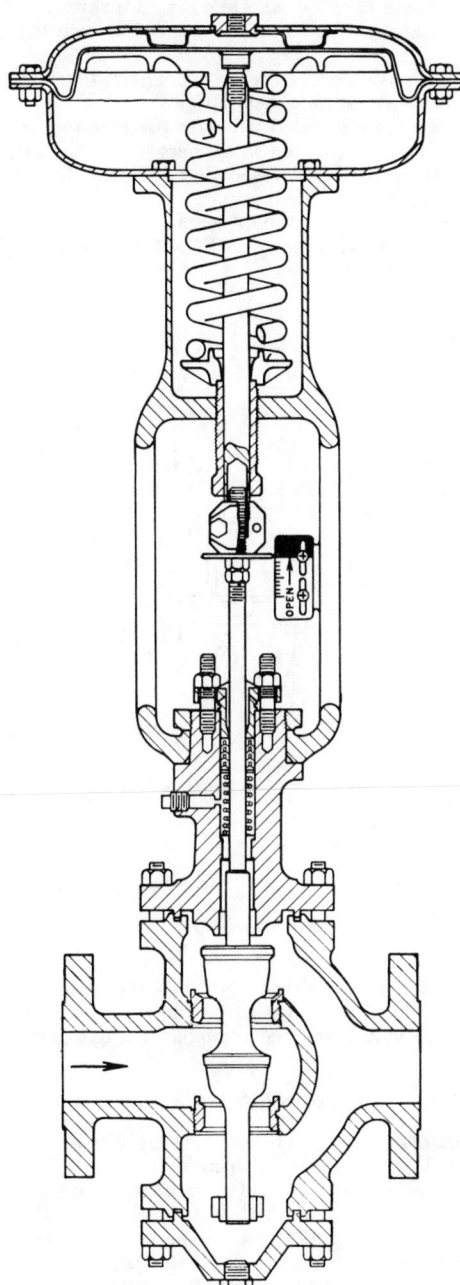

FIG. 12-16. Typical spring-loaded motor valve.   (*Courtesy of Fisher Governor Co.*)

sure constant regardless of how the sales line pressure varies. The two control valves fix the pressure drop across the choke, with the flow rate being determined by the choke setting.

Where very high formation pressures are encountered one or more "storm chokes" in the well proper make a desirable installation.

Figure 12-15 shows a spring-loaded valve for pressure-reduction service. This is a popular valve for pressure regulation in services where the rate of flow is not large. The pivot point on the arm is so located that it ratios the force on the inner valve down to where the spring can control properly.

Figure 12-16 shows a double-port diaphragm motor valve that would be controlled by a separate pilot, such as that shown in Fig. 12-13. Figure 12-17 shows several of

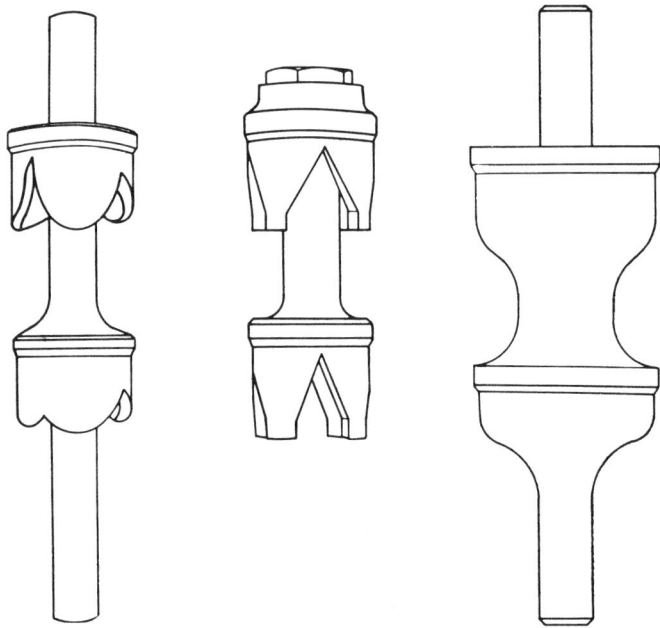

Fig. 12-17. Several types of inner valves used in double-port valves. (*Courtesy of Fisher Governor Co.*)

the different types of inner valves that might be used in the double-port valve shown. The shape used depends on the service and the type of control desired. The same general shapes of inner valves are also available in single-port valves.

Control of Field Compressors

Most of the controls on a field booster compressor are designed to protect the equipment and facilitate operation, with minimum attention, for it is theoretically possible to operate the system with little more than manual control. The exact scheme used will of course vary with the application, but that shown in Fig. 12-18 is typical of small-lease operations where low-pressure gas is compressed in one stage.

No control and cooling system is shown for the engine since this will depend on the engine manufacturer. On most small portable units the engine is self-contained with its own radiator and pump. If two, or more, stage compression is used, the controls shown for the inlet scrubber would be duplicated for each interstage scrubber. A provision would also have to be made for interstage gas cooling.

The back-pressure controller shown on the vent is to prevent overpressuring of the separator in case the compressor plant is down. The other back-pressure valve on the suction line is to prevent the plant from lowering the separator pressure by drawing off gas faster than it is produced. It should be set several pounds lower than the valve on the vent line.

The meter run is shown at the plant, although it could be conveniently located at the separator. Check valve (12) is included to prevent the backflow which may result when multiple units feed the same compressor.

Butterfly valve (14) is an optional but desirable item to control the compressor suction pressure. All compressors are rated using a given suction and discharge pressure, and this valve simply prevents the former from getting too low and overloading the unit. This valve is particularly desirable if the deliverability of gas to the plant is widely variant.

The inlet scrubber is primarily a protective device to keep liquid out of the cylinders and should not be used as a primary oil and gas separator. This vessel serves simply

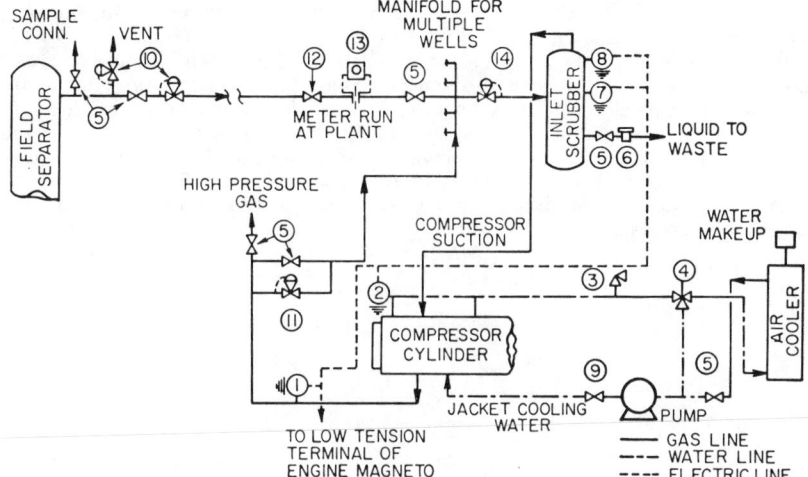

Fig. 12-18. Typical control system for field compression of natural gas. 1. High-pressure shutdown switch. 2. Water-temperature safety switch. 3. Low-pressure liquid-relief valve. 4. Water-temperature bypass control. 5. Plug valve. 6. Trap-type level control. 7. High-level shutdown. 8. Low-pressure shutdown switch. 9. Globe valve. 10. Low-pressure back-pressure controllers. 11. Relief valve. 12. Check valve. 13. Orifice meter. 14. Low-pressure pilot-controlled butterfly valve.

as a liquid sump and a convenient device on which to hang certain necessary controls. As a convenient rule of thumb, this vessel should have a cross-sectional area of at least 100 sq in./MMcf/D of gas processed. The minimum size is normally 12 in. A float-operated trap (6) is very satisfactory for controlling the liquid level.

Switches (1), (2), (7), and (8) constitute the basic safety shut-down system. These switches are normally open but if the condition at any one goes beyond set limits it closes, grounding out the engine magneto, which in turn stops the engine. All are simple and inexpensive and afford positive protection. A horn and/or remote indicator may be incorporated that is actuated at any time the compressor stops.

Switches (1) and (8) are high- and low-pressure shut-down, respectively. They serve to keep these pressures within the limits set up for the compressor. Switch (2) is a high-temperature shut-down that is actuated by the hot water leaving the cylinder jacket. It shuts down the unit when any failure occurs in the cooling system.

Switch (8) is a high-level shut-down that operates when the liquid level becomes too high in the scrubber because of either failure of valve (6) or an excess quantity of liquid entering the plant.

Bypass valve (5) is desirable for it provides a means of taking the load off the compressor, particularly during start-up. During normal start-up this valve would be open and gradually closed once the compressor and engine reached running speed.

The bypass relief valve (11) is an optional and, to a certain extent, a luxury item for it duplicates the protection offered by switch (1). It provides relief in the event the outlet or bypass plug valves are inadvertently closed, without shutting down the compressor. If used it would normally be set to open 5 to 10 psig before the high-pressure switch closes.

The water-temperature bypass control (4) serves to control the jacket water temperature by governing the amount of water to the cooler. In its simplest and cheapest form it consists of an automobile-radiator-type thermostat in a three-way cast-iron valve body. It is substantially the same device used on most oil-field engines. A conventional temperature control would of course be satisfactory but its cost cannot be justified unless it is a large installation or is used where the complexity of the system does not lend itself to this type of control. In some cases where several services are handled by the same cooler it is often more satisfactory to control the temperature by varying the speed or pitch of the fan.

Although no scale trap is shown it is normally a good policy to have one to prevent accumulation and possible system damage. Some provision for water make-up is necessary; so a small surge tank on top of the cooler should be provided for this purpose. Drains should be provided so that the system may be completely drained.

Pop-off valve (3) is primarily to prevent overpressure of the system, particularly the radiator. A simple brass valve $\frac{1}{2}$ in. in size is normally sufficient.

On large systems a standpipe may be used ahead of the pump suction to handle surges and serve as a water reservoir.

Chapter 13

LEASE-OPERATED HYDROCARBON-RECOVERY SYSTEMS AND GAS-TREATING SYSTEMS

By Edwin C. Young

Director, Product Planning
Black, Sivalls & Bryson, Inc.
Oklahoma City, Okla.

LEASE-OPERATED HYDROCARBON-RECOVERY SYSTEMS

In lease production of natural gas it is important to consider the marketing specifications as prescribed by gas contracts in selecting the best system for processing wellhead gas. Natural gas at the wellhead can contain hydrocarbons which can be liquefied, free water, water vapor, acid gases, and other undesirable components. In order to make wellhead gas merchantable it is necessary to reduce these components to a quantity that will satisfy the marketing specifications. This section is devoted to the removal of liquefiable hydrocarbons. The section following this one relates to the removal of the other undesirable components.

The removal of liquefiable hydrocarbons, henceforth referred to as condensate, is necessary to effect efficient gas-transmission operation. When the hydrocarbons condense in the pipeline, additional horsepower is required to overcome the increased pressure drop created. Where the calorific heat content of the natural gas is specified by gas contracts, close control of the condensate must be effected to satisfy these limitations. A final consideration for removal of condensate is to realize an additional revenue over that derived from the sale of natural gas. In many instances this additional revenue can readily pay out the cost of process equipment required to produce gas of merchantable quality.

There are several possible methods of producing gas wells to effect a removal of condensate. These methods are discussed below.

Low-temperature Separation Systems

Theoretical Consideration. Before discussing the methods of removing condensate from natural gas, it is necessary to examine the various physical phenomena which are responsible for the formation of condensate.

Retrograde condensation is a phenomenon which occurs near the critical point of a hydrocarbon mixture, the critical point being defined as the point where the vapor dew-point curve and the liquid bubble-point curve merge. In the retrograde-condensation region, condensate forms with a reduction in pressure and no change in temperature, which is contrary to normal condensation phenomena. Thus, when the pressure of natural gas containing condensate in a vapor form above the critical point is lowered, the condensate will liquefy in this retrograde-condensation region and can be separated.

A second phenomenon to be considered in condensate removal is the Joule-Thomson effect. When natural gas expands from a high pressure (below 5,000 psig) to a lower pressure without heat transfer or work (constant-enthalpy expansion), there is an accompanying temperature drop or refrigeration effect which is normally referred to as the Joule-Thomson effect. Advantage can be taken of the available pressure drop to lower the separation temperature of the hydrocarbon mixture, causing more liquids to drop out of the natural gas. Figure 13-1 shows a typical temperature drop that can be expected for a pressure differential starting at a given initial wellstream pressure.

A third phenomenon which must be considered is the formation of hydrates of natural gas. Hydrates are unstable, solid chemical compounds of natural gas and water which exist in snowlike form at temperatures above 32°F under pressure but decompose at atmospheric pressure. They appear to be hydrates of a mixture of the component gases and not a mixture of the hydrates of the individual gases. Thus

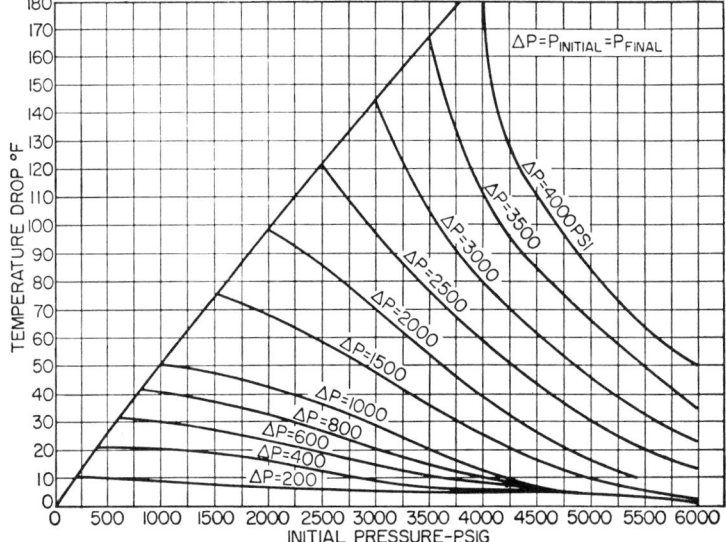

Fig. 13-1. Temperature drop associated with a given pressure drop.

these hydrates form at a temperature for a given gas mixture rather than at the hydrate temperature for the individual pure components in the mixture. It is also a known fact that the presence of liquid water is generally considered necessary for the formation of hydrates. Turbulence accelerates the formation of hydrates and freezing occurs frequently downstream from valves, regulators, chokes, orifice plates, sharp bends, etc. Until the first hydrate crystal forms, there exists no nucleus for further formation; but once started, hydrates form rapidly from the available free water. Hydrate-formation curves for various specific gravity gases can be seen in Fig. 13-2.

A necessary condition for hydrate formation is the presence of liquid water. It is therefore necessary to be able to predict the temperature where free water will occur in natural gas. The chart shown in Fig. 13-3 shows the water-vapor content of natural gas as a function of temperature and pressure. As the temperature decreases at a given pressure the water-vapor content for saturation also decreases, which results in condensation of water vapor to free liquid for a gas stream of given water content. As an example, suppose a well is flowing 1 MMscf/D at 1,000 psi, is saturated with water vapor but contains no liquid water at 110°F, and is cooled to 60°F because of ground and atmospheric cooling. At 1,000 psia and 110°F the gas contains 80 lb per million water content and at 1,000 psia and 60°F it contains 17 lb per million.   For a day's production 63 lb of free water are formed because of this cooling effect.   Referring to Fig. 13-2, if the gas flowing has a specific gravity greater than 0.60 it is more than likely that hydrates will form in the flow line at some point of turbulence.

Constant-enthalpy Expansion Systems.   The constant-enthalpy expansion systems utilize the refrigeration effect resulting from an appreciable pressure drop taken on a high-pressure wellstream.   This expansion is taken across a choke and the resulting refrigeration effect is dependent upon the temperature on the upstream side of the choke and the pressure differential across the choke.   For obtaining the maximum removal of liquefiable hydrocarbons from the gas streams for a given pressure differential and sales-gas pressure, the lowest possible temperature within reasonable limits should be attained in the separator.   This in turn means the lowest possible temperature ahead of the choke.   From the discussion above on hydrate formation it can be concluded that hydrates must be taken into account in these systems.   Two basic methods commonly used to accomplish condensate removal are low-temperature separation with or without hydrate inhibitors.   Each method is discussed below.

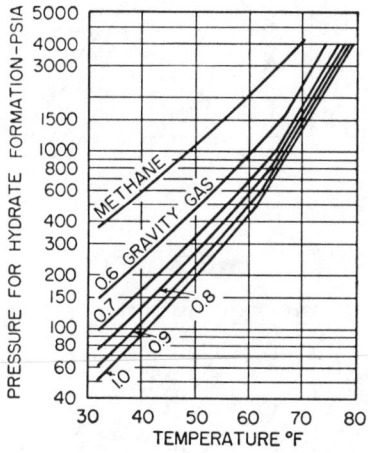

Fig. 13-2. Limiting temperature conditions for various operating pressures below which hydrate formation occurs.   (*Courtesy of Dr. Donald F. Katz, AIME Tech. Paper* 1748.)

Low-temperature Separation without Hydrate Inhibitor.   The basic unit for low-temperature separation without hydrate inhibitor includes essentially a choke, separator, and heat-exchange coils.   Assuming that the inlet wellstream contains a minimum amount of free water and is of sufficient temperature to prevent formation of hydrates upstream of the choke, the operation is as follows: The wellstream enters the unit (see Fig. 13-4) through the heat-exchange coil where it is cooled through heat exchange with the liquid external to the coil.   The wellstream then passes through an adjustable choke which is used to control the flow rate through the system and establish a means for introducing the necessary pressure drop.   The turbulence and temperature drop created by the expansion across the choke cause the formation of hydrates and the condensation of the liquefiable hydrocarbons.   The hydrates and condensate are separated from the gas by means of centrifugal force, normally generated by locating the choke tangential to the shell of the separator, and by gravity.   The hydrates and condensate collect in the bottom of the separator where they absorb heat from the inlet coil, causing the hydrates to be melted.   The liquid level is maintained by a level controller such that the coils are always submerged in the liquid.

It is apparent that two possible operating problems might occur in this simple system.   Either the wellstream can be near the hydrate temperature on entering the

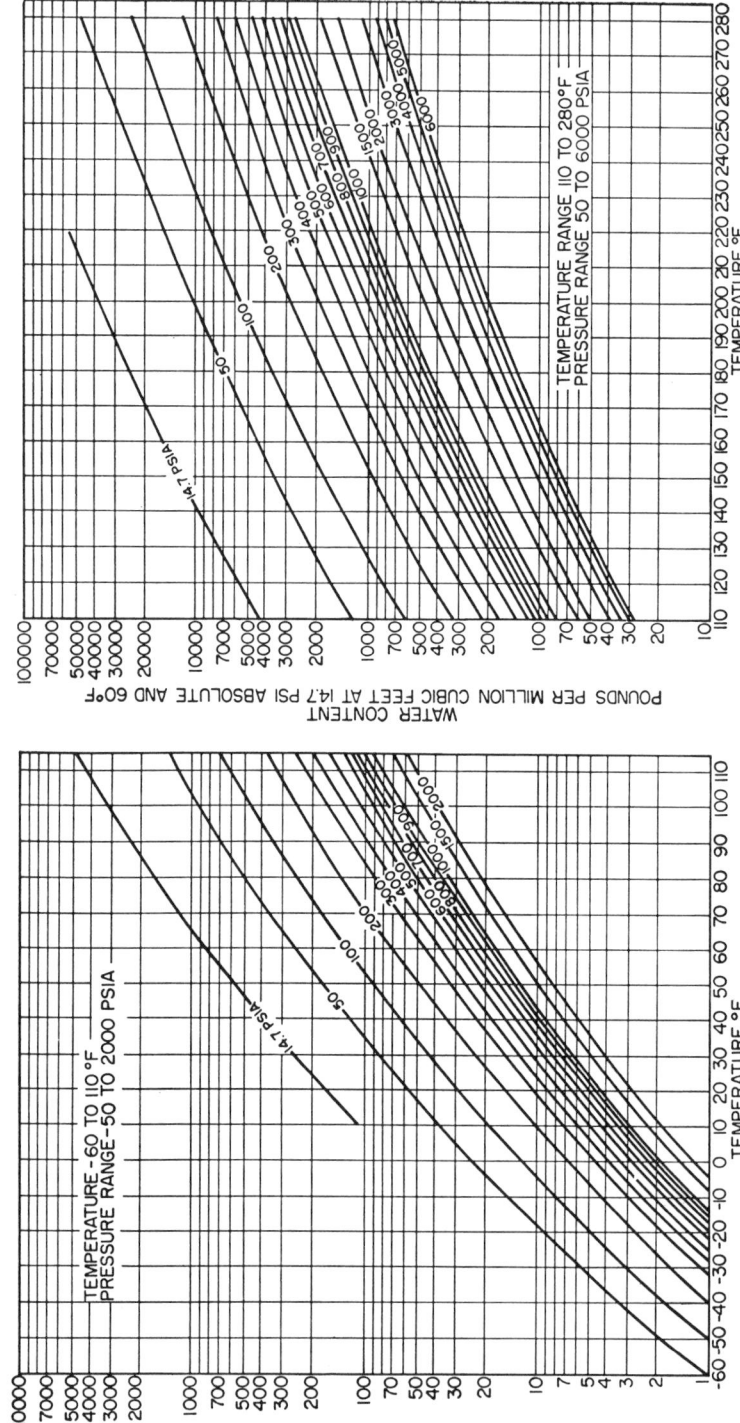

FIG. 13-3. Water-vapor content of natural gas at saturation. (From E. L. McCarthy, W. L. Boyd, and L. S. Reid, AIME San Antonio Meeting, Oct. 5, 1949.)

13–4

coil and further cooling can create hydrates upstream of the choke or there is insufficient heating of the liquid bottoms causing hydrates to build up inside the separator. In either case the system will malfunction.   To overcome this there are two possible solutions.

One common solution which has been successful in the past is to install an indirect heater upstream of the low-temperature separator.   The indirect heater temperature is maintained at a level to assure wellstream gas temperatures above the hydrate temperature.   Heat transfer is accomplished by flowing the wellstream through the coils of the indirect heater and the gas temperature is controlled by a thermostat located in the outlet end of the coil.   A second thermostat can be located in the liquid section of the low-temperature separator to override the heater controls in the event that the liquid temperature is too low.

A more recent solution has been the use of a steam generator in place of the indirect heater.   The wellstream temperature upstream of the choke is controlled by regulating the flow through coils in the steam generator.   However, the bottoms of the low-

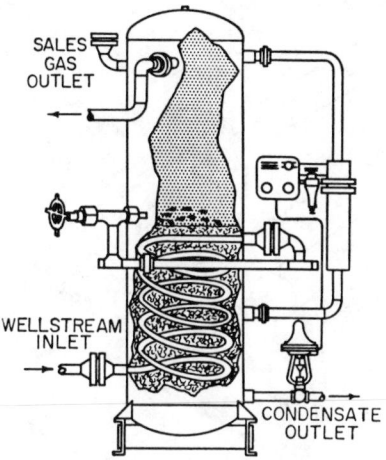

FIG. 13-4. Typical low-temperature separator.

temperature separator are maintained at a given temperature through use of a steam coil in place of the wellstream inlet coil mentioned above.   The thermostat regulates the steam flow through this coil to control the bottoms temperature.   This system affords good control and has the advantage of being totally skid-mounted for portability and ease of field installation.   These units are most popular in areas where ambient temperatures are relatively low in the winter.

For the simple system outlined above the prime concern was to keep the temperature high enough upstream of the choke to assure continuous operation.   One of the necessary elements for hydrate formation, as pointed out above, is the presence of free water.   In cases where free water and liquid hydrocarbons are present in the wellstream and where these liquids are formed because of the chilling effect in the inlet coil, it is desirable to place a high-pressure separator between the coil and the choke. The liquids separated in this vessel are dumped at a relatively warm temperature into the bottom of the low-temperature separator and combined with the liquids therein. The advantage derived from use of this inlet separator is to reduce the amount of free water and liquid hydrocarbons passing through the choke.   This allows more net chilling to occur since the sensible heat transferred to these liquids can be used for cooling the gas and condensing additional hydrocarbon vapors.   It also reduces the amount of hydrates formed by minimizing the amount of free water passing through the choke.

A further refinement to this system is possible for increasing the condensate removed from the wellstream.   This includes the addition of a heat exchanger located between the inlet high-pressure liquid separator and the choke.   The high-pressure wellstream flows through the tube side of this heat exchanger and cold sales gas off the top of the low-temperature separator flows through the shell side.   The amount of sales gas flowing on the shell side is controlled by a three-way bypass valve which is actuated by a temperature controller upstream of the choke.   In this manner the upstream temperature at the choke can be maintained at a minimum value, but still above hydrate temperature.   From the analysis given above the lower this inlet temperature the lower will be the temperature in the separator and the greater will be the condensate removed.

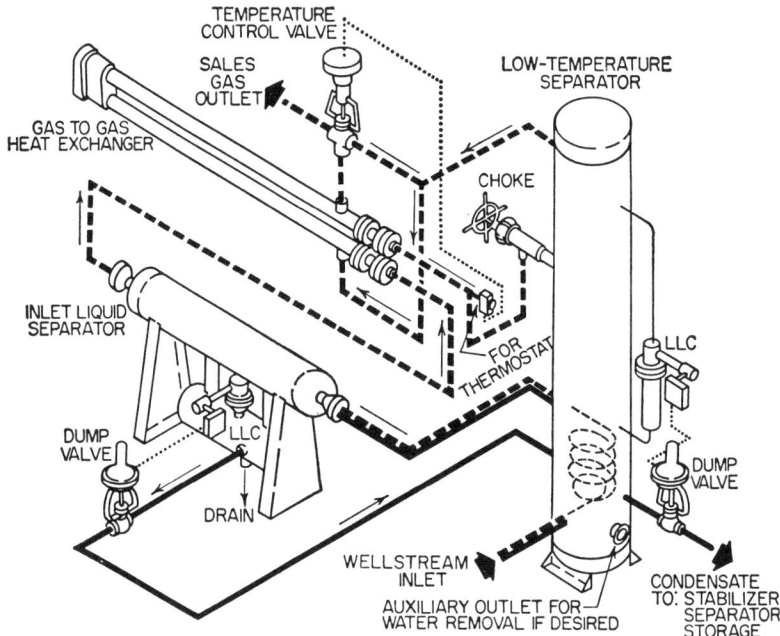

Fig. 13-5. Typical LTS system with inlet separator and intermediate heat exchanger.

The complete system is shown in Fig. 13-5.   The wellstream flows through the coil in the low-temperature separator where it is slightly chilled, then to the inlet high-pressure liquid separator where free liquids are separated from the gas.   The gas then flows through the gas-to-gas heat exchanger, through the choke, and into the low-temperature separator.   The cold gas flows from the separator, through the gas-to-gas heat exchanger, and into the sales-gas line.   The liquids from the bottom of the low-temperature separator are dumped to some form of stabilization prior to going into storage.

In summary, the following considerations are necessary for operation of low-temperature separation systems without hydrate inhibitors: The controlled temperature of the high-pressure stream must be kept slightly above the hydrate temperature in order to prevent freezing upstream of the choke.   The hydrate temperature can be determined by reference to the hydrate curve for natural gas (Fig. 13-2).   The temperature of the low-temperature separator can be predicted from pressure-temperature drop curves for natural gas (Fig. 13-1).   Allowances must be made for the liquid content, which will slightly reduce the temperature drop if the liquid hydrocarbons are not separated in a high-pressure separator upstream of the choke.

On wellstreams with low flowing temperatures it may be necessary to use a heater upstream of the low-temperature unit. In such cases the temperature is controlled with the heater and the gas-to-gas heat exchanger may not be required. If a well makes little free water and/or no waxy distillates or free condensate, the inlet high-pressure liquid separator can be eliminated.

This type of system is economically feasible from a liquid-recovery standpoint on gas streams with liquid content of a few barrels up to about 100 bbl per MMscf of gas. The optimum recovery pressure will vary with different wellstreams but may be as low as 350 psig.

A rough rule of thumb is that 0.05 bbl of additional liquid can be recovered per MMscf of gas for each degree lowering of the temperature. Below 20°F the increase in recovery becomes lower, and in some cases only slight additional recovery of net stock-tank liquid can be realized by lower temperatures.

Low-temperature Separation with Hydrate Inhibitor. In the type of system just covered it was evident that the formation of hydrates could be troublesome. It is

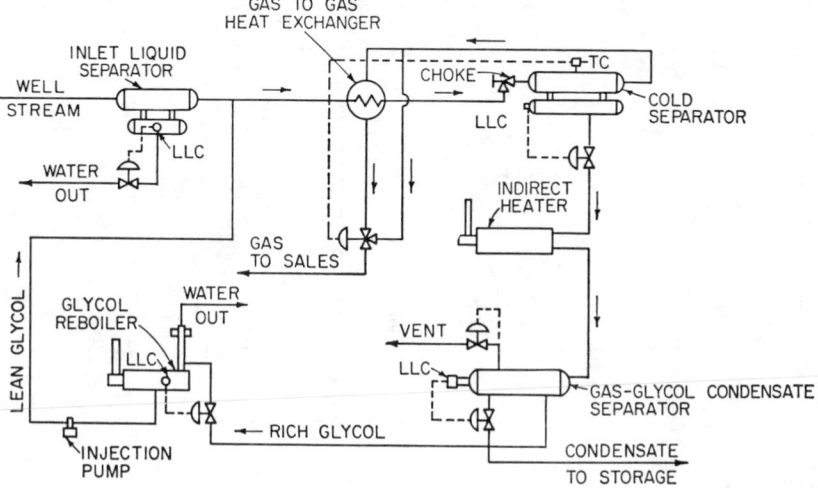

Fig. 13-6. Schematic flow diagram of a glycol injection LTS system.

possible through the use of hydrate inhibitors to prevent the formation of hydrates and effect a better condensate removal from the wellstream. The system is similar to the one described above except that the inhibitor is injected between the inlet high-pressure separator and the regenerative heat exchanger. The inhibitor mixes with the free water formed on cooling and consequently prevents hydrate formation. A typical system is shown in Fig. 13-6.

The presence of the inlet high-pressure liquid separator is very important in this system. The produced water must be removed in this inlet separator to prevent contamination of the glycol, which is usually used as the hydrate inhibitor, and to keep the regeneration equipment from having to handle this extra vaporization load. This contamination occurs as excessive dilution of the glycol, thus reducing its inhibiting qualities; as salt water, which is detrimental to the regeneration system; and as solids, which can cause foaming and other problems in the separation and regeneration system. If the wellstream contains waxy heavy ends, it is very important that these be removed and kept out of the low-temperature separator where they would build up and cause the system to malfunction.

Glycol, which has been processed through a reboiler to remove the water picked up in the system, is pumped from a storage tank to an injection point downstream of the inlet separator. The glycol rate is controlled by setting the speed of the pump, usually a gas-powered reciprocating pump. The rate is established by calculating the amount of water to be inhibited in going from the saturated condition downstream of the inlet separator to a saturated condition in the low-temperature separator. The glycol concentration, resulting from dilution with this water to be picked up, must be maintained sufficiently above the freezing point of the solution to prevent malfunction in the low-temperature separator or the regenerative heat exchanger. There are curves published by the suppliers of glycol that can be used in this calculation.

The wellstream thus inhibited passes through the regenerative heat exchanger, to the choke and into the low-temperature separator. The cold sales gas off the separator passes through the shell side of the heat exchanger. A three-way valve is used to control the rate of heat transferred from the wellstream to the sales gas to maintain a given temperature in the low-temperature separator. This valve is actuated by a

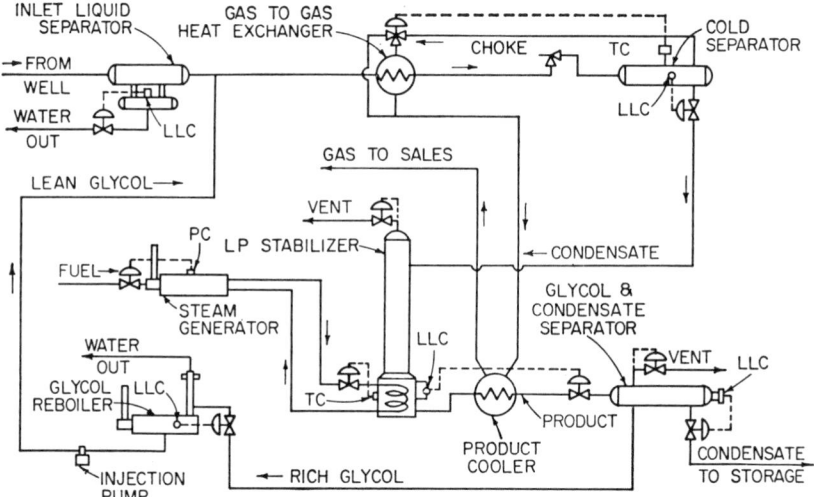

Fig. 13-7. Schematic flow diagram of a glycol injection LTS system with low-temperature stabilization.

temperature controller located in the low-temperature separator. Since the inhibited wellstream can be cooled below hydrate temperature ahead of the choke, lower temperatures are possible in this system. Thus more liquefiable hydrocarbons are condensed out of the wellstream and separated along with the rich glycol.

The liquids from the low-temperature separator contain condensate and rich glycol. The next step is to separate these liquids so that the glycol can be processed for reuse and the condensate stored for sale with a minimum of losses. This can be accomplished by discharging the mixture to a gas-glycol-condensate separator. Since the mixture is usually very cold, the liquids are quite viscous and cannot be easily separated. One method of handling this problem is to pass the liquids through an indirect heater, as seen in Fig. 13-6, to bring the temperature up to a level where separation can be achieved. However, it is more common to stabilize the condensate to effect a more favorable economic return through higher stock-tank recoveries. This system is shown in Fig. 13-7 and will be discussed in more detail below. However, it can be noted that the total mixture flows through the stabilizer and is separated in a glycol-condensate separator located downstream from the stabilizer.

The glycol thus separated is rich in water and must be reconcentrated before it can be recirculated. This is accomplished in the glycol reboiler as shown in Figs. 13-6 and 13-7. The rich glycol is fed into a still column where it contacts the steam rising from the reboiler proper. This serves to preheat the glycol, strip out any dissolved gases, and condense any glycols that may be entrained in the steam vapors. With diethylene glycol the reboiler is operated at around 240 to 250°F to provide outlet glycol concentrations of about 80 to 85 per cent. The glycol-condensate separator is usually designed to act as a surge to take up the slack in the event that glycol might be temporarily accumulated elsewhere in the system.

Since glycols are expensive, it is important that this system be designed and operated to keep these losses at a minimum. These losses occur because of the slight solubility of glycols in condensate and the vaporization of glycols in the regeneration systems. Proper equipment design and sizing for separation in the low-temperature separator and the glycol-condensate separator can keep other mechanical losses to a minimum. In considering the type of glycol best suited for these systems it is necessary to look at both the solubility and vaporization characteristics of each. Ethylene glycol has the least solubility in condensates but the highest vaporization losses. The vaporization losses can be reduced through a more elaborate regeneration system but at a higher initial equipment cost. Triethylene glycol has the least vaporization loss but is the most soluble. Thus diethylene glycol is usually used as a good compromise. In a typical condensate diethylene glycol of 70 to 80 per cent concentration is about 0.04 weight per cent soluble. Higher concentrated solutions are more soluble, but seldom would these be encountered in the glycol injection systems. Aromatic hydrocarbons tend to increase the solubility, and higher losses can be expected when they are present in the condensate. In installations where extreme care is exercised to eliminate glycol losses of a mechanical nature, such as leakage past the pump packing and spillage, glycol losses have been found to be in the order of 0.2 gal per MMcf of gas processed or less.

Hydrocarbons separated in the inlet high-pressure liquid separator can be recombined in the low-temperature separator provided they are not of a waxy base. The solution gas flashed in discharging from the high-pressure separator can be recombined with the sales gas and the liquids recombined with the condensate prior to stabilization. Waxy-base hydrocarbon liquids are best discharged directly to the stabilizer where the temperatures are higher and they are more easily handled.

In summary the low-temperature separation system with hydrate inhibitor eliminates the formation of hydrates and allows the gas to be cooled below the hydrate temperature before expansion. This results in an increase in the amount of condensate removed from the wellstream. The operating costs are higher than for the system using expansion without inhibitor, but the increased recovery will normally more than offset this. It can be used more effectively on wellstreams where the pressure drop is lower than can the straight expansion system.

Mechanical-refrigeration Systems. Up to this point all discussion has been concerned with condensate removal from wellstreams of high pressures. Much of the gas produced does not have sufficient pressure for an expansion system. In many cases it is tail gas off low-pressure separators, emulsion treaters, etc., which has been gathered and recompressed for sale to a pipeline. These systems contain heavier hydrocarbons, which cause the problems cited in the beginning of the chapter and require removal. These can be removed through low-temperature systems using mechanical refrigeration or through selective adsorption systems discussed below.

In the mechanical-refrigeration system essentially the same problems encountered in the low-temperature systems must be considered. The systems are therefore quite similar. The basic difference is in the fact that the choke in the low-temperature-separators systems is replaced by a chiller in the mechanical-refrigeration systems. Because it is desirable to chill to 0°F and below in these systems some type of preventive measure must be taken against hydrate formation.

Although glycol-injection systems are extensively used there have been installations where inlet dehydration is used to get the water dew point of the gas below the operating temperature in the chiller. There is some merit to this system since the glycol does not come in contact with the condensate and glycol losses are less. Some of the other operating problems such as good separation of glycol and condensate are also eliminated. The dehydrator would be placed between the inlet liquid separator and the chiller and could be either the glycol type or granular-desiccant type.

The inlet liquid separator is necessary to remove waxy condensate and salt water as was described in the section above.   Figure 13-8 shows a typical refrigeration system using absorption refrigeration and stabilization.

Absorption Refrigeration.   In the ammonia-absorption system shown, liquid ammonia in the condenser flows to the chiller through a level-control system.   The liquid ammonia in the chiller is vaporized by the inlet gas stream flowing through the chiller coils.   Ammonia vapors flow from the chiller to the absorber, where they are absorbed by a weak ammonia-liquor spray.   The absorption of the ammonia vapors by the weak ammonia liquor generates a considerable amount of heat.   This heat must be removed from the absorber by an outside source of cooling.   The absorption of the ammonia vapor by the weak liquor forms a strong ammonia liquor.

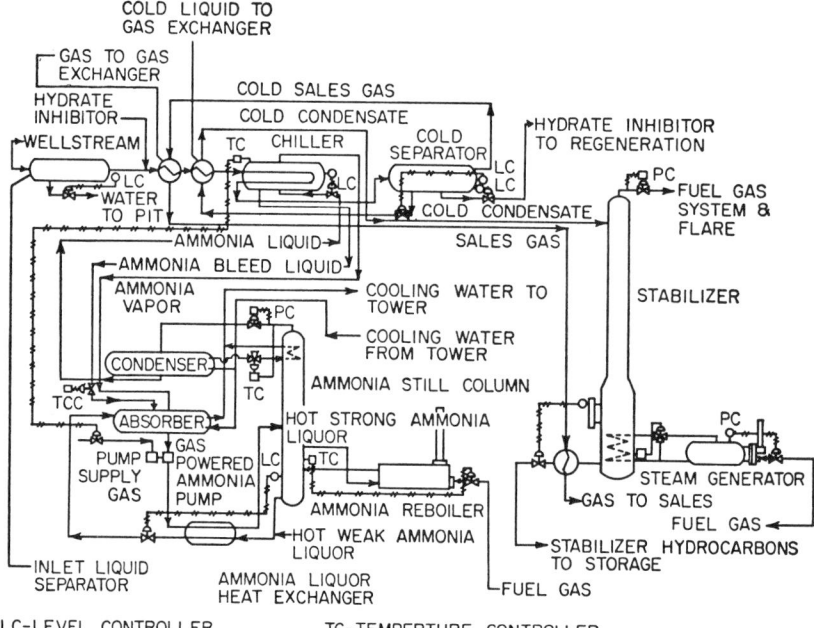

FIG. 13-8. Hydrocarbon-liquid recovery system with absorption refrigeration and stabilization.

The strong ammonia liquor is pumped from the bottom of the absorber through an ammonia-liquor heat exchanger to a still column operated at an elevated pressure. The strong liquor picks up heat from the hot weak ammonia liquor from the bottom of the still column in this heat exchanger.

Ammonia is vaporized from the strong ammonia liquor in the still column by heat as supplied to the still column by the ammonia-liquor reboiler.   Hot weak ammonia liquor flows from the bottom of the still to the ammonia-liquor heat exchanger.   The cooled weak ammonia liquor then flows to the absorber.

Water vapor is condensed from the hot ammonia vapors in the top of the still column by reflux from a water-cooled partial condenser.   Virtually pure ammonia vapor is obtained overhead from the still.

Ammonia vapor from the top of the still column flows to an ammonia condenser. The ammonia vapor is cooled and condensed at approximately the same pressure as the still-column pressure.   The liquid ammonia collects in the bottom of the condenser and flows into the chiller on demand of the liquid-level-control system.

Figure 13-9 shows the vapor-pressure curves for ammonia, water, and propane. Considering the process just described, assume that it is desirable to operate the chiller at $-10°F$. It can be seen from this curve that the chiller must operate at a pressure of 24 psia. The absorber must also be operated at this pressure. If the cooling water will allow cooling the pure ammonia vapor off the top of the still column to 100°F, then the condenser must be operated at 216 psia as shown by the vapor-pressure curve. Thus the only pressure increase required of the ammonia pump is from 24 to 216 psia. For 216 psia still-column pressure the bottoms temperature would have to be 386°F to vaporize all the ammonia out of the water. However, since the weak ammonia liquor from the still bottoms is used to absorb the ammonia vapors from the chiller it is not necessary to remove all the ammonia from the water. The bottoms temperature can be around 310°F and produce a solution of approximately 85 per cent water and 15 per cent ammonia, which is satisfactory for this operation.

Compression-refrigeration System. The compression-refrigeration system (Fig. 13-10) accomplishes the identical result as does the absorption system. The inlet gas stream flowing through the chiller coils causes the refrigerant (assumed to be propane for this example) to boil. The cold propane vapors flow out of the chiller through a back-pressure valve which maintains the pressure in the chiller at a set value. A propane vapor–propane liquid heat exchanger is included to further cool the liquid and heat the vapor to prevent condensation.

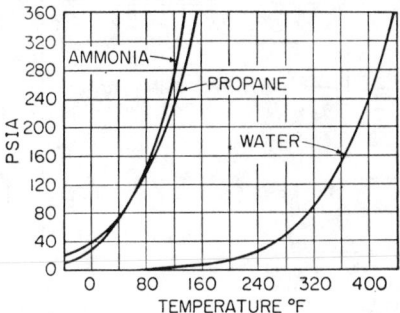

Fig. 13-9. Vapor pressures of ammonia, propane, and water.

The propane vapors then enter an accumulator which is included to remove all traces of liquid that may be entrained in the vapor prior to compression. The warm propane liquid flows through a coil in the bottom of this scrubber to boil off any liquids that may accumulate and return them to a vapor phase for recompression.

The propane vapors are then compressed in a reciprocating compressor. This compressor is normally driven by a natural-gas engine since the gas is readily available. Since the compressor requires lubrication, it is difficult to prevent oil from being entrained in the compressed vapors. It is necessary to drain this oil from the refrigerant periodically since it would eventually build up in the chiller and decrease the efficiency of the system. For this reason there are oil drains located in the receiver, chiller, and accumulator for removing these lubricating oils.

The propane vapors are then liquefied in the condenser by cooling with either water or air cooling. The liquid propane is then stored in the receiver until required in the chiller. The propane liquid flows through the coils of the gas scrubber to the expansion valve, which is actuated by the level controller on the chiller. As the propane level decreases in the chiller because of the boiling action caused in chilling the wellstream, the level controller opens the expansion valve, allowing more liquid to flow into the chiller.

Referring to Fig. 13-9 for propane, if the chiller is to be operated at $-10°F$, then the chiller pressure has to be set at 31 psia. If water cooling is available and 100°F cooling water can be assumed, then the discharge pressure of the compressor must be 188 psia. If air cooling is to be used, this pressure will have to be increased to provide sufficient temperature differential to assure sufficient cooling for condensing the propane.

Ammonia is a common refrigerant in this type of service. It has advantages and disadvantages over propane. It has a heat of vaporization about $3\frac{1}{2}$ times that of propane. This means that the circulation rate of the ammonia will be roughly one-third that of propane for the same refrigeration load. The ammonia requires higher compressor discharge pressures to allow for the condensation of the ammonia vapors. Other refrigerants are available, including Freon, butanes, and lithium chloride–water solution, but their vapor pressure–temperature characteristics are normally not suited for this low-temperature operation (0°F and below).

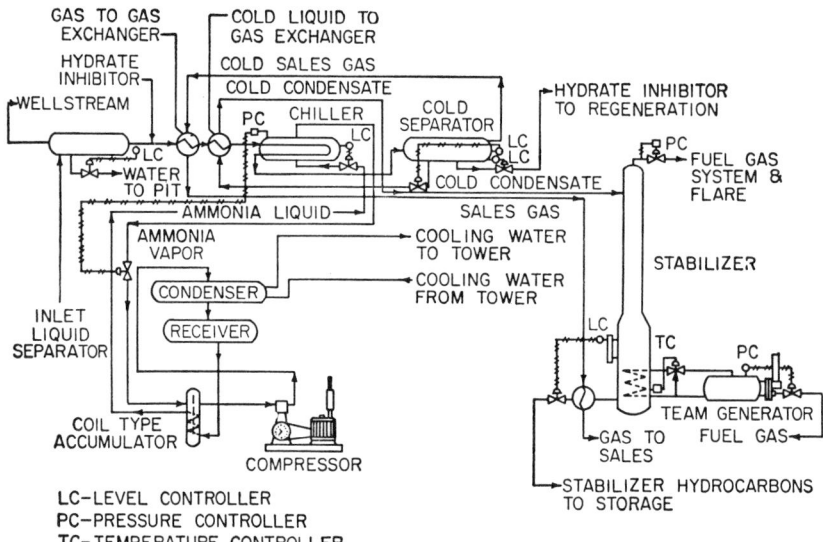

FIG. 13-10. Hydrocarbon-liquid recovery system with mechanical refrigeration and stabilization.

The refrigeration load on the chiller for a given flow rate is a function of the wellstream analysis, pressure, and inlet temperature to the chiller. The two factors involved in this cooling are the sensible heat required to reduce the wellstream from flowing temperatures to chiller temperature and the latent heat required to condense the liquefiable hydrocarbons. It is obvious that the richer the wellstream the greater the refrigeration required. The chiller and refrigeration system must be designed to meet the requirements of each individual installation and must be based on the wellstream analysis, pressure, and temperature.

The system must be designed to utilize as much of the cooling as possible. This can be done by taking the cold gas and condensate from the low-temperature separator and passing them through heat exchangers to cool the inlet gas upstream of the chiller. In most cases pipelines will not accept gas if it is too low in temperature, and this will allow the sales gas to be warmed. This cooling effect can be used to reduce the refrigeration tonnage required and increase the over-all efficiency of the process. In some cases the cold gas is used to cool the stabilized condensate before it is sent to storage. These heat exchangers are shown in the flow diagrams of Figs. 13-8 and 13-10.

Selective Adsorption Systems

On lean wellstreams where economic justification and pay-out of equipment for hydrocarbon removal by refrigeration are not possible, consideration of a selective adsorption system should be made. This type of system will normally recover more hydrocarbons than is possible with refrigeration on very lean streams.

The selective adsorption system consists basically of two or more adsorption towers filled with a dry desiccant, normally a silica gel. These towers are controlled on a time cycle to be absorbing, regenerating, and/or cooling. Alternate use is made of these beds to absorb the desired hydrocarbons from the gas stream. When the bed becomes saturated, the gas stream is switched through another bed. The saturated bed is then regenerated by passing hot gas through the bed, which vaporizes and drives off the hydrocarbons which have been adsorbed on the desiccant. During the regeneration cycle the bed and some of the steel parts of the adsorber become heated and must be cooled prior to using the bed on the adsorbing cycle.

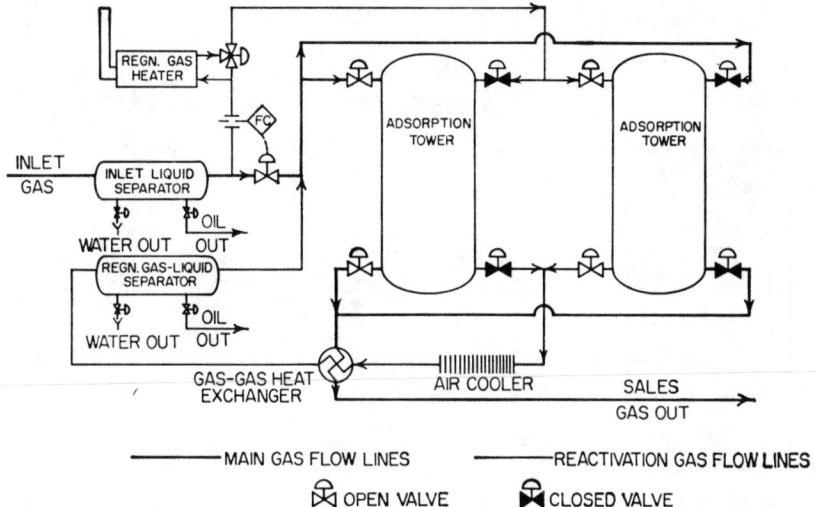

Fig. 13-11. Typical two-tower open-cycle selective hydrocarbon-absorption system.

This cycle is the same as has been used for many years as a dry-desiccant dehydrator. The basic difference is in the time allowed for the length of the cycle. The dehydrators normally operated on an 8-hour cycle. These units operate on a much shorter cycle and have been called short-cycle or quick-cycle units.

In studying the adsorption of natural gas on solid desiccants such as silica gel, the adsorption begins with methane, ethane, propane, etc., in that order. As the gas progresses through the bed the heavier hydrocarbons displace the lighter ones and eventually the water vapor displaces the hydrocarbons. In past operation of dry-desiccant dehydrators the presence of hydrocarbons in the water condensate removed from the unit has often been evident. The reason that more were not detected is the long time cycle used on these units. The secret of operation of these units is to determine the point where the split is most desirable from a pipeline and recovery standpoint. Usually this has to be a compromise since it must be done on a time basis because of instrumentation presently available.

Figure 13-11 shows a typical installation for the selective adsorption system. The wellstream flows into an inlet-liquid separator to remove any free liquids and thus cut down on possible desiccant contamination. The gas then flows through a pressure-reducing valve, used to control the flow of gas through the regeneration and cooling cycles, and into a manifold for switching to the tower on stream by the time-cycle controller. As the gas passes through the desiccant bed the heavier hydrocarbons and water vapor are adsorbed. Stripped dry gas leaves the tower and flows through the gas-to-gas heat exchanger into the sales-gas line.

The tower being regenerated has been saturated through previous contact with the main gas stream. Gas for regeneration is taken off the main gas line upstream of the pressure-reducing value, and the flow rate through the regeneration system is controlled by the pressure drop across this valve. The regeneration gas flows through the heater where it is heated and then to the tower being regenerated. The heavier hydrocarbons and water vapor which were adsorbed are now driven off by the hot gases. The gas and vaporized fluids pass through an air-cooled heat exchanger where the temperature is decreased, condensing some of these fluids. Additional cooling is

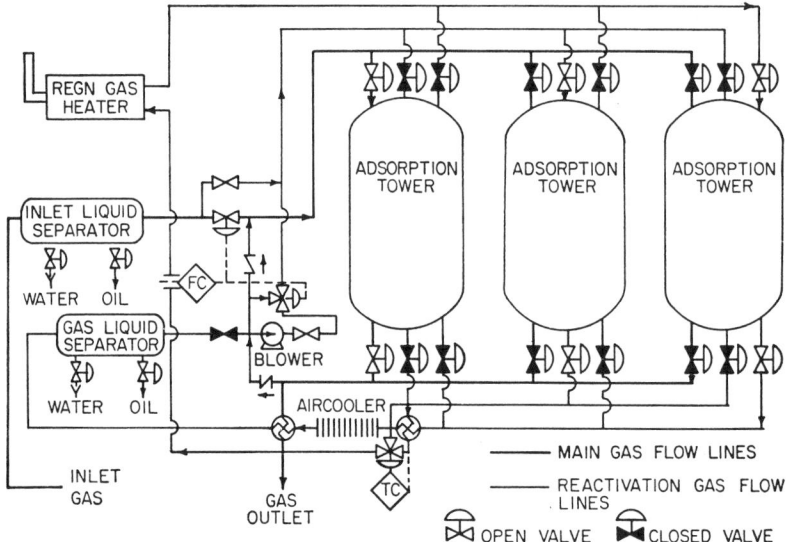

FIG. 13-12. Typical three-tower closed-cycle selective hydrocarbon-adsorption system.

obtained in the main gas-to-gas heat exchanger where further condensation results. The regeneration gas and condensates are passed through the regeneration-system separator where the condensates are removed from the gas. The gas off the separator flows back into the main gas stream downstream of the pressure-reducing valve. The condensates are separated and the water is dumped to a pit and the hydrocarbon liquid to a stabilizer.

The system just described is commonly referred to as an open-type regeneration system. This means that the regeneration gas flows continuously out and into the main gas stream on either side of the pressure-reducing valve. This requires that a pressure drop be taken in the main gas stream. In applications where pressure drops cannot be tolerated a closed-type regeneration system can be used. Such a system can be seen in Fig. 13-12.

A blower is used to recirculate the regeneration gas through the regeneration heating and cooling cycles. The blower picks up gas downstream from the regeneration-liquid separator and boosts the pressure sufficiently to produce the required circulation rate of the regeneration gas. Although the system shown in Fig. 13-12 is for a three-tower system, to be described below, the blower will work equally well on the two-tower system shown in Fig. 13-11. The blower discharge would connect into the meter run going to the regenerative gas heater.   The pressure-reducing valve and extra piping shown in Fig. 13-12 are included to ensure continuous operation while the blower is shut in for maintenance.   Under these circumstances the unit operates as an open-cycle system.   To compensate for varying pressures in the reactivation-gas system due to temperature changes, equalizer lines are connected into the system with check valves.   In the event that gas is required in the system, dry gas is taken from the sales-gas end of the system.   If the reverse is the case, then gas within the regeneration system is discharged ahead of the adsorber so that wet gas can be processed before entering the sales-gas line.

One of the advantages of the closed system is the fact that the regeneration gas never becomes a factor in the drying cycle.   Essentially the same gas is used over and over again.   This results in slightly higher recoveries with an additional operating expense which requires an economic study for justification.   The inclusion of the blower in the system adds considerably to the maintenance expense and operating problems encountered over the open-type system.   The main advantage of the closed-type system is the fact that the pressure drop on the main gas stream can be held to a minimum.

As noted in Fig. 13-12, the system can include more than two adsorption towers. The three-tower system shown allows for equal adsorption, heating, and cooling cycles on a time basis.   In the two-tower system the adsorption cycle equals the sum of the heating and cooling cycles timewise.   Since the weight of desiccant required is proportional to the weight of vapors adsorbed, the shorter the time cycle the less desiccant is required because less vapor passes through the bed.   Thus it can be seen that for three towers the same vapors can be removed with three-fourths as much desiccant as for the two-tower system.   This means that with less desiccant the tower size can be reduced for the same capacity and the three-tower system may not have any more first costs than the two-tower system.

A four-tower system is also a possibility.   This system would be comparable with the three-tower system in design but would use the fourth tower in parallel to the tower on the adsorption cycle.   This would mean that one tower would be heating, one cooling, and two adsorbing.   This system would allow for handling twice the flow capacity with the addition of one tower and its controls plus a slight increase in the size of the regeneration-system components.

Another possible variation to this system is to include a second set of towers using activated charcoal downstream of these towers using silica gel.   The second set of towers is designed to adsorb the propanes and butanes while the first set of towers adsorbs the pentanes plus.   This system is used principally where the propane and butane content is sufficiently high to merit consideration and where the market for these products is available.

As was pointed out, the size of the beds is a function of the amount of liquids to be removed.   This quantity of liquid may be obtained from a small volume of rich gas or a large volume of lean gas.   The diameter of the tower is established from the allowable velocity of the gas through the bed.   At low pressures this diameter can become quite large if a given capacity must be satisfied.   The depth of the bed is determined by the amount of desiccant required, the allowable pressure drop, or the minimum bed depth.   The length of the time cycle affects the size of the bed for a given amount of liquid removed.   The amount of desiccant decreases with decreasing time but the heating and cooling requirements increase as the cycle is shortened.   The heat required is a function only of the pounds of liquids to be removed and the materials to be heated such as the desiccant and portions of the towers.   The heating and cooling rates are thus inversely proportional to the time of the cycle.

For a given wellstream it can be concluded that the design of the equipment and the operation and control are most important in effecting liquid removal.   The time cycle is important and is good only for a range of variation in the wellstream analysis. If the wellstream becomes richer, the cycle may be too long and all liquids are not removed.   If the wellstream becomes leaner, the cycle is too short and the desiccant is not utilized to the maximum.

The quality of process cooling can also affect the process efficiency.   If sufficient cooling is not accomplished, condensation of the liquefiable hydrocarbons will not be complete. In the open cycle this means that the regeneration gas will carry these vapors back into the bed to be adsorbed again. It can be seen that this could result in a considerable amount of recycling of hydrocarbon vapors.

The nonhydrocarbons present in the natural gas will have some effect on the process. This is especially true of the water vapors which eventually replace the hydrocarbons adsorbed in the bed and allow them to be expelled. The short-cycle unit is an excellent dehydrator as well as a hydrocarbon-removal unit. Presence of hydrogen sulfide has little effect on the process unless oxygen is present. In this event the oxygen causes free sulfur to form which will tend to foul the desiccant. Carbon dioxide, nitrogen, and other gases occasionally found in natural gas do not affect the process significantly.

In selecting a short-cycle unit the following can be used as a guide: When the butanes and heavier to be adsorbed amount to 10 bbl/MMscf of gas or less, then the application of this type of system is normally feasible. Between 10 and 15 bbl/MMscf the choice must be made between the quick-cycle and the refrigeration system. Only through an economic analysis of both these systems can the proper choice be made. On wellstreams in excess of 15 bbl/MMscf the refrigeration system is more feasible. The normal application for the quick-cycle unit is downstream of low-temperature separation systems in which the reservoir pressure has decreased to the extent that the refrigeration from expansion cannot effectively remove the liquefiable hydrocarbons.

Hydrocarbon Stabilization

The previous discussion covers the processes in which a maximum removal of liquefiable hydrocarbons from the gaseous phase of the wellstream is accomplished to satisfy pipeline specifications and to derive additional revenue from these liquid hydrocarbons. Unless these liquid hydrocarbons are properly handled after separation from the main gas stream, the revenue to be derived will not be a maximum. In order to obtain a maximum revenue from these products, it is necessary to retain the maximum volume of separated hydrocarbon liquids in atmospheric storage. It is also necessary to salvage the maximum amount of light vapors from the separated liquids.

In order to store a liquid at atmospheric pressure without losses, it must have a vapor pressure equal to atmospheric pressure at a temperature which will be the maximum encountered in the storage tank. This vapor pressure would be referred to as the true vapor pressure. In practice it is more common to use a standard vapor pressure determined by sampling the liquid and measuring its vapor pressure under controlled conditions. This empirical pressure is normally referred to as the Reid vapor pressure (RVP) and is taken at 100°F in a controlled water bath. It is therefore possible to determine the RVP of a bottom product under actual operating conditions.

Referring to Fig. 13-13, it can be seen that, if atmospheric temperature is such that it will not be higher than 64°F at 14.5 psia pressure, a 26-lb RVP product can be stored. On the other hand, if the temperature can be expected to run as high as 105°F at 14.5 psia, a 12-lb RVP product can be stored. The chart is helpful then in selecting what products can be stored in atmospheric storage tanks. If pressure tanks are to be used, it provides a means of determining for a given RVP product and storage temperature what working pressure must be held on the tanks to assure no vapor losses.

When the hydrocarbon liquids are dumped from the high-pressure separator, the liquids are at their boiling point for the pressures involved. Each reduction in pressure causes some vapors to be boiled off. If the liquids were dumped directly to a storage tank, violent boiling would take place, resulting in a loss of not only the lighter vapors but also some of the heavier ends. By taking the pressure reduction in stages these losses are reduced. Increasing the number of stages of separation results in greater stock-tank recovery. Regardless of the number of stages used, some recoverable hydrocarbons that are normally liquid are lost with the solution vapors from each stage of separation. Considerable volumes of low-pressure gas are released from each stage and are costly to salvage. A maximum volume of hydrocarbon liquid stable under stock-tank conditions with a minimum volume of solution vapors removed at relatively high pressure can be accomplished by fractionation of the first-stage separator liquid.   This process is commonly referred to as stabilization, and different systems are outlined below.

Figure 13-14 shows a flow diagram of a stabilizer used with a heated-liquid-type low-temperature separation system.   In this system the condensate feed stream to the stabilizer is preheated.   Condensate comes from the low-temperature separator at about 80 to 90°F and is preheated in a heat exchanger with the bottom product to approximately the same temperature as the stabilizer at the point of entry.   A temperature controller regulates a bypass valve in the feed line so that a constant temperature can be maintained in the feed to the stabilizer.   The hydrocarbon mixture

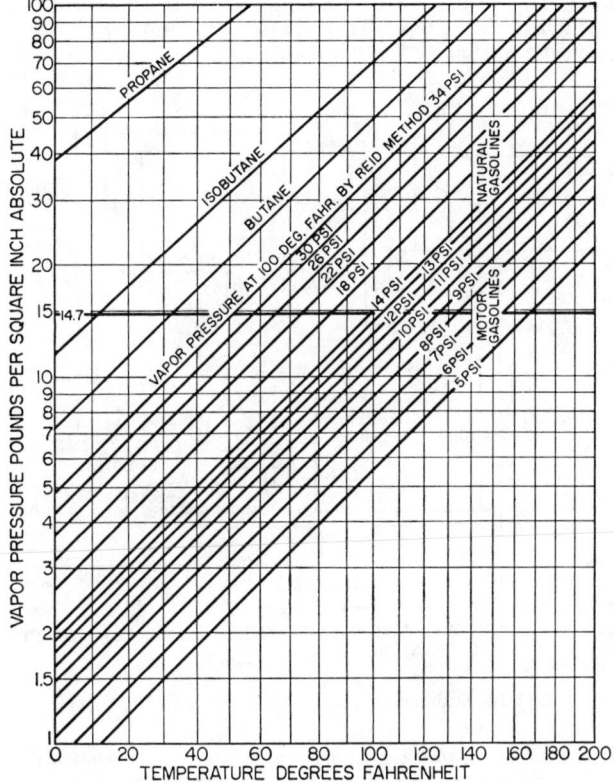

Fig. 13-13. Vapor pressure–temperature curves for motor and natural gasolines.   (*From the NGSMA Handbook.*)

is fractionated and the lighter components pass overhead in the vapor state.   The stable liquid is withdrawn from the bottom of the stabilizer.   A portion of the overhead vapors is condensed either by cooling water or by the cold gas stream from the low-temperature separator in a heat exchanger.   The liquid is separated and returned to the stabilizer as reflux.

Gas from the reflux accumulator is vented for fuel and instrument gas.   If the excess is great enough, it may be recompressed and added to the sales gas, but it may have to be dehydrated after compression.

Heat is supplied to the stabilizer by circulating the liquid that has passed through the fractionating section through an indirect-fired salt-bath heater.   This provides stripping vapors for the liquid as it flows down the tower.   The remaining liquid is automatically discharged by a liquid-level controller in the bottom of the stabilizer. This liquid is partially cooled in the feed preheater and further cooled with air coolers. Final cooling to atmospheric temperature is done with the cold gas from the low-temperature separator. After cooling, the bottom product is stored in a stock tank.

A number of variations of this system are possible, depending upon the utilities available at the particular location. Where these units are used in conjunction with normal recovery methods, cooling water or a fan cooler may be used in place of the cold gas.

Figure 13-15 shows a flow diagram of a stabilizer used with a glycol-injection cold-liquid-type low-temperature separation system. The system uses cold feed from a glycol-injection system for the feed stream to the stabilizer. Condensate at 0 to 25°F is fed into the stabilizer at the top. This cold feed creates its own reflux and requires no other equipment for refluxing the stabilizer.

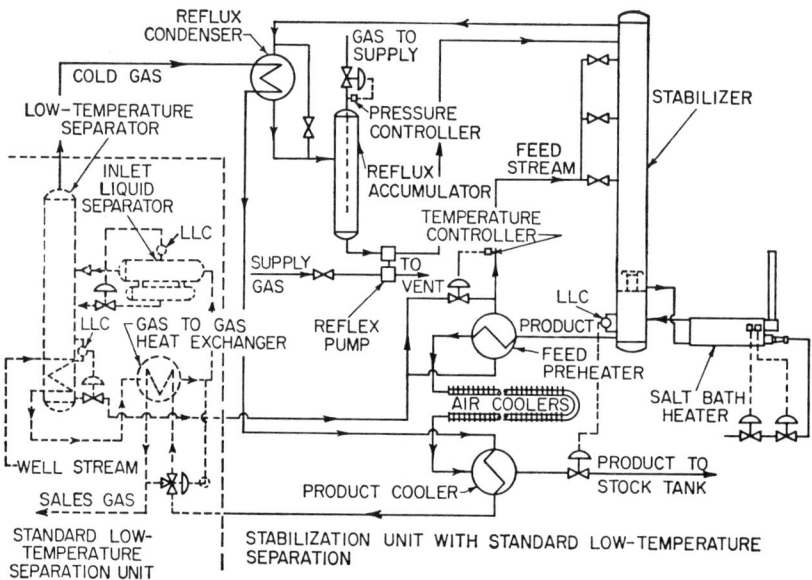

FIG. 13-14. Stabilization unit with standard LTS system.

Condensate is fractionated by the same process used in the system described with Fig. 13-14. The light components pass overhead as vapor, and the stable product is withdrawn from the bottom of the tower. The bottom product is cooled in a heat exchanger either by the cold gas from the low-temperature separator or by cooling water, whichever the case may be. Overhead gas may be used for fuel and supply gas. If the volume warrants, it may be recompressed for sales gas. Heat is supplied with an indirect-fired salt-bath heater.

To determine the pressure and temperature at which the maximum recovery will be achieved, Fig. 13-16 is included. The curves are drawn for 14.5 psia. The example shown is for a low-pressure stabilizer using a steam generator for a bottoms heater. For temperatures and pressure above this range the high-pressure stabilizer and salt-bath heater combination are used.

It has been found that, where the feed to the stabilizer is at low temperatures, as in glycol-injection systems, good fractionation can be obtained by feeding the cold liquid on the top tray, causing the column to reflux itself. This eliminates the relatively expensive reflux system required on stabilizers where the feed is at higher temperatures. The elimination of reflux condenser, reflux control, and reflux pump

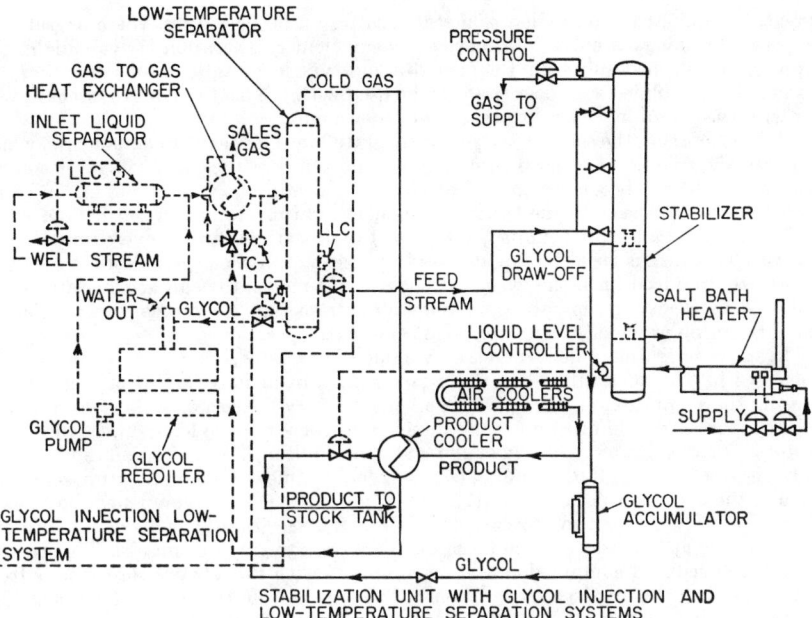

Fig. 13-15. Stabilization unit with glycol-injection LTS system.

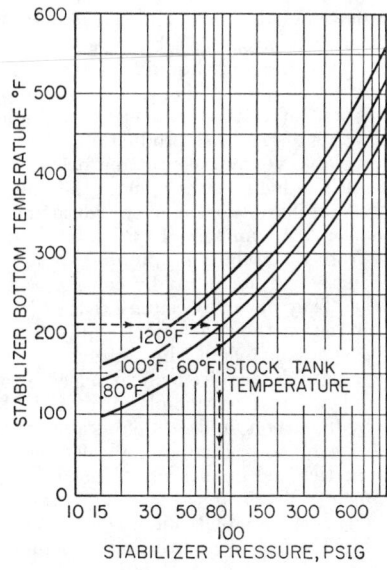

Fig. 13-16. Stabilizer operating conditions. Initial settings for determining the point of maximum recovery.

greatly simplifies the operation of a stabilizer on an oil-field lease where operational supervision is very limited. In most cases sufficient refrigeration is available in the system to chill the liquid from the heated-liquid-type low-temperature separation system. The simplified stabilizer can then be used with the heated-liquid system as well as with the glycol-injection low-temperature system.

By this method, the separator liquid is separated into its heavier components, which will remain a liquid at atmospheric pressure and temperatures and its lighter components, which will become a gas at atmospheric conditions. A minimum of liquid components are lost with the lighter components in this method of separation.

For selective adsorption units the liquefied hydrocarbons are recovered on a batch basis. This means that the liquids build up fast over a short period of time and no more are produced until the cycle switches. This means that an accumulator must be used between the separator and the stabilizer so that a more continuous flow of liquids can be provided to effect efficient stabilizer operation.

In stage separation all the increased volume of normally liquid hydrocarbons is not reflected in the stock tanks because a larger amount of it is carried out as a vapor during the separation of the lighter components. By the use of stabilization almost all the increased volume of normally liquid components in the low-temperature separator is retained in the stock tanks under stable conditions. In addition to producing a larger stock-tank volume of liquid from a given volume of low-temperature separator liquid, the stabilizer produces all the lighter normally gaseous components overhead at one point in the system at relatively high pressures, 175 psig or higher. This low-pressure gas at this pressure can be compressed back to gas-transmission line pressure at a much reduced compression cost as compared with the low-pressure vapors from the same system using stage separation. The vapors from the stabilizer are also lean in heavy hydrocarbon components and therefore more desirable in a gas-transmission line than the gasoline-laden vapors from stage separation.

When the overhead vapors from a stabilizer are compressed into the sales-gas line and the stabilized liquid is stored in a vaportight tank, every pound of the produced well fluid with the exception of that used for fuel gas in lease heaters (if any) and the stabilizer reboiler can be marketed.

Where a high API gravity condensate from a low-temperature separation system is being stabilized on the lease it is often desirable to go one step further and install a low-pressure fractionator on the discharge liquid from the stabilizer to produce natural gasoline to proper specification of vapor and end point overhead and residue oil off the bottom. This further refinement of the condensate on the lease will often increase substantially the market value of the lease production.

Where there is an appreciable volume of propane being produced in the low-temperature separator liquid, it is in many cases economically desirable to add a de-ethanizer column ahead of the stabilizer to remove the methane and most of the ethane from the feed to the stabilizer. A commercial LPG mixture can then be produced by condensing the overhead from the stabilizer column.

These latter two possibilities are not normally considered to be in the category of lease-operated equipment. They normally require that at least one operator be present at all times. For this reason their inclusion is only for the purpose of showing that further refinements are possible to effect higher revenues from a given wellstream.

In order to be able to evaluate the requirements of a lease from an equipment standpoint, it is necessary to understand the principles of material balance, especially as it relates to equilibrium in hydrocarbon fluids. Before undertaking such an evaluation the properties of the wellstream, in particular the wellstream analysis, pressure, and temperature, and the properties and quantities of fluid both gas and liquid that can be marketed must be known. The latter knowledge is essential since a pay-out for the equipment can exist only if the product can be sold. With this information available it is possible to calculate the recoveries utilizing the equilibrium methods outlined below.

The wellstream or, in chemical-process terms, the feed F in moles is composed of hydrocarbons in the liquid phase L in moles, and the vapor phase V in moles, thus

$$F = L + V \qquad (1)$$

If the individual hydrocarbon components of the wellstream, methane, ethane, propane, etc., are considered, they will exist as mole fractions of the liquid x_i, mole fractions of the vapor y_i, and mole fractions of the wellstream z_i. The material balance for each component can be written

$$x_i L + y_i V = z_i F \tag{2}$$

By definition the equilibrium constant k_i for a given component is the ratio of the moles of the component in the vapor y_i to that in the liquid x_i.

$$k_i = \frac{y_i}{x_i} \tag{3}$$

The value of k_i for a given component is a function of the pressure and temperature of the system. Thus it is necessary to know the pressure and temperature of the wellstream and also the pressure and temperature at the point under consideration. The latter could be the sales-gas condition in the separator, the conditions at the overhead or bottom of the stabilizer, stage-separator conditions, or stock-tank conditions.

The summation by definition of the mole fractions in the liquid, in the vapor, or in the feed is equal to unity.

$$\Sigma x_i = 1$$
$$\Sigma y_i = 1$$
$$\Sigma z_i = 1$$

To simplify the calculations it is possible to consider 1 mole of feed and with some algebraic manipulation arrive at the following:

$$L + V = 1$$
$$y_i = k_i x_i$$
$$x_i L + k_i x_i V = z_i$$
$$x_i L \left(1 + k_i \frac{V}{L}\right) = z_i$$
$$x_i L = \frac{z_i}{1 + k_i(V/L)}$$
$$\sum x_i L = L = \sum \frac{z_i}{1 + k_i(V/L)} \tag{4}$$

Assuming a value for V/L, the following table can be set up for the calculation and summation of $z_i/[1 + k_i(V/L)]$.

Component	Symbol	z_i	k_i	$\dfrac{z_i}{1 + k_i(V/L)}$
Methane................	C_1	z_{C_1}	k_{C_1}	
Ethane.................	C_2	z_{C_2}	k_{C_2}	
Propane................	C_3	z_{C_3}	k_{C_3}	
Isobutane..............	iC_4	z_{iC_4}	k_{iC_4}	
Normal butane..........	nC_4	z_{nC_4}	k_{nC_4}	
Isopentane.............	iC_5	z_{iC_5}	k_{iC_5}	
Normal pentane.........	nC_5	z_{nC_5}	k_{nC_5}	
Hexanes...............	C_6	z_{C_6}	k_{C_6}	
Heptanes plus..........	C_7^+	$z_{C_7}^+$	k_{C_7}	
		$\sum zi = 1.00$		$\sum \dfrac{z_i}{1 + k_i(V/L)}$

From Eq. (4) it can be seen that this summation must be equal to L, and from Eq. (1)

$$L = \frac{1}{1 + (V/L)}$$

If the summation is less than L then a higher V/L must be assumed and the calculation repeated until by trial and error the summation becomes equal to L, as seen in Eq. (4).

This method of calculation is normally used where the liquids in the wellstream are small such as in a gas-condensate well. For cases where the liquids predominate it is more convenient to solve Eq. (2) for

$$\sum y_i V = V$$

This form would be used in calculating the liquid recovered and vapor released from solution in stage-separation systems, stabilizers, and stock tanks. The calculation is made for a given pressure and temperature that can be expected to be normal in operation for that part of the system in question. It can be seen that this could be a considerable chore if the operation is for the purpose of finding the optimum pressure and temperature conditions to give maximum recovery. In most cases the calculations are performed on electric computing machines that are usually found at universities or at companies supplying this type of equipment.

Once the moles of liquid and moles of vapor have been determined for the given set of conditions under study, i.e., pressure and temperature in the separator, stabilizer, stock tank, etc., it becomes necessary to convert the mole into more common units of measurement. Primarily these units are barrels of liquid hydrocarbons produced per million standard cubic feet of wellstream flowing.

It is necessary to make an equilibrium calculation every time the liquid is flashed or separated at different pressure and temperature conditions to account for the vapors lost in the flash. For example, if in the initial separation only 0.20 mole of liquid is recovered, in the second-stage separation only 0.75 mole of the liquid is recovered, and in the stock tank only 0.90 mole of the liquid is recovered, the actual moles of liquid recovered in the stock tank will be the 0.20 times the 0.75 times the 0.90, or 0.135 mole of stock-tank liquid per mole of feed.

Each mole of stock-tank liquid contains a mixture of the various hydrocarbons in equilibrium. Each hydrocarbon component can be expressed as a fraction of the total liquid or in other words a mole fraction. By multiplying these mole fractions by the molecular weight of the particular hydrocarbon component and summing up these products by multiplication, it is possible to get the molecular weight of the stock-tank liquid.

The density of each of the hydrocarbon components can be obtained from any standard reference on properties of hydrocarbons. This density is listed as a standard density and if used the standard temperature and pressure should be noted. For example, this normally would be referred to 60°F and 14.696 psia. By dividing the product of the molecular weight and the mole fraction as calculated above by the density of the particular hydrocarbon component it is possible to obtain the standard volume per mole. By summing up these dividends the volume per mole of the total liquid can be obtained.

The total number of moles in the original feed multiplied by the moles of stock-tank liquid per mole of feed will give the total number of moles of recovered liquid in the stock tank. The volume of the recovered stock-tank liquid is obtained by multiplying the moles of stock-tank liquid.

It is common to express recoveries in terms of barrels per million standard cubic feet of feed or in gallons per thousand cubic feet. Therefore, it is necessary to convert cubic feet of stock-tank liquid to gallons or barrels and moles of feed to standard cubic feet. This can be accomplished by multiplying the cubic feet of stock-tank liquid by 0.1781 bbl/cu ft or by 7.48 gal/cu ft. To convert moles of feed to standard cubic feet it is only necessary to multiply the moles by 379 cu ft/mole.

By dividing the molecular weight of the stock-tank liquid by the volume per mole calculated above, it is possible to determine the density of the liquid. This density is necessary in calculating the revenues derived from the recovered liquids because normally the price per barrel is based on the API gravity of the liquid.

A word of caution: When evaluating calculations made by others it is necessary to know what equilibrium constants have been used.   No attempt will be made to recommend the constants to be used in these calculations because of the existence of variance of opinions of this subject.   Short-cut approximations also exist that can be used to make rough calculations on hydrocarbon recoveries.   These are used only for the purpose of investigating whether or not further calculations are warranted and should not be used past this point.

In the case of hydrocarbon recoveries from short-cycle adsorption units no attempt will be made to present the methods of calculations since the equilibrium constants or adsorption factors are still in the embryo stage.   These are determined from actual experimental and operational data and require gathering, compilation, and consolidation before they can be used in these calculations.   In evaluating these systems, it is also necessary to check each calculation for the source of the constants used to obtain an equitable comparison.

GAS-TREATING SYSTEMS FOR REMOVAL OF WATER VAPOR, CARBON DIOXIDE, AND HYDROGEN SULFIDE

Natural gas can contain any number of nonhydrocarbon impurities in the formation or wellhead condition.   Some of these are detrimental to efficient pipeline operation while others have no effect on operation but do affect the heat content or Btu rating of the natural gas.

In almost every case natural gas contains water vapor to some extent.   The characteristics of the rock in the formation will determine largely the extent to which water occurs.   In some cases the gas is supersaturated, which means that free water will be present.   In other cases the gas is saturated at reservoir conditions, which would mean that at producing condition it will be supersaturated.   Finally the water content can be much lower than saturation but higher than specifications to be satisfied for pipeline acceptance.   The formation of free water with pressure and/or temperature reduction can result in the formation of hydrates if the temperature falls below the hydrate-forming temperature.   This phenomenon is discussed more fully in the preceding section.   In addition to the problems of hydrates the formation of free water due to condensation can add to the horsepower requirements for pipelines because of increased pressure drops caused when water collects in low spots in the line and reduces the flow area of the gas.   This condition is also conducive to corrosion in the pipe.   It is sufficient to say that water vapors must be removed from the gas, and various methods used for this removal will be discussed below.

Sour gas is the name commonly given to natural gas containing hydrogen sulfide. This hydrogen sulfide is found in concentrations varying from a trace on up to 30 mole per cent.   The presence of hydrogen sulfide causes severe corrosion to occur when free water is present in natural-gas pipelines.   When burned it forms sulfur dioxide, which is very toxic and can be a serious problem on the marketing end of the pipeline.   Various methods for removal of hydrogen sulfide will be discussed below.

A companion to hydrogen sulfide is carbon dioxide.   It occurs quite frequently in natural gas but is not nearly so serious a detriment as hydrogen sulfide.   The main difficulty encountered is the corrosive characteristics of carbon dioxide in the presence of water.   Since it is not combustible, it lowers the heat content of the natural gas, and this becomes a factor especially where large volumes of carbon dioxide are present. The same systems that are used to remove the hydrogen sulfide can also remove the carbon dioxide.   The presence of both these acid gases in the same wellstream will require larger recirculation and regeneration equipment than if only one were present.

Other impurities occur in natural gas, but their occurrence is infrequent.   Mercaptans, compounds similar to alcohols but with sulfur replacing the oxygen, RSH instead of ROH, are found occasionally but are not detrimental.   Nitrogen is commonly found in natural gas, and in some instances it is injected to control the heat content. It has no detrimental effects.   Oxygen is sometimes encountered but the quantities are usually so low that they can be discounted.   Another impurity that is only rarely encountered is helium.   The importance of this inert gas to the defense industries as well as other industries has led the government, through the Bureau of Mines, to construct plants in areas where helium is prevalent.   Since this is a specialized low-temperature process it will not be covered here.

Removal of Water Vapor

In the preceding pages the removal of liquefiable hydrocarbon is discussed.   The basic processes used for this removal of hydrocarbons invariably result in the removal of water vapors.   Experience has shown that the water-vapor dew point of the gas leaving the low-temperature separator in these processes is from 10 to 12°F below LTS temperature for systems not using hydrate inhibitors and from 20 to 40°F below LTS temperature for systems using hydrate inhibitors.   Dew-point depressions for selective adsorption systems will be discussed further, and the use of liquid desiccants will be covered for the field of gas dehydration in this section.

To understand water-vapor dew point and dew-point depression better, reference is made to Fig. 13-3.   As was explained, this curve shows the saturation conditions for water vapor in natural gas.   The water dew-point temperature is the same as the saturation temperature for a given pressure.   Assume that gas is flowing into a dehydration unit at 1,000 psia and 100°F and that it must be dehydrated to 7 lb of water/MMscf of gas to meet contract specifications.   At 1,000 psia and 100°F the gas contains 62 lb of water.   The inlet water-vapor dew-point temperature is 100°F.   From the chart for 1,000 psia and 7 lb water/MMscf the outlet water-vapor dew-point temperature is 33°F.   The dehydrator must be capable of producing a 67°F dew-point depression and removing 55 lb of water/MMscf of gas.

Dehydration by Adsorption.   One of the most common methods for water-vapor removal is the use of a dry desiccant as an adsorption medium.   This type of dehydration unit has been used in the chemical industry for many years for drying gases.   Although some dry-desiccant dehydrators were used prior to 1940 in the natural-gas industry, they have been more extensively used since World War II.

The process of adsorption is largely a form of adhesion between the solid surface of the desiccant and the water vapor which appears as a very thin film and is held by the attraction between the two materials.   The amount of water adsorbed varies with the nature and the surface area of the desiccant being used.   The most effective desiccants then are those possessing the greatest ratio of surface area to volume displacement.   It is generally believed that the adhesion of the water to the solid surface is also supplemented by capillary condensation.   Thus some of the water is condensed and retained in the capillary-size channels within the desiccant.   Although these desiccants appear to be hard and smooth, they are in reality honeycombed with microscopic pores which result in large-surface-area structures.

A typical dry-desiccant dehydration unit is shown in Fig. 13-17.   The main gas stream flows through an inlet separator where free liquids are removed.   These liquids can be harmful to the dehydration process in that free water will reduce the capacity of the unit if not removed and hydrocarbons can poison the bed if not properly regenerated.   The main gas stream then flows through a pressure-reducing valve which controls the flow of the regeneration gas by inducing a pressure drop in the main gas stream.   The gas then flows through one of the two adsorption towers where it contacts the desiccant and the water vapors are removed.   The main gas flows to the sales-gas line through a gas-to-gas heat exchanger where heat is added to the main gas stream from the regeneration gas.

The second adsorption tower is regenerated while the other tower adsorbs water vapors from the main gas stream.   Regeneration gas is taken from the main gas stream upstream of the pressure-reducing valve and passed through an indirect heater where the temperature is raised to 350 to 450°F depending on the desiccant used.   The hot gas then passes through the desiccant bed.   The water adsorbed in the bed is evaporated and swept out of the bed by the regeneration gas.   The hot wet regeneration gas passes through the gas-to-gas heat exchanger where it is cooled by heat transfer to the main gas stream.   The water condensed out of the gas is then separated in the regeneration gas scrubber.   The regeneration gas flows back into the main gas stream downstream of the pressure-reducing valve.   Normally about 10 per cent of the main gas stream is used for regeneration and approximately a 25 psig pressure drop is required to generate the flow of this regeneration gas through the system.

The control of this unit is automatic and is done on a time-cycle basis. Normally an 8-hour time is set for the adsorption and reactivation cycles. This requires that the towers be sized to handle 8 hours of flow from a water-vapor-capacity standpoint and that the heating and cooling requirements must be satisfied on the same basis. The time-cycle controller switches the three-way valves shown to place one tower on stream and the other on regeneration. The three-way valve on the heater system is controlled by the time-cycle controller so that, when the heating cycle is completed, the valve switches to allow cool gas to flow through the system to cool off the desiccant and tower prior to placing it on the adsorption cycle.

Some of the significant factors that must be considered in the design of these units are gas pressure and temperature, gas velocity, desired outlet-water content, adsorption capacity of the desiccant, and free liquids to be removed from the main gas stream. In addition the following precautions should be taken to assure good operation. It is necessary to eliminate low spots in the flow lines and equipment where

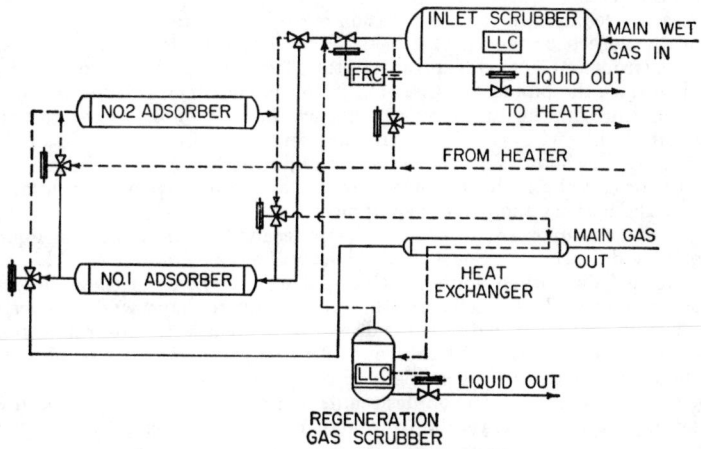

FIG. 13-17. Dry-desiccant dehydrator.

water might collect during the regeneration cycle. Proper sequencing of the valve-switching operation must be accomplished so that no unusual pressure or velocity surge will occur and so that no wet gas is allowed to pass from the unit to the sales-gas line. Finally, precautions should be taken to assure that no high temperatures occur in the main gas stream.

The granular desiccants used are basically silica gels or activated aluminas. Raw silica gel is a high-silica material in the form of highly irregular shaped particles. It is usually supplied in an 8-mesh screened size with a bulk density of 45 lb/cu ft. Refined silica gel, Mobilbead, is supplied in the form of beads of fairly uniform size and a bulk density of 48 to 50 lb/cu ft. Activated alumina is aluminum oxide in porous granular form having a bulk density of about 51 lb/cu ft. Several grades are available, and some bulk densities as high as 55 lb/cu ft are available.

The absorptive capacities of these desiccants vary. The initial desiccant capacity may indicate that it is possible to pick up in excess of 20 lb of water per 100 lb of desiccant. However, experience has shown that these capacities drop off rapidly to around 10 per cent and then gradually taper off until the desiccant becomes ineffective and must be replaced. The capacity and life of the desiccant depend almost entirely on the nature of the application. Under ideal operating conditions life in excess of

10 years has been experienced on one hand, while under severe fouling conditions the life may be reduced to less than 1 year. The design capacity used for desiccants must be accomplished through an economic balance between the first cost of the unit and the additional costs for desiccant replacement.

The desiccants are normally reactivated at a temperature well in excess of the boiling point for the water. This is necessary to effect efficient removal of the water as well as hydrocarbon fractions that may be present. Continuous regeneration of the silica gels above 450°F can cause some loss of adsorption capacity. On the other hand, the activated aluminas may be regenerated at temperatures in excess of 600°F. Since the heating and cooling requirements must be satisfied within the time cycle set, it is normally unnecessary to use high temperatures for the 8-hour cycles. The range of operation is usually set between 350 and 450°F.

The selection of desiccant is usually a matter of economics. For a given job, the greater the bulk density possessed by a desiccant, the smaller will be the unit from an adsorption standpoint. The regeneration system remains essentially the same in any event. When sour gas is present the alumina-type desiccants are seriously affected and reduced capacities result. Caution must be taken in the event that oxygen is present under these conditions because free sulfur can be formed which will tend to foul the pores of the desiccant.

The heating required in the regeneration cycle is equal to the heat of vaporization of the water adsorbed; the sensible heat required to raise the desiccant, water, and water vapor from ambient temperatures to the regeneration temperature; and the heat required to raise the piping, vessels, etc., from ambient temperature up to regeneration temperatures. The fuel requirements are directly proportional to these heat requirements. Likewise, the cooling requirements are directly proportional to heat requirements. A good design of the unit to minimize the heat requirements for only heating the desiccant and driving off the water vapors can have a substantial effect on the size of the heating and cooling equipment.

It is extremely important to protect the desiccant beds from slugs of liquid water and liquid hydrocarbons. Some of the better desiccants now available are highly susceptible to failure when doused with liquid water. Some of these desiccants are available in a specially treated form that is resistant to liquid-water failure. These water-resistant forms of the desiccants do not have good water-adsorption properties, however, and should be limited to about 10 to 15 per cent of the total bed. They should be placed at the main-gas-inlet end of the adsorber.

Slugs of liquid hydrocarbons on desiccants can cause fouling and reduced capacity for adsorbing water. This results from higher-molecular-weight hydrocarbons plugging up the many tiny pores in the desiccant pellets. Repeated regenerations at relatively high temperatures may remove some of these heavy hydrocarbons so that the capacity for adsorbing water is increased.

Protection of the beds is sufficiently important that an inlet separator is included as an integral part of the unit.

Another condition that results in foul desiccant beds is the presence of minute particles of heavy oils such as compressor oil. The tiny particles of oil are frequently so small that many of them pass through conventional separation equipment placed ahead of the dry-desiccant beds. When this condition exists, the installation of a precontactor has often helped to prolong the life of the desiccant. The precontactor usually consists of a vessel containing fouled desiccant or a less expensive grade of dry desiccant. The precontactor acts as an efficient mist-extracting section, removing the tiny particles of compressor oils.

Severe fouling of the dry-desiccant bed may occur in a very short time when treating a gas stream containing both hydrogen sulfide and oxygen. Although the relative concentrations of these two components may be very small, the desiccant acts as a catalyst to convert the hydrogen sulfide to free sulfur and water. The formation of free sulfur in the pores of the desiccant plugs up the pores so that the desiccant has little capacity for removing water vapor.

Corrosion is usually not a serious problem in dry-desiccant dehydration. However, where considerable carbon dioxide and hydrogen sulfide are present, corrosion may occur in the regeneration-gas heat exchanger. At this point, free water is condensing inside the heat exchanger in the presence of the acid gases. Very extreme corrosion has been noted where both carbon dioxide and oxygen are present in the gas to be dehydrated.

Occasionally corrosion in the regeneration equipment has been combated by the injection of ammonia ahead of the regeneration-gas cooler. Although this usually helps to control the pH of the water that is being removed, it has a severe effect upon the operation of the dry desiccant. Ammonia and carbon dioxide react to form an unstable white solid which plugs up the pores in the desiccant. Upon termination of the injection of ammonia and repeated regeneration of the bed, much of the ammonium carbonate that has been formed will decompose restoring some of the desiccant capacity for removing water.

Dehydration by Absorption. Since 1949, the removal of water vapor from natural gas with organic liquid desiccants has become one of the most accepted methods of dehydration. The most widely used organic liquids for dehydration are the glycols. From field experience and physical properties it has been found that the most accepta-

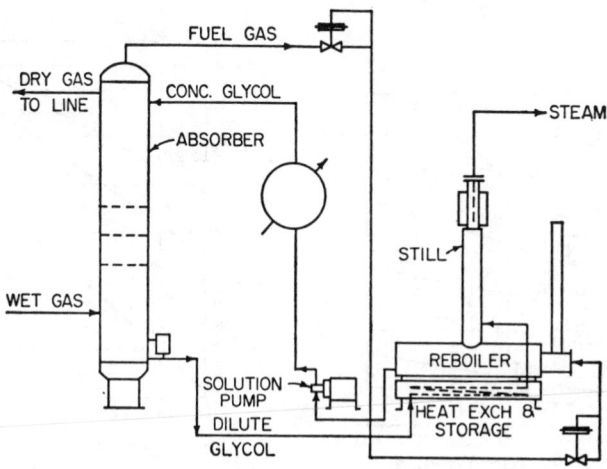

FIG. 13-18. Glycol-absorption gas dehydrator.

ble glycol is triethylene glycol (TEG). The advent of TEG in 1949 was a predominant factor in the success of dehydration with liquid desiccants. Prior to 1949, dehydration plants used diethylene glycol (DEG) and were not as acceptable for reasons explained below.

As shown in Fig. 13-18, the absorption for dehydration of natural gas is much less complicated than the adsorption process just described above. Wet gas enters the absorber and flows up through a series of two or more countercurrent stages, coming in contact with highly concentrated glycol. The glycol removes from 75 to 95 per cent of the incoming water vapor, depending on the efficiency of the over-all system. This results in dew-point depressions of from 50 to 85°F. The dehydrated gas leaves the absorber at the top and flows into the sales-gas line.

The dilute glycol leaves the bottom of the absorber and flows through a heat exchanger in the storage tank where it cools the reconcentrated glycol and picks up heat prior to discharging into the still column. The heated glycol flashes off solution gas as it enters the still column and comes in countercurrent contact with the rising vapors from the reboiler. These vapors are essentially steam but also contain hydrocarbon vapors and glycol vapors. The cooler glycol feed tends to condense the glycol vapors but does not appreciably affect the steam or hydrocarbon vapors which are discharged from the top of the still column. The dilute glycol then dumps into the reboiler where it is heated up to the temperature required for producing glycol of sufficient concentration to allow the outlet-gas dew point desired to be attained. The regenerated glycol overflows a weir in the reboiler and flows down into the storage tank. Glycol from the storage tank is then pumped onto the top tray of the absorber, where it comes in contact with the gas being dehydrated. The glycol flows by gravity down through the absorber, removing water vapors from the gas as it progresses. Since the gas contains more water with each subsequent lower stage, the water picked up on the lower trays is greater than on the upper trays. The dilute glycol is dumped from the absorber by a liquid-level controller.

The principal application for this type of unit has been on wellheads. For many of these installations the prime purpose is to dehydrate the gas so that hydrates will not form between the wellhead and a main gas-processing plant. This requires dew-point depressions of 65°F or less in most cases.

As was mentioned the first liquid desiccant to come into use was diethylene glycol (DEG), more recently replaced by triethylene glycol (TEG). This trend has resulted principally from the fact that greater dew-point depressions are possible and less loss of glycol is encountered when using TEG. For equal concentrations less than 98

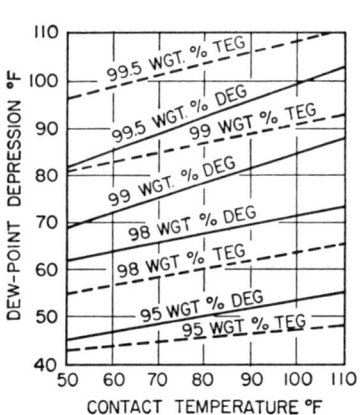

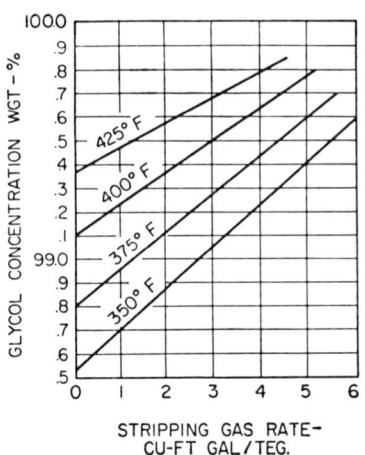

Fig. 13-19. Maximum dew-point depressions with glycol dehydration.

Fig. 13-20. Triethylene glycol concentration with stripping gas through reboiler.

per cent glycol DEG can theoretically produce greater dew-point depressions than is possible with TEG. However, for the range of operations normally encountered, above 98 per cent concentrations, greater depressions are possible using TEG because it can be regenerated to higher concentrations than DEG without serious degradation occurring. DEG decomposes at 328°F whereas TEG decomposes at 404°F. This allows about 2 per cent higher concentrations for TEG and consequently higher dew-point depressions.

Figure 13-19 shows the theoretical maximum dew-point depressions possible for DEG and TEG for various contact temperatures in the absorber and for various glycol concentrations when an infinite number of contacting trays are used. Glycol concentrations of 98.5 to 99 per cent may be obtained with simple regeneration equipment for TEG. For DEG only concentrations of from 98 to 98.5 per cent are obtainable with like equipment. When higher concentrations than these are desired, more elaborate regeneration equipment must be used. By using stripping gas in the reboiler it is possible to obtain higher concentrations for the same reboiler temperature, as is indicated in Fig. 13-20.

When selecting the desiccant for these systems, it has been seen that the use of DEG is limited to areas where dew-point depression required is relatively low, 65°F or less. TEG has a much wider operating range, as shown above. An important factor in selection is the glycol losses that can be expected. These losses result from vaporization, mechanical entrainment as mist in the absorber, and vaporization in the still column. TEG is more favorable from a loss or replacement standpoint because its consumption due to vapor losses is less than DEG for the same operating conditions. The vapor losses are directly proportional to the vapor pressures of the liquids, and the vapor pressure of TEG is less than that for DEG. Glycol consumption can be kept to less than 0.1 gal/MMscf of gas under normal operating conditions of contact temperatures below 100°F and pressures above 200 psig.

There are practical limitations in using TEG for dehydration from both a dehydration-efficiency and operating-cost standpoint. The lower the temperature of contact, the greater the viscosity of the glycol solution. As the viscosity of the solution increases, the efficiency of contact decreases, resulting in less water-vapor removal. At temperatures below 50°F a very pronounced reduction in efficiency has been noted. Below 40°F the solution becomes so viscous that it becomes impossible to move the liquid solution through the system. As the contact temperature increases, the vapor pressure of the solution increases, resulting in higher vaporization losses of glycol and higher outlet-water-vapor content of the gas. The normal upper temperature limit has been established at 100°F. For cases where higher temperatures are encountered up to 120°F the glycol losses due to vaporization can be three times as much as those at 100°F. However, since these losses are small to start with, tripling them has very little effect on the over-all glycol losses from the system.

It was once believed by the industry that there was a definite pressure limitation to dehydration with glycols. This stemmed from the publication of laboratory data which have since been found to be in error. From recent data taken at pressures up to 2,000 psig and correlation of these data with theoretical calculations, there appears to be no pressure limitations for all practical purposes. It appears that the maximum theoretical dew-point depression increases with pressures up to 500 psig and then remains essentially constant for pressures up to 3,000 psig.

The higher the ratio of glycol circulated to the water vapor removed from the gas, the less will be the dilution on the trays, and the dew-point depression will be increased theoretically. However, since the dilution on the top tray is relatively small, the over-all effect is not appreciable. For example, if the glycol rate is doubled, the dew-point depression is increased only a few degrees. The over-all effect would be the same if more trays were added so that the same water content is present in the gas entering the top tray. From an economic standpoint, it appears that a solution rate of 3 gal/lb of water absorbed is best for most applications.

Theoretically the greater the number of trays the greater the dew-point depression. For cases where only a minimum dew-point depression of 50 to 55°F is required for wellhead dehydration for transmission to a central processing plant, two trays are sufficient. For the normal case where 65 to 75°F dew-point depression is required, four trays are normally used. When higher dew-point depressions are desired, it becomes necessary to consider not only the number of trays but also the glycol concentrations. Under laboratory field testing conditions dew-point depressions in excess of 130°F have been obtained for cases where glycol concentrations of 99.95 per cent were obtained and 10 contact trays were used.

Contaminants due to operations under varying conditions can prove to be troublesome. Small amounts of liquid water entering the absorber have no serious effects on the system. If the water contains salt, these salts are deposited on the firebox of the reboiler, causing reduced efficiencies of heat transfer, resulting in hot spots and fire-tube failures. Large quantities of water tend to overload the regeneration equipment, causing inefficient regeneration of the glycol plus other operational difficulties.

Liquid hydrocarbons are a potential source of trouble in the system. It is normally recommended that inlet separators be used to prevent free liquids, both water and hydrocarbons, from entering the absorber. Presence of liquid hydrocarbons tends to clog the filter and flood the still column and reboiler. In the event that this occurs, a serious fire hazard may develop if the overhead from the still column is not piped away from the unit. Certain liquid hydrocarbons cause the glycol to foam in the absorber, thus reducing seriously the capacity of the unit and a high loss of glycol from the system. The heavier hydrocarbon liquids accumulate and cannot be separated from the glycol in the system. This causes the glycol to become discolored and to lose its effectiveness as a desiccant.

Corrosion in these systems occurs only when carbon dioxide or hydrogen sulfide is present. They do not affect the dehydration process except for the corrosion caused. The system must be specially designed when these gases are known to be present.

Other Methods of Dehydration

Dehydration systems using calcium chloride have been used for removing water vapors from natural gas. Basically the system consists of charging a unit with calcium chloride crystals at the top of the dehydration tower. As these crystals adsorb water vapors they dissolve until they are finally a brine solution. This brine solution is then used further on conventional bubble-cap trays where it picks up additional water vapors. The brine solution is then dumped to a pit. Although these units provide reasonable dew-point depressions, they are subject to operational problems and require recharging on a periodic basis. Disposal of the salt brine is sometimes a problem, and carry-over of the calcium chloride crystals can result in downstream corrosion. These units have been used only in limited applications and have the advantage of requiring less gas for operation than do the units described above.

The use of refrigeration either from natural expansion or of one of mechanical types described earlier in this chapter is fairly common. Another method of dehydration is compression and cooling of the natural gas. Referring to Fig. 13-3, the water content for natural gas at 300 psia and 80°F is 90 lb/MMscf. If this gas is compressed to 1,000 psia and cooled to 80°F the water content is 33 lb/MMscf. Thus by compressing the gas and cooling it, it would be possible to remove 57 lb of water vapor from the gas. By reducing the pressure to 300 psia it is possible to have a dew-point depression of 28°F, discounting any additional effects that might be derived from cooling caused in the expansion process. It can be assumed that this method is not practical over the other methods described above.

Removal of Acid Gases

The presence of acid gases, hydrogen sulfide and carbon dioxide, in natural gas is undesirable from many standpoints, but the principal objection is the corrosion that results when free water is present. For this reason it is necessary to remove the hydrogen sulfide and carbon dioxide at the wellhead or relatively close to it. Although several systems can be used for removal of acid gases, the amine-type desulfurizers are the most common.

A simplified flow diagram of a typical amine-type desulfurization unit is shown in Fig. 13-21. Note the similarity between the flow diagram for amine-type desulfurizers and that for glycol dehydration units as indicated on Fig. 13-18. Here again is an absorber where the undesirable component of the inlet gas stream is removed and a regeneration system where the undesirable component is discharged from the circulating solution. In this process, a water and amine solution that may vary from about 10 to 20 per cent amine is utilized for removing hydrogen sulfide and carbon dioxide from the incoming gas stream. The principle of this process is based upon the fact that acid gases (hydrogen sulfide and carbon dioxide) will react with amine at ordinary temperatures, but the reaction is reversed in the regenerator at temperatures of about 220 to 240°F. The sour gas passes up through the absorber, contacting the lean amine solution passing down the absorber. The foul solution is discharged from the bottom of the absorber and passes through a heat exchanger before it discharges into the top of the still column. The amine solution is boiled in the amine reboiler by the application of heat. This boiling action supplies steam vapors that pass up through the still column, sweeping the hydrogen sulfide and carbon dioxide from the incoming solution.

The regenerated amine leaving the reboiler then passes through the amine-to-amine heat exchanger to an amine storage tank and is recirculated with the amine pump.

The hydrogen sulfide and carbon dioxide leaving the top of the still column have a considerable volume of steam with them. In order to keep down the quantity of make-up water required, this overhead product is usually cooled to around 120°F. This allows most of the steam to condense so that it can be returned to the amine-solution system.

Three types of amine are used in the process: monethanolamine, diethanolamine, and triethanolamine. Monethanolamine (MEA) is preferred in most operations. This is because it is a much stronger base, having a higher affinity for the acid gases. It also has a lower molecular weight, resulting in smaller quantities of amine being circulated per unit volume of acid gas removed. A rule-of-thumb comparison between MEA and DEA is that in a given unit approximately 1.7 times as much DEA is required to be circulated as MEA for doing a specific job of removing acid gases. Triethanolamine requires a greater circulation rate than the DEA. One factor affecting the choice of DEA over MEA is that MEA is reputed to react with carbonyl sulfide (COS); this gaseous compound is often present in flue gases and refinery gases. The result of this reaction is unregenerative compounds which tie up the amine. This reduces the capacity of the solution for removing the acid gases in the absorber.

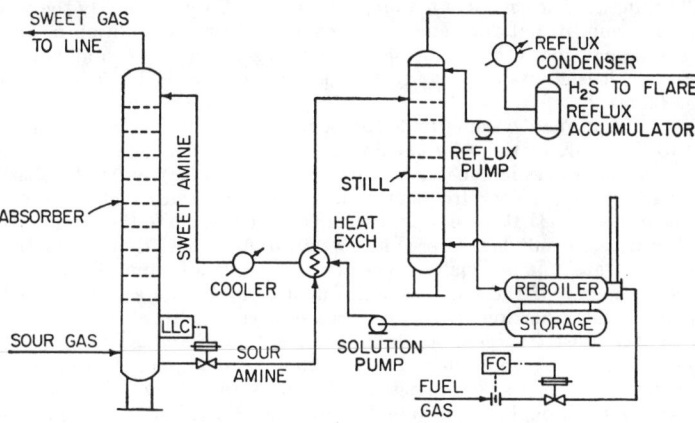

Fig. 13-21. Amine gas desulfurizer.

In many units corrosion is perhaps the greatest operating problem. As a general rule, this corrosion occurs in the reboiler, storage tank, still column, heat exchangers, and occasionally in the absorber. Most of these corrosion problems can be minimized greatly by conservative design. For instance, one cause of corrosion is the release of carbon dioxide and hydrogen sulfide from the amine solution after the pressure has been reduced and the solution has been preheated. The presence of this carbon dioxide and hydrogen sulfide may cause serious corrosion to occur in the heat exchanger and adjacent piping. Several steps can be taken to minimize corrosion at this point. For instance, a back pressure can be maintained on the amine solution after it leaves the absorber until after it has passed through the amine-to-amine heat exchanger. This higher pressure minimizes the amount of carbon dioxide and hydrogen sulfide breaking out of the solution. Another effective step in controlling this type of corrosion is to limit the amount of acid-gas pickup per unit volume of solution. As a general rule, it is not a good practice to allow the amine to pick up more than about 0.33 mole of acid gas per mole of amine. In some cases, it is desirable to refrain from preheating the foul solution above 180 to 190°F. The higher this temperature the greater the volume of carbon dioxide and hydrogen sulfide that is released by the solution.

Corrosion occurring in the reboiler and still column is very frequently the result of too high regeneration temperatures and pressures. As a general rule the regeneration temperature should be in the range of 220 to 240°F. Where most of the acid gas being removed is hydrogen sulfide, it is preferable to use 220 to 230°F regeneration temperatures. When most of the acid gas is carbon dioxide, slightly better regeneration can be obtained without greatly increased corrosion rates by operating at about 230 to 240°F.

In some instances, it has been reported that corrosion occurred in steam-heated reboilers because boiler tubes were too closely spaced. The corrosion rate was decreased by allowing a greater boiler-tube spacing, permitting more of the carbon dioxide to be quickly emitted from the tube bundle.

As a rule, absorbers are free from corrosion. However, stress corrosion has occurred in or near welded seams when this vessel was not stress-relieved. It is considered good practice to stress-relieve all vessels in an amine desulfurization plant.

A few cases have been reported of severe corrosion on the bubble caps in the lower portion of absorber towers where the ratio of carbon dioxide to hydrogen sulfide is great. This corrosion is not carbon dioxide corrosion but hydrogen sulfide corrosion.

Another severe problem that is frequently encountered in amine-type desulfurizers is foam. Most frequently this foaming condition occurs in the absorber, resulting in very excessive amine losses. However, in some cases severe foaming has occurred in the still column. The causes of foaming are many. Very frequently the actual cause is never determined, but the condition is controlled by the addition of an antifoam agent. Although many antifoam agents have been developed and have met with some success, it is advisable to contact a specialist in this field to handle a particular foam problem.

Amine solution may become fouled in several ways. All solutions in service are subject to the accumulation of iron sulfide. This iron sulfide may occur as the result of corrosion somewhere in the desulfurizer system, or it may enter the absorber with the sour-gas stream. Very frequently the volume of iron sulfide in a desulfurizer leaves the impression that the unit is corroding away at an extremely high rate. However, when this iron sulfide is filtered and weighed, it is found that it represents a very low corrosion rate. It is usually necessary to include an amine filter somewhere in the amine system. If the unit is small, full-stream filters are usually used. If the unit is large, only a portion of the total stream need be filtered.

Perhaps the most troublesome fouling that occurs in amine solution results from the presence of oxygen somewhere in the system. Sometimes the oxygen enters the absorber with the sour gas. Sometimes it enters the system through the vent on storage vessels or through the packing on the suction side of circulating pumps. When oxygen and hydrogen sulfide are both present in the incoming gas stream, amine thiosulfates usually collect in the solution. This amine product cannot be regenerated in the conventional regeneration equipment. A similar compound is formed when cyanates are present in the incoming gas stream.

When amine reaction products are formed in an amine solution that cannot be regenerated in the conventional equipment, an amine reclaimer should be installed. This reclaimer takes a side stream of the total solution flowing and distills the entire quantity of amine and water overhead. The vapor product is fed into the still column near the bottom. By charging the side reclaimer with soda ash, the amine that has been tied up is released. Caustic soda is sometimes used instead of soda ash. The reclaimer not only removes the heat-stable amine compounds but also dissolved solids that may have been introduced with make-up water.

Chapter 14

SURFACE FACILITIES FOR WATERFLOODING
AND SALT-WATER DISPOSAL

By W. F. Ellison

Civil Engineering Section Chief
Mobil Oil Company

and

R. H. Lasater

Senior Production Engineer
Socony Mobil Oil Company, Inc.

The purpose of this chapter is to present general information and design criteria that may be used in considering appropriate methods to employ in the collection, treatment, storage, and injection of brine. A combined discussion of the subjects of waterflood plants and salt-water-disposal plants is presented since many of the basic components in the two types of plants are similar.

The scope of operations discussed will be confined to topics for consideration in planning and installing surface facilities. Information on reservoir studies and subsurface injection problems may be found in other sections of the handbook. Even though corrosion is of utmost importance in the design of waterflood and salt-water-disposal facilities, comments on corrosion in this chapter are necessarily limited.

Salt water is a by-product obtained from the production of oil for which there is no present economic value except in its use as a reservoir repressuring or flooding agent. It is a waste product that is often produced in large quantities with the recovery of crude from an underground reservoir. Salt water is an expensive item to the oil producer. The cost of lifting a barrel of salt water from the subsurface oil-bearing formation is the same as the cost of lifting a barrel of commercial crude. Once the oil-water mixture has reached the surface, the oil fraction becomes a commercial product from which revenue is immediately available to the producer. Salt water, on the other hand, is a liability that continues to be an expense until it is disposed of by evaporation or controlled stream dilution, or until it is returned to its origin or to another formation that is capable of receiving additional volumes of fluids by pressure or gravity injection.

State legislation has been a decisive factor in encouraging producers to provide adequate disposal facilities as soon as possible after the first salt-water production. On some projects it is difficult to justify the collection of data over a long period of time, and prolonged engineering studies on small "stripper" leases are unwarranted. The oil producer must comply with state statutes, determine the expenditure that his lease will justify, and arrive at an early solution for the salt-water-disposal problem. He must carefully study and consider the possibilities of profitable reinjection of produced brine, with or without the addition of supplementary fluid, to the producing reservoir. The Woodbine Sand of the East Texas field is an excellent example of profitable disposal. Waste fluid is used in the East Texas field as a tool in accomplishing forced migration of crude in the subsurface oil-bearing formation.

As a general rule, proration of production obtained by secondary recovery methods is a function of state regulatory agencies upon application of the producer. The states usually require testimony on reservoir data and mechanics, and depend upon the operator's recommendations for reasonable and prudent injection and recovery rates without damage to the reservoir. In some states proration of production obtained by secondary methods is not regulated. The operator must consider specific local conditions and regulations in the final analysis of economic data in order to arrive at a sound conclusion on the feasibility of developing a proposed waterflood project.

State Pollution Legislation

In recent years, the legislative bodies of the Mid-Continent and Gulf Coast oil-producing states of Kansas, Oklahoma, Texas, and Louisiana have passed legislation for preventing and abating surface and subsurface pollution of fresh waters. Other states are faced with the pollution problem resulting from oil production within their territorial boundaries. Some have passed antipollution legislation; others will inevitably be confronted with the problem in the future.

Kansas. The pollution problem was recognized by the state of Kansas as early as 1934, when laws were enacted for the prevention of contamination of the state's fresh-water resources resulting from the exploration for and the exploitation of gas and oil. The Oil Field Section of the Kansas State Board of Health is charged with the responsibility for preventing pollution. Legislation in Kansas has been periodically supplemented and amended as recently as 1957. Highlights of the current Kansas legislation are interpreted as follows:

1. In a 1957 Regular Session in the Kansas legislature, House Bill 219 authorized the State Board of Health to deny or revoke a permit for the surface and subsurface storage or disposal of domestic, industrial, or sewage wastes in any case where it finds such storage is causing or likely to cause pollution.

2. Surface casing for each oil well is set below all fresh water. Regulation of surface pipe setting rests with the Kansas Corporation Commission.

3. Surface and other pipe is cemented below fresh and other usable water strata as determined by the State Corporation Commission in accordance with the recommendations of the State Board of Health, State Geological Survey, and State Water Resources Board.

Oklahoma. Oklahoma enacted antipollution legislation in 1909 under the control of the Game and Fish Department (29 O.S.A. 409) which "Prohibits placing, throwing, depositing, or permitting to be deposited any crude or other deleterious substances into streams, lakes, or ponds of this state, or where same might run or be washed into any of the streams, lakes, or ponds." Because of lack of rigid enforcement of the 1909 and subsequent legislation, however, they failed to accomplish their objective purposes prior to 1955.

More stringent legislation introduced in 1955 (House Bill 569) placed control of pollution in the state of Oklahoma under the jurisdiction of four state agencies: (1) the Oklahoma Corporation Commission, (2) the Planning and Resources Board, (3) the State Game and Fish Department, and (4) the Board of Public Health.

The Corporation Commission is vested with the authority to regulate the handling, storage, and disposition of salt water, mineral brines, and other substances so as to prevent the pollution of surface and subsurface waters in the state. The Division of Water Resources of the Planning and Resources Board and the Game and Fish Department are authorized to assist the Corporation Commission and cooperate in the investigations, gathering evidence, filing reports and complaints, etc.

Texas. In the state of Texas, prevention of pollution and the control of salt water are functions of the Railroad Commission. Rule 20, established by the Railroad Commission and pertaining to the disposal of waste brine, states in part: "Fresh water, whether above or below the surface, shall be protected from pollution whether in drilling, plugging, or disposing of salt water already produced." Tex. Rev. Civ. Stat. Art. 4444 is a general statute that prohibits the pollution of public bodies of water by salt water and oil. These regulations clearly indicate the necessity for the proper handling and disposal of waste products obtained from the production of crude.

In addition to the control exercised by the Railroad Commission, the State Board of Health, the Fish and Game Commission, the Board of Water Engineers, and the Attorney General all deal with pollution and the control of salt water.

Louisiana. In the state of Louisiana, the Commissioner of Conservation is empowered to require drilling, casing, and plugging of wells to be done in such a manner as to prevent the pollution of fresh-water supplies by oil, gas, or salt water. Operators of a well may, however, drain water from wells, reservoirs, or tanks into the rivers, bayous, streams, and other waterways between Oct. 1 and Dec. 31 of each year but are prohibited to do so between Jan. 1 and Sept. 30 of each year.

The primary objectives of these state statutes are, of course, to prevent permanent damage to the surface for growing crops; to preserve diminishing fresh-water resources for individual consumption, growing industrial, residential, and commercial requirements; and to promote the conservation of fish and wild life.

In the past, engineers considered the normal municipal water demand to be 100 gal per capita per day. A terrific increase in per capita demand has been noticed during the past decade. This increase can be largely attributed to the increasing demand brought about by the installation of air conditioners, automatic dishwashers, automatic washing machines, automatic lawn sprinkling systems, etc. As a result, the figure for municipal fresh water demand now exceeds 150 gal/capita/day. In many cities, it has been necessary to restrict the use of potable water in order to provide sufficient quantities for the necessities of life.

Previously mentioned state legislation is an example of the emphasis that has been placed upon the growing need for the preservation and protection of the nation's fresh-water reserves. The oil industry has met the problem by expending vast sums of money for the disposal of waste fluids produced in the oil-production process. It is estimated, conservatively, that approximately 3 bbl of waste fluids are produced for each bbl of oil produced on a national scale. In Oklahoma alone, as a result of the recent antipollution statutes, the direct cost for the satisfactory disposal of salt water has been estimated at $25 million. Because it may not be economically feasible to produce "stripper" wells and leases that must support their share of disposal facilities, the lost production in Oklahoma may amount to a figure approaching $300 million in the future.[1]

TYPES OF SYSTEMS

The type of brine-conditioning plant to be constructed is largely determined by the efficient intake capacity of the underground reservoir and the chemical characteristics and volume of fluids anticipated. If, from testing or from information obtained from previously drilled wells, the reservoir is capable of handling large volumes of fluids without restriction, an elaborate treating plant is an unnecessary expenditure. If, however, the formation is of low permeability, extensive treatment may be required to condition the brine for pressure injection. Economic factors and effective injection rates normally influence the type of brine-conditioning plant considered for construction. Such plants are generally classified as open or closed.

Open Systems

In an open system, the brine is aerated for the purpose of releasing dissolved elements. Chemicals are added to either keep the remaining components in a state of equilibrium or to flocculate suspended solids. If a flocculant is used, the fluid is allowed to pass through a reservoir where sufficient retention time is provided and flocculated solids are settled. Residual suspended solid material may be removed by filtration.

Closed Systems

It is often found more economical to allow the existence of moderate corrosion, sedimentation, and scale conditions rather than to include extensive chemical treatment in the plant design.

Closed systems are constructed to pass salt water through the plant in a manner that will provide an effluent in as near its original state as possible. This is accomplished by providing auxiliary equipment that will prevent the contact of brine with atmospheric oxygen, maintaining dissolved elements in solution A shallow oil blanket or a low-pressure gas blanket is maintained on collection, treatment, and storage vessels in order to ensure closed conditions. Some systems consist of a combination of the desirable features contained in both the open- and closed-type systems. Usually an oil blanket is maintained on the accumulator and storage equipment as an economical means of keeping most of the dissolved elements in solution and as a means of preventing the formation of excessive quantities of suspended or precipitated solids. Solution gases that may accumulate in treating vessels are vented to the atmosphere. Many plant designs incorporate the use of pressure-vacuum-relief valves on siphon overflow pipes to minimize air entrainment and reduce corrosion. This also prevents the formation of undesirable solid precipitates.

If conditions are suitable for such an installation, some advantages are (1) the elimination of the cost for auxiliary treating equipment; (2) the elimination of the cost of a gas supply for maintaining a completely closed treating plant; (3) the elimination of the cost for extensive chemical treatment; and (4) the attendant cost of settling basins, pumps, and filter equipment.

COMPONENTS OF WATERFLOOD AND DISPOSAL SYSTEMS

The four major components of waterflood and salt-water-disposal systems are (1) the gathering system, (2) the treating plant, (3) the collection or storage facilities, and (4) the injection system.

Gathering System

Waterflood and salt-water-disposal gathering systems may be defined as *pipelines and accessory equipment used in the transportation of salt water from an oil-water separation vessel or from a water-supply source to the treating-storage-injection plant area.*

If supplementary fluid is required and a sufficient source is available, it is advantageous to locate water-supply wells in close proximity to the treating-plant area. Such an arrangement eliminates added cost for gathering lines and intermediate pumping and storage equipment. Figure 14-2 is an alignment plat and Fig. 14-3 is a profile plat of a typical gathering system. Figure 14-6 shows a typical gunbarrel hookup. The foregoing illustrations are discussed later in this chapter under Design.

Treating Plant

The treating plant consists of all piping, controls, pumps, vessels, aerators, chemical feeders, mixing chambers, flumes, pits, filters, and appurtenances in the processing-plant area. Chemical characteristics of the injection fluid are controlled in the treating area. The purpose of this section of the plant is to prepare the water, through aeration, chemical treatment, sedimentation, and filtration, for storage and later injection. Figure 14-1 is a schematic flow diagram of a typical treating-storage-injection plant area and is discussed in more detail later in this chapter.

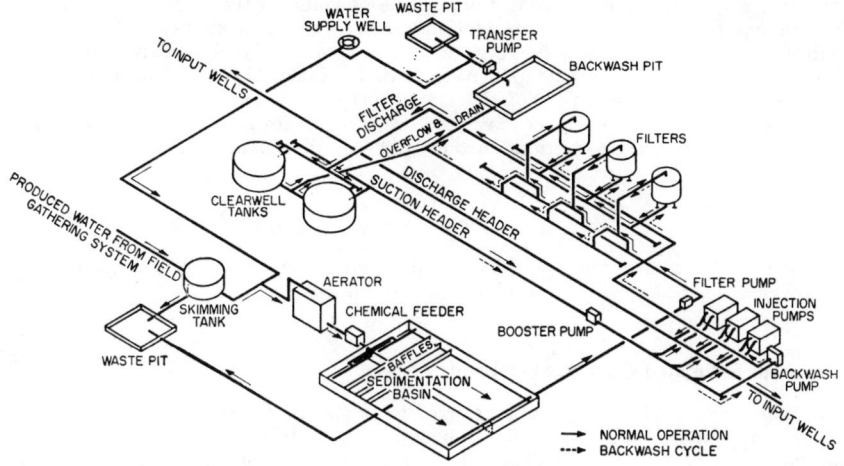

FIG. 14-1. Plant layout.

Storage Facilities

Clear well storage in the plant area is usually included to provide a flooded suction for injection pumps and to provide emergency storage for processed fluid when mechanical failures occur in the injection system. Simplified salt-water-disposal plants include the installation of a gravity gathering system, accumulator-storage tank, and injection lines. In such a minimum installation, the storage vessel or accumulator tank provides retention time for settlement of suspended solids. A salt-water-discharge line from a gunbarrel siphon connected directly to the disposal well, without benefit of controlled flow through a collection vessel, allows excessive air entrainment at the siphon. This condition is undesirable and often results in formation plugging and aggravated corrosion problems.

Injection System

The surface injection system includes that portion of the waterflood or salt-water-disposal plant from the outlet valves on the storage vessel up to and including the injection or salt-water-disposal wellhead connections. Since the design and selection of suction headers and injection pumping equipment are interrelated, suction headers are considered a part of the injection system. Other elements of the injection system are prime movers, pumps, automatic controls, desurgers, discharge headers, distribution pipelines, injection headers, injection pipelines, and wellhead connections.

DESIGN

Many factors influence the actual design of waterflood and salt-water-disposal systems and must be given consideration in the preliminary planning of such projects. The economic aspect of the project is of primary importance. For example, the additional oil that will be recovered must be compared with the cost of the flooding operation. Extensive reservoir studies, including the geology and reservoir characteristics, are necessary in determining the feasibility of flooding. The economic analysis of a salt-water-disposal system varies from the economic analysis of a waterflood system since the disposal of water must be treated as an expense item without the realization of increased income from additional production. No attempt will be made in this section to discuss reservoir studies or economic analysis in detail. The importance of considering these items in the final design of the system, however, must be emphasized.

In presenting design information that will be of value to the design engineer, we shall assume that preliminary investigations, such as reservoir studies and economic studies, have been completed. We shall further assume, for illustrative purposes, that a system containing all component parts is feasible and proceed to discuss the design procedures for each part of the system. In this manner, all phases will be discussed and the design engineer may proceed with the design of a system using the facilities dictated by the conditions encountered on individual projects.

Field Data

Prior to the design of any waterflood or disposal system, the following field data, upon which the design will be based, must be obtained:

Maximum Estimated Quantities of Fluid

1. Water produced with the oil is referred to as *produced water*.
2. *Supplementary water* is obtained from supply wells drilled into relatively shallow salt-water reservoirs, from shallow wells drilled into fresh-water sands, or from streams, ponds, or lakes. Water from these sources is generally necessary in floods to supplement the produced water in order to furnish prescribed quantities and rates of injection.

Compatibility of Waters

Varying characteristics of waters from different sources require that the design engineer have a knowledge of the quality of water to be processed. In the injection of salt water for disposal or for flooding it is usually necessary to remove suspended solids in order to prevent plugging of the formation into which the water is being injected. It is possible, in some instances, to inject the water directly into the formation through a closed system, if the quality of water is suitable.

The degree of compatibility of commingled waters must be analyzed and the resulting characteristics determined so that proper treating facilities may be included in the design. Reference is made to Sec. 3, Reservoir Engineering, for a complete discussion of water qualities.

Corrosivity of Fluids

Many problems confront the engineer when planning and designing disposal and flood projects, and one of the most important of these is the proper method of corrosion control. Generally, corrosion, both external and internal, is the principal cause for maintenance required on injection systems. When considering internal corrosion, it is essential to know the corrosive qualities of the fluid so that a proper preventive program may be included in the early life of the system. Failure to provide these measures could result in costly equipment replacements during the life of the system and could possibly be the determining factor in a profitable or unprofitable operation.

The following methods of determining corrosion severity are available to the design engineer:

1. Water analysis
2. Visual inspection of water samples
3. Coupon tests
4. Examination of existing equipment
5. Corrosion history of similar operations in area

Corrective measures employed in corrosion control are:

1. Chemical treatment
2. Cathodic protection
3. Corrosion-resistant materials

The degree to which corrosion-preventive methods are incorporated must be considered in the economic analysis of the system. Ordinarily the cost to reduce the fluid to a minimum corrosivity is prohibitive and a reduction to a moderate rate is economically feasible.

Studies of the corrosion-control problem have been made by many individuals, and detailed discussions of these studies are available in published technical papers. No attempt will be made in this section to give full technical consideration to the corrosion aspect of injection systems, but the importance of corrosion is stressed and emphasis should be placed on this problem in the final design.

Field Survey

A field survey should be conducted and the following information obtained prior to beginning the design of the facilities:

1. Alignment and ground profile along proposed center line of all gathering and injection lines.

2. Center-line measurement or *plus* on all property lines with a distance shown along the property line to the nearest established corner and surface ownership noted.

3. Ties to all surface improvements passed along the right of way which are within 100 ft of the center line, including wells and tank batteries.

4. Cross section of all major streams, drainage canals, roads, highways, and railroads crossed. Location of right-of-way widths on roads, highways, railroads, and drainage canals.

5. Ties along center line of roads, highways, railroads, and canals that require crossing permits.

a. Highways—tie to bridge, culvert, stream, or other road crossings that can be readily identified. In the absence of above, tie to nearest established land corner.

b. Railroads—tie to nearest milepost, bridge, or culvert that has milepost thereon.

c. Canal—tie to nearest established land corner.

6. Center-line *plusses* and width of all foreign pipelines, utilities lines, ravines, ditches, and secondary road embankments crossed. Depth of ravines and ditches and the height of road embankments.

7. Type of soil and depth to rock, gravel, or water-bearing formation if it falls above normal ditch depth.

8. Cultivation and timber lines with comments on type and quantity.

9. Elevation of bottom of water-separation equipment and elevations of overflow on siphon pipe.

10. Nameplate data including recommended maximum operating pressure and actual working pressure of water-separation equipment.

11. Location of proposed surface tract for plant area with ties from tract corners to nearest established corner.

12. Best possible routing for access road into plant area.

13. Cross section on all existing storage pits or proposed sites for storage pits to be constructed.

14. Location of power and/or fuel systems.

15. State and Federal requirements for pipeline road crossings.

Gathering System

Hydraulic Calculations

The first step in the design of the gathering system is the determination of the pipe sizes required to transport a stipulated quantity of water over a given period of time from the produced and/or supply sources to the collection terminal at the treating plant. The selection of the proper pipe size depends primarily on the available head and the friction loss incurred by the flow of the liquid through the pipe. The available head is the head resulting from the difference in elevation between the source and the terminus plus the actual operating pressure of any vessel at the source. In a gravity line, the elevation head is expressed as a positive value and the flow is from the source to the terminus by gravitational force, whereas the elevation head is expressed as a negative value in a pressure line where the source is at a lower elevation than the terminus.

In the calculation of the loss of head due to friction in a pipeline, the Williams-Hazen formula, an empirical formula commonly used in pipeline design, is recommended. This formula gives accurate values only when the kinematic viscosity of the fluid corresponds to water at 60°F, which is generally considered at normal conditions. The kinematic viscosity of water varies with the temperature from 1.8 at 32°F to 0.29 cs at 212°F. Kinematic viscosity should be calculated and applied in any case where the temperature of the fluid varies significantly from 60°F, since calculations based on the formula may increase the friction loss as much as 20 per cent at 32°F and decrease as much as 20 per cent at 212°F.

The Williams-Hazen formula is expressed in the following form:

$$f = 0.2083 \left(\frac{100}{C}\right)^{1.85} \frac{Q^{1.85}}{d^{4.8655}}$$

in which f = friction head loss, ft of liquid/100 ft of pipe
$\quad\quad d$ = inside diameter of pipe, in.
$\quad\quad Q$ = flow, gal/min
$\quad\quad C$ = constant for surface roughness

The value of C, the coefficient of roughness, varies from 80 to 140 and is dependent upon the type and condition of the pipe to be used. C values of 140 and over have been recommended for various pipes that are to be installed new; however, the design engineer should consider the deposition of sludge and the build-up of scale inside the pipe after the pipe has been in service. Experience has shown that a C value of 120 is practical for new pipe installations such as asbestos-cement, plastic, cement-lined steel, or plastic-lined steel pipe. For installations of used pipe or types of pipe other than those mentioned above, the design engineer should investigate the condition of the interior of the pipe and adjust the C value accordingly.

Table 14-1 shows friction-loss values based on the Williams-Hazen formula for commonly used pipe sizes.

Following is a sample calculation for determining the necessary line size to meet set conditions:

Given:

Maximum estimated flow Q = 8,000 B/D
Length of line from gunbarrel to collection tank = 2,850 ft
Elevation water outlet at gunbarrel = 125.0
Elevation pipe invert at gunbarrel = 113.0
Elevation overflow at collection tank = 95.0
Temperature = 60°F
Specific gravity = 1.0

Required: Minimum size of pipe required for gravity flow from gunbarrel to collection tank.

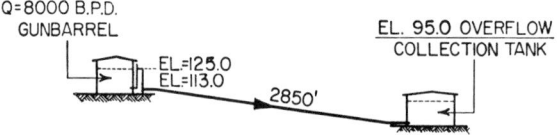

Table 14-1. Friction Loss (in Feet of Liquid) per 100 ft of Pipe Length Based on Williams-Hazen Formula*

Flow Q		3-in. asbestos cement 3.0 in. ID			3-in. steel pipe, cement-lined 2.818 in. ID			4-in. asbestos cement 3.95 in. ID			4-in. steel pipe, cement-lined 3.714 in. ID		
B/D	Gal/min	C = 100	C = 120	C = 140	C = 100	C = 120	C = 140	C = 100	C = 120	C = 140	C = 100	C = 120	C = 140
1,000	29.2	0.5	0.4	0.3	0.7	0.5	0.4	0.1	0.1	0.1	0.2	0.1	0.1
2,000	58.3	1.8	1.3	1.0	2.5	1.8	1.3	0.5	0.3	0.3	0.6	0.5	0.3
4,000	116.7	6.6	4.7	3.5	9.1	6.4	4.8	1.7	1.2	0.9	2.3	1.7	1.2
6,000	175.0	14.0	10.0	7.5	19.1	13.6	10.2	3.7	2.6	1.9	4.9	3.5	2.6
8,000	233.3	23.8	17.0	12.8	32.4	23.1	17.3	6.3	4.5	3.3	8.4	6.1	4.5
10,000	291.7	36.1	25.8	19.3	49.1	35.0	26.2	9.5	6.8	5.1	12.8	9.1	6.8
12,000	350.0	50.5	36.0	20.0	68.7	48.9	36.7	13.3	9.5	7.1	17.9	12.8	9.6
14,000	408.3	....	....	....	....	....	....	17.6	12.6	9.4	23.5	17.0	12.7
16,000	466.7	....	....	....	....	....	....	22.6	16.1	12.0	30.5	21.7	16.3
18,000	525.0	....	....	....	....	....	....	28.1	20.0	15.0	37.9	27.0	20.3
20,000	583.3	....	....	....	....	....	....	34.2	24.4	18.2	46.2	32.9	24.7

Flow Q		6-in. asbestos cement 5.85 in. ID			6-in. steel pipe, cement-lined 5.565 in. ID			8-in. asbestos cement 7.85 ID			8-in. steel pipe, cement-lined 7.571 in. ID		
B/D	Gal/min	C = 100	C = 120	C = 140	C = 100	C = 120	C = 140	C = 100	C = 120	C = 140	C = 100	C = 120	C = 140
4,000	116.7	0.3	0.2	0.1	0.7	0.5	0.4	0.2	0.2	0.1	0.3	0.2	0.1
6,000	175.0	0.5	0.4	0.3	1.2	0.8	0.6	0.3	0.3	0.2	0.4	0.3	0.2
8,000	233.3	0.9	0.7	0.5	1.8	1.3	0.9	0.5	0.4	0.3	0.6	0.4	0.3
10,000	291.7	1.4	1.0	0.7	2.5	1.8	1.3	0.6	0.7	0.4	0.7	0.5	0.4
12,000	350.0	1.9	1.4	1.1	3.5	2.4	1.8	0.8	0.9	0.5	0.9	0.8	0.5
14,000	408.3	2.6	1.9	1.4	4.3	3.0	2.3	1.1	1.3	0.6	1.2	1.2	0.6
16,000	466.7	3.3	2.4	1.8	5.5	3.7	2.8	1.3	1.8	1.1	1.4	1.5	0.8
18,000	525.0	4.1	2.9	2.2	6.5	4.5	3.5	1.8	2.4	1.4	2.0	2.2	1.6
20,000	583.3	5.0	3.6	2.7	9.1	6.9	5.2	2.5	3.1	1.9	3.0	2.9	2.2
25,000	729.2	7.6	5.4	5.7	13.7	12.9	7.3	3.4	3.9	2.3	4.0	3.7	2.8
30,000	875.0	10.7	7.6	7.6	18.1	16.6	9.7	4.4	4.7	2.9	5.2	4.6	3.5
35,000	1,020.8	14.2	10.0	9.7	23.3	20.6	12.4	5.4	6.6	3.5	6.5	5.6	4.2
40,000	1,166.6	18.3	13.0	12.1	28.9	25.1	15.4	6.6	8.8	4.9	7.9	5.9	5.9
45,000	1,312.5	22.6	16.1	14.7	35.2	....	18.8	9.2	11.2	6.6	11.0	10.5	7.8
50,000	1,458.3	27.6	19.7	....	....	....	....	12.3	13.9	8.4	14.6	13.4	10.0
60,000	1,750.0	....	....	....	....	....	....	15.7	17.0	10.5	18.8	16.2	12.5
70,000	2,041.6	....	....	....	....	....	....	19.5	....	12.7	23.3	20.2	15.1
80,000	2,333.3	....	....	....	....	....	....	23.8	....	....	28.3	....	....
90,000	2,624.9	....	....	....	....	....	....	....	....	....	....	....	....
100,000	2,916.6	....	....	....	....	....	....	....	....	....	....	....	....

* Williams-Hazen formula:

$$h_f \text{ per 100 ft} = 0.2083 \left(\frac{100}{C}\right)^{1.85} \frac{Q^{1.85}}{d^{4.8165}}$$

where h_f per 100 in. = head loss due to friction, ft of liquid
C = coefficient of roughness for pipe interior
Q = flow, gal/min
d = inside pipe diam, in.
Water temperature at 60°F
Specific gravity = 1.0

Solution: Adjusted water-outlet elevation at gunbarrel:

$$125.0 - 113.0 = 12.0 \therefore 12.0(0.8) = 9.6 \text{ ft}$$
$$113.0 + 9.6 = \underline{122.6}$$

(See page **14**–17 for discussion of reduction of 20 per cent between water outlet and pipe invert at gunbarrel to compensate for fittings loss.)

$$\text{Available static head} = 122.6 - 95.0 = 27.6 \text{ ft}$$

$$\text{Allowable head loss in feet per 100 ft of pipe} = \frac{27.6}{28.5} = 0.97$$

From Table 14-1: At $Q = 8,000$ B/D (233.3 gal/min), using a C value of 120,

6-in. asbestos-cement pipe (5.85 in. ID) shows a head loss of 0.7 ft/100 ft;
       0.7 ft/100 ft $<$ 0.97 ft/100 ft   O.K.; use
6-in. steel cement-lined pipe (5.565 in. ID) shows a head loss of 0.8 ft/100 ft;
       0.8 ft/100 ft $<$ 0.97 ft/100 ft   O.K.; use
4-in. asbestos-cement pipe (3.95 in. ID) shows a head loss of 4.5 ft/100 ft;
       4.5 ft/100 ft $>$ 0.97 ft/100 ft   too small; do not use

NOTE: To check capacity of calculated line size in the above problem: From Table 14-1, using a C value of 120, under the calculated line size, find the head loss per 100 ft of pipe that approximates the calculated allowable head loss per 100 ft; read the Q value directly.
Example from Above Problem. 6-in. asbestos-cement pipe (5.85 in. ID) at $C = 120$:

0.7 ft at 8,000 B/D
0.97 ft at capacity (B/D)
1.0 ft at 10,000 B/D

By interpolation, capacity of 6-in. asbestos-cement pipe (5.85 in. ID) = 9,800 B/D (285.8 gal/min) for conditions given in above problem.

This method gives a close approximation of the capacity of a calculated line size and is well within the limits of general usage; however, to obtain the exact calculated capacity, the Williams-Hazen formula should be used.

Example from Above Problem.

$$h_f/100 \text{ ft} = 0.2083 \left(\frac{100}{C}\right)^{1.85} \frac{Q^{1.85}}{d^{4.8655}}$$
$$0.97 = 0.1487 \frac{Q^{1.85}}{5,403}$$
$$Q^{1.85} = \frac{0.97 \times 5,403}{0.1487}$$
$$Q^{1.85} = 35,244.8$$
$$Q = 287.0 \text{ gal/min} = 9,840 \text{ B/D} = \text{calculated capacity of 6-in. asbestos-cement}$$
$$\text{pipe (5.85 in. ID) for conditions in above problem}$$

In transporting fluid from one point to another through a pipeline, the ideal condition of gravity flow does not always exist, and in many instances the operator finds it necessary to provide the flow by the use of a pump. Following is a sample calculation to meet given conditions requiring the use of a pump:

Given:
       Maximum estimated flow $Q = 8,000$ B/D
       Size of line = 4-in. steel cement-lined pipe, ID = 3.714 in.
       Length of line from reservoir to collection tank = 2,850 ft
       Elevation at pump discharge = 95.0
       Elevation overflow collection tank = 125.0
       Elevation high point on line (see sketch) at Sta. 16 + 00 = 135.0

Required: Pump and motor (size and type) to furnish required total discharge head at given conditions. (Assume no minor head losses through fittings.)

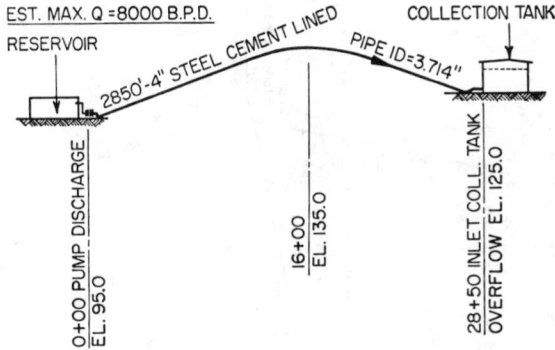

Solution:

From Sta. 0 + 00 to Sta. 16 + 00:

Available static head = 95.0 − 135.0 = −40.0 ft

From Table 14-1, head loss per 100 ft of pipe due to friction for 4-in. steel cement-lined **pipe**
= 6.0 ft (ID = 3.714 in., Q = 8,000 B/D, C = 120)

Total head loss due to friction from Sta. 0 + 00 to Sta. 16 + 00 = 6.0 × 16.0 = 96.0 ft

Total discharge head required from Sta. 0 + 00 to Sta. 16 + 00 = 96.0 + 40.0 = 136 ft

From Sta. 16 + 00 to Sta. 28 + 50:

Static head = 135.0 − 125.0 = 10 ft

From Table 14-1, head loss per 100 ft of pipe due to friction for 4-in. steel cement-lined pipe
= 6.0 ft (ID = 3.714, Q = 8,000 B/D, C = 120)

Total head loss due to friction from Sta. 16 + 00 to Sta. 28 + 50 = 6.0 × 12.5 = 75.0 ft

Total discharge head required from Sta. 16 + 00 to Sta. 28 + 50 = 75.0 − 10.0 = 65.0 ft

Total discharge head required from Sta. 0 + 00 to Sta. 28 + 50 = 136.0 + 65.0 = 201 ft

From performance curves for pumps select a pump capable of furnishing a total discharge head of 201 ft (87.1 psi) at a discharge rate of 8,000 B/D. The horsepower required to drive the pump is shown for all points on the performance curve. The motor size may be selected to furnish horsepower requirements.

The preceding illustration was based on a given size of pipe and field conditions, and the problem was to select the pump and motor to satisfy these conditions. In many instances this problem is reversed and the problem is to find the minimum size of pipe to meet given pump, motor, and field conditions. The problem is basically the same, the only variation being that the allowable head losses due to friction are determined and the proper pipe size selected from the head-loss tables. In the preceding illustration the specific gravity of the liquid was not taken into account in the conversion of the total discharge head to psi. In actual calculations where the specific gravity of the fluid is known, the following formula would apply:

$$\frac{\text{psi} \times 2.31}{\text{sp gr}} = \text{head, ft}$$

The velocity head $V^2/2g = h_{ft}$ was also omitted in the determination of the total discharge head required for the pump in the preceding illustration. The velocity head in most cases is negligible but should be considered when the total head is low and/or the suction lift is high. The recommended maximum head loss and velocity of various pipe sizes are as follows:

1. Water lines of 4-in. size or less should have a head loss not exceeding 2.5 ft/100 ft of pipe.

2. Water lines of over 4-in. size should be set for a maximum velocity of ft/sec.

Gathering systems for disposal or flood projects ordinarily consist of a network of pipelines with laterals tying into a main line or lines at irregular intervals along its length. The calculation of the required line sizes for a complex system of this type

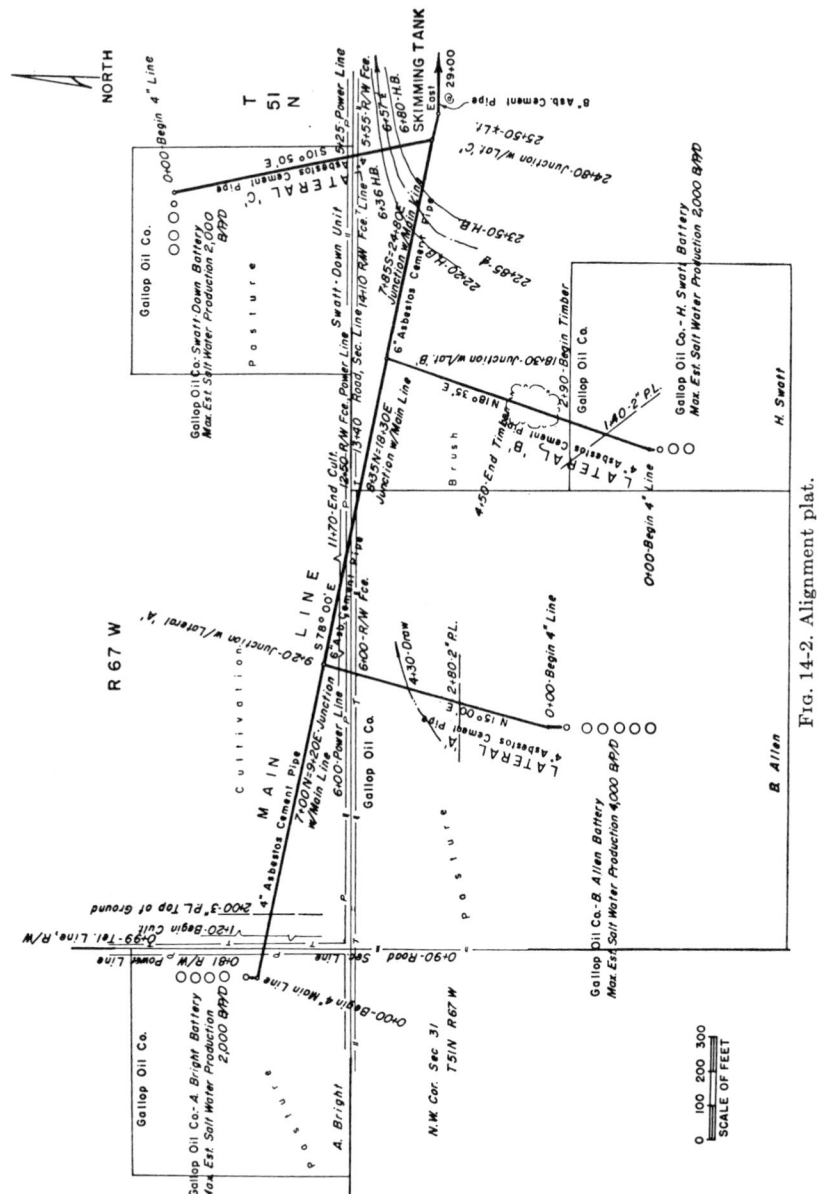

FIG. 14-2. Alignment plat.

0   100   200   300

SCALE OF FEET

14–12

is more complicated than for a relatively simple system containing no laterals; however, the basic principle of computing the proper line sizes is the same and is based on the available static head and the friction loss through the pipe. The desired result in a system containing a main and laterals is to size the lines so that the pressure at junction points will allow the entry of fluid from the laterals into the main line with unrestricted flow through the main line to the point of collection.

Figures 14-2 and 14-3 show typical alignment and profile sheets for a gravity-flow gathering system consisting of a main line with lateral tie-ins. In a gravity-flow system of this type, an ideal hydraulic gradient for flow would be one that is at the same elevation as the profile of the pipe transporting the fluid. Ideal conditions do not exist in the field because of elevation differentials along the finished pipe grade, and it is necessary that the design engineer approach the problem of line sizing with the objective in mind of keeping the hydraulic gradient as low as is practical with respect to the finished pipe grades. At any point of connection of a lateral with the main line, the finished hydraulic gradient must be lower than any source on the lateral to produce gravity flow.

The recommended procedure for designing a gravity-flow system is to size the main-line portions first, treating each portion as a separate unit for calculations. The calculations are based on the available static head and the friction loss. The hydraulic gradient is established by starting with the elevation of the collection point or terminus and progressing upstream along the main line, adding the calculated head loss from points of entry or junctions of the laterals with the main line, thereby making the junctions control points on the gradient. The hydraulic gradient is ordinarily plotted on a profile working sheet which shows an over-all graphic presentation and affords an excellent basis for analysis.

After the pipe for the main line has been sized, the size of pipe for the lateral lines must be determined, using the available head and friction loss through the pipe. The available head used in the lateral calculations is the elevation at the water outlet of the treater or gunbarrel at the tank battery plus any operating pressure, less the elevation of the hydraulic gradient calculated for the main line at the point of junction or the invert elevation of the pipe grade at this point using the highest of these two elevations. Actually, in plotting the hydraulic gradient, the value is never shown below the invert elevation of the pipe since the hydraulic gradient is drawn from the control points (points of entry or junctions). If at any point this gradient line passes beneath the pipe invert, a corrected gradient must be drawn. This corrected gradient is shown beginning at the point of intersection with the invert elevation of the pipe and is considered to run along the invert grade of the pipe on its upward course as long as the slope of the pipe invert is greater than the slope of the hydraulic gradient line. At the point on the invert pipe grade where the slope of the hydraulic gradient becomes greater than that of the invert pipe grade, a revised hydraulic gradient is drawn parallel to the original gradient. In many gathering systems the size of the lateral lines is specified as a minimum allowable size even though calculations may show a smaller-sized pipe would meet the requirements. Experience has shown that the use of small-sized pipe (2 in. diameter or less) is not feasible for the following reasons:

1. Maximum produced water rates are estimated, and even though this total amount for the entire system may be correct, the produced water from individual tank batteries may fluctuate, with one battery increasing for a period and another battery decreasing and, in turn, reversing this trend.

2. The cost differential between the small-sized pipe, 2 in. and under, vs. 3-in. pipe is not great enough to offset the added safety factor gained by use of larger pipe.

3. Cleaning operations for small-sized pipe are more difficult than for a larger pipe.

As in the case of most procedures or usages, there are exceptions and on smaller systems and/or systems where the produced water rate can be accurately determined, the design engineer must use proper judgment and size the lateral lines accordingly, disregarding the use of a specified minimum pipe size.

In systems where a specified minimum-sized lateral line is used and the calculations indicate a smaller pipe could be used, there is naturally an excess of available head over the calculated head set up at the point of entry or junction point with the main

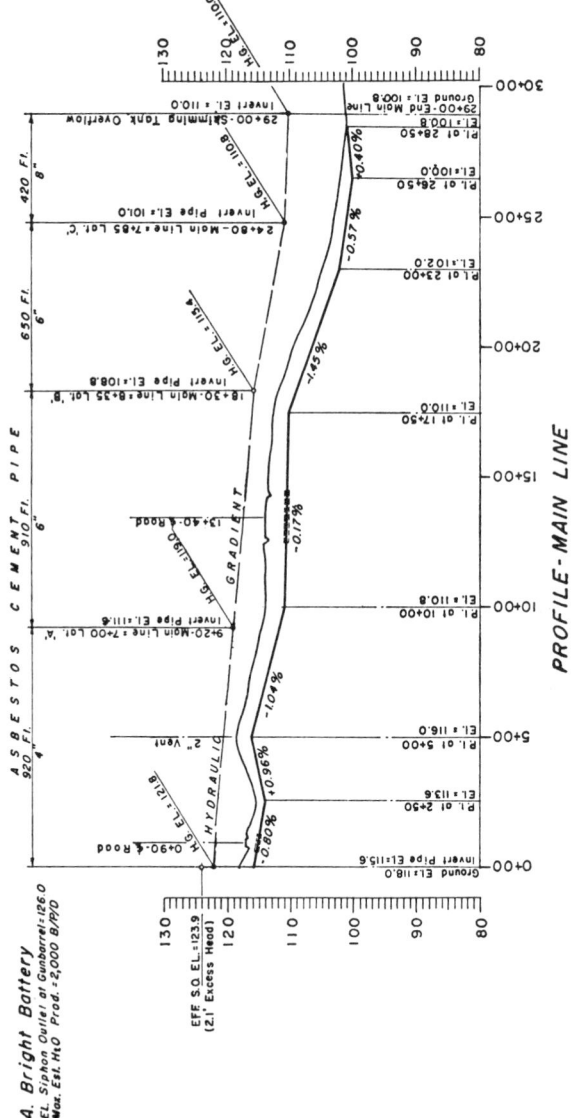

PROFILE - MAIN LINE

A. Bright Battery
El. Siphon Outlet at Gunbarrel = 126.0
Max. Est. H₂O Prod. = 2,000 B/P/D

14-14

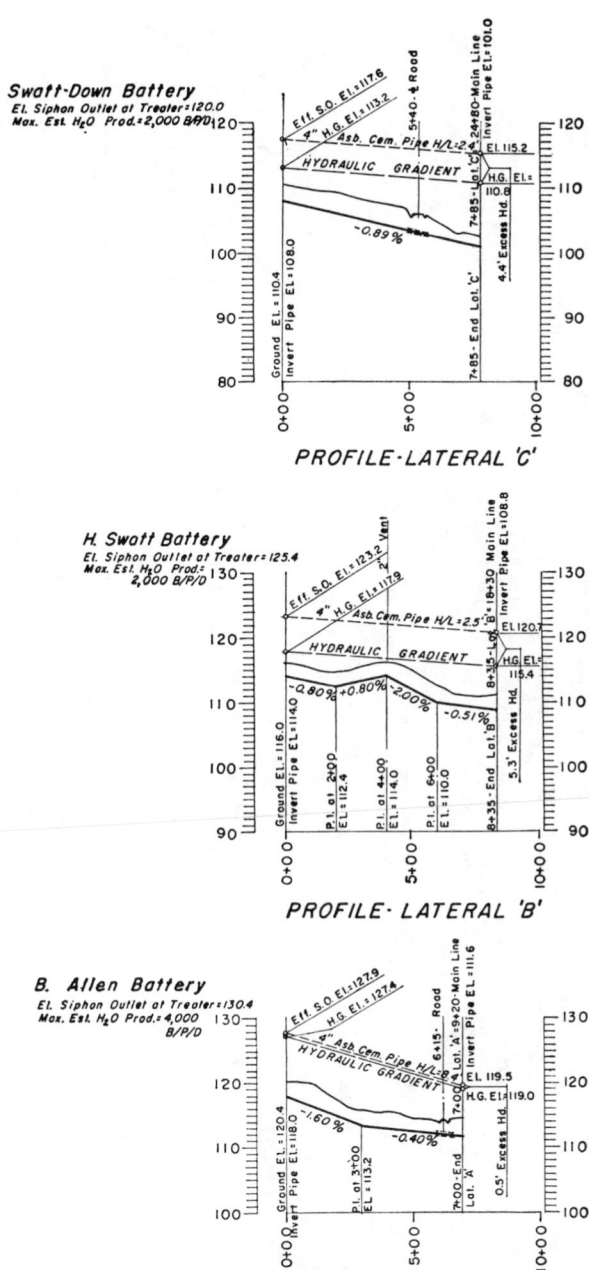

FIG. 14-3. Profiles—gathering system.

14–15

Table 14-2. Sample Hydraulic Calculations—Line Size for Gathering Systems as Shown in Figs. 14-2 and 14-3

Head loss due to friction based on Williams-Hazen formula $\left[h_f/100 \text{ ft} = 0.2083 \left(\dfrac{100}{C}\right) 1.85 \dfrac{Q^{1.85}}{d^{4.8155}} \right]$. $C = 120$ for all pipe

Line	Q (flow), B/D	Q (flow), gal/min	Length, ft	Line size, nom. in.	Head loss per 100 ft, ft	Total head loss, ft	Hydraulic-gradient elev.	Pipe-invert elev.	H_2O outlet elev. at battery	Adjusted H_2O outlet elev. at battery	Remarks
Main Line:											
29 + 00 − 24 + 80 Jct. w/Lat C	10,000	292.0	420	8-in. asbestos cement	0.2	0.8	110.0	......	......	......	Overflow elevation at skimming tank
24 + 80 − 18 + 30 Jct. w/Lat B	8,000	233.3	650	6-in. asbestos cement	0.7	4.6	110.8	101.0	......	......	Hyd. grad. controls—above pipe invert
18 + 30 − 9 + 20 Jct. w/Lat A	6,000	175.0	910	6-in. asbestos cement	0.4	3.6	115.4	108.8			Hyd. grad. controls—above pipe invert
9 + 20 − 0 + 00	2,000	58.3	920	4-in. asbestos cement	0.3	2.8	119.0	111.6			Hyd. grad. controls—above pipe invert
A. Bright Gunbarrel							121.8	115.6	126.0	123.9	O.K. 123.9 > 121.8 − 2.1 ft excess head
Lateral C: At Jct. w/Main Line (7 + 85 Lat C = 24 + 80 M.L.)							110.8	101.0			Hyd. grad. controls—above pipe invert
Lateral C Swatt-Down Treater	2,000	58.3	785	3-in. asbestos cement	1.3	10.2	121.0	108.0	120.0	117.6	Won't go −117.6 < 121.0 Try 4-in. Transite
Lateral C Swatt-Down Treater	2,000	58.3	785	4-in. asbestos cement	0.3	2.4	113.2	108.0	120.0	117.6	O.K. 117.6 > 113.2. Use 4-in. Transite 4.4 ft excess head
Lateral B: At Jct. w/Main Line (8 + 35 Lat B = 18 + 30 M.L.)							115.4	108.8			Hyd. grad. controls—above pipe invert
Lateral B H. Swatt Treater	2,000	58.3	835	3-in. asbestos cement	1.3	10.9	126.3	114.0	125.4	123.2	Won't go −123.2 < 126.3. Try 4-in. Transite
Lateral B H. Swatt Treater	2,000	58.3	835	4-in. asbestos cement	0.3	2.5	117.9	114.0	125.4	123.2	O.K. 123.2 > 117.9. Use 4-in. Transite 5.3 ft excess head
Lateral A: At Jct. w/Main Line (7 + 00 Lat A = 9 + 20 M.L.)							119.0	111.6			Hyd. grad. controls—above pipe invert
Lateral A B. Allen Treater	4,000	116.7	700	4-in. asbestos cement	1.2	8.4	127.4	118.0	130.4	127.9	O.K. 127.9 > 127.4 − 0.5 ft excess head

line. This excess head is available for friction loss, and it is possible that the size of the main line may be reduced. However, if the main-line size is reduced, new head-loss calculations are made using the reduced-sized pipe, and the revised hydraulic-gradient height is shown on the profile sheet.

In most instances where an excess of available head over the calculated head exists at the junction point caused by the adherence to a specified minimum size of the lateral, it is preferable to keep the main line at the size originally calculated and show this excess head as available on the profile sheet. The reason for this is that the fluctuations of produced water at the battery are carried to the main line. If the size of the main line is left as originally calculated, sufficient capacity is available to absorb these fluctuations. At first this may appear to be oversizing the lines. However, experience has shown that the estimated maximum quantity of produced water is difficult to forecast accurately, and allowances must be made for fluctuating volumes of fluid.

All hydraulic calculations are based on an even flow of water over a given period of time, even though this condition seldom exists. Irregular rates of produced water are caused by varying production schedules. For this reason, a safety factor is applied when sizing the lines for a system.

Complete and accurate records of water production should be kept on all systems after they are in operation, and based on these records, design reviews should be made periodically to determine the actual conditions with relation to the design conditions. These design reviews afford the engineer an opportunity to foresee possible difficulties in the system and take the remedial measures to furnish the desired capacities with a minimum shutdown time.

For further clarification and illustrative purposes a complete set of hydraulic calculations for the sample gathering system shown in Figs. 14-2 and 14-3 is presented in Table 14-2.

Reference is made to the adjusted water-outlet elevation at the battery shown on the calculation sheet. In order to compensate for fitting losses in an atmospheric treater or gunbarrel siphon hookup, the difference in elevation between the water outlet on the siphon riser and the pipe invert at the siphon down leg is reduced by 20 per cent. This figure of 20 per cent is a rule of thumb dictated by experience and has proved feasible. Another method, though more laborious, is by converting each fitting in the hookup to an equivalent length of pipe and calculating the head losses through the fittings.

Gunbarrel and Treater Piping

Piping installations at batteries vary and are dependent upon the type of treaters used.

Figure 14-6 shows a typical hookup of a gunbarrel or atmospheric treater with a siphon arrangement and overflow provisions.

At batteries where pressure treaters are used it is recommended that a surge column or "boot" be installed on the downstream side of the treater. This surge column consists of a large-sized pipe (12 to 14 in.) of sufficient height to provide the necessary static head. The purpose of the surge column is to allow for the escape of gas which prevents gas locks in the gathering lines. It also provides a static head by absorbing the surging discharge of the treater. Figure 14-4 shows a typical hookup of a surge column at a pressure treater. If the elevation of the treater is low, with respect to the remainder of the system, and it is necessary to utilize the treater pressure for flow into the system, it may not be advantageous to install a surge column because of the required height of the column to furnish the necessary static head. When this condition exists, the treater is tied directly into the gathering line, the operating treater pressure is utilized to produce the flow, and the release of gas is accomplished by using line vents downstream. A discussion of line vents (types, locations, and use) is presented later in this chapter. Figure 14-5 is an illustration of a pressure-treater hookup made directly into the line. The determination of the available static head at batteries where pressure treaters are employed is basically the same as for an atmospheric treater or gunbarrel. When a surge column is installed down-

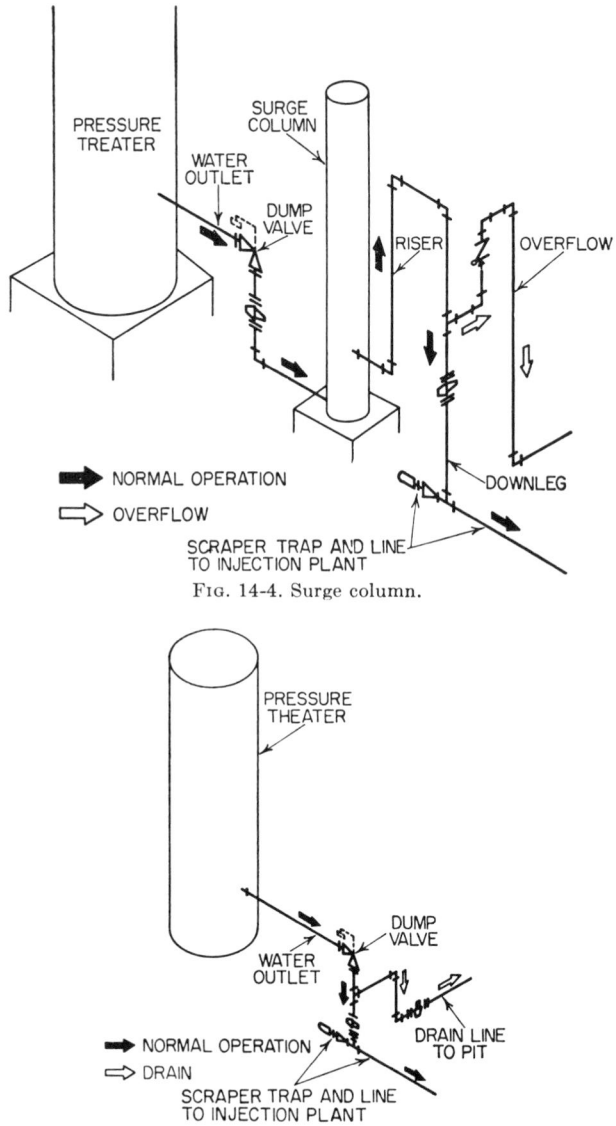

FIG. 14-4. Surge column.

FIG. 14-5. Pressure treater.

stream from the pressure treater, the determination of the available static head is *exactly* the same as it would be for an atmospheric treater or gunbarrel. The treater pressure is used to raise the fluid to the level of the outlet on the surge column, and being exposed to the atmosphere, the pressure is dissipated. The elevation of the water outlet on the column is used to determine the available static head. Where the pressure treater is tied directly into the line, the operating pressure of the treater, generally expressed in pounds per square inch, is converted to feet of water (pounds per square inch × 2.31 = feet of water at 60°F), and the elevation of the theoretical water outlet is established and is used in calculating the available static head.

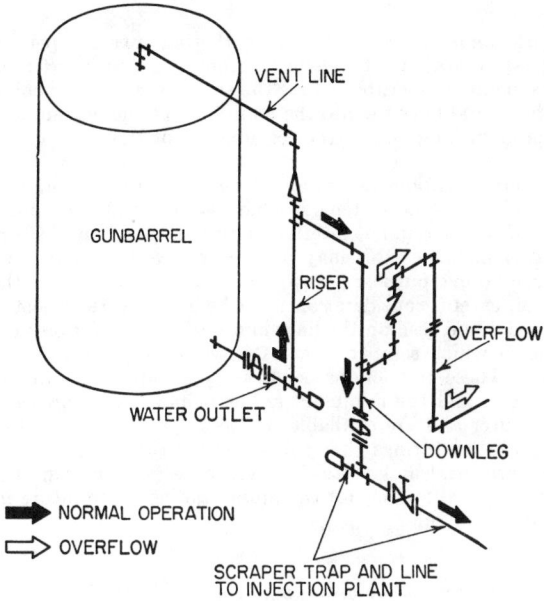

NORMAL OPERATION

OVERFLOW

SCRAPER TRAP AND LINE
TO INJECTION PLANT

FIG. 14-6. Gunbarrel.

Vents

In gathering systems designed for gravity flow all lines are laid to a calculated grade. Unfortunately, all gravity lines in gathering systems cannot be laid to a constant grade because of the changes in topography. At high points, or peaks, on the grade line (where a positive grade meets a negative grade along the direction of flow) vents are installed to allow the release of gas and to prevent gas locks in the line capable of stopping or seriously impeding the flow. Vent design consists of two types, one designed to operate above the hydraulic gradient, and the other capable of operating below the hydraulic gradient at the vent point. Vents designed to operate above the hydraulic gradient are very simple and consist of a tee in the line with a vertical piece of pipe of sufficient height to be above the calculated hydraulic gradient. A valve is installed on the vertical riser to provide shut-off. A vent of this type is not too satisfactory because the required height of the vertical riser is often excessive. Also, because of the spasmodic or irregular flow in the lines, air is allowed to reach the water, resulting in troublesome operation. Vents designed to operate below the hydraulic gradient consist of a tee in the line, a vertical riser, a valve on the riser, and an upper- and lower-seat vent valve. The main constituent in a vent assembly of this type is naturally the vent valve. Several types of upper- and lower-seat vent valves are manufactured today. They are made of asbestos cement, plastic, cast iron, and other materials. The principle of operation for a vent valve is as follows: With the pipe flowing full, the buoyant ball is seated in the upper seat, allowing no fluid to pass. Any gas accumulating at the vent point will displace the fluid in the valve, dropping the ball from the seat and allowing the gas to escape. As the gas is released, the fluid level rises in the valve until the ball is again seated in the upper seat. In instances where the flow in the line is not full, the level of the fluid in the valve drops, allowing the ball to seat in the lower seat, thereby preventing the entrance of air into the line. This type of vent valve is in use on many gathering systems and has proved very satisfactory in eliminating the problem of gas lock on gravity-flow lines.

Scraper Traps

In order to provide facilities for cleaning gathering lines, scraper traps are installed throughout the system at points where it is necessary to insert and to remove the scraper. These points are located where the size of the pipeline changes; at junction points where the lateral lines tie into the main line; at the beginning of all lines, both laterals and the main line; and at the termination of the main line of the gathering system.

Scraper traps are of various design and depend upon the desired method of operation. For example, on some systems it is necessary that the cleaning of a particular line or segment of the system not interfere with the operation of the remainder of the system. In other instances this may not be applicable and the shutdown time of the system for cleaning purposes may not be detrimental. In the design of the gathering system, careful consideration must be given to the selection of the proper valves and fittings to be used on the lines in order to allow for passage of the scraper. The limitations to which scrapers are restricted vary in accordance with different scraper designs. These restrictions, such as types of valves and fittings that the scraper will traverse and the minimum radius of pipe curvature, are set out by the scraper manufacturer and are available to the design engineer. In addition to the selection of valves and fittings that will allow for the passage of the scraper, it is necessary that horizontal and vertical curves be established on the alignment and grade of the pipe with allowance for the proper radius of curvature in order to eliminate sharp bends in the line.

Materials

The selection of materials for use in a salt-water-disposal or waterflood system is perhaps the most important and at the same time the most perplexing problem faced by the design engineer. Many types of materials are available for selection, and the choice must be governed by several factors, such as economics, types of fluid to be handled, and terrain encountered in the installation. It is not the intent in the following discussion of materials to rate one product above another; the purpose is to point out recommended usage for given conditions, and observations are based on experience gained in the field from systems now in operation.

Types of Pipe. *Asbestos-cement Pipe.* Because of its resistance to corrosion, asbestos-cement pipe is highly recommended for use as gathering lines on gravity or low-pressure systems (200 psi maximum working pressure). Asbestos-cement pipe is manufactured under the trade names of Transite, Century, and others with the joint connection consisting of asbestos-cement couplings with rubber rings. The pipe itself is not flexible, but a deflection of 6° can be obtained at the coupling. This proves advantageous when it is necessary to lay pipe on horizontal or vertical curves eliminating abrupt bends. Care must be exercised in the actual laying of the pipe by providing a conditioned ditch for the pipe. Installation guides have been published by the manufacturers of asbestos-cement pipe and are available to the design engineer upon request.

Cement-lined Steel Pipe. Cement-lined steel pipe is recommended in areas where pressures are in excess of 200 psi. Its use is also recommended in areas where the cost of ditching and burying would be excessive because of rough rocky terrain. In some areas where this condition exists, cement-lined steel pipe has been laid on top of the ground successfully; however, the possibility of freezing of the exposed lines should be analyzed. The problem of interior corrosion protection to exposed metal at joints between the termination of cement lining at ends of the pipe must be considered. Several methods are now in use to provide corrosion protection at the joints of cement-lined steel pipe, namely:

1. Use of a mandrel to cement-line the joint in the field after make-up for plain-end, threaded and coupled, or grooved-end pipe.

2. Use of a cement-varnish mixture or coal-tar-epoxy lining at the joints for screwed pipe.

3. Use of an asbestos welding gasket compressed between the ends of the pipe for welded joints.

Cast-iron Pipe. Very satisfactory installations of cast-iron pipe have been made on systems where pressures are in excess of 200 psi and not over 350 psi. Cast-iron pipe has a high corrosion-resistant quality. Because of a higher initial cost, this pipe is recommended only on systems where the estimated life of the system is long and the economic studies show a pay-out resulting from savings in replacement costs. In ordinary disposal or flood projects, experience has shown that cement-lined steel pipe will last the life of the system and because of a lower initial cost it is used more widely than cast-iron pipe. The use of cast-iron pipe is normally limited to buried systems with moderate pressures.

Plastic Pipe. Rapid progress has been made in the development of plastic pipe in the past decade for use in oil-field operations. The improvement in material properties and increase in engineering knowledge of the plastic materials have been responsible for the more widespread use of these materials in disposal and flood projects.

The desirable features of plastic pipe are the very high corrosion-resistant qualities, a relatively high C value (coefficient of roughness), and the ease of handling for field installation.

The limitations of plastic pipe are the temperature-strength characteristics and the creep characteristics.

Generally speaking, the most common type of plastics used in disposal or flood projects are the extruded plastics. Of these extruded plastics, polyvinyl chloride pipe (PVC) is the most widely used because of its relatively higher flexural strength and low water absorption. Reinforced-plastic pipe offers higher operating pressures and desirable temperature characteristics.

Steel Pipe, Plastic-lined. Various processes have been developed for lining the interior of steel pipe with plastics, epoxy resins, etc., for the purpose of furnishing corrosion protection. These processes are worthy of consideration, and their use will prove beneficial on certain installations. Information concerning these linings is available to the design engineer from the various processing companies upon request.

Valves. Space will not permit an adequate discussion of the types of valves available for use on disposal or flood projects because of the unlimited number of the different types of valves presently on the market. Literature is available in manufacturers' catalogs describing the construction features of different valves. In the selection of valves, the design engineer must determine the specifications to which the valve must conform. This includes pressure rating, type of metals used in valve construction to afford resistance to corrosion, method of operation, and other factors deemed necessary to perform satisfactorily in the system.

Fittings. Various types of fittings such as cast iron, ductile iron, steel, asbestos cement, and plastic are available for use on disposal or flood systems. These fittings are available in screwed, flanged, plain end, or grooved end. The selection of fittings is governed by pressure requirements, resistance to corrosion, and desired operational features.

On low-pressure gravity systems, the use of asbestos-cement or cast-iron screwed fittings has proved successful. On higher-pressure systems, cement- or plastic-lined steel fittings are generally recommended.

Treating-plant Design

Aeration

Water routed to the treating-plant area in an "open-type" system is usually passed through a common header immediately upstream of aeration facilities. The header is constructed of corrosion-resistant materials and is well anchored for stability to resist forces transmitted through expansion and contraction of influent-gathering lines. The header must be designed of sufficient size to pass the maximum anticipated volume of produced and supply waters without restriction. Produced water contains a certain amount of residual oil which should be removed prior to processing the fluid through the treating plant. Locating a skimming chamber ahead of the aerator will assist in removing oil particles which are a frequent source of trouble.

Aeration is provided in an "open system" to release dissolved gases such as free carbon dioxide and hydrogen sulfide. Aeration also oxidizes soluble ferrous compounds, thereby forming insoluble ferric compound precipitates. Soluble bicarbonate compounds are changed to insoluble carbonate compounds through oxidation. Through aeration, the temperature of the water and anaerobic bacterial activity are decreased.

Water may be aerated by one of several methods: (1) exposing it to the atmosphere in open reservoirs; (2) flowing over cascades, weirs, steps, etc.; (3) flowing through perforated or slatted trays and highly porous rock or coke beds; (4) spraying through nozzles into the air; (5) injecting air beneath the surface through perforated pipes, porous plates, strainers, etc.; (6) flowing through forced-draft towers; and other methods.

The atmospheric or splash tower is the most commonly used method of aeration in salt-water disposal and waterflood plants. In this type of aerator, the fluid falls through the aerator and is broken into small droplets upon contact with slatted or perforated diffusing trays. Care should be exercised in the design of aerator trays to assure enough openings in each tray to allow a free flow of the maximum water volume under the available hydrostatic head.

The towers are constructed of a yellow pine, redwood, or cypress superstructure on a concrete collection base. They are assembled with galvanized hardware. The use of creosoted timber in aerator construction is not recommended because of the tendency for creosote to be washed from the wood and be deposited on filter beds and other equipment in the treating-plant area.

Chemical Treatment

The major objective in any salt-water-disposal or waterflood treating-plant operation is to produce a water that will not cause precipitation of insoluble compounds in the distribution system or on the face of the subsurface formation in the input or disposal wells. The first step in determining the proper treatment is to obtain a complete biochemical analysis of the raw water to determine its chemical and bacteriological qualities. Other items that should be considered before attempting to arrive at a definite water-treating program are (1) corrosion tests; (2) review of corrosion, scaling, and precipitate history of the formation fluid; (3) examination of equipment used in processing similar fluid. A workable treating program can then be established and revised as the need arises by using the laboratory analysis in conjunction with periodic field tests of the effluent from each treating process. Changes in the quantity of various chemical additives used are often required after the plant has been in operation for an extended period of time.

It is often necessary to use chlorine, an oxidizing agent, to supplement oxidation obtained through aeration. Chlorination is used in the control of algae and bacteriological growths and will aid in the oxidation of iron particles and in the flocculation of iron compounds. As a result of its oxidizing reaction with hydrogen sulfide, chlorine assists in preventing the formation of ferrous sulfide.

Two sources of chlorine have been found to be economical for producing the required dosage in brine-treating plants: (1) chlorine generated by the electrolytic process and (2) liquid chlorine which is available in cylinders. Experiments with other methods of chlorination such as the use of calcium hypochlorite compounds have been made, but their costs were found to be prohibitive.

The settling of suspended solids may be accelerated by injecting chemical additives that will form a flocculant precipitate. Several coagulants commonly used for this purpose are (1) lime and iron, (2) alum, (3) alum and lime, (4) alum and soda ash, and (5) sodium aluminate.

Hydrated lime, one of the most frequently used for water-treating compounds, reacts with calcium and magnesium bicarbonates to form carbonate precipitates. Part of the lime additive will go into solution and some lime will settle to the bottom of the settling chamber, carrying iron particles with it.

Alum, or aluminum sulfate, is often used as a flocculating agent in the treatment of water. By the addition of alum to the water, large insoluble gelatinous precipitates will form which will absorb and entrain suspended and colloidal matter in the settling process.

Detailed explanations of water-treatment problems and their solutions are available in Babbitt and Doland[8] and in Theroux, Eldridge, and Mallmann.[9]

Chemical feeders are located at any convenient and accessible point between the aerator and settling basin. Dry-feed machines equipped with constant-speed electric motors, rate-of-feed gauges, and recording scales are desirable so that a thorough check of injection rates can be maintained. Thorough mixing of the chemical additives with raw water is accomplished by providing some form of violent agitation immediately following the addition of treating compounds to the raw water. A good method of dry chemical injection is to mount the chemical feeder in a position above a narrow open channel through which water flows from the aerator. Baffles or other protrusions in the channel will create the turbulence necessary for thorough mixing of dry chemicals with the water. The violent agitation needed for mixing should be followed by a period of gentle agitation. The period of time required for this conditioning can be regulated so as to develop particles of floc that will settle readily in the sedimentation basin.

Sedimentation

Large quantities of suspended and settleable solids are removed in the plant area by plain sedimentation. After water passes through the aerator and chemical feeder, it is routed to a settling basin. The object of this treating phase is to provide a retention period during which a slow fluid velocity allows suspended particles to settle by gravity, thereby decreasing the load on filters.

Most sedimentation basins are designed using the principle that water will enter and leave the basin at the same rate. The less efficient fill-and-draw method of operation is not used extensively on salt-water-disposal or waterflood installations.

With few exceptions, circular sedimentation basins are less desirable than those of rectangular shape. A lower first cost is obtained by using a *square shape* for single basins.

The following factors should be given special consideration in the design of rectangular sedimentation basins: (1) inlet and outlet devices, (2) retention period, (3) capacity of basins, (4) velocity of flow, (5) depth of basins, (6) wind and wave protection, and (7) provision for cleaning. Fluid entering and leaving the basin is directed through devices that provide an even lateral distribution of flow from top to bottom through the basin. Perforated noncorrosive conduits, perforated baffles, sharp-crested weirs, and overflow troughs are commonly used for flow distribution.

The *retention period* is defined as the time interval determined by dividing the volume of the basin by the volumetric rate of flow through the basin. This period may vary from a fraction of an hour to several days and is dependent upon tests made to determine the settling time required for the particular fluid being treated in each plant.

Once the retention period is established, *settling-basin capacity* is calculated by multiplying the retention period by the volume of flow through the basin.

The *velocity of flow* in a plain sedimentation basin is equal to the rate of flow through the basin divided by the vertical cross-sectional area of the basin. Basins should never be designed for a velocity exceeding 1 ft/min, and many have velocities less than $\frac{1}{10}$ ft/min.

Since the particles have less distance to fall in shallow basins, settling efficiency, within limits, increases with a decrease in basin depth. Practical application of this principle has shown that the best results are obtained from basins where the relationship between depth, length, and width is considered. Limits on basin depths range from 10 to 15 ft.

Cross currents and excessive construction expense are avoided and wind action is reduced when the ratio of the flowing through channel length exceeds basin width by more than 4:1. Channel width should be limited to approximately 40 ft. Intermediate round-the-end baffles may be constructed of low-cost material and may be spaced so that length-width conditions are satisfied.

Removal of sludge from the basin should be provided for and is accomplished by shaping the basin bottom so that sediment will collect and may be subsequently drawn off from a low point. Sedimentation basins built for service on waterflood or salt-water-disposal projects are usually constructed of concrete, sprayed concrete slurry, asphalt sheets, or other relatively impervious materials. Redwood, cypress, or steel tanks coated with corrosion-resistant lining or equipped with cathodic protection are frequently installed as sedimentation-collection vessels on small projects.

Filtration

In order to remove small floc particles or undissolved solids that remain in suspen⁻ sion after chemical treatment and sedimentation, it is often necessary to treat the water further by the filtration process. The removal of the floc particles or undissolved solids prevents the plugging of the formation and also reduces damage to injection equipment. The filtration process is relatively simple and consists of passing the water through layers of sand, graded aggregate, or other media.

Several types of filters are in use and consist of numerous design features employing various filter media to filter the water effectively. The two most common types of filters used in disposal and waterflood projects are

1. Pressure-type rapid mechanical filters utilizing beds of graded sand and gravel, anthracite, or graphitic ores

2. Diatomite filters utilizing diatomaceous earth as a filter medium

Pressure-type Mechanical Filters. Pressure-type rapid mechanical filters are constructed of a steel shell and are capable of operating at pressures from 45 to 100 psi. Dimensions of the filters vary with sizes ranging from 4 ft in diameter by 5 ft high to 12 ft in diameter by 5 ft high. Designs of pressure-type rapid mechanical filters vary with manufacturers' specifications for spreader plates at the inlet, underdrains at the outlet, methods of supporting the filter media, etc. These factors should be considered by the engineer in the selection of filter equipment. The choice of several types of filter media is available for use in the filter, such as (1) graded sand and gravel, (2) anthracite-coal granulars, (3) graphitic ore, or (4) a layer of permeable plates constructed of aluminum oxide supporting a bed of single-grade fine filter media. Selection of the media is dependent upon (1) required rates of filtration, (2) quality of water to be filtered, (3) availability, and (4) cost.

Capacities of pressure-type rapid mechanical filters are empirical values and are usually expressed in gallons per minute per square foot of filter-bed cross section. Rates of flow vary between 2 and 5 gal/min/sq ft of filter-bed cross section with an average of 2.5 gal/min/sq ft of filter-bed cross section. The variation in these rates is due to the type of filter medium used, the quality of the water treated, etc.

After a filter has been in operation for a short period of time (usually 24 to 48 hours) the filter bed becomes loaded with floc particles and the effectiveness of filtering is decreased. In order to restore the bed to effective operation, it is necessary to remove the accumulated deposit. This is accomplished by reversing the flow or backwashing through the filter. Care must be taken to furnish the proper rate of flow for backwashing as an excessive backwash rate will unload the filter media whereas an insufficient backwash rate will not thoroughly clean the filter media and will result in the buildup of a relatively impervious layer or "cake" on the face of the media. The size, shape, and density of the filter media determine the backwash rate required for the filter. Backwash rates for common types of filter media vary from 10 to 20 gal/min/sq ft of filter area. The design engineer should obtain recommended backwash rates from the filter-media supplier or manufacturer. The frequency of required backwashing is dependent upon the quantity and characteristics of the suspended solids entering the filter bed. A pressure drop of 2 to 4 psi across the filter bed indicates the need for backwashing common types of filter media. Rate-of-flow indicators or controllers with manometers are recommended for each filter in order that proper backwash and flow rates may be maintained.

Table 14-3 shows the *average* quantities of filter media recommended to charge certain pressure filters used on disposal or flood projects.

Table 14-3. Filter-media Sizes and Volumes

Depth of bed, in.	Filter-media size		Volume required, cu ft			
	Sand and gravel	Anthracite-coal granulars	4 ft diam 5 ft high	6 ft diam 5 ft high	8 ft diam 5 ft high	10 ft diam 5 ft high
24	Filter sand, 0.55–0.60 mm	No. 1, 0.6–0.8 mm	24	56	100	156
6	Gravel, 1/16–3/32 in.	No. 2, 3/32–3/16 in.	6	14	25	39
6	Gravel, 3/16–1/4 in.	No. 4, 5/16–9/16 in.	6	14	25	39
6	Gravel, 3/8–1/2 in.	No. 5, 9/16–13/16 in.	6	14	25	39
6	Gravel, 3/4–1 in.	No. 6, 13/16–15/8 in.	6	14	25	39

Table 14-4 shows *average* capacities of various sizes of pressure-type rapid mechanical filters charged with graded sand and gravel filter media.

Table 14-4. Filter Capacities and Backwash Rates, Graded Sand and Gravel Media

Nominal shell size, diam × height, ft	Nominal working pressure, psi	Filter area, sq ft	Water capacity, B/D	Backwash water required, gal (at 15 gal/min/ sq ft area)
4×5	40	12.3	1,070	1,845
6×5	40	27.9	2,430	4,185
8×5	40	49.7	4,325	7,455
10×5	40	77.9	6,780	11,685

Table 14-5 shows *average* capacities of various sizes of pressure-type rapid mechanical filters charged with anthracite-coal granulars, commonly referred to as "Anthrafilt."

Table 14-5. Filter Capacities and Backwash Rates, Anthracite-coal Granular Filter Media

Nominal shell size, diam × height, ft	Nominal working pressure, psi	Filter area, sq ft	Water capacity, B/D	Backwash water required, gal (at 10 gal/min/ sq ft area)
4 × 5	40	12.3	1,260	1,230
6 × 5	40	27.9	2,850	2,790
8 × 5	40	49.7	5,100	4,970
10 × 5	40	77.9	7,950	7,790

Diatomaceous-earth Filters. On disposal or flood projects where the water has not been previously treated (chemically or by sedimentation) and a very high percentage of solids removal is required, diatomaceous-earth filters are generally used.

The principle of filtration by the diatomaceous-earth process is the use of diatomaceous earth as a filter aid. This is accomplished by the addition of a slurry mixture containing the diatomaceous earth to the water to be filtered, which forms a permeable "cake" to retain or filter out the solids. The design features of diatomaceous-earth filters vary as do the pressure-type rapid mechanical filters; however, the two most common types are the vertical leaf and the horizontal tray.

The vertical-leaf type consists of several vertical leaves suspended in the tank or vessel. These leaves are constructed of noncorrosive materials such as stainless steel and carborundum and are precoated with a material such as asbestos fiber which forms a fine filter medium and also retains the diatomaceous earth.

The horizontal-tray type consists of several horizontal trays mounted in the tank or vessel. The trays contain a perforated plate on top of which is placed a layer of sand, gravel, or silica and covered by a fibrous material such as plastic or metal screen, synthetic fabric, or permeable paper filter pads. The diatomaceous earth is retained on the fibrous cover material during the filtering operation.

In the normal operation of the diatomaceous-earth filter, the addition of the slurry mixture containing diatomaceous earth to the water being filtered is continued until the allowable pressure differential is reached or the through-put volume is at a minimum. The length of this filtering cycle is dependent upon the amount of solids removed from the water. If the maximum pressure differential is reached or the through-put volume is insufficient during normal operation, the filter is backwashed by reversing the flow through the filter. Many filters employ high-pressure jets to assist in the removal of cake during backwashing operations. Manufacturers' specifications and recommended flow rates for filter and backwash cycles should be obtained for the operation of diatomaceous-earth filters.

Corrosion protection should be provided for filter vessels. This may be accomplished by lining or coating the interior with plastic or other suitable lining material. Cathodic protection is also used in the reduction or elimination of damage from corrosion.

The number of pressure filters required for a disposal or flood system is determined by dividing the estimated maximum quantity of water to be processed by the specified capacity of the filter. Filters are connected in parallel to obtain the capacity of each filter by a selective arrangement of valves, fittings, and pipe, commonly referred to as the filter manifold. The filter manifold is designed to permit backwashing of any individual filter without disturbing the normal operation of the remaining filters in the battery.

The selection of the valves and fittings to make up the filter manifold should be studied carefully in order to furnish corrosion-resistant materials and ease of operation and to allow for the removal of various fittings and valves for maintenance purposes without disturbing the remainder of the filter manifold or the normal operation of the filter battery during periods of repair.

A centrifugal pump is used to transport the fluid from the sedimentation pit, through the filters, into the accumulator or clear-well tanks. This pump is referred to as the filter pump and is sized to furnish the required rate of flow plus the total discharge head used in the filter-battery design. To backwash filters, water is taken from the accumulator or clear-well tanks and is pumped through the filters (reversing the normal flow for filtration) and into a backwash or sludge pit. A centrifugal pump, designated the backwash pump, is used in this operation. The backwash pump is sized to furnish the specified backwash rate for the filters.

Storage (Accumulation) of Treated Water

Upon completion of the treating processes (aeration, chemical treatment, sedimentation, and filtration) the fluid is transported to storage or accumulation tanks or basins. The purpose of the storage facilities is to furnish an adequate supply of treated water to (1) injection pumps for pressure injection and (2) the backwash pump for the cleaning of filters. On systems where pressure injection is not required, the storage facilities may be designed to furnish a constant supply of treated water and sufficient static head for gravity injection. The required size desired, type, and proper location of the storage facilities should be determined.

Size. The volume of water required for storage varies with the scope of the operation for different systems. The engineer should attempt to arrive at a storage volume that will ensure an adequate supply for the injection pumps without adversely affecting the pumping cycle. Provision must be made for water required for backwashing filters.

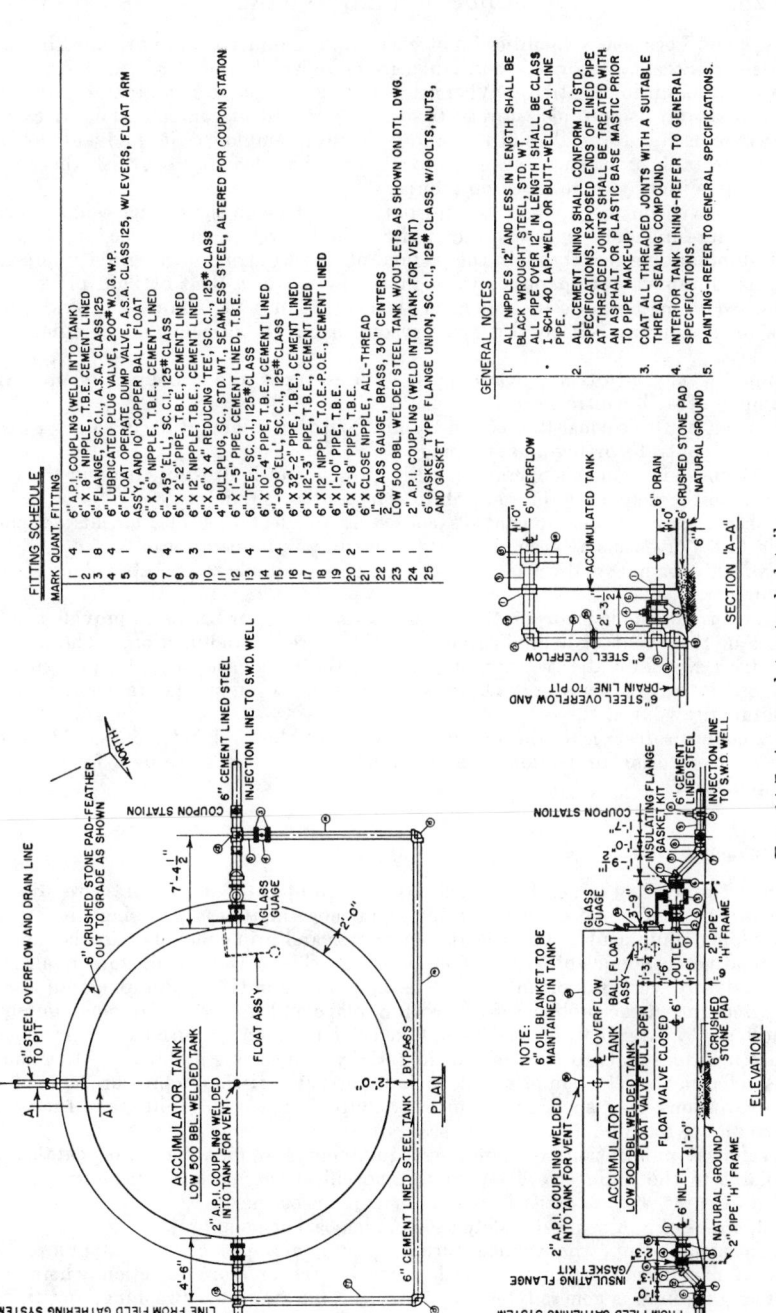

Fig. 14-7. Accumulator-tank details.

Type and Location. Facilities for storage and accumulation are provided by tanks or basins. Steel tanks or redwood tanks are more widely used because of the smaller area required for installation. Where the limits of the plant area are not critical and tne topography is suitable, storage basins constructed of concrete or lined earthen basins are used. Regardless of the storage facilities employed, it is advantageous to locate the tank or basin at an elevation of sufficient height to furnish the flooded suction required by some injection pumps.

Liquid-level controls are used to control the fluid level in the storage tanks or basin. On pressure-injection systems the desired fluid level is maintained by starting and stopping pumps through the action of the controls. On gravity injection systems dump valves operating through the action of a float or fluid pressure are employed to maintain desired operating levels. Figure 14-7 shows a typical storage tank for a salt-water-disposal gravity system using the principle of the dump valve and float.

Liquid-level controls are available in various types and principles of operation. Examples of such controls are

1. Float controls consisting of a float and float switch actuating the starter box of pumps to control starting and stopping

2. Liquid-level controls operating on the principle of hydrostatic head in the vessel to actuate the diaphragm of a switch to start and stop pumps

3. Electrically regulated controls consisting of electrodes or uninsulated points set in tanks or basins at desired levels to control pump operation

Hydraulic or pneumatic float switches are also available to operate valves or other equipment.

An overflow line is incorporated on the storage tanks or basins to provide a safety outlet in the event of a liquid-level-control failure or malfunction. The overflow line discharges into the sedimentation basin, the backwash pit, or a pit especially designed for overflow water. Drain lines are installed on storage tanks or basins to facilitate drawdown.

Cathodic protection or the lining or coating of the tank interior should be provided for corrosion protection on systems where steel tanks are used for storage or accumulation.

Pumps and Prime Movers

In the analysis of the cost of disposal or flood projects requiring pressure injection, perhaps the component or phase of operation reflecting the largest single investment is pumping equipment. The selection of pumps and prime movers must be made on the relative economics of available equipment. The corrosion-resistant qualities of materials are very important in this economic evaluation. Pump manufacturers have recognized the problem of corrosion damage and failure in pumping equipment handling oil-field salt water and have taken definite steps to furnish equipment constructed of materials to eliminate or materially reduce this problem. Other factors considered in the selection of pumps include capacity, discharge pressure, suction lift, load variations, floor-space requirements, pump efficiency, flexibility, and the type of prime mover required.

Technical publications on pumping equipment and manufacturers' catalogs are available to the engineer. They contain specifications, performance curves, operational features, etc., to assist in the equipment selection.

The types of pumps most widely used on disposal or flood projects are the positive-displacement pump, the vertical-turbine pump, and the centrifugal pump. The positive-displacement pump is used primarily for pressure injection whereas the centrifugal pump is generally employed for the filtration, backwashing, and transfer operations. The vertical-turbine pump is used for installation on water-supply wells and may also be used for injection and other pumping operations.

The following general information is listed to assist the engineer in the selection and installation of rotating equipment:

Positive-displacement Pumps. *Duplex-piston Type.* Generally used in systems where the required discharge pressure is below 500 psi.   Has a relatively high mechanical efficiency.

Triplex-plunger Type.   Generally used on systems where the required discharge pressure is above 500 psi.   Has a high rate of mechanical efficiency.

Centrifugal Pumps.   Generally used where low pressures and high volumes are required.   Limited to installations where the required discharge pressure is below 200 psi.   Mechanical efficiency varies from 40 to 85 per cent.

Vertical-turbine Pumps   Multiple installations are very adaptable to changing pressure and volume requirements; low initial installation costs; easily maintained.

Prime Movers.   Electric motors and gas engines—widely used in oil-field operations today.   Selection governed by the relative costs and the availability of electric power and engine fuel.

Three types of drives are employed, namely:

1. Direct drive with a flexible coupling between the drive shafts of the prime mover and the pump, with the speed of the mover and pump synchronous
2. Direct drive with a flexible coupling between the drive shafts of the prime mover and the pump, with a gear-type speed reducer where the speed of the mover and pump is nonsynchronous
3. Belt drive between the mover and pump with the speed of the pump being governed by sheave sizes

Of the three types of drives listed above, the direct drive through a flexible coupling with the speed of the mover and the pump synchronous is more desirable.   The problem of alignment between the prime mover and the pump must be given careful attention.   If the pump is direct-driven through a flexible coupling, the shafts must be precisely aligned and the proper gap left between the end of the prime-mover drive shaft and the end of the pump shaft.   Flexible couplings are designed for normal operations and *minor* misalignment of the shafts due to machine deflection, wear, foundation settling, etc., but *not* for shaft misalignment in excess of prescribed tolerances during installation.   It is important on belt-driven equipment that the pump sheave and prime-mover sheave be carefully aligned to ensure long belt and bearing life.

Foundations.   For adequate support to maintain alignment and to reduce vibration, a foundation of sufficient size and strength should be provided.   Steel-reinforced-concrete foundations are ordinarily used for rotating equipment and are recommended.   The pump and prime mover must be set level to ensure good operation. To accomplish this, the pump and mover are mounted on a skid base; the skid base is set on the concrete foundation, leveled, and approximately 1 in. of grout is used to set the equipment.   For proper location of the anchor or foundation bolts, manufacturers' certified prints should be obtained for all equipment.

The required dimensions of the foundation will vary relative to the size and shape of the equipment.   The depth to which the foundation must be carried depends upon the soil conditions where the foundation is to be set.   The foundation should have sufficient bearing area, which is calculated by using the allowable soil-bearing capacity.   The balanced design of steel-reinforced-concrete foundations for reciprocating equipment is complicated because of unknown shock or vibratory forces encountered, and a "rule of thumb" is employed in many cases to determine foundation design. This "rule of thumb" is that the weight of the concrete mass (foundation) should be from 1.5 to 2 times the weight of the reciprocating equipment.   The size and shape of the skid base will determine the linear dimensions of the foundation, and with acceptable soil conditions, the depth of the foundation is carried to a point that will furnish the required mass.   Temperature stresses in normal concrete foundations for pumps and engines govern the amount of steel reinforcing used.   The amount of such steel is generally determined by the following:

Area of steel, sq in./sq ft of slab area $= 0.002 \times$ cross-sectional area, sq in. of

concrete slab

with maximum spacing between bars not to exceed 18 in.

For heavy equipment, the required reinforcing steel should be determined by the moment and shear in the foundation.

Piping Hookup. More operating difficulties within the plant are attributable to poor piping hookup than to any other source. For this reason, careful consideration and planning must be given to the piping layout. Regardless of the price or quality of equipment, good operation cannot be achieved unless this equipment is properly connected.

The following items, generally accepted in good piping practice, are listed and should be given attention in the piping layout:

General—All Piping

1. Should be as short and direct as possible with a minimum of turns, valves, fittings, or restrictions.

2. Should be independently supported to eliminate strain on the pump and/or piping.

Suction Piping. It is essential that a flooded suction be furnished the positive-displacement pump. A pump should never be allowed to run "dry" or "starved." The net positive suction head recommended by the manufacturer is shown on the performance curves for the pump and must be provided. To furnish this head and ensure a flooded suction at all times, it is necessary that (1) the storage tank or basin supplying the pump be set at a sufficient elevation above the fluid end of the pump, and (2) that the suction piping be of sufficient size to minimize friction losses in the pipe between the storage tank or basin and the pump. In cases where it is impossible to secure sufficient elevation head between the storage tank and pump, a centrifugal pump, commonly referred to as a "booster pump," is employed. The "booster pump" is normally tied into the storage tank and delivers the water in sufficient quantity to the suction header of the injection pumps to furnish the flooded suction and provide the required net positive suction head. Centrifugal pumps do not require a flooded suction as they are capable of a suction lift varying with elevation and characteristics of the liquid. The following features relative to suction-piping installations should be provided:

1. Suction pipe should be as large as or preferably larger than the pump suction inlet size.

2. Long-radius elbows are recommended to eliminate sharp turns.

3. Suction lines should be laid to a constant grade from the pump to storage tank to eliminate high points where vapor may accumulate.

4. An air-volume chamber should be installed in the pump suction manifold or in the suction piping adjacent to the suction fluid end of the positive-displacement pump to relieve pulsation and vibration on the suction side. Basically, the air-volume chamber allows the pump to fill properly by relieving excessive acceleration and deceleration of the fluid with each stroke of the pump. The required size of an air-volume chamber and its air space depends upon the type of pump, displacement per revolution, and the speed of the pump. The air-volume chamber may vary from two to eight times the piston displacement of a single stroke. The air-volume chamber is normally constructed of 6- or 8-in. pipe of sufficient length to furnish required volume, capped on one end and swaged on one end for threaded connection into the pump manifold. Petcocks are tapped into the cap and near the base for bleeding the fluid. A sight glass is also installed for gauging the liquid level in the chamber.

5. The suction piping should be flushed out and cleaned prior to starting the pump to remove slag, mill scale, rust, welding splatter, etc.

Discharge Piping. As in the suction piping, the discharge piping should be well planned with a minimum of turns, fittings, restrictions, etc. The discharge piping should be of sufficient size to minimize friction losses in the pipe in order to furnish the required pressure of the pump discharge. Other factors to be considered in discharge piping are

1. A pressure-relief valve must be employed on positive-displacement pumps in the discharge line ahead of any other valve or restriction.

2. A bypass line should be provided in order that positive-displacement pumps may be started under no load.   This bypass normally consists of a line and valve at least half the size of the discharge line, connecting suction and discharge lines, and is manually operated.   Automatically operated bypass lines may be installed in the same manner utilizing a pressure-controlled diaphragm valve.

3. A pulsation damper, or desurger, should be installed in the discharge line near the pump to relieve shock or vibratory forces.   These forces are the result of pressure variations, or surges, prevalent in positive-displacement pump operation and also result from water hammer due to valve closures and restrictions in the line.

The design and theory of pulsation dampers, or desurgers, are based on the concept that a constant pressure can be maintained if the liquid can be accumulated as the pressure increases and discharged as the pressure decreases.

Several types of dampers, or desurgers, are available.   Operational features should be investigated and a damper, or desurger, selected to fit each condition.

4. On installations where the fluid is pumped to a level higher than the pump outlet, a gate valve or check valve should be placed downstream of the pressure-relief valve near the pump in the discharge line.   This permits the shut-off of fluid backing through the pump while pump valves or plungers are being serviced.

The general practice is to connect pumps in parallel through a common suction and discharge header on systems where two or more positive-displacement pumps are installed.   Headers should be sized to ensure sufficient capacity for satisfactory operation.   On such installations, *each* pump should have its *own* separate pressure-relief valve to ensure protection regardless of which pump may be shut down or out of service.

Plant Buildings

An injection-station building is provided where operations are extensive and economics will allow the expenditure.   This building is normally of the prefabricated-steel type with a concrete foundation and slab floor.   The building is of sufficient size to house all pumping equipment and control panels and to provide office space for operating personnel.

Wellhead Connections

Wellhead design for disposal and injection wells should be made as simple as possible yet provide sufficient equipment for practical and safe operation.   Provision should be made for backflowing, pressure-vacuum gauging, and air release.   Valves are installed for positive shut-off for the well and for the water line to the well.   Displacement-type flowmeters are installed on some installations immediately upstream of the wellhead rather than at the field-line distribution header.   Fittings must be selected with pressure ratings that will meet injection-pressure requirements.   Using past experience as a guide, most operators establish standard wellhead assemblies for uniformity, interchangeability of parts, and reduced construction and maintenance costs.

PLANS

Preparation of adequate plans covering the construction details of waterflood and salt-water-disposal systems is highly desirable.   Such plans enable the engineer to have a complete picture of essential features, thereby eliminating numerous costly field trips and changes in materials and mechanics of operation as the project progresses.   During the planning stage, emphasis is placed on terrain, fluid volumes, fluid characteristics, and disposal-well characteristics.   Any unusual operational features can be considered at that time and incorporated in the plans.

Detailed drawings, complete with identifying marks and accurate measurements, facilitate the preparation of bills of material and cost estimates.   Typical plans for an accumulator-tank installation are illustrated in Fig. 14-7.   Through the use of these drawings, selection, fabrication, purchase, and delivery of materials may be made prior to the commencement of construction.   At the same time, provision can be made for including the installation of equipment necessary for maintenance.

Space requirements are often critical in the plant area.   Well-prepared plans are the only means of assurance that arrangement and positioning of equipment will fit the allocated space.

The alignment plat is used in securing necessary rights of way for surface installations.   It serves as a permanent reference for use in relocating buried lines in the future after the disappearance of surface identification.   It provides a reference for the relative position of components of the entire system.

Profiles of the terrain traversed by gathering lines and relative elevations in the plant area are essential for use not only in hydraulic calculations but also in determining construction grades.

It is especially desirable that plans be prepared with ample detail when it is anticipated that competitive bids will be obtained from contractors for the installation. This provides contractors with a complete understanding of the contemplated work. The bids received should therefore encompass all the work intended and should result in a satisfactory completion of the installation.   Regardless of whether the facilities are installed by contractors or others, detailed plans are extremely valuable to the inspector on the job and provide an excellent record for future reference.

Using completed plans as a guide, a rigid inspection program during construction ensures the desired quality of workmanship in all phases of the work as it progresses. Through such a program, the owner maintains close contact with the project and is satisfied that his plans are an accurate record of the completed installation.

SPECIFICATIONS

As a general rule, specifications are divided into two fundamental parts: *specific clauses* and *general clauses*.

Specific Clauses

For clarity and understanding, plans usually show the quantities, proportions, and relative position of various components of an anticipated structural installation. Plans also contain descriptive phrases pertaining to materials selected for use during construction.   Space for detailed specifications is limited, and a thorough discussion of workmanship and materials is usually conveyed more clearly by means of a separate document.

Specific clauses in specifications place emphasis on particulars that are confusing or might tend to obscure the plan.   They describe materials and workmanship and define the work from an engineering standpoint.   Following are examples of specific clauses:

Concrete.   Shall be either ready-mixed concrete conforming to latest ASTM Standard Specification C94 or job-mixed concrete using the water-cement-ratio method conforming to latest Joint Committee Report of American Concrete Institute on Recommended Practice and Standard Specifications for proportions as follows:

1. Assume 28-day strength.. 3,000 psi
2. Max size coarse aggregate.. 1 in.
3. Min sacks of cement (94 lb)/cu yd.. 5.75
4. Max net water, gal/sack.. $6\frac{1}{2}$
   (includes surface moisture but not absorbed by aggregate)
5. Range in percentage fine aggregate to total aggregate by weight...................... 30–50
6. Range in slump... 2–6 in.
7. Portland cement shall comply with the Standard Specifications for Portland Cement (ASTM C 150) or the Tentative Specifications for Air-entraining Portland Cement (ASTM C 175) and shall be type I unless plans or other parts of these specifications show otherwise

Forms.   Shall be constructed so concrete will conform to shape, lines, grades, and dimensions indicated on drawings without deformation or deflection.   Forms shall not be removed until concrete has hardened sufficiently to support its own weight and any loads due to construction which may occur upon it.   Forms shall not be removed in any case less than 24 hours after placing concrete. Forms shall not permit excess leakage of mortar.

Reinforcement. Shall be as indicated on drawings. Reinforcing bars shall conform to the requirements of the Standard Specifications for Billet Steel Bars for Concrete Reinforcement (ASTM A 15) and deformation on bars shall conform to ASTM A 305. Welded-wire fabric or cold-drawn wire for concrete reinforcement shall conform to the requirements of Standard Specifications for Cold-drawn Steel Wire of Concrete Reinforcement (ASTM A 82) or Standard Specifications for Welded Steel Wire Fabric for Concrete Reinforcement (ASTM A 185). All metal reinforcement shall be as shown on plans, free from rust, oil, or foreign substances. Bars shall be placed as shown, or noted, on plans, and shall be wired securely in place and properly supported so that they will not be disturbed or moved when concrete is poured. All steel shall return 24 in. at corners and shall be lapped 24 diameters at all splices.

General Clauses

Because of the generality involved in their application, certain clauses in the specifications dealing with business and legal matters of the parties concerned are defined as *general clauses.* Some such clauses are only remotely related to actual construction. They might actually apply to several phases of the work because of word usage and phraseology. Opinions differ concerning the relative merits of making general clauses a part of the specifications rather than part of the contract. For example, attorneys often prefer that clauses relating to extra work and damage to persons or property be made express covenants of the contract.[7] Following are examples of *general clauses:*

Shop Drawings. The contractor shall submit, for the owner's representative's approval, two copies of all shop or setting drawings required for work of various trades. The contractor shall make any corrections required by the owner's representative and return two corrected copies for owner's files. The owner's representative's approval of such drawings shall not relieve the contractor from responsibility for deviations from the owner's drawings or specifications, unless he has called attention to such deviations in writing at time of submission, nor shall it relieve him from responsibility for errors in drawings.

Superintendent. The contractor shall keep, at all times during progress of the work, a competent superintendent on the work. Directions given to the superintendent in the contractor's absence shall be as binding as if given to the contractor. Important directions shall be confirmed in writing to the contractor.

Changes in the Work. The owner, without invalidating the contract, may order extra work or make changes by altering, adding to, or deducting from the work. Orders for such changes or additions shall be in writing. The contract sum shall be adjusted accordingly and at unit prices agreed upon.

Subcontracts. The contractor shall submit a list of subcontractors for approval of the owner. The contractor shall be fully responsible to the owner for the acts and omissions of his subcontractors and their employees. Nothing contained in the contract documents shall create any contractual relations between any subcontractor and the owner.

Thoroughly prepared specifications serve to convey the exact intent of the design. The owner has the opportunity to define what is expected of the contractor by adequately covering all points not precisely clear in the plans or contract documents. This is accomplished through the use of detailed descriptions and references to accepted standards of workmanship and materials. Specifications aid the contractor by defining the required conditions for successful completion of the contract.

CONSTRUCTION

Bids

Subsequent to the completion of plans and specifications, the owner or operator of a given project must decide on a source of labor for construction. Oil producers usually depend on outside labor from experienced contractors for the construction of relatively large-scale projects for several reasons:

1. Regular company employees are occupied with routine work and are unable to devote the time required to special projects in order to complete the work within a reasonable length of time.

2. Other concerns specializing in such construction are staffed with trained personnel and have equipment available with which to provide efficient results at a reduced cost.

3. Competitive bids may be obtained from several qualified contractors enabling the operator to determine the actual cost of the installation prior to the start of construction. Bidders are often instructed to quote prices on separate items. Excessive cost on any item may result in a reevaluation and change in plans prior to signing the contract.

Selection of contractors qualified to bid on construction is dependent upon (1) proved ability to perform the work in a satisfactory manner, (2) financial status, (3) reputation, (4) insurance qualifications, (5) availability of labor and equipment, etc.

Bids are requested through a letter to bidders containing instructions regarding

(COMPANY NAME)

________________ Date ________________

____

____

Gentlemen:

You are requested to furnish us with your turn-key bid proposal to furnish all necessary labor, materials (except as noted), equipment, tools, transportation and insurance to perform the work listed below:

I. WORK TO BE PERFORMED:

II. LOCATION OF WORK:

Lease: ________________

Location: __________, __________ Co., __________

III. (Company Name) will furnish materials and/or services indicated below and at sites designated:

IV. All work shall be performed in accordance with the attached plans and specifications, and shall be subject to inspection and approval by (Company representative).

V. ATTACHMENTS:

CONTRACTOR'S BID

Item I-A $ ________ Work shall commence on or before ________.
Item I-B $ ________
Item I-C $ ________ Working days required to complete work ________.
Item I-D $ ________
Item I-E $ ________ Days per week ____. Hours per day ____.
Item I-F $ ________

Total ________ ________________
Contractor

By: ________________

Please fill in above and sign as your bid. Return one copy with the specifications to:

Mr. __________, (Title), P. O. Box ____, __________

not later than __________.

Yours very truly,

____
(Company Representative)

FIG. 14-8. Typical bid form.

the form in which bids will be received. The final date that bids will be accepted must be clearly specified. It is often advantageous for those with a considerable amount of such work to provide bidders with a printed form containing all the necessary information for a direct comparison of bids. A typical bid form is illustrated in Fig. 14-8.

A careful and prudent selection of responsible bidders, combined with a complete explanation of the scope of the work intended in the plans and specifications, assures good competitive bids that may be compared on an equitable basis. Accomplishment of the foregoing leaves little latitude for error in awarding the final contract.

Contracts

The American Law Institute defines a contract as "a promise or a set of promises for the breach of which the law gives a remedy or the performance of which the law in some way recognizes a duty."[7] Valid contracts may be either *express* or *implied* contracts. *Express* contracts are those either oral or written agreements among the principal parties. *Implied* contracts are those agreements in which the parties have obligated themselves by "circumstantial evidence of intention" to perform certain acts. For our terms of reference, the *express* written contract will be considered as the usual method employed for contracting the construction of salt-water-disposal and waterflood plants.

The essential elements in a contract are that the parties be competent, that the subject matter be legal, that the parties have mutually agreed, and that there be valuable consideration involved. The engineer or other agent of the owner charged with the responsibility of preparing the contract does so with the primary intent of assuring diligent performance by the contractor of the acts stipulated in the contract supported by the plans and specifications. The wording of the contract may provide for partial payment for work completed at various stages of construction. Payment can also be made on unit prices agreed upon for completion of certain items of work or it can be made in lump-sum payment for fulfillment of the entire contract. Although contracts are written to include either of the above methods of payment or a combination of several methods, it is usually desirable, on salt-water-disposal and waterflood projects, to make payment for the entire performance in a lump sum.

Field Inspection

Prior to construction, it is necessary for the engineer to establish the location and elevations for gathering and injection facilities, equipment foundations, and structures in the processing-plant area. He usually acts as the inspector during construction, works very closely with construction forces, and is available for consultation on questions that inevitably arise regardless of the thoroughness with which plans and specifications are prepared. The inspector must be familiar with manufacturers' recommendations regarding installation of specialty items. He must know the contents of plans and specifications in order to interpret their intent. He must evaluate the quality of workmanship in all phases of construction. Substandard connection work can be determined before completion of the project by pressure-testing gathering and injection lines. If the pressure test indicates failures in the system, repairs can be made to eliminate costly future maintenance.

When conditions arise during the progress of construction that necessitate changes in the plans or specifications, the inspector must be able to select an alternate method of approach that will provide the desired operational features at the least cost. In arriving at a solution to construction problems, an exchange of ideas on special construction techniques gained through experience invariably results in a reduction of labor and material costs. All changes in the original design should be recorded and made a part of corrected plans at the conclusion of construction for reference purposes. A complete check of the operation of gathering facilities, pumps, vessels, controls in the processing plant, and injection facilities should be made by the inspector before the release of construction forces and prior to the assignment of the plant to regular operating personnel.

A completion report prepared by the inspector should include any unusual conditions encountered during construction. It should evaluate the quality of workmanship and should include a detailed cost analysis, especially on large projects. Comments on the reasoning applied in making changes to plans or specifications are valuable for use in the design and construction of similar future projects.

OPERATION—MAINTENANCE

Responsibility for the operation and maintenance of salt-water-disposal and waterflood plants is normally delegated to personnel with a limited knowledge of the technological problems involved in their design. A simplified operation-maintenance guide, written for the purpose of explaining procedures of operation and maintenance of the plant and associated equipment, will greatly assist such personnel in the performance of their duties.

When a plant is relatively large and involves complex flow patterns, treating cycles, etc., a school is necessary for teaching fundamental operating techniques. Familiarizing operating personnel with occasional problems with which they will be confronted often eliminates costly errors in judgment by untrained personnel. Equipment failures and reservoir damage, through the injection of improperly treated fluid or the injection of fluids at abnormal rates, are often the result of a lax educational program. A concentrated effort toward preparing plans for adequate facilities, conscientious installation of those facilities, the use of efficient injection rates, and instructing personnel in operation and maintenance will pay large dividends by increasing the probability of success for the flooding or disposal project.

Periodic inspection of the plant and related facilities is desirable from the standpoint of minimizing repairs and maintenance. A study of inspection reports will indicate the frequency required for repairs and maintenance and will reveal the degree of corrosion and deposition on mechanical equipment, filters, storage vessels, and pipelines. A maintenance record is helpful in determining costs per barrel of fluid injected and also helps in pinpointing trouble spots. These reports furnish information from which equipment and materials may be selected to improve other projects.

ACKNOWLEDGMENT

The authors gratefully acknowledge the assistance of Mobil Oil Company, a Division of Socony Mobil Oil Company, Inc., and its employees for their generosity and participation in making this section of the handbook possible.

References

1. Knappen, R. S.: The Effects of Recent Legislation on the Petroleum Industry in Oklahoma, Sixth Oklahoma Conference on Industrial Wastes, October, 1955.
2. The Staff of East Texas Salt Water Disposal Company, Salt Water Disposal—East Texas Oil Field, 2d ed., Kilgore and Tyler, Tex., July, 1958.
3. Water Flooding, issued by the University of Oklahoma Business and Industrial Services and State Board for Vocational Education, Department of Trade and Industrial Education in Cooperation with American Petroleum Institute, Division of Production, Committee on Vocational Training, 1956.
4. Power Pump Data, Bethlehem Supply Company, Tulsa, Okla., Operation and Maintenance Instructions, sec. TP-1, p. 1.
5. Ellison, W. F.: Salt Water Disposal, Paper 885-G, presented at 32d Annual Fall Meeting, Society of Petroleum Engineers of AIME in Dallas, Tex., Oct. 6–9, 1957.
6. Russell, George E.: *Hydraulics*, Henry Holt and Company, Inc., New York, 1948.
7. Kirby, R. S.: *The Elements of Specification Writing*, 4th ed., John Wiley & Sons, Inc., New York, 1947.
8. Babbitt, Harold E., and James J. Doland: *Water Supply Enginerring*, 5th ed., McGraw-Hill Book Company, Inc., New York, 1955.
9. Theroux, Frank R., Edward F. Eldridge, and W. LeRoy Mallmann: *Laboratory Manual for Chemical and Bacterial Analysis of Water and Sewage*, 3d ed., McGraw-Hill Book Company, Inc., New York , 1943

Chapter 15

AUTOMATION OF LEASE EQUIPMENT

By DON R. PATTERSON

Production Engineer
The Atlantic Refining Company

Automatic controls are not new to the oil- and gas-producing industry. They have been in common use on almost every producing oil and gas lease for years. But automation is more than the automatic control of single simple functions or series of such functions. It is the linking together of instruments and controls for optimum operation of diverse functions in a self-regulating system. Automation, as it applies to the oil- and gas-producing industry, might be defined as "a self-regulating system of instruments and control devices which automatically perform lease-operating functions in an optimum manner."

For convenience, lease-operating functions may be broken down into seven categories in so far as automation is concerned: (1) automatic well control, (2) automatic well testing, (3) automatic tank-battery control, (4) lease automatic custody transfer, (5) automatic lease-process control, (6) automation supervisory control, and (7) office-machine automation.

The automatic well controls are the ones which control the well's flow, i.e., the controls to place the well on production, to shut in the well, to divert the well's production through the test facilities, time controllers which control the particular times and lengths of time that the well is produced, pump-off controls which shut down the pumping unit when no fluid is being produced, automatic variable-flow controls which control the well's rate of production, etc.

The automatic well-testing controls are the ones which accomplish the automatic testing of each well. They include instruments and control devices to make the automatic well controls switch each well's production into the test facilities in the desired sequence and for the desired length of time, and to measure and record the quantitative and qualitative results of each test and identify the well to which the data belong. If the produced oil and water are not separated before being measured, the well-testing controls must also include an automatic sampling device which will catch and keep segregated a representative sample of each well's production while on test.

The automatic tank-battery controls include devices to permit filling each tank in sequence to a predetermined level, automatically switch the production stream into the next tank available for filling when that level is reached, prevent filling into a tank at the same time it is being run to the pipeline, and shut down all production on the lease when no tank is available for filling. Also in this category may be found controls automatically to recirculate tank "bottoms" or bleed off water accumulation. While not really automatic in the true sense of the word, ground-level tank gauges are also generally associated with this category of lease automation.

Lease automatic custody transfer is the automatic running of produced oil or gas into the connected pipeline on an unattended basis in accordance with any time schedules the pipeline might require. It entails the automatic determination of the quantity and quality of the oil or gas so run and control devices to prevent running production of unacceptable quality or volumes in excess of legal allowables into the pipeline.

Automatic lease-process control is a catch-all category. It includes the automatic control and operation of such production facilities as water-conditioning plants, injection-pumping stations, gas-handling equipment, and compressor installations. Among the operations to be automatically performed in this category are the back-washing of filters in water-conditioning plants; the control of injection pressures, rates, and/or volumes delivered by pumping facilities for disposal, flooding, and pressure-maintenance projects; the cycling and drying of desiccant beds in gas-dehydration equipment; and the start-up, shutdown, and control of operating conditions of gas compressors.

Automation supervisory control refers to the remote supervision and control of individual units of automation from the master-control point of an automation system. The supervision and control is generally accomplished through the use of either a direct-control electric-wire system, a telemetering system, or a radio or microwave system. It entails primarily the sending and receiving of coded signals representing the existing conditions or the desired conditions between these two points over one of these communication media.

Office-machine automation has reference to computers and data-handling machines which automatically perform manual accounting and statistical paper work, and to similar types of computers which perform routine but complex mathematical calculations for engineering and research personnel. The data may be fed into these machines directly by means of an automation supervisory-control system or be manually fed into the machines on magnetic tapes, punched tapes, or punched cards.

Any time that two or more of these categories of lease automation are combined into a system of automation, there will also be an interlocking system of automatic safety devices. These automatic safety devices will protect components of the automation system against malfunction of individual control devices and instruments.

The amount of automation which can be justified under any given set of circumstances is normally a function of pure economics: automatic operation will normally replace manual operation only when the costs incurred are offset by the economies realized in a reasonable length of time. The needs for greater safety and control of operations can, of course, constitute justification for the inclusion of some automatic controls. Complete automation of all operating functions will probably never be accomplished on every producing oil and gas lease for the simple reason that it will not be economical to do so. However, there are some areas of production operations on a large percentage of the oil and gas leases where automation can and will be used to economic advantage.

A number of potential economic benefits are possible through the use of automation. The use of automation can

1. Reduce the capital investment in lease production equipment
2. Reduce operating expenses through savings in labor costs, maintenance expenses, travel expenses, depreciation, and power and fuel costs
3. Conserve the volume and gravity of the produced liquid hydrocarbons
4. Make possible the salvage of some existing equipment on manually operated leases
5. Provide greater accuracy of volumetric measurement and reservoir-performance data
6. Make possible the more efficient use of personnel and equipment
7. Provide relief from inflationary pressures
8. Increase management control of company operations
9. Increase the safety of lease operations

The maximum gain in operating efficiency and economy with lease automation occurs when the number of points at which supervisory and control functions must be exercised are reduced to the minimum practical limit. Consequently, the use of lease automation frequently causes changes in conventional operating and accounting practices.   Individual-well flow lines up to a mile and longer in length may carry full wellhead pressures to central well manifolds.   Wells may be choked and controlled at central manifolds rather than at the wellheads.   All production from a lease or operating unit, or even a whole field, may be gathered to one central point for measurement and transfer to the pipeline.   Production transferred to the pipeline may be measured quantitatively and qualitatively by automatic measuring devices without any manual gauging or thiefing.   A single printed meter-delivery ticket each month may replace a multitude of daily tank-gauge reports and pipeline-run tickets for a large number of tanks on a lease or operating unit.   An automatic data-handling machine may automatically receive production data from the lease, automatically enter the data in a number of records, and even automatically write and mail the royalty checks.

In spite of all the changes in lease equipment and operating procedural concepts attributed to automation, the fact remains that much of the automatic control equipment which goes to make up an automation system is not new to lease operations. What *is* new is the way that these automatic controls have been combined into self-regulating systems.   This point could, perhaps, best be illustrated by first discussing some of the more commonly used automatic control equipment and then depicting some of the more common automation systems.

AUTOMATIC PRODUCTION-CONTROL EQUIPMENT

Automatically Controlled Valves and Accessories

Automatic control valves can be classified in a number of ways, but the method most pertinent to automation is to classify them according to the energy medium which actuates the valve operator.   Using this method of classification, automatic control valves can be grouped into three major categories: fluid-controlled valves, electrically controlled valves, and fluid-electric-controlled valves.   In the latter category a fluid energy is generally used to operate the valve and electric energy is used to control the fluid-energy source.

Fluid-controlled Valves.   The most common types of automatic fluid-controlled valve operators are diaphragm operators and fluid cylinders.   Both these types of valve operators can be used on any style of valve body whose inner valve can be positioned by longitudinal displacement of the valve stem.   However, only the fluid cylinder operator is normally used with valve-body styles requiring 90° rotation for operation.   Diaphragm operators are most commonly applied to valves having globe, angle, butterfly, and Saunders-type valve bodies.   Fluid-cylinder operators are more commonly used with plug valves.

In oil-field applications, the most common fluid used to actuate both these valve operators is natural gas, generally taken directly off a separator or heater-treater on the lease.   If natural gas is not available, or if for some reason the available natural-gas supply is not suitable, a bottled gas (oxygen, nitrogen, etc.), compressed air, or hydraulic fluid could be used.   Diaphragm operators normally only require 15 to 20 psi fluid pressure to actuate the valve.   Pressures up to 100 psi and over are often desired for the fluid cylinders because the higher the fluid pressure available to operate the cylinder, the smaller size the cylinder may be, and consequently the lower the cost. Valves using these types of operators, as a class, are frequently referred to as pneumatic control valves even though the control fluid may be something other than air.

Some fluid-controlled valves can be controlled with the fluid flowing in the line in which the valve is located.   These types of valves generally utilize the differential-pressure principle for control purposes.   A reference control pressure is established by spring-loading or pressure-loading the valve operator.   The control valve is actuated when the line pressure upstream and/or downstream sensed by the valve operator algebraically exceeds the reference control pressure; i.e., the valve can be actuated by pressures either excessively high or excessively low, or both.   This feature makes this type of valve particularly suited to use as safety shut-in valves on wellheads.

Electrically Controlled Valves. Automatic electrically controlled valve operators are of two general types, electric-solenoid or magnetic, and electric-motor. Magnetic operators are used for valves requiring longitudinal motion to position the inner valve. The use of magnetic operators is generally limited to valves 2 in. and smaller in size of relatively low working pressures. Electric-motor operators can be used with any type of valve but in all cases must include accessories which provide a torque-limiting means and a limit switch to prevent damaging the motor when either extreme valve position is reached. On valves requiring longitudinal motion to seat the inner valve electric-motor operators must also include a gear rack and pinion to convert the motor's rotary motion to longitudinal displacement. Because of the relative expense of electric-motor operators, they are normally used only on large-sized valves and/or valves having high working pressures.

Fluid-electric Controlled Valves. Self-contained valve operators in the third category are generally hydroelectric-type operators. Operators of this type essentially consist of a self-contained reservoir of hydraulic fluid, a small electric motor, a pump, and a fluid-cylinder device—all within a single housing. The fluid-cylinder principle limits this type of operator to valves requiring longitudinal motion or 90° rotation to seat the inner valve. Valve operators of this type are available for a wide variety of valve sizes and working-pressure ranges.

In addition to the hydroelectric-type operators, any of the fluid-controlled operators mentioned above can be made combination-type operators. By the addition of electric-solenoid valves in the fluid-control lines, an electric signal can be used to control the release of fluid energy to the valve operator. Combination-type operators of this kind are commonly referred to as electropneumatic operators.

Valve Switches. It is frequently essential that an automatic control system be able to sense the position of certain valves whether automatically or manually operated. This is accomplished by means of a "valve switch" coupled directly to the stem of the valve in question. In electrical control systems, the valve switch may be either a mercury switch or a microswitch. In pneumatic control systems, the "valve switch" is a three-way pilot valve. The switches may be adjusted to open or close a circuit as the valve opens and vice versa as the valve closes. One of the most common applications of valve switches is on tank-run valves, in which case they are generally called "pipeline valve switches." Another common use of valve switches is to indicate remotely the operational position (open, closed, etc.) of automatic control valves on wellheads, well manifolds, metering-tank inlets and outlets, etc. In these general applications, valve switches will normally be referred to as "limit switches." When interlocked with an automatic control system, valve switches perform the very important function of preventing subsequent steps in an automatic operation from proceeding unless certain valves are in the proper position.

Automatic Production Programmers

Time-cycle Controller. Automatic production programmers are scheduling devices which control the particular times and lengths of time that operating functions are performed. The simplest form of automatic production programmer is a time-cycle controller. A time-cycle controller basically consists of a clock with a timing wheel or wheels, containing a number of programming points at regular intervals around its circumference. The clock may be electrically driven, gas driven, or mechanically driven by a spring. It may have a 1-, 2-, 4-, 6-, 8-, 12-, or 24-hour rotation period, the rotation period being the time required for the timing wheel(s) to make one complete revolution. Programming is accomplished by positioning the contacts on the timing wheel(s) such that the rotation of the wheel(s) generates the proper control signal to open or close valves controlled by the time-cycle controller at the proper times.

As commonly applied, a time-cycle controller in conjunction with a diaphragm control valve comprises a "stopcock controller" and/or an "intermitter controller." The primary difference in a stopcock controller and an intermitter controller is in the application. A stopcock controller is generally installed in a well's flow line at the Christmas tree. It controls the times that the well is opened up to be produced, normally for short intervals several times a day. An "intermitter controller" is installed in high-pressure-gas supply line at the wellhead of a well being gas lifted intermittently.   It controls the times that gas is admitted to the well to actuate the gas-lift valves and lift the fluid to the surface. A time-cycle controller in conjunction with any type of automatic control valve may be used to produce a naturally flowing well where it is desired to produce the well less than 24 hours per day and/or 7 days a week.

A time-cycle controller plus a motor starter basically comprises an automatic production programmer for an electrically driven rod-pumping unit. The rod-pumping unit controls also generally contain several safety devices: undervoltage releasing relay which drops out on power failure, overload relays to prevent burning up the motor, lightning arrester, circuit-breaking devices, etc.

Any time the above automatic production-programming devices are electrically actuated, the control point for individual wells may be centralized at the well manifolds, a central point on the lease, or even a point remote from the field.   The time-cycle controllers, automatic control valves, motor starters, etc., may still remain physically located at the wellheads while control is exercised remotely.   This is not true for similar devices which are pneumatically actuated unless the pilot gas for these devices is electrically controlled.   Too much dampening and distortion occurs in pneumatic control signals for effective control when transmitted distances over about 150 ft.

Automatic-sequence Well Tester.   At these centralized automatic control points may be found another automatic programming device, an automatic-sequence well tester.   The automatic-sequence well tester may be either an electric or a pneumatic programming device.   The electric well tester consists primarily of stepping relays, latching relays, switching relays, cycle timers, and adjustable reset-type timers. Economics and experience have indicated that in so far as possible all components of these control panels should be of the plug-in variety.   Electric well testers may provide anywhere from a single adjustable test interval to an adjustable test interval for each well connected to the control panel.   In fact, individual intermitter controls for each well may be provided in the control panel.   Electric control panels offer almost unlimited flexibility to accomplish any programming schedules desired.

Pneumatic well testers basically operate like a rotary selector switch. A master timer, which is essentially a time-cycle controller, operates a mechanical ratcheting device by means of a pneumatic controller.   Each operation of the ratchet sends a signal to the automatic control valve of the next well in the program schedule, which diverts that well's production through the test facilities.   In this fashion, each well in the program schedule is sequentially tested for the time set by the master timer. The pneumatic well-test control panel may also include pneumatic relays, regulators, switches, etc., in its make-up which were not specifically alluded to above.   Pneumatic control panels do not offer the same degree of flexibility as electric panels and as a general rule are slightly more expensive.

An important part of any well-test control panel is the recording of the results of each well's production while on test and the identification of the well to which the data belong.   This is normally accomplished by transmitting the necessary data to either a strip-chart recorder or a data-print-out machine.   Strip-chart recorders may be either electrically driven or mechanically driven by a spring.   To date, data-print-out machines are available only for electrical operation.   Both strip-chart recorders and data-print-out machines will be discussed in a later section.

Other Programmers.   There are other automatic production programmers which utilize principles similar to those just discussed.   Included would be control panels for automatic custody transfer facilities, automatic filter backwash cycles, or any other lease operational process which requires a sequence of operations for proper attainment.

PRODUCTION SAFETY CONTROLS

In some respects, virtually all automatic control equipment is also safety-control equipment: automatic control equipment is nearly always made to be "fail safe"; i.e., upon loss of power from the controlling energy medium the controls return to the position which will result in the safest condition. Some automation controls, however, primarily perform safety functions rather than normal operational functions. These include high-low-pressure safety shut-in valves, excess-flow valves, pressure and temperature switches, and pump-off controls.

Safety Shut-in Valves. High-low-pressure safety shut-in valves and excess-flow valves are both fluid-controlled valves of the type which is actuated by line fluid. This valve type was briefly discussed in the section on automatic control valves. The use of an excess-flow valve or low-pressure control with a safety shut-in valve primarily safeguards against a flow-line break and the resultant loss of oil and surface property damage. High-pressure control with a safety shut-in valve guards against pressures in excess of the allowable limit building up in the flow line. Either of these two kinds of valves would normally be installed at the wellhead.

Pressure Switches. Another means of protection against excessive flow-line pressures and/or flow-line breaks is the use of a pressure switch and an automatic control valve. Pressure switches are available which produce either an electric or pneumatic signal, as required, to actuate the automatic control valve. On rod-pumped wells, the control signal from the pressure switch must also shut down the pumping unit, i.e., turn off the switch on an electric motor or ground the magneto on an internal-combustion engine. On rod-pumped wells which have no tendency to "head" or flow when the pumping unit is shut down, the automatic control valve may be omitted.

A "pressure switch" in the sense to which it is referred to here consists primarily of a pressure-sensing element, limit pressure contact(s), and an electrical, mechanical, or pneumatic means to transmit the control signal to the object(s) controlled by the pressure switch. The pressure-sensing element is commonly a bourdon tube, though some requirements could necessitate the use of a helical-, spiral-, diaphragm-, piston-, or bellows-type pressure-sensing element. In electrical control systems, the displacement of the pressure-sensing element is made to "make" or "break" an electrical switch, normally a mercury or microswitch switch, when the line pressure reaches the preset pressure limit(s). In pneumatic control systems, reaching the preset pressure limit(s) may actuate a pneumatic transmitter, relay, or slide valve or a magnetic switch. The former are used when purely fluid-controlled devices are involved. The latter is used primarily to shut down internal-combustion engines. Actuating the magnetic switch produces an electrical signal (by inducing voltage in the windings of a coil through displacement of a magnet in its core) which is used to ground the engine's magneto. The magnetic switch does not require an external electric-power source.

Automatic Pump-off Control. Another automatic safety-control device which can be installed at the wellhead is a "pump-off control" for rod-pumped wells. Whenever no fluid flows in the line for an interval equal to that of a time-delay relay used in conjunction with the pump-off control, the controls shut down the pumping unit. A time controller may then be used to restart the well again after a predetermined interval. Because of the relative expense of controls to restart internal-combustion engines automatically, pump-off controls are normally only used on electric-driven pumping units. The only type of pump-off control currently available is essentially a spring-loaded check valve with an electric switch and a time-delay relay coupled to its valve stem. This type of pump-off control has one serious limitation in that the flow of gas will give exactly the same indication as the flow of liquid.

Liquid-level Controls. Another automatic safety-control device, which also frequently performs an operational-control function, is a liquid-level controller. These devices are commonly used to control liquid levels in separators, heater-treaters, storage tanks, surge tanks, accumulator vessels, metering vessels, etc. They may be used to control high liquid levels to prevent running over a vessel; low liquid levels to maintain pump submergence; intermediate operational levels to open and close dump valves, to start and stop pumps, etc.; or to maintain the interface of two liquids at a given level.

There are five basic types of liquid-level controls: (1) floatless level controls, (2) float-operated level switches, (3) induced-voltage level switches, (4) electric probes, and (5) ground-level tank-gauge switches. A floatless level-control switch may control liquid level on the basis of either differential or static pressure head. In either case, a pressure-sensing element creates a control signal when the desired liquid level is reached. The differential-pressure type of liquid-level-control equipment is commonly used as one form of "pilot-operated dump valve" on pressure vessels. The static-pressure type of liquid-level-control equipment is more commonly used for well-shutdown service and level control in surge tanks. A float-operated level switch consists of a spherical or cylindrical float on one end of a mechanical lever, with either an electrical switch or a pneumatic relay on the other end. When the float is displaced by the rise and/or fall of the liquid level being controlled, it produces a signal which can be used to actuate other control devices.

One type of induced-voltage switch is essentially a vibrating paddle mechanically linked to an electrical motor-generator arrangement. Electric-current input to the motor end causes the paddle to vibrate by following the action of its armature. The paddle's vibration in turn causes the armature action in the generator end to induce an emf in the generator coils. When the paddle is immersed in liquid, its amplitude of vibration is damped and the generator output drops to virtually zero. The induced emf is sufficient to actuate other electrical control devices.

Another type of induced-voltage switch consists essentially of a transmitter, a receiver, and two crystal transducers. The transmitter applies r-f energy to one of the crystal transducers, setting up mechanical vibrations in that crystal transducer which impinge upon the other crystal transducer and generate an r-f voltage of the same frequency. The second crystal transducer is coupled to the receiver, which amplifies the signal as a d-c voltage to operate a control relay. The intensity of the signal received by the second transducer is dependent upon the density of the transmitting medium and therefore can be used to control liquid levels and/or interfaces.

Electric-probe-type level controls consist of an electrode and an electrical or electronic relay. The probe may produce a control signal on the basis of either the capacitance or the conductivity of the liquid coming in contact with it. In either event, the liquid level coming in contact with the electrode completes an electric circuit, producing an electrical signal which can be used to actuate other control devices.

Liquid levels can also be controlled by the use of limit switches actuated by the tape drum of a ground-level tank gauge. Ground-level tank gauges include a mechanism to maintain a constant tension in the gauge tape. This mechanism causes the tape drum to rotate in unison with the displacement of the tank-gauge float by the rise and fall of the liquid level in the vessel. By extending the tape drum shaft and using the appropriate cams, gearing, etc., electrical or pneumatic control systems may be actuated at programmed liquid levels. The electric switches are generally microswitches, the pneumatic switches slide valves or pneumatic relays. For remote reading and/or control of liquid levels with ground-level tank gauges, electrical or electronic control devices may also be mounted on the gauge head. These devices are primarily built around telephone-type stepping relays.

Automatic Tank-switching Controls

Automatic tank-switching controls essentially consist of automatic control valves on the tank-fill lines, valve switches on the pipeline-run valves, high-level liquid-level controls in each tank, and an automatic tank-switcher control panel. High-level liquid-level controls in each pressure vessel and a safety shut-in valve(s) upstream of all pressure vessels will also normally be integrated into this type of control system. The controls may be either electrically or pneumatically actuated.

Automatic Electric Tank Switcher. An automatic electric tank switcher commonly uses a rotary stepping switch for sequential switching and relays to provide for bypassing tanks not available for filling and safety shutdown in case no tanks are available for filling. An electric switch is also provided to make it possible to remove any tank(s) manually from the automatic control system. The relays and stepping switch are generally hermetically sealed and of plug-in design to simplify maintenance and to protect against corrosion. Electric tank-switcher control panels also generally have a small light representing each of the major control components in the system. These lights are illuminated as the various controls are actuated, thus indicating their position.

Automatic Pneumatic Tank Switcher. There are basically two types of automatic pneumatic tank switcher. The first type uses pneumatic pilots interconnected to switch sequentially from one tank to the next upon receiving the appropriate signal from the high-level control in the tank, and pneumatic relays to perform exactly the same functions as the electric relays above. The second type uses a rotary selector valve driven by an air motor or a pneumatically actuated ratcheting device to perform the sequential switching. Manually operated control valves are provided in the control circuit to each tank with either type of pneumatic tank switcher to permit any tank(s) to be removed from the automatic control system. Pneumatic tank-switcher control panels can also be equipped with indicators on the front of the panel to show the position of the various automatic-control components.

Engine-driven Electric Generators. Any of the types of automatic control valves, liquid-level controls, valve switches, etc., previously described may be used in an automatic tank-switching control system. The nonavailability of commercial electricity does not necessarily rule out the possibility of installing an electric or electro-pneumatic control system. Electric power may be generated on the lease by means of an engine-driven generator, a gas-turbine-driven generator, or a thermopile generator. Engine-driven and/or gas-turbine-driven generators have one bad feature where very accurate timing is required by the automatic-control system; the frequency output of such a generator generally is not so constant as desirable, and this adversely affects the sensitivity of time controls. Also, unless there are other demands for electric power on the lease, the smallest engine-driven generator presently available has a power output many times that required by the average automatic-control system. The gas-turbine-driven generator can be used only when an ample supply of gas of sufficient working pressure is available.

Thermopile Generators. Most components used in automatic control systems on the lease require very little current to actuate, on the order of 3 ma. This low current demand, plus the fact that it is seldom necessary to actuate electrically too many components simultaneously, makes it possible to furnish the electric power with a thermopile generator. A thermopile generator is nothing more than a bank of pilot generators, such as would be used on a burner control, and an electrical resistor. The pilot generator burns a small volume of fuel gas to create heat at one end of a thermocouple. This causes the thermocouple to develop an electromotive force (emf) which, when coupled with the electrical resistor, produces sufficient power to actuate the control devices. The thermopile generator can be interconnected with a standby battery to provide an emergency power supply should source gas to the thermopile fail.

Automatic Quantitative Measurement

There are two classes of quantitative measuring devices which are commonly used at present for automatic liquid measurement on the lease: positive-volume meters and positive-displacement meters. A third class which may become more common in the years ahead is the mass-flow meter. The primary difference between a positive-volume meter and a positive-displacement meter is that the measuring element in the former is essentially static and in the latter is mobile. Positive-volume meters include weir tanks, volume-type dump tanks or meters, and metering separators and heater-treaters. Positive-displacement meters include rotary-vane, rotary-bucket, modified-lobed-impeller, nutating-disk, oscillating-piston, and conventional-piston types of meters.

Weir Tanks. A weir tank is essentially an ordinary lease storage tank with high- and low-level weir boxes and liquid-level controls added. The weir boxes and liquid-level controls may be either internally or externally mounted on the tank. A calibrated volume is measured between the knife-edges of the weir boxes on each cycle. One complete cycle would entail filling the tank to the upper-level control above the upper weir box, drawing the liquid level in the tank down to the top of the upper weir through the overflow connection, releasing the measured volume out the tank outlet—thus lowering the liquid level to the top of the lower weir. A counter actuated by the automatic control valve on the tank outlet will record each dump. The number of dumps times the calibrated volume between the weirs gives the total gross volume measured. The gross volume must be corrected for temperature to obtain the net volume.

Positive-volume Dump Meters. Volume-type dump tanks, or meters, and metering separators and heater-treaters work on exactly the same principle as weir tanks. Many of the volume-type dump tanks, particularly in the larger sizes, require exactly the same cycle as that described for the weir tank. All volume-type dump tanks and metering separators and heater-treaters eliminate the bottom weir and rely solely upon a liquid-level control for shutting the outlet-control valve when the run is complete. The smaller-sized volume-type dump tanks and metering separators and heater-treaters eliminate the upper weir also and rely upon a liquid-level control always to shut the inlet-control valve at the same level in the vessel. Some volume-type dump tanks will have seraphin necks on the top and bottom of the vessel, ostensibly to increase accuracy. However, experience has shown that, if the rate of flow is too high when the liquid level rises into the seraphin neck, the accuracy of the meter is adversely affected. For that reason, in such cases it is desirable to reduce automatically the rate of fill into the vessel when the liquid level approaches the seraphin neck.

Volume-type dump tanks, or meters, have been built in a variety of shapes and volumes. Capacities per dump have ranged from $\frac{1}{4}$ bbl to several hundred barrels. The smaller sizes have generally resembled small dished-head pressure vessels, some having the seraphin necks discussed above added. The larger sizes have more resembled welded tanks and have been of both vertical and horizontal design. The vertical designs have generally had cone bottoms. Metering separators and heater-treaters are essentially standard-design vessels which have had volume-type dump meters of relatively small capacity incorporated as an integral part of the vessel. The meter chambers are normally located in the lower part of the vessel.

Positive-displacement Meters. A positive-displacement meter, regardless of specific type, consists of two primary elements, a stationary case and a mobile element which acts to isolate within the case a fixed volume of fluid each cycle of operation. The mobile element may be a rotor with sliding vanes, rotatable vanes, or rotatable buckets. It may be two rotors which mesh somewhat similarly to two helical or cycloidal gears as they rotate. The mobile element may be a disk which nutates about a camlike follower in three-dimensional motion or a cylinder which oscillates about a cam follower in two-dimensional motion. Or, finally, the mobile element could be a conventional piston such as that found in a power pump. Most positive-displacement meters are, in fact, closely akin to positive-displacement pumps.

In almost every instance, positive-displacement meters used in automatic-custody-transfer installations will be automatically temperature-compensated to give gross volume metered at a base temperature of 60°F. The temperature compensation is accomplished through a temperature-sensing bulb, capillary, and compensating-bellows assembly coupled with an infinitely variable transmission. The temperature-sing bulb is installed in a thermowell either in the meter housing or in adjacent piping. Since atmospheric temperatures also affect the accuracy of the compensation, another compensating-bellows assembly is incorporated to correct for variations in ambient temperatures and as a result the net movement of the transmission is a reflection of line temperature only.

Care must be exercised in the installation design for a positive-displacement meter. All free gas must be removed upstream to avoid spinning the meter and causing erroneous readings, possibly damaging the meter too. For greatest accuracy, a constant flow rate should be maintained through the meter and at a rate at least 15 per cent or greater of the rated capacity of the meter. Standards for calibration frequency, methods, etc., are set forth in API Code 1101 (revised January, 1952).

Integrating Gas Meters. Measurement of gas volumes on the lease has been accomplished almost exclusively by differential-pressure flowmeters (rate meters) to this time. When incorporated into automatic systems, it is desirable that these meters be made direct-reading. This is accomplished by the addition of an integrator to the flowmeter recorder. The integrator is a device which computes the area under the differential-pressure curve traced by the recording pen, extracts the square root of the result, and provides the answer locally on a counter and/or remotely for recording on a strip-chart recorder or data-print-out device. If a high degree of accuracy is required, pressure and temperature compensators can be added with the integrator to adjust automatically for variations in static pressure and line temperature. Some integrators integrate continuously; others integrate only at 5-, 12-, or 15-second intervals. The integrators may be basically pneumatic-, electric-, or electronic-type instruments.

In recent months, there has been a growing trend toward the use of positive-displacement gas meters in place of differential-pressure flowmeters. The meters used to date have been of two types, diaphragm and rotary (the "rotary" positive-displacement gas meter is similar in design to the "lobed-impeller" or gear-type positive-displacement liquid meter). The positive-displacement gas meter is generally more accurate than the differential-pressure flowmeter and is capable of accurately measuring over a range of 15:1. An integrating differential-pressure flowmeter is limited to a range of about 4:1, preferably less. Care must be exercised with the positive-displacement gas meter, however, to prevent liquid accumulation within the measuring element(s). The volume measured by a positive-displacement gas meter may be read directly from a counter on the meter and/or transmitted for remote recording. The integrated readings may also be corrected for variations in static pressure and line temperature.

Mass Flowmeters. There is much in favor of the future application of mass flowmeters on the lease for the measuring of both liquids and gases. None has actually been used to date, though research on their development is in progress. A mass flowmeter will basically consist of rate- and density-sensing elements. Its biggest advantage lies in metering fluids which have a variable density. Its first oil-field application will probably be for measuring full well-stream production from gas wells for direct transmission to the pipeline or gasoline plant.

Automatic Qualitative Measurement

B.S. & W. Monitors. Next to volume, measurement of B.S. & W. is the most important test made on oil at the lease. It helps to determine the net volume for which the producer will be paid. Manually the B.S. & W. is determined by grinding out a sample from each tender in a centrifuge. The advent of automation created the need for an instrument which would continuously and automatically determine B.S. & W. content. To date, two basic types of instruments have been developed, though only one has found very widespread use. This one determines quality by measuring the dielectric constant of crude oil flowing past a capacitor. The other method uses the differential pressure between columns of filtered and unfiltered oil. Presently these devices are being used only to monitor the oil and divert it back through the treating facilities or shut in the production if the B.S. & W. exceeds acceptable limits. Samples are being caught for manual shake-out for accounting purposes. In time, these or similar devices will surely eliminate the need for automatic samplers.

The capacitance-type instrument basically consists of a capacitance cell in the pipeline, an electronic oscillator, a self-balancing bridge, and a recorder. The cell may be formed by two concentric cylinders, two parallel plates, two rod-type probes, or a single probe which uses surrounding piping as the other electrode. The cell can be installed in the main flow stream or in a bypass line through which only a part of the stream is diverted. The cell is commonly installed in a vertical riser on the premise that more uniform mixing of all components in the flowing stream will result and consequently the accuracy of the instrument will be increased. The accuracy and sensitivity of the instrument are affected little, if any, by variations in pressure; however, the instrument must be compensated for temperature because of the variations in dielectric constants of oil which occur with temperature.

The differential-pressure-cell method of B.S. & W. measurement compares a column of clean oil devoid of all water and other impurities with an equivalent column of crude oil. Any head differential existing between the two columns is a direct indication of the percentage of impurities present in the crude. This method requires a sensitive differential-pressure cell which will respond to very small forces. This means that the amplification of the force differential must be large and the error tolerance small.

Automatic Samplers. An automatic sampler is a device which removes a representative volume of fluid from a flowing stream and retains it in a container for later analysis of B.S. & W. content and gravity. All automatic samplers basically consist of four major functional components: a thiefing element, a metering element, a proportioning means, and a sample container. Two or more of these components may be combined into a single device in a specific automatic sampler. The thiefing element may be a plunger or piston type which isolates a volume of fluid each cycle. It may be the suction inlet to a small pump, or it might be just a simple eductor tube which depends upon a small differential pressure to draw the sample into the sampler. The thiefing element may take the sample from a single point or take a sample from the whole cross section. The thiefing element may be fixed or it may rotate. The metering element is simply a device which controls the volume of sample taken per cycle. Some samplers accomplish this by adjusting the length of plunger travel, the volume of sample tube or chamber, the amount of back pressure on the pump discharge, the pump rpm, etc.

The proportioning means is the controller which regulates the rate of sampling activity. It may regulate on the basis of either time or volume flowing past the sampling point. The regulator proportional to time is commonly either an electric or electronic servomechanism (synchronous electric motor, multivibrator, etc.). The regulator proportional to flow normally consists of either an impeller or positive-displacement metering element which, through a gear train, cam, or mechanical linkage, actuates a sampling valve.

For samples which must be retained under pressure, the sample container may be a metal case with a rubber or synthetic diaphragm which rides on top of the oil, a plastic bag inside a metal case with back-pressure checks, or a piston operating in a cylinder in such a way as to maintain the sample under line pressure. For samples requiring only a few ounces to no pressure, the sample container may be a calibrated glass beaker or a fruit jar.

Where the price structure of a crude oil is based on gravity, it is very important that the sample be maintained in the container under conditions which will prevent weathering, i.e., under pressure. The volume of sample withdrawn must be of sufficient size to permit all the necessary tests to be made. The taking of too large a sample should be avoided, however, because of the potential source of error introduced by having to take a representative sample of the original sample.

There are four further basic requirements which should be met for efficient operation of automatic samplers: (1) the sampler should be located as close as possible to the pipeline, (2) the sampler should be located so as to avoid areas of vibrations from high-pressure lines, (3) the lines and sampler should be installed such that the stream is turbulent flowing past and/or through the sampling unit, and (4) the sampler should be installed such as to permit manual purging of the system at desired intervals. For more detailed discussion, see API Standard 2500.

Automatic Temperature Measurements. There are three basic types of temperature-measuring systems: (1) filled-thermal systems, (2) resistance-bulb systems, and (3) thermocouple systems. A filled-thermal system works on the principle that a fluid expands or contracts with changes in temperature. This type of system consists of a temperature-sensitive bulb connected by capillary tubing to an expansible element sensitive to pressure change. The bulb may be filled with a liquid, a liquid and its vapors, or a gas. The expansible element may be a diaphragm, a bellows, or a bourdon tube—the latter being the most common. The pressure-sensitive element is suitably linked to a stylus for direct recording or to an electrical or pneumatic transducer for transmission to a remote recorder.

A resistance-bulb system works on the principle that a change in resistance of a wire is directly related to a change in temperature of the wire. This is the most accurate of the three types of systems in the range from $-100°F$ to $+600°F$. It consists of a resistance element (the measuring element) whose resistance is measured by a self-balancing or deflection-type bridge (modified Wheatstone bridge) and recorded directly in degrees Fahrenheit. Power for this type of system can be furnished by either battery or rectified alternating current. The bridge circuits are designed so that effects of ambient temperature and supply-voltage changes are eliminated.

A thermocouple system works on the principle that heat applied to one end of two strips of metal of different composition which are bonded at either end causes the development of an electromotive force (emf) whose magnitude is directly related to the amount of heat (temperature) applied. Thermocouples may be of the wire type, in which both elements are in wire form, or of the Pyod type, in which one element is a closed tube and the other a wire welded to the inside bottom of the tube. In thermocouple systems the detecting circuit is a self-balancing potentiometer instead of a bridge because the electrical quantity is an emf instead of a resistance change. Thermocouple systems are the primary temperature-measurement means where temperatures exceed $1000°F$.

A variation of the thermocouple-type system, which is not dependent upon the emf developed, is sometimes used in place of the thermal-filled system. In this case, the bimetallic element consists of strips of two metals having greatly different coefficients of expansion joined together and wound in a helical coil. Temperature changes around the element cause the free end to move angularly in proportion to the temperature change. This movement is transmitted through a mechanical linkage to a chart and recorded in terms of temperature.

There are two kinds of temperature measurements required in lease operations: spot measurements and average measurements. Spot measurements are made by individual temperature elements, but by elements of sufficient dimension to extend completely through the areas for which the average temperature is required. Individual spot measurements can also be brought into a single sensing device and be recorded as an average temperature.

Automatic Gravity Measurement. There are four basic methods of automatic gravity determination presently available. These are based upon the measurement of buoyancy, weight, differential pressure, and intensity of radioactive radiation, respectively. Any of these methods may be used to obtain a continuous measurement of gravity. However, with a continuous-measuring gravity instrument, the gravity measurement is an instantaneous valve which is proportional to time and not to rate of flow. In order to measure the average gravity, which is an essential quantity in automatic custody transfer, the rate of flow must be taken into account. One method of doing this would be to drive the recording chart with pulses from the flowmeter, then integrate the chart with respect to flow to get an average. Another method would be to regulate the flow to produce a constant rate. For weir-tank systems and positive-volume dump tanks or meters, instantaneous measurements of gravity taken by buoyancy or differential-pressure methods just prior to releasing the measured volume to the line are, in effect, average-gravity measurement.

The automatic determination of gravity by the buoyancy method is merely an elaboration of the manual-hydrometer method. A float is submerged in the liquid for which the gravity is to be determined, the position of the float being determined by the resultant of its weight and buoyancy in the liquid. Changes in the specific gravity of the liquid cause the float to ride higher or lower in the liquid dependent upon whether the specific gravity decreases or increases. The movement of the float is transmitted by mechanical, electrical, pneumatic, or some combination of these means to a recorder.

The weight method of automatic gravity determination weighs a small known volume of the liquid on a knife-edge balance. A small volume of the flowing stream of liquid is continually bypassed through a pressuretight container which is supported on the knife-edge balance. A recording pen is linked directly to the balance arm and records variations in specific gravity as indicated by displacements of the balance arm.

The differential-pressure method of automatic gravity determination is based on the principle of comparing the hydrostatic pressure of a constant head of variable-density liquid against a constant, stable reference pressure or head of liquid. Because of the small pressure changes which will normally be encountered as the result of gravity variations in lease production operations, differential-pressure cells used for this purpose will have to be very sensitive narrow-range instruments—such as the bell-type differential-pressure cell, for example. Differential-pressure cells can be obtained which will produce either an electric or a pneumatic signal for transmitting to a recorder.

The fourth method of automatic gravity determination presently available uses a source of radioactive radiation (gamma rays) on one side of a pipe or tank and a detector (geiger-counter tubes and electronic amplifier) to measure the intensity of radiation received on the opposite side. It works on the principle that the intensity of the radiation received depends upon the density of the material separating the source and the detector. Radiations received and amplified by the detector are converted into an appropriate signal and transmitted to a recorder. At the present stage of development, instruments of this type are not applicable to lease automation because they do not have the desired sensitivity. With further refinements in application technique, however, they could become quite acceptable in the future. This tool would become quite important if the need should ever develop to measure or control gravity in some lease process where the liquid was at extreme temperatures or too viscous to be used with the other methods cited above.

The true gravity of oil at 60°F is generally the basis for determining the price paid for the crude. For this reason, it is necessary either to simultaneously record the temperature of the liquid and manually correct the observed gravity reading, or to include automatic temperature compensation in the configuration of the automatic gravity-measuring device. If for any reason pressure should also be a factor, some models of these automatic gravity-measurement instruments can be obtained which will simultaneously record the pressure.

Automatic Recording Instruments

Circular-chart Recorders. The most common type of automatic recording instrument used in lease operations today is the circular-chart recorder. This type of recorder is almost universally used in conjunction with orifice meters (as long as the meter reading is not integrated before being recorded) and is also commonly used for recording temperatures, pressures, B.S. & W. content, etc. The recorder may be considered to be basically a mechanical, pneumatic, electrical, or electronic instrument, depending upon how the signal of the quantity to be recorded is received by the element controlling the recording stylus.

Mechanical recorders must be located in close proximity to the point where the quantity to be recorded is measured because the recording stylus is coupled directly to the measuring element by a suitable linkage. Pneumatic, electrical, or electronic recorders may be located either at the point where the measurement is made or at some convenient remote point. Pneumatic recorders are generally limited to locations within about 200 ft, however, because of signal distortion and dissipation which occur at greater distances. Some electrical measurements are similarly restricted where a high degree of sensitivity is required and line losses can reduce accuracy. Regardless of whether the input signal to the recording instrument is by pneumatic, electrical, or electronic means, it is translated into mechanical motion proportional to the range of the instrument. This motion governs the displacement of the recording stylus, and thus in every case the actual recording of data is by mechanical means. It is possible to mount several styli on the same instrument to record several pieces of data simultaneously.

Strip-chart Recorders. Any measured quantity which can properly be recorded on a circular-chart recorder may also be recorded on a strip-chart recorder. The principal advantage of the strip chart over the circular chart is its capacity to record data for up to 30 days without changing charts as opposed to a maximum of 7 days with the circular chart.   The strip chart is unwound from an idler roller by sprockets attached to either end of a driven roller which mesh with perforations in the paper and pull it along as the record is made.   The motive power for the drive roller may be mechanical springs, synchronous motors, or gas timers similar to those used for chart drives for circular-chart recorders.   Chart speeds available range from $\frac{3}{4}$ to 12 in./hr, with $1\frac{1}{2}$ in. being the most common.   The strip-chart recorder also is susceptible to multiple-pen recording.

One special version of the multiple-pen strip-chart recorder, which is particularly applicable for recording automatic well-test data, is what is known as an operation recorder.   The chart drive and writing system of this type of strip-chart recorder are exactly the same as for any other strip-chart recorder.   However, instead of drawing continuous curves representing the quantities being measured, the operation recorder gives a simultaneous set of on-off and/or digital-type records for up to 20 channels of information.

Each recording pen, which is controlled by a small electromagnet, is offset a small fixed distance when actuated.   The pen may be held in the offset position to indicate the period of actuation, producing a "rectangle-pattern" type of record.   This type of record is used in automatic well testing to indicate the duration of the test and, where each well is identified by a separate pen, the particular well on test.   Other well-test data, however, are generally recorded as an "impulse-pattern" type of record.   This type of record is produced by actuating the pen only momentarily. Pulses representing units of measurement for each quantity being recorded are fed into the respective pens as the unit quantity is produced, resulting in a series of horizontal marks.   Since the chart is driven at a constant rate of speed, the space between marks represents the time that it took to produce that unit of measure. The relative spacing of marks on adjacent channels is representative of the rate of production of one quantity with respect to the other(s).

In effect, the "impulse-pattern" type of record is a digital record, for by merely counting the marks, the total quantity measured by each channel may be determined. Even this chore may be lessened by the use of some of the available channels as decade-counting channels.   Some quantities being measured might require two or more decade counters.

Automatic Data-print-out Machines.   The automatic recording of data in printed form has generally been accomplished in one of two ways to date, with an adaptation of (1) the electric adding machine or (2) the electric typewriter.   The primary difference in the records obtainable from these machines is the number of digits which can be recorded in the data read-out and the form of the printed record.   The adaptation of the electric adding machine prints a record on adding-machine tape and consequently is limited to 8 or 10 horizontal positions.   The first three of these positions are generally reserved for code information (well or meter designation, quantity being recorded, etc.) and only the last five or six positions are normally available for recording quantitative results.   Successive quantitative results to be recorded from the same source, or other sources, are printed one below the other.   With the electric typewriter, the number of horizontal positions available are limited only by the width of the typewriter carriage.   Successive quantitative results may be recorded side by side or one below the other, or both, as desired.   It is even possible to use a preprinted form and automatically fill in the appropriate blanks as the signals are called for in fixed sequence.

With either of these types of data-print-out machines, it is necessary to use a programmer.   The programmer contains the counting channels and scanning, coding, selector, and timing circuits.   The counting channels are commonly 10-position stepping switches with as many switches cascaded as necessary to obtain the number of digits desired in the answer.   The remaining electric circuits—which are composed primarily of stepping relays, latching relays, switching relays, timers, etc.—select the point(s) from which the data are to be read, the sequence in which they are read. and the time of the read-out; supply the necessary code to identify the point from which the data are read; and between logging cycles can scan off-normal alarm points.

Coded Digital Data Recorders.   The ultimate in automatic recording, in so far as lease automation is concerned, is to record the data in such a fashion that they can be either manually or automatically fed into automatic office machines for final processing. The automatic recording machines which are most applicable for this purpose at present are those capable of producing coded digital data on punched tapes, punched cards, or magnetic tapes. Functionally these types of recording machines perform in a manner very similar to an electric typewriter or adding machine and their respective programmers. However, instead of creating records of printed data using the alphabet and arabic numerals, they create records of coded perforations on tape or card, or coded magnetic spots on tape. These are the sensible languages of automatic office machines.

Initially these machines will probably be used only in the case of very large field operations, or in areas of large concentrations of automatic leases, and they will be in addition to the present printed records. As automation of an operator's leases in an area increases, coded data from each intelligence point will be fed directly into a single machine at a central location. Then any printed records required in production offices or on the lease will probably be prepared at the central office and returned to those points. The use of this type of recording machine, either on the lease or in some remote office, will not eliminate the need or the desirability for also producing a written record intelligible to the operating personnel.

TYPICAL AUTOMATIC-CONTROL INSTALLATIONS

Automatic Well Control

Automatic Wellhead Controls. Wells may be controlled at the wellhead or at the well manifold. Frequently it is found to be necessary or desirable to control them at both places. Figure 15-1 depicts three different types of automatic control valves which could be installed at the wellhead immediately adjacent to the tubing wing valve. While Fig. 15-1 pictures a naturally flowing well, the same types of automatic controls would be applicable for artifically lifted wells of all types, if required. The excess-flow valve shown in Fig. 15-1a is generally used only to protect against flow-line breaks when the wells are choked and controlled at the well manifold. The high-low pressure shut-in valve in Fig. 15-1b may be used whether the well is choked at the well or at the well manifold. It is protection against both flow-line breaks and chokes cutting out or plugging. The control valve and separate pressure-sensing element shown in Fig. 15-1c perform exactly the same functions as the high-low pressure shut-in valve.

Rod-pumped-well Control. In Fig. 15-2 is shown the typical automatic-control system for a rod-pumped well. The high-low pressure safety shut-in valve is necessary only when the well has a tendency to flow naturally when the pumping unit is shut

(a) EXCESS FLOW SHUT-IN CONTROL VALVE

(b) HI-LOW PRESSURE SHUT-IN CONTROL VALVE

CHRISTMAS TREE

(c) AUTOMATIC CONTROL VALVE WITH PRESSURE SWITCH

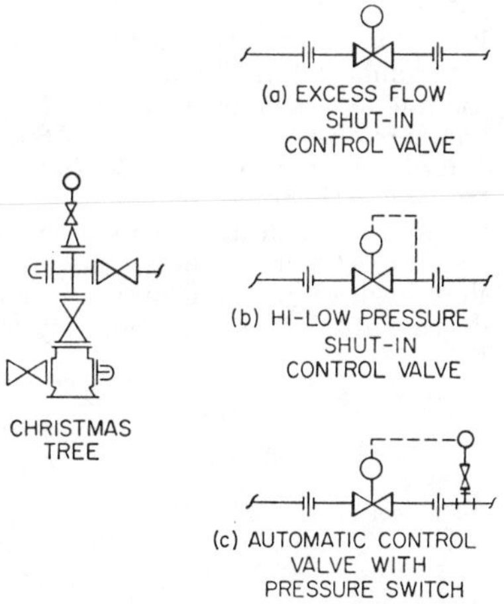

Fig. 15-1. Automatic wellhead safety controls. (a) Excess flow shut-in control valve; (b) high-low-pressure shut-in control valve; (c) automatic control valve with pressure switch.

down. The excess-flow valve, again, is protection against flow-line breaks. Some operators use them; others do not. They are not always effective unless line pressures are high enough, and the size of the break large enough, to create a substantial pressure drop. The pressure switch is the most common automatic safety control used with rod-pumped wells, particularly where the wells are remotely controlled. Regardless of which of these three types of controls are used, when the control pressure is reached, that automatic control must furnish a signal to shut down the pumping unit. This is accomplished by grounding the magneto of a gas engine or

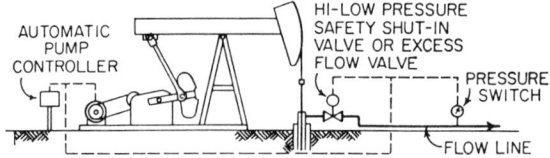

Fɪɢ. 15-2. Automatic controls for rod-pumped well.

shutting off an electric motor. A pump-off control, if used, would be installed in the flow line immediately adjacent to the pumping tee.

Gas-lift-well Control. Figure 15-3 shows a typical arrangement of controls on the gas-supply line to a well which is produced by an intermitter-type gas-lift installation. The "time-cycle controller" shown on the right is an automatic production programmer. It automatically opens and closes the diaphragm control valve, to which

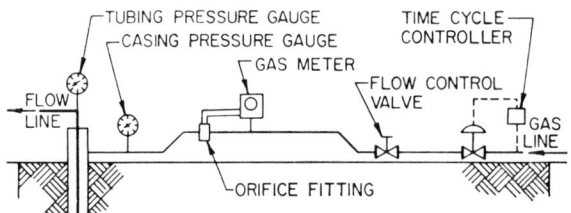

Fɪɢ. 15-3. Typical automatic control of gas-lift well.

it is connected by instrument lines, according to the schedule manually created in the programmer. The "flow-control valve" is a manually actuated valve used to control the rate at which gas is admitted to a well. Automatic-control valves on the flow line, if required, would be one of the types shown in Fig. 15-1.

Hydraulic-pumped-well Control. Figure 15-4 depicts the typical automatic controls for a hydraulic pumping system. A high-low pressure switch protects the triplex pump and its prime mover against overloading from abnormally low suction pressures and/or high discharge pressures. In either case, the pressure switch would shut down the prime mover. Automatic control valve V-1 in the manifold bypass is generally a diaphragm-type regulator valve which is normally closed. It would

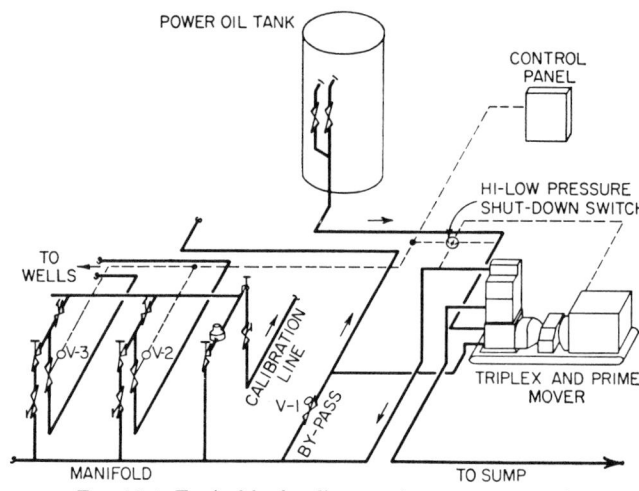

Fɪɢ. 15-4. Typical hydraulic-pumping-system control.

open at a pressure slightly under the setting of the high-low pressure shutdown switch and divert sufficient power oil back to the power-oil tank to maintain system pressure at a safe level. Automatic control valves V-2 and V-3 are in the power-oil lines to individual wells. They would be automatically closed in the event the pressure switch shut down the triplex and prime mover. With an appropriate programmer, they could also be used to produce individual wells selectively on an intermittent schedule.

Automatic Well Manifolds. In Figs. 15-5 and 15-6 are shown two typical automatic well manifolds designed for controlling the wells at the well manifold rather than at

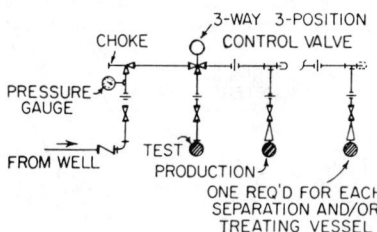

FIG. 15-5. Typical single-wing automatic well manifold.

the wellhead. The single-wing well manifold shown in Fig. 15-5 has a maximum of flexibility to meet any system of stage separation and/or treating that might arise. It has another advantage in that it could be installed initially on new leases as they are developed without the automatic-control valve and still add the valve later with a minimum of expense. The dual-wing well manifold shown in Fig. 15-6 is limited to situations where all production in a well manifold is processed through a single vessel or a common sequence of vessels. Both these manifold designs would require flow lines capable of withstanding full wellhead pressure and would choke and control the wells at the manifold.

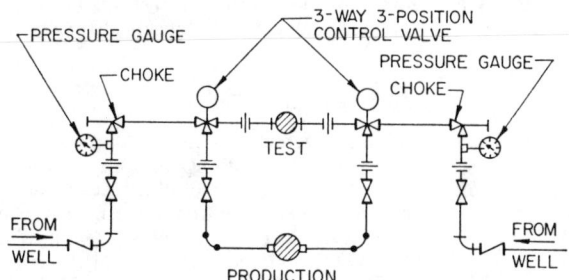

FIG. 15-6. Typical dual-wing automatic well manifold.

Some operators prefer to use three-way two-position control valves in the well manifold and to control the wells at the wellhead. Automatic-control valves of the types shown in Fig. 15-1 would then be installed at the wellhead in addition to the control valves in the well manifold. Other operators would prefer to use a two-way control valve in each riser to each pressure vessel served by the well manifold.

Automatic Well Testing

A typical automatic well-testing system is illustrated in Fig. 15-7. Upon receiving the proper signal from the well-test control panel, each well's automatic three-way control valve in the well manifold is actuated and its production is diverted through the test vessel. The test vessel may be either a separator or a heater-treater. It may have the liquid-metering elements as an integral part of the vessel, or they may be separate components. In Fig. 15-7 they are shown as separate components. If a three-phase separator or a heater-treater is used as the test vessel, the oil, water, and gas would be metered individually. If only a two-phase separator is used as the test vessel, the measured quantities will be gas and liquid. In this case it will be necessary to install a fluid sampler immediately downstream of the fluid meter to catch and keep segregated a representative sample of each well's production while on test. Each production and test vessel in an automatic well-test system will normally have an emergency high-level float switch which would shut in all production through that vessel in the event it were actuated.

The accuracy requirement for fluid measuring and sampling is not nearly so great for automatic well testing as it is for automatic custody transfer. An accuracy of

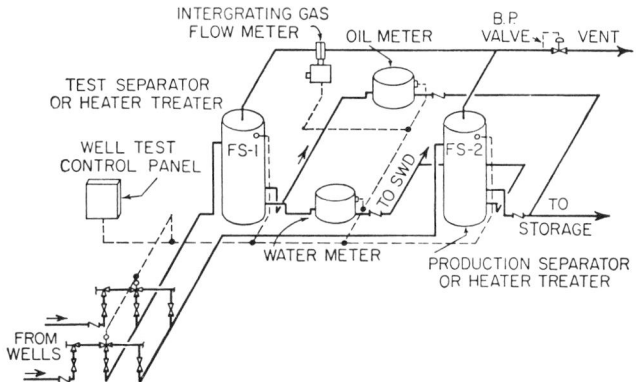

Fig. 15-7. Typical automatic well-testing system.

± 2 per cent is generally acceptable for automatic well testing, as compared with the accuracy requirement of $\frac{1}{10}$ of 1 per cent generally specified for automatic custody transfer.

Automatic Tank Battery

Automatic Tank-switching Control System. In Fig. 15-8 is shown a schematic flow diagram of a typical tank-battery installation containing an automatic tank-switching and circulating system. For purposes of illustration, assume that the upper left-hand tank is empty and available for filling. Automatic control valve V-1 on the tank-fill line opens and clean oil from the treating facility (heater-treater, gunbarrel, etc.) enters the tank. Valve V-1 remains open until the oil level in the tank rises until it comes in contact with float switch FS-3. If float switch FS-3 should fail to actuate, float switch FS-2 would still protect the tank against running over. When float switch FS-3 is actuated, valve V-1 is closed and the automatic tank switcher begins its search for the next tank available for filling. If the upper right-hand tank were the next tank in the sequence, and it were available for filling, automatic control valve V-7 would open and the cycle would be repeated for that tank. If that tank were full or had been manually locked out of the circuit for repairs, cleaning, etc., the automatic tank switcher would continue searching for an available tank into which to produce. If no tank were available for filling, the automatic tank switcher would sense this fact and initiate action to shut in all wells producing into that tank battery. The same signal would be given in the event of a high level in the treating facility as sensed by float switch FS-1. If the wells were controlled at the well manifold, simultaneous control signals would be sent to the automatic-control valve in each well's manifold. If the wells were controlled at the wellhead, a single safety shut-in valve would probably be installed in the common flow line upstream of the separating and treating facilities, and this valve would be the recipient of the tank switcher's signal. The buildup of flow-line pressures which would then result could be sensed by a pressure switch or a high-low pressure safety shut-in valve at the wellhead and shut in the wells.

In an automatic tank battery, the pipeline-run valves (valves V-9, V-10, V-11, and V-12 in Fig. 15-8) would be manually operated valves, but they would have a valve switch mounted on the valve stem. This valve switch would be so integrated in the automatic-control system that, when that particular tank was being run to the pipeline, the automatic-control valve on its fill line could not be opened.

Automatic-circulating Control System. For automatic circulating of tank bottoms, an automatic-control valve would have to be installed on the circulating line of each tank (valves V-3, V-4, V-5, and V-6 in Fig. 15-8). When the pipeline valve was closed upon completion of the run, the circulating valve would open and the circulating pump would be started. An automatic timer would permit the circulating pump to operate for a predetermined time, then shut down the pump, close the automatic circulating valve, and signal the control panel that the tank was again available for filling. This type of system would require that the circulating pump either be a gas-operated pump or have an electric prime mover or a battery-actuated ignition system to permit a gas-engine prime mover to be automatically started and stopped.

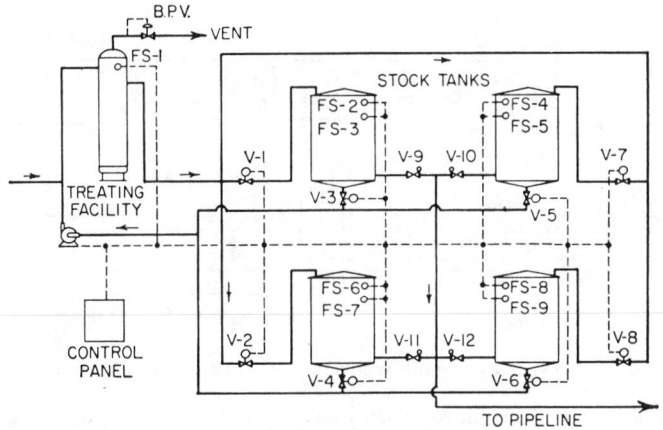

Fig. 15-8. Automatic tank-switching and circulating system.

Automatic Water-bleed-off Control System. Where free water in the bottom of the tank was the main concern, an automatic-control system could be installed to keep the water bled off the tank bottom. A capacitance-type probe would be installed in the tank shell between the lower chime and the pipeline connection. When the water level in the tank came in contact with the probe an automatic-control valve on the tank drain line would be opened. It would be held in the open position by an automatic time control for a predetermined time sufficient for the water to drain and then would be permitted to close.

Automatic Custody Transfer

The first efforts to design an acceptable lease automatic-custody-transfer installation tried to utilize the existing equipment on the lease and familiar operating principles in so far as possible. Thus, understandably, the first officially accepted LACT system was a weir-tank system installed by the Gulf Oil Corporation on its Ames Lease in the Bloomer field, Kansas, in 1955. The Shell Oil Company also pioneered in the development of the weir-tank-type LACT system on its leases in the Antelope and Wasson fields in Texas, beginning unofficial experiments as early as 1948. The next significant development in LACT system design was the meter-tank-type system.

The meter-tank-type system is closely akin to the weir-tank system in many respects, but it perhaps deserves consideration as a separate category because these vessels were designed solely as measuring vessels. The great similarity between measurement with the larger-sized positive-volume dump meters and conventional lease tanks assured their early acceptance. Officially accepted LACT installations of this type of the Phillips Petroleum Company and the Pan American Petroleum Company in Oklahoma and Texas followed closely on the heels of the Gulf weir-tank-type system in Kansas. The third type of LACT design which has gained wide acceptance to date is the positive-displacement-meter-type system. The Humble Oil & Refining Company was perhaps the strongest early proponent of this type of system, and they performed much development work on their leases in South Texas. Today, this is the type of LACT system which seems to be favored with the greatest acceptance by potential users. A fourth type of LACT system, which is based upon mass-flow metering, is reported to have been installed by the Creole Petroleum Corporation in Venezuela, but very little information is available on this type of system.

Weir-tank LACT System. A typical schematic flow diagram of a weir-tank-type LACT installation is shown in Fig. 15-9. Basically the system works in the following manner: Clean oil from the treating facility is alternately directed into the left and right tanks as they are available for filling. As the oil leaves the treating facility, it

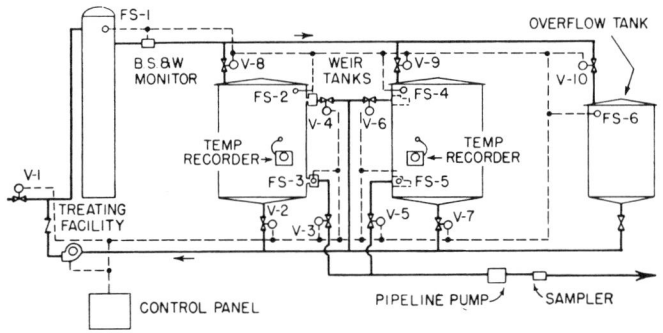

Fig. 15-9. Typical weir-tank-type automatic-custody-transfer system.

flows past a B.S. & W. monitor which would cause the fill valve on the weir tank (valve V-8 or V-9) to close and the fill valve V-10 on the overflow tank to open any time the B.S. & W. content exceeded the limit set on the monitor. When the B.S. & W. content was again within limits, the oil would be diverted back into the proper weir tank.

Assuming that the left tank is the one being filled, valve V-8 is held open until the fluid level reaches float switch FS-2. The valve V-8 closes and valves V-4 and V-9 are opened. At the same time, a timer is actuated which controls the length of time that the tank is weathered before it is run to the pipeline, and the volume of oil between the float switch FS-2 and the lip of the upper weir is drawn off by the circulating pump. When the weathering time is up, valve V-3 is opened and the pipeline pump is started. When the fluid level falls to the lip of the lower weir box and float switch FS-3 is actuated, valve V-3 is closed, the pipeline pump is shut down, valve V-2 is opened, and the circulating pump is started. After a predetermined time the circulating pump is shut down, valve V-2 is closed, and that tank is again available for filling.

A pipeline sampler is provided downstream of the pipeline pump to catch a representative sample of the oil for manual determination of gravity and B.S. & W. content. A safety shut-in valve V-1 is provided to shut in all production in the event the allowable for the day or month is run and/or the fluid level reaches the emergency high-level float switches in the treating facility (FS-1) and/or the overflow tank (FS-6).

Some weir-tank-type LACT installations have only a single weir tank. In that event, the treating facility or overflow tank must have sufficient surge capacity to contain the normal through-put until the weir tank has completed its cycle and is available to receive more oil. The sequence of operations for the weir tank is exactly the same as with the two weir tanks in parallel. Also, some weir tanks will have internal weir boxes, others external weir boxes. This arrangement is shown in the right and left tanks, respectively, of Fig. 15-9.

Positive-volume Dump-meter LACT System. A typical schematic flow diagram of a metering-dump-tank-type LACT installation is shown in Fig. 15-10. Clean oil from the treating facility flows into a surge tank. The surge-tank fluid level normally operates in the range from a level between float switches FS-7 and FS-8 and float switch FS-7. The surge tank is sized to retain each barrel of oil run through the dump meters for a length of time established by the connected pipeline as that necessary to weather the crude sufficiently. When the oil level in the surge tank reaches float switch FS-7, the transfer pump is started and automatic control valve V-3 is opened to permit oil to enter the metering vessel. Oil is pumped into the metering

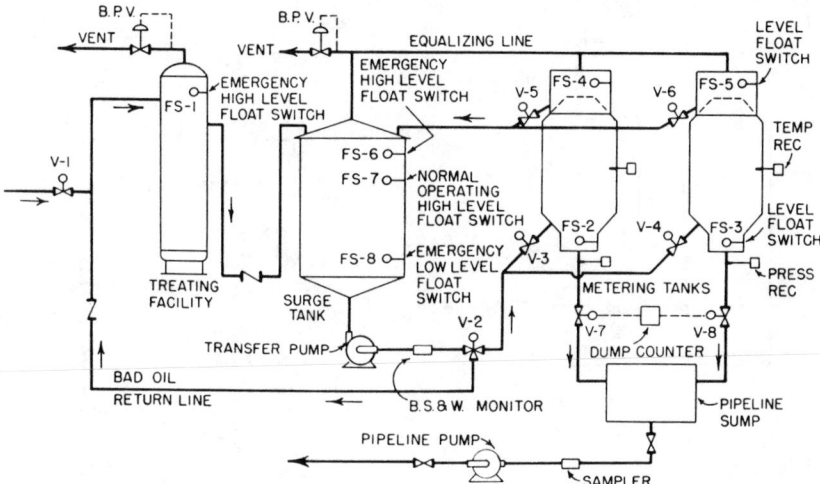

Fig. 15-10. Typical automatic-custody-transfer system using metering dump tanks.

vessel until the fluid level reaches float switch FS-4, at which time valve V-3 is closed, the transfer pump is shut down, and valve V-5 is opened. A time-delay switch is actuated at the same time that float switch FS-4 is actuated. The time delay is of sufficient duration to permit all oil above the top of the weir to drain back into the surge tank by gravity. When that time interval is up, valve V-5 is closed, valve V-7 is opened, and the pipeline pump (if one is required) is started. When the fluid level drops to float switch FS-2, valve V-7 is closed and the pipeline pump is shut down. This completes one-half cycle if two parallel metering tanks are used or a complete cycle if only a single tank is used.

This system contains much the same safety controls as the weir-tank system. The treating facility has an emergency high-level float switch FS-1 which will close the lease shut-in valve V-1 in the event it is actuated. The surge tank also has an emergency high-level float switch FS-6 which performs the same function, and an emergency low-level float switch FS-8 which maintains a flooded suction for the transfer pump. There is a B.S. & W. monitor between the surge tank and metering tank which monitors the B.S. & W. content and automatically actuates diverting valve V-2 to bypass unacceptable-quality oil back through the treating facility.

In addition, each metering tank has a pressure tap at its bottom and a temperature probe at its mid-point which produces continuous records of pressure and temperature on an automatic recorder.   A record of the number of dumps is obtained by counting the number of times that the run valve (valves *V*-7 and *V*-8) is opened (or closed). The pipeline sampler catches a representative sample of each dump and maintains it under pressure in its container until it can be manually evaluated to determine its gravity and B.S. & W. content.

The metering-tank design shown in Fig. 15-10 is basically the system developed by the Phillips Petroleum Company.   It has found rather wide acceptance with the larger-sized metering vessels.   Other metering-tank-type LACT systems work on almost exactly the same principles as those outlined above.

Positive-displacement-meter LACT System.   In Fig. 15-11 are shown two typical arrangements for positive-displacement-meter-type LACT installations.   Note that up to the diverting valve this system is identical to the metering-tank-type system, except for the addition of a strainer and a gas eliminator between the transfer pump and the diverting valve.   The wire mesh in the strainer is not too fine because experience has shown that, if the mesh is very fine, difficulty is encountered from plugging

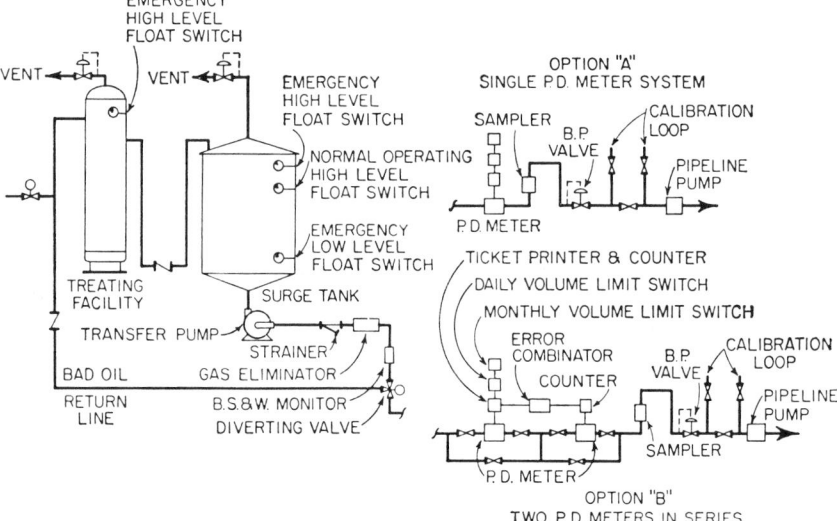

FIG. 15-11. Typical automatic-custody-transfer systems using positive-displacement meters.

with paraffin, hydrates, etc.   The purpose of the gas eliminator is to remove the last vestiges of free gas from the oil in order to improve the accuracy of the meter.   If not removed, the free gas would occupy space passing through the meter and would be registered as a volume of oil.

Downstream of the diverting valve, two types of positive-displacement-meter systems have been used: a single-positive-displacement-meter type (Fig. 15-11, option *A*) and two positive-displacement meters in tandem (Fig. 15-11, option *B*). The type using two positive-displacement meters in tandem was strongly recommended at first, but recently the sentiment has been more in favor of a single-positive-displacement-meter type of system.   With the two positive-displacement meters, each meter is temperature-compensated and has a barrel counter.   In addition, the first meter has a printing head and monthly-volume-limit switch and can be furnished with a daily-volume-limit switch if desired.   The purpose of these limit switches is to prevent running a volume in excess of legal allowables to the pipeline within the stated interval.   The readings of the two meter counters are sometimes combined in an "error combinator," which is a device that subtracts one reading from the other. Any time one reading is more than some predetermined percentage (usually about 5 per cent) different from the other, either a warning signal is actuated or the production is shut in. Some designs have flowed continuously through both meters. Other designs have flowed through both meters only for short periods at regular intervals, using the second meter solely as a reference meter but functioning in the same fashion just described.

In the single-positive-displacement meter-type LACT design, the positive-displacement meter has exactly the same accessories as the first positive-displacement meter in the tandem-meter LACT design. One factor which has contributed to swinging sentiment over in favor of the single positive-displacement meter is the difficult and time-consuming nature of calibrating the tandem meters. In order to use the error combinator effectively, the two meters must be calibrated to obtain approximately the same meter-calibration factor.

Downstream of the positive-displacement meter or meters, there is generally provided a calibration loop (so that the meters may be calibrated in place), a pipeline sampler, pipeline pump (if required), and a back-pressure valve. The purpose of the back-pressure valve is to keep a constant head on the positive-displacement meter and to hold to a minimum the "flashing" of gas through the meter. The pipeline sampler operates in exactly the same manner as those previously described.

Automatic Lease Process Control

There are many normal lease-operating processes which may be automated or which are already completely automated and not recognized as such by the average individual. Space limitations will permit only a brief look at a few of these control systems to show what can be and is being done.

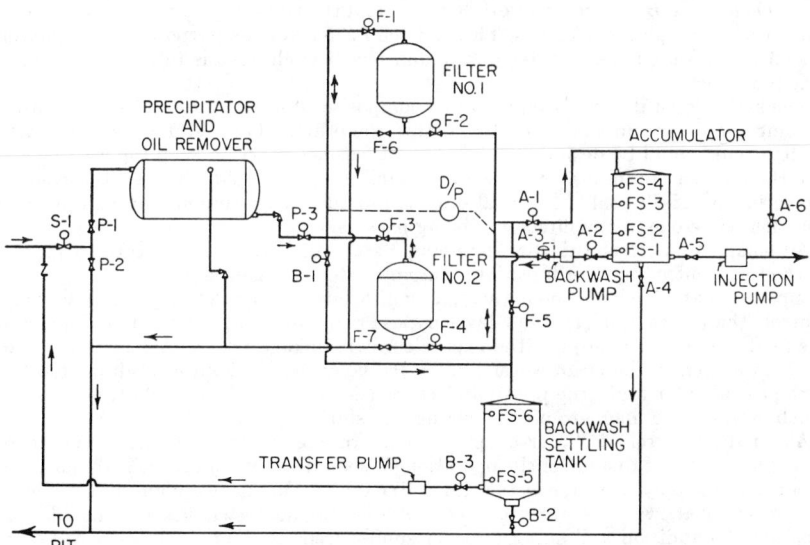

FIG. 15-12. Automatic backwash of rapid sand filters in water-treatment plant.

Automatic Water-treating Plant. Looking first to an area of lease operations that is growing tremendously in importance, Fig. 15-12 depicts a rather elaborate automatic backwash system for rapid sand filters in water-treating plants. Normal flow is from the precipitator and oil remover through the sand filters into the accumulator. When the differential pressure across the bank of filters reaches a predetermined value, the backwash cycle is automatically initiated. Valves P-3, F-1, F-3, F-4, and A-1 are closed; valve A-2 is opened; and the backwash pump is started. After a slight delay, valves F-1 and B-1 are opened and filter 1 is backwashed into the backwash-settling tank for a predetermined, but adjustable, time. At the end of this time, valves B-1 and A-2 are closed and valves P-3 and F-5 are opened. Normal flow is permitted through filter 1 into the backwash-settling tank for a short interval to settle the filter bed. At the end of this interval, valves P-3 and F-5 are closed, valve A-2 and F-4 are opened, and the backwash pump is started. After a slight delay, valve F-3 opens and the same cycle is completed for filter 2.

Four float switches are required in the accumulator. Float switch FS-1 is an emergency low-level float switch which maintains a flooded pump suction and prevents gas from locking the pump since the accumulator will normally be gas-blanketed. The volume between float switches FS-1 and FS-2 is large enough to backwash the filters. Normally the fluid level is not permitted to fall below FS-2. If it should, the injection pump is shut down if it has an electric prime mover, or valve A-6 is opened and the injection-pump output is bypassed back into the accumulator if the injection pump has a gas-engine prime mover. When the fluid level reaches float switch FS-3, the normal injection process is resumed. Float switch FS-4 is an emergency high-level control which would cause valve S-1 to close to prevent running over the accumulator.

Valve A-3 is shown as a back-pressure valve which is intended to keep a constant head on the backwash pump. The backwash pump will probably be a centrifugal pump because of the high rate normally recommended for proper backwashing. If the injection process ceases for the backwash cycle, then gas pressure applied to the top of the accumulator can be used in place of the backwash pump.

After all the filters have been backwashed and settled into the backwash-settling tank, the solids in the water are permitted to settle out in the bottom of the tank. Then valve B-2 is automatically opened to permit the solids to be washed out to the pit. Then valve B-2 closes, valve B-3 opens, and the transfer pump returns the clear water back through the system. Float switch FS-5 is for the purpose of maintaining a flooded suction on the transfer pump, and float switch FS-6 is to prevent running over the vessel.

The system just described represents a composite situation. All automatic water-treating plants would not have to be this elaborate. For example, a backwash-settling tank would be desirable only where it was necessary to keep the water going into the pit at a minimum. On the other hand, by a few small changes, the systems shown in Fig. 15-12 could also be altered to provide for continuous through-put and injection while one of the filters was being backwashed.

Automatic Control of Injection-pumping Rate. In Fig. 15-13 is shown a typical method of controlling the injection-pumping rate of a gas-engine-driven injection pump. A float switch and pilot valve, acting through a snap-acting pneumatic relay, controls the position of (1) a low-level bypass regulator, and (2) a bellows-operated pneumatic motor that adjusts the engine throttle linkage relative to the position of the float switch in the clean-water tank. In the event the fluid level drops too low in the clean-water tank, the pilot valve sends a signal to a low-level shutdown switch which grounds the magneto on the engine and shuts it down.

Automatic Control of Water-supply Wells. In Fig. 15-14 is shown a method of using float switches to control the operation of several water-supply wells to maintain an adequate supply of water in the raw-water tank. As always, high- and low-level emergency float switches are provided. Additional float switches are included to program the addition and subtraction of supply wells feeding the system to assure always an adequate volume of water in the raw-water tank. The well-on float switches would be actuated by a dropping fluid level, and the well-off float switches by a rising fluid level.

At the water-supply wells, there are several ways in which to control the pumping equipment. If the pump is electrically driven, it might only be necessary to start up and shut down the pump motor as called for. If the water-supply well were artesian or had a tendency to flow naturally, it would, of course, be necessary to furnish a shut-in valve. If the pump is driven by a gas engine, it would be necessary either to provide the engine with an electric ignition system (battery or electric motor) and a start-up sequence programmer or to install a diverting valve and leave the engine running while diverting production back into the casing annulus.

Automatic Control of Dry-desiccant-type Gas Dehydrators. As a final example, let us consider a lease process which has been fully automatic since its inception, but one which is rarely thought of in terms of automation: the automatic cycling of desiccant beds in dry-desiccant-type gas dehydrators. Figure 15-15 is a schematic flow diagram of a typical dry-desiccant-type dehydrator. The wet gas stream enters

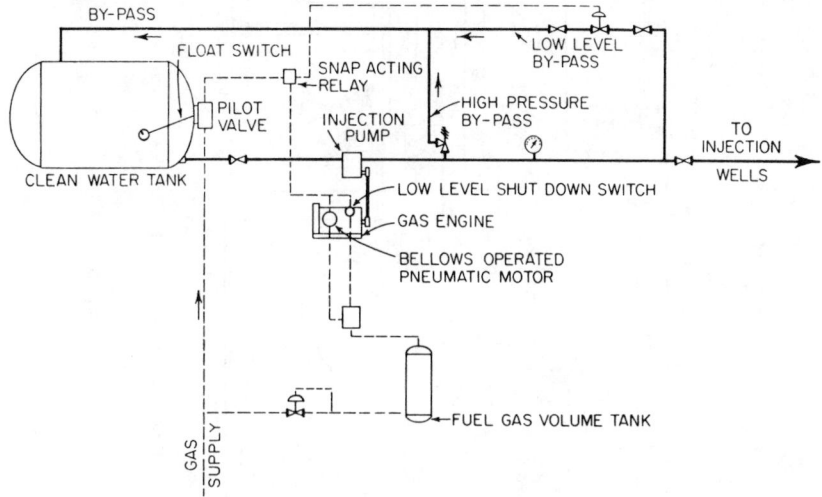

FIG. 15-13. Typical method of controlling injection-pumping rate.

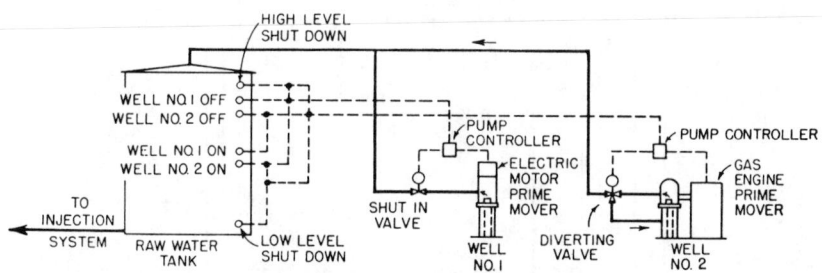

FIG. 15-14. Automatic control of water-supply wells.

the horizontal separator and is divided, with a part of the gas going to the regeneration stream and the remainder continuing in the main gas stream through the dehydrating tower. The proportioning of the flow between the two streams is controlled by the regeneration-rate controller. The rate of flow in the regeneration gas line is measured by a differential-pressure cell and transmitted to the regeneration-rate controller. The regeneration-rate controller, in turn, acts to position automatic-control valve V-10 to maintain the predetermined rate of flow of gas through the regeneration system.

Automatic-control valve V-11 in the regeneration gas line is controlled by controller B. Each time the controller rotates until the pin on the next trip clamp unlatches the pilot arm, valve V-11 reverses its position. In the one position, it diverts gas through the heater to provide hot gas for expelling moisture from the desiccant bed of the tower being regenerated. In the other position, it bypasses the heater and provides unheated gas to cool the desiccant bed in the same tower before

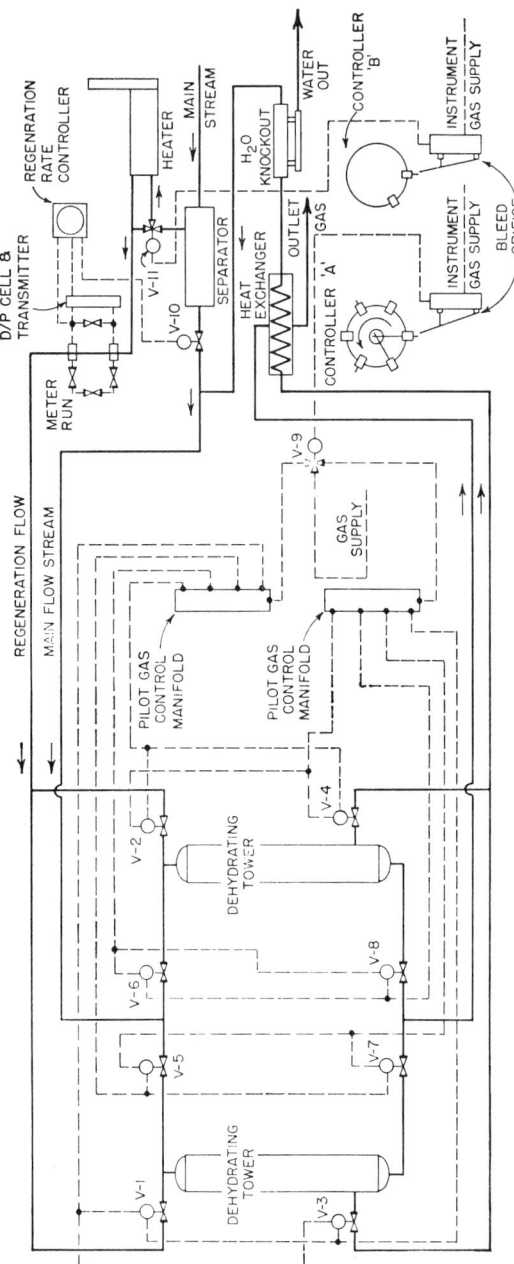

Fig. 15-15. Automatic cycling of desiccant beds in dry-desiccant-type gas dehydrators.

placing it back into service. By the time the controller rotates one more position, the regeneration valves on the towers will have switched so that the hot gas goes to the other tower.

Automatic-control valves V-1, V-2, V-3, and V-4 control the flow of regeneration gas to dehydrating towers, and valves V-5, V-6, V-7, and V-8 control the flow of the main gas stream. Valves V-1, V-3, V-6, and V-8 are always in the opposite position from valves V-2, V-4, V-5, and V-7. The main-stream valves and the regeneration-stream valves are manifolded in such a manner that only one tower at a time receives the main-stream gas and that tower is blocked off from the regeneration gas. The other tower receives the regeneration gas and is blocked off from the main-stream gas. The position of all these valves is controlled by controller A acting through relay valve V-9 and the pilot-gas-control manifolds. Each time the controller rotates until the pin on the next trip clamp unlatches the pilot arm, instrument gas will flow through the bleed orifice instead of flowing to the relay valve V-9. Relay valve V-9 will then reposition itself and allow instrument gas to flow to the other pilot-gas-control manifold and vent the gas from the pilot-gas-control manifold supplied in its original position. This, in turn, will cause each of these control valves to reverse their positions, and thus the flows of main and regeneration gas streams will also reverse. The length of each cycle is controlled by the spacing of the trip clamps on the controller.

References

1. Atkinson, M. H., and A. H. Newberg: Crude-oil Measurement Is Going Automatic, *Oil and Gas J.*, June 4, 1956, p. 102.
2. Barrett, M. L., Jr.: Meter Proving, *Oil and Gas J.*, Feb. 24, 1958, p. 153; Mar. 10, 1958, p. 201; Mar. 24, 1958, p. 213; Apr. 21, 1958, p. 179; May 5, 1958, p. 133.
3. Bayless, C. R., and F. J. Mikeska: Automatic Control of Production, *Oil and Gas J.*, June 4, 1956, p. 78; June 11, 1956, p. 129; June 25, 1956, p. 110.
4. Beach, Frank W.: Fail-safe LACT Unit; Here's How It Works, *World Oil*, November, 1957, p. 133.
5. Brainerd, Henry A., and John J. Piros: New Controller Recorder Gravitometer, *Oil and Gas J.*, Dec. 2, 1957, p. 78.
6. DeVerter, P. L., and W. E. Scovill: Part I: Continuous Automatic Sampling, *Oil and Gas J.*, Apr. 2, 1956, p. 125. Warren, F. H.: Part II: Continuous Automatic Sampling, *Oil and Gas J.*, Apr. 9, 1956, p. 124. Johnson, R. P.: Part III: Continuous Automatic Sampling, *Oil and Gas J.*, Apr. 23, 1956, p. 119. Berglund, J. H.: Part IV: Continuous Automatic Sampling, *Oil and Gas J.*, Apr. 30, 1956, p. 210.
7. EnDean, Howard J.: Oil Field "Watchman" Checks BS&W Content, *World Oil*, November, 1957, p. 151.
8. Foster, K. W.: Centralia Water Flood: Pre-planned Automation Pays Off, *Pet. Engr.*, March, 1958, p. B-116.
9. Hebard, G. G.: Automatic Lease Custody Transfer, *Oil and Gas J.*, Nov. 5, 1956, p. 86.
10. Hill, Ralph W.: Factory-built LACT Unit Is Gas Operated, *Oil and Gas J.*, May 6, 1957, p. 98.
11. Hubby, L. M.: Automatic Production Controls, API Paper 926-1-C, presented at the Spring Meeting of the Southern District, Division of Production, San Antonio, Tex., Mar. 9, 1956.
12. LeVelle, James A.: New Production Programming System, *Pet. Engr.*, April, 1956, p. B-30.
13. McGhee, Ed: Automatic Switching, 9-mile Radio Link, *Oil and Gas J.*, Sept. 10, 1956, p. 114.
14. McGhee, Ed: How Cities Service Is Using P.D. Meters for LACT, *Oil and Gas J.*, Jan. 13, 1958, p. 74.
15. McGhee, Ed: How Shell's Antelope LACT Works, *Oil and Gas J.*, June 3, 1957, p. 90.
16. McGhee, Ed: It's Automatic—Even to Sample Taking, *Oil and Gas J.*, Feb. 13, 1956, p. 104.
17. McGhee, Ed: LACT—And Why We Like It, *Oil and Gas J.*, Jan. 20, 1958, p. 131.
18. McGhee, Ed: When a Field Outgrows Its Facilities, *Oil and Gas J.*, Apr. 15, 1957, p. 108.
19. McKinley, Dee C.: P.D. Meters Get the Job Done, *Oil and Gas J.*, Oct. 1, 1956, p. 87.
20. Meyers, D. C.: How Shell Designs an Automatic Lease, *Oil and Gas J.*, Oct. 17, 1955, p. 111.

21. Northern, T. P.: Automatic Lease Operations Weeks Island Field, Paper 283-G, presented at the Fall Meeting of the Petroleum Branch, AIME, in Dallas, Tex., Oct. 19–21, 1953.
22. Packard, H. C.: Part I: General Considerations; Kelley, Harold S.: Part II: From the Producer's Viewpoint; Newburg, A. H.: From the Pipeliner's Viewpoint: Three-part paper, Automatic Custody Transfer of Crude Oil, presented to Group Session of the Division of Production during the 36th Annual Meeting of the API, Chicago, Ill., Nov. 13, 1956.
23. Patterson, D. R.: Production Automation, *Pet. Engr.*, January, 1959, p. B-31.
24. Pope, S. H., and R. M. Stuntz: Lease Automatic Custody Transfer Becomes a Reality, *Oil and Gas J.*, Apr. 23, 1956, p. 96.
25. Resen, Larry: Humble Tries LACT, Gives A Stamp of Approval, *Oil and Gas J.*, Mar. 4, 1957, p. 94.
26. Saye, Hugh A.: Automatic Well Testing, *Oil and Gas J.*, Jan. 6, 1958, p. 102.
27. Scott, J. O.: Automation Pays Off in Big Mineral Producing Operations, *Oil and Gas J.*, Sept. 19, 1955, p. 114.
28. Scott, Vernon B.: Automatic Lease Operation, paper presented at West Texas Oil Lifting Short Course, Texas Technological College, Lubbock, Tex., Apr. 11–12, 1957.
29. Shatto, H. L.: Comments on the Status and Future of ACT from the Production Viewpoint, paper presented at the ASME Mechanical Engineering Conference, Denver, Colo., Sept. 21–24, 1958.
30. Shatto, H. L., and A. H. Hall: Greater Rewards from LACT, *Oil and Gas J.*, Apr. 7, 1958, p. 133.
31. Stormont, D. H.: Tank Bottoms Are Recycled, *Oil and Gas J.*, Nov. 12, 1956, p. 173.
32. Taylor, Donald M.: New Auto-pneumatic Lease Programming System, *Pet. Engr.*, December, 1956, p. B-28.
33. Todd, Morris: Automation Applied to Flooding at Naval Reserve Pool, *Oil and Gas J.*, Mar. 4, 1957, p. 84.
34. Travis, R. H.: Complete Automation in Water Injection, *Pet. Engr.*, February, 1957, p. B-76.
35. Warren, F. H.: Automatic Gaging, Sampling, and Testing, *Oil and Gas J.*, Nov. 8, 1951, p. 271.
36. Wasicek, J. J., K. B. Kleppinger, and W. W. Grovenburg: An Integrated Design of Lease Programming and Custody Transfer Facilities, paper 1125-G presented at the 33d Annual Fall Meeting of the Society of Petroleum Engineers, AIME, in Houston, Tex., Oct. 3–8, 1958.
37. Wrightsman, L. S.: Experience with P.D. Meters and Fixed-volume Tank-measurement Procedures in LACT, paper presented at the ASME Mechanical Engineering Conference, Denver, Colo., Sept. 21–24, 1958.
38. Automatic Custody Transfer, *Oil and Gas J.*, July 11, 1956, p. 110.
39. Automatic Lease Operation, *Control Specialty Corporation Bull.* 601.
40. Automatic Sale Slated, *Oil and Gas J.*, Feb. 13, 1956, p. 90.
41. Automation, *Pet. Week*, Nov. 16, 1956, p. 71.
42. First LACT System for Low Gravity, Viscous Crudes, *Oil and Gas J.*, Dec. 2, 1957, p. 82.
43. LACT: A Youngster Now, Soon a Giant, *Oil and Gas J.*, Sept. 22, 1958, p. 74.
44. LACT Is for Stripper Leases, Too, *Oil and Gas J.*, Dec. 15, 1958, p. 70.
45. Lease Automatic Custody Transfer, *API Bull.* 2509A, August, 1956.
46. Lease Is Fully Automatic, *Pet. Week*, Feb. 15, 1957, p. 11.
47. Pneumatic LACT System, *Pet. Engr.*, January, 1957, p. B-104.
48. Principles of Lease Automation, *Pet. Equipment*, 5th issue, 1957, p. 21.
49. Production Automation Forges Ahead, *Pet. Week*, July 26, 1957, p. 21.
50. Water-flood Project Is Fully Automatic, *Oil and Gas J.*, July 7, 1958, p. 135.
51. Weight Measures Flow in New Unit, *Oil and Gas J.*, Sept. 8, 1958, p. 66.
52. What's Ahead for Oil in Automation, *Oil and Gas J.*, June 27, 1955, p. 62.

Chapter 16

MEASURING, SAMPLING, AND TESTING CRUDE OIL

API Standard 2500

AMERICAN PETROLEUM INSTITUTE

FOREWORD

API Standard 2500 supersedes Part 2 and 3* of the 7th edition (June 1948) of *API Code 25: "Measuring, Sampling, and Testing Crude Oil."*

This standard has been formulated by, and represents the unqualified consensus of, the members† of the API Committee on Code 25, who represent all branches of the oil industry which have any interest in the subject matter of this standard with respect to the production, transportation, inspection, storage, and refining of most of the crude oil in the United States.

The purpose of this standard is to unify methods and practices employed in measuring, sampling, and testing crude oil. In those instances where it has not been possible to obtain national agreement upon a single method or practice, exceptions are noted and, in some cases, alternative methods are described. This procedure is obvious after study of the widely varying conditions under which crude oil is produced and handled in different parts of the country.

It is not intended that this standard be retroactive, nor that it take precedence over contractual agreements. Existing codes and manuals, whenever practicable, have been used in the preparation of this standard.

The American Petroleum Institute takes no position as to whether any method, apparatus, or product mentioned herein is covered by an existing patent, nor as to the validity of any patent alleged to cover any such method. Furthermore, nothing contained in this standard grants any right, by implication or otherwise, for manufacture, sale, or use in connection with any method, apparatus, or product covered by letters patent; nor does it insure anyone against liability for infringement of letters patent.

This standard may be used by anyone desiring to do so, but the American Petroleum Institute shall not be held responsible or liable in any way either for any loss or damage resulting therefrom or for any violation of any federal, state, or municipal regulations with which it may conflict.

---

* Part 1 of *API Code 25* has been superseded by *API Standard 2501: "Crude-Oil Tank Measurement and Calibration,"* 1st edition, Sept. 1955.

† The 1954 membership of the API Committee on Code 25 is recorded in Appendix "A" of this standard.

PART I—GENERAL

1000. INTRODUCTION

The determination of net quantity for the purchase, sale, receipt, delivery, or inventory of crude oil involves two important factors. These are gross volume, as ascertained by measurement; and correct adjustments, as ascertained by representative samples properly tested. The measurement for observed volume is affected by the accuracy of gages and by the temperature above or below the basic 60 F. Accurate gages and accurate temperature readings at the time of measurement are required. The correct adjustments are determined by API gravity at 60 F and by the amount of extraneous material or foreign matter in suspension in crude oil which is known as BS&W (basic sediment and water).*

The producer, purchaser, or receiving company is interested primarily in obtaining accurate measurement of crude oil properly settled and as free as possible of water, sediment, and other impurities.

The procedure for measuring, sampling, and testing crude oil is performed by a person, known to the industry as a "gager."

Procedures for measuring, sampling, and testing crude oil are established by practical and theoretical means, and are published by the American Petroleum Institute as *Standard 2500*. ASTM and other methods have been endorsed whenever applicable throughout this standard. Supplementary instructions applicable to such measurement, sampling, and testing may be agreed upon by the parties involved.

Laboratory tests are preferred, but these are not practical in many oil fields. This necessitates the performance of the tests in field areas so as to duplicate as closely as practicable the laboratory methods. The gager should be sufficiently equipped to perform all of his duties in a workmanlike manner.

A regular routine should be followed on the "turn-on," i.e., taking the opening measurement of liquid level, temperature of the oil, samples for the observed gravity and temperature, samples for BS&W test, and samples for inspection of settled BS&W in the oil at the bottom of the tank. On the "shut-off," the second or closing measurement of liquid level should be taken; and, if required, the temperature of the oil remaining in the tank should be taken, and an inspection of settled BS&W in the remaining oil should be made.

In the measuring, sampling, and testing of crude oil the gager should keep in mind the hazards involved, using every precaution for personal protection as well as protection to storage and equipment. Gaging tanks by the manual method should be avoided during electrical storms. Gas masks should be worn in toxic gas areas.

In cases where alternate methods are described, the first method should be the preferred method of test.

1001. MEASURING LIQUID VOLUME (GAGING)

1001.1 Gaging Equipment

A. Gage line: For gaging tanks for liquid level, a steel tape—length and width optional; graduated in feet, inches, and to at least eighths of an inch; and fitted with an innage or outage plumb bob—is recommended. The accuracy of the tape should be at least equal to $\frac{1}{8}$ in. per 100 ft at 60 F, although no tape corrections should be made for tank temperature. The tape should be one continuous line, with reversed numerals on the inside for easy reading. Kinked or spliced tapes (or other tapes which do not meet the accuracy tolerances of new equipment) should not be used. The working tape with bob attached should be checked for accuracy when new, and at least annually thereafter. The zero point of the working tape with bob attached should check within $\frac{1}{32}$ in. of the zero point of the "master" tape with weight

---

* Hereinafter, throughout this standard, the terms "basic sediment and water" and "water and sediment" will be referred to simply by the abbreviation BS&W.

attached, as recommended by the National Bureau of Standards—both tapes suspended in a vertical position.

B. Master tape: The master tape shall be certified as to accuracy at 60 F by the National Bureau of Standards.

C. Innage bob: If the innage method is to be used, the bob—similar to the one shown in Fig. 16-1—should be of sufficient weight to keep the tape taut and vertical during gaging. The bob may be: round or square, graduated to at least eighths of an inch, pointed, made of metal of low sparking tendency, 1 in. in diameter, 6 in. to 12 in. long, and weigh a minimum of 20 oz. The tip of the bob and the insert for the eye should be made of hard low-sparking-tendency metal to reduce wear such as would occur were a soft metal used in these parts. The zero point of the innage tape will be the tip of the bob with the tape attached.

D. Outage bob: If the outage method is to be used, the bob should be made of low-sparking-tendency metal, similar to the one shown in Fig. 16-2. It may be square in cross section, and graduated to at least eighths of an inch—the scale reading upward and downward from a zero point on the bob. The side of the outage bob may be grooved so as to prevent errors caused by creepage. The grooves should be $\frac{1}{16}$ in. deep, $\frac{1}{32}$ in. wide, and should be spaced at least $\frac{1}{8}$ in. apart. Each graduation and groove should be accurate within $\frac{1}{32}$ in. The innage tape—similar to the one shown in Fig. 16-1—graduated in feet, inches, and to at least eighths of an inch, should be used with this type of outage bob. An outage steel tape with the zero point at the bottom of the snap and an outage bob reading downward from the zero point— similar to the one shown in Fig. 16-3—and graduated in inches to at least eighths of an inch and weighing at least 14 oz, may be used in lieu of the innage tape and outage bob previously described. The eye of the outage bob should be of hard low-sparking-tendency metal to reduce wear.

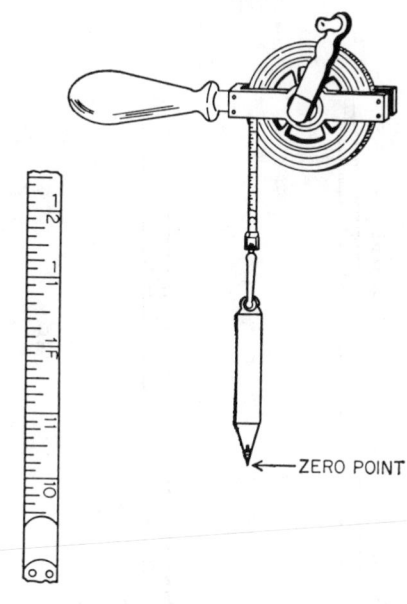

←—ZERO POINT

Fig. 16-1. Typical innage gage tape and bob.

1001.2. Gaging Methods

The innage method or the outage method may be used to measure the liquid level in a tank. Care should be taken when either method is employed that the final figure obtained represents accurately the depth of the oil in the tank to at least the nearest $\frac{1}{8}$ in.; however, on tanks of 1,000-bbl nominal capacity, or less, the gage should be determined to at least the nearest $\frac{1}{4}$ in.

An accurate permanent record of the gage measurement should be made at the time the readings are taken. No gage should be taken until the foam has subsided or has been cleared from the oil surface beneath the gaging hatch, or until the surface of the oil is at rest. Sufficient time should be allowed before gaging a tank to permit the oil to free itself from entrained air and gas.

The tape or bob may be rubbed with a suitable oil-indicating paste if difficulties are experienced in obtaining a well-defined liquid-level mark. Chalk should never be used for this purpose, as oil has a tendency to creep on a chalked line.

The same gaging procedure, with matched gaging apparatus, should be used for both the opening and closing measurements. The gages should be taken through the same gage hatch and at the same reference point, obtaining at least two identical gage readings for each measurement.

Gage measurements should be taken as close as practicable to the time of beginning and of ending each run of oil.

A. Innage method: The innage method determines the liquid content of the tank in feet, inches, and fractions of an inch. The procedure employed is to measure the distance from the bottom of the tank, or from the datum plate, to the surface of the liquid. The gage measurement should be taken as near as possible to the pipeline connection except in instances where this connection is provided with an upturned ell or other appurtenance inside the shell of the tank, or where "wet oil" (oil with a

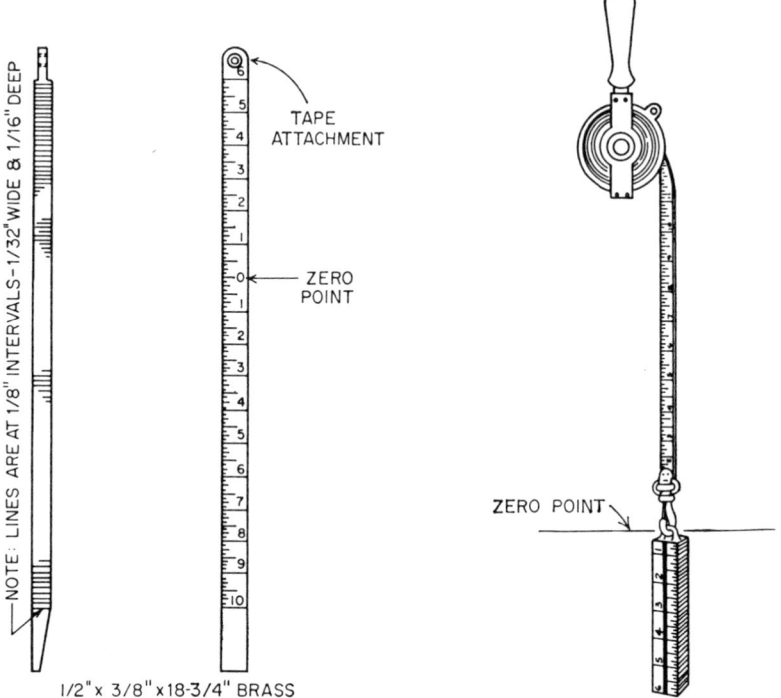

Fɪɢ. 16-2. Typical outage bob for innage tape.

Fɪɢ. 16-3. Typical outage tape and bob.

BS&W content greater than permitted by pipeline specifications) is encountered, or where sample cocks are used as sampling devices. In the latter 2 exceptions a minimum of 6 ft circumferentially should separate the main hatch and the pipeline outlet. The reference point on the hatch should be chosen and marked so that no obstruction will be encountered by the bob. The exact distance from the bottom of the tank to the reference point should be stenciled on the roof of the tank near the hatch. Care should be taken that the bob touches the bottom, or the datum plate, of the tank so lightly that the bob will not deviate from a vertical position. Whenever possible, the datum plate and the reference-point marker should be attached to the shell of the tank.

B. Outage method: The outage method determines the liquid content of the tank in feet, inches, and fractions of an inch. The procedure employed is to measure the distance from the surface of the liquid to the reference point at the top of the tank. Deduction of this measurement from the gaging height will give the innage in the tank.

The reference point on the gage hatch used in outage gaging should be definite and fixed, preferably attached to the shell instead of to the gage hatch.   The exact distance from the bottom of the tank to the reference point should be stenciled on the roof near the hatch, and is known as the reference depth.   Standing on the tank roof should be avoided whenever possible when outage gages are taken.   If it is necessary to stand on the roof of a tank during gaging, the number of men required for gaging operations should be limited, and the same number of men should be used for both opening and closing gages.   Outage gages should be taken in such a manner as to avoid any changes in the distance from the bottom of the tank to the reference point. The tape should be lowered slowly until the bob is in the crude oil with the tape indicating, at the reference point, an even foot or inch graduation mark.   The tape reading at the reference point should be recorded.   The tape should be withdrawn quickly, and the oil-cut mark should be read and recorded as the outage.   When an outage tape and bob are used, the outage gage is the sum of the tape and bob readings.

The adjusted outage gage is obtained by subtracting some number of feet or inches (usually 1 ft, 2 ft, or 3 ft) from the reference depth and suspending into the tank that amount of gage line at the reference point.   The subtracted number of feet or inches is then added to the gage measurement of the crude oil obtained; for example:

	Feet	Inches
Reference depth............................	41	$2\frac{5}{8}$
Suspended gage at reference point............	40	$2\frac{5}{8}$
Difference................................	1	0
Crude-oil reading on tape...................	38	$2\frac{1}{2}$
Sum (innage gage)........................	39	$2\frac{1}{2}$

1001.3. Floating-roof Tanks

There are 4 types of floating-roof tanks generally used in crude-oil service, viz.: 1, pan-type; 2, outer pontoon-type; 3, outer and inner pontoon-type; and, 4, double-deck.   They are used primarily to retard evaporation losses, to reduce corrosion in handling sour crudes, and to assist in the prevention of fire.

That portion of the floating roof which displaces a quantity of oil is considered deadwood, and is distributed, according to the construction of the deck, between the elevation where the oil reaches the lowest point of the roof, when the roof rests on its normal supports, and the elevation where the oil floats the roof freely.   The weight of the volume of oil displaced is equal to the weight of the roof and attached deadwood. Therefore, the gravity of the oil must be taken into consideration along with the weight of the roof, as stenciled on the roof manhole, when the necessary gage-table corrections are made for the calculation of crude-oil volumes.   Standard gage tables are used to calculate the volume of oil from the bottom of the tank to a point or measurement at which the oil just touches the lowest section of the roof, and from a point or measurement where the roof floats freely to top-oil tank height.   That section or measurement between the point where the oil touches the roof and the point where the roof floats freely may be computed.

Should the submergence of the floating roof be increased due to water, snow, or ice, it is necessary to remove or estimate the additional weight in order to compute displacement.   Should the gravity of the oil be increased or decreased, the change should be figured—unless tables covering such changes are on hand—in order to obtain a more nearly accurate gage.

The computed distribution of a floating roof as deadwood is subject to considerable error.   It is essential, therefore, that the opening and closing measurements be taken with the roof floating freely or completely supported on its legs, or supports, and with the oil level below the low point of the roof.   For the closest approach to accuracy, the roof should be floating freely for both the opening and closing gages.

Gaging contents of floating-roof tanks: There are two manual methods of measuring the contents of tanks with floating roofs, viz.: a, measurements from the roof; and, b, measurements from the gaging platform.

a. MEASUREMENTS FROM THE ROOF: When the roof is floating freely, the measurements should be taken from the bottom of the tank, or from the datum plate, to the liquid surface in the gage hatch with an innage tape and bob. To determine whether the roof is floating freely, all of the legs should be checked to see that they are loose in the sleeves or that the sleeves are not resting on the bottom of the tank. When the roof is resting on its normal supports, measurements should be taken from the bottom of the tank, or from the datum plate, to the liquid level. This method of gaging on the tank roof is used when there is no objection, or when there is no danger involved from highly volatile or sour crudes.

b. MEASUREMENTS FROM THE GAGING PLATFORM

(1) *Outage method:* A reference point should be constructed of a fixed arm attached to the shell approximately 4 ft above the top of the tank on the gager's platform, directly above the gage hatch. The distance from the surface of the oil to the reference point is the outage gage measurement. The exact distance from the bottom of the tank to the reference point should be stenciled on the gager's platform.

(2) *Innage method:* Measurements should be taken from the bottom of the tank, or from the datum plate, to the liquid level. This may be done from the gaging platform by opening the gage hatch with a sash cord, taking measurement, then allowing the hatch to close by its own weight.

1001.4 Automatic Gaging Devices

If mutually agreeable, automatic gaging devices of known accuracy may be used to determine measurements of crude-oil movements. Details are set out in Part III, Sect. 1200, hereinafter.

1001.5 Metering Crude Oil

ASME-API Code No. 1101: "Code for the Installation, Proving, and Operation of Positive-Displacement Meters in Liquid-Hydrocarbon Service" (short title: *Petroleum PD Meter Code*) should be referred to for the measurement of crude oil by meter.

1002. TEMPERATURE MEASUREMENT

1002.1. Thermometers

A. Cup-case thermometer: The cup-case thermometer (total immersion type, similar to the one shown in Fig. 16-4) may be used to determine tank-temperature measurements. This thermometer has a suitable range; is graduated in single-degree divisions etched on the stem and spaced a minimum of 1 mm apart, with an accuracy of plus or minus ½ F. The bulb should be mercury-filled, with nitrogen gas above

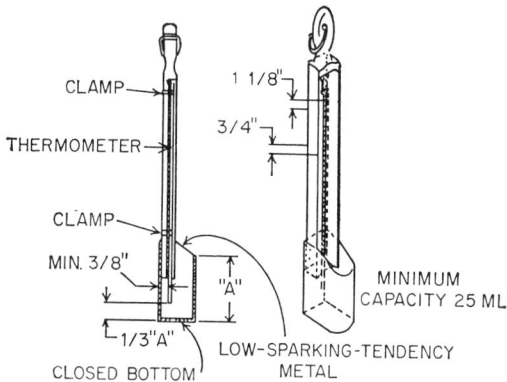

FIG. 16-4. API cup-case thermometer.

the mercury column. The case may be of varnished hardwood, or of other suitable material, with a cup made of low-sparking-tendency metal whose capacity is at least 25 ml. The bulb should have a clearance of at least ⅜ in. to the nearest wall, and should extend downward into the cup a distance equal to two-thirds of the minimum depth of the cup. The thermometer should be handled carefully, and should be well protected when in use or in transit. A thermometer with the mercury column parted (discontinuous), or with the pigment on its scale faded or missing, should not be used. Defective thermometers should be replaced with thermometers which meet these requirements of accuracy. The cup-case thermometer should be equipped with a cord, marked so that the thermometer can be lowered to the desired point in the tank. When new, the cup-case thermometer should be checked for accuracy at one or more places on the scale, and should be checked at least annually thereafter with a "master" thermometer.

B. **Master thermometer:** The master thermometer shall be certified as to accuracy by the National Bureau of Standards.

1002.2. Procedure

The cup-case thermometer should be suspended at the desired point in the crude oil for a period of not less than 5 min. The thermometer should be raised and lowered several times in order to assist temperature adjustment by intimate contact with the crude oil. The thermometer should be carefully and rapidly withdrawn, and the temperature read to the nearest degree fahrenheit before the oil is poured from the cup. This temperature should be immediately recorded. Special care should be taken that the temperature recorded, especially during adverse weather conditions, accurately represents the temperature of the contents of the tank. The point of suspension should be 12 in. or more from the shell of the tank. Crude oil should not be accepted by pipelines at a temperature above 120 F, except when higher temperatures are desirable to facilitate transportation of extremely viscous or high pour-point oils.

A. **Tanks of less than 5,000-bbl capacity:** On tanks of less than 5,000-bbl capacity, one temperature only may be required. The thermometer should be suspended midway (vertically) in the oil.

B. **Tanks of 5,000-bbl capacity or more:** On tanks with a capacity of 5,000 bbl or more, the following procedure should be used:

a. When the level of the oil is 15 ft or more, 3 temperature readings should be taken: viz., the first, 3 ft from the top; the second, in the middle (vertically) of the oil; and the third, 3 ft from the bottom, but never closer than 1 ft above the nonmerchantable oil line. The temperature recorded should be the average of the three temperatures taken.

b. When the level of the oil is between 10 ft and 15 ft, 2 temperature readings should be taken: viz., the first, 3 ft from the top; and the second, 3 ft from the bottom, but never closer than 1 ft above the nonmerchantable oil line. The temperature recorded should be the average of the two temperatures taken.

c. When the level of the oil is less than 10 ft, 1 temperature reading may be taken in the middle (vertically) of the oil.

d. The temperature may be determined at any greater number of depths (vertically) as mutually agreed, and the average of these readings shall be recorded as the temperature of the oil in the tank. In special cases additional temperature measurements in the horizontal cross section may be taken and included with the vertical readings to obtain the average temperature. When two or more temperatures are taken in the horizontal cross section, they should be averaged, and the results obtained at each level (vertically) should then be averaged to determine the average tank temperature.

C. **Automatic temperature devices:** If mutually agreeable, automatic temperature devices of known accuracy may be used to determine tank temperature. Details are set out in Part IV, Sect. 1300, hereinafter.

D. **Temperature corrections and calculations:** Volumes should be corrected to 60 F. The standard practice is to adjust the quantity determined at the high gage from the observed temperature to 60 F and subtract therefrom the quantity shown at the low gage, similarly adjusted from the observed temperature to 60 F. The difference indicates the gross volume, in barrels, at 60 F. This standard method is recommended in the purchase, sale, or exchange of crude oil as handled on receiving and delivery gage tickets, as well as in runs made from field tanks and handled on run tickets.

By mutual agreement, volumes on run tickets covering oil run from lease tanks may be corrected to 60 F by using the alternate method, i.e., subtracting the quantity as shown on the low gage from the quantity as shown on the high gage, the difference being corrected to 60 F, using temperature at opening gage, and indicating the gross volume in barrels at 60 F.

To determine net quantities at 60 F, Table 7: "Reduction of Volume to 60 F Against API Gravity at 60 F (Abridged Table)" of the *ASTM-IP Petroleum Measurement Tables (ASTM Designation D 1250; IP Designation 200*—see Appendix "C" hereinafter) was prepared to meet the demand from the oil industry for a short and convenient table for adjusting crude-oil volumes at any observed temperature to crude-oil volumes at 60 F. This table is intended to replace various abridged tables heretofore used by the industry. Table 7 has been set up in 8 ranges of API gravity as follows:

Group No.	Range of Group, API Gravity at 60 F	Coefficient of Expansion Per Degree Fahrenheit at 60 F	Corresponding API Gravity at 60 F
0	0 to 14.9	0.00035	6.0
1	15.0 to 34.9	0.00040	22.0
2	35.0 to 50.9	0.00050	44.0
3	51.0 to 63.9	0.00060	58.0
4	64.0 to 78.9	0.00070	72.0
5	79.0 to 88.9	0.00080	86.0
6	89.0 to 93.9	0.00085	91.0
7	94.0 to 100.0	0.00090	97.0

It is important to note that the group classification of the crude oil is determined by its API gravity at 60 F. Large errors (up to 0.5 per cent) may arise if the gravity at the observed temperature is used to determine the group, because this error may place the oil in the wrong group.

This table must be entered with API gravity at 60 F. If the API gravity is known only at the observed temperature, the API gravity at 60 F must first be found from Table 5: "Reduction of Observed API Gravity to API Gravity at 60 F" of the *ASTM-IP Petroleum Measurement Tables (ASTM Designation D 1250; IP Designation 200*—see Appendix "B" hereinafter).

1003. SAMPLING

Samples of crude oil for the gravity and BS&W tests should be taken according to the following methods of sampling, and should be thoroughly representative of the oil to be tested. That portion of the sample used for the test should be thoroughly representative of the sample itself. It is imperative to obtain representative samples, and that they be handled so that no change in composition occurs before testing. The importance of sampling and sample handling cannot be too strongly emphasized.

1003.1. Sampling Equipment

A. Thief: A thief (core-type) made of low-sparking-tendency metal, similar to those shown in Fig. 16-5, may be employed—with a uniform cross section and bottom closure, and with capacity depending upon the size of the sample required. The thief should be: capable of penetrating the material in the tank to the required level, mechanically equipped, to permit filling at any desired level, and capable of being withdrawn without undue contamination of the contents. The thief may be equipped as follows:

a. Sample cocks for obtaining samples for the BS&W tests.

b. Extension rods for use in obtaining samples at levels corresponding with requirements for high connections or for samples to determine high settled BS&W level.

c. BS&W gage for determining height of BS&W in the thief.

d. Windshield to be used when taking the gravity and temperature of the oil.

e. Opener to break the tension on the valve or slide.

f. Hook to hang the thief in the hatch vertically.

g. A thief cord marked so that sample can be taken at any depth in the vertical cross section of the tank. The thief should be kept in good working order at all times.

B. Beaker or bottle: A beaker made of low-sparking-tendency metal, or a glass bottle, similar to the one shown in Fig. 16-6, of suitable capacity, with a weighted bottom, may be used if desired. The opening should be from ¾ in. to 1½ in. in diameter—the size being determined by the nature of

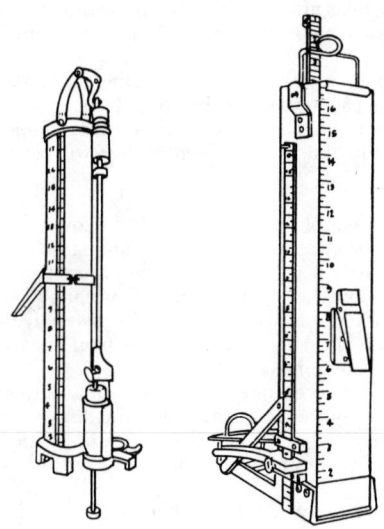

Fig. 16-5. Typical oil thiefs—core-type.

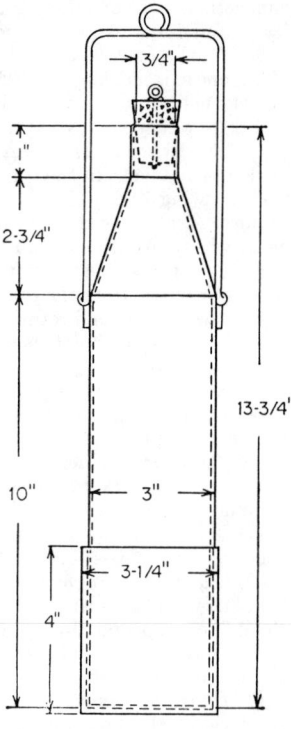

Fig. 16-6. Typical beaker sampler.

crude oil being sampled. The stopper should incorporate a small eyebolt with attached cord.

C. Test glass: A test glass, 2 in. wide by 4 in. long, made of crystal or plate glass with smooth edges, may be used for detecting the BS&W line.

D. Measuring cup: A cup of suitable size to proportion a composite sample taken through sample cocks may be used.

E. Composite sampler: An hydrometer cylinder (see Par. 1004.3-A hereinafter), equipped additionally with sample cocks at regular intervals of the vertical section, may be used to proportion a composite tank sample for the hydrometer and centrifugal tests.

1003.2. Sampling Methods

A. Tank samples: Samples may be taken from tanks by mutual agreement as follows: composite spot, middle spot, all-levels, running samples, or sample cocks. Additional samples may be taken as deemed necessary.

a. COMPOSITE SPOT SAMPLE: Spot samples should be mixed in equal proportions for a composite sample, or they may be tested separately and the results averaged.

(1) *Three-way:* On tanks larger than 1,000-bbl capacity which contain in excess of 15 ft of oil, samples should be taken at the upper, middle, and lower or outlet connection of the merchantable oil—in the order named.   On tanks of 1,000-bbl capacity and under, this method may be used also.

(2) *Two-way:* On tanks larger than 1,000-bbl capacity which contain in excess of 10 ft and up to 15 ft of oil, samples should be taken at the upper and lower or outlet connection of the merchantable oil—in the order named.   On tanks of 1,000-bbl capacity and under, this method may be used also.

b. MIDDLE SPOT SAMPLE: On tanks larger than 1,000-bbl capacity with 10 ft or less of oil, one sample, known as the middle spot, should be taken as near the center of the vertical column of oil as possible with either thief, beaker, or sample cock.   On tanks of 1,000-bbl capacity and under, this method may be used also.

c. ALL-LEVELS SAMPLE: An all-levels sample may be taken by lowering a stoppered beaker or bottle from the top of the oil to the level of the bottom of the outlet connection or swing line, pulling stopper, and returning sampler to the top of the oil at a uniform rate of speed such that the beaker or bottle is nearly full (maximum 85 per cent) when withdrawn from the oil.

d. RUNNING SAMPLE: A running sample may be taken by lowering the unstoppered beaker or bottle from the top of the oil to the level of the bottom of the outlet connection or swing line, and returning it to the top of the oil at a uniform rate of speed such that the beaker or bottle is nearly full (maximum 85 per cent) when withdrawn from the oil.

e. SAMPLING METHODS DESCRIBED

(1) *Upper sample:* In taking the upper sample, the thief should be lowered so as to obtain a sample 12 in. below the top of the oil, the thief tripped, and slowly raised to avoid agitation.   When the beaker or bottle is used, it should be lowered so that the opening of the beaker or bottle is 12 in. below the top of the oil.   The cork should then be pulled, time allowed to fill, and the beaker or bottle raised slowly to avoid agitation.

(2) *Middle sample:* The middle sample is taken as near the vertical center of the column of oil as possible, with either the thief, beaker, or bottle.

(3) *Lower- or outlet-connection sample:* The lower- or outlet-connection sample should be taken with the thief at the bottom of the outlet connection or swing line.   The thief should be tripped at this point and raised slowly.   When the beaker or bottle is used, it should be lowered so that the opening of the beaker or bottle is level with the bottom of the outlet connection.

(4) *Clearance sample:* The clearance sample is a spot sample obtained 4 in. below the level of the tank outlet.   It is used only to determine the acceptability of the crude oil at the bottom of the outlet connection.

(5) *Bottom thiefing sample:* The bottom thiefing sample is obtained with a thief to determine the amount of nonmerchantable material at the bottom of the tank.

f. SAMPLE COCK: Samples may be taken through sample cocks properly placed in the shell of the tank.

(1) *Location of sample cocks:* Upper sample cocks shall be located 18 in. below the top of the tank shell; the lower sample cock shall be located level with the bottom of the outlet connection or at the top of an upturned elbow or other similar fitting if installed on the outlet connection; and the middle sample cock shall be located halfway between the upper and lower sample cocks.   An additional cock for the clearance sample should be located 4 in. below the bottom of the outlet connection to determine if the level of merchantable oil is at least below this point.   The sample cocks should be located a minimum of 6 ft distant circumferentially from the pipeline outlet and drain connections, and 8 ft from the filling-line connection.   The sample cocks should be $\frac{3}{4}$-in. size, and the lines should be $\frac{3}{4}$-in. nominal diameter for 18-deg API-gravity crude oil or less.   For lighter oils $\frac{1}{2}$-in.-size cocks, with $\frac{1}{2}$-in.-nominal-diameter lines, should be used.   The lines should extend a minimum of 4 in. inside the tank shell, except on floating-roof tanks where flush installations are necessary.   All sample cocks should be equipped with sealable valves and plugged inspection tees.

On tanks of more than 10,000-bbl capacity, at least 2 sets of sample cocks shall be installed, located equidistant apart, around the circumference of the tank.   It is recommended that five or more sample cocks be installed per set, evenly spaced between lower and upper sample levels.

(2) *Procedure*

Check for merchantable oil should be made at the clearance sample cock.

Flush each sample connection until all oil from the previous run has been removed and sample lines filled with fresh oil from the tank.

On tanks of 10,000-bbl capacity or smaller, samples of equal amounts shall be taken from the lower, middle, and upper sample connections. A measuring cup of proper size may be used to assure the drawing of the proper quantity from each sample cock.

On tanks of more than 10,000-bbl capacity, samples of equal amounts shall be taken from each of the sample connections at each set of sample connections.

All samples shall be mixed in equal proportions for a composite sample, or the samples may be tested separately and the results averaged.

When crude oil in a tank fails to reach the upper or middle sample cocks on a tank equipped with three sample cocks, it is suggested that the sample for the run be obtained as follows: If the level of the oil is nearer the upper sample cock than the middle, two-thirds of the sample shall be taken from the middle sample cock and one-third from the lower. If the level of oil is nearer the middle sample cock than the upper, one-half of the sample shall be taken from the middle and one-half from the lower. If the level of the oil is below the middle sample cock, all of the sample shall be taken from the lower cock.

B. Line samples: The connection for taking line samples should be placed in a vertical line, whenever possible, and as near as practicable to the point where the oil passes to the custody of the receiver. When it is necessary to take samples from a horizontal line, the connection should enter the line above the horizontal diameter. For this purpose $\frac{1}{2}$-in. pipe should be used, and it should extend to the center of the line pipe, be perforated or the end beveled at a 45-deg angle, and the beveled edge faced upstream. The sampling lines should be cleared before the samples are taken. Samples of $\frac{1}{2}$ pt or more should be taken in a sample bottle or in a can every hour or less—whichever is thought necessary. By mutual agreement, the sample period may be increased to 2-hour intervals. It is important that the size of the samples and the intervals between the sampling operations be uniform for each run. The sample bottle may be of clear or brown glass. Sample cans may be used, provided the seams are soldered on the exterior surface—using a flux of rosin in a suitable solvent. Cork, glass, or screw caps may be used. The sample should be placed in a closed container; and at the end of a 24-hour period, or less if desired, the combined samples should be gently yet thoroughly mixed, and a composite sample taken for test purposes. The sample container should be vaporproof, equipped with a delivery tube extending through the top to within $\frac{1}{2}$ in. of the bottom, and with a funnel and positive closure to allow for submerged filling. The sample container should be stored in a cool, dry place; and exposure to direct sunlight should be avoided. The sample bottle, or can, and container before use should be cleaned by rinsing with a suitable solvent, and carefully dried. Duplicate line samples obtained for BS&W and gravity tests may be taken according to the instructions for sampling, and the tests made at that time. A record of the results of such tests should be kept and averaged for a 24-hour period. The composite or average of hourly samples is acceptable.

C. Mechanical samplers: If mutually agreeable, mechanical samplers of known accuracy, when properly connected to lines covering the movement of crude oil, may be used to obtain samples for the gravity and BS&W tests.

D. Inspection of tank bottoms: The maximum level of nonmerchantable oil and water at the bottom of a tank should be at least 4 in. below the bottom of the outlet connection of the lowest measurement from which oil may be run from the tank by gravity. On tanks with stationary connections, the height of the tank connection should be determined by taking the measurement from the bottom of the outlet to the bottom of the tank. The height of the outlet connection should be stenciled on the shell of the tank. The thief, with valve or slide open, should be lowered to the bottom of the tank slowly. The oil and BS&W should be given sufficient time to reach their proper level in the thief, and then the thief should be tripped and withdrawn slowly so as not to disturb the contents. The contents of the thief should be poured back into the tank, in a small flat stream over the test glass, in order to detect the BS&W line. As soon as the BS&W shows up, the thief should be returned to a vertical position and the BS&W measured. When it is desired to determine the amount of free water in the tank, the valve or slide should be cracked, and the free water drawn from the bottom of the thief and measured. The BS&W should not be disturbed any more than necessary when the thief is being operated. Tank bottoms should be thiefed before and, if thought necessary, after each run or delivery. On tanks equipped with sample cocks, the sample shall be taken by means of a cock located 4 in. below the outlet connection.

Note: Sampling for Reid vapor-pressure determination is given in Sect. 1005 hereinafter of this standard.

1004. GRAVITY DETERMINATION

The API gravity of crude oil and petroleum products, normally handled as liquids, should be determined in accordance with the standards of the American Society for Testing Materials, viz., *ASTM Designation D 287-39: "Standard Method of Test for Gravity of Petroleum and Petroleum Products by Means of the Hydrometer."* In addition, certain permissible exceptions and improvements in procedures are given hereinafter to improve applicability to field operations.

(*Note:* The paragraphs set out hereinafter in *italic type* are quoted verbatim from *ASTM Designation D 287-39*. The paragraphs in arabic type are the permissible exceptions.)

Scope

1. (a) This method covers the determination of the specific gravity and the A.P.I. gravity of crude petroleum and petroleum products normally handled as liquids. The determination of the gravity of mixtures of petroleum products with other substances is treated as a special case owing to the fact that the coefficients of expansion of such mixtures may not be the same as those of petroleum or its products.

(b) The determination of the specific gravity of road oils, road tars, asphalt cements, and soft tar pitches is covered by the Standard Method of Test for Specific Gravity of Road Oils, Road Tars, Asphalt Cements, and Soft Tar Pitches (A.S.T.M. Designation: D 70) of the American Society for Testing Materials* and the testing of these products is, therefore, specifically excluded from the scope of this method.

Definitions

2. (a) Specific Gravity.—The specific gravity of a petroleum oil and of mixtures of petroleum products with other substances is the ratio of the weight of a given volume of the material at a temperature of 60 F. (15.56 C.) to the weight of an equal volume of distilled water at the same temperature, both weights being corrected for the buoyancy of air.

(b) A.P.I. Gravity.—The A.P.I. gravity scale is an arbitrary one which is related to the specific gravity of a petroleum oil in accordance with the formula:

$$Degrees\ A.P.I. = \frac{141.5}{sp.\ gr.\ 60/60\ F.} - 131.5$$

A table showing the equivalent specific gravity, pounds per gallon and gallons per pound, at 60 F. for each degree A.P.I. from 0 to 100° A.P.I. is given in the Appendix to this method.

Apparatus

There are two kinds of hydrometers in common use, the plain type and the combined thermometer and hydrometer (Fig. 16-7), known as a thermo-hydrometer. Although the thermo-hydrometer type of instrument is sufficiently satisfactory for routine use, the thermometer incor-

* *1949 Book of A.S.T.M. Standards, Part 3.*

porated in it possesses certain inherent defects of design which render it unfit for use when results of unquestioned accuracy are desired. Therefore, in all referee tests the temperature of the sample being tested must be determined by means of a separate thermometer.

3. (a) Hydrometer Calibrations.—The hydrometer may be calibrated either in terms of specific gravity or degrees A.P.I. It shall be of glass of the conventional constant mass and variable displacement type, with a scale of suitable material clearly marked with black ink. The range may be any suitable portion of the interval between 0 and 100° A.P.I. (1.0760 to 0.6112 sp. gr.). The A.P.I. hydrometer scale (Note 1) shall be divided into 0.1° A.P.I., numbered at each multiple of 1°

A.P.I. and each fifth division denoted by a longer line. The specific gravity hydrometer scale shall be divided in 0.0005 of a unit of specific gravity, numbered at each multiple of 0.01 and each 0.001 division denoted by a longer line. The smallest scale subdivision shall be not less than 1 mm. (0.039 in.) or more than 2 mm. (0.079 in.) in width. The accuracy of calibration of the hydrometer shall be such that the error at any point of the scale shall not exceed the value of one smallest scale division. The scale, or an extension thereof, of the hydrometer shall have plainly marked on it the name of the manufacturer, a serial number, and the definition of the scale. There shall be a mark on the stem of the hydrometer corresponding to a fixed mark on the scale, to provide a check against possible displacement of the scale.

PERMISSIBLE EXCEPTION: A short line etched at 60 F. and another at the highest gravity range will provide necessary check points.

Note 1.—In the case of A.P.I. hydrometers the scale is defined by the expression:

$$\text{"Degrees } A.P.I. = \frac{141.5}{sp.\ gr.\ 60/60\ F.} - 131.5\text{"}$$

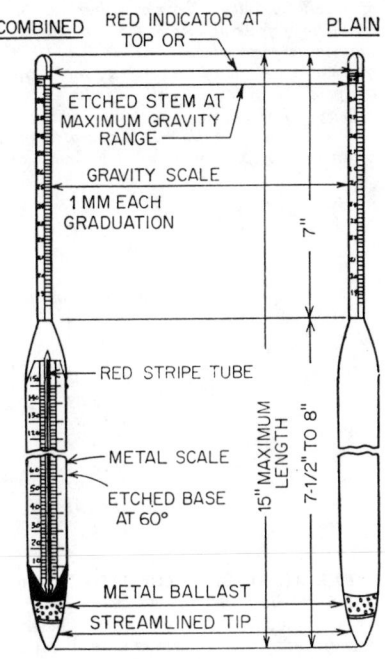

Fig. 16-7. Hydrometers.

In the case of specific gravity hydrometers the inscription "sp. gr. 60/60 F. Petroleum" is sufficient to denote that the hydrometer is intended to determine specific gravities at 60 F. relative to water at 60 F. when the readings are taken at 60 F.

The long axis of the hydrometer shall assume a vertical position when the instrument is floating freely in the sample. Any solid material, such as shot, paper, etc., used in the weighting of the hydrometer shall be firmly secured in place by the use of a suitable cement, the softening point of which lies well above 215 F. (102 C.). When mercury is used for weighting, it shall be placed in a small bulb below the main bulb of the hydrometer and completely separated from the bulb by means of a glass partition.

(b) *Thermometer.*—An A.S.T.M. Gravity Thermometer, total immersion, graduated in either Centigrade or Fahrenheit degrees as specified, having a range of −5 to +215 F. or −20 to +102 C. and conforming to the requirements for this thermometer as prescribed in the Standard Specifications for A.S.T.M. Thermometers (A.S.T.M. Designation: E 1) of the American Society for Testing Materials.

(c) *Thermometer for Thermo-hydrometer.*—The thermometer incorporated in the thermo-hydrometer type of instrument shall have a range of from 20 to 130 F. or 60 to 220 F. depending upon the range of the hydrometer. The temperature scale shall be graduated in 2 F. divisions accurate to plus or minus 1 F. (Note 2) and, when located in the stem of the hydrometer, shall be marked in red ink to avoid any possibility of its being confused with the black gravity scale.

PERMISSIBLE EXCEPTION: The thermometer incorporated in the hydrometer-thermometer type of instrument for field and station use may have a range of 0 to 150 F. The temperature scale should be graduated in 2-F divisions, accurate to ± 1 F.

Note 2.—This approximates the limit of accuracy which it is possible to obtain in this type of thermometer. It becomes at once obvious, therefore, in view of the following facts, that a high degree of accuracy in the determination of the gravity of an oil cannot be expected when this type of thermometer is used for the determination of the temperature of the sample undergoing test.

Between 10 and 11° A.P.I., one degree A.P.I. is equivalent to 0.0070 of a unit of specific gravity. Between 90 and 91° A.P.I., one degree A.P.I. is equivalent to only 0.0028 of a unit of specific gravity. In correcting the observed gravity of an oil of 10° A.P.I. for temperature, an error of plus or minus 2 F. in the determination of the temperature of the oil will introduce maximum error of only 0.1° A.P.I. (0.0007 sp. gr.) in the gravity. In correcting the observed gravity of an oil of 90° A.P.I. for temperature, an error of 1 F. in the determination of the temperature of the oil will introduce a maximum error of 0.3° A.P.I. (0.00084 sp. gr.) in the gravity. For convenience, the following table is given which shows the errors at each tenth degree A.P.I. from 10 to 100° A.P.I. which may be introduced into a corrected gravity as the result of an error of plus or minus 1 F. in the determination of the observed temperature:

Observed Gravity, deg. A.P.I.	Resultant Maximum Error in Corrected Gravity, deg. A.P.I. per plus or minus 1 F. Error in Observed Temperature
10 to 11	0.1
20 to 21	0.1
30 to 31	0.1
40 to 41	0.1
50 to 51	0.2
60 to 61	0.2
70 to 71	0.2
80 to 81	0.2
90 to 91	0.3
At 99	0.3

PERMISSIBLE EXCEPTION: An ASTM thermometer, viz., *ASTM Designation E 1-53: "Standard Specifications for ASTM Thermometers,"* should be used with the plain or combined hydrometer in reference work when a more accurate temperature designation is required. The readings must be accurate on both the hydrometer and the thermometer, the hydrometer to be read to one-tenth of a degree and the thermometer in single degrees.

(d) Hydrometer Cylinder.—The hydrometer cylinder in which the sample for the gravity test is confined may be made of metal or clear glass and shall be cylindrical in shape. For convenience in pouring it may have a lip on the rim. The inside diameter of the cylinder shall be at least 2.54 cm. (1.0 in.) greater than the outside diameter of the hydrometer used in it. The height of the cylinder shall be such that the length of the column of sample it contains is greater by at least 2.54 cm. (1.0 in.) than the portion of the hydrometer which is immersed beneath the surface of the sample after a state of equilibrium has been reached.

Temperature of Test, Crude Petroleum and Its Products

4. (a) The determination of the gravity of crude petroleum or its products may be made at any suitable temperature between 0 and 195 F. in accordance with the procedure described in Section 6. The observed gravity at the observed temperature shall be corrected to the gravity at 60 F. as described in Section 7.

(b) Crude petroleum or a product thereof with an initial boiling point below 250 F. (121.1 C.) and an A.P.I. gravity below 70 deg. shall be cooled in the original closed container to a temperature of 65 F. (18.3 C.) or lower before pouring it into the hydrometer cylinder. Crude petroleum or a product thereof having an A.P.I. gravity of 70 deg. or greater shall be cooled in the original closed container to a temperature of 35 F. (1.7 C.) or lower before pouring it into the hydrometer cylinder. Crude petroleum having an initial

boiling point below 250 F. (121.1 C.) which has too high a pour point or is too viscous at 65 F. (18.3 C.) to permit an accurate hydrometer reading at 65 F. (18.3 C.) or below should be heated to the minimum temperature which will give sufficient fluidity to permit an accurate hydrometer reading.

PERMISSIBLE EXCEPTION: That part of Par. 6(b) [under the heading "Temperature of Test, Crude Petroleum and Its Products"] of *ASTM Designation D 287-39* which specifies the cooling of samples of certain types of crude oils shall not be mandatory as applied to crude oil under this standard.   However, it should be noted that these cooling requirements are permissible, and are strongly recommended, for light crude oil where the sample has a high temperature—provided the sample shall not be cooled to the temperature below which the oil ceases to be homogeneous.   It is desirable that the determination of the gravity of samples be made at temperatures between 40 F and 80 F in order to avoid possible errors in certain crude oils introduced by a difference in the coefficient of expansion from that employed in the computation of standard gravity-correction tables.   When the crude oil to be tested is of low gravity or is viscous, the sample must be heated to a minimum temperature at which the oil is sufficiently fluid to give an accurate hydrometer reading.

(c) *The thermometer, hydrometer, and hydrometer cylinder shall be at approximately the same temperature as the sample to be tested.   Precaution shall be taken to prevent the temperature of the sample from changing appreciably during the time necessary to complete the test.   This may be done when testing nonvolatile and nonviscous samples by choosing a temperature of test only slightly different from the room temperature.   When volatile samples (those having initial boiling points below 250 F. (121.1 C.) and also those having A.P.I. gravities greater than 70 deg.) are cooled, or viscous samples are heated, the test cylinder shall be placed in a bath maintained at the necessary temperature during the time of test.   In determining the gravity of any crude petroleum or product, the temperature of the surrounding medium should not differ from the temperature of the sample by more than 5 F. (2.8 C.).*

Temperature of Test, Mixtures of Petroleum and Other Substances

5. *The gravity of mixtures of petroleum products with other substances shall be determined at a temperature of 60 F. in accordance with the procedure described in Section 6, since there are no nationally recognized tables giving the coefficients of expansion of such mixtures.*

Procedure

6. (a) *The sample to be tested for gravity shall be poured into the clean hydrometer cylinder without splashing, so as to avoid the formation of air bubbles and to reduce to a minimum the evaporation of the lower boiling constituents of the lighter oils.   If air bubbles are formed they shall be removed after they have collected on the surface, by touching them with a piece of clean blotting paper or filter paper before the hydrometer is placed in the sample.*

(b) *The cylinder containing the prepared sample shall be placed in a vertical position in a place free from air currents.   The hydrometer shall be carefully lowered into the sample to a level two smallest scale divisions below that at which it will float and shall then be released.   When the hydrometer has come to rest, floating freely away from the walls of the cylinder, the gravity shall be read as the point at which the surface of the sample apparently cuts the hydrometer scale.   In the case of samples sufficiently transparent this point shall be determined by placing the eye slightly below the level of the liquid and slowly raising it until the surface of the sample first seen as a distorted ellipse seems to become a straight line cutting the hydrometer scale.   In the case of nontransparent samples where this procedure cannot be followed, the point on the hydrometer scale to which the sample rises above the main surface of the liquid shall be read with the eye placed slightly above the plane of the surface of the sample.   This reading shall then be corrected by subtracting in the case of A.P.I. hydrometers or adding in the case of specific-gravity hydrometers, an amount equal to the height which the sample rises on the hydrometer stem above the main liquid surface.*

This height will vary for different oils and different hydrometers and the amount of correction necessary will depend upon the width of the hydrometer scale graduations. The necessary correction factor shall be determined, therefore, for the particular hydrometer in use by observing the height above the main surface of the liquid to which the oil rises on the hydrometer scale when the hydrometer in question is immersed in a transparent oil having a surface tension similar to that of the sample under test (Note 3).

Note 3.—In the routine testing of opaque crude petroleum with the usual type of hydrometer with a 12-deg. range, it is customary and permissible to correct the reading taken as prescribed above for nontransparent samples by an arbitrary deduction of 0.1° A.P.I. from the observed gravity reading.

(c) *The temperature of the sample shall be determined from the reading of the separate thermometer placed in the sample or from that of the thermometer contained in the hydrometer when the thermo-hydrometer type of instrument is used (see Note 4).*

Note 4.—Although it is usually satisfactory to determine the temperature of the sample immediately after reading the hydrometer, it is recommended that in all referee tests this temperature be determined both before and after the hydrometer is read.

Calculation

7. (a) *In the case of crude petroleum and petroleum products the determinations made in Section 6 are commonly referred to as "observed gravity and observed temperature." These observations shall be corrected to the gravity at 60 F.*

PERMISSIBLE EXCEPTION: With some paraffin-base crudes it is necessary at times, especially in cold weather, to heat the sample for the hydrometer test to a temperature of 60 F to 80 F, or from 10 F to 20 F above a point where the oil congeals. The sample may be heated by immersing the cylinder in a water bath at the required temperature for a sufficient length of time for the temperature of the oil to approximate the temperature of the bath. The sample should be gently, yet thoroughly, shaken after heating so that an average temperature of the sample will result.

Reproducibility of Results*

8. (a) *Duplicate determinations shall agree within 0.1° A.P.I. or the equivalent thereof in units of specific gravity at the particular gravity being determined when the same hydrometer and thermometer are used in the tests.*

(b) *Separate laboratories using different hydrometers and thermometers should obtain duplicate results agreeing within 0.5° A.P.I. or the equivalent thereof in units of specific gravity at the particular gravity being determined, provided the observed temperatures do not vary from 60 F. (15.5 C.) by more than plus or minus 18 F. (10 C.). When extreme accuracy is desired, instruments certified by the National Bureau of Standards shall be used, and the necessary corrections made.*

CALCULATION: In the case of crude oil and petroleum products gravity determinations are commonly referred to as "observed gravity" and "observed temperature." These observations shall be corrected to the gravity at 60 F by the use of Table 5: "Reduction of Observed API Gravity to API Gravity at 60 F" of the *ASTM-IP Petroleum Measurement Tables (ASTM Designation D 1250; IP Designation 200*—see Appendix, below).

APPENDIX

ASTM Designation D 287

The following is an abridgement of Table 8: "Pounds Per U.S. Gallon and U.S. Gallons Per Pound" of the *ASTM-IP Petroleum Measurement Tables (ASTM Designation D 1250; IP Designation 200)*, which contains similar data for each 0.1 deg API from 0 to 100 deg API, inclusive.

* *Editorially revised in 1942.*

TABLE SHOWING SPECIFIC GRAVITIES, POUNDS PER GALLON, AND GALLONS PER POUND AT 60 F, CORRESPONDING TO DEGREES API

Degrees API	Specific Gravity at 60/60 F	Pounds Per Gallon at 60 F	Gallons Per Pound at 60 F
0	1.0760	8.962	0.11158
1	1.0679	8.895	0.11243
2	1.0599	8.828	0.11328
3	1.0520	8.762	0.11413
4	1.0443	8.697	0.11498
5	1.0366	8.634	0.11583
6	1.0291	8.571	0.11668
7	1.0217	8.509	0.11752
8	1.0143	8.448	0.11837
9	1.0071	8.388	0.11922
10	1.0000	8.328	0.12007
11	0.9930	8.270	0.12092
12	0.9861	8.212	0.12177
13	0.9792	8.155	0.12262
14	0.9725	8.099	0.12347
15	0.9659	8.044	0.12432
16	0.9593	7.989	0.12517
17	0.9529	7.935	0.12602
18	0.9465	7.882	0.12687
19	0.9402	7.830	0.12772
20	0.9340	7.778	0.12857
21	0.9279	7.727	0.12942
22	0.9218	7.676	0.13027
23	0.9159	7.627	0.13112
24	0.9100	7.578	0.13197
25	0.9042	7.529	0.13282
26	0.8984	7.481	0.13367
27	0.8927	7.434	0.13452
28	0.8871	7.387	0.13537
29	0.8816	7.341	0.13622
30	0.8762	7.296	0.13707
31	0.8708	7.251	0.13792
32	0.8654	7.206	0.13877
33	0.8602	7.162	0.13962
34	0.8550	7.119	0.14047
35	0.8499	7.076	0.14132
36	0.8448	7.034	0.14217
37	0.8398	6.992	0.14302
38	0.8348	6.951	0.14387
39	0.8299	6.910	0.14472
40	0.8251	6.870	0.14557
41	0.8203	6.830	0.14642
42	0.8156	6.790	0.14727
43	0.8109	6.751	0.14812
44	0.8063	6.713	0.14897
45	0.8017	6.675	0.14982
46	0.7972	6.637	0.15067
47	0.7927	6.600	0.15152
48	0.7883	6.563	0.15237
49	0.7839	6.527	0.15322
50	0.7796	6.491	0.15407
51	0.7753	6.455	0.15492
52	0.7711	6.420	0.15577
53	0.7669	6.385	0.15662
54	0.7628	6.350	0.15747
55	0.7587	6.316	0.15832
56	0.7547	6.283	0.15917
57	0.7507	6.249	0.16002
58	0.7467	6.216	0.16087
59	0.7428	6.183	0.16172
60	0.7389	6.151	0.16257
61	0.7351	6.119	0.16342
62	0.7313	6.087	0.16427
63	0.7275	6.056	0.16512

TABLE SHOWING SPECIFIC GRAVITIES, POUNDS PER GALLON, AND GALLONS
PER POUND AT 60 F, CORRESPONDING TO DEGREES API (*Continued*)

Degrees API	Specific Gravity at 60/60 F	Pounds Per Gallon at 60 F	Gallons Per Pound at 60 F
64	0.7238	6.025	0.16597
65	0.7201	5.994	0.16682
66	0.7165	5.964	0.16767
67	0.7128	5.934	0.16853
68	0.7093	5.904	0.16938
69	0.7057	5.875	0.17023
70	0.7022	5.845	0.17108
71	0.6988	5.816	0.17193
72	0.6953	5.788	0.17278
73	0.6919	5.759	0.17363
74	0.6886	5.731	0.17448
75	0.6852	5.704	0.17533
76	0.6819	5.676	0.17618
77	0.6787	5.649	0.17703
78	0.6754	5.622	0.17788
79	0.6722	5.595	0.17873
80	0.6690	5.569	0.17958
81	0.6659	5.542	0.18043
82	0.6628	5.516	0.18128
83	0.6597	5.490	0.18213
84	0.6566	5.465	0.18298
85	0.6536	5.440	0.18384
86	0.6505	5.415	0.18469
87	0.6476	5.390	0.18554
88	0.6446	5.365	0.18639
89	0.6417	5.341	0.18724
90	0.6388	5.317	0.18809
91	0.6360	5.293	0.18894
92	0.6331	5.269	0.18979
93	0.6303	5.245	0.19064
94	0.6275	5.222	0.19149
95	0.6247	5.199	0.19234
96	0.6220	5.176	0.19319
97	0.6193	5.153	0.19404
98	0.6166	5.131	0.19490
99	0.6139	5.109	0.19575
100	0.6112	5.087	0.19660

1005. VAPOR-PRESSURE DETERMINATION*

This procedure is limited to crude oils with a Reid vapor pressure of 26 psia or less.

1005.1. Sampling Procedure

The utmost care and precaution should be taken in obtaining and handling samples of highly volatile crude oil and petroleum blends due to their extreme sensitivity to evaporation losses. Procedures given in *API RP 50B: "Recommended Practice for Measuring, Sampling, and Testing Natural Gasoline and Other Light Liquid Petroleum Hydrocarbons"* should be used.

PERMISSIBLE EXCEPTION: The sample obtained should thoroughly represent the product to be tested, and that portion of the sample used for the test should thoroughly represent the sample itself. Samples should be taken by a gager or inspector especially trained for sampling petroleum products. If this is not possible, the gager should work under the direction of a supervisor who has had previous experience with this type of sampling. Samples may be taken from open tanks, pressure tanks, pressure locks, sample cocks, sample lines, or from a line in which the product is moving.

* This section, viz., vapor-pressure determination, is based on, and abstracted from, *ASTM Designation D 323-43: "Standard Method of Test for Vapor Pressure of Petroleum Products (Reid Method)"* and *API RP 50B: "Recommended Practice for Measuring, Sampling, and Testing Natural Gasoline and Other Light Liquid Petroleum Hydrocarbons."*

This method of sampling, the points of sampling, and the number of samples may be mutually agreed upon by the parties involved.   Composite samples, however, are not acceptable.

The sample container should be carefully examined for leaks after a sample has been taken.   If leaks are observed, the sample should be discarded and a new sample in a tight container obtained.

In the event samples are to be shipped by common carrier, the sample container should be enclosed in a wood box crate to comply with ICC regulations (*ICC Specification 15C: "Wooden Boxes, Nailed."*)

PERMISSIBLE EXCEPTION: Necessary precautions should be taken to guard against fire and explosion when flushing or purging the lines and the sample containers.

A. Equipment

a. OPEN SAMPLE CONTAINERS: Open-type containers with single openings, when properly weighted, may be used for sampling by immersion in open tanks.   This type of container may also be used for obtaining samples from closed or pressure tanks.

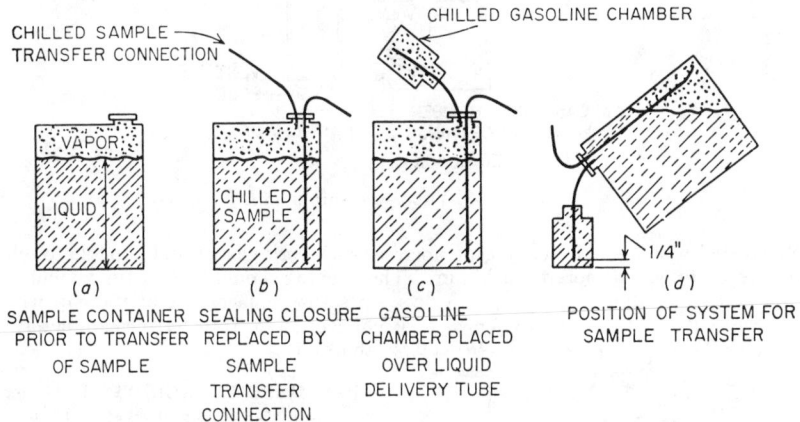

FIG 16-8. Simplified sketches outlining method of transferring sample to gasoline chamber from open-type containers.

In both cases the containers should be rinsed with the product to be sampled immediately prior to obtaining the sample.   The transfer connection for the open-type container, as shown in Fig. 16-8(*b*), should consist of an air tube and a liquid delivery tube assembled in a cap or stopper.   One end of the delivery tube should be flush with the inside face of the cap or stopper, the air tube and a liquid delivery tube should be flush with the inside face of the cap or stopper, and the air tube should be long enough to reach the bottom of the gasoline chamber while the sample is being transferred to the chamber.

(1) *Glass-bottle sample container:* The glass-bottle sample container should be of clear, colorless flint glass, approximately 9 in. in height, $3\frac{5}{8}$ in. in outside diameter, 32-oz capacity, with a narrow mouth to accommodate a No. 8 taper cork stopper. New No. 8 corks, size $1\frac{1}{16}$ by $\frac{7}{8}$ by $\frac{1}{16}$, at least equal to XXXX quality should be used on each sample taken.   The use of the glass-bottle sample container, equipped with screw caps which are lined with cork, is permissible.

(2) *Metal-can sample container:* The metal-can sample container, as shown in Fig. 16-8(*a*) should be of at least 1-qt but not more than 2-gal capacity, with a square or rectangular bottom and with corresponding sides and top.   The metal used should

be of sufficient weight to withstand safely the pressure to which it may be subjected. A 135-lb tin plate with its body paneled will satisfy this requirement.   The top should

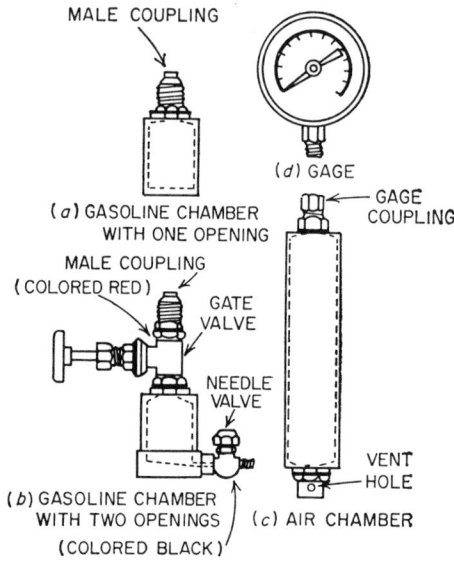

Fig. 16-9. Vapor-pressure bomb.

be provided with a single screw-type opening with cork gasket and cap, the pitch of the threads to be not more than $\frac{1}{10}$ in.   The opening should be of a type which permits the replacement of the cap with a connection for transferring samples at the laboratory.

PERMISSIBLE EXCEPTION: The gasoline chamber, one-opening-type, of the Reid vapor-pressure bomb, as shown in Fig. 16-9(a), may be used as an open sample container, in lieu of the glass-bottle and the metal-can sample container, if suitable means of closing is provided.

b. APPARATUS FOR CHILLING SAMPLES: A chilled sampling apparatus, for use in obtaining a chilled sample (as shown in Fig. 16-10), should consist of a bath of sufficient size to accommodate both the sample container and the cooling coil, and should be formed of at least $\frac{1}{4}$-in.-OD No. 20 gage copper tubing.   One end of the cooling coil should be provided with connections suitable for attaching to the sampling connection, and the other should be provided with an $\frac{1}{8}$-in. needle valve of high quality.   For introducing the sample into the container, this valve should have at its open end a removable

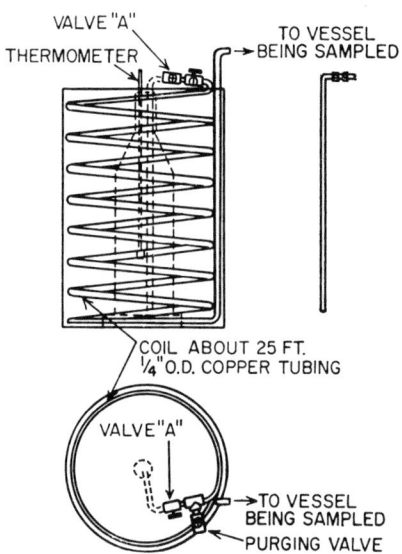

Fig. 16-10. Chilled sampling apparatus.

tube of $\frac{1}{4}$-in.-OD copper tubing of sufficient length to reach the bottom of the sample container.

c. CLOSED SAMPLE CONTAINERS: The closed type of sample container is recommended for obtaining samples on closed vessels or product lines with a product of 12 psia to 26 psia Reid vapor pressure. The transfer connection for the closed type of container should consist of a single tube with a connection suitable for attaching to the opening of the sample container. The tube should be long enough to reach the bottom of the gasoline chamber while the sample is being transferred.

(1) *Single-valve steel cylinder:* This type of sample container should have a capacity of 1 gal, and should conform in construction and maintenance to ICC regulations. The container should be made of steel, and should be cylindrical in shape, approximately 6 in. in diameter, 13 in. high, and 0.156 in. in wall thickness. The sample container should have a single opening in the top tapped with a ¾-in. pipe thread. The sample container should be equipped with a liquefied-petroleum-gas cylinder valve, which is provided also with a safety-relief device with an initial setting of 375 psig (±25 psig) and with a full opening at 450 psig (+0 −50 psig). The cylinder should be provided with a cap for the protection of the outlet valve. These design features fulfill the requirements of *ICC Specification 4B 240: "Welded and Brazed Steel Cylinders"*; and cylinders so designed, if adequately maintained, are suitable for shipment, by common carrier, of products which have a vapor pressure less than 320 psig at 130 F, or approximately 240 psig at 100 F.

(2) *Double-valve steel cylinder:* This type of sample container (*CNGA* Bulletin TS-341: "California Natural Gasoline Association Tentative Standard Method for Gaging Natural Gasoline in Pressure Storage"*) consists of a 13-in. overall length of 4-in. seamless drawn tubing with standard welding caps, or with orange-peel ends which have a diameter equal to the diameter of the tubing and which contain an unequal number of segments. Brass angle valves with a working pressure of 225 psig and with key handles are provided at the upper end; one valve is connected to the top of the cylinder, and the other is fastened to a ¼-in. pipe which leads to the bottom of the container. The top valve is painted red, and the bottom valve black. This arrangement is virtually the same as if the container had a valve at both ends, and hence permits either water displacement or vapor displacement of the sample. A skirt is attached to the lower end of the cylinder which allows the cylinder to stand upright. The lower end of the cylinder has two plugs. One plug is at the extreme end and permits the removal of scale which may form in the cylinder, and the other is placed in the unwelded portion of the shell and permits inspection of the thickness of the metal. A bail is provided for greater ease in carrying. A thermometer well is also provided in the cylinder. The cylinder should be tested to a 300-psig pressure with cold water, and should have a working pressure of 200 psig.

PERMISSIBLE EXCEPTION: The gasoline chamber, two-opening type, of the Reid vapor-pressure bomb, as shown in Fig. 16-9(*b*), may be used in lieu of the closed-type sample container.

B. Procedure

Samples may be obtained by immersing the sample container through the open gage hatch or the pressure lock, or from sample cocks located below the liquid level and extending at least 6 in. within the tank, or from a sample connection in a vertical or horizontal product line—the extension to reach the middle of the pipe.

One-quarter-inch copper tubing should be used to connect the sample valve, on the tank or line which contains the product to be sampled, to the inlet valve on the sample container or chilled sampling apparatus. For sampling products with a Reid vapor pressure of 26 psia or less, open-type containers are adequate. If the product to be sampled is in an open vessel, the product may be sampled by immersion. If the product to be sampled is in a closed vessel or pipeline, the chilled sampling procedure or closed-type sampling container with its designated procedure may be used. Prior to the sampling operation, the sampling connections should be purged by slowly withdrawing twice their capacity of the product to be sampled. This should be done through a loose connection at the inlet valve in the sample container or chilled sampling apparatus. Upon completion of the purging of the sampling connections, the

* California Natural Gasoline Assn.

loose connection should be tightened and the sampling operation should be started immediately. If a gage glass is the only available sampling entrance to the tank, it should be emptied at least twice before each flow of the product through the sampling connections. As a record for identification of future reports, each sample should be tagged and marked at the time the sample is taken. The sample container should be inspected for leaks by completely immersing the container in water. The results of the inspection for leaks should be made a part of the sample record. Samples in containers found to be leaking should not be considered as representative of the material sampled.

a. SAMPLING BY IMMERSION: The empty sample container should first be immersed in the liquid to be sampled and allowed to fill while being lowered and raised through the liquid. The first filling is for the purpose of equalizing the temperature of the container and the contents, and for washing the container. The container should then be emptied and refilled. On this second filling, the sample container should be lowered and raised at such a rate that it will be nearly, but not quite, full when withdrawn. Enough of the contents should be poured off immediately so that the portion remaining should fill the sample container to not less than 70 per cent and not more than 80 per cent of its capacity. The sample container should be promptly and tightly closed, and should be kept cool (preferably in an ice bath) until delivery to the laboratory.

b. PROCEDURE FOR CHILLING SAMPLES: Having purged the sampling connections and filled the bath or baths with water and cracked ice, the chilling-coil inlet should be connected to the tubing in the sampling connection. The chilling-coil outlet valve should be closed and the valve in the sampling connection opened, thus allowing the tank or line pressure to be exerted to the chilling-coil outlet valve. The chilling coil should be purged by allowing an excess of the capacity of the coil to be wasted through the coil, during which operation the outlet valve should be throttled so as to maintain a back pressure on the coil approximately the same as that of the vessel being sampled. After purging the chilling coil, the sample container should be immersed in the ice bath, and the $\frac{1}{4}$-in. copper tubing from the chilling-coil outlet valve should be connected and should extend to the bottom of the sample container. The chilling-coil outlet valve should be slightly opened, allowing enough of the sample to collect in the sample container for thorough rinsing. After the container has been rinsed, it should be returned to an ice bath and filled to between 70 and 80 per cent of the capacity of the sample container—maintaining a back pressure on the cooling coil approximately the same as that of the vessel or the line being sampled. The rate of withdrawal should be such that the temperature of the sample will not exceed 40 F. When the sample has been collected, the container should be immediately closed.

c. SAMPLING INTO SINGLE-VALVE STEEL CYLINDERS: After sampling connections have been purged, a small quantity of the product to be sampled should be collected in the sample container. The container should then be disconnected and allowed to vent for a period from 3 min to 5 min in an upright position, after which the cylinder should be inverted, allowing the remaining liquid to be expelled. After this purging of the sample container, the valve on the sample container should be closed and loosely connected to the sampling connections, which should then be purged again. The sample container should be completely filled with liquid. This is best ascertained by weighing. To expedite the filling of the cylinder, it may be necessary to reduce the vapor pressure of the material in the sample container by placing the container in an ice bath or by cooling by other means. When the sample container has been filled, all valves should be closed; the sample container immediately should be disconnected and inverted, and enough sample allowed to escape to provide for an outage of approximately 20 per cent. The container valve should be closed while the cylinder is in the inverted position. The container valve should be plugged immediately.

d. SAMPLING INTO DOUBLE-VALVE STEEL CYLINDERS

(1) *By vapor displacement:* Having purged the sampling connections, the valve (black) leading to the bottom of the sample container should be opened, thus throttling the valve (red) from the top of the sample container so as to maintain a back pressure approximately the same as that of the vessel which is being sampled during the sampling operation. The sample should be withdrawn by allowing the product to flow through the sampling system until a volume equal to at least twice that of the sample container has been passed. All the valves should then be closed and the container

disconnected.   If it is necessary to transport the sample some distance to an ice bath, a 5-per-cent vapor space should be provided in the container by allowing 100 ml of liquid, or its approximate equivalent in vapor and liquid, to escape through the bottom (black) valve.   Should the vapor pressure of the product be insufficient to force liquid from the container, it is permissible to open both valves to facilitate the withdrawal of the specified outage.   Both sample-container valves should be tightly plugged immediately after completion of the sampling operation.

(2) *By water displacement:* Before the double-valve steel cylinder is used for sampling, it should be thoroughly purged with live steam for at least 5 min by hanging it in an inverted position and introducing the steam through the black valve which leads to the bottom.   After steaming, the valve packing should be inspected and replaced if necessary.   The container should then be tested for leaks at 50-psig air pressure by immersion in water.   The sample container should be filled with water by connecting the black valve leading to the bottom of the container to the water supply and filling the container completely; and the necessary precautions should be taken to remove any entrained air.   Closed-type sample containers may be used for obtaining samples from closed vessels by either of 2 methods, viz.: 1, by purging with gasoline; or, 2, by water displacement.

PERMISSIBLE EXCEPTION: The water-displacement method is preferable only when the flow involved in the purging process may create a hazard.

It is recommended that the sample container be immersed in cracked ice during transportation to and from the point of sampling.   The sampling connection should be joined to the upper (red) valve of the sample container.   With all valves closed, following the purging of the sampling connections the valve in the sampling connection should be opened, then the top (red) valve should be opened and, last, the bottom (black) valve should be slowly opened to allow the water to be withdrawn.   The rate at which the water is withdrawn should be kept sufficiently slow so that the pressure on the liquid in the sample container will be substantially the same as it is in the liquid in the tank or pipeline.   When the product appears at the black valve, in order to check the fullness of the container, the container should be inverted and the product should be allowed to flow slowly through the black valve.   If product continues to flow, the container is full.   In case there is a doubt that the first product drawn into the container is representative of the material to be sampled, an amount of product equal to the volume of the container should be slowly passed through the cylinder, care being taken not to lower the pressure of the sample container substantially below the tank pressure.   To disconnect the sample container, the black valve should first be closed; next, the red valve; and, last, the valve at the sampling connection on the tank being sampled.   If the sample can be placed at once in an ice bath and maintained at a temperature lower than the sampling temperature, no vapor space should be allowed.   Otherwise a 5-per-cent vapor space should be provided in the container by allowing 100 ml of liquid, or its approximate equivalent in vapor and liquid, to escape from the bottom (black) valve.   Should the vapor pressure of the product be insufficient to force liquid from the container, it will be permissible to open both valves to facilitate the withdrawal of the specified outage.   Both valves should be tightly plugged immediately upon completion of the sampling operation.   All samples not to be immediately tested should be stored in a cool place, preferably a cold room, as soon as their containers have been inspected and approved.

1005.2. Vapor-pressure Test

The determination of vapor pressure of volatile, nonviscous crude oil and petroleum blends should be made according to *ASTM Designation D 323-43: "Standard Method of Test for Vapor Pressure of Petroleum Products (Reid Method)"*—using the Reid vapor-pressure bomb, with open or closed liquid chambers and with a vapor-pressure gage.

A. Equipment: The vapor-pressure bomb shown in Fig. 16-9 consists of 2 sections or chambers, viz.: an upper section or air chamber, and a lower section or gasoline chamber.   The ratio of the volume of the air chamber to the volume of the gasoline chamber should be between the limits of 3.8 and 4.2.   To determine the volume of the air chamber, insert a ¼-in. plug in the gage coupling, invert the chamber, fill with water up to and including the portion of the coupling device attached permanently to the air chamber, and then carefully measure the volume of water. To determine the volume of the gasoline chamber, fill with water up to and including the portion of the coupling device attached permanently to the gasoline chamber, and then carefully measure the volume of water.

a. AIR CHAMBER: The upper section, or air chamber [see Fig. 16-9(*c*)], should be a cylindrical vessel 2 in. to 2⅛ in. in diameter and 10 in. ± ⅛ in. in length, inside dimensions. In one end of the air chamber a ¼-in. standard pipe thread should be tapped to receive the gage coupling. The internal diameter of the connection between the air chamber and the pressure gage should be not less than 3/16 in. Other means of connecting the air chamber with the pressure gage may be employed, provided necessary requirements are fulfilled. In the other end of the air chamber an opening approximately ½ in. in diameter should be provided for the purpose of coupling the air chamber with the gasoline chamber. The nature of this opening will depend upon the method of coupling employed. Any method of coupling the air chamber and the gasoline chamber may be employed; e.g., a simple thread, a union, or a clamp. The sole provision in this respect is that the assembly should be free of leaks during the test. Responsibility for freedom from leaks lies with the user. The air chamber must drain completely from either end when held in a vertical position and, for this reason, the ends may be slightly convex.

b. ONE-OPENING GASOLINE CHAMBER: The lower-section 1-opening gasoline chamber [see Fig. 16-9(*a*)] should be a cylindrical vessel of the same inside diameter as the air chamber and 2½ in. ± 1/16 in. in inside length. In one end of the gasoline chamber an opening approximately ½ in. in diameter should be provided for the purpose of coupling the gasoline chamber with the air chamber. This opening will depend upon the method of coupling employed. The other end of the gasoline chamber should be completely closed. The gasoline chamber must drain completely when inverted and, for this reason, the top may be slightly convex. The vertical dimensions of the gasoline chamber proper should be such that the assembly fulfills necessary requirements for this type of construction.

c. TWO-OPENING GASOLINE CHAMBER: The lower-section 2-opening gasoline chamber shown in Fig. 16-9(*b*) should be the same as described for the 1-opening gasoline chamber, except that a ¼-in. needle valve should be attached near the bottom of the gasoline chamber and a ½-in. gate valve should be inserted between the gasoline chamber and the air chamber. The capacity of the gasoline chamber should be considered as that below the gate-valve closure. The volume above the gate-valve closure, including the portion of the coupling permanently attached to the gasoline chamber, should be considered as a part of the air-chamber capacity. Before placing new apparatus in service and as often as necessary thereafter, the assembled vapor-pressure bomb should be checked for freedom from leaks by filling the bomb with air to a pressure of 100 psig and completely immersing the bomb in a water bath. Only apparatus which will stand this test without leaking should be used.

d. PRESSURE GAGE: The pressure gage [see Fig. 16-9(*d*)] should be a bourdon-type spring gage of test-gage quality, 4½ in. to 5½ in. in diameter, with a passageway not less than 3/16 in. in diameter from the bourdon tube to the atmosphere. The range of the pressure gage used should be governed by the vapor pressure of the sample being tested, as follows:

		Gage to be Used*	
		Numbered	Intermediate
Reid Vapor Pressure	Scale Range	Intervals	Graduations
(PSIA at 100 F)	(PSIG)	(PSIG)	(PSIG)
12 and under	0 to 15	3	0.1
10 to 36	0 to 45	5	0.2
30 to 55	0 to 60	10	0.25
50 and higher	0 to 100	10	0.5

* A gage of 0- to 30-psig range, 5-psig numbered intervals, and 0.2-psig intermediate graduations may be used for products with a Reid vapor pressure of from 10 to 26 psia.

Only accurate gages should be used. When the "gage correction" exceeds 1 per cent of the scale range, the gage should be considered inaccurate.

e. COOLING BATH: A cooling bath should be provided of such dimensions that the sample containers and gasoline chambers may be completely immersed. Means for maintaining the bath at a temperature of 32 F to 40 F should be provided.

f. WATER BATH: The water bath should be of such dimensions that the vapor-pressure bomb may be immersed to at least 1 in. above the top of the air chamber. Means for maintaining the bath at a constant temperature of 100 F ±0.2 F should be provided.

Water-bath temperature: An ASTM Reid vapor-pressure thermometer, graduated in degrees fahrenheit, with a range of 94 F to 108 F, which conforms with *ASTM Designation E 1-53: "Specifications for ASTM Thermometers,"* should be used.

g. AIR-CHAMBER THERMOMETER: An ASTM air-chamber thermometer, graduated in degrees fahrenheit, with a range of −40 F to +120 F, which conforms with *ASTM Designation E 1-42*, should be used.

B. Preparation of equipment: The air chamber should be thoroughly purged of any liquid gasoline or vapors from previous tests. This may be accomplished by filling the air chamber with warm water (above 90 F) and allowing it to drain. This operation should be repeated at least five times. Pressure gages should be purged of residual gasoline from the previous test by directing a small stream of air into the bourdon tube for at least 5 min. The pressure gage should be attached to the air chamber, and the air thermometer should be inserted into the air chamber for three-fourths of the chamber's length. The thermometer bulb should not be permitted to rest on the wall of the air chamber. It should be held in place by a loosely fitting or slotted stopper inserted in the end of the air chamber. The thermometer should be left in the air chamber for a sufficient length of time for an accurate determination of "initial air temperature." If this temperature reading has been constant for 0.5 F for 5 min, and if this temperature does not differ more than 2 F from the air temperature (room temperature) adjacent to the bomb, then the correct "initial air temperature" has been determined. This temperature reading should be recorded. The water bath should be inspected and adjusted for correct temperature (100 ±0.2 F).

C. Transfer of sample from sample container to gasoline chamber

a. ONE-OPENING GASOLINE CHAMBER: With the chilled-sample transfer connection, the sample to be tested should be transferred to the 1-opening chamber [Fig. 16-9(*a*)]. The gasoline chamber should be placed over the sample delivery tube [Fig. 16-8(*c*)] of the transfer connection. The entire system should be rapidly inverted [Fig. 16-8(*d*)] so that the gasoline chamber is finally in an upright position with the delivery tube extending to within ¼ in. of the bottom of the gasoline chamber. The gasoline chamber should then be filled to overflowing. The 1-opening gasoline chamber should then be immediately attached to the air chamber [Fig. 16-9(*c*)].

b. TWO-OPENING GASOLINE CHAMBER: The same procedure as outlined for the 1-opening chamber should be used for the 2-opening chamber [Fig. 16-9(*b*)], except that the upper valve should not be opened until the system has reached its final position. The gasoline chamber should be immediately connected to the air chamber.

D. Procedure: The assembled vapor-pressure bomb should be turned upside down and shaken vigorously. This should be repeated several times. The bomb should then be righted and immersed in the water bath to at least 1 in. above the top of the air chamber. The water-bath temperature should be maintained at a constant temperature of 100 F ±0.2 F, as determined by a bath thermometer which is well immersed in the bath throughout the vapor-pressure determination. While the bomb is immersed, it should be closely checked for leaks. Liquid leaks are much more difficult to detect than vapor leaks; and, as the much-used coupling device is normally in the liquid section of the apparatus, it should be given special attention. When at any time in the course of a test a leak is detected, the test should be discarded and a new sample taken. After 5 min the bomb should be withdrawn from the bath, inverted, shaken vigorously, and replaced in the bath. This procedure should be repeated at intervals of not less than 2 min. Vigorous shaking should be performed quickly to avoid cooling the bomb and contents. Prior to each removal of the bomb from the bath, the gage reading should be observed. The gage should be tapped slightly before each reading. These operations should be continued for at least 20 min to insure equilibrium. After this period, if consecutive gage readings observed are constant, the value of the readings should be recorded as the "uncorrected vapor pressure" compared with that of a mercury column. The correction thus determined should be recorded as the "gage correction."

E. Calculations: To calculate the Reid vapor pressure of the sample under test, the "uncorrected vapor pressure" should be corrected for the pressure-gage error, if any, and for the change in the pressure of the water and air in the air chamber due to the differences between the "initial air temperature" and the temperature of the water bath. The following tabulation shows the corrections to apply for "initial air temperatures" ranging from 32 F to 110 F. The value which results from these corrections should be recorded as the Reid vapor pressure.

CORRECTIONS TO BE APPLIED TO CONVERT UNCORRECTED VAPOR PRESSURES
TO REID VAPOR PRESSURES

	Corrections (in Pounds Per Square Inch, Absolute) for Various Temperatures, Calculated for Normal Barometric Pressures of:				
Initial Air Temperature*	760 Milli-meters	745 Milli-meters	700 Milli-meters	650 Milli-meters	600 Milli-meters
32 F (0 C)	−2.9	−2.9	−2.7	−2.6	−2.5
40 F (4.4 C)	−2.6	−2.6	−2.4	−2.3	−2.2
50 F (10 C)	−2.2	−2.2	−2.1	−2.0	−1.9
60 F (15.6 C)	−1.8	−1.8	−1.7	−1.6	−1.6
70 F (21.1 C)	−1.4	−1.4	−1.3	−1.3	−1.2
80 F (26.7 C)	−1.0	−1.0	−1.0	−0.9	−0.9
90 F (32.2 C)	−0.5	−0.5	−0.5	−0.5	−0.5
100 F (37.8 C)	0.0	0.0	0.0	0.0	0.0
110 F (43.3 C)	+0.6	+0.6	+0.5	+0.5	+0.5

$$\text{Correction factor} = \frac{(P_a - P_t)(t - 100)}{460 + t} - (P_{100} - P_t)$$

where: t = the air chamber temperature at beginning of test, degrees fahrenheit.

P_t = the vapor pressure of water, pounds per square inch, absolute, at t degrees fahrenheit.

P_{100} = the vapor pressure of water, pounds per square inch, absolute, at 100 F (37.8 C).

P_a = the normal barometric pressure in pounds per square inch at the place where the test is conducted.

* For intermediate air temperatures, the corrections should be interpolated to the nearest 0.1 psia.

F. Reproducibility of results: With care and strict attention, duplicate tests for vapor pressures should not differ from each other by more than 0.2 psia, plus 1 per cent of the vapor pressure, as determined.

PART II—BS&W

WATER AND SEDIMENT

1100. INTRODUCTION

There are four well-established methods for determining BS&W, as follows:

(1) API Standard Method (*ASTM Designation D 96-46: "Standard Method of Test for Water and Sediment in Petroleum Products by Means of Centrifuge"*).

(2) API Base Method (*ASTM Designation D 95-46: "Standard Method of Test for Water in Petroleum Products and Other Bituminous Materials"; and ASTM Designation D 473-48: "Standard Method of Test for Sediment in Fuel Oil by Extraction"*).

(3) Field centrifuge method.
(4) Gravity-settling method.

1101. API STANDARD METHOD

It is generally agreed that ASTM Method D 96-46 for the determination of BS&W is the most nearly accurate method for routine testing. However, due to economic conditions, it is not possible at the present time to standardize on this method throughout the country. ASTM Method D 96-46 is recommended for use wherever practicable, but recognition is necessarily given to the hand centrifuge method for field operations where laboratory facilities are not available, and to the gravity-settling method now well established in certain parts of the country.

Solvents other than benzol shall be permitted when tests demonstrate that such solvents provide equivalent results or are necessary to obtain correct results. The use of a demulsifier (resolving agent) with solvents shall be permitted, subject to the mutual consent of all parties concerned when tests demonstrate that correct results cannot otherwise be determined. The following solvents and demulsifiers have been reported as satisfactory for certain crudes:

Solvents	Demulsifiers
Benzol, Industrial 90	Commercial crude-oil demulsifiers
Toluol	Phenol
Aviation-gasoline base	Nitrogen bases
White gasoline	Naphthenic acids
75 per cent aviation-gas-line base and 25 per cent carbon bisulfide	

Increased ratios of solvent to crude oil are successfully employed with certain crudes. Solvents are toxic, and care should be exercised in their use. Gasoline containing tetraethyllead should never be used.

When using any demulsifier, care should be taken not to overtreat the oil sample. It should also be known that the demulsifier will completely disperse in the oil sample to be tested so that correct BS&W determinations will result. There are no known universal solvents or demulsifying agents for use with crude oil.

To avoid inclusion of waxy material in the BS&W, it may be necessary to heat the mixture of oil and solvent to 140 F before centrifuging. The temperature of the mixture of oil and solvent shall be not less than 115 F at completion of the test on such crudes which have a high wax content. A heated centrifuge may be necessary.

1102. API BASE METHOD

The sum of the results obtained by ASTM Method D 95-46 and the per cent by weight (see note) obtained by ASTM Method D 473-48 shall be assumed to give the correct results. These tests shall be considered as the API Base Method, and shall be used when agreement cannot be reached between buyer and seller on the API Standard Method. The API Base Method shall be used as a criterion to compare the effectiveness of solvents, with or without demulsifiers, used in the API Standard Method.

Note: For crude oils which contain sediment-by-extraction values in excess of 0.02 per cent by weight, the results should be converted to a volume basis. The result of water-by-distillation is in per cent by volume, and the result of sediment-by-extraction is in per cent by weight. BS&W values are commonly reported in per cent by volume. The result from the sediment-by-extraction should be corrected to per cent by volume. As the major portion of the sediment would probably be sand (silicon dioxide, which has a specific gravity of 2.32) and a small amount of other natural-occurring earthy materials (with a specific gravity lower than that of sand), an arbitrary specific gravity of 2 shall be used for the resulting sediment. This means that the sediment-by-extraction result, in per cent by weight, shall be converted to per cent by volume by dividing by 2.

1103. FIELD CENTRIFUGE METHOD

1103.1. Equipment

A centrifuge of the type illustrated in Fig. 16-11 or 16-12 may be employed. Centrifuge tubes of 12.50-ml, or greater, capacity in the calibrated portion are permitted (see Par. 1105 hereinafter).

1103.2. Procedure

Fill 2 tubes to the 50-per-cent mark with the solvent, with or without a demulsifier (such as listed in Par. 1101 hereinbefore), and then to the 100-per-cent mark with the sample of oil to be tested. Shake the tubes until the contents are thoroughly mixed, place them in the centrifuge, and revolve at the rate of 1,500 rpm for from 3 min to 10 min, depending upon the character of the sample. Remove the tubes, and record the combined volume of water and sediment (BS&W) in each tube to the nearest 0.1 per cent.

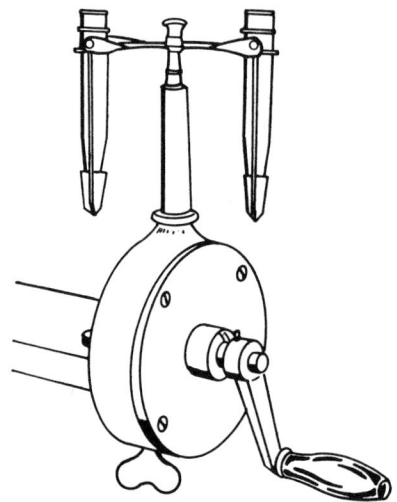

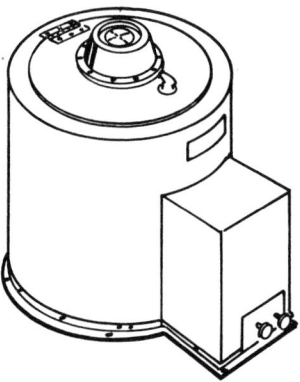

FIG. 16-11. Hand centrifuge.   FIG. 16-12. Power centrifuge.

Replace the tubes in the centrifuge, and revolve again for from 3 min to 10 min. Again record the combined volume of water and sediment (BS&W). If there is a difference of more than 0.2 per cent between the first and second readings, continue centrifuging until 2 consecutive readings check within 0.2 per cent. The sum of the final readings on both tubes represents the percentage of BS&W in the oil.

To avoid including waxy material with BS&W in the testing of certain types of crude oil, it may be necessary to heat the mixture of oil and solvent to 140 F before centrifuging. The temperature of the mixture of oil and solvent shall be not less than 115 F at completion of the test. A heated centrifuge may be necessary.

1104. GRAVITY-SETTLING METHOD

1104.1. Equipment

A special flat-bottom glass cylinder (see Fig. 16-14) is employed (see **Par. 1105** hereinafter).

1104.2. Procedure

Fill the special graduated cylinder to the 100-per-cent mark with the sample of oil to be tested.   Place the cylinder and sample in a heater, and maintain at 120 F for 24 hours.   Remove the cylinder from the heater, and read the per cent of water and sediment (BS&W) at the bottom of the cylinder.   It is desirable, whenever possible, to provide thermostatic control of the temperature of the heater.

1105. SPECIFICATIONS FOR 12.50-ML CENTRIFUGE TUBES AND FLAT-BOTTOM GRAVITY GAGE-GLASS SETTLING TUBES

1105.1. 12.50-Ml Centrifuge Tubes

The standard centrifuge tube in the small size shall be 12.50-ml capacity in the calibrated portion, with capacity, dimensions, graduations, tolerances, and markings, as shown in Fig. 16-13.

Note: Larger sizes of centrifuge tubes shall be in accordance with ASTM specifications (ASTM Method D 96-46).

Capacity

Indicated Percentage	Milliliters
1	0.125
2	0.250
3	0.375
5	0.625
10	1.250
15	1.875
20	2.500
25	3.125
30	3.750
35	4.375
40	5.000
45	5.625
50	6.250
100	12.500

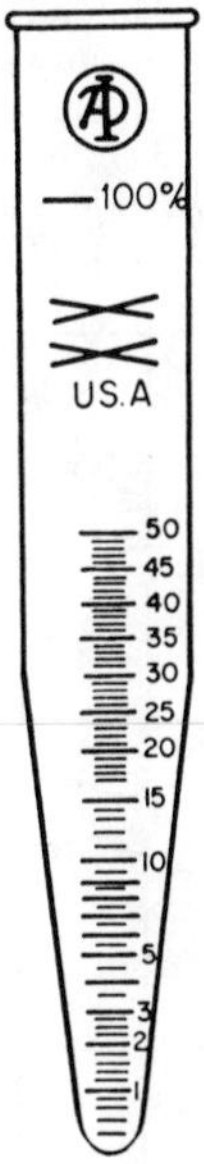

Marking

API monogram, ¼ in. high, etched on tube, as shown.   Manufacturer's mark or name etched on tube directly below monogram.

Graduations

Graduations shall be marked as follows:

0 to 3 per cent	0.2 of 1 per cent
3 to 10 per cent	0.5 of 1 per cent
10 to 50 per cent	1.0 per cent
50 to 100 per cent	blank

FIG. 16-13. Standard centrifuge tube.

Specifications

Length, overall: 118 mm ± 2 mm.
Length, 0 to 50 per cent: 66 mm ± 4 mm.
Length, 50 to 100 per cent: 35 mm ± 3 mm.
Length, tapered part: 56 mm to 62 mm.
Length, untapered part: 58 mm to 60 mm.
Rim thickness: 2 mm to 3 mm, included in overall measurement.
Diameter, untapered: 17 mm ± 0.25 mm.
Diameter, bottom, at the 0.3-per-cent marking: 5 mm ± 1 mm.
Normal thickness: perfect semi-circle bottom.

Limit of Error

Limit of error (plus or minus tolerance) is based on total calibrated volume of tube, as follows:

	Tolerance	
Range (Per Cent)	(Per Cent)	Volumetric Capacity (Milliliters)
0 to 1	±0.1	±0.0125
1 to 2	±0.15	±0.0188
2 to 3	±0.2	±0.0250
3 to 5	±0.2	±0.0250
5 to 10	±0.4	±0.0500
10 to 25	±0.5	±0.0625
25 to 50	±1.0	±0.1250
50 to 100	±1.0	±0.1250

Molded tubes are preferred. If blown tubes can comply with the stipulations on uniform wall thickness, they will be considered satisfactory.

All centrifuge tubes shall be retempered to remove manufacturing strains.

The lower end of the centrifuge tube must be clear and perfectly rounded inside, with the same thickness of glass as in the main body of the tube.

A. Tests for accuracy of centrifuge tubes: Centrifuge tubes may be tested for accuracy by the purchaser with a microburette, using air-free distilled water at 68 F (20 C), in accordance with ASTM Method D 96-46.

B. Auxiliary equipment: Aluminum or spun-brass shields are satisfactory for 12.50-ml tubes, for either hand-operated or electric-driven machines.

C. Disputes: In case of disagreement between the purchaser and vendor of crude oil on the accuracy of the 12.50-ml centrifuge tubes, such tubes may be tested by the burette method stipulated in Par. 1105.1-A hereinbefore. The tube found to be accurate according to this test shall be considered satisfactory.

As an alternate test, a master tube, calibrated and certified by the National Bureau of Standards as complying with these specifications, may be used. The test of the crude oil shall be made with the master tube, and similar tests shall be made with a tube furnished by the buyer and a tube furnished by the vendor, and compared with the test made with the master tube. The tube producing like or similar results to the master tube shall be considered satisfactory.

Samples of crude oil used in these BS&W tests shall be representative of the material in question, and the portion used for the test shall be thoroughly representative of the sample itself. The procedure for conducting these tests shall be as prescribed herein (see Part I, Sect. 1003, hereinbefore).

1105.2. Gravity-settling Tubes

F I G.   16-14. Flat-bottom gravity gage-glass settling tube.

The standard size of a gravity-settling tube shall be 1-in.-ID by 16 in. in length, with dimensions, tolerances, graduations, and markings as shown in Fig. 16-14.

All tubes shall be made of carefully selected tubing. The bottom shall be flat and square with the side walls, and the inside radius of the filler between the bottom and side shall not exceed 0.03 in. The tubes shall be annealed to remove manufacturing strains.

Tests for accuracy of gravity-settling tubes: The graduations of the lower 10 per cent of the tube and the inside radius of the fillet between the bottom and the sides shall be tested for accuracy with a plug gage 0.96 in. in diameter. Such gage shall be made of metal accurately marked in a lathe, and the diameter below the ¼-per-cent marking shall be reduced to 0.89 in.   The bottom of the plug gage shall be concaved $\frac{1}{32}$ in., except for an annular ring $\frac{1}{32}$ in. wide on the outside of the bottom which shall be left flat.   The graduations from 10 to 100 per cent shall be tested for accuracy with an accurately graduated scale.

Marking

Monogram size, $\frac{1}{2}$ in., etched on settling tubes which meet API specifications and limit of error.
Manufacturer's mark or name etched on tube directly below monogram.

Specifications

Length, overall..16 in.
Diameter (inside)..1 in. ± 0.03 in.
Minimum outside diameter of rolled edge................................1$\frac{1}{8}$ in.
Length graduated..14 in.
Graduations to start from inside face of bottom.
All graduations up to 5 per cent to be marked in 4 quadrants.

Graduations

Range (Per Cent)	Divisions (Per Cent)	Subdivisions (Per Cent)	Limit of Error (Inch)
0 to 2	1	0.25	±0.006
2 to 5	1	0.50	±0.01
5 to 100	10	1.00	±0.02

1106. API MONOGRAM AND COMPLIANCE

All 12.50-ml centrifuge tubes and all gravity-settling tubes, made in accordance with these specifications, shall be marked by all authorized manufacturers* with the API monogram and the manufacturer's name or identifying mark.   Authority to use the monogram will be granted in accordance with the rules and conditions contained in the note hereinafter.

The monogram and manufacturer's name or mark shall be etched plainly on the side of the tube where it will not conflict with the graduations specified.

Tubes not complying with these specifications shall not be marked with the API monogram or with the letters "API."

The manufacturer is responsible for complying with all of the provisions of this specification.   The purchaser may make any investigation necessary to satisfy himself of compliance by the manufacturer, and may reject any material which does not comply with this specification.

Note

Use of Monogram

The foregoing specifications are for the use of all manufacturers desiring to use them.

Manufacturers desiring to warrant that articles manufactured or sold by them conform with these specifications may under certain conditions obtain the license to use the official API monogram.

The following resolution, adopted by the Board of Directors of the American Petroleum Institute, October 20, 1924, embodies the purpose and the conditions under which such official monogram may be used:

WHEREAS, there has been a movement in the petroleum industry to simplify, standardize, and improve oil-country drilling equipment and methods, and

WHEREAS, the cooperation of the American Petroleum Institute was sought in order

* Doerr Glass Co., Vineland, N. J. (centrifuge tubes only).   Kimble Glass Co., Vineland, N. J.   The Western Machinery Co., Wichita, Kans. (centrifuge tubes only).

that there might be a national forum for the discussion, consideration, and adoption or rejection of such proposed standards, and

WHEREAS, it appears desirable that the American Petroleum Institute adopt an official monogram to be used for identifying materials that comply with such standards or specifications (where such specifications or standards call for the use of such monogram) that may hereafter be adopted by the Board of Directors of the American Petroleum Institute, and

WHEREAS, it also appears desirable that the use of such monogram be encouraged wherever and whenever possible to inform the public that material so marked is manufactured in accordance with such specifications,

Now THEREFORE, BE IT RESOLVED: That the following monogram is hereby adopted as the official monogram of the American Petroleum Institute;

BE IT FURTHER RESOLVED: That the general secretary or assistant general secretary be and they are hereby directed to authorize anyone desiring to do so to use such monogram under the following conditions:

Anyone desiring to use the monogram of the American Petroleum Institute shall apply to the American Petroleum Institute, New York 20, N. Y., using the form shown below, entitled: "Application to use official monogram of the American Petroleum Institute." Upon receipt of this application, properly acknowledged, and accompanied by a statement satisfactory to the Institute of the applicant's qualifications (when applicant is a manufacturer) to comply with the specification stated in the application, the secretary shall issue a certificate of authority to use the said monogram in the form shown below entitled: "Certificate of Authority to Use Official Monogram of the American Petroleum Institute."

Statement of Manufacturer's Qualifications to Use API Monogram

The information requested below must accompany all applications to use the monogram of the American Petroleum Institute on material to be manufactured in accordance with its specifications and intended for sale. All applicants are subject to investigation before licenses are granted. Applications may be rejected if information supplied does not warrant the issuing of the license.

(*Note:* If applicant has previously qualified as a licensee on material where serial-number gages are required, and certificates are desired for numbering additional gages, this statement is not necessary. It is also not necessary when applications are required for serial numbers of gages by users or consumers who desire to purchase gages for their own use or to control material not intended for sale.)

Material covered:...

(Give title and number of API specification covering the material on which applicant desires to use monogram.)

  1. Name:................... ....
                              (of applicant)
  2. Location of principal office and factory:.................................
....
                          (city, state, or country)
  3. Class of ownership:...
                     (corporation, partnership, or individual)
  4. Capital invested:...
  5. When organized:..
                       (year)
  6. Is the applicant actually manufacturing this material now?.................
                             ("Yes" or "No")
  7. State the length of time applicant has made the material and supplied it to the oil industry:..
                      (years and months)
  8. Approximately what proportion is this material to the average yearly output of all material made by applicant? ....

9. Give the names and addresses of five representative users of this equipment in the oil industry to whom applicant has sold this material:

Name   Company   Address

....

....

....

....

10. If applicant has not supplied this or similar material to the oil industry, state here the industries or other uses for which such material has been supplied:

....

....

....

11. Is the applicant thoroughly familiar with all stipulations given in the API specification covering the material?...

....

....

12. Does the applicant now possess the necessary equipment and personnel for conducting any tests required in the API specification covering this material?..........

PART III—AUTOMATIC GAGING DEVICES

1200. INTRODUCTION

If mutually agreeable, automatic tank gaging devices of known accuracy and which meet the following standards may be used to determine oil levels in atmospheric or low-pressure lease, field, storage, and working tanks for the purpose of custody transfer. The use of these standards as set forth herein should assist in assuring maximum measurement accuracies and dependability of results.

1201. DESCRIPTION OF GAGES

1201.1. Automatic Tank Gages

In contrast to hand gages (meaning those taken manually with a gage line), automatic tank gages are direct-reading gages which measure liquid level by various mechanical or combination mechanical-electrical means. Only 2 types of gages are described herein, viz.: 1, the float-actuated; and, 2, the surface-sensing. Such gages read directly at tank-top, ground, or eye level on either a graduated tape, dial inditor, or a mechanical counter. This does not preclude the use of other types of devices when they meet the standards of precision given herein and are mutually acceptable to the parties concerned.

The float-actuated–type gage measures changes in liquid level as a function of float travel. The float acts upon a counterbalanced tape which moves past a fixed point or reference mark, or upon a nongraduated tape or cable which moves a dial indicator or counter. The surface-sensing–type gage replaces the float type with a sensing element which detects changes in liquid level as a condition of unbalance in an electronic circuit which, by means of a reversible a-c drive motor, acts to restore balance by repositioning the sensing element in accordance with the liquid-level change. Readings are at tank-top or ground level on a mechanical counter driven directly from the control motor shaft.

1201.2. Remote-reading Automatic Tank Gages

The automatic tank gage may be made to read at a remote point from the tank, or tanks, by superimposing a secondary system known as remote transmission. Two combinations of this system are normally employed. The first is in conjunction with a tank-reading automatic gage where readings are available both at the tank and at a remote location. The second system is nonindicating, in that no visible means is provided for reading the automatic gage at the tank—the only readings being available at a remote location.   These systems are referred to, in order, as: 1, combination automatic and remote-reading gages; and, 2, remote-reading automatic gages.

Remote transmitting systems used with automatic tank gages are electric or electronic in principle, and are divided into the following types which make them suitable for single or selective tank installation as noted:

Impulse motor—single.
Single selsyn—single.
Selective single selsyn—selective.
Double selsyn—selective.
Step contact—selective.
Wheatstone-bridge electronic—selective.
Balanced input electronic—selective.
Impulse scanning—selective.
Voice telemetering transmitter—selective.

1201.3. Definitions of Terms Used

Automatic gaging tapes: The flexible measuring or connecting element—a section of which is graduated generally in feet, inches, and eighths of an inch—which is used to measure the liquid level in tanks by the automatic gage method: The length, width, and thickness of the tape—which may be either solid or perforated—depend upon the gage design, with the limits of accuracy of the tape length being $\pm \frac{1}{8}$ in. per 100 ft at 60 F.

Pressure lock: A manually operated semiautomatic gaging device, self-enclosed, which is used for the prevention of vapor losses in the gaging of atmospheric-pressure, variable-vapor-space, and high-pressure tanks.

Float: Buoyant member in a float-actuated automatic gage which floats on the measured medium and provides the force to position the graduated tape or dial indicator in accordance with liquid-level changes.

Sensing element: Detecting unit in an electronic surface-sensing automatic gage which directs the operation of the reversible a-c motor through the electronic control circuit.

Float guide wires or cables: Solid wire or flexible stranded cable used to guide the travel of an automatic gage float.

Positioning wires or cables: Solid or stranded wire or cable which connects the float to the tape or which drives the dial indicator or transmitter.

Anchor weight: A specified weight to which the float guide wires or cables are attached to hold them taut and plumb.

Tape entry: Point of cable or tape entry into tank.

Seal unit: Assembly used in tank installations to seal off the gage assembly from the tank vapors.

Sheaves: Support wheels over which tape, wire, or cable rides.

Float well: Cylindrical structure built into the roof of a floating-roof tank to contain and guide the float.

Gaging well or stilling well: Vertical, cylindrical gaging well or float well built into the tank for gaging or to guide the float or the sensing element so as to reduce errors arising from turbulence.

Dial indicator: Pointer and fixed-number dial, reading in calibrated increments.

Mechanical counter: Indicator composed of graduated wheels which align in proper sequence at a fixed index to indicate liquid-level reading.

Look box: That portion of the gage housing which contains a shielded or glassed-in opening through which a gage reading is observed.

Gravity compensator: Double index scale against which fixed reference pointer may be moved to correct for variations in gravity from a base point computed for water at 60 F.   The compensator is marked in both specific-gravity and API units.

Tape tester or manual-operation checker: A mechanical device, knob, or lever—which can be engaged through its connecting tape or cable—to lift or rock the float in order to assure that the float is free.

Counterweight: Device which exerts force or tension on tape or cable to hold connecting elements tight.

Remote transmission and telemetering: A separate or integral instrument system used in conjunction with some other basic measuring means—such as an automatic tank gage—which transmits the basic reading to some place other than the point of measurement.

Transmitter: That portion of a remote transmission system which constitutes the sending element.

Receiver: Companion instrument to transmitter in remote transmission system which remotely indicates or records tank-gage readings.

Single-tank remote gage: A remote transmission system which requires a separate receiver for each tank transmitter.

Selective-tank remote gage: A single receiver used with a remote transmission system which permits the use of one or more tank transmitters so that selective readings can be obtained by switching from one tank to another.

Selsyn: Type of electric a-c motor used to transmit motion and position.

Repeatability or reproducibility: The inherent ability of a gage or instrument to duplicate previous readings within established accuracy limits.

Calibration: The process or procedure of setting or bringing gages or instruments into agreement with the established reference standard or master.

Sensitivity: Term applied to the amount of indicated liquid-level change (plus or minus, measured in fractions of an inch) which is required to start the movement of a gage float or a sensing element.

Flotation level: The depth of submergence of a buoyant automatic gage float in a liquid of known density or weight.

1202. TESTING OF AUTOMATIC GAGES

The acceptance and use of direct- and remote-reading automatic tank gages in custody transfer requires that the basic accuracy and performance characteristics of such equipment should be established by means of a suitable shop-test method.   The required accuracy limits of either or both the direct- and remote-reading gage shall be within the tolerance specified.

1203. STANDARDS OF INSTALLATION

1203.1. General Installation Details

Any direct- and/or remote-reading automatic tank gage installed on any tank containing crude oil, which is or may be involved in custody transfer, must be installed in strict accordance with the instructions supplied by the manufacturer.   Properly qualified and authorized representatives of the joint parties involved shall make a final check and written report on the installation, before it is placed in service, to determine that all provisions set forth in the manufacturer's instructions have been complied with.   A copy of this report should be retained at the field location for ready reference.   Further, all such installations shall be in compliance with any governmental regulations.

The dependability and continuing accuracy of an automatic tank-gage installation is directly dependent upon the condition of the tank upon which it is installed.   Old and incorrectly erected tanks—particularly those with unstable bottoms, shells, or roofs—will introduce an appreciable amount of error and variation which no gage can correct.   For these reasons it is recommended that all tanks proposed for automatic gage installations should be carefully checked for their compliance with established construction and maintenance codes and standards.

Automatic tank gages can be installed either on tanks not in service or on tanks in service.   However, the installation of gages on tanks in service presents certain problems which may require some modification of the standard method of installation.   Such modifications shall be held to a minimum.   Automatic tank gages, the installations of which vary substantially from standard practice, may be used in custody transfer only when agreed to by the parties involved.   Because these installations are critical, the standard installation procedure shall be that for tanks not in service which will constitute the approved method of installation.

Automatic gages should be located in close proximity to the gaging hatch, yet sufficiently distant from the suction and filling lines to minimize disturbing effect of eddies, currents, or turbulence arising from these sources.

Either the ground-level or tank-top reading device should be at a convenient height or distance from the ground or the gaging platform to assure easy reading and to avoid reading errors.

The automatic gage-tape entry point should be such as to eliminate errors due to roof movement.

The datum plate directly under the gage hatch normally used should not be a part of the bottom of a tank the stability of which, under varying load conditions, is questionable.   The datum plate should be attached to and supported from the tank shell at a fixed distance from the bottom.

Excessive tank turbulence or agitation caused either by high emptying-filling rates or by mechanical agitators will seriously affect automatic gages.   The results may be severe enough to throw the unit out of calibration if it is a float-actuated unit, or may damage the sensing element if it is an electronic surface-sensing element.   Where these conditions exist, it may be necessary to enclose the measuring element in a stilling well, regardless of the tank type or the gage entry point.

1203.2. Standard Installation Procedure (Tanks Not in Service)

In other than floating-roof tank installations, the measuring element, unless surface sensing, must be guided or contained in a gaging well or stilling well.   The use of gaging wells or stilling wells for either type of gage on all types of tanks is recommended in order to increase accuracy and to minimize the effects of tank turbulence and agitation.

In floating-roof tank installations, it is recommended that gages be installed in a float well or, alternately, in a gaging well or stilling well, rather than attaching the actuating cable directly to the roof.   The float well should be of a proper size for the float, and should have a baffle or retainer in the bottom so as to prevent the float from escaping if the roof stops on its support legs when oil is pulled below the bottom of a well.   Entry hole must be of sufficient size to allow free movement of oil into and out of the float well for equalization of liquid level.   No floating-roof gage installation should have any tape exposed outside the tape pipe so as to minimize errors due to wind drift.   Exposed connecting link to the float should be maximum-diameter $\frac{1}{16}$-in. stainless-steel flexible cable.   Top elbow or pulley should be centered over cable hole in float-well cover.

All gages must be mounted securely to the tank shell, with sufficient brackets properly attached and adequately spaced to hold the gage rigidly in place and in proper alignment at all points.   The top horizontal tape conduit (extension arm) must be braced by support members from the top angle only.   When the gage is mounted, the tape line should center, and it must not touch or rub inside the tape pipe.

When a gage is installed in corrosive service, adequate provisions for sealing off or preventing vapors from entering the gage should be included, and the last exposed sheave assembly should be of a durable corrosion-resistant construction.   This provision does not apply to floating-roof tanks which utilize top entry unless a float stilling well is used.

Float guide wires should be installed plumb, properly centered, free of kinks or twists, and pulled tight under proper spring tension.   Float travel through the normal range from top to bottom of the tank should be smooth and free, with minimum of binding or friction.   The sensing element of an electronic gage should also be checked for unimpeded movement through its range of travel.

Tape, cable, counterweight assembly, and all components of the entire mechanism on both types of gages should be tried through the entire operating range to assure freedom of action.

When the gage installation is remote-reading only or remote-reading in addition to direct-reading, the installation-procedure check, described in the preceding paragraph, should be made both before and after the remote transmitter is connected into the drive mechanism. The transmitter should be checked for smoothness and freedom of movement prior to installation on the automatic gage.

The method of electrical tie-in and the receiver-installation details in a remote transmission system vary widely, depending upon the type and make of system employed. However, these installation details are well standardized, and the electrical tests to prove the system are definite and exact. For these reasons it is recommended that the manufacturer's instructions, including those of the company making the installation, should be followed.

1203.3. Installation Procedure (Tanks in Service)

The standard installation procedure applies only on tanks not in service. Except for the following special conditions, the same installation shall apply also when automatic gaging equipment is installed on tanks in service. The principal difference between the installation of an automatic gage on a tank in service and on one not in service is in the provision for guiding the float in a float-operated gage. An electronic gage, however, does not require guides for the sensing element. On the other hand, for both the electronic and float types, the tape conduit must be secured without using brackets welded to the vessel.

In the case of the float guides, it is common practice to use guide cables which are stranded and flexible instead of more rigid solid-construction guide wires. The lower ends of the cable are secured by attaching a suspended weight of sufficient mass to hold the guide cables straight. The weight is located just above the bottom of the tank. It should be the responsibility of the authorized inspector to assure that the weight is of sufficient mass that it is properly suspended at the right elevation from the bottom of the tank, and that the cables have been installed free of any kinks or loops which would interfere with the free operation of the float. The installation must be made when the tank is almost empty, and the entire mechanism can be checked by actual trial throughout its entire range to assure freedom of movement.

The method of attaching the gage to the tank may be by any appropriate means, but the attachment must be to the tank shell and must be sufficiently strong to hold the gage rigidly in place and in alignment. The operation of the tape or cable over the pulley should be checked carefully to assure that the tape does not crowd to one side or the other and create undue friction against the pulley flanges or rub at any point against the tape conduit.

A written report covering this type of installation shall be made, and a copy should be retained at the field location for ready reference for as long as the gage is continued in service. If this type of installation is replaced by one installed when the tank is out of service, the report shall be destroyed and a new one prepared in accordance with the standard installation procedure (see Par. 1203.2 hereinbefore).

1204. CALIBRATION PROCEDURE

1204.1. General Considerations

An automatic tank gage should be calibrated as part of the erection or installation of such equipment, and as often thereafter as is deemed essential by operating experience to insure dependable service and established accuracy within prescribed limits, except that the maximum period which any gage shall remain in service without recalibration must not exceed one year.

The basic measuring standard by which the automatic and/or remote-reading gages should be calibrated for accuracy is the manual gage. Such gages shall be in accordance with the procedure outlined in Part I, Sect. 1001, "Measuring Liquid Volume (Gaging)," of this standard, or other mutually agreeable methods.

Gages should be set or reset to agree with the manual gages obtained as outlined herein. Such settings should be done in accordance with the manufacturer's instructions.

Before any calibration is begun, sufficient waiting time should be allowed for the surface of the liquid in the tank to come to rest. An initial check period, at least equal to several cycles of filling the tank, should be allowed on any new or reconditioned installation or on any installation after a major change has been made. If after this period of time no appreciable change has been noted in the gage operation or reading, it may be assumed that the installation is stabilized, and calibration may be made.

Calibration of automatic gaging equipment should be avoided under extremes of temperature, high winds, or dust storms, and should approximate atmospheric and weather conditions similar to those under which the gage is normally used in custody transfer.

1204.2. Calibration (Hand-Line Method)

The standard gage line of certified accuracy, as outlined in Par. 1001.1-A hereinbefore of this standard, shall be used.

In general, the procedure for taking either an innage or an adjusted outage gage on fixed-roof or floating-roof tanks, as outlined in Par. 1001.2 hereinbefore of this standard, can be used.

Variable-vapor-space and pressure tanks require special gaging procedure because of their construction. For this reason, when gaging these types of tanks, reference should be made to *ASTM Designation D 1085-52T: "Gaging Petroleum and Petroleum Products."*

Two identical gage readings should be obtained with the tank contents at rest and recorded at each of several tank levels selected for calibration points. The automatic gage should be set to this or to these reference levels and rechecked. The method of setting varies between different makes and types of gages, and will be dependent upon the degree of correction required. In each instance the manufacturer's setting procedure should be followed.

1205. INSPECTION AND MAINTENANCE

A regular schedule of inspection and maintenance should be set up to insure the original installation accuracy of direct- and/or remote-reading tank gages. The frequency with which inspections should be made and the proper time interval for corrective maintenance can hardly be established as a fixed rule because varying contributing factors affecting the operation differ widely in various locations and in different types of service. The particular service conditions under which any given gage operates should be studied by the user in order to determine the correct routine of inspection and maintenance best suited to his individual needs.

PART IV—AUTOMATIC TEMPERATURE DEVICES

1300. INTRODUCTION

Automatic temperature devices are those by which the temperature is determined merely by observation of a dial, meter, or scale. No manual operations are involved other than the manipulation of a lever or an electrical switch. These devices may be used for temperature determinations on custody change measurements if mutually agreed to by the parties involved.

1301. ANGLE-STEM INDUSTRIAL-TYPE GLASS THERMOMETER

The angle-stem thermometer is installed in the tank by using a standard metal-separable well or socket. The glass stem of the thermometer shall be at least 3 ft long (for vertical tanks of less than 5,000-bbl capacity the stem may be 12 in. long) and protected with a light metal tube. The sensitive portion of the thermometer shall not exceed 2.5 in., and the stem may have an angle of 90 deg or greater to conform with the contour of the tank shell. A thermometer with a separate graduated scale is acceptable, provided the markings on the scale are permanently engraved, and provided temperature lines at approximately 80-F intervals are etched on the glass stem of the thermometer, coinciding with the corresponding lines on the scale.

1302. BIMETAL-ACTUATED DIAL THERMOMETER

The bimetal-actuated thermometer with dial indicator is installed in the tank by the use of a standard metal-separable well or socket. The stem of the thermometer shall be at least 3 ft long (for vertical tanks of less than 5,000-bbl capacity the stem may be 12 in. long) and the sensitive portion not more than 2.5 in. long.

1303. MERCURY-ACTUATED DIAL THERMOMETER

A mercury-actuated dial thermometer is installed in the tank by the use of a standard metal-separable well or socket. The stem of the thermometer shall be at least 3 ft long (for vertical tanks of less than 5,000-bbl capacity the stem may be 12 in. long) and the sensitive portion shall conform to the manufacturer's recommendation for the particular range involved. This thermometer may be connected through nonsensitve tube systems to a dial indicator or a recorder located not more than 60 ft from the thermometer bulb.

1304. GENERAL

The angle-stem, the bimetal-actuated, and the mercury-actuated dial thermometers shall be accurate to ± 1 F. They should be checked for accuracy by comparison with a National Bureau of Standards certified thermometer, or its equivalent, before being installed in the tank; they should also be checked at yearly intervals thereafter and, in addition, at any time they appear to have become inaccurate for any reason. These same provisions apply to dial indicators or recording devices which are connected to mercury-actuated bulb elements through nonsensitive tube systems.

1305. ELECTRICAL-RESISTANCE THERMOMETER FOR SPOT TEMPERA-TURES

The electrical-resistance thermometer operates on the basic principle that metals change their electrical resistance with changes in temperature. Inasmuch as the temperature coefficients of resistance of these metals are uniform, a measure of the change in these coefficients is used to indicate temperature.

A resistance thermometer consists of one or more wire resistors and a meter assembly for the indication of temperature. The meter assembly consists of a resistance network based upon the Wheatstone-bridge principle, a voltage supply, and a galvanometer calibrated in temperature units (degrees fahrenheit). A typical circuit is shown in Fig. 16-15. A ratio-type meter or its equivalent may be used in the circuit. The ratio-type meter is a modification of the conventional Wheatstone-bridge network, and is designed to eliminate errors caused by variations in voltage. If a standard bridge circuit is used, means must be provided for control of the voltage.

The resistance bulb referred to consists of a wire resistance unit, suitably housed and provided with leads. The housing shall be corrosion-resistant, made of low-sparking-tendency metal, with leads sealed so as to protect against contamination of conductors or connections. The individual resistance bulb shall be installed through the tank shell at the required level through conventional, separable sockets. For portable use, the bulb may be attached to a flexible cable, permitting it to be lowered through the gaging hatch to any desired level.

The galvanometer or meter scale should be graduated in single degrees fahrenheit over the range required, and it shall be calibrated for the type of wire used in the resistance units.   The meter may be located at the top of the tank, at ground level, or at any convenient location for remote reading.

If a given tank is equipped with more than one resistor bulb in order that spot temperatures may be determined at different points in the tank, a multi-point selector switch shall be used to connect the desired resistor to the meter.   Should one meter located at a central point be used to determine the temperature from single resistor bulbs in a number of different tanks, a selector switch shall be used to connect the desired resistor to the meter.

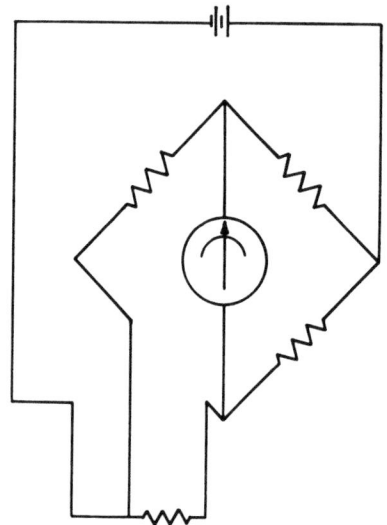

Fig. 16-15. Typical Wheatstone-bridge circuit.

1306. ELECTRICAL-RESISTANCE THER-MOMETER FOR AVERAGE TEM-PERATURES

In using the electrical-resistance thermometer for determining the average temperature of the vertical column of oil in a tank, the same basic principles apply as outlined in Sect. 1304 and 1305 hereinbefore, which cover electrical-resistance thermometers for spot temperatures.

In the averaging-type thermometer the resistance bulb (Fig. 16-16) consists of an assembly of insulated resistance units of various lengths, each unit being of equal resistance which is evenly distributed over the bulb's entire length.   The units are assembled in cable form and inserted in a flexible hose or thin-walled pipe to form the bulb.   The flexible hose or pipe shall be made of corrosion-resistant low-sparking-tendency metal.   The insulation used to cover the individual resistance units must be capable of withstanding the maximum temperature to which it may be subjected.

The number of individual resistance units which make up the bulb will depend upon the height of the tank, but in all cases the entire working range of the tank shall be

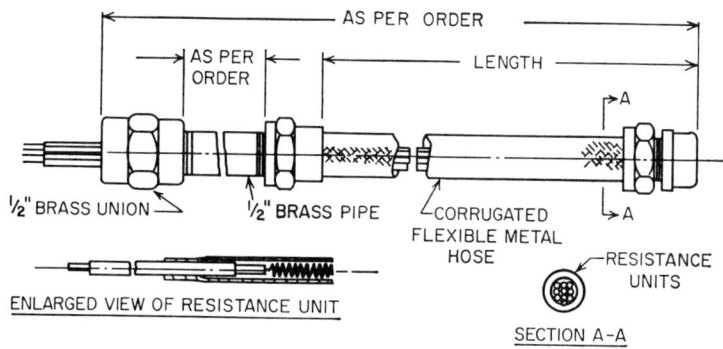

Fig. 16-16. Averaging-thermometer assembly.

covered [see Fig. 16-17 (a), (b), and (c)].   In tanks where a closing gage of 3 ft or less is sometimes necessary, the bulb shall be equipped with a spot-reading resistor at the 2-ft level.   The nonmerchantable oil line shall be maintained at least 1 ft below the spot-reading resistor.

The flexible hose, or the pipe conductor which contains the bundle of resistors, shall be suspended vertically in the tank by passing it through a flange in the tank roof located not less than 18 in. from the shell of the tank.

For a floating-roof tank installation, the flexible hose shall be suspended vertically from an angle bracket located on top of the tank shell, and shall pass through the

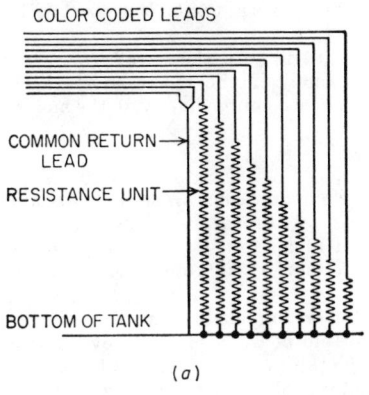

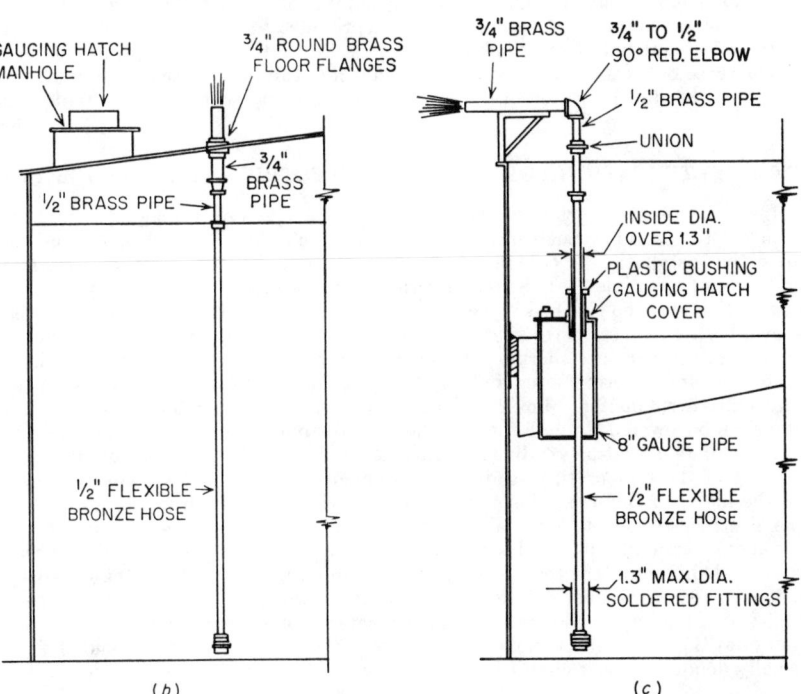

Fig. 16-17. (a) Schematic diagram of averaging-type resistance bulb.   (b) Cone-roof tank. (c) Floating-roof tank.

gaging hatch or other opening on the floating roof at least 18 in. from the tank shell. The angle bracket should be installed high enough to prevent damage by the floating roof in case of overfilling.

A multipoint selector switch shall be used to permit the separate connection to the meter of each resistor contained in the averaging-thermometer bulb.   The switch dial shall be marked to indicate the range of oil level served by the respective point for each resistor.

For installations in floating-roof tanks, the switch dial marking shall be corrected for the depth of oil in the roof gaging pipe because the temperature of the oil contained in the pipe may be several degrees different from the temperature of the main body of oil in the tank. In other words, the bundle or bulb is not to be energized within the roof level.

In operating the assembly, it is only necessary to turn the selector switch to the setting which corresponds to the longest completely submerged resistor. When the current is applied, the average temperature is indicated immediately on the meter scale.

1307. BULB-POSITIONING DEVICE

Where one or three sensitive thermometer elements—such as spot electrical-resistance thermometers or conventional mercury-actuated recording or dial thermometers with nonsensitive tube systems—are installed in a tank, the sensitive elements or bulbs shall be positioned in the same vertical column by suitable mechanical means in the tank.

In the case of a 3-spot assembly, one resistor or bulb shall be suspended 3 ft below the oil surface; the second, 3 ft above the bottom of the tank, but never lower than 1 ft above the nonmerchantable oil line; and the third shall be located at the mid-point of the oil height in such a manner that its position will be maintained regardless of the level of oil in the tank. Means shall also be provided to permit checking the position of the mid-point bulb from time to time to assure that it is in the proper location.

The three bulbs thus installed may be connected through nonsensitive tube systems to either the dial indicator or a recording instrument located on the tank shell at ground level.

1308. CERTIFICATION FOR ACCURACY (ELECTRICAL-RESISTANCE TYPES)

Electrical-resistance thermometers, of either the spot- or averaging-type, shall be accurate to ± 1.0 F. Such installations shall be checked for accuracy immediately after the installation is completed, at least at annual intervals thereafter, and, in addition, at any time that the reading appears to be inaccurate for any reason. The installation shall be checked by comparing the reading shown on the meter with that shown by a cup-case thermometer of known accuracy. In checking these spot temperatures, the cup-case thermometer shall be lowered to the same point as the spot-bulb resistance thermometer and to the same distance from the tank shell as the spot-bulb thermometer. For the averaging-type thermometer, the cup-case thermometer shall be lowered through the roof the same distance from the shell, and a sufficient number of temperature readings at various levels shall be carefully obtained. The average of the temperature readings shall be compared with the temperature shown on the meter of the averaging thermometer at the same depth in the tank. Should the electrical-resistance type fail to agree within 1 F of the cup-case determination, the meter assembly should be checked by comparing the meter reading with that shown when a standard resistor is substituted for the resistor bulb connected to the meter. A slow response on the meter indicator denotes low operating voltage. An "off-scale" reading on the upper end of the scale denotes an open circuit in a resistance unit or at the terminals or leads. An "off-scale" reading on the lower end of the scale usually denotes a short circuit in a resistance unit or in the leads.

MARINE—TANKSHIPS AND BARGES*

2000. MEASURING LIQUID VOLUME (GAGING)

A. Standards for measuring liquid volume (gaging) are set out in detail in Part I, Sect. 1001, hereinbefore. In addition, the requirements of the following paragraph shall apply also.

* Collectively referred to herein as "ship."

B. When loading or discharging a ship, shore-tank gages shall be "official." Two or more measurements shall be taken at each gaging of shore tanks until two identical readings are obtained.

2001. TEMPERATURE MEASUREMENT

Standards for temperature measurement are set out in detail in Part I, Sect. 1002, hereinbefore.

2002. SAMPLING

2002.1. Preliminary Examination of Shore Tanks

Tanks shall be examined for BS&W at the bottom before and after all loading or discharging operations. Water-finding paste is recommended for this purpose. Thieving paper or chalk should not be used so as to avoid errors caused by creepage. With heavier oils, a box thief of the bottom-closure type should be used. If it is not practicable to measure BS&W in this manner before and after every loading and discharging, the tanks should be examined at least once or twice a month, depending upon the number of loading and discharging (receiving) operations.

2002.2. Taking of Samples

Samples shall be taken:
  a. From the shore tanks before loading, and both before and after discharging.
  b. From the pipeline during loading and discharging.
  c. From the ship's tanks after loading and before discharging.

2002.3. Procuring Samples

A. Shore-tank samples: Shore-tank samples shall preferably be an "all-levels" sample as described in Part I, Par. 1003.2-A-*c* hereinbefore, or a running sample as described in Part I, Par. 1003.2-A-*d*.
  B. Pipeline samples: Pipeline samples for checking purposes only shall be taken as described in Part I, Par. 1003.2-B hereinbefore.
  C. Ship's tank samples: An "all-levels" sample as described in Part I, Par. 1003.2-A-*c* hereinbefore, or a running sample as described in Part I, Par. 1003.2-A-*d*, shall be obtained from the ship's cargo tanks, as follows:

Number of Grades	*Minimum Number of Samples*
1	3 *compartments*

Number of Compartments Containing One Grade	
1 or 2	Each *compartment*
3 to 6	2 *compartments*
7 or more	3 *compartments*

Additional samples to be taken if requested by the inspector.

2002.4. Size of Container

The size of the container shall be governed by the quantity of the sample required to supply all interested parties with the amount required for test purposes and to leave a like amount to be retained for future reference.

2002.5. Official Samples

When loading a ship, shore-tank samples shall be "official." However, ship's tank samples shall also be tested for BS&W and for quality, when required; and the results of these tests, together with tests of shore-tank samples, shall be shown on the cargo certificate. When discharging a ship, ship's tank samples shall be "official."

2003. GRAVITY DETERMINATION

Details for gravity determination are set out in Part I, Sect. 1004, hereinbefore.

2004. SEALING

A general practice of sealing tank outlets is not deemed necessary for marine storage terminals, but it may be done at the request of the buyer's or the seller's representative or inspector.

When so requested, suction gates and bleeder valves shall be sealed by lead-pellet-wire meter seals or other suitable seals. Padlocks and chains should not be used, as they might hinder the transfer of oil from the tank in case of fire.

2005. BS&W (WATER AND SEDIMENT)

ASTM Designation D 96-46: "Standard Method of Test for Water and Sediment in Petroleum Products by Means of Centrifuge" shall be used for the determination of BS&W, except that the field centrifuge method, described in Part II, Sect. 1103, of this standard, may be used when no suitable power is available at the marine terminal

2006. CORRECTIONS AND CONVERSIONS

All crude-oil volume shall be corrected to 60 F.

Table 7: "Reduction of Volume to 60 F Against API Gravity at 60 F (Abridged Table)" of the *ASTM-IP Petroleum Measurement Tables* (ASTM Designation D 1250; IP Designation 200—see Appendix "C" hereinafter) shall be used in making the correction, except where the method conflicts with governmental regulations.

For the conversion of volume measurement to weight, Table 8: "Pounds Per U.S. Gallon at 60 F and U.S. Gallons at 60 F Per Pound Against API Gravity at 60 F" of the *ASTM-IP Petroleum Measurement Tables* shall be used. An abridgement of this table appears in the appendix to Part I, Sect. 1004, "Gravity Determination," p. **16-12**, hereinbefore.

2007. DISPLACEMENT OF OIL IN PIPELINES

Shore pipelines shall be left in the same condition (full or empty) after loading or discharging as they were before these operations were commenced. It is recommended that shore pipelines be kept full of the commodity to be handled at the time opening and closing gages are taken.

A shore pipeline to be used for loading or discharging a ship shall be displaced if it contains a grade of oil in sufficient quantities to degrade seriously the oil to be loaded or discharged. At some sea loading or discharging terminals, water is required by loading regulations, and in such cases water may be used as a displacing medium.

Whenever oil or water is used for displacement, completion of the operation shall be determined by the quality of the shore-line samples and checked by tank gages.

2008. INSPECTION OF SHIP'S TANKS

All ship's tanks shall be inspected for dryness before loading and after discharging by both the supplier's and the consignee's inspectors, and this information shall be recorded on the *Ship's Ullage Report*.

Samples shall be taken from the ship's tanks, in accordance with Par. 2002.3-C hereinbefore, immediately after loading has been completed and before discharging has commenced.   When cargo is heated, the temperature of oil in the ship's tanks should also be measured by taking a single temperature measurement at the middle of the oil in each tank, in accordance with the procedure given in Part I, Par. 1002.2, of this standard.   When cargo is not heated, the following temperatures are to be obtained from the ship's tanks:

Number of Grades	Minimum Number of Temperature Measurements
1	3 *compartments*

Number of Compartments Containing One Grade	
1 or 2	Each *compartment*
3 to 6	2 *compartments*
7 or more	3 *compartments*

Ship's officers and shore representatives shall take joint readings of ullages and temperatures of the ship's tanks, and this information shall be recorded on the *Ship's Ullage Report.*

2009. GENERAL REMARKS

When a ship is loading or discharging, no withdrawals shall be made from the shore tanks or pipelines which are being used by the ship.

When a tankship is loaded from or discharged into barges, etc., the tankship's ullages and temperatures before and after, and the barge's ullages and temperatures before and after, shall be very carefully taken, and a report covering this information shall be forwarded to the supplier, the consignee, and the ship's owner or operator. This quantity of cargo loaded or discharged by the barge shall be determined by gaging the shore tank at the point at which the barge is loaded or discharged.

2009.1. Cargo Intake or Outturn Certificates

Cargo intake or outturn certificates shall be prepared for each loading or discharging of a tankship or barge, and a copy shall be furnished the supplier, the consignee, and the ship's owner or operator.   These certificates shall include the following information:

A. Cargo intake or outturn certificate (shore tanks)

Name of ship.
Loading or discharging terminal.
Date.
Shore tank No.
Grade of crude.
API gravity at 60 F.
Opening: gage, temperature, quantity at observed temperature, and quantity converted to 60 F (when required).
Closing: gage, temperature, quantity at observed temperature, and quantity converted to 60 F (when required).
Coefficient of expansion or multiplier.
Gross quantity (barrels) loaded or discharged at 60 F.
BS&W, per cent and quantity.
Net quantity (barrels) loaded or discharged at 60 F, excluding BS&W.
Quantity in long tons (when required).
Condition of shore pipelines before loading or discharging (full or empty).
Condition of shore pipelines after loading or discharging (full or empty).

B. Ship's ullage report

Name of ship.

Date.

Loading or discharging terminal.

The following information for each ship's cargo tank:

Number of ship's tanks.

Grade of crude.

Condition (empty, or inches of BS&W) or ullage before loading or discharging.

Condition (empty, or inches of BS&W) or ullage after loading or discharging.

Temperature, degrees fahrenheit.

Any irregularity which occurred during loading or discharging, such as cargo overflow, bursting of hose, leakage, etc., and an estimate of the quantity lost thereby.

Ship's draft (fore and aft) before loading and after loading.

Ship's draft (fore and aft) before discharging and after discharging.

This report should be signed by the cargo inspector and the ship's senior deck officer on duty.

APPENDIX "A"

COMMITTEE ON CODE 25 OF THE AMERICAN PETROLEUM INSTITUTE

(1954)

Officers

H. C. Packard (*Chairman*)	Shell Oil Co	New York, N. Y.
G. H. Supple (*Vice Chairman*)	General Petroleum Corp	Los Angeles, Calif.
R. Charles Nicholson (*Vice Chairman*)	Shell Pipe Line Corp	Houston, Texas
E. O. Mattocks (*Secretary*)	American Petroleum Institute	New York, N. Y.

Members

H. H. Anderson	Trans-Mountain Oil Pipe Line Co	Vancouver, British Columbia, Canada
F. D. Arthur (alternate to S. F. Spencer)	Keystone Shipping Co	Houston, Texas
F. L. Aurin	Southland Royalty Co	Fort Worth, Texas
G. E. Baque	The Buckeye Pipe Line Co	Lima, Ohio
F. B. Behrens	Wilshire Oil Co., Inc	Los Angeles, Calif.
Walter Biery	Mid-Continent Pipe Line Co	Tulsa, Okla.
Bowman Brannon	Charles Martin and Co	Port Arthur, Texas
Floyd Brett	Sinclair Oil and Gas Co	Tulsa, Okla.
R. C. Buchan	Humble Oil and Refining Co	Houston, Texas
L. W. Burdett (alternate to J. A. Sleeth)	Union Oil Co. of California	Brea, Calif.
E. D. Butcher	Butcher-Arthur, Inc	Houston, Texas
D. H. Carpenter	Sohio Petroleum Co	Oklahoma City, Okla.
A. S. Chamberlain	Ashland Oil and Refining Co	Ashland, Ky.
R. J. Cooke	Gulf Oil Corp	New York, N. Y.
J. R. Dean (alternate to O. D. Stallard, Jr.)	Magnolia Pipe Line Co	Wichita Falls, Texas
P. L. DeVerter	Humble Oil and Refining Co	Baytown, Texas
S. H. Dowdell	The British American Oil Co., Ltd	Toronto, Ontario, Canada
L. W. Dyer	The Globe Oil and Refining Co	Wichita, Kans.
Roger Enders	The Hancock Oil Co. of California	Long Beach, Calif.
J. E. Gosline	Standard Oil Co. of California	San Francisco, Calif.
R. A. Hamill (alternate to A. H. Newberg)	Service Pipe Line Co	Tulsa, Okla.
H. M. Hancock	The Atlantic Refining Co	Philadelphia, Pa.
J. K. Haraway	Midwest Oil Corp	Denver, Colo.

D. L. Harlan......................The Texas Co................Houston, Texas
C. G. Herrigton...................The Carter Oil Co............Tulsa, Okla.
C. K. Hewes......................Richfield Oil Corp...........Wilmington, Calif.
E. L. Hoffman....................Socony-Vacuum Oil Co., Inc...New York, N. Y.
F. P. Irwin......................Imperial Oil Limited.........Toronto, Ontario, Canada
H. S. Kelly......................Phillips Petroleum Co........Bartlesville, Okla.
S. G. Kershner...................The Texas Pipe Line Co.......Houston, Texas
Karl Krech.......................The Atlantic Refining Co.....Philadelphia, Pa.
P. K. Kuhne......................Gulf Oil Corp................Pittsburgh, Pa.
E. R. Laughner
  (alternate to A. S. Chamberlain)..Ashland Oil and Refining Co...Ashland, Ky.
Ben Leuty........................Cities Service Oil Co.
                                   (Delaware)................Bartlesville, Okla.
Harry Levin......................The Texas Co.,
                                   Beacon Research Laboratories.Beacon, N. Y.
J. G. Light......................McColl-Frontenac Oil Co., Ltd. Montreal, Quebec, Canada
R. E. Luton......................The Ohio Oil Co..............Findlay, Ohio
C. H. Lynam......................Standard Oil Co. of California. El Segundo, Calif.
Paschal Martin...................The Pure Oil Co..............Chicago, Ill.
J. H. McClintock.................Esso Standard Oil Co.........New York, N. Y.
J. T. McCoy......................Tide Water Associated Oil Co..Bayonne, N. J.
D. C. McKinley...................Interstate Oil Pipe Line Co...Shreveport, La.
J. W. Meehan.....................Pure Transportation Co.......Chicago, Ill.
R. H. Meyer......................Sinclair Pipe Line Co........Independence, Kans.
A. E. Miller.....................Sinclair Refining Co.........New York, N. Y.
F. W. Miller.....................Esso Shipping Co.............New York, N. Y.
L. Mittelman.....................Tide Water Associated Oil Co..Associated, Calif.
A. H. Newberg....................Service Pipe Line Co.........Tulsa, Okla.
W. C. Nidever
  (alternate to W. C. Roberts).....Shell Oil Co.................Los Angeles, Calif.
S. D. Osborne....................National Transit Co..........Oil City, Pa.
R. K. Paine......................Standard Oil Co. of California..San Francisco, Calif.
E. O. Perkins....................The Texas Co.................New York, N. Y.
W. C. Roberts....................Shell Oil Co.................Los Angeles, Calif.
J. H. Robinson...................Union Oil Co. of California...Los Angeles, Calif.
L. D. Sage.......................Richfield Oil Corp...........Long Beach, Calif.
Hill Sanders.....................Sun Pipe Line Co. (Texas)....Beaumont, Texas
W. W. Scheumann..................Cities Service Research
                                   and Development Co.......New York, N. Y.
M. H. Shanahan...................Continental Oil Co...........Ponca City, Okla.
W. L. Shannon....................Gulf Oil Corp................Houston, Texas
J. R. Shipley, Jr................Sohio Pipe Line Co...........St. Louis, Mo.
J. A. Sleeth.....................Union Oil Co. of California...Los Angeles, Calif.
R. H. Smith......................Signal Oil and Gas Co........Los Angeles, Calif.
W. E. Soden......................Sun Oil Co...................Philadelphia, Pa.
S. F. Spencer....................Keystone Shipping Co.........Philadelphia, Pa.
H. C. Spindell...................E. W. Saybolt and Co.........Elizabeth, N. J.
O. D. Stallard, Jr...............Magnolia Pipe Line Co........Dallas, Texas
O. J. Thompson...................Standard Oil Co. (Indiana)...Whiting, Ind.
T. C. Towl.......................Southern Pipe Line Co........Pittsburgh, Pa.
J. H. Tubbs......................Deep Rock Oil Corp...........Tulsa, Okla.
J. E. Young
  (alternate to F. C. Whiteside)....Continental Pipe Line Co.....Ponca City, Okla.
W. H. Wallace....................Phillips Pipe Line Co........Bartlesville, Okla.
F. H. Warren.....................The Ohio Oil Co..............Findlay, Ohio
F. C. Whiteside..................Continental Pipe Line Co.....Ponca City, Okla.
J. Harry Wood, Jr................Atlantic Pipe Line Co........Dallas, Texas
L. S. Wrightsman.................Humble Pipe Line Co..........Houston, Texas
Joseph Zaba......................Standard Oil and Gas Co......Tulsa, Okla.

Ex-officio Members

General Chairman, API Financial and Accounting Committee:
Max Lorimore.....................Union Oil Co. of California....Los Angeles, Calif.

Chairman, API Central Committee on Pipeline Transportation:

Ralph B. McLaughlin . . . . The Texas Pipe Line Co . . . . Houston, Texas

Chairman, API Committee on Tank Vessels:

William G. Anderson . . . . The Atlantic Refining Co . . . . . . Philadelphia, Pa.

Chairman, ASTM Division II of Committee D-2:

C. A. Neusbaum . . . . Standard Oil Development Co . . Linden, N. J.

APPENDIX "B"
TABLE 5*

REDUCTION OF OBSERVED API GRAVITY TO API GRAVITY AT 60° F

This table gives the values of API gravity at 60° F corresponding to API gravities observed with a glass hydrometer at temperatures other than 60° F. The expression "API Gravity at Observed Temperature" appears in Table 5 since it is the term most generally used in industry. A more exact expression would be "API hydrometer indication at the observed temperature." The API hydrometer indication at temperature $t°$ F differs slightly from the true API gravity because of the change in volume of the glass hydrometer from that at the calibration temperature 60° F.

It is generally impracticable to determine an API gravity at exactly 60° F, although it is at this temperature only that strictly correct results are obtained with a standard soft glass hydrometer calibrated at 60° F. In converting an API gravity at the observed temperature $t°$ F (API hydrometer indication) to the corresponding API gravity at 60° F, two corrections are necessary: the first arises from the change in volume of the glass hydrometer with temperature, and the second from the change in volume of the oil. Both have been applied in this table.

This table must be entered with API gravities (hydrometer indications) measured with a soft hydrometer calibrated at 60° F.

EXAMPLE NO. 1

If the API gravity reading observed on a hydrometer in an oil at 76° F is 38.4°, what is its API gravity at 60° F?

Enter the table in the column "API Gravity at Observed Temperature," headed
38° API, and note that against an "Observed Temperature" of 76° F the corresponding API gravity at 60 F is . . . . 36.8° API

Likewise, note that for 39° API at 76° F the corresponding API gravity at 60° is . 37.8° API

This represents an increase of 1.0° API at 60° F for an increase of 1.0° API in the value at 76° F. Therefore, by simple proportion, an increase at 76° F from 38 to 38.4° API increases the corresponding API gravity at 60° F by 0.4 × 1.0 or . . . . 0.4° API

Then, the API gravity at 60° F corresponding to the observed API gravity of
38.4 at 76° F is 36.8 +0.4 or . . . . 37.2° API

When interpolation according to the above procedure gives a result to two decimal places, it is rounded off to the nearest tenth of a degree API. When the figure in the second decimal place is 4 or less, it is dropped. When the figure in the second decimal place is 5 or greater, the figure in the first decimal place is increased one unit.

* Reproduced herein by permission of the copyright owner, The American Socy. for Testing Materials, 1916 Race St., Philadelphia 3, Pa.

EXAMPLE NO. 2

If the API gravity reading observed on a hydrometer in an oil at 77° F is 63.5°, what is its API gravity at 60° F?

Enter the table in the column "API Gravity at Observed Temperature," headed
63° API, and note that against an "Observed Temperature" of 77° F the corresponding API gravity at 60° F is....................................... 61.0° API
Likewise, note that for 64° API at 77° F the corresponding API gravity at 60° F
is... 61.9° API
This represents an increase of 0.9° API at 60° F for an increase of 1.0° API at
77° F.   Therefore, by simple proportion, an increase at 77° F from 63 to 63.5°
API increases the corresponding API gravity at 60° F by 0.5×0.9=0.45
which becomes... 0.5° API
Then, the API gravity of 60° F corresponding to the observed API gravity at
63.5 at 77° F is 61.0+0.5 or... 61.5° API

The following table provides a convenient means for obtaining interpolation values according to the above procedure.   The figures taken from this table are to be added to API gravities at 60° F corresponding to the whole number of degrees "observed API gravity."

Difference at 60° F per Degree Observed API Gravity	Fractional Degrees Observed API Gravity								
	0.1	0.2	0.3	0.4	0.5	0.6	0.7	0.8	0.9
0.8......	0.1	0.2	0.2	0.3	0.4	0.5	0.6	0.6	0.7
0.9......	0.1	0.2	0.3	0.4	0.5	0.5	0.6	0.7	0.8
1.0......	0.1	0.2	0.3	0.4	0.5	0.6	0.7	0.8	0.9
1.1......	0.1	0.2	0.3	0.4	0.6	0.7	0.8	0.9	1.0
1.2......	0.1	0.2	0.4	0.5	0.6	0.7	0.8	1.0	1.1

PRODUCTION EQUIPMENT

Table 5

API Gravity Reduction to 60° F. ASTM—IP

Observed Temperature, °F.	API Gravity at Observed Temperature									
	0	1	2	3	4	5	6	7	8	9
	Corresponding API Gravity at 60° F.									
0	2.6	3.6	4.7	5.7	6.8	7.9	8.9	10.0	11.0	12.1
1	2.5	3.6	4.6	5.7	6.7	7.8	8.9	9.9	11.0	12.0
2	2.5	3.5	4.6	5.6	6.7	7.8	8.8	9.9	10.9	12.0
3	2.4	3.5	4.5	5.6	6.6	7.7	8.8	9.8	10.9	11.9
4	2.4	3.4	4.5	5.5	6.6	7.7	8.7	9.8	10.8	11.9
5	2.3	3.4	4.4	5.5	6.6	7.6	8.7	9.7	10.8	11.8
6	2.3	3.3	4.4	5.4	6.5	7.6	8.6	9.7	10.7	11.8
7	2.2	3.3	4.3	5.4	6.5	7.5	8.6	9.6	10.7	11.7
8	2.2	3.3	4.3	5.4	6.4	7.5	8.5	9.6	10.6	11.6
9	2.2	3.2	4.3	5.3	6.4	7.4	8.5	9.5	10.6	11.6
10	2.1	3.2	4.2	5.3	6.3	7.4	8.4	9.5	10.5	11.5
11	2.1	3.1	4.2	5.2	6.3	7.3	8.4	9.4	10.5	11.5
12	2.0	3.1	4.1	5.2	6.2	7.3	8.3	9.4	10.4	11.4
13	2.0	3.0	4.1	5.1	6.2	7.2	8.3	9.3	10.3	11.4
14	1.9	3.0	4.0	5.1	6.1	7.2	8.2	9.3	10.3	11.3
15	1.9	2.9	4.0	5.0	6.1	7.1	8.2	9.2	10.2	11.3
16	1.9	2.9	3.9	5.0	6.0	7.1	8.1	9.2	10.2	11.2
17	1.8	2.9	3.9	4.9	6.0	7.0	8.1	9.1	10.1	11.2
18	1.8	2.8	3.8	4.9	5.9	7.0	8.0	9.1	10.1	11.1
19	1.7	2.8	3.8	4.8	5.9	6.9	8.0	9.0	10.0	11.1
20	1.7	2.7	3.8	4.8	5.8	6.9	7.9	9.0	10.0	11.0
21	1.6	2.7	3.7	4.7	5.8	6.8	7.9	8.9	9.9	11.0
22	1.6	2.6	3.7	4.7	5.7	6.8	7.8	8.8	9.9	10.9
23	1.6	2.6	3.6	4.7	5.7	6.7	7.8	8.8	9.8	10.9
24	1.5	2.5	3.6	4.6	5.6	6.7	7.7	8.7	9.8	10.8
25	1.5	2.5	3.5	4.6	5.6	6.6	7.7	8.7	9.7	10.8
26	1.4	2.5	3.5	4.5	5.6	6.6	7.6	8.6	9.7	10.7
27	1.4	2.4	3.4	4.5	5.5	6.5	7.6	8.6	9.6	10.7
28	1.3	2.4	3.4	4.4	5.5	6.5	7.5	8.5	9.6	10.6
29	1.3	2.3	3.4	4.4	5.4	6.4	7.5	8.5	9.5	10.6
30	1.3	2.3	3.3	4.3	5.4	6.4	7.4	8.4	9.5	10.5
31	1.2	2.2	3.3	4.3	5.3	6.3	7.4	8.4	9.4	10.5
32	1.2	2.2	3.2	4.2	5.3	6.3	7.3	8.4	9.4	10.4
33	1.1	2.2	3.2	4.2	5.2	6.3	7.3	8.3	9.3	10.4
34	1.1	2.1	3.1	4.2	5.2	6.2	7.2	8.3	9.3	10.3
35	1.0	2.1	3.1	4.1	5.1	6.2	7.2	8.2	9.2	10.2
36	1.0	2.0	3.0	4.1	5.1	6.1	7.1	8.2	9.2	10.2
37	1.0	2.0	3.0	4.0	5.0	6.1	7.1	8.1	9.1	10.1
38	0.9	1.9	3.0	4.0	5.0	6.0	7.0	8.1	9.1	10.1
39	0.9	1.9	2.9	3.9	4.9	6.0	7.0	8.0	9.0	10.0
40	0.8	1.8	2.9	3.9	4.9	5.9	6.9	8.0	9.0	10.0
41	0.8	1.8	2.8	3.8	4.9	5.9	6.9	7.9	8.9	9.9
42	0.7	1.8	2.8	3.8	4.8	5.8	6.8	7.9	8.9	9.9
43	0.7	1.7	2.7	3.8	4.8	5.8	6.8	7.8	8.8	9.8
44	0.7	1.7	2.7	3.7	4.7	5.7	6.7	7.8	8.8	9.8
45	0.6	1.6	2.6	3.7	4.7	5.7	6.7	7.7	8.7	9.7
46	0.6	1.6	2.6	3.6	4.6	5.6	6.7	7.7	8.7	9.7
47	0.5	1.6	2.6	3.6	4.6	5.6	6.6	7.6	8.6	9.6
48	0.5	1.5	2.5	3.5	4.5	5.5	6.6	7.6	8.6	9.6
49	0.5	1.5	2.5	3.5	4.5	5.5	6.5	7.5	8.5	9.5

Table 5 (*Continued*)

ASTM—IP   API Gravity Reduction to 60° F.   0–9° API

Observed Temper- ature, °F.	API Gravity at Observed Temperature									
	0	1	2	3	4	5	6	7	8	9
	Corresponding API Gravity at 60° F.									
50	0.4	1.4	2.4	3.4	4.4	5.5	6.5	7.5	8.5	9.5
51	0.4	1.4	2.4	3.4	4.4	5.4	6.4	7.4	8.4	9.4
52	0.3	1.3	2.3	3.4	4.4	5.4	6.4	7.4	8.4	9.4
53	0.3	1.3	2.3	3.3	4.3	5.3	6.3	7.3	8.3	9.3
54	0.2	1.3	2.3	3.3	4.3	5.3	6.3	7.3	8.3	9.3
55	0.2	1.2	2.2	3.2	4.2	5.2	6.2	7.2	8.2	9.2
56	0.2	1.2	2.2	3.2	4.2	5.2	6.2	7.2	8.2	9.2
57	0.1	1.1	2.1	3.1	4.1	5.1	6.1	7.1	8.1	9.1
58	0.1	1.1	2.1	3.1	4.1	5.1	6.1	7.1	8.1	9.1
59	0.0	1.0	2.0	3.0	4.0	5.0	6.0	7.0	8.0	9.0
60	...	1.0	2.0	3.0	4.0	5.0	6.0	7.0	8.0	9.0
61	...	1.0	2.0	3.0	4.0	5.0	6.0	7.0	8.0	9.0
62	...	0.9	1.9	2.9	3.9	4.9	5.9	6.9	7.9	8.9
63	...	0.9	1.9	2.9	3.9	4.9	5.9	6.9	7.9	8.9
64	...	0.8	1.8	2.8	3.8	4.8	5.8	6.8	7.8	8.8
65	...	0.8	1.8	2.8	3.8	4.8	5.8	6.8	7.8	8.8
66	...	0.7	1.7	2.7	3.7	4.7	5.7	6.7	7.7	8.7
67	...	0.7	1.7	2.7	3.7	4.7	5.7	6.7	7.7	8.7
68	...	0.7	1.7	2.7	3.6	4.6	5.6	6.6	7.6	8.6
69	...	0.6	1.6	2.6	3.6	4.6	5.6	6.6	7.6	8.6
70	...	0.6	1.6	2.6	3.6	4.5	5.5	6.5	7.5	8.5
71	...	0.5	1.5	2.5	3.5	4.5	5.5	6.5	7.5	8.5
72	...	0.5	1.5	2.5	3.5	4.5	5.4	6.4	7.4	8.4
73	...	0.5	1.4	2.4	3.4	4.4	5.4	6.4	7.4	8.4
74	...	0.4	1.4	2.4	3.4	4.4	5.4	6.3	7.3	8.3
75	...	0.4	1.4	2.3	3.3	4.3	5.3	6.3	7.3	8.3
76	...	0.3	1.3	2.3	3.3	4.3	5.3	6.3	7.3	8.2
77	...	0.3	1.3	2.3	3.2	4.2	5.2	6.2	7.2	8.2
78	...	0.2	1.2	2.2	3.2	4.2	5.2	6.2	7.1	8.1
79	...	0.2	1.2	2.2	3.2	4.1	5.1	6.1	7.1	8.1
80	...	0.2	1.1	2.1	3.1	4.1	5.1	6.1	7.1	8.0
81	...	0.1	1.1	2.1	3.1	4.1	5.0	6.0	7.0	8.0
82	...	0.1	1.1	2.0	3.0	4.0	5.0	6.0	7.0	7.9
83	...	0.0	1.0	2.0	3.0	4.0	5.0	5.9	6.9	7.9
84	...	...	1.0	2.0	2.9	3.9	4.9	5.9	6.9	7.8
85	...	...	0.9	1.9	2.9	3.9	4.9	5.8	6.8	7.8
86	...	...	0.9	1.9	2.9	3.8	4.8	5.8	6.8	7.8
87	...	...	0.9	1.8	2.8	3.8	4.8	5.7	6.7	7.7
88	...	...	0.8	1.8	2.8	3.7	4.7	5.7	6.7	7.7
89	...	...	0.8	1.7	2.7	3.7	4.7	5.7	6.6	7.6
90	...	...	0.7	1.7	2.7	3.7	4.6	5.6	6.6	7.6
91	...	...	0.7	1.7	2.6	3.6	4.6	5.6	6.5	7.5
92	...	...	0.6	1.6	2.6	3.6	4.5	5.5	6.5	7.5
93	...	...	0.6	1.6	2.6	3.5	4.5	5.5	6.5	7.4
94	...	...	0.6	1.5	2.5	3.5	4.5	5.4	6.4	7.4
95	...	...	0.5	1.5	2.5	3.4	4.4	5.4	6.4	7.3
96	...	...	0.5	1.5	2.4	3.4	4.4	5.3	6.3	7.3
97	...	...	0.4	1.4	2.4	3.4	4.3	5.3	6.3	7.2
98	...	...	0.4	1.4	2.3	3.3	4.3	5.3	6.2	7.2
99	...	...	0.4	1.3	2.3	3.3	4.2	5.2	6.2	7.1

PRODUCTION EQUIPMENT

Table 5 (Continued)

0-9° API   API Gravity Reductions to 60° F.   ASTM—IP

Observed Temperature, °F.	API Gravity at Observed Temperature									
	0	1	2	3	4	5	6	7	8	9
	Corresponding API Gravity at 60° F.									
100	. . .	. . .	0.3	1.3	2.3	3.2	4.2	5.2	6.1	7.1
101	. . .	. . .	0.3	1.2	2.2	3.2	4.1	5.1	6.1	7.1
102	. . .	. . .	0.2	1.2	2.2	3.1	4.1	5.1	6.0	7.0
103	. . .	. . .	0.2	1.2	2.1	3.1	4.1	5.0	6.0	7.0
104	. . .	. . .	0.1	1.1	2.1	3.0	4.0	5.0	5.9	6.9
105	. . .	. . .	0.1	1.1	2.0	3.0	4.0	4.9	5.9	6.9
106	. . .	. . .	0.1	1.0	2.0	3.0	3.9	4.9	5.9	6.8
107	. . .	. . .	0.0	1.0	2.0	2.9	3.9	4.8	5.8	6.8
108	. . .	. . .	. . .	0.9	1.9	2.9	3.8	4.8	5.8	6.7
109	. . .	. . .	. . .	0.9	1.9	2.8	3.8	4.8	5.7	6.7
110	. . .	. . .	. . .	0.9	1.8	2.8	3.7	4.7	5.7	6.6
111	. . .	. . .	. . .	0.8	1.8	2.7	3.7	4.7	5.6	6.6
112	. . .	. . .	. . .	0.8	1.7	2.7	3.7	4.6	5.6	6.5
113	. . .	. . .	. . .	0.7	1.7	2.7	3.6	4.6	5.5	6.5
114	. . .	. . .	. . .	0.7	1.7	2.6	3.6	4.5	5.5	6.5
115	. . .	. . .	. . .	0.6	1.6	2.6	3.5	4.5	5.5	6.4
116	. . .	. . .	. . .	0.6	1.6	2.5	3.5	4.4	5.4	6.4
117	. . .	. . .	. . .	0.6	1.5	2.5	3.4	4.4	5.4	6.3
118	. . .	. . .	. . .	0.5	1.5	2.4	3.4	4.4	5.3	6.3
119	. . .	. . .	. . .	0.5	1.4	2.4	3.4	4.3	5.3	6.2
120	. . .	. . .	. . .	0.4	1.4	2.4	3.3	4.3	5.2	6.2
121	. . .	. . .	. . .	0.4	1.4	2.3	3.3	4.2	5.2	6.1
122	. . .	. . .	. . .	0.4	1.3	2.3	3.2	4.2	5.1	6.1
123	. . .	. . .	. . .	0.3	1.3	2.2	3.2	4.1	5.1	6.0
124	. . .	. . .	. . .	0.3	1.2	2.2	3.1	4.1	5.0	6.0
125	. . .	. . .	. . .	0.2	1.2	2.1	3.1	4.0	5.0	6.0
126	. . .	. . .	. . .	0.2	1.1	2.1	3.0	4.0	5.0	5.9
127	. . .	. . .	. . .	0.1	1.1	2.1	3.0	4.0	4.9	5.9
128	. . .	. . .	. . .	0.1	1.1	2.0	3.0	3.9	4.9	5.8
129	. . .	. . .	. . .	0.1	1.0	2.0	2.9	3.9	4.8	5.8
130	. . .	. . .	. . .	0.0	1.0	1.9	2.9	3.8	4.8	5.7
131	. . .	. . .	. . .	. . .	0.9	1.9	2.8	3.8	4.7	5.7
132	. . .	. . .	. . .	. . .	0.9	1.8	2.8	3.7	4.7	5.6
133	. . .	. . .	. . .	. . .	0.8	1.8	2.7	3.7	4.6	5.6
134	. . .	. . .	. . .	. . .	0.8	1.8	2.7	3.7	4.6	5.6
135	. . .	. . .	. . .	. . .	0.8	1.7	2.7	3.6	4.6	5.5
136	. . .	. . .	. . .	. . .	0.7	1.7	2.6	3.6	4.5	5.5
137	. . .	. . .	. . .	. . .	0.7	1.6	2.6	3.5	4.5	5.4
138	. . .	. . .	. . .	. . .	0.6	1.6	2.5	3.5	4.4	5.4
139	. . .	. . .	. . .	. . .	0.6	1.5	2.5	3.4	4.4	5.3
140	. . .	. . .	. . .	. . .	0.5	1.5	2.4	3.4	4.3	5.3
141	. . .	. . .	. . .	. . .	0.5	1.4	2.4	3.3	4.3	5.2
142	. . .	. . .	. . .	. . .	0.5	1.4	2.4	3.3	4.2	5.2
143	. . .	. . .	. . .	. . .	0.4	1.4	2.3	3.3	4.2	5.1
144	. . .	. . .	. . .	. . .	0.4	1.3	2.3	3.2	4.2	5.1
145	. . .	. . .	. . .	. . .	0.3	1.3	2.2	3.2	4.1	5.1
146	. . .	. . .	. . .	. . .	0.3	1.2	2.2	3.1	4.1	5.0
147	. . .	. . .	. . .	. . .	0.2	1.2	2.1	3.1	4.0	5.0
148	. . .	. . .	. . .	. . .	0.2	1.1	2.1	3.0	4.0	4.9
149	. . .	. . .	. . .	. . .	0.2	1.1	2.1	3.0	3.9	4.9

Table 5 (*Continued*)

API Gravity Reduction to 60° F.

Observed Temperature, °F.	API Gravity at Observed Temperature									
	0	1	2	3	4	5	6	7	8	9
	Corresponding API Gravity at 60° F.									
150	...	...	...	...	0.1	1.1	2.0	3.0	3.9	4.8
151	...	...	...	...	0.1	1.0	2.0	2.9	3.8	4.8
152	...	...	...	...	0.0	1.0	1.9	2.9	3.8	4.7
153	...	...	...	...	...	0.9	1.9	2.8	3.8	4.7
154	...	...	...	...	...	0.9	1.8	2.8	3.7	4.7
155	...	...	...	...	...	0.8	1.8	2.7	3.7	4.6
156	...	...	...	...	...	0.8	1.7	2.7	3.6	4.6
157	...	...	...	...	...	0.8	1.7	2.6	3.6	4.5
158	...	...	...	...	...	0.7	1.7	2.6	3.5	4.5
159	...	...	...	...	...	0.7	1.6	2.6	3.5	4.4
160	...	...	...	...	...	0.6	1.6	2.5	3.5	4.4
161	...	...	...	...	...	0.6	1.5	2.5	3.4	4.3
162	...	...	...	...	...	0.5	1.5	2.4	3.4	4.3
163	...	...	...	...	...	0.5	1.4	2.4	3.3	4.3
164	...	...	...	...	...	0.5	1.4	2.3	3.3	4.2
165	...	...	...	...	...	0.4	1.4	2.3	3.2	4.2
166	...	...	...	...	...	0.4	1.3	2.3	3.2	4.1
167	...	...	...	...	...	0.3	1.3	2.2	3.1	4.1
168	...	...	...	...	...	0.3	1.2	2.2	3.1	4.0
169	...	...	...	...	...	0.2	1.2	2.1	3.1	4.0
170	...	...	...	...	...	0.2	1.1	2.1	3.0	3.9
171	...	...	...	...	...	0.2	1.1	2.0	3.0	3.9
172	...	...	...	...	...	0.1	1.1	2.0	2.9	3.9
173	...	...	...	...	...	0.1	1.0	1.9	2.9	3.8
174	...	...	...	...	...	0.0	1.0	1.9	2.8	3.8
175	...	...	...	...	...	...	0.9	1.9	2.8	3.7
176	...	...	...	...	...	...	0.9	1.8	2.7	3.7
177	...	...	...	...	...	...	0.8	1.8	2.7	3.6
178	...	...	...	...	...	...	0.8	1.7	2.7	3.6
179	...	...	...	...	...	...	0.8	1.7	2.6	3.5
180	...	...	...	...	...	...	0.7	1.6	2.6	3.5
181	...	...	...	...	...	...	0.7	1.6	2.5	3.5
182	...	...	...	...	...	...	0.6	1.6	2.5	3.4
183	...	...	...	...	...	...	0.6	1.5	2.5	3.4
184	...	...	...	...	...	...	0.5	1.5	2.4	3.3
185	...	...	...	...	...	...	0.5	1.4	2.4	3.3
186	...	...	...	...	...	...	0.4	1.4	2.3	3.2
187	...	...	...	...	...	...	0.4	1.3	2.3	3.2
188	...	...	...	...	...	...	0.4	1.3	2.2	3.1
189	...	...	...	...	...	...	0.3	1.2	2.2	3.1
190	...	...	...	...	...	...	0.3	1.2	2.1	3.1
191	...	...	...	...	...	...	0.2	1.2	2.1	3.0
192	...	...	...	...	...	...	0.2	1.1	2.0	3.0
193	...	...	...	...	...	...	0.1	1.1	2.0	2.9
194	...	...	...	...	...	...	0.1	1.0	2.0	2.9
195	...	...	...	...	...	...	0.1	1.0	1.9	2.8
196	...	...	...	...	...	...	0.0	0.9	1.9	2.8
197	...	...	...	...	...	...	...	0.9	1.8	2.7
198	...	...	...	...	...	...	...	0.9	1.8	2.7
199	...	...	...	...	...	...	...	0.8	1.7	2.7

PRODUCTION EQUIPMENT

Table 5 (*Continued*)

API Gravity Reduction to 60° F.

Observed Temper- ature, °F.	API Gravity at Observed Temperature									
	0	1	2	3	4	5	6	7	8	9
	Corresponding API Gravity at 60° F.									
200	...	...	...	...	...	...	...	0.8	1.7	2.6
201	...	...	...	...	...	...	...	0.7	1.6	2.6
202	...	...	...	...	...	...	...	0.7	1.6	2.5
203	...	...	...	...	...	...	...	0.6	1.6	2.5
204	...	...	...	...	...	...	...	0.6	1.5	2.4
205	...	...	...	...	...	...	...	0.5	1.5	2.4
206	...	...	...	...	...	...	...	0.5	1.4	2.3
207	...	...	...	...	...	...	...	0.5	1.4	2.3
208	...	...	...	...	...	...	...	0.4	1.3	2.3
209	...	...	...	...	...	...	...	0.4	1.3	2.2
210	...	...	...	...	...	...	...	0.3	1.2	2.2
211	...	...	...	...	...	...	...	0.3	1.2	2.1
212	...	...	...	...	...	...	...	0.2	1.2	2.1
213	...	...	...	...	...	...	...	0.2	1.1	2.0
214	...	...	...	...	...	...	...	0.1	1.1	2.0
215	...	...	...	...	...	...	...	0.1	1.0	1.9
216	...	...	...	...	...	...	...	0.1	1.0	1.9
217	...	...	...	...	...	...	...	0.0	0.9	1.9
218	...	...	...	...	...	...	...	...	0.9	1.8
219	...	...	...	...	...	...	...	...	0.8	1.8
220	...	...	...	...	...	...	...	...	0.8	1.7
221	...	...	...	...	...	...	...	...	0.8	1.7
222	...	...	...	...	...	...	...	...	0.7	1.6
223	...	...	...	...	...	...	...	...	0.7	1.6
224	...	...	...	...	...	...	...	...	0.6	1.5
225	...	...	...	...	...	...	...	...	0.6	1.5
226	...	...	...	...	...	...	...	...	0.5	1.5
227	...	...	...	...	...	...	...	...	0.5	1.4
228	...	...	...	...	...	...	...	...	0.4	1.4
229	...	...	...	...	...	...	...	...	0.4	1.3
230	...	...	...	...	...	...	...	...	0.4	1.3
231	...	...	...	...	...	...	...	...	0.3	1.2
232	...	...	...	...	...	...	...	...	0.3	1.2
233	...	...	...	...	...	...	...	...	0.2	1.1
234	...	...	...	...	...	...	...	...	0.2	1.1
235	...	...	...	...	...	...	...	...	0.1	1.0
236	...	...	...	...	...	...	...	...	0.1	1.0
237	...	...	...	...	...	...	...	...	0.0	1.0
238	...	...	...	...	...	...	...	...	...	0.9
239	...	...	...	...	...	...	...	...	...	0.9
240	...	...	...	...	...	...	...	...	...	0.8
241	...	...	...	...	...	...	...	...	...	0.8
242	...	...	...	...	...	...	...	...	...	0.7
243	...	...	...	...	...	...	...	...	...	0.7
244	...	...	...	...	...	...	...	...	...	0.6
245	...	...	...	...	...	...	...	...	...	0.6
246	...	...	...	...	...	...	...	...	...	0.5
247	...	...	...	...	...	...	...	...	...	0.5
248	...	...	...	...	...	...	...	...	...	0.5
249	...	...	...	...	...	...	...	...	...	0.4
250	...	...	...	...	...	...	...	...	...	0.4

Table 5 (*Continued*)

API Gravity Reduction to 60° F.

Observed Temperature, °F.	API Gravity at Observed Temperature									
	10	11	12	13	14	15	16	17	18	19
	Corresponding API Gravity at 60° F.									
0	13.1	14.2	15.2	16.3	17.3	18.3	19.4	20.4	21.5	22.5
1	13.1	14.1	15.2	16.2	17.2	18.3	19.3	20.4	21.4	22.5
2	13.0	14.1	15.1	16.1	17.2	18.2	19.3	20.3	21.4	22.4
3	13.0	14.0	15.0	16.1	17.1	18.2	19.2	20.3	21.3	22.4
4	12.9	13.9	15.0	16.0	17.1	18.1	19.2	20.2	21.2	22.3
5	12.8	13.9	14.9	16.0	17.0	18.1	19.1	20.1	21.2	22.2
6	12.8	13.8	14.9	15.9	17.0	18.0	19.0	20.1	21.1	22.2
7	12.7	13.8	14.8	15.9	16.9	17.9	19.0	20.0	21.1	22.1
8	12.7	13.7	14.8	15.8	16.8	17.9	18.9	20.0	21.0	22.0
9	12.6	13.7	14.7	15.7	16.8	17.8	18.9	19.9	20.9	22.0
10	12.6	13.6	14.7	15.7	16.7	17.8	18.8	19.8	20.9	21.9
11	12.5	13.6	14.6	15.6	16.7	17.7	18.8	19.8	20.8	21.9
12	12.5	13.5	14.5	15.6	16.6	17.7	18.7	19.7	20.8	21.8
13	12.4	13.5	14.5	15.5	16.6	17.6	18.6	19.7	20.7	21.7
14	12.4	13.4	14.4	15.5	16.5	17.5	18.6	19.6	20.7	21.7
15	12.3	13.3	14.4	15.4	16.5	17.5	18.5	19.6	20.6	21.6
16	12.3	13.3	14.3	15.4	16.4	17.4	18.5	19.5	20.5	21.6
17	12.2	13.2	14.3	15.3	16.3	17.4	18.4	19.4	20.5	21.5
18	12.2	13.2	14.2	15.3	16.3	17.3	18.3	19.4	20.4	21.4
19	12.1	13.1	14.2	15.2	16.2	17.3	18.3	19.3	20.4	21.4
20	12.0	13.1	14.1	15.1	16.2	17.2	18.2	19.3	20.3	21.3
21	12.0	13.0	14.1	15.1	16.1	17.1	18.2	19.2	20.2	21.3
22	11.9	13.0	14.0	15.0	16.1	17.1	18.1	19.1	20.2	21.2
23	11.9	12.9	13.9	15.0	16.0	17.0	18.1	19.1	20.1	21.1
24	11.8	12.9	13.9	14.9	15.9	17.0	18.0	19.0	20.1	21.1
25	11.8	12.8	13.8	14.9	15.9	16.9	17.9	19.0	20.0	21.0
26	11.7	12.8	13.8	14.8	15.8	16.9	17.9	18.9	19.9	21.0
27	11.7	12.7	13.7	14.8	15.8	16.8	17.8	18.9	19.9	20.9
28	11.6	12.7	13.7	14.7	15.7	16.8	17.8	18.8	19.8	20.9
29	11.6	12.6	13.6	14.6	15.7	16.7	17.7	18.7	19.8	20.8
30	11.5	12.5	13.6	14.6	15.6	16.6	17.7	18.7	19.7	20.7
31	11.5	12.5	13.5	14.5	15.6	16.6	17.6	18.6	19.7	20.7
32	11.4	12.4	13.5	14.5	15.5	16.5	17.6	18.6	19.6	20.6
33	11.4	12.4	13.4	14.4	15.5	16.5	17.5	18.5	19.5	20.6
34	11.3	12.3	13.4	14.4	15.4	16.4	17.4	18.5	19.5	20.5
35	11.3	12.3	13.3	14.3	15.3	16.4	17.4	18.4	19.4	20.4
36	11.2	12.2	13.3	14.3	15.3	16.3	17.3	18.3	19.4	20.4
37	11.2	12.2	13.2	14.2	15.2	16.3	17.3	18.3	19.3	20.3
38	11.1	12.1	13.1	14.2	15.2	16.2	17.2	18.2	19.2	20.3
39	11.1	12.1	13.1	14.1	15.1	16.1	17.2	18.2	19.2	20.2
40	11.0	12.0	13.0	14.1	15.1	16.1	17.1	18.1	19.1	20.1
41	11.0	12.0	13.0	14.0	15.0	16.0	17.0	18.1	19.1	20.1
42	10.9	11.9	12.9	13.9	15.0	16.0	17.0	18.0	19.0	20.0
43	10.9	11.9	12.9	13.9	14.9	15.9	16.9	17.9	19.0	20.0
44	10.8	11.8	12.8	13.8	14.9	15.9	16.9	17.9	18.9	19.9
45	10.8	11.8	12.8	13.8	14.8	15.8	16.8	17.8	18.8	19.9
46	10.7	11.7	12.7	13.7	14.7	15.8	16.8	17.8	18.8	19.8
47	10.7	11.7	12.7	13.7	14.7	15.7	16.7	17.7	18.7	19.7
48	10.6	11.6	12.6	13.6	14.6	15.6	16.7	17.7	18.7	19.7
49	10.6	11.6	12.6	13.6	14.6	15.6	16.6	17.6	18.6	19.6

Table 5 (*Continued*)

10–19° API   API Gravity Reduction to 60° F.   ASTM—IP

Observed Temperature, °F.	API Gravity at Observed Temperature									
	10	11	12	13	14	15	16	17	18	19
	Corresponding API Gravity at 60° F.									
50	10.5	11.5	12.5	13.5	14.5	15.5	16.5	17.6	18.6	19.6
51	10.5	11.5	12.5	13.5	14.5	15.5	16.5	17.5	18.5	19.5
52	10.4	11.4	12.4	13.4	14.4	15.4	16.4	17.4	18.5	19.5
53	10.4	11.4	12.4	13.4	14.4	15.4	16.4	17.4	18.4	19.4
54	10.3	11.3	12.3	13.3	14.3	15.3	16.3	17.3	18.3	19.3
55	10.2	11.3	12.3	13.3	14.3	15.3	16.3	17.3	18.3	19.3
56	10.2	11.2	12.2	13.2	14.2	15.2	16.2	17.2	18.2	19.2
57	10.1	11.2	12.2	13.2	14.2	15.2	16.2	17.2	18.2	19.2
58	10.1	11.1	12.1	13.1	14.1	15.1	16.1	17.1	18.1	19.1
59	10.0	11.1	12.1	13.1	14.1	15.1	16.1	17.1	18.1	19.1
60	10.0	11.0	12.0	13.0	14.0	15.0	16.0	17.0	18.0	19.0
61	10.0	10.9	11.9	12.9	13.9	14.9	16.0	16.9	17.9	18.9
62	9.9	10.8	11.9	12.9	13.9	14.9	15.9	16.9	17.9	18.9
63	9.9	10.8	11.8	12.8	13.8	14.8	15.8	16.8	17.8	18.8
64	9.8	10.8	11.8	12.8	13.8	14.8	15.8	16.8	17.8	18.8
65	9.8	10.7	11.7	12.7	13.7	14.7	15.7	16.7	17.7	18.7
66	9.7	10.7	11.7	12.7	13.7	14.7	15.7	16.7	17.7	18.7
67	9.7	10.6	11.6	12.6	13.6	14.6	15.6	16.6	17.6	18.6
68	9.6	10.6	11.6	12.6	13.6	14.6	15.6	16.6	17.6	18.5
69	9.6	10.6	11.5	12.5	13.5	14.5	15.5	16.5	17.5	18.5
70	9.5	10.5	11.5	12.5	13.5	14.5	15.5	16.5	17.4	18.4
71	9.5	10.4	11.4	12.4	13.4	14.4	15.4	16.4	17.4	18.4
72	9.4	10.4	11.4	12.4	13.4	14.4	15.4	16.3	17.3	18.3
73	9.4	10.3	11.3	12.3	13.3	14.3	15.3	16.3	17.3	18.3
74	9.3	10.3	11.3	12.3	13.3	14.3	15.2	16.2	17.2	18.2
75	9.3	10.2	11.2	12.2	13.2	14.2	15.2	16.2	17.2	18.2
76	9.2	10.2	11.2	12.2	13.2	14.2	15.1	16.1	17.1	18.1
77	9.2	10.2	11.1	12.1	13.1	14.1	15.1	16.1	17.1	18.0
78	9.1	10.1	11.1	12.1	13.1	14.0	15.0	16.0	17.0	18.0
79	9.1	10.1	11.0	12.0	13.0	14.0	15.0	16.0	17.0	17.9
80	9.0	10.0	11.0	12.0	13.0	13.9	14.9	15.9	16.9	17.9
81	9.0	10.0	10.9	11.9	12.9	13.9	14.9	15.9	16.8	17.8
82	8.9	9.9	10.9	11.9	12.9	13.8	14.8	15.8	16.8	17.8
83	8.9	9.9	10.8	11.8	12.8	13.8	14.8	15.8	16.7	17.7
84	8.8	9.8	10.8	11.8	12.8	13.7	14.7	15.7	16.7	17.7
85	8.8	9.8	10.7	11.7	12.7	13.7	14.7	15.6	16.6	17.6
86	8.7	9.7	10.7	11.7	12.7	13.6	14.6	15.6	16.6	17.5
87	8.7	9.7	10.6	11.6	12.6	13.6	14.6	15.5	16.5	17.5
88	8.6	9.6	10.6	11.6	12.5	13.5	14.5	15.5	16.5	17.4
89	8.6	9.6	10.5	11.5	12.5	13.5	14.5	15.4	16.4	17.4
90	8.5	9.5	10.5	11.5	12.4	13.4	14.4	15.4	16.4	17.3
91	8.5	9.5	10.4	11.4	12.4	13.4	14.3	15.3	16.3	17.3
92	8.4	9.4	10.4	11.4	12.3	13.3	14.3	15.3	16.2	17.2
93	8.4	9.4	10.3	11.3	12.3	13.3	14.2	15.2	16.2	17.2
94	8.4	9.3	10.3	11.3	12.2	13.2	14.2	15.2	16.1	17.1
95	8.3	9.3	10.2	11.2	12.2	13.2	14.1	15.1	16.1	17.1
96	8.3	9.2	10.2	11.2	12.1	13.1	14.1	15.1	16.0	17.0
97	8.2	9.2	10.2	11.1	12.1	13.1	14.0	15.0	16.0	17.0
98	8.2	9.1	10.1	11.1	12.0	13.0	14.0	15.0	15.9	16.9
99	8.1	9.1	10.1	11.0	12.0	13.0	13.9	14.9	15.9	16.8

Table 5 *(Continued)*

ASTM—IP   API Gravity Reduction to 60° F.   10–19° API

Observed Temperature, °F.	API Gravity at Observed Temperature									
	10	11	12	13	14	15	16	17	18	19
	Corresponding API Gravity at 60° F.									
100	8.1	9.0	10.0	11.0	11.9	12.9	13.9	14.9	15.8	16.8
101	8.0	9.0	10.0	10.9	11.9	12.9	13.8	14.8	15.8	16.7
102	8.0	8.9	9.9	10.9	11.8	12.8	13.8	14.7	15.7	16.7
103	7.9	8.9	9.9	10.8	11.8	12.8	13.7	14.7	15.7	16.6
104	7.9	8.8	9.8	10.8	11.7	12.7	13.7	14.6	15.6	16.6
105	7.8	8.8	9.8	10.7	11.7	12.7	13.6	14.6	15.6	16.5
106	7.8	8.8	9.7	10.7	11.6	12.6	13.6	14.5	15.5	16.5
107	7.7	8.7	9.7	10.6	11.6	12.6	13.5	14.5	15.5	16.4
108	7.7	8.7	9.6	10.6	11.5	12.5	13.5	14.4	15.4	16.4
109	7.6	8.6	9.6	10.5	11.5	12.5	13.4	14.4	15.3	16.3
110	7.6	8.6	9.5	10.5	11.5	12.4	13.4	14.3	15.3	16.3
111	7.6	8.5	9.5	10.4	11.4	12.4	13.3	14.3	15.2	16.2
112	7.5	8.5	9.4	10.4	11.4	12.3	13.3	14.2	15.2	16.1
113	7.5	8.4	9.4	10.3	11.3	12.3	13.2	14.2	15.1	16.1
114	7.4	8.4	9.3	10.3	11.3	12.2	13.2	14.1	15.1	16.0
115	7.4	8.3	9.3	10.2	11.2	12.2	13.1	14.1	15.0	16.0
116	7.3	8.3	9.2	10.2	11.2	12.1	13.1	14.0	15.0	15.9
117	7.3	8.2	9.2	10.2	11.1	12.1	13.0	14.0	14.9	15.9
118	7.2	8.2	9.1	10.1	11.1	12.0	13.0	13.9	14.9	15.8
119	7.2	8.1	9.1	10.1	11.0	12.0	12.9	13.9	14.8	15.8
120	7.1	8.1	9.1	10.0	11.0	11.9	12.9	13.8	14.8	15.7
121	7.1	8.1	9.0	10.0	10.9	11.9	12.8	13.8	14.7	15.7
122	7.0	8.0	9.0	9.9	10.9	11.8	12.8	13.7	14.7	15.6
123	7.0	8.0	8.9	9.9	10.8	11.8	12.7	13.7	14.6	15.6
124	7.0	7.9	8.9	9.8	10.8	11.7	12.7	13.6	14.6	15.5
125	6.9	7.9	8.8	9.8	10.7	11.7	12.6	13.6	14.5	15.5
126	6.9	7.8	8.8	9.7	10.7	11.6	12.6	13.5	14.5	15.4
127	6.8	7.8	8.7	9.7	10.6	11.6	12.5	13.5	14.4	15.4
128	6.8	7.7	8.7	9.6	10.6	11.5	12.5	13.4	14.4	15.3
129	6.7	7.7	8.6	9.6	10.5	11.5	12.4	13.4	14.3	15.3
130	6.7	7.6	8.6	9.5	10.5	11.4	12.4	13.3	14.3	15.2
131	6.6	7.6	8.5	9.5	10.4	11.4	12.3	13.3	14.2	15.2
132	6.6	7.5	8.5	9.4	10.4	11.3	12.3	13.2	14.2	15.1
133	6.5	7.5	8.4	9.4	10.3	11.3	12.2	13.2	14.1	15.1
134	6.5	7.4	8.4	9.3	10.3	11.2	12.2	13.1	14.1	15.0
135	6.5	7.4	8.4	9.3	10.2	11.2	12.1	13.1	14.0	15.0
136	6.4	7.4	8.3	9.3	10.2	11.1	12.1	13.0	14.0	14.9
137	6.4	7.3	8.3	9.2	10.2	11.1	12.0	13.0	13.9	14.9
138	6.3	7.3	8.2	9.2	10.1	11.0	12.0	12.9	13.9	14.8
139	6.3	7.2	8.2	9.1	10.1	11.0	11.9	12.9	13.8	14.8
140	6.2	7.2	8.1	9.1	10.0	11.0	11.9	12.8	13.8	14.7
141	6.2	7.1	8.1	9.0	10.0	10.9	11.8	12.8	13.7	14.7
142	6.1	7.1	8.0	9.0	9.9	10.9	11.8	12.7	13.7	14.6
143	6.1	7.0	8.0	8.9	9.9	10.8	11.7	12.7	13.6	14.5
144	6.0	7.0	7.9	8.9	9.8	10.8	11.7	12.6	13.6	14.5
145	6.0	6.9	7.9	8.8	9.8	10.7	11.6	12.6	13.5	14.4
146	6.0	6.9	7.8	8.8	9.7	10.7	11.6	12.5	13.5	14.4
147	5.9	6.9	7.8	8.7	9.7	10.6	11.6	12.5	13.4	14.3
148	5.9	6.8	7.8	8.7	9.6	10.6	11.5	12.4	13.4	14.3
149	5.8	6.8	7.7	8.6	9.6	10.5	11.5	12.4	13.3	14.2

Table 5 (*Continued*)

10–19° API   API Gravity Reduction to 60° F.   ASTM—IP

Observed Temperature, °F.	API Gravity at Observed Temperature									
	10	11	12	13	14	15	16	17	18	19
	Corresponding API Gravity at 60° F.									
150	5.8	6.7	7.7	8.6	9.5	10.5	11.4	12.3	13.3	14.2
151	5.7	6.7	7.6	8.6	9.5	10.4	11.4	12.3	13.2	14.1
152	5.7	6.6	7.6	8.5	9.4	10.4	11.3	12.2	13.2	14.1
153	5.6	6.6	7.5	8.5	9.4	10.3	11.3	12.2	13.1	14.0
154	5.6	6.5	7.5	8.4	9.4	10.3	11.2	12.1	13.1	14.0
155	5.6	6.5	7.4	8.4	9.3	10.2	11.2	12.1	13.0	14.0
156	5.5	6.4	7.4	8.3	9.3	10.2	11.1	12.1	13.0	13.9
157	5.5	6.4	7.3	8.3	9.2	10.2	11.1	12.0	12.9	13.9
158	5.4	6.4	7.3	8.2	9.2	10.1	11.0	12.0	12.9	13.8
159	5.4	6.3	7.2	8.2	9.1	10.1	11.0	11.9	12.8	13.8
160	5.3	6.3	7.2	8.1	9.1	10.0	10.9	11.9	12.8	13.7
161	5.3	6.2	7.2	8.1	9.0	10.0	10.9	11.8	12.7	13.7
162	5.2	6.2	7.1	8.0	9.0	9.9	10.8	11.8	12.7	13.6
163	5.2	6.1	7.1	8.0	8.9	9.9	10.8	11.7	12.6	13.6
164	5.1	6.1	7.0	8.0	8.9	9.8	10.8	11.7	12.6	13.5
165	5.1	6.0	7.0	7.9	8.8	9.8	10.7	11.6	12.5	13.5
166	5.1	6.0	6.9	7.9	8.8	9.7	10.7	11.6	12.5	13.4
167	5.0	6.0	6.9	7.8	8.8	9.7	10.6	11.5	12.4	13.4
168	5.0	5.9	6.8	7.8	8.7	9.6	10.6	11.5	12.4	13.3
169	4.9	5.9	6.8	7.7	8.7	9.6	10.5	11.4	12.4	13.3
170	4.9	5.8	6.7	7.7	8.6	9.5	10.5	11.4	12.3	13.2
171	4.8	5.8	6.7	7.6	8.6	9.5	10.4	11.3	12.3	13.2
172	4.8	5.7	6.7	7.5	8.5	9.5	10.4	11.2	12.2	13.1
173	4.7	5.7	6.6	7.5	8.5	9.4	10.3	11.2	12.2	13.1
174	4.7	5.6	6.6	7.5	8.4	9.4	10.3	11.2	12.1	13.0
175	4.7	5.6	6.5	7.5	8.4	9.3	10.2	11.2	12.1	13.0
176	4.6	5.5	6.5	7.4	8.3	9.3	10.2	11.1	12.0	12.9
177	4.6	5.5	6.4	7.4	8.3	9.2	10.2	11.1	12.0	12.9
178	4.5	5.5	6.4	7.3	8.2	9.2	10.1	11.0	11.9	12.8
179	4.5	5.4	6.3	7.3	8.2	9.1	10.1	11.0	11.9	12.8
180	4.4	5.4	6.3	7.2	8.2	9.1	10.0	10.9	11.8	12.7
181	4.4	5.3	6.3	7.2	8.1	9.0	10.0	10.9	11.8	12.7
182	4.3	5.3	6.2	7.1	8.1	9.0	9.9	10.8	11.7	12.6
183	4.3	5.2	6.2	7.1	8.0	8.9	9.9	10.8	11.7	12.6
184	4.3	5.2	6.1	7.0	8.0	8.9	9.8	10.7	11.6	12.5
185	4.2	5.1	6.1	7.0	7.9	8.9	9.8	10.7	11.6	12.5
186	4.2	5.1	6.0	7.0	7.9	8.8	9.7	10.7	11.6	12.5
187	4.1	5.1	6.0	6.9	7.8	8.8	9.7	10.6	11.5	12.4
188	4.1	5.0	5.9	6.9	7.8	8.7	9.6	10.6	11.5	12.4
189	4.0	5.0	5.9	6.8	7.7	8.7	9.6	10.5	11.4	12.3
190	4.0	4.9	5.8	6.8	7.7	8.6	9.6	10.5	11.4	12.3
191	3.9	4.9	5.8	6.7	7.7	8.6	9.5	10.4	11.3	12.2
192	3.9	4.8	5.8	6.7	7.6	8.5	9.5	10.4	11.3	12.2
193	3.9	4.8	5.7	6.6	7.6	8.5	9.4	10.3	11.2	12.1
194	3.8	4.7	5.7	6.6	7.5	8.4	9.4	10.3	11.2	12.1
195	3.8	4.7	5.6	6.5	7.5	8.4	9.3	10.2	11.1	12.0
196	3.7	4.6	5.6	6.5	7.4	8.3	9.3	10.2	11.1	12.0
197	3.7	4.6	5.5	6.5	7.4	8.3	9.2	10.2	11.1	11.9
198	3.6	4.6	5.5	6.4	7.3	8.3	9.2	10.1	11.0	11.9
199	3.6	4.5	5.4	6.4	7.3	8.2	9.1	10.1	11.0	11.9

Table 5 (*Continued*)

ASTM--IP
API Gravity Reduction to 60° F.
10–19° API

Observed Temperature, °F.	API Gravity at Observed Temperature									
	10	11	12	13	14	15	16	17	18	19
	Corresponding API Gravity at 60° F.									
200	3.5	4.5	5.4	6.3	7.2	8.2	9.1	10.0	10.9	11.8
201	3.5	4.4	5.3	6.3	7.2	8.1	9.0	10.0	10.9	11.8
202	3.5	4.4	5.3	6.2	7.2	8.1	9.0	9.9	10.8	11.7
203	3.4	4.3	5.3	6.2	7.1	8.0	9.0	9.9	10.8	11.7
204	3.4	4.3	5.2	6.1	7.1	8.0	8.9	9.8	10.7	11.6
205	3.3	4.2	5.2	6.1	7.0	7.9	8.9	9.8	10.7	11.6
206	3.3	4.2	5.1	6.0	7.0	7.9	8.9	9.7	10.6	11.5
207	3.2	4.2	5.1	6.0	6.9	7.8	8.8	9.7	10.6	11.5
208	3.2	4.1	5.0	6.0	6.9	7.8	8.7	9.6	10.6	11.4
209	3.1	4.1	5.0	5.9	6.8	7.8	8.7	9.6	10.5	11.4
210	3.1	4.0	4.9	5.9	6.8	7.7	8.6	9.6	10.5	11.4
211	3.1	4.0	4.9	5.8	6.7	7.7	8.6	9.5	10.4	11.3
212	3.0	3.9	4.9	5.8	6.7	7.6	8.5	9.5	10.4	11.3
213	3.0	3.9	4.8	5.7	6.7	7.6	8.5	9.4	10.3	11.2
214	2.9	3.8	4.8	5.7	6.6	7.5	8.4	9.4	10.3	11.2
215	2.9	3.8	4.7	5.6	6.6	7.5	8.4	9.3	10.2	11.1
216	2.8	3.7	4.7	5.6	6.5	7.4	8.4	9.3	10.2	11.1
217	2.8	3.7	4.6	5.5	6.5	7.4	8.3	9.2	10.2	11.0
218	2.7	3.7	4.6	5.5	6.4	7.3	8.3	9.2	10.1	11.0
219	2.7	3.6	4.5	5.5	6.4	7.3	8.2	9.1	10.1	10.9
220	2.6	3.6	4.5	5.4	6.3	7.3	8.2	9.1	10.0	10.9
221	2.6	3.5	4.4	5.4	6.3	7.2	8.1	9.0	10.0	10.9
222	2.6	3.5	4.4	5.3	6.2	7.2	8.1	9.0	9.9	10.8
223	2.5	3.4	4.4	5.3	6.2	7.1	8.0	9.0	9.9	10.8
224	2.5	3.4	4.3	5.2	6.2	7.1	8.0	8.9	9.8	10.7
225	2.4	3.3	4.3	5.2	6.1	7.0	7.9	8.9	9.8	10.7
226	2.4	3.3	4.2	5.1	6.1	7.0	7.9	8.8	9.7	10.6
227	2.3	3.3	4.2	5.1	6.0	6.9	7.9	8.8	9.7	10.6
228	2.3	3.2	4.1	5.0	6.0	6.9	7.8	8.7	9.6	10.6
229	2.2	3.2	4.1	5.0	5.9	6.8	7.8	8.7	9.6	10.5
230	2.2	3.1	4.0	5.0	5.9	6.8	7.7	8.6	9.6	10.5
231	2.2	3.1	4.0	4.9	5.8	6.8	7.7	8.6	9.5	10.4
232	2.1	3.0	3.9	4.9	5.8	6.7	7.6	8.5	9.5	10.4
233	2.1	3.0	3.9	4.8	5.7	6.7	7.6	8.5	9.4	10.3
234	2.0	2.9	3.9	4.8	5.7	6.6	7.5	8.5	9.4	10.3
235	2.0	2.9	3.8	4.7	5.7	6.6	7.5	8.4	9.3	10.2
236	1.9	2.8	3.8	4.7	5.6	6.5	7.4	8.4	9.3	10.2
237	1.9	2.8	3.7	4.6	5.6	6.5	7.4	8.3	9.2	10.2
238	1.8	2.8	3.7	4.6	5.5	6.4	7.4	8.3	9.2	10.1
239	1.8	2.7	3.6	4.5	5.5	6.4	7.3	8.2	9.1	10.1
240	1.7	2.7	3.6	4.5	5.4	6.3	7.3	8.2	9.1	10.0
241	1.7	2.6	3.5	4.5	5.4	6.3	7.2	8.1	9.1	10.0
242	1.7	2.6	3.5	4.4	5.3	6.3	7.2	8.1	9.0	9.9
243	1.6	2.5	3.4	4.4	5.3	6.2	7.1	8.0	9.0	9.9
244	1.6	2.5	3.4	4.3	5.2	6.2	7.1	8.0	8.9	9.8
245	1.5	2.4	3.4	4.3	5.2	6.1	7.0	8.0	8.9	9.8
246	1.5	2.4	3.3	4.2	5.1	6.1	7.0	7.9	8.8	9.7
247	1.4	2.3	3.3	4.2	5.1	6.0	6.9	7.9	8.8	9.7
248	1.4	2.3	3.2	4.1	5.1	6.0	6.9	7.8	8.7	9.6
249	1.3	2.3	3.2	4.1	5.0	5.9	6.8	7.8	8.7	9.6
250	1.3	2.2	3.1	4.0	5.0	5.9	6.8	7.7	8.6	9.6

PRODUCTION EQUIPMENT

Table 5 (*Continued*)

20–29° API   API Gravity Reduction to 60° F.   ASTM—IP

Observed Temperature, °F.	API Gravity at Observed Temperature									
	20	21	22	23	24	25	26	27	28	29
	Corresponding API Gravity at 60° F.									
0	23.6	24.6	25.7	26.7	27.8	28.9	30.0	31.0	32.0	33.1
1	23.5	24.6	25.6	26.7	27.7	28.8	29.8	30.9	32.0	33.0
2	23.5	24.5	25.6	26.6	27.7	28.7	29.8	30.8	31.9	33.0
3	23.4	24.4	25.5	26.5	27.6	28.7	29.7	30.8	31.8	32.9
4	23.3	24.4	25.4	26.5	27.5	28.6	29.6	30.7	31.8	32.8
5	23.3	24.3	25.4	26.4	27.5	28.5	29.6	30.6	31.7	32.8
6	23.2	24.3	25.3	26.4	27.4	28.5	29.5	30.6	31.6	32.7
7	23.2	24.2	25.2	26.3	27.3	28.4	29.4	30.5	31.6	32.6
8	23.1	24.1	25.2	26.2	27.3	28.3	29.4	30.4	31.5	32.5
9	23.0	24.1	25.1	26.2	27.2	28.3	29.3	30.4	31.4	32.5
10	23.0	24.0	25.0	26.1	27.1	28.2	29.2	30.3	31.3	32.4
11	22.9	23.9	25.0	26.0	27.1	28.1	29.2	30.2	31.3	32.3
12	22.8	23.9	24.9	26.0	27.0	28.1	29.1	30.2	31.2	32.3
13	22.8	23.8	24.9	25.9	26.9	28.0	29.0	30.1	31.1	32.2
14	22.7	23.8	24.8	25.8	26.9	27.9	29.0	30.0	31.1	32.1
15	22.7	23.7	24.7	25.8	26.8	27.9	28.9	30.0	31.0	32.1
16	22.6	23.6	24.7	25.7	26.8	27.8	28.8	29.9	30.9	32.0
17	22.5	23.6	24.6	25.6	26.7	27.7	28.8	29.8	30.9	31.9
18	22.5	23.5	24.5	25.6	26.6	27.7	28.7	29.7	30.8	31.8
19	22.4	23.5	24.5	25.5	26.6	27.6	28.6	29.7	30.7	31.8
20	22.4	23.4	24.4	25.5	26.5	27.5	28.6	29.6	30.7	31.7
21	22.3	23.3	24.4	25.4	26.4	27.5	28.5	29.5	30.6	31.6
23	22.2	23.3	24.3	25.3	26.4	27.4	28.4	29.5	30.5	31.6
23	22.2	23.2	24.2	25.3	26.3	27.3	28.4	29.4	30.5	31.5
24	22.1	23.1	24.2	25.2	26.2	27.3	28.3	29.3	30.4	31.4
25	22.1	23.1	24.1	25.1	26.2	27.2	28.2	29.3	30.3	31.4
26	22.0	23.0	24.1	25.1	26.1	27.1	28.2	29.2	30.2	31.3
27	21.9	23.0	24.0	25.0	26.0	27.1	28.1	29.1	30.2	31.2
28	21.9	22.9	23.9	25.0	26.0	27.0	28.0	29.1	30.1	31.1
29	21.8	22.8	23.9	24.9	25.9	27.0	28.0	29.0	30.0	31.1
30	21.8	22.8	23.8	24.8	25.9	26.9	27.9	28.9	30.0	31.0
31	21.7	22.7	23.7	24.8	25.8	26.8	27.9	28.9	29.9	30.9
32	21.6	22.7	23.7	24.7	25.7	26.8	27.8	28.8	29.8	30.9
33	21.6	22.6	23.6	24.6	25.7	26.7	27.7	28.7	29.8	30.8
34	21.5	22.5	23.6	24.6	25.6	26.6	27.7	28.7	29.7	30.7
35	21.5	22.5	23.5	24.5	25.5	26.6	27.6	28.6	29.6	30.7
36	21.4	22.4	23.4	24.5	25.5	26.5	27.5	28.6	29.6	30.6
37	21.3	22.4	23.4	24.4	25.4	26.4	27.5	28.5	29.5	30.5
38	21.3	22.3	23.3	24.3	25.4	26.4	27.4	28.4	29.4	30.5
39	21.2	22.2	23.3	24.3	25.3	26.3	27.3	28.4	29.4	30.4
40	21.2	22.2	23.2	24.2	25.2	26.2	27.3	28.3	29.3	30.3
41	21.1	22.1	23.1	24.2	25.2	26.2	27.2	28.2	29.2	30.3
42	21.0	22.1	23.1	24.1	25.1	26.1	27.1	28.2	29.2	30.2
43	21.0	22.0	23.0	24.0	25.0	26.1	27.1	28.1	29.1	30.1
44	20.9	21.9	23.0	24.0	25.0	26.0	27.0	28.0	29.0	30.1
45	20.9	21.9	22.9	23.9	24.9	25.9	26.9	28.0	29.0	30.0
46	20.8	21.8	22.8	23.8	24.9	25.9	26.9	27.9	28.9	29.9
47	20.8	21.8	22.8	23.8	24.8	25.8	26.8	27.8	28.8	29.9
48	20.7	21.7	22.7	23.7	24.7	25.7	26.8	27.8	28.8	29.8
49	20.6	21.6	22.7	23.7	24.7	25.7	26.7	27.7	28.7	29.7

Table 5 (*Continued*)

API Gravity Reduction to 60° F.

Observed Temperature, °F.	API Gravity at Observed Temperature									
	20	21	22	23	24	25	26	27	28	29
	Corresponding API Gravity at 60° F.									
50	20.6	21.6	22.6	23.6	24.6	25.6	26.6	27.6	28.6	29.7
51	20.5	21.5	22.5	23.5	24.6	25.6	26.6	27.6	28.6	29.6
52	20.5	21.5	22.5	23.5	24.5	25.5	26.5	27.5	28.5	29.5
53	20.4	21.4	22.4	23.4	24.4	25.4	26.4	27.4	28.5	29.5
54	20.3	21.4	22.4	23.4	24.4	25.4	26.4	27.4	28.4	29.4
55	20.3	21.3	22.3	23.3	24.3	25.3	26.3	27.3	28.3	29.3
56	20.2	21.2	22.2	23.2	24.2	25.2	26.3	27.3	28.3	29.3
57	20.2	21.2	22.2	23.2	24.2	25.2	26.2	27.2	28.2	29.2
58	20.1	21.1	22.1	23.1	24.1	25.1	26.1	27.1	28.1	29.1
59	20.1	21.1	22.1	23.1	24.1	25.1	26.1	27.1	28.1	29.1
60	20.0	21.0	22.0	23.0	24.0	25.0	26.0	27.0	28.0	29.0
61	20.0	21.0	21.9	22.9	23.9	24.9	25.9	26.9	27.9	28.9
62	19.9	20.9	21.9	22.9	23.9	24.9	25.9	26.9	27.9	28.9
63	19.8	20.8	21.8	22.8	23.8	24.8	25.8	26.8	27.8	29.8
64	19.8	20.8	21.8	22.8	23.8	24.8	25.8	26.7	27.7	28.7
65	19.7	20.7	21.7	22.7	23.7	24.7	25.7	26.7	27.7	28.7
66	19.7	20.7	21.6	22.6	23.6	24.6	25.6	26.6	27.6	28.6
67	19.6	20.6	21.6	22.6	23.6	24.6	25.6	26.6	27.6	28.5
68	19.5	20.5	21.5	22.5	23.5	24.5	25.5	26.5	27.5	28.5
69	19.5	20.5	21.5	22.5	23.5	24.4	25.4	26.4	27.4	28.4
70	19.4	20.4	21.4	22.4	23.4	24.4	25.4	26.4	27.4	28.3
71	19.4	20.4	21.4	22.3	23.3	24.3	25.3	26.3	27.3	28.3
72	19.3	20.3	21.3	22.3	23.3	24.3	25.3	26.2	27.2	28.2
73	19.3	20.2	21.2	22.2	23.2	24.2	25.2	26.2	27.2	28.2
74	19.2	20.2	21.2	22.2	23.2	24.1	25.1	26.1	27.1	28.1
75	19.1	20.1	21.1	22.1	23.1	24.1	25.1	26.1	27.0	28.0
76	19.1	20.1	21.1	22.0	23.0	24.0	25.0	26.0	27.0	28.0
77	19.0	20.0	21.0	22.0	23.0	24.0	24.9	25.9	26.9	27.9
78	19.0	20.0	20.9	21.9	22.9	23.9	24.9	25.9	26.9	27.8
79	18.9	19.9	20.9	21.9	22.9	23.8	24.8	25.8	26.8	27.8
80	18.9	19.8	20.8	21.8	22.8	23.8	24.8	25.7	26.7	27.7
81	18.8	19.8	20.8	21.8	22.7	23.7	24.7	25.7	26.7	27.6
82	18.8	19.7	20.7	21.7	22.7	23.7	24.6	25.6	26.6	27.6
83	18.7	19.7	20.7	21.6	22.6	23.6	24.6	25.6	26.5	27.5
84	18.6	19.6	20.6	21.6	22.6	23.5	24.5	25.5	26.5	27.5
85	18.6	19.6	20.5	21.5	22.5	23.5	24.5	25.4	26.4	27.4
86	18.5	19.5	20.5	21.5	22.4	23.4	24.4	25.4	26.4	27.3
87	18.5	19.5	20.4	21.4	22.4	23.4	24.3	25.3	26.3	27.3
88	18.4	19.4	20.4	21.3	22.3	23.3	24.3	25.3	26.2	27.2
89	18.4	19.3	20.3	21.3	22.3	23.2	24.2	25.2	26.2	27.1
90	18.3	19.3	20.3	21.2	22.2	23.2	24.2	25.1	26.1	27.1
91	18.3	19.2	20.2	21.2	22.2	23.1	24.1	25.1	26.0	27.0
92	18.2	19.2	20.1	21.1	22.1	23.1	24.0	25.0	26.0	27.0
93	18.1	19.1	20.1	21.1	22.0	23.0	24.0	25.0	25.9	26.9
94	18.1	19.1	20.0	21.0	22.0	22.9	23.9	24.9	25.9	26.8
95	18.0	19.0	20.0	20.9	21.9	22.9	23.9	24.8	25.8	26.8
96	18.0	18.9	19.9	20.9	21.9	22.8	23.8	24.8	25.7	26.7
97	17.9	18.9	19.9	20.8	21.8	22.8	23.7	24.7	25.7	26.6
98	17.9	18.8	19.8	20.8	21.7	22.7	23.7	24.7	25.6	26.6
99	17.8	18.8	19.7	20.7	21.7	22.7	23.6	24.6	25.6	26.5

Table 5 (*Continued*)

API Gravity Reduction to 60° F.

Observed Temperature, °F.	API Gravity at Observed Temperature									
	20	21	22	23	24	25	26	27	28	29
	Corresponding API Gravity at 60° F.									
100	17.8	18.7	19.7	20.7	21.6	22.6	23.6	24.5	25.5	26.5
101	17.7	18.7	19.6	20.6	21.6	22.5	23.5	24.5	25.4	26.4
102	17.6	18.6	19.6	20.5	21.5	22.5	23.4	24.4	25.4	26.3
103	17.6	18.6	19.5	20.5	21.5	22.4	23.4	24.3	25.3	26.3
104	17.5	18.5	19.5	20.4	21.4	22.4	23.3	24.3	25.3	26.2
105	17.5	18.4	19.4	20.4	21.3	22.3	23.3	24.2	25.2	26.1
106	17.4	18.4	19.4	20.3	21.3	22.2	23.2	24.2	25.1	26.1
107	17.4	18.3	19.3	20.3	21.2	22.2	23.1	24.1	25.1	26.0
108	17.3	18.3	19.2	20.2	21.2	22.1	23.1	24.0	25.0	26.0
109	17.3	18.2	19.2	20.2	21.1	22.1	23.0	24.0	24.9	25.9
110	17.2	18.2	19.1	20.1	21.1	22.0	23.0	23.9	24.9	25.8
111	17.2	18.1	19.1	20.0	21.0	22.0	22.9	23.9	24.8	25.8
112	17.1	18.1	19.0	20.0	20.9	21.9	22.9	23.8	24.8	25.7
113	17.1	18.0	19.0	19.9	20.9	21.8	22.8	23.8	24.7	25.7
114	17.0	18.0	18.9	19.9	20.8	21.8	22.7	23.7	24.6	25.6
115	16.9	17.9	18.9	19.8	20.8	21.7	22.7	23.6	24.6	25.5
116	16.9	17.8	18.8	19.8	20.7	21.7	22.6	23.6	24.5	25.5
117	16.8	17.8	18.8	19.7	20.7	21.6	22.6	23.5	24.5	25.4
118	16.8	17.7	18.7	19.6	20.6	21.6	22.5	23.5	24.4	25.4
119	16.7	17.7	18.6	19.6	20.5	21.5	22.4	23.4	24.3	25.3
120	16.7	17.6	18.6	19.5	20.5	21.4	22.4	23.3	24.3	25.2
121	16.6	17.6	18.5	19.5	20.4	21.4	22.3	23.3	24.2	25.2
122	16.6	17.5	18.5	19.4	20.4	21.3	22.3	23.2	24.2	25.1
123	16.5	17.5	18.4	19.4	20.3	21.3	22.2	23.2	24.1	25.1
124	16.5	17.4	18.4	19.3	20.3	21.2	22.2	23.1	24.1	25.0
125	16.4	17.4	18.3	19.3	20.2	21.2	22.1	23.0	24.0	24.9
126	16.4	17.3	18.3	19.2	20.2	21.1	22.0	23.0	23.9	24.9
127	16.3	17.3	18.2	19.2	20.1	21.0	22.0	22.9	23.9	24.8
128	16.3	17.2	18.2	19.1	20.0	21.0	21.9	22.9	23.8	24.8
129	16.2	17.2	18.1	19.0	20.0	20.9	21.9	22.8	23.8	24.7
130	16.2	17.1	18.0	19.0	19.9	20.9	21.8	22.8	23.7	24.6
131	16.1	17.0	18.0	18.9	19.9	20.8	21.8	22.7	23.6	24.6
132	16.1	17.0	17.9	18.9	19.8	20.8	21.7	22.6	23.6	24.5
133	16.0	16.9	17.9	18.8	19.8	20.7	21.6	22.6	23.5	24.5
134	15.9	16.9	17.8	18.8	19.7	20.6	21.6	22.5	23.5	24.4
135	15.9	16.8	17.8	18.7	19.7	20.6	21.5	22.5	23.4	24.3
136	15.8	16.8	17.7	18.7	19.6	20.5	21.5	22.4	23.3	24.3
137	15.8	16.7	17.7	18.6	19.5	20.5	21.4	22.4	23.3	24.2
138	15.7	16.7	17.6	18.6	19.5	20.4	21.4	22.3	23.2	24.2
139	15.7	16.6	17.6	18.5	19.4	20.4	21.3	22.2	23.2	24.1
140	15.6	16.6	17.5	18.4	19.4	20.3	21.2	22.2	23.1	24.0
141	15.6	16.5	17.5	18.4	19.3	20.3	21.2	22.1	23.1	24.0
142	15.5	16.5	17.4	18.3	19.3	20.2	21.1	22.1	23.0	23.9
143	15.5	16.4	17.4	18.3	19.2	20.1	21.1	22.0	22.9	23.9
144	15.4	16.4	17.3	18.2	19.2	20.1	21.0	22.0	22.9	23.8
145	15.4	16.3	17.3	18.2	19.1	20.0	21.0	21.9	22.8	23.8
146	15.3	16.3	17.2	18.1	19.1	20.0	20.9	21.8	22.8	23.7
147	15.3	16.2	17.1	18.1	19.0	19.9	20.9	21.8	22.7	23.6
148	15.2	16.2	17.1	18.0	18.9	19.9	20.8	21.7	22.7	23.6
149	15.2	16.1	17.0	18.0	18.9	19.8	20.7	21.7	22.6	23.5

Table 5 (*Continued*)

API Gravity Reduction to 60° F.   **20–29° API**

Observed Temperature, °F.	API Gravity at Observed Temperature									
	20	21	22	23	24	25	26	27	28	29
	Corresponding API Gravity at 60° F.									
150	15.1	16.1	17.0	17.9	18.8	19.8	20.7	21.6	22.5	23.5
151	15.1	16.0	16.9	17.9	18.8	19.7	20.6	21.6	22.5	23.4
152	15.0	16.0	16.9	17.8	18.7	19.7	20.6	21.5	22.4	23.3
153	15.0	15.9	16.8	17.8	18.7	19.6	20.5	21.4	22.4	23.3
154	14.9	15.9	16.8	17.7	18.6	19.5	20.5	21.4	22.3	23.2
155	14.9	15.8	16.7	17.6	18.6	19.5	20.4	21.3	22.3	23.2
156	14.8	15.7	16.7	17.6	18.5	19.4	20.4	21.3	22.2	23.1
157	14.8	15.7	16.6	17.5	18.5	19.4	20.3	21.2	22.1	23.1
158	14.7	15.7	16.6	17.5	18.4	19.3	20.2	21.2	22.1	23.0
159	14.7	15.6	16.5	17.4	18.4	19.3	20.2	21.1	22.0	22.9
160	14.6	15.5	16.5	17.4	18.3	19.2	20.1	21.1	22.0	22.9
161	14.6	15.5	16.4	17.3	18.3	19.2	20.1	21.0	21.9	22.8
162	14.5	15.4	16.4	17.3	18.2	19.1	20.0	20.9	21.9	22.8
163	14.5	15.4	16.3	17.2	18.1	19.1	20.0	20.9	21.8	22.7
164	14.4	15.3	16.3	17.2	18.1	19.0	19.9	20.8	21.7	22.7
165	14.4	15.3	16.2	17.1	18.0	19.0	19.9	20.8	21.7	22.6
166	14.3	15.2	16.2	17.1	18.0	18.9	19.8	20.7	21.6	22.5
167	14.3	15.2	16.1	17.0	17.9	18.8	19.8	20.7	21.6	22.5
168	14.2	15.1	16.1	17.0	17.9	18.8	19.7	20.6	21.5	22.4
169	14.2	15.1	16.0	16.9	17.8	18.7	19.7	20.6	21.5	22.4
170	14.1	15.0	16.0	16.9	17.8	18.7	19.6	20.5	21.4	22.3
171	14.1	15.0	15.9	16.8	17.7	18.6	19.5	20.5	21.4	22.3
172	14.0	14.9	15.9	16.8	17.7	18.6	19.5	20.4	21.3	22.2
173	14.0	14.9	15.8	16.7	17.6	18.5	19.4	20.3	21.3	22.2
174	13.9	14.8	15.8	16.7	17.6	18.5	19.4	20.3	21.2	22.1
175	13.9	14.8	15.7	16.6	17.5	18.4	19.3	20.2	21.1	22.0
176	13.8	14.8	15.7	16.6	17.5	18.4	19.3	20.2	21.1	22.0
177	13.8	14.7	15.6	16.5	17.4	18.3	19.2	20.1	21.0	21.9
178	13.7	14.6	15.6	16.5	17.4	18.3	19.2	20.1	21.0	21.9
179	13.7	14.6	15.5	16.4	17.3	18.2	19.1	20.0	20.9	21.8
180	13.6	14.5	15.5	16.4	17.3	18.2	19.1	20.0	20.9	21.8
181	13.6	14.5	15.5	16.3	17.2	18.1	19.0	19.9	20.8	21.7
182	13.5	14.5	15.4	16.3	17.2	18.1	19.0	19.9	20.8	21.7
183	13.5	14.4	15.3	16.2	17.1	18.0	18.9	19.8	20.7	21.6
184	13.5	14.4	15.3	16.2	17.1	18.0	18.9	19.8	20.6	21.5
185	13.4	14.3	15.2	16.1	17.0	17.9	18.8	19.7	20.6	21.5
186	13.4	14.3	15.2	16.1	17.0	17.9	18.7	19.6	20.5	21.4
187	13.3	14.2	15.1	16.0	16.9	17.8	18.7	19.6	20.5	21.4
188	13.3	14.2	15.1	16.0	16.9	17.7	18.6	19.5	20.4	21.3
189	13.2	14.1	15.0	15.9	16.8	17.7	18.6	19.5	20.4	21.3
190	13.2	14.1	15.0	15.9	16.8	17.6	18.5	19.4	20.3	21.2
191	13.1	14.0	14.9	15.8	16.7	17.6	18.5	19.4	20.3	21.2
192	13.1	14.0	14.9	15.8	16.7	17.5	18.4	19.3	20.2	21.1
193	13.0	13.9	14.8	15.7	16.6	17.5	18.4	19.3	20.2	21.1
194	13.0	13.9	14.8	15.7	16.5	17.4	18.3	19.2	20.1	21.0
195	12.9	13.8	14.7	15.6	16.5	17.4	18.3	19.2	20.1	20.9
196	12.9	13.8	14.7	15.6	16.4	17.3	18.2	19.1	20.0	20.9
197	12.8	13.7	14.6	15.5	16.4	17.3	18.2	19.1	20.0	20.8
198	12.8	13.7	14.6	15.5	16.3	17.2	18.1	19.0	19.9	20.8
199	12.7	13.6	14.5	15.4	16.3	17.2	18.1	19.0	19.8	20.7

Table 5 (*Continued*)

20-29° API   API Gravity Reduction to 60° F.   ASTM—IP

Observed Temperature, °F.	API Gravity at Observed Temperature									
	20	21	22	23	24	25	26	27	28	29
	Corresponding API Gravity at 60° F.									
200	12.7	13.6	14.5	15.4	16.3	17.1	18.0	18.9	19.8	20.7
201	12.7	13.5	14.4	15.3	16.2	17.1	18.0	18.9	19.7	20.6
202	12.6	13.5	14.4	15.3	16.2	17.0	17.9	18.8	19.7	20.6
203	12.6	13.4	14.3	15.2	16.1	17.0	17.9	18.8	19.6	20.5
204	12.5	13.4	14.3	15.2	16.1	16.9	17.8	18.7	19.6	20.5
205	12.5	13.4	14.2	15.1	16.0	16.9	17.8	18.6	19.5	20.4
206	12.4	13.3	14.2	15.1	16.0	16.9	17.7	18.6	19.5	20.4
207	12.4	13.3	14.1	15.0	15.9	16.8	17.7	18.5	19.4	20.3
208	12.3	13.2	14.1	15.0	15.9	16.7	17.6	18.5	19.4	20.2
209	12.3	13.2	14.0	14.9	15.8	16.7	17.6	18.4	19.3	20.2
210	12.2	13.1	14.0	14.9	15.8	16.6	17.5	18.4	19.3	20.1
211	12.2	13.1	14.0	14.8	15.7	16.6	17.5	18.3	19.2	20.1
212	12.1	13.0	13.9	14.8	15.7	16.5	17.4	18.3	19.2	20.0
213	12.1	13.0	13.9	14.7	15.6	16.5	17.4	18.2	19.1	20.0
214	12.1	12.9	13.8	14.7	15.6	16.4	17.3	18.2	19.1	19.9
215	12.0	12.9	13.8	14.6	15.5	16.4	17.3	18.1	19.0	19.9
216	12.0	12.8	13.7	14.6	15.5	16.3	17.2	18.1	19.0	19.8
217	11.9	12.8	13.7	14.5	15.4	16.3	17.2	18.0	18.9	19.8
218	11.9	12.7	13.6	14.5	15.4	16.2	17.1	18.0	18.9	19.7
219	11.8	12.7	13.6	14.4	15.3	16.2	17.1	17.9	18.8	19.7
220	11.8	12.7	13.5	14.4	15.3	16.1	17.0	17.9	18.8	19.6
221	11.7	12.6	13.5	14.4	15.2	16.1	17.0	17.8	18.7	19.6
222	11.7	12.6	13.4	14.3	15.2	16.0	16.9	17.8	18.6	19.5
223	11.6	12.5	13.4	14.3	15.1	16.0	16.9	17.7	18.6	19.5
224	11.6	12.5	13.3	14.2	15.1	15.9	16.8	17.7	18.5	19.4
225	11.6	12.4	13.3	14.2	15.0	15.9	16.8	17.6	18.5	19.4
226	11.5	12.4	13.3	14.1	15.0	15.9	16.7	17.6	18.4	19.3
227	11.5	12.3	13.2	14.1	14.9	15.8	16.7	17.5	18.4	19.3
228	11.4	12.3	13.2	14.0	14.9	15.8	16.6	17.5	18.3	19.2
229	11.4	12.2	13.1	14.0	14.8	15.7	16.6	17.4	18.3	19.2
230	11.3	12.2	13.1	13.9	14.8	15.7	16.5	17.4	18.2	19.1
231	11.3	12.2	13.0	13.9	14.8	15.6	16.5	17.3	18.2	19.1
232	11.2	12.1	13.0	13.8	14.7	15.6	16.4	17.3	18.1	19.0
233	11.2	12.1	12.9	13.8	14.7	15.5	16.4	17.2	18.1	19.0
234	11.2	12.0	12.9	13.7	14.6	15.5	16.3	17.2	18.0	18.9
235	11.1	12.0	12.8	13.7	14.6	15.4	16.3	17.1	18.0	18.8
236	11.1	11.9	12.8	13.7	14.5	15.4	16.2	17.1	17.9	18.8
237	11.0	11.9	12.8	13.6	14.5	15.3	16.2	17.0	17.9	18.7
238	11.0	11.9	12.7	13.6	14.4	15.3	16.1	17.0	17.8	18.7
239	10.9	11.8	12.7	13.5	14.4	15.2	16.1	16.9	17.8	18.6
240	10.9	11.8	12.6	13.5	14.3	15.2	16.0	16.9	17.7	18.6
241	10.9	11.7	12.6	13.4	14.3	15.1	16.0	16.8	17.7	18.5
242	10.8	11.7	12.5	13.4	14.2	15.1	15.9	16.8	17.6	18.5
243	10.8	11.6	12.5	13.3	14.2	15.0	15.9	16.7	17.6	18.4
244	10.7	11.6	12.4	13.3	14.1	15.0	15.8	16.7	17.5	18.4
245	10.7	11.5	12.4	13.2	14.1	15.0	15.8	16.7	17.5	18.3
246	10.6	11.5	12.3	13.2	14.1	14.9	15.8	16.6	17.5	18.3
247	10.6	11.5	12.3	13.2	14.0	14.9	15.7	16.6	17.4	18.2
248	10.6	11.4	12.3	13.1	14.0	14.8	15.7	16.5	17.4	18.2
249	10.5	11.4	12.2	13.1	13.9	14.8	15.6	16.5	17.3	18.1
250	10.5	11.3	12.2	13.0	13.9	14.7	15.6	16.4	17.3	18.1

Table 5 (*Continued*)

API Gravity Reduction to 60° F.

Observed Temperature, °F.	API Gravity at Observed Temperature									
	30	31	32	33	34	35	36	37	38	39
	Corresponding API Gravity at 60° F.									
0	34.2	35.3	36.3	37.4	38.5	39.6	40.7	41.8	42.9	44.0
1	34.1	35.2	36.3	37.3	38.4	39.5	40.6	41.7	42.8	43.9
2	34.0	35.1	36.2	37.3	38.3	39.4	40.5	41.5	42.7	43.8
3	34.0	35.0	36.1	37.2	38.3	39.3	40.4	41.5	42.6	43.7
4	33.9	35.0	36.0	37.1	38.2	39.3	40.3	41.4	42.5	43.6
5	33.8	34.9	36.0	37.0	38.1	39.2	40.3	41.3	42.4	43.5
6	33.7	34.8	35.9	36.9	38.0	39.1	40.2	41.3	42.3	43.4
7	33.7	34.7	35.8	36.9	37.9	39.0	40.1	41.2	42.3	43.3
8	33.6	34.7	35.7	36.8	37.9	38.9	40.0	41.1	42.2	43.3
9	33.5	34.6	35.7	36.7	37.8	38.9	39.9	41.0	42.1	43.2
10	33.5	34.5	35.6	36.6	37.7	38.8	39.8	40.9	42.0	43.1
11	33.4	34.4	35.5	36.6	37.6	38.7	39.8	40.8	41.9	43.0
12	33.3	34.4	35.4	36.5	37.6	38.6	39.7	40.8	41.8	42.9
13	33.2	34.3	35.4	36.4	37.5	38.5	39.6	40.7	41.7	42.8
14	33.2	34.2	35.3	36.3	37.4	38.5	39.5	40.6	41.7	42.7
15	33.1	34.2	35.2	36.3	37.3	38.4	39.4	40.5	41.6	42.7
16	33.0	34.1	35.1	36.2	37.2	38.3	39.4	40.4	41.5	42.6
17	33.0	34.0	35.1	36.1	37.2	38.2	39.3	40.4	41.4	42.5
18	32.9	33.9	35.0	36.0	37.1	38.1	39.2	40.3	41.3	42.4
19	32.8	33.9	34.9	36.0	37.0	38.1	39.1	40.2	41.2	42.3
20	32.7	33.8	34.8	35.9	36.9	38.0	39.0	40.1	41.2	42.2
21	32.7	33.7	34.8	35.8	36.9	37.9	39.0	40.0	41.1	42.1
22	32.6	33.6	34.7	35.7	36.8	37.8	38.9	39.9	41.0	42.1
23	32.5	33.6	34.6	35.7	36.7	37.8	38.8	39.9	40.9	42.0
24	32.5	33.5	34.5	35.6	36.6	37.7	38.7	39.8	40.8	41.9
25	32.4	33.4	34.5	35.5	36.6	37.6	38.7	39.7	40.8	41.8
26	32.3	33.4	34.4	35.4	36.5	37.5	38.6	39.6	40.7	41.7
27	32.3	33.3	34.3	35.4	36.4	37.5	38.5	39.5	40.6	41.6
28	32.2	33.2	34.3	35.3	36.3	37.4	38.4	39.5	40.5	41.6
29	32.1	33.1	34.2	35.2	36.3	37.3	38.3	39.4	40.4	41.5
30	32.0	33.1	34.1	35.1	36.2	37.2	38.3	39.3	40.4	41.4
31	32.0	33.0	34.0	35.1	36.1	37.1	38.2	39.2	40.3	41.3
32	31.9	32.9	34.0	35.0	36.0	37.1	38.1	39.1	40.2	41.2
33	31.8	32.9	33.9	34.9	36.0	37.0	38.0	39.1	40.1	41.1
34	31.8	32.8	33.8	34.9	35.9	36.9	38.0	39.0	40.0	41.1
35	31.7	32.7	33.8	34.8	35.8	36.8	37.9	38.9	39.9	41.0
36	31.6	32.7	33.7	34.7	35.7	36.8	37.8	38.8	39.9	40.9
37	31.6	32.6	33.6	34.6	35.7	36.7	37.7	38.8	39.8	40.8
38	31.5	32.5	33.5	34.6	35.6	36.6	37.6	38.7	39.7	40.7
39	31.4	32.4	33.5	34.5	35.5	36.5	37.6	38.6	39.6	40.7
40	31.4	32.4	33.4	34.4	35.4	36.5	37.5	38.5	39.6	40.6
41	31.3	32.3	33.3	34.3	35.4	36.4	37.4	38.4	39.5	40.5
42	31.2	32.2	33.3	34.3	35.3	36.3	37.3	38.4	39.4	40.4
43	31.1	32.2	33.2	34.2	35.2	36.2	37.3	38.3	39.3	40.3
44	31.1	32.1	33.1	34.1	35.2	36.2	37.2	38.2	39.2	40.3
45	31.0	32.0	33.0	34.1	35.1	36.1	37.1	38.1	39.2	40.2
46	30.9	32.0	33.0	34.0	35.0	36.0	37.0	38.1	39.1	40.1
47	30.9	31.9	32.9	33.9	34.9	35.9	37.0	38.0	39.0	40.0
48	30.8	31.8	32.8	33.8	34.9	35.9	36.9	37.9	38.9	39.9
49	30.7	31.7	32.8	33.8	34.8	35.8	36.8	37.8	38.8	39.9

PRODUCTION EQUIPMENT

Table 5 (*Continued*)

30–39° API   API Gravity Reduction to 60° F.   ASTM—IP

Observed Temperature, °F.	API Gravity at Observed Temperature									
	30	31	32	33	34	35	36	37	38	39
	Corresponding API Gravity at 60° F.									
50	30.7	31.7	32.7	33.7	34.7	35.7	36.7	37.8	38.8	39.8
51	30.6	31.6	32.6	33.6	34.6	35.7	36.7	37.7	38.7	39.7
52	30.5	31.5	32.6	33.6	34.6	35.6	36.6	37.6	38.6	39.6
53	30.5	31.5	32.5	33.5	34.5	35.5	36.5	37.5	38.5	39.5
54	30.4	31.4	32.4	33.4	34.4	35.4	36.4	37.5	38.5	39.5
55	30.3	31.3	32.3	33.4	34.4	35.4	36.4	37.4	38.4	39.4
56	30.3	31.3	32.3	33.3	34.3	35.3	36.3	37.3	38.3	39.3
57	30.2	31.2	32.2	33.2	34.2	35.2	36.2	37.2	38.2	39.2
58	30.1	31.1	32.1	33.1	34.1	35.1	36.1	37.1	38.2	39.2
59	30.1	31.1	32.1	33.1	34.1	35.1	36.1	37.1	38.1	39.1
60	30.0	31.0	32.0	33.0	34.0	35.0	36.0	37.0	38.0	39.0
61	29.9	30.9	31.9	32.9	33.9	34.9	35.9	36.9	37.9	38.9
62	29.9	30.9	31.9	32.9	33.9	34.9	35.9	36.9	37.8	38.8
63	29.8	30.8	31.8	32.8	33.8	34.8	35.8	36.8	37.8	38.8
64	29.7	30.7	31.7	32.7	33.7	34.7	35.7	36.7	37.7	38.7
65	29.7	30.7	31.7	32.7	33.6	34.6	35.6	36.6	37.6	38.6
66	29.6	30.6	31.6	32.6	33.6	34.6	35.6	36.6	37.5	38.5
67	29.5	30.5	31.5	32.5	33.5	34.5	35.5	36.5	37.5	38.5
68	29.5	30.5	31.5	32.4	33.4	34.4	35.4	36.4	37.4	38.4
69	29.4	30.4	31.4	32.4	33.4	34.4	35.3	36.3	37.3	38.3
70	29.3	30.3	31.3	32.3	33.3	34.3	35.3	36.3	37.2	38.2
71	29.3	30.3	31.3	32.2	33.2	34.2	35.2	36.2	37.2	38.2
72	29.2	30.2	31.2	32.2	33.2	34.1	35.1	36.1	37.1	38.1
73	29.1	30.1	31.1	32.1	33.1	34.1	35.1	36.0	37.0	38.0
74	29.1	30.1	31.0	32.0	33.0	34.0	35.0	36.0	36.9	37.9
75	29.0	30.0	31.0	32.0	32.9	33.9	34.9	35.9	36.9	37.9
76	28.9	29.9	30.9	31.9	32.9	33.9	34.8	35.8	36.8	37.8
77	28.9	29.9	30.8	31.8	32.8	33.8	34.8	35.7	36.7	37.7
78	28.8	29.8	30.8	31.8	32.7	33.7	34.7	35.7	36.7	37.6
79	28.8	29.7	30.7	31.7	32.7	33.7	34.6	35.6	36.6	37.6
80	28.7	29.7	30.6	31.6	32.6	33.6	34.6	35.5	36.5	37.5
81	28.6	29.6	30.6	31.6	32.5	33.5	34.5	35.5	36.5	37.4
82	28.6	29.5	30.5	31.5	32.5	33.4	34.4	35.4	36.4	37.3
83	28.5	29.5	30.4	31.4	32.4	33.4	34.3	35.3	36.3	37.3
84	28.4	29.4	30.4	31.4	32.3	33.3	34.3	35.2	36.2	36.2
85	28.4	29.3	30.3	31.3	32.3	33.2	34.2	35.2	36.1	37.1
86	28.3	29.3	30.3	31.2	32.2	33.2	34.1	35.1	36.1	37.0
87	28.2	29.2	30.2	31.2	32.1	33.1	34.1	35.0	36.0	37.0
88	28.2	29.1	30.1	31.1	32.1	33.0	34.0	35.0	35.9	36.9
89	28.1	29.1	30.1	31.0	32.0	33.0	33.9	34.9	35.9	36.8
90	28.0	29.0	30.0	31.0	31.9	32.9	33.9	34.8	35.8	36.7
91	28.0	29.0	29.9	30.9	31.9	32.8	33.8	34.7	35.7	36.7
92	27.9	28.9	29.9	30.8	31.8	32.8	32.7	34.7	35.6	36.6
93	27.9	28.8	29.8	30.8	31.7	32.7	33.7	34.6	35.6	36.5
94	27.8	28.8	29.7	30.7	31.7	32.6	35.6	34.5	35.5	36.5
95	27.7	28.7	29.7	30.6	31.6	32.5	33.5	34.5	35.4	36.4
96	27.7	28.6	29.6	30.6	31.5	32.5	33.4	34.4	35.4	36.3
97	27.6	28.6	29.5	30.5	31.5	32.4	33.4	34.3	35.3	36.2
98	27.5	28.5	29.5	30.4	31.4	32.3	33.3	34.3	35.2	36.2
99	27.5	28.4	29.4	30.4	31.3	32.2	33.2	34.2	35.1	36.1

Table 5 (*Continued*)

ASTM—IP   API Gravity Reduction to 60° F.   30–39° API

Observed Temperature, °F.	API Gravity at Observed Temperature									
	30	31	32	33	34	35	36	37	38	39
	Corresponding API Gravity at 60° F.									
100	27.4	28.4	29.3	30.3	31.3	32.2	33.2	34.1	35.1	36.0
101	27.4	28.3	29.3	30.2	31.2	32.1	33.1	34.0	35.0	35.9
102	27.3	28.3*	29.2	30.2	31.1	32.1	33.0	34.0	34.9	35.9
103	27.2	28.2	29.1	30.1	31.1	32.0	33.0	33.9	34.9	35.8
104	27.2	28.1	29.1	30.0	31.0	31.9	32.9	33.8	34.8	35.7
105	27.1	28.1	29.0	30.0	30.9	31.9	32.8	33.8	34.7	35.7
106	27.0	28.0	29.0	29.9	30.9	31.8	32.8	33.7	34.6	35.6
107	27.0	27.9	28.9	29.8	30.8	31.7	32.7	33.6	34.6	35.5
108	26.9	27.9	28.8	29.8	30.7	31.7	32.6	33.6	34.5	35.4
109	26.9	27.8	28.8	29.7	30.7	31.6	32.5	33.5	34.4	35.4
110	26.8	27.7	28.7	29.6	30.6	31.5	32.5	33.4	34.4	35.3
111	26.7	27.7	28.6	29.6	30.5	31.5	32.4	33.4	34.3	35.2
112	26.7	27.6	28.6	29.5	30.5	31.4	32.3	33.3	34.2	35.2
113	26.6	27.6	28.5	29.5	30.4	31.3	32.3	33.2	34.2	35.1
114	26.5	27.5	28.4	29.4	30.3	31.3	32.2	33.2	34.1	35.0
115	26.5	27.4	28.4	29.3	30.3	31.2	32.1	33.1	34.0	35.0
116	26.4	27.4	28.3	29.3	30.2	31.1	32.1	33.0	34.0	34.9
117	26.4	27.3	28.3	29.2	30.1	31.1	32.0	32.9	33.9	34.8
118	26.3	27.2	28.2	29.1	30.1	31.0	31.9	32.9	33.8	34.7
119	26.2	27.2	28.1	29.1	30.0	30.9	31.9	32.8	33.7	34.7
120	26.2	27.1	28.1	29.0	29.9	30.9	31.8	32.7	33.7	34.6
121	26.1	27.1	28.0	28.9	29.9	30.8	31.7	32.7	33.6	34.5
122	26.1	27.0	27.9	28.9	29.8	30.8	31.7	32.6	33.5	34.5
123	26.0	26.9	27.9	28.8	29.8	30.7	31.6	32.5	33.5	34.4
124	25.9	26.9	27.8	29.8	29.7	30.6	31.5	32.5	33.4	34.3
125	25.9	26.8	27.8	28.7	29.6	30.6	31.5	32.4	33.3	34.3
126	25.8	26.8	27.7	28.6	29.6	30.5	31.4	32.3	33.3	34.2
127	25.8	26.7	27.6	28.6	29.5	30.4	31.4	32.3	33.2	34.1
128	25.7	26.6	27.6	28.5	29.4	30.4	31.3	32.2	33.1	34.1
129	25.6	26.6	27.5	28.4	29.4	30.3	31.2	32.1	33.1	34.0
130	25.6	26.5	27.4	28.4	29.3	30.2	31.2	32.1	33.0	33.9
131	25.5	26.5	27.4	28.3	29.2	30.2	31.1	32.0	32.9	32.8
132	25.5	26.4	27.3	28.2	29.1	30.1	31.0	31.9	32.9	33.8
133	25.4	26.3	27.3	28.2	29.1	30.0	31.0	31.9	32.8	33.7
134	25.3	26.3	27.2	28.1	29.0	30.0	30.9	31.8	32.7	33.6
135	25.3	26.2	27.1	28.1	29.0	29.9	30.8	31.7	32.7	33.6
136	25.2	26.1	27.1	28.0	28.9	29.8	30.8	31.7	32.6	33.5
137	25.2	26.1	27.0	27.9	28.9	29.8	30.7	31.6	32.5	33.4
138	25.1	26.0	27.0	27.9	28.8	29.7	30.6	31.6	32.5	33.4
139	25.0	26.0	26.9	27.8	28.7	29.7	30.6	31.5	32.4	33.3
140	25.0	25.9	26.8	27.8	28.7	29.6	30.5	31.4	32.3	33.2
141	24.9	25.9	26.8	27.7	28.6	29.5	30.4	31.4	32.3	33.2
142	24.9	25.8	26.7	27.6	28.5	29.5	30.4	31.3	32.2	33.1
143	24.8	25.7	26.6	27.6	28.5	29.4	30.3	31.2	32.1	33.0
144	24.7	25.7	26.6	27.5	28.4	29.3	30.3	31.2	32.1	33.0
145	24.7	25.6	26.5	27.4	28.4	29.3	30.2	31.1	32.0	32.9
146	24.6	25.6	26.5	27.4	28.3	29.2	30.1	31.0	31.9	32.8
147	24.6	25.5	26.4	27.3	28.2	29.1	30.1	31.0	31.9	32.8
148	24.5	25.4	26.3	27.3	28.2	29.1	30.0	30.9	31.8	32.7
149	24.4	25.4	26.3	27.2	28.1	29.0	29.9	30.8	31.7	32.6

Table 5 (Continued)

API Gravity Reduction to 60° F.

Observed Temperature, °F.	API Gravity at Observed Temperature									
	30	31	32	33	34	35	36	37	38	39
	Corresponding API Gravity at 60° F.									
150	24.4	25.3	26.2	27.1	28.1	29.0	29.9	30.8	31.7	32.6
151	24.3	25.3	26.2	27.1	28.0	28.9	29.8	30.7	31.6	32.5
152	24.3	25.2	26.1	27.0	27.9	28.8	29.7	30.6	31.5	32.4
153	24.2	25.1	26.0	27.0	27.9	28.8	29.7	30.6	31.5	32.4
154	24.2	25.1	26.0	26.9	27.8	28.7	29.6	30.5	31.4	32.3
155	24.1	25.0	25.9	26.8	27.7	28.6	29.6	30.5	31.4	32.2
156	24.0	25.0	25.9	26.8	27.7	28.6	29.5	30.4	31.3	32.2
157	24.0	24.9	25.8	26.7	27.6	28.5	29.4	30.3	31.2	32.1
158	23.9	24.8	25.8	26.7	27.6	28.5	29.4	30.3	31.2	32.0
159	23.9	24.8	25.7	26.6	27.5	28.4	29.3	30.2	31.1	32.0
160	23.8	24.7	25.6	26.5	27.4	28.3	29.2	30.1	31.0	31.9
161	23.7	24.7	25.6	26.5	27.4	28.3	29.2	30.1	31.0	31.9
162	23.7	24.6	25.5	26.4	27.3	28.2	29.1	30.0	30.9	31.8
163	23.6	24.5	25.5	26.4	27.3	28.2	29.1	29.9	30.8	31.7
164	23.6	24.5	25.4	26.3	27.2	28.1	29.0	29.9	30.8	31.7
165	23.5	24.4	25.3	26.2	27.1	28.0	28.9	29.8	30.7	31.6
166	23.5	24.4	25.3	26.2	27.1	28.0	28.9	29.8	30.7	31.5
167	23.4	24.3	25.2	26.1	27.0	27.9	28.8	29.7	30.6	13.5
168	26.3	24.3	25.2	26.1	27.0	27.9	28.7	29.6	30.5	31.4
169	23.3	24.2	25.1	26.0	26.9	27.8	28.7	29.6	30.5	31.3
170	23.2	24.1	25.0	25.9	26.8	27.7	28.6	29.5	30.4	31.3
171	23.2	24.1	25.0	25.9	26.8	27.7	28.6	29.4	30.3	31.2
172	23.1	24.0	24.9	25.8	26.7	27.6	28.5	29.4	30.3	31.1
173	23.1	24.0	24.9	25.8	26.7	27.5	28.4	29.3	30.2	31.1
174	23.0	23.9	24.8	25.7	26.6	27.5	28.4	29.3	30.1	31.0
175	22.9	23.8	24.8	25.7	26.5	27.4	28.3	29.2	30.1	31.0
176	22.9	23.8	24.7	25.6	26.5	27.4	28.3	29.1	30.0	30.9
177	22.8	23.7	24.6	25.5	25.4	27.3	28.2	29.1	30.0	30.8
178	22.8	23.7	24.6	25.5	26.4	27.2	28.1	29.0	29.9	30.8
179	22.7	23.6	24.5	25.4	26.3	27.2	28.1	29.0	29.8	30.7
180	22.7	23.6	24.5	25.4	26.2	27.1	28.0	28.9	29.8	30.6
181	22.6	23.5	24.4	25.3	26.2	27.1	27.9	28.8	29.7	30.6
182	22.6	23.4	24.3	25.2	26.1	27.0	27.9	28.8	29.6	30.5
183	22.5	23.4	24.3	25.2	26.1	27.0	27.8	28.7	29.6	30.5
184	22.4	23.3	24.2	25.1	26.0	26.9	27.8	28.6	29.5	30.4
185	22.4	23.3	24.2	25.1	26.0	26.8	27.7	28.6	29.5	30.3
186	22.3	23.2	24.1	25.0	25.9	26.8	27.6	28.5	29.4	30.3
187	22.3	23.2	24.1	24.9	25.8	26.7	27.6	28.5	29.3	30.2
188	22.2	23.1	24.0	24.9	25.8	26.7	27.5	28.4	29.3	30.1
189	22.2	23.1	23.9	24.8	25.7	26.6	27.5	28.3	29.2	30.1
190	22.1	23.0	23.9	24.8	25.7	26.5	27.4	28.3	29.2	30.0
191	22.1	22.9	23.8	24.7	25.6	26.5	27.4	28.2	29.1	30.0
192	22.0	22.9	23.8	24.7	25.5	26.4	27.3	28.2	29.0	29.9
193	21.9	22.8	23.7	24.6	25.5	26.4	27.2	28.1	29.0	29.8
194	21.9	22.8	23.7	24.5	25.4	26.3	27.2	28.0	28.9	29.8
195	21.8	22.7	23.6	24.5	25.4	26.2	27.1	28.0	28.8	29.7
196	21.8	22.7	23.5	24.4	25.3	26.2	27.1	27.9	28.8	29.6
197	21.7	22.6	23.5	24.4	25.3	26.1	27.0	27.9	28.7	29.6
198	21.7	22.6	23.4	24.3	25.2	26.1	26.9	27.8	28.7	29.5
199	21.6	22.5	23.4	24.3	25.1	26.0	26.9	27.7	28.6	29.5

Table 5 (*Continued*)

API Gravity Reduction to 60° F.

Observed Temperature, °F.	API Gravity at Observed Temperature									
	40	41	42	43	44	45	46	47	48	49
	Corresponding API Gravity at 60° F.									
0	45.1	46.2	47.3	48.4	49.5	50.6	51.8	52.9	54.0	55.2
1	45.0	46.1	47.2	48.3	49.4	50.5	51.6	52.8	53.9	55.0
2	44.9	46.0	47.1	48.2	49.3	50.4	51.5	52.7	53.8	54.9
3	44.8	45.9	47.0	48.1	49.2	50.3	51.4	52.6	53.7	54.8
4	44.7	45.8	46.9	48.0	49.1	50.2	51.3	52.5	53.6	54.7
5	44.6	45.7	46.8	47.9	49.0	50.1	51.2	52.3	53.5	54.6
6	44.5	45.6	46.7	47.8	48.9	50.0	51.1	52.2	53.4	54.5
7	44.4	45.5	46.6	47.7	48.8	49.9	51.0	52.1	53.3	54.4
8	44.3	45.4	46.5	47.6	48.7	49.8	50.9	52.0	53.1	54.3
9	44.3	45.3	46.4	47.5	48.6	49.7	50.8	51.9	53.0	54.2
10	44.2	45.2	46.3	47.4	48.5	49.6	50.7	51.8	52.9	54.0
11	44.1	45.2	46.2	47.3	48.4	49.5	50.6	51.7	52.8	53.9
12	44.0	45.1	46.2	47.2	48.3	49.4	50.5	51.6	52.7	53.8
13	43.9	45.0	46.1	47.1	48.2	49.3	50.4	51.5	52.6	53.7
14	43.8	44.9	46.0	47.1	48.1	49.2	50.3	51.4	52.5	53.6
15	43.7	44.8	45.9	47.0	48.0	49.1	50.2	51.3	52.4	53.5
16	43.6	44.7	45.8	46.9	48.0	49.0	50.1	51.2	52.3	53.4
17	43.6	44.6	45.7	46.8	47.9	48.9	50.0	51.1	52.2	53.3
18	43.5	44.5	45.6	46.7	47.8	48.8	49.9	51.0	52.1	53.2
19	43.4	44.4	45.4	46.6	47.7	48.7	49.8	50.9	52.0	53.1
20	43.3	44.4	45.4	46.5	47.6	48.7	49.7	50.8	51.9	53.0
21	43.2	44.3	45.3	46.4	47.5	48.6	49.6	50.7	51.8	52.9
22	43.1	44.2	45.2	46.3	47.4	48.5	49.5	50.6	51.7	52.8
23	43.0	44.1	45.2	46.2	47.3	48.4	49.4	50.5	51.6	52.7
24	42.9	44.0	45.1	46.1	47.2	48.3	49.3	50.4	51.5	52.6
25	42.9	43.9	45.0	46.0	47.1	48.2	49.2	50.3	51.4	52.4
26	42.8	43.8	44.9	46.0	47.0	48.1	49.1	50.2	51.3	52.3
27	42.7	43.7	44.8	45.9	46.9	48.0	49.0	50.1	51.2	52.2
28	42.6	43.7	44.7	45.8	46.8	47.9	48.9	50.0	51.1	52.1
29	42.5	43.6	44.6	45.7	46.7	47.8	48.9	49.9	51.0	52.0
30	42.4	43.5	44.5	45.6	46.6	47.7	48.8	49.8	50.9	51.9
31	42.4	43.4	44.5	45.5	46.6	47.6	48.7	49.7	50.8	51.8
32	42.3	43.3	44.4	45.4	46.5	47.5	48.6	49.6	50.7	51.7
33	42.2	43.2	44.3	45.3	46.4	47.4	48.5	49.5	50.6	51.6
34	42.1	43.1	44.2	45.2	46.3	47.3	43.3	49.4	50.5	51.5
35	42.0	43.1	44.1	45.1	46.2	47.2	48.3	49.3	50.4	51.4
36	41.9	43.0	44.0	45.1	46.1	47.1	48.2	49.2	50.3	51.3
37	41.9	42.9	43.9	45.0	46.0	47.0	48.1	49.1	50.2	51.2
38	41.8	42.8	43.8	44.9	45.9	47.0	48.0	49.0	50.1	51.1
39	41.7	42.7	43.8	44.8	45.8	46.9	47.9	48.9	50.0	51.0
40	41.6	42.6	43.7	44.7	45.7	46.8	47.8	48.9	49.0	50.9
41	41.5	42.6	43.6	44.6	45.7	46.7	47.7	48.8	49.8	50.8
42	41.4	42.5	43.5	44.5	45.6	46.6	47.6	48.7	49.7	50.7
43	41.4	42.4	43.4	44.4	45.5	46.5	47.5	48.6	49.6	50.6
44	41.3	42.3	43.3	44.4	45.4	46.4	47.4	48.5	49.5	50.5
45	41.2	42.2	43.2	44.3	45.3	46.3	47.3	48.4	49.4	50.4
46	41.1	42.1	43.2	44.2	45.2	46.2	47.3	48.3	49.3	50.3
47	41.0	42.1	43.1	44.1	45.1	46.1	47.2	48.2	49.2	50.2
48	41.0	42.0	43.0	44.0	45.0	46.1	47.1	48.1	49.1	50.1
49	40.9	41.9	42.9	43.9	44.9	46.0	47.0	48.0	49.0	50.0

PRODUCTION EQUIPMENT

Table 5 (*Continued*)

40–49° API · API Gravity Reduction to 60° F. · ASTM—IP

Observed Temper- ature, °F.	API Gravity at Observed Temperature									
	40	41	42	43	44	45	46	47	48	49
	Corresponding API Gravity at 60° F.									
50	40.8	41.8	42.8	43.8	44.9	45.9	46.9	47.9	48.9	50.0
51	40.7	41.7	42.7	43.8	44.8	45.8	46.8	47.8	48.8	49.9
52	40.6	41.6	42.7	43.7	44.7	45.7	46.7	47.7	48.7	49.8
53	40.6	41.6	42.6	43.6	44.6	45.6	46.6	47.6	48.6	49.7
54	40.5	41.5	42.5	43.5	44.5	45.5	46.5	47.5	48.6	49.6
55	40.4	41.4	42.4	43.4	44.4	45.4	46.4	47.5	48.5	49.5
56	40.3	41.3	42.3	43.3	44.3	45.3	46.4	47.4	48.4	49.4
57	40.2	41.2	42.2	43.3	44.3	45.3	46.3	47.3	48.3	49.3
58	40.2	41.2	42.2	43.2	44.2	45.2	46.2	47.2	48.2	49.2
59	40.1	41.1	42.1	43.1	44.1	45.1	46.1	47.1	48.1	49.1
60	40.0	41.0	42.0	43.0	44.0	45.0	46.0	47.0	48.0	49.0
61	39.9	40.9	41.9	42.9	43.9	44.9	45.9	46.9	47.9	48.9
62	39.8	40.8	41.8	42.8	43.8	44.8	45.8	46.8	47.8	48.8
63	39.8	40.8	41.8	42.8	43.7	44.7	45.7	46.7	47.7	48.7
64	39.7	40.7	41.7	42.7	43.7	44.7	45.6	46.6	47.6	48.6
65	39.6	40.6	41.6	42.6	43.6	44.6	45.6	46.6	47.5	48.5
66	39.5	40.5	41.5	42.5	43.5	44.5	45.5	46.5	47.5	48.4
67	39.5	40.4	41.4	42.4	43.4	44.4	45.4	46.4	47.4	48.3
68	39.4	40.4	41.4	42.3	43.3	44.3	45.3	46.3	47.3	48.3
69	39.3	40.3	41.3	42.3	43.2	44.2	45.2	46.2	47.2	48.2
70	39.2	40.2	41.2	42.2	43.2	44.1	45.1	46.1	47.1	48.1
71	39.1	40.1	41.1	42.1	43.1	44.1	45.0	46.0	47.0	48.0
72	39.1	40.0	41.0	42.0	43.0	44.0	45.0	45.9	46.9	47.9
73	39.0	40.0	41.0	41.9	42.9	43.9	44.9	45.8	46.8	47.8
74	38.9	39.9	40.9	41.9	42.8	43.8	44.8	45.8	46.7	47.7
75	38.8	39.8	40.8	41.8	42.7	43.7	44.7	45.7	46.6	47.6
76	38.8	39.7	40.7	41.7	42.7	43.6	44.6	45.6	46.6	47.5
77	38.7	39.7	40.6	41.6	42.6	43.6	44.5	45.5	46.5	47.4
78	38.6	39.6	40.6	41.5	42.5	43.5	44.4	45.4	46.4	47.4
79	38.5	39.5	40.5	41.4	42.4	43.4	44.4	45.3	46.3	47.3
80	38.5	39.4	40.4	41.4	42.3	43.3	44.3	45.2	46.2	47.2
81	38.4	39.4	40.3	41.3	42.3	43.2	44.2	45.2	46.1	47.1
82	38.3	39.3	40.2	41.2	42.2	43.1	44.1	45.1	46.0	47.0
83	38.2	39.2	40.2	41.1	42.1	43.1	44.0	45.0	45.9	46.9
84	38.2	39.1	40.1	41.1	42.0	43.0	43.9	44.9	45.9	46.8
85	38.1	39.0	40.0	41.0	41.9	42.9	43.9	44.8	45.8	46.7
86	38.0	39.0	39.9	40.9	41.9	42.8	43.8	44.7	45.7	46.6
87	37.9	38.9	39.9	40.8	41.8	42.7	43.7	44.6	45.6	46.6
88	37.9	38.8	39.8	40.7	41.7	42.7	43.6	44.6	45.5	46.5
89	37.8	38.7	39.7	40.7	41.6	42.6	43.5	44.5	45.4	46.4
90	37.7	38.7	39.6	40.6	41.5	42.5	43.4	44.4	45.3	46.3
91	37.6	38.6	39.5	40.5	41.4	42.4	43.4	44.3	45.3	46.2
92	37.6	38.5	39.5	40.4	41.4	42.3	43.3	44.2	45.2	46.1
93	37.5	38.4	39.4	40.3	41.3	42.2	43.2	44.1	45.1	46.0
94	37.4	38.4	39.3	40.3	41.2	42.2	43.1	44.1	45.0	45.9
95	37.3	38.3	39.2	40.2	41.1	42.1	43.0	44.0	44.9	45.9
96	37.3	38.2	39.2	40.1	41.1	42.0	43.0	43.9	44.8	45.8
97	37.2	38.1	39.1	40.0	41.0	41.9	42.9	43.8	44.8	45.7
98	37.1	38.1	39.0	40.0	40.9	41.8	42.8	43.7	44.7	45.6
99	37.0	38.0	38.9	39.9	40.8	41.8	42.7	43.6	44.6	45.5

Table 5 (*Continued*)

ASTM—IP

API Gravity Reduction to 60° F.

40-49° API

Observed Temper- ature, °F.	API Gravity at Observed Temperature									
	40	41	42	43	44	45	46	47	48	49
	Corresponding API Gravity at 60° F.										
100	37.0	37.0	38.9	39.8	40.7	41.7	42.6	43.6	44.5	45.4
101	36.9	37.8	38.8	39.7	40.7	41.6	42.5	43.5	44.4	45.4
102	36.8	37.8	38.7	39.7	40.6	41.5	42.5	43.4	44.3	45.3
103	36.7	37.7	38.6	39.6	40.5	41.5	42.4	43.3	44.3	45.2
104	36.7	37.6	38.6	39.5	40.4	41.4	42.3	43.2	44.2	45.1
105	36.6	37.5	38.5	39.4	40.4	41.3	42.2	43.2	44.1	45.0
106	36.5	37.5	38.4	39.4	40.3	41.2	42.1	43.1	44.0	44.9
107	36.5	37.4	38.3	39.3	40.2	41.1	42.1	43.0	43.9	44.8
108	36.4	37.3	38.3	39.2	40.1	41.1	42.0	42.9	43.8	44.8
109	36.3	37.3	38.2	39.1	40.1	41.0	41.9	42.8	43.8	44.7
110	36.2	37.2	38.1	39.0	40.0	40.9	41.8	42.8	43.7	44.6
111	36.2	37.1	38.0	39.0	39.9	40.8	41.8	42.7	43.6	44.5
112	36.1	37.0	38.0	38.9	39.8	40.7	41.7	42.6	43.5	44.4
113	36.0	37.0	37.9	38.8	39.7	40.7	41.6	42.5	43.4	44.3
114	36.0	36.9	37.8	38.7	39.7	40.6	41.5	42.4	43.4	44.3
115	35.9	36.8	37.7	38.7	39.6	40.5	41.4	42.4	43.3	44.2
116	35.8	36.7	37.7	38.6	39.5	40.4	41.4	42.3	43.2	44.1
117	35.7	36.7	37.6	38.5	39.4	40.4	41.3	42.2	43.1	44.0
118	35.7	36.6	37.5	38.5	39.4	40.3	41.2	42.1	43.0	43.9
119	35.6	36.5	37.5	38.4	39.3	40.2	41.1	42.0	43.0	43.9
120	35.5	36.5	37.4	38.3	39.2	40.1	41.0	42.0	42.9	43.8
121	35.5	36.4	37.3	38.2	39.1	40.1	41.0	41.9	42.8	43.7
122	35.4	36.3	37.2	38.2	39.1	40.0	40.9	41.8	42.7	43.6
123	35.3	36.2	37.2	38.1	39.0	39.9	40.8	41.7	42.6	43.5
124	35.3	36.2	37.1	38.0	38.9	39.8	40.7	41.6	42.6	43.5
125	35.2	36.1	37.0	37.9	38.9	39.8	40.7	41.6	42.5	43.4
126	35.1	36.0	36.9	37.9	38.8	39.7	40.6	41.5	42.4	43.3
127	35.0	36.0	36.9	37.8	38.7	39.6	40.5	41.4	42.3	43.2
128	35.0	35.9	36.8	37.7	38.6	39.5	40.4	41.3	42.2	43.1
129	34.9	35.8	36.7	37.6	38.6	39.5	40.4	41.3	42.2	43.1
130	34.8	35.8	36.7	37.6	38.5	39.4	40.3	41.2	42.1	43.0
131	34.8	35.7	36.6	37.5	38.4	39.3	40.2	41.1	42.0	42.9
132	34.7	35.6	36.5	37.4	38.3	39.2	40.1	41.0	41.9	42.8
133	34.6	35.5	36.5	37.4	38.3	39.2	40.1	41.0	41.8	42.7
134	34.6	35.5	36.4	37.3	38.2	39.1	40.0	40.9	41.8	42.7
135	34.5	35.4	36.3	37.2	38.1	39.0	39.9	40.8	41.7	42.6
136	34.4	35.3	36.2	37.1	38.0	38.9	39.8	40.7	41.6	42.5
137	34.4	35.3	36.2	37.1	38.0	38.9	39.8	40.6	41.5	42.4
138	34.3	35.2	36.1	37.0	37.9	38.8	39.7	40.6	41.5	42.3
139	34.2	35.1	36.0	36.9	37.8	38.7	39.6	40.5	41.4	42.3
140	34.1	35.1	36.0	36.9	37.8	38.6	39.5	40.4	41.3	42.2
141	34.1	35.0	35.9	36.8	37.7	38.6	39.5	40.3	41.2	42.1
142	34.0	34.9	35.8	36.7	37.6	38.5	39.4	40.3	41.2	42.0
143	33.9	34.8	35.7	36.6	37.5	38.4	39.3	40.2	41.1	42.0
144	33.9	34.8	35.7	36.6	37.5	38.4	39.2	40.1	41.0	41.9
145	33.8	34.7	35.6	36.5	37.4	38.3	39.2	40.0	40.9	41.8
146	33.7	34.6	35.5	36.4	37.3	38.2	39.1	40.0	40.9	41.7
147	33.7	34.6	35.5	36.4	37.2	38.1	39.0	39.9	40.8	41.6
148	33.6	34.5	35.4	36.3	37.2	38.1	38.9	39.8	40.7	41.6
149	33.5	34.4	35.3	36.2	37.1	38.0	38.9	39.8	40.6	41.5

Table 5 (Continued)

40–49° API   API Gravity Reduction to 60° F.   ASTM—IP

Observed Temperature, °F.	API Gravity at Observed Temperature									
	40	41	42	43	44	45	46	47	48	49
	Corresponding API Gravity at 60° F.									
150	33.5	34.4	35.3	36.1	37.0	37.9	38.8	39.7	40.6	41.4
151	33.4	34.3	35.2	36.1	37.0	37.8	38.7	39.6	40.5	41.3
152	33.3	34.2	35.1	36.0	36.9	37.8	38.7	39.5	40.4	41.3
153	33.3	34.2	35.1	35.9	36.8	37.7	38.6	39.5	40.3	41.2
154	33.2	34.1	35.0	35.9	36.8	37.6	38.5	39.4	40.3	41.1
155	33.1	34.0	34.9	35.8	36.7	37.6	38.4	39.3	40.2	41.0
156	33.1	34.0	34.9	35.7	36.6	37.5	38.4	39.2	40.1	41.0
157	33.0	33.9	34.8	35.7	36.5	37.4	38.3	39.2	40.0	40.9
158	32.9	33.8	34.7	35.6	36.5	37.3	38.2	39.1	40.0	40.8
159	32.9	33.8	34.6	35.5	36.4	37.3	38.1	39.0	39.9	40.7
160	32.8	33.7	34.6	35.5	36.3	37.2	38.1	38.9	39.8	40.7
161	32.7	33.6	34.5	35.4	36.3	37.1	38.0	38.9	39.7	40.6
162	32.7	33.6	34.4	35.3	36.2	37.1	37.9	38.8	39.7	40.5
163	32.6	33.5	34.4	35.3	36.1	37.0	37.9	38.7	39.6	40.4
164	32.5	33.4	34.3	35.2	36.1	36.9	37.8	38.7	39.5	40.4
165	32.5	33.4	34.2	35.1	36.0	36.9	37.7	38.6	39.4	40.3
166	32.4	33.3	34.2	35.0	35.9	36.8	37.6	38.5	39.4	40.2
167	32.3	33.2	34.1	35.0	35.8	36.7	37.6	38.4	39.3	40.1
168	32.3	33.2	34.0	34.9	35.8	36.6	37.5	38.4	39.2	40.1
169	32.2	33.1	34.0	34.8	35.7	36.6	37.4	38.3	39.2	40.0
170	32.2	33.0	33.9	34.8	35.6	36.5	37.4	38.2	39.1	39.9
171	32.1	33.0	33.8	34.7	35.6	36.4	37.3	38.2	39.0	39.9
172	32.0	32.9	33.8	34.6	35.5	36.4	37.2	38.1	38.9	39.8
173	32.0	32.8	33.7	34.6	35.4	36.3	37.2	38.0	38.9	39.7
174	31.9	32.8	33.6	34.5	35.4	36.2	37.1	37.9	38.8	39.6
175	31.8	32.7	33.6	34.4	35.3	36.2	37.0	37.9	38.7	39.6
176	31.8	32.6	33.5	34.4	35.2	36.1	36.9	37.8	38.6	39.5
177	31.7	32.6	33.4	34.3	35.2	36.0	36.9	37.7	38.6	39.4
178	31.6	32.5	33.4	34.2	35.1	36.0	36.8	37.7	38.5	39.4
179	31.6	32.4	33.3	34.2	35.0	35.9	36.7	37.6	38.4	39.3
180	31.5	32.4	33.2	34.1	35.0	35.8	36.7	37.5	38.4	39.2
181	31.4	32.3	33.2	34.0	34.9	35.8	36.6	37.4	38.3	39.1
182	31.4	32.2	33.1	34.0	34.8	35.7	36.5	37.4	38.2	39.1
183	31.3	32.2	33.0	33.9	34.8	35.6	36.5	37.3	38.1	39.0
184	31.3	32.1	33.0	33.8	34.7	35.5	36.4	37.2	38.1	38.9
185	31.2	32.1	32.9	33.8	34.6	35.5	36.3	37.2	38.0	38.8
186	31.1	32.0	32.9	33.7	34.6	35.4	36.3	37.1	37.9	38.8
187	31.1	31.9	32.8	33.6	34.5	35.3	36.2	37.0	37.9	38.7
188	31.0	31.9	32.7	33.6	34.4	35.3	36.1	37.0	37.8	38.6
189	30.9	31.8	32.7	33.5	34.4	35.2	36.1	36.9	37.7	38.6
190	30.9	31.7	32.6	33.4	34.3	35.1	36.0	36.8	37.7	38.5
191	30.8	31.7	32.5	33.4	34.2	35.1	35.9	36.8	37.6	38.4
192	30.8	31.6	32.5	33.3	34.2	35.0	35.9	36.7	37.5	38.3
193	30.7	31.5	32.4	33.2	34.1	34.9	35.8	36.6	37.4	38.3
194	30.6	31.5	32.3	33.2	34.0	34.9	35.7	36.5	37.4	38.2
195	30.6	31.4	32.3	33.1	34.0	34.8	35.6	36.5	37.3	38.1
196	30.5	31.4	32.2	33.1	33.9	34.7	35.6	36.4	37.2	38.1
197	30.4	31.3	32.1	33.0	33.8	34.7	35.5	36.3	37.2	38.0
198	30.4	31.2	32.1	32.9	33.8	34.6	35.4	36.3	37.1	37.9
199	30.3	31.2	32.0	32.9	33.7	34.5	35.4	36.2	37.0	37.9
200	30.3	31.1	32.0	32.8	33.6	34.5	35.3	36.1	37.0	37.8

Table 5 (*Continued*)

ASTM—IP API Gravity Reduction to 60° F. 50–59° API

Observed Temperature, °F.	API Gravity at Observed Temperature									
	50	51	52	53	54	55	56	57	58	59
	Corresponding API Gravity at 60° F.									
0	56.3	57.4	58.5	59.7	60.8	61.9	63.0	64.2	65.3	66.4
1	56.2	57.3	58.4	59.5	60.7	61.8	62.9	64.0	65.2	66.3
2	56.1	57.2	58.3	59.4	60.5	61.7	62.8	63.9	65.0	66.1
3	56.0	57.1	58.2	59.3	60.4	61.5	62.7	63.8	64.9	66.0
4	55.8	57.0	58.1	59.2	60.3	61.4	62.5	63.6	64.8	65.9
5	55.7	56.9	58.0	59.1	60.2	61.3	62.4	63.5	64.6	65.8
6	55.6	56.7	57.8	59.0	60.1	61.2	62.3	63.4	64.5	65.6
7	55.5	56.6	57.7	58.8	59.9	61.0	62.2	63.3	64.4	65.5
8	55.4	56.5	57.6	58.7	59.8	60.9	62.0	63.1	64.3	65.4
9	55.3	56.4	57.5	58.6	59.7	60.8	61.9	63.0	64.1	65.2
10	55.2	56.3	57.4	58.5	59.6	60.7	61.8	62.9	64.0	65.1
11	55.1	56.2	57.3	58.4	59.5	60.6	61.7	62.8	63.9	65.0
12	54.9	56.1	57.2	58.3	59.3	60.4	61.5	62.6	63.7	64.8
13	54.8	55.9	57.0	58.1	59.2	60.3	61.4	62.5	63.6	64.7
14	54.7	55.8	56.9	58.0	59.1	60.2	61.3	62.4	63.5	64.6
15	54.6	55.7	56.8	57.9	59.0	60.1	61.2	62.3	63.4	64.5
16	54.5	55.6	56.7	57.8	58.9	60.0	61.1	62.1	63.2	64.3
17	54.4	55.5	56.6	57.7	58.8	59.8	60.9	62.0	63.1	64.2
18	54.3	55.4	56.5	57.6	58.6	59.7	60.8	61.9	63.0	64.1
19	54.2	55.3	56.4	57.4	58.5	59.6	60.7	61.8	62.9	63.9
20	54.1	55.2	56.2	57.3	58.4	59.5	60.6	61.7	62.7	63.8
21	54.0	55.0	56.1	57.2	58.3	59.4	60.5	61.5	62.6	63.7
22	53.8	54.9	56.0	57.1	58.2	59.3	60.3	61.4	62.5	63.6
23	53.7	54.8	55.9	57.0	58.1	59.1	60.2	61.3	62.4	63.4
24	53.6	54.7	55.8	56.9	57.9	59.0	60.1	61.2	62.2	63.3
25	53.5	54.6	55.7	56.8	57.8	58.9	60.0	61.0	62.1	63.2
26	53.4	54.5	55.6	56.7	57.7	58.8	59.9	60.9	62.0	63.1
27	53.3	54.4	55.5	56.5	57.6	58.7	59.7	60.8	61.9	62.9
28	53.2	54.3	55.4	56.4	57.5	58.6	59.6	60.7	61.7	62.8
29	53.1	54.2	55.2	56.3	57.4	58.4	59.5	60.6	61.6	62.7
30	53.0	54.1	55.1	56.2	57.3	58.3	59.4	60.4	61.5	62.6
31	52.9	54.0	55.0	56.1	57.2	58.2	59.3	60.3	61.4	62.4
32	52.8	53.9	54.9	56.0	57.0	58.1	59.2	60.2	61.3	62.3
33	52.7	53.7	54.8	55.9	56.9	58.0	59.0	60.1	61.1	62.2
34	52.6	53.6	54.7	55.8	56.8	57.9	58.9	60.0	61.0	62.1
35	52.5	53.5	54.6	55.6	56.7	57.8	58.8	59.9	60.9	62.0
36	52.4	53.4	54.5	55.5	56.6	57.6	58.7	59.7	60.8	61.8
37	52.3	53.3	54.4	55.4	56.5	57.5	58.6	59.6	60.7	61.7
38	52.2	53.2	54.3	55.3	56.4	57.4	58.5	59.5	60.5	61.6
39	52.1	53.1	54.2	55.2	56.3	57.3	58.3	59.4	60.4	61.5
40	52.0	53.0	54.1	55.1	56.1	57.2	58.2	59.3	60.3	61.3
41	51.9	52.9	54.0	55.0	56.0	57.1	58.1	59.2	60.2	61.2
42	51.8	52.8	53.8	54.9	55.9	57.0	58.0	59.0	60.1	61.1
43	51.7	52.7	53.7	54.8	55.8	56.9	57.9	58.9	60.0	61.0
44	51.6	52.6	53.6	54.7	55.7	56.7	57.8	58.8	59.8	60.9
45	51.5	52.5	53.5	54.6	55.6	56.6	57.7	58.7	59.7	60.7
46	51.4	52.4	53.4	54.5	55.5	56.5	57.5	58.6	59.6	60.6
47	51.3	52.3	53.3	54.4	55.4	56.4	57.4	58.5	59.5	60.5
48	51.2	52.2	53.2	54.2	55.3	56.3	57.3	58.3	59.4	60.4
49	51.1	52.1	53.1	54.1	55.2	56.2	57.2	58.2	59.3	60.3

PRODUCTION EQUIPMENT

Table 5 (*Continued*)

API Gravity Reduction to 60° F.

Observed Temperature, °F.	API Gravity at Observed Temperature									
	50	51	52	53	54	55	56	57	58	59
	Corresponding API Gravity at 60° F.									
50	51.0	52.0	53.0	54.0	55.1	56.1	57.1	58.1	59.1	60.2
51	50.9	51.9	52.9	53.9	54.9	56.0	57.0	58.0	59.0	60.0
52	50.8	51.8	52.8	53.8	54.8	55.9	56.9	57.9	58.9	59.9
53	50.7	51.7	52.7	53.7	54.7	55.8	56.8	57.8	58.8	59.8
54	50.6	51.6	52.6	53.6	54.6	55.6	56.7	57.7	58.7	59.7
55	50.5	51.5	52.5	53.5	54.5	55.5	56.5	57.6	58.6	59.6
56	50.4	51.4	52.4	53.4	54.4	55.4	56.4	57.4	58.5	59.5
57	50.3	51.3	52.3	53.3	54.3	55.3	56.3	57.3	58.3	59.3
58	50.2	51.2	52.2	53.2	54.2	55.2	56.2	57.2	58.2	59.2
59	50.1	51.1	52.1	53.1	54.1	55.1	56.1	57.1	58.1	59.1
60	50.0	51.0	52.0	53.0	54.0	55.0	56.0	57.0	58.0	59.0
61	49.9	50.9	51.9	52.9	53.9	54.9	55.9	56.9	57.9	58.9
62	49.8	50.8	51.8	52.8	53.8	54.8	55.8	56.8	57.8	58.8
63	49.7	50.7	51.7	52.7	53.7	54.7	55.7	56.7	57.7	58.7
64	49.6	50.6	51.6	52.6	53.6	54.6	55.6	56.6	57.6	58.5
65	49.5	50.5	51.5	52.5	53.5	54.5	55.5	56.5	57.4	58.4
66	49.4	50.4	51.4	52.4	53.4	54.4	55.4	56.3	57.3	58.3
67	49.3	50.3	51.3	52.3	53.3	54.3	55.3	56.2	57.2	58.2
68	49.2	50.2	51.2	52.2	53.2	54.2	55.1	56.1	57.1	58.1
69	49.1	50.1	51.1	52.1	53.1	54.1	55.0	56.0	57.0	58.0
70	49.1	50.0	51.0	52.0	53.0	54.0	54.9	55.9	56.9	57.9
71	49.0	49.9	50.9	51.9	52.9	53.9	54.8	55.8	56.8	57.8
72	48.9	49.8	50.8	51.8	52.8	53.8	54.7	55.7	56.7	57.6
73	48.8	49.8	50.7	51.7	52.7	53.6	54.6	55.6	56.6	57.5
74	48.7	49.7	50.6	51.6	52.6	53.5	54.5	55.5	56.5	57.4
75	48.6	49.6	50.5	51.5	52.5	53.4	54.4	55.4	56.3	57.3
76	48.5	49.5	50.4	51.4	52.4	53.3	54.3	55.3	56.2	57.2
77	48.4	49.4	50.3	51.3	52.3	53.2	54.2	55.2	56.1	57.1
78	48.3	49.3	50.3	51.2	52.2	53.1	54.1	55.1	56.0	57.0
79	48.2	49.2	50.2	51.1	52.1	53.0	54.0	54.0	55.9	56.9
80	48.1	49.1	50.1	51.0	52.0	52.9	53.9	54.9	55.8	56.8
81	48.0	49.0	50.0	50.9	51.9	52.8	53.8	54.8	55.7	56.7
82	48.0	48.9	49.9	50.8	51.8	52.7	53.7	54.7	55.6	56.6
83	47.9	48.8	49.8	50.7	51.7	52.6	53.6	54.5	55.5	56.4
84	47.8	48.7	49.7	50.6	51.6	52.5	53.5	54.4	55.4	56.3
85	47.7	48.6	49.6	50.5	51.5	52.4	53.4	54.3	55.3	56.2
86	47.6	48.5	49.5	50.5	51.4	52.4	53.3	54.2	55.2	56.1
87	47.5	48.5	49.4	50.4	51.3	52.3	53.2	54.1	55.1	56.0
88	47.4	48.4	49.3	50.3	51.2	52.2	53.1	54.0	55.0	55.9
89	47.3	48.3	49.2	50.2	51.1	52.1	53.0	53.9	54.9	55.8
90	47.2	48.2	49.1	50.1	51.0	52.0	52.9	53.8	54.8	55.7
91	47.2	48.1	49.0	50.0	50.9	51.9	52.8	53.7	54.7	55.6
92	47.1	48.0	48.9	49.9	50.8	51.8	52.7	53.6	54.6	55.5
93	47.0	47.9	48.9	49.8	50.7	51.7	52.6	53.5	54.5	55.4
94	46.9	47.8	48.8	49.7	50.6	51.6	52.5	53.4	54.4	55.3
95	46.8	47.7	48.7	49.6	50.5	51.5	52.4	53.3	54.3	55.2
96	46.7	47.7	48.6	49.5	50.5	51.4	52.3	53.2	54.2	55.1
97	46.6	47.6	48.5	49.4	50.4	51.3	52.2	53.1	54.1	55.0
98	46.5	47.5	48.4	49.3	50.3	51.2	52.1	53.0	54.0	54.9
99	46.5	47.4	48.3	49.2	50.2	51.1	52.0	52.9	53.9	54.8

Table 5 (*Continued*)

ASTM—IP   API Gravity Reduction to 60° F.   50–59° API

Observed Temperature, °F.	API Gravity at Observed Temperature									
	50	51	52	53	54	55	56	57	58	59
	Corresponding API Gravity at 60° F.									
100	46.4	47.3	48.2	49.2	50.1	51.0	51.9	52.8	53.8	54.7
101	46.3	47.2	48.1	49.1	50.0	50.9	51.8	52.7	53.7	54.6
102	46.2	47.1	48.0	49.0	49.9	50.8	51.7	52.7	53.6	54.5
103	46.1	47.0	48.0	48.9	49.8	50.7	51.6	52.6	53.5	54.4
104	46.0	47.0	47.9	48.8	49.7	50.6	51.5	52.5	53.4	54.3
105	45.9	46.9	47.8	48.7	49.6	50.5	51.4	52.4	53.3	54.2
106	45.9	46.8	47.7	48.6	49.5	50.4	51.4	52.3	53.2	54.1
107	45.8	46.7	47.6	48.5	49.4	50.3	51.3	53.2	53.1	54.0
108	45.7	46.6	47.5	48.4	49.3	50.3	51.2	52.1	53.0	53.9
109	45.6	46.5	47.4	48.3	49.3	50.2	51.1	52.0	52.9	53.8
110	45.5	46.4	47.3	48.3	49.2	50.1	51.0	51.9	52.8	53.7
111	45.4	46.3	47.3	48.2	49.1	50.0	50.9	51.8	52.7	53.6
112	45.3	46.3	47.2	48.1	49.0	49.9	50.8	51.7	52.6	53.5
113	45.3	46.2	47.1	48.0	48.9	49.8	50.7	51.6	52.5	53.4
114	45.2	46.1	47.0	47.9	48.8	49.7	50.6	51.5	52.4	53.3
115	45.1	46.0	46.9	47.8	48.7	49.6	50.5	51.4	52.3	53.2
116	45.0	45.9	46.8	47.7	48.6	49.5	50.4	51.3	52.2	53.1
117	44.9	45.8	46.7	47.6	48.5	49.4	50.3	51.2	52.1	53.0
118	44.8	45.8	46.7	47.6	48.4	49.3	50.2	51.1	52.0	52.9
119	44.8	45.7	46.6	47.5	48.4	49.3	50.1	51.0	51.9	52.8
120	44.7	45.6	46.5	47.4	48.3	49.2	50.1	50.9	51.8	52.7
121	44.6	45.5	46.4	47.3	48.2	49.1	50.0	50.8	51.7	52.6
122	44.5	45.4	46.3	47.2	48.1	49.0	49.9	50.8	51.6	52.5
123	44.4	45.3	46.2	47.1	48.0	48.9	49.8	50.7	51.5	52.4
124	34.4	45.2	46.1	47.0	47.9	48.8	49.7	50.6	51.5	52.3
125	44.3	45.2	46.1	47.0	47.8	48.7	49.6	50.5	51.4	52.2
126	44.2	45.1	46.0	46.9	47.8	48.6	49.5	50.4	51.3	52.1
127	44.1	45.0	45.9	46.8	47.7	48.5	49.4	50.3	51.2	52.0
128	44.0	44.9	45.8	46.7	47.6	48.5	49.3	50.2	51.1	52.0
129	43.9	44.8	45.7	46.6	47.5	48.4	49.2	50.1	51.0	51.9
130	43.9	44.8	45.6	46.5	47.4	48.3	49.2	50.0	50.9	51.8
131	43.8	44.7	45.6	46.4	47.3	48.2	49.1	49.9	50.8	51.7
132	43.7	44.6	45.5	46.4	47.2	48.1	49.0	49.8	50.7	51.6
133	43.6	44.5	45.4	46.3	47.2	48.0	48.9	49.8	50.6	51.5
134	43.5	44.4	45.3	46.2	47.1	47.9	48.8	49.7	50.5	51.4
135	43.5	44.3	45.2	46.1	47.0	47.8	48.7	49.6	50.4	51.3
136	43.4	44.3	45.1	46.0	46.9	47.8	48.6	49.5	50.3	51.2
137	43.3	34.2	45.1	45.9	46.8	47.7	48.5	49.4	50.3	51.1
138	43.2	44.1	45.0	45.9	46.7	47.6	48.5	49.3	50.2	51.0
139	43.2	44.0	44.9	45.8	46.6	47.5	48.4	49.2	50.1	50.9
140	43.1	43.9	44.8	45.7	46.6	47.4	48.3	49.1	50.0	50.8
141	43.0	43.9	44.7	45.6	46.5	47.3	48.2	49.0	49.9	50.8
142	42.9	43.8	44.7	45.5	46.4	47.3	48.1	49.0	49.8	50.7
143	42.8	43.7	44.6	45.4	46.3	47.2	48.0	48.9	49.7	50.6
144	42.8	43.6	44.5	45.4	46.2	47.1	47.9	48.8	49.6	50.5
145	42.7	43.6	44.4	45.3	46.1	47.0	47.8	48.7	49.5	50.4
146	42.6	43.5	44.3	45.2	46.1	46.9	47.8	48.6	49.5	50.3
147	42.5	43.4	44.3	45.1	46.0	46.8	47.7	48.5	49.4	50.2
148	42.4	43.3	44.2	45.0	45.9	46.7	47.6	48.4	49.3	50.1
148	42.4	43.2	44.1	45.0	45.8	46.7	47.5	48.4	49.2	50.0
150	42.3	43.2	44.0	44.9	45.7	46.6	47.4	48.3	49.1	49.9

Table 5 (Continued)

API Gravity Reduction to 60° F.

Observed Temperature, °F.	API Gravity at Observed Temperature									
	60	61	62	63	64	65	66	67	68	69
	Corresponding API Gravity at 60° F.									
0	67.5	68.7	69.8	70.9	72.1	73.2	74.3	75.5	76.5	77.7
1	67.4	68.5	69.7	70.8	71.9	73.0	74.2	75.3	76.4	77.6
2	67.3	68.4	69.5	70.6	71.8	72.9	74.0	75.2	76.3	77.4
3	67.1	68.3	69.4	70.5	71.6	72.8	73.9	75.0	76.1	77.3
4	67.0	68.1	69.2	70.4	71.5	72.6	73.7	74.9	76.0	77.1
5	66.9	68.0	69.1	70.2	71.3	72.5	73.6	74.7	75.8	76.9
6	66.7	67.9	69.0	70.1	71.2	72.3	73.4	74.6	75.7	76.8
7	66.6	67.7	68.8	69.9	71.1	72.2	73.3	74.4	75.5	76.6
8	66.5	67.6	68.7	69.8	70.9	72.0	73.1	74.3	75.4	76.5
9	66.3	67.4	68.6	69.7	70.8	71.9	73.0	74.1	75.2	76.3
10	66.2	67.3	68.4	69.5	70.6	71.7	72.8	74.0	75.1	76.2
11	66.1	67.2	68.3	69.4	70.5	71.6	72.7	73.8	74.9	76.0
12	65.9	67.0	68.1	69.2	70.4	71.5	72.6	73.7	74.8	75.9
13	65.8	66.9	68.0	69.1	70.2	71.3	72.4	73.5	74.6	75.7
14	65.7	66.8	67.9	69.0	70.1	71.2	72.3	73.4	74.5	75.6
15	65.5	66.6	67.7	68.8	69.9	71.0	72.1	73.2	74.3	75.4
16	65.4	66.5	67.6	68.7	69.8	70.9	72.0	73.1	74.2	75.3
17	65.3	66.4	67.5	68.6	69.7	70.7	71.8	72.9	74.0	75.1
18	65.2	66.2	67.3	68.4	69.5	70.6	71.7	72.8	73.9	75.0
19	65.0	66.1	67.2	68.3	69.4	70.5	71.6	72.6	73.7	74.8
20	64.9	66.0	67.1	68.2	69.2	70.3	71.4	72.5	73.6	74.7
21	64.8	65.9	66.9	68.0	69.1	70.2	71.3	72.4	73.4	74.5
22	64.6	65.7	66.8	67.9	69.0	70.0	71.1	72.2	73.3	74.2
23	64.5	65.6	66.7	67.7	68.8	69.9	71.0	72.1	73.1	74.2
24	64.4	65.5	66.5	67.6	68.7	69.8	70.8	71.9	73.0	74.1
25	64.3	65.3	66.4	67.5	68.6	69.6	70.7	71.8	72.9	73.9
26	64.1	65.2	66.3	67.3	68.4	69.5	70.6	71.6	72.7	73.8
27	64.0	65.1	66.1	67.2	68.3	69.4	70.4	71.5	72.6	73.6
28	63.9	64.9	66.0	67.1	68.1	69.2	70.3	71.4	72.4	73.5
29	63.8	64.8	65.9	66.9	68.0	69.1	70.1	71.3	72.3	73.3
30	63.6	64.7	65.8	66.8	67.9	68.9	70.0	71.1	72.1	73.2
31	63.5	64.6	65.6	66.7	67.7	68.8	69.9	70.9	72.0	73.1
32	63.4	64.4	65.5	66.6	67.6	68.7	69.7	70.8	71.8	72.9
33	63.3	64.3	65.4	66.4	67.5	68.5	69.6	70.6	71.7	72.8
34	63.1	64.2	65.2	66.3	67.3	68.4	69.5	70.5	71.6	72.6
35	63.0	64.1	65.1	66.2	67.2	68.3	69.3	70.4	71.4	72.5
36	62.9	63.9	65.0	66.0	67.1	68.1	69.2	70.2	71.3	72.3
37	62.8	63.8	64.8	65.9	66.9	68.0	69.0	70.1	71.1	72.2
38	62.6	63.7	64.7	65.8	66.8	67.9	68.9	70.0	71.0	72.0
39	62.5	63.6	64.6	65.6	66.7	67.7	68.8	69.8	70.9	71.9
40	62.4	63.4	64.5	65.5	66.6	67.6	68.6	69.7	70.7	71.8
41	62.3	63.3	64.3	65.4	66.4	67.5	68.5	69.5	70.6	71.6
42	62.1	63.2	64.2	65.3	66.3	67.3	68.4	69.4	70.4	71.5
43	62.0	63.1	64.1	65.1	66.2	67.2	68.2	69.3	70.3	71.3
44	61.9	62.9	64.0	65.0	66.0	67.1	68.1	69.1	70.2	71.2
45	61.8	62.8	63.8	64.9	65.9	66.9	68.0	69.0	70.0	71.1
46	61.7	62.7	63.7	64.7	65.8	66.8	67.8	68.9	69.9	70.9
47	61.5	62.6	63.6	64.6	65.6	66.7	67.7	68.7	69.8	70.8
48	61.4	62.4	63.5	64.5	65.5	66.5	67.6	68.6	69.6	70.6
49	61.3	62.3	63.3	64.4	65.4	66.4	67.4	68.5	69.5	70.5

Table 5 (*Continued*)

ASTM—IP   API Gravity Reduction to 60° F.   60–69° API

Observed Temperature, °F.	API Gravity at Observed Temperature									
	60	61	62	63	64	65	66	67	68	69
	Corresponding API Gravity at 60° F.									
50	61.2	62.2	63.2	64.2	65.3	66.3	67.3	68.3	69.3	70.4
51	61.1	62.1	63.1	64.1	65.1	66.2	67.2	68.2	69.2	70.2
52	60.9	62.0	63.0	64.0	65.0	66.0	67.0	68.1	69.1	70.1
53	60.8	61.8	62.8	63.9	64.9	65.9	66.9	67.9	68.9	70.0
54	60.7	61.7	62.7	63.7	64.8	65.8	66.8	67.8	68.8	69.8
55	60.6	61.6	62.6	63.6	64.6	65.6	66.6	67.7	68.7	69.7
56	60.5	61.5	62.5	63.5	64.5	65.5	66.5	67.5	68.5	69.5
57	60.4	61.4	62.4	63.4	64.4	65.4	66.4	67.4	68.4	69.4
58	60.2	61.2	62.2	63.2	64.2	65.3	66.3	67.3	68.3	69.3
59	60.1	61.1	62.1	63.1	64.1	65.1	66.1	67.1	68.1	69.1
60	60.0	61.0	62.0	63.0	64.0	65.0	66.0	67.0	68.0	69.0
61	59.9	60.9	61.9	62.9	63.9	64.9	65.9	66.9	67.9	68.9
62	59.8	60.8	61.8	62.8	63.8	64.7	65.7	66.7	67.7	68.7
63	59.7	60.6	61.6	62.6	63.6	64.6	65.6	66.6	67.6	68.6
64	59.5	60.5	61.5	62.5	63.5	64.5	65.5	66.5	67.5	68.5
65	59.4	60.4	61.4	62.4	63.4	64.4	65.4	66.4	67.3	68.3
66	59.3	60.3	61.3	62.3	63.3	64.2	65.2	66.2	67.2	68.2
67	59.2	60.2	61.2	62.2	63.1	64.1	65.1	66.1	67.1	68.1
68	59.1	60.1	61.0	62.0	63.0	64.0	65.0	66.0	67.0	67.9
69	59.0	59.9	60.9	61.9	62.9	63.9	64.8	65.8	66.8	67.8
70	58.9	59.8	60.8	61.8	62.8	63.8	64.7	65.7	66.7	67.7
71	58.7	59.7	60.7	61.7	62.7	63.6	64.6	65.6	66.6	67.5
72	58.6	59.6	60.6	61.6	62.5	63.5	64.5	65.5	66.4	67.4
73	58.5	59.5	60.5	61.4	62.4	63.4	64.4	65.3	66.8	67.3
74	58.4	59.4	60.3	61.3	62.3	63.3	64.2	65.2	66.2	67.1
75	58.3	59.3	60.2	61.2	62.2	63.1	64.1	65.1	66.1	67.0
76	58.2	59.1	60.1	61.1	62.1	63.0	64.0	65.0	65.9	66.9
77	58.1	59.0	60.0	61.0	61.9	62.9	63.9	64.8	65.8	66.8
78	58.0	58.9	59.9	60.8	61.8	62.8	63.7	64.7	65.7	66.6
79	57.8	58.8	59.8	60.7	61.7	62.7	63.6	64.6	65.5	66.5
80	57.7	58.7	59.7	60.6	61.6	62.5	63.5	64.5	65.4	66.4
81	57.6	58.6	59.5	60.5	61.5	62.4	63.4	64.3	65.3	66.2
82	57.5	58.5	59.4	60.4	61.3	62.3	63.3	64.2	65.2	66.1
83	57.4	58.4	59.3	60.3	61.2	62.2	63.1	64.1	65.0	66.0
84	57.3	58.2	59.2	60.2	61.1	62.1	63.0	64.0	64.9	65.9
85	57.2	58.1	59.1	60.0	61.0	61.9	62.9	63.8	64.8	65.7
86	57.1	58.0	59.0	59.9	60.9	61.8	62.8	63.7	64.7	65.6
87	57.0	57.9	58.9	59.8	60.8	61.7	62.7	63.6	64.5	65.5
88	56.9	57.8	58.8	59.7	60.6	61.6	62.5	63.5	64.4	65.4
89	56.8	57.7	58.6	59.6	60.5	61.5	62.4	63.4	64.3	65.2
90	56.6	57.6	58.5	59.5	60.4	61.4	62.3	63.2	64.2	65.1
91	56.5	57.5	58.4	59.4	60.3	61.2	62.2	63.1	64.1	65.0
92	56.4	57.4	58.3	59.2	60.2	61.1	62.1	63.0	63.9	64.9
93	56.3	57.3	58.2	59.1	60.1	61.0	61.9	62.9	63.8	64.7
94	56.2	57.1	58.1	59.0	60.0	60.9	61.8	62.8	63.7	64.6
95	56.1	57.0	58.0	58.9	59.8	60.8	61.7	62.6	63.6	64.5
96	56.0	56.9	57.9	58.8	59.7	60.7	61.6	62.5	63.4	64.4
97	55.9	56.8	57.8	58.7	59.6	60.5	61.5	62.4	63.3	64.3
98	55.8	56.7	57.6	58.6	59.5	60.4	61.4	62.3	63.2	64.1
99	55.7	56.6	57.5	58.5	59.4	60.3	61.2	62.2	63.1	64.0

PRODUCTION EQUIPMENT

Table 5 (Continued)

API Gravity Reduction to 60° F.

Observed Temperature, °F.	API Gravity at Observed Temperature									
	60	61	62	63	64	65	66	67	68	69
	Corresponding API Gravity at 60° F.									
100	55.6	56.5	57.4	58.4	59.3	60.2	61.1	62.0	63.0	63.9
101	55.5	56.4	57.3	58.2	59.2	60.1	61.0	61.9	62.8	63.8
102	55.4	56.3	57.2	58.1	59.1	60.0	60.9	61.8	62.7	63.6
103	55.3	56.2	57.1	58.0	58.9	59.9	60.8	61.7	62.6	63.5
104	55.2	56.1	57.0	57.9	58.8	59.7	60.7	61.6	62.5	63.4
105	55.1	56.0	56.9	57.8	58.7	59.6	60.5	61.5	62.4	63.3
106	55.0	55.9	56.8	57.7	58.6	59.5	60.4	61.3	62.3	63.2
107	54.9	55.8	56.7	57.6	58.5	59.4	60.3	61.2	62.1	63.0
108	54.8	55.7	56.6	57.5	58.4	59.3	60.2	61.1	62.0	62.9
109	54.7	55.6	56.5	57.4	58.3	59.2	60.1	61.0	61.9	62.8
110	54.6	55.5	56.4	57.3	58.2	59.1	60.0	60.9	61.8	62.7
111	54.5	55.4	56.3	57.2	58.1	59.0	59.9	60.8	61.7	62.6
112	54.4	55.3	56.2	57.1	58.0	58.9	59.8	60.7	61.6	62.5
113	54.3	55.2	56.1	56.9	57.8	58.7	59.6	60.5	61.4	62.3
114	54.2	55.1	56.0	56.8	57.7	58.6	59.5	60.4	61.3	62.2
115	54.1	55.0	55.8	56.7	57.6	58.5	59.4	60.3	61.2	62.1
116	54.0	54.9	55.7	56.6	57.5	58.4	59.3	60.2	61.1	62.0
117	53.9	54.8	55.6	56.5	57.4	58.3	59.2	60.1	61.0	61.9
118	53.8	54.7	55.5	56.4	57.3	58.2	59.1	60.0	60.9	61.8
119	53.7	54.6	55.4	56.3	57.2	58.1	59.0	59.9	60.8	61.6
120	53.6	54.5	55.3	56.2	57.1	58.0	58.9	59.8	60.6	61.5
121	53.5	54.4	55.2	56.1	57.0	57.9	58.8	59.6	60.5	61.4
122	53.4	54.3	55.1	56.0	56.9	57.8	58.6	59.5	60.4	61.3
123	53.3	54.2	55.0	55.9	56.8	57.7	58.5	59.4	60.3	61.2
124	53.2	54.1	54.9	55.8	56.7	57.6	58.4	59.3	60.2	61.1
125	53.1	54.0	54.8	55.7	56.6	57.4	58.3	59.2	60.1	61.0
126	53.0	53.9	54.7	55.6	56.5	57.3	58.2	59.1	60.0	60.8
127	52.9	53.8	54.6	55.5	56.4	57.2	58.1	59.0	59.9	60.7
128	52.8	53.7	54.5	55.4	56.3	57.1	58.0	58.9	59.7	60.6
129	52.7	53.6	54.4	55.3	56.2	57.0	57.9	58.8	59.6	60.5
130	52.6	53.5	54.3	55.2	56.1	56.9	57.8	58.7	59.5	60.4
131	52.5	53.4	54.3	55.1	56.0	56.8	57.7	58.5	59.4	60.3
132	52.4	53.3	54.2	55.0	55.9	56.7	57.6	58.4	59.3	60.2
133	52.4	53.2	54.1	54.9	55.8	56.6	57.5	58.3	59.2	60.1
134	52.3	53.1	54.0	54.8	55.7	56.5	57.4	58.2	59.1	59.9
135	52.2	53.0	53.9	54.7	55.6	56.4	57.2	58.1	59.0	59.8
136	52.1	52.9	53.8	54.6	55.5	56.3	57.1	58.0	58.9	59.7
137	52.0	52.8	53.7	54.5	55.4	56.2	57.0	57.9	58.8	59.6
138	51.9	52.7	53.6	54.4	55.3	56.1	56.9	57.8	58.6	59.5
139	51.8	52.6	53.5	54.3	55.2	56.0	56.8	57.7	58.5	59.4
140	51.7	52.5	53.4	54.2	55.1	55.9	56.7	57.6	58.4	59.3
141	51.6	52.5	53.3	54.1	55.0	55.8	56.6	57.5	58.3	59.2
142	51.5	52.4	53.2	54.0	54.9	55.7	56.5	57.4'	58.2	59.1
143	51.4	52.3	53.1	53.9	54.8	55.6	56.4	57.3	58.1	59.0
144	51.3	52.2	53.0	53.8	54.7	55.5	56.3	57.2	58.0	58.8
145	51.2	52.1	52.9	53.7	54.6	55.4	56.2	57.1	57.9	58.7
146	51.1	52.0	52.8	53.7	54.5	55.3	56.1	57.0	57.8	58.6
147	51.1	51.9	52.7	53.6	54.4	55.2	56.0	56.8	57.6	58.5
148	51.0	51.8	52.6	53.5	54.3	55.1	55.9	56.7	57.6	58.4
149	50.9	51.7	52.5	53.4	54.2	55.0	55.8	56.6	57.5	58.3
150	50.8	51.6	52.5	53.3	54.1	54.9	55.7	56.5	57.4	58.2

Table 5 (*Continued*)

ASTM—IP   API Gravity Reduction to 60° F.   70–79° API

Observed Temperature, °F.	API Gravity at Observed Temperature									
	70	71	72	73	74	75	76	77	78	79
	Corresponding API Gravity at 60° F.									
0	78.9	80.0	81.1	82.3	83.4	84.6	85.7	86.9	88.1	89.2
1	78.7	79.8	81.0	82.1	83.3	84.4	85.6	86.7	87.9	89.0
2	78.5	79.7	80.8	82.0	83.1	84.2	85.4	86.5	87.7	88.8
3	78.4	79.5	80.7	81.8	82.9	84.1	85.2	86.4	87.5	88.7
4	78.2	79.4	80.5	81.6	82.8	83.9	85.0	86.2	87.3	88.5
5	78.1	79.2	80.3	81.5	82.6	83.7	84.9	86.0	87.1	88.3
6	77.9	79.0	80.2	81.3	82.4	83.6	84.7	85.8	87.0	88.1
7	77.8	78.9	80.0	81.1	82.3	83.4	84.5	85.7	86.8	87.9
8	77.6	78.7	79.8	81.0	82.1	83.2	84.3	85.5	86.6	87.7
9	77.4	78.6	79.7	80.8	81.9	83.0	84.2	85.3	86.4	87.6
10	77.3	78.4	79.5	80.6	81.8	82.9	84.0	85.1	86.3	87.4
11	77.1	78.2	79.4	80.5	81.6	82.7	83.8	85.0	86.1	87.2
12	77.0	78.1	79.2	80.3	81.4	82.5	83.7	84.8	85.9	87.0
13	76.8	77.9	79.0	80.2	81.3	82.4	83.5	84.6	85.7	86.8
14	76.7	77.8	78.9	80.0	81.1	82.2	83.3	84.4	85.5	86.7
15	76.5	77.6	78.7	79.8	80.9	82.0	83.1	84.3	85.4	86.5
16	76.4	77.5	78.6	79.7	80.8	81.9	83.0	84.1	85.2	86.3
17	76.2	77.3	78.4	79.5	80.6	81.7	82.8	83.9	85.0	86.1
18	76.1	77.2	78.2	79.3	80.4	81.5	82.6	83.7	84.8	86.0
19	75.9	77.0	78.1	79.2	80.3	81.4	82.5	83.6	84.7	85.8
20	75.8	76.8	77.9	79.0	80.1	81.2	82.3	83.4	84.5	85.6
21	75.6	76.7	77.8	78.9	80.0	81.0	82.1	83.2	84.3	85.4
22	75.5	76.5	77.6	78.7	79.8	80.9	82.0	83.1	84.2	85.3
23	75.3	76.4	77.5	78.6	79.6	80.7	81.8	82.9	84.0	85.1
24	75.2	76.2	77.3	78.4	79.5	80.6	81.6	82.7	83.8	84.9
25	75.0	76.1	77.2	78.2	79.3	80.4	81.5	82.6	83.6	84.7
26	74.9	75.9	77.0	78.1	79.2	80.2	81.3	82.4	83.5	84.6
27	74.7	75.8	76.9	77.9	79.0	80.1	81.2	82.2	83.3	84.4
28	74.6	75.6	76.7	77.8	78.8	79.9	81.0	82.1	83.1	84.2
29	74.4	75.5	76.5	77.6	78.7	79.8	80.8	81.9	83.0	84.0
30	74.3	75.3	76.4	77.5	78.5	79.6	80.7	81.7	82.8	83.9
31	74.1	75.2	76.2	77.3	78.4	79.4	80.5	81.6	82.6	83.7
32	74.0	75.0	76.1	77.2	78.2	79.3	80.3	81.4	82.5	83.5
33	73.8	74.9	75.9	77.0	78.1	79.1	80.2	81.2	82.3	83.4
34	73.7	74.7	75.8	76.8	77.9	79.0	80.0	81.1	82.1	83.2
35	73.5	74.6	75.6	76.7	77.7	78.8	79.9	80.9	82.0	83.0
36	73.4	74.4	75.5	76.5	77.6	78.6	79.7	80.8	81.8	82.9
37	73.2	74.3	75.3	76.4	77.4	78.5	79.5	80.6	81.6	82.7
38	73.1	74.1	75.2	76.2	77.3	78.3	79.4	80.4	81.5	82.5
39	72.9	74.0	75.0	76.1	77.1	78.2	79.2	80.3	81.3	82.4
40	72.8	73.8	74.9	75.9	77.0	78.0	79.1	80.1	81.2	82.2
41	72.7	73.7	74.7	75.8	76.8	77.9	78.9	80.0	81.0	82.0
42	72.5	73.6	74.6	75.6	76.7	77.7	78.8	79.8	80.8	81.9
43	72.4	73.4	74.4	75.5	76.5	77.6	78.6	79.6	80.7	81.7
44	72.2	73.3	74.3	75.3	76.4	77.4	78.4	79.5	80.5	81.6
45	72.1	73.1	74.2	75.2	76.2	77.3	78.3	79.3	80.4	81.4
46	71.9	73.0	74.0	75.0	76.1	77.1	78.1	79.2	80.2	81.2
47	71.8	72.8	73.9	74.8	75.9	76.9	78.0	79.0	80.0	81.1
48	71.7	72.7	73.7	74.7	75.8	76.8	77.8	78.8	79.9	80.9
49	71.5	72.5	73.6	74.6	75.6	76.6	77.7	78.7	79.7	80.7

PRODUCTION EQUIPMENT

Table 5 (*Continued*)

API Gravity Reduction to 60° F.

Observed Temperature, °F.	API Gravity at Observed Temperature									
	70	71	72	73	74	75	76	77	78	79
	Corresponding API Gravity at 60° F.									
50	71.4	72.4	73.4	74.4	75.5	76.5	77.5	78.5	79.6	80.6
51	71.2	72.3	73.3	74.3	75.3	76.3	77.4	78.4	79.4	80.4
52	71.1	72.1	73.1	74.2	75.2	76.2	77.2	78.2	79.2	80.3
53	71.0	72.0	73.0	74.0	75.0	76.0	77.1	78.1	79.1	80.1
54	70.8	71.8	72.9	73.9	74.9	75.9	76.9	77.9	78.9	79.9
55	70.7	71.7	72.7	73.7	74.7	75.7	76.8	77.8	78.8	79.8
56	70.5	71.6	72.6	73.6	74.6	75.6	76.6	77.6	78.6	79.6
57	70.4	71.4	72.4	73.4	74.4	75.4	76.4	77.5	78.5	79.5
58	70.3	71.3	72.3	73.3	74.3	75.3	76.3	77.3	78.3	79.3
59	70.1	71.1	72.1	73.1	74.1	75.1	76.1	77.2	78.2	79.2
60	70.0	71.0	72.0	73.0	74.0	75.0	76.0	77.0	78.0	79.0
61	69.9	70.9	71.9	72.9	73.9	74.9	75.9	76.8	77.8	78.8
62	69.7	70.7	71.7	72.7	73.7	74.7	75.7	76.7	77.7	78.7
63	69.6	70.6	71.6	72.6	73.6	74.6	75.6	76.5	77.5	78.5
64	69.5	70.4	71.4	72.4	73.4	74.4	75.4	76.4	77.4	78.4
65	69.3	70.3	71.3	72.3	73.3	74.3	75.3	76.2	77.2	78.2
66	69.2	70.2	71.2	72.1	73.1	74.1	75.1	76.1	77.1	78.1
67	69.1	70.0	71.0	72.0	73.0	74.0	75.0	75.9	76.9	77.9
68	68.9	69.9	70.9	71.9	72.9	73.8	74.8	75.8	76.8	77.8
69	68.8	69.8	70.7	71.7	72.7	73.7	74.7	75.7	76.6	77.6
70	68.7	69.7	70.6	71.6	72.6	73.5	74.5	75.5	76.5	77.5
71	68.5	69.5	70.5	71.4	72.4	73.4	74.4	75.4	76.3	77.3
72	68.4	69.4	70.3	71.3	72.3	73.3	74.2	75.2	76.2	77.2
73	68.3	69.2	70.2	71.2	72.1	73.1	74.1	75.1	76.0	77.0
74	68.1	69.1	70.1	71.0	72.0	73.0	73.9	74.9	75.9	76.9
75	68.0	69.0	69.9	70.9	71.9	72.8	73.8	74.8	75.7	76.7
76	67.9	68.8	69.8	70.8	71.7	72.7	73.7	74.6	75.6	76.6
77	67.7	68.7	69.7	70.6	71.6	72.6	73.5	74.5	75.4	76.4
78	67.6	68.6	69.5	70.5	71.4	72.4	73.4	74.3	75.3	76.3
79	67.5	68.4	69.4	70.3	71.3	72.3	73.2	74.2	75.2	76.1
80	67.4	68.3	69.3	70.2	71.2	72.1	73.1	74.0	75.0	76.0
81	67.2	68.2	69.1	70.1	71.0	71.9	72.9	73.9	74.9	75.8
82	67.1	68.0	69.0	69.9	70.9	71.8	72.8	73.8	74.7	75.7
83	66.9	67.9	68.9	69.8	70.8	71.7	72.7	73.6	74.6	75.5
84	66.8	67.8	68.7	69.7	70.6	71.6	72.5	73.5	74.4	75.4
85	66.7	67.6	68.6	69.5	70.5	71.4	72.4	73.3	74.3	75.2
86	66.6	67.5	68.5	69.4	70.4	71.3	72.2	73.2	74.1	75.1
87	66.5	67.4	68.3	69.3	70.2	71.2	72.1	73.0	74.0	74.9
88	66.3	67.3	68.2	69.1	70.1	71.0	72.0	72.9	73.8	74.8
89	66.2	67.1	68.1	69.0	69.9	70.9	71.8	72.8	73.7	74.6
90	66.1	67.0	67.9	68.9	69.8	70.7	71.7	72.6	73.6	74.5
91	65.9	66.9	67.8	68.7	69.7	70.6	71.5	72.5	73.4	74.4
92	65.8	66.7	67.7	68.6	69.5	70.5	71.4	72.3	73.3	74.2
93	65.7	66.6	67.5	68.5	69.4	70.3	71.3	72.2	73.1	74.1
94	65.6	66.5	67.4	68.3	69.3	70.2	71.1	72.1	73.0	73.9
95	65.4	66.4	67.3	68.2	69.1	70.1	71.0	72.0	72.9	73.8
96	65.3	66.2	67.2	68.1	69.0	69.9	70.9	71.8	72.7	73.6
97	65.2	66.1	67.0	68.0	68.9	69.8	70.7	71.7	72.6	73.5
98	65.1	66.0	66.9	67.8	68.7	69.7	70.6	71.5	72.4	73.4
99	64.9	65.9	66.8	67.7	68.6	69.5	70.5	71.4	72.3	73.2

Table 5 (*Continued*)

API Gravity Reduction to 60° F.

Observed Temperature, °F.	API Gravity at Observed Temperature									
	70	71	72	73	74	75	76	77	78	79
	Corresponding API Gravity at 60° F.									
100	64.8	65.7	66.6	67.6	68.5	69.4	70.3	71.2	72.2	73.1
101	64.7	65.6	66.5	67.4	68.4	69.3	70.2	71.1	72.0	72.9
102	64.6	65.5	66.4	67.3	68.2	69.1	70.1	71.0	71.9	72.8
103	64.4	65.4	66.3	67.2	68.1	69.0	69.9	70.8	71.7	72.7
104	64.3	65.2	66.1	67.1	68.0	68.9	69.8	70.6	71.6	72.5
105	64.2	65.1	66.0	66.9	67.8	68.7	69.7	70.5	71.5	72.4
106	64.1	65.0	65.9	66.8	67.7	68.6	69.5	70.4	71.3	72.2
107	64.0	64.9	65.8	66.7	67.6	68.5	69.4	70.3	71.2	72.1
108	63.8	64.7	65.6	66.5	67.5	68.4	69.3	70.2	71.1	72.0
109	63.7	64.6	65.5	66.4	67.3	68.2	69.1	70.0	70.9	71.8
110	63.6	64.5	65.4	66.3	67.2	68.1	69.0	69.9	70.8	71.7
111	63.5	64.4	65.3	66.2	67.1	68.0	68.9	69.8	70.7	71.6
112	63.4	64.3	65.2	66.0	66.9	67.8	68.7	69.6	70.5	71.4
113	63.2	64.1	65.0	65.9	66.8	67.7	68.6	69.5	70.4	71.3
114	63.1	64.0	64.9	65.8	66.7	67.6	68.5	69.4	70.3	71.1
115	63.0	63.9	64.8	65.7	66.6	67.5	68.3	69.2	70.1	71.0
116	62.9	63.8	64.7	65.6	66.4	67.3	68.2	69.1	70.0	70.9
117	62.8	63.7	64.5	65.4	66.3	67.2	68.1	69.0	69.9	70.7
118	62.6	63.5	64.4	65.3	66.2	67.1	68.0	68.8	69.7	70.6
119	62.5	63.4	64.3	65.2	66.1	66.9	67.8	68.7	69.6	70.5
120	62.4	63.3	64.2	65.1	65.9	66.8	67.7	68.6	69.5	70.3
121	62.3	63.2	64.1	64.9	65.8	66.7	67.6	68.5	69.3	70.2
122	62.2	63.1	63.9	64.8	65.7	66.6	67.4	68.3	69.2	70.1
123	62.1	62.9	63.8	64.7	65.6	66.4	67.3	68.2	69.1	69.9
124	61.9	62.8	63.7	64.6	65.4	66.3	67.2	68.1	68.9	69.8
125	61.8	62.7	63.6	64.5	65.3	66.2	67.1	67.9	68.8	69.7
126	61.7	62.6	63.5	64.3	65.2	66.1	66.9	67.8	68.7	69.5
127	61.6	62.5	63.3	64.2	65.1	66.0	66.8	67.7	68.6	69.4
128	61.5	62.4	63.2	64.1	65.0	65.8	66.7	67.6	68.4	69.3
129	61.4	62.2	63.1	64.0	64.8	65.7	66.6	67.4	68.3	69.2
130	61.3	62.1	63.0	63.9	64.7	65.6	66.4	67.3	68.2	69.0
131	61.1	62.0	62.9	63.7	64.6	65.5	66.3	67.2	68.0	68.9
132	61.0	61.9	62.8	63.6	64.5	65.3	66.2	67.1	67.9	68.8
133	60.9	61.8	62.6	63.5	64.4	65.2	66.1	66.9	67.8	68.6
134	60.8	61.7	62.5	63.4	64.2	65.1	65.9	66.8	67.7	68.5
135	60.7	61.5	62.4	63.3	64.1	65.0	65.8	66.7	67.5	68.4
136	60.6	61.4	62.3	63.1	64.0	64.9	65.7	66.6	67.4	68.3
137	60.5	61.3	62.2	63.0	63.9	64.7	65.6	66.4	67.3	68.1
138	60.4	61.2	62.1	62.9	63.8	64.6	65.5	66.3	67.2	68.0
139	60.2	61.1	61.9	62.8	63.6	64.5	65.3	66.2	67.0	67.9
140	60.1	61.0	61.8	62.7	63.5	64.4	65.2	66.1	66.9	67.7
141	60.0	60.9	61.7	62.6	63.4	64.3	65.1	65.9	66.8	67.6
142	59.9	60.8	61.6	62.4	63.3	64.1	65.0	65.8	66.7	67.5
143	59.8	60.6	61.5	62.3	63.2	64.0	64.9	65.7	66.5	67.4
144	59.7	60.5	61.4	62.2	63.1	63.9	64.7	65.6	66.4	67.2
145	59.6	60.4	61.3	62.1	62.9	63.8	64.6	65.5	66.3	67.1
146	59.5	60.3	61.2	62.0	62.8	63.7	64.5	65.3	66.2	67.0
147	59.4	60.2	61.0	61.9	62.7	63.5	64.4	65.2	66.0	66.9
148	59.3	60.1	60.9	61.8	62.6	63.4	64.3	65.1	65.9	66.7
149	59.1	60.0	60.8	61.6	62.5	63.3	64.1	65.0	65.8	66.6
150	59.0	59.9	60.7	61.5	62.4	63.2	64.0	64.9	65.7	66.5

PRODUCTION EQUIPMENT

Table 5 (*Continued*)

API Gravity Reduction to 60° F.

Observed Temperature, °F.	API Gravity at Observed Temperature									
	80	81	82	83	84	85	86	87	88	89
	Corresponding API Gravity at 60° F.									
0	90.4	91.6	92.7	93.9	95.1	96.3	97.5	98.7	99.9	.....
1	90.2	91.4	92.5	93.7	94.9	96.1	97.3	98.5	99.7	.....
2	90.0	91.2	92.3	93.5	94.7	95.9	97.0	98.2	99.4	.....
3	89.8	91.0	92.1	93.3	94.5	95.7	96.8	98.0	99.2	.....
4	89.6	90.8	91.9	93.1	94.3	95.4	96.6	97.8	99.0	.....
5	89.4	90.6	91.8	92.9	94.1	95.2	96.4	97.6	98.8	100.0
6	89.2	90.4	91.6	92.7	93.9	95.0	96.2	97.4	98.6	99.7
7	89.1	90.2	91.4	92.5	93.7	94.8	96.0	97.2	98.3	99.5
8	88.9	90.0	91.2	92.3	93.5	94.6	95.8	97.0	98.1	99.3
9	88.7	89.8	91.0	92.1	93.3	94.4	95.6	96.7	97.9	99.1
10	88.5	89.6	90.8	91.9	93.1	94.2	95.4	96.5	97.7	98.9
11	88.3	89.5	90.6	91.7	92.9	94.0	95.2	96.3	97.5	98.6
12	88.1	89.3	90.4	91.5	92.7	93.8	95.0	96.1	97.3	98.4
13	88.0	89.1	90.2	91.3	92.5	93.6	94.8	95.9	97.1	98.2
14	87.8	88.9	90.0	91.2	92.3	93.4	94.6	95.7	96.8	98.0
15	87.6	88.7	89.8	91.0	92.1	93.2	94.4	95.5	96.6	97.8
16	87.4	88.5	89.6	90.8	91.9	93.0	94.2	95.3	96.4	97.6
17	87.2	88.3	89.5	90.6	91.7	92.8	94.0	95.1	96.2	97.4
18	87.1	88.2	89.3	90.4	91.5	92.6	93.8	94.9	96.0	97.1
19	86.9	88.0	89.1	90.2	91.3	92.4	93.6	94.7	95.8	96.9
20	86.7	87.8	88.9	90.0	91.1	92.2	93.4	94.5	95.6	96.7
21	86.5	87.6	88.7	89.8	90.9	92.1	93.2	94.3	95.4	96.5
22	86.4	87.4	88.5	89.6	90.8	91.9	93.0	94.1	95.2	96.3
23	86.2	87.3	88.4	89.5	90.6	91.7	92.8	93.9	95.0	96.1
24	86.0	87.1	88.2	89.3	90.4	91.5	92.6	93.7	94.8	95.9
25	85.8	86.9	88.0	89.1	90.2	91.3	92.4	93.5	94.6	95.7
26	85.6	86.7	87.8	88.9	90.0	91.1	92.2	93.3	94.4	95.5
27	85.5	86.6	87.6	88.7	89.8	90.9	92.0	93.1	94.2	95.3
28	85.3	86.4	87.5	88.5	89.6	90.7	91.8	92.9	94.0	95.1
29	85.1	86.2	87.3	88.4	89.4	90.5	91.6	92.7	93.8	94.9
30	85.0	86.0	87.1	88.2	89.3	90.3	91.4	92.5	93.6	94.7
31	84.8	85.9	86.9	88.0	89.1	90.2	91.2	92.3	93.4	94.5
32	84.6	85.7	86.7	87.8	88.9	90.0	91.0	92.1	93.2	94.3
33	84.4	85.5	86.6	87.6	88.7	89.8	90.9	91.9	93.0	94.1
34	84.3	85.3	86.4	87.5	88.5	89.6	90.7	91.7	92.8	93.9
35	84.1	85.2	86.2	87.3	88.3	89.4	90.5	91.6	92.6	93.7
36	83.9	85.0	86.0	87.1	88.2	89.2	90.3	91.4	92.4	93.5
37	83.8	84.8	85.9	86.9	88.0	89.0	90.1	91.2	92.2	93.3
38	83.6	84.6	85.7	86.8	87.8	88.9	89.9	91.0	92.0	93.1
39	83.4	84.5	85.5	86.6	87.6	88.7	89.7	90.8	91.9	92.9
40	83.3	84.3	85.4	86.4	87.5	88.5	89.6	90.6	91.7	92.7
41	83.1	84.1	85.2	86.2	87.3	88.3	89.4	90.4	91.5	92.5
42	82.9	84.0	85.0	86.1	87.1	88.1	89.2	90.2	91.3	92.3
43	82.8	83.8	84.8	85.9	86.9	88.0	89.0	90.1	91.1	92.1
44	82.6	83.6	84.7	85.7	86.7	87.8	88.8	89.9	90.9	92.0
45	82.4	83.5	84.5	85.5	86.6	87.6	88.6	89.7	90.7	91.8
46	82.3	83.3	84.3	85.4	86.4	87.4	88.5	89.5	90.5	91.6
47	82.1	83.1	84.2	85.2	86.2	87.3	88.3	89.3	90.4	91.4
48	81.9	83.0	84.0	85.0	86.0	87.1	88.1	89.1	90.2	91.2
49	81.8	82.8	83.8	84.8	85.9	86.9	87.9	89.0	90.0	91.0

Table 5 (*Continued*)

ASTM—IP   API Gravity Reduction to 60° F.   80–89° API

Observed Temperature, °F	API Gravity at Observed Temperature									
	80	81	82	83	84	85	86	87	88	89
	Corresponding API Gravity at 60° F.									
50	81.6	82.6	83.7	84.7	85.7	86.7	87.7	88.8	89.8	90.8
51	81.4	82.5	83.5	84.5	85.5	86.6	87.6	88.6	89.6	90.6
52	81.3	82.3	83.3	84.3	85.4	86.4	87.4	88.4	89.4	90.5
53	81.1	82.1	83.2	84.2	85.2	86.2	87.2	88.2	89.3	90.3
54	81.0	82.0	83.0	84.0	85.0	86.0	87.0	88.1	89.1	90.1
55	80.8	81.8	82.8	83.8	84.8	85.9	86.9	87.9	88.9	89.9
56	80.6	81.6	82.7	83.7	84.7	85.7	86.7	87.7	88.7	89.7
57	80.5	81.5	82.5	83.5	84.5	85.5	86.5	87.5	88.5	89.5
58	80.3	81.3	82.3	83.3	84.3	85.3	86.3	87.4	88.4	89.4
59	80.2	81.2	82.2	83.2	84.2	85.2	86.2	87.2	88.2	89.2
60	80.0	81.0	82.0	83.0	84.0	85.0	86.0	87.0	88.0	89.0
61	79.8	80.8	81.8	82.8	83.8	84.8	85.8	86.8	87.8	88.8
62	79.7	80.7	81.7	82.7	83.7	84.7	85.7	86.7	87.6	88.6
63	79.5	80.5	81.5	82.5	83.5	84.5	85.5	86.5	87.5	88.5
64	79.4	80.4	81.4	82.3	83.3	84.3	85.3	86.3	87.3	88.3
65	79.2	80.2	81.2	82.2	83.2	84.2	85.1	86.1	87.2	88.1
66	79.1	80.0	81.0	82.0	83.0	84.0	85.0	86.0	86.9	87.9
67	78.9	79.9	80.9	81.9	82.3	83.8	84.8	85.8	86.8	87.8
68	78.7	79.7	80.7	81.7	82.7	83.7	84.6	85.6	86.6	87.6
69	78.6	79.6	80.6	81.5	82.5	83.5	84.5	85.4	86.4	87.4
70	78.4	79.4	80.4	81.4	82.3	83.3	84.3	85.3	86.3	87.2
71	78.3	79.3	80.2	81.2	82.2	83.2	84.1	85.1	86.1	87.1
72	78.1	79.1	80.1	81.1	82.0	83.0	84.0	84.9	85.9	86.9
73	78.0	78.9	79.9	80.9	81.9	82.8	83.8	84.8	85.7	86.7
74	77.8	78.8	79.8	80.7	81.7	82.7	83.6	84.6	85.6	86.5
75	77.7	78.6	79.6	80.6	81.5	82.5	83.5	84.4	85.4	86.4
76	77.5	78.5	79.5	80.4	81.4	82.3	83.3	84.3	85.2	86.2
77	77.4	78.3	79.3	80.3	81.2	82.2	83.1	84.1	85.1	86.0
78	77.2	78.2	79.1	80.1	81.1	82.0	83.0	83.9	84.9	85.8
79	77.1	78.0	79.0	79.9	80.9	81.9	82.8	83.8	84.7	85.7
80	76.9	77.9	78.8	79.8	80.7	81.7	82.7	83.6	84.6	85.5
81	76.8	77.7	78.7	79.6	80.6	81.5	82.5	83.4	84.4	85.3
82	76.6	77.6	78.5	79.5	80.4	81.4	82.3	83.3	84.2	85.2
83	76.5	77.4	78.4	79.3	80.3	81.2	82.2	83.1	84.1	85.0
84	76.3	77.3	78.2	79.2	80.1	81.1	82.0	82.9	83.9	84.8
85	76.2	77.1	78.1	79.0	80.0	80.9	81.8	82.8	83.7	84.7
86	76.0	77.0	77.9	78.9	79.8	80.7	81.7	82.6	83.6	84.5
87	75.9	76.8	77.8	78.7	79.6	80.6	81.5	82.5	83.4	84.3
88	75.7	76.7	77.6	78.5	79.5	80.4	81.4	82.3	83.2	84.2
89	75.6	76.5	77.5	78.4	79.3	80.3	81.2	82.1	83.1	84.0
90	75.4	76.4	77.3	78.2	79.2	80.1	81.0	82.0	82.9	83.8
91	75.3	76.2	77.2	78.1	79.0	80.0	80.9	81.8	82.7	83.7
92	75.1	76.1	77.0	77.9	78.9	79.8	80.7	81.7	82.6	83.5
93	75.0	75.9	76.9	77.8	78.7	79.6	80.6	81.5	82.4	83.3
94	74.9	75.8	76.7	77.6	78.6	79.5	80.4	81.3	82.3	83.2
95	74.7	75.6	76.6	77.5	78.4	79.3	80.3	81.2	82.1	83.0
96	74.6	75.5	76.4	77.3	78.3	79.2	80.1	81.0	81.9	82.9
97	74.4	75.3	76.3	77.2	78.1	79.0	79.9	80.9	81.8	82.7
98	74.3	75.2	76.1	77.0	78.0	78.9	79.8	80.7	81.6	82.5
99	74.1	75.1	76.0	76.9	77.8	78.7	79.6	80.6	81.5	82.4

Table 5 (*Continued*)

　　　API Gravity Reduction to 60° F.　　　　ASTM—IP

Observed Temperature, °F.	API Gravity at Observed Temperature									
	80	81	82	83	84	85	86	87	88	89
	Corresponding API Gravity at 60° F.									
100	74.0	74.9	75.8	76.7	77.7	78.6	79.5	80.4	81.3	82.2
101	73.9	74.8	75.7	76.6	77.5	78.4	79.3	80.2	81.1	82.1
102	73.7	74.6	75.5	76.4	77.4	78.3	79.2	80.1	81.0	81.9
103	73.6	74.5	75.4	76.3	77.2	78.1	79.0	79.9	80.8	81.7
104	73.4	74.3	75.2	76.2	77.1	78.0	78.9	79.8	80.7	81.6
105	73.3	74.2	75.1	76.0	76.9	77.8	78.7	79.6	80.5	81.4
106	73.1	74.1	75.0	75.9	76.8	77.7	78.6	79.5	80.4	81.3
107	73.0	73.9	74.8	75.7	76.6	77.5	78.4	79.3	80.2	81.1
108	72.9	73.8	74.7	75.6	76.5	77.4	78.3	79.2	80.1	80.9
109	72.7	73.6	74.5	75.4	76.3	77.2	78.1	79.0	79.9	80.8
110	72.6	73.5	74.4	75.3	76.2	77.1	78.0	78.9	79.7	80.6
111	72.4	73.3	74.2	75.1	76.0	76.9	77.8	78.7	79.6	80.5
112	72.3	73.2	74.1	75.0	75.9	76.8	77.7	78.5	79.4	80.3
113	72.2	73.1	74.0	74.8	75.7	76.6	77.5	78.4	79.3	80.2
114	72.0	72.9	73.8	74.7	75.6	76.5	77.4	78.2	79.1	80.0
115	71.9	72.8	73.7	74.6	75.4	76.3	77.2	78.1	79.0	79.9
116	71.8	72.6	73.5	74.4	75.3	76.2	77.1	77.9	78.8	79.7
117	71.6	72.5	73.4	74.3	75.2	76.0	76.9	77.8	78.7	79.6
118	71.5	72.4	73.3	74.1	75.0	75.9	76.8	77.6	78.5	79.4
119	71.4	72.2	73.1	74.0	74.9	75.7	76.6	77.5	78.4	79.2
120	71.2	72.1	73.0	73.9	74.7	75.6	76.5	77.4	78.2	79.1
121	71.1	72.0	72.8	73.7	74.6	75.5	76.3	77.2	78.1	78.9
122	70.9	71.8	72.7	73.6	74.4	75.3	76.2	77.1	77.9	78.8
123	70.8	71.7	72.6	73.4	74.3	75.2	76.0	76.9	77.8	78.6
124	70.7	71.6	72.4	73.3	74.2	75.0	75.9	76.8	77.6	78.5
125	70.5	71.4	72.3	73.2	74.0	74.9	75.8	76.6	77.5	78.3
126	70.4	71.3	72.1	73.0	73.9	74.7	75.6	76.5	77.3	78.2
127	70.3	71.1	72.0	72.9	73.7	74.6	75.5	76.3	77.2	78.0
128	70.1	71.0	71.9	72.7	73.6	74.5	75.3	76.2	77.0	77.9
129	70.0	70.9	71.7	72.6	73.5	74.3	75.2	76.0	76.9	77.7
130	69.9	70.7	71.6	72.5	73.3	74.2	75.0	75.9	76.7	77.6
131	69.8	70.6	71.5	72.3	73.2	74.0	74.9	75.7	76.6	77.5
132	69.6	70.5	71.3	72.2	73.0	73.9	74.8	75.6	76.5	77.3
133	69.5	70.3	71.1	72.1	72.9	73.8	74.6	75.5	76.3	77.2
134	69.4	70.2	71.0	71.9	72.8	73.6	74.5	75.3	76.2	77.0
135	69.2	70.1	70.9	71.8	72.6	73.5	74.3	75.2	76.0	76.9
136	69.1	70.0	70.8	71.6	72.5	73.3	74.2	75.0	75.9	76.7
137	69.0	69.8	70.7	71.5	72.4	73.2	74.0	74.9	75.7	76.6
138	68.8	69.7	70.5	71.4	72.2	73.1	73.9	74.7	75.6	76.4
139	68.7	69.6	70.4	71.2	72.1	72.9	73.8	74.6	75.4	76.3
140	68.6	69.4	70.3	71.1	71.9	72.8	73.6	74.5	75.3	76.1
141	68.5	69.3	70.1	71.0	71.8	72.7	73.5	74.3	75.2	76.0
142	68.3	69.2	70.0	70.8	71.7	72.5	73.4	74.2	75.0	75.9
143	68.2	69.0	69.9	70.7	71.5	72.4	73.2	74.0	74.9	75.7
144	68.1	68.9	69.7	70.6	71.4	72.2	73.1	73.9	74.7	75.6
145	68.0	68.8	69.6	70.4	71.3	72.1	72.9	73.8	74.6	75.4
146	67.8	68.7	69.5	70.3	71.1	72.0	72.8	73.6	74.5	75.3
147	67.7	68.5	69.4	70.2	71.0	71.8	72.7	73.5	74.3	75.1
148	67.6	68.4	69.2	70.1	70.9	71.7	72.5	73.4	74.2	75.0
149	67.5	68.3	69.1	69.9	70.7	71.6	72.4	73.2	74.0	74.9
150	67.3	68.1	69.0	69.8	70.6	71.4	72.3	73.1	73.9	74.7

Table 5 (*Continued*)

API Gravity Reduction to 60° F.

Observed Temperature, °F.	API Gravity at Observed Temperature									
	90	91	92	93	94	95	96	97	98	99
	Corresponding API Gravity at 60° F.									
0	.....	....	....	....	....	....	....	....	....	....
1	.....	....	....	....	....	....	....	....	....	....
2	.....	....	....	....	....	....	....	....	....	....
3	.....	....	....	....	....	....	....	....	....	....
4	.....	....	....	....	....	....	....	....	....	....
5	.....	....	....	....	....	....	....	....	....	....
6	.....	....	....	....	....	....	....	....	....	....
7	.....	....	....	....	....	....	....	....	....	....
8	.....	....	....	....	....	....	....	....	....	....
9	.....	....	....	....	....	....	....	....	....	....
10	100.0	....	....	....	....	....	....	....	....	....
11	99.8	....	....	....	....	....	....	....	....	....
12	99.6	....	....	....	....	....	....	....	....	....
13	99.4	....	....	....	....	....	....	....	....	....
14	99.1	....	....	....	....	....	....	....	....	....
15	98.9	....	....	....	....	....	....	....	....	....
16	98.7	99.9	....	....	....	....	....	....	....	....
17	98.5	99.6	....	....	....	....	....	....	....	....
18	98.3	99.4	....	....	....	....	....	....	....	....
19	98.1	99.2	....	....	....	....	....	....	....	....
20	97.9	99.0	....	....	....	....	....	....	....	....
21	97.6	98.8	99.9	....	....	....	....	....	....	....
22	97.4	98.6	99.7	....	....	....	....	....	....	....
23	97.2	98.3	99.5	....	....	....	....	....	....	....
24	97.0	98.1	99.2	....	....	....	....	....	....	....
25	96.8	97.9	99.0	....	....	....	....	....	....	....
26	96.6	97.7	98.8	99.9	....	....	....	....	....	....
27	96.4	97.5	98.6	99.7	....	....	....	....	....	....
28	96.2	97.3	98.4	99.5	....	....	....	....	....	....
29	96.0	97.1	98.2	99.3	....	....	....	....	....	....
30	95.8	96.9	98.0	99.1	....	....	....	....	....	....
31	95.6	96.7	97.8	98.8	99.9	....	....	....	....	....
32	95.4	96.5	97.5	98.6	99.7	....	....	....	....	....
33	95.2	96.2	97.3	98.4	99.5	....	....	....	....	....
34	95.0	96.0	97.1	98.2	99.2	....	....	....	....	....
35	94.8	95.8	96.9	98.0	99.1	....	....	....	....	....
36	94.6	95.6	96.7	97.8	98.9	99.9	....	....	....	....
37	94.4	95.4	96.5	97.6	98.7	99.7	....	....	....	....
38	94.2	95.2	96.3	97.4	98.4	99.5	....	....	....	....
39	94.0	95.0	96.1	97.2	98.2	99.3	....	....	....	....
40	93.8	94.8	95.9	97.0	98.0	99.1	....	....	....	....
41	93.6	94.6	95.7	96.8	97.8	98.9	99.9	....	....	....
42	93.4	94.4	95.5	96.5	97.6	98.7	99.7	....	....	....
43	93.2	94.2	95.3	96.3	97.4	98.5	99.5	....	....	....
44	93.0	94.0	95.1	96.1	97.2	98.2	99.3	....	....	....
45	92.8	93.9	94.9	95.9	97.0	98.0	99.1	....	....	....
46	92.6	93.7	94.7	95.7	96.8	97.8	98.9	99.9	....	....
47	92.4	93.5	94.5	95.5	96.6	97.6	98.7	99.7	....	....
48	92.2	93.3	94.3	95.3	96.4	97.4	98.4	99.5	....	....
49	92.0	93.1	94.1	95.1	96.2	97.2	98.2	99.3	....	....

PRODUCTION EQUIPMENT

Table 5 *(Continued)*

API Gravity Reduction to 60° F.

ASTM—IP

Observed Temperature, °F.	API Gravity at Observed Temperature									
	90	91	92	93	94	95	96	97	98	99
	Corresponding API Gravity at 60° F.									
50	91.9	92.9	93.9	94.9	96.0	97.0	98.0	99.1	....	....
51	91.7	92.7	93.7	94.7	95.8	96.8	97.8	98.9	99.9	....
52	91.5	92.5	93.5	94.5	95.6	96.6	97.6	98.6	99.7	....
53	91.3	92.3	93.3	94.4	95.4	96.4	97.4	98.4	99.5	....
54	91.1	92.1	93.1	94.2	95.2	96.2	97.2	98.2	99.2	....
55	90.9	91.9	92.9	94.0	95.0	96.0	97.0	98.0	99.0	....
56	90.7	91.7	92.8	93.8	94.8	95.8	96.8	97.8	98.8	99.8
57	90.6	91.6	92.6	93.6	94.6	95.6	96.6	97.6	98.6	99.6
58	90.4	91.4	92.4	93.4	94.4	95.4	96.4	97.4	98.4	99.4
59	90.2	91.2	92.2	93.2	94.2	95.2	96.2	97.2	98.2	99.2
60	90.0	91.0	92.0	93.0	94.0	95.0	96.0	97.0	98.0	99.0
61	89.8	90.8	91.8	92.8	93.8	94.8	95.8	96.8	97.8	98.8
62	89.6	90.6	91.6	92.6	93.6	94.6	95.6	96.6	97.6	98.6
63	89.5	90.4	91.4	92.4	93.4	94.4	95.4	96.4	97.4	98.4
64	89.3	90.3	91.3	92.2	93.2	94.2	95.2	96.2	97.2	98.2
65	89.1	90.1	91.1	92.1	93.0	94.0	95.0	96.0	97.0	98.0
66	88.9	89.9	90.9	91.9	92.9	93.8	94.8	95.8	96.8	97.8
67	88.7	89.7	90.7	91.7	92.7	93.6	94.6	95.6	96.6	97.6
68	88.6	89.5	90.5	91.5	92.5	93.5	94.4	95.4	96.4	97.4
69	88.4	89.4	90.3	91.3	92.3	93.3	94.2	95.2	96.2	97.2
70	88.2	89.2	90.2	91.1	92.1	93.1	94.0	95.0	96.0	97.0
71	88.0	89.0	90.0	90.9	91.9	92.9	93.9	94.8	95.8	96.8
72	87.9	88.8	89.8	90.8	91.7	92.7	93.7	94.6	95.6	96.6
73	87.7	88.6	89.6	90.6	91.5	92.5	93.5	94.4	95.4	96.4
74	87.5	88.5	89.4	90.4	91.4	92.3	93.3	94.2	95.2	96.2
75	87.3	88.3	89.3	90.2	91.2	92.1	93.1	94.0	95.0	96.0
76	87.2	88.1	89.1	90.0	91.0	91.9	92.9	93.9	94.8	95.8
77	87.0	87.9	88.9	89.9	90.8	91.8	92.7	93.7	94.6	95.6
78	86.8	87.8	88.7	89.7	90.6	91.6	92.5	93.5	94.4	95.4
79	86.6	87.6	88.5	89.5	90.4	91.4	92.3	93.3	94.2	95.2
80	86.5	87.4	88.4	89.3	90.3	91.2	92.2	93.1	94.0	95.0
81	86.3	87.2	88.2	89.1	90.1	91.0	92.0	92.9	93.9	94.8
82	86.1	87.1	88.0	89.0	89.9	90.8	91.8	92.7	93.7	94.6
83	85.9	86.9	87.8	88.8	89.7	90.7	91.6	92.5	93.5	94.4
84	85.8	86.7	87.7	88.6	89.5	90.5	91.4	92.4	93.3	94.2
85	85.6	86.5	87.5	88.4	89.4	90.3	91.2	92.2	93.1	94.0
86	85.4	86.4	87.3	88.3	89.2	90.1	91.1	92.0	92.9	93.8
87	85.3	86.2	87.1	88.1	89.0	89.9	90.9	91.8	92.7	93.6
88	85.1	86.0	87.0	87.9	88.8	89.8	90.7	91.6	92.5	93.5
89	84.9	85.9	86.8	87.7	88.7	89.6	90.5	91.4	92.4	93.3
90	84.8	85.7	86.6	87.6	88.5	89.4	90.3	91.2	92.2	93.1
91	84.6	85.5	86.5	87.4	88.3	89.2	90.2	91.1	92.0	92.9
92	84.4	85.4	86.3	87.2	88.1	89.1	90.0	90.9	91.8	92.7
93	84.3	85.2	86.1	87.0	88.0	88.9	89.8	90.7	91.6	92.5
94	84.1	85.0	85.9	86.9	87.8	88.7	89.6	90.5	91.4	92.3
95	83.9	84.9	85.8	86.7	87.6	88.5	89.4	90.3	91.3	92.2
96	83.8	84.7	85.6	86.5	87.4	88.3	89.3	90.2	91.1	92.0
97	83.6	84.5	85.4	86.4	87.3	88.2	89.1	90.0	90.9	91.8
98	83.5	84.4	85.3	86.2	87.1	88.0	88.9	89.8	90.7	91.6
99	83.3	84.2	85.1	86.0	86.9	87.8	88.7	89.6	90.5	91.4

Table 5 (*Continued*)

ASTM—IP   API Gravity Reduction to 60° F.   90–99° API

Observed Temperature, °F.	API Gravity at Observed Temperature									
	90	91	92	93	94	95	96	97	98	99
	Corresponding API Gravity at 60° F.									
100	83.1	84.0	84.9	85.8	86.7	87.7	88.6	89.5	90.4	91.3
101	83.0	83.9	84.8	85.7	86.6	87.5	88.4	89.3	90.2	91.1
102	82.8	83.7	84.6	85.5	86.4	87.3	88.2	89.1	90.0	90.9
103	82.6	83.5	84.4	85.3	86.2	87.1	88.0	88.9	89.8	90.7
104	82.5	83.4	84.3	85.2	86.1	87.0	87.9	88.8	89.6	90.5
105	82.3	83.2	84.1	85.0	85.9	86.8	87.7	88.6	89.5	90.4
106	82.2	83.1	84.0	84.8	85.7	86.6	87.5	88.4	89.3	90.2
107	82.0	82.9	83.8	84.7	85.6	86.5	87.3	88.2	89.1	90.0
108	81.8	82.7	83.6	84.5	85.4	86.3	87.2	88.1	88.9	89.8
109	81.7	82.6	83.5	84.3	85.2	86.1	87.0	87.9	88.8	89.7
110	81.5	82.4	83.3	84.2	85.1	86.0	86.8	87.7	88.6	89.5
111	81.4	82.3	83.1	84.0	84.9	85.8	86.7	87.5	88.4	89.3
112	81.2	82.1	83.0	83.9	84.7	85.6	86.5	87.4	88.2	89.1
113	81.1	81.9	82.8	83.7	84.6	85.4	86.3	87.2	88.1	88.9
114	80.9	81.8	82.7	83.5	84.4	85.3	86.2	87.0	87.9	88.8
115	80.7	81.6	82.5	83.4	84.2	85.1	86.0	86.9	87.7	88.6
116	80.6	81.5	82.3	83.2	84.1	85.0	85.8	86.7	87.6	88.4
117	80.4	81.3	82.2	83.1	83.9	84.8	85.7	86.5	87.4	88.3
118	80.3	81.1	82.0	82.9	83.8	84.6	85.5	86.4	87.2	88.1
119	80.1	81.0	81.9	82.7	83.6	84.5	85.3	86.2	87.0	87.9
120	80.0	80.8	81.7	82.6	83.4	84.3	85.2	86.0	86.9	87.7
121	79.8	80.7	81.5	82.4	83.3	84.1	85.0	85.9	86.7	87.6
122	79.7	80.5	81.4	82.3	83.1	84.0	84.8	85.7	86.5	87.4
123	79.5	80.4	81.2	82.1	83.0	83.8	84.7	85.5	86.4	87.2
124	79.4	80.2	81.1	81.9	82.8	83.7	84.5	85.4	86.2	87.1
125	79.2	80.1	80.9	81.8	82.6	83.5	84.3	85.2	86.0	86.9
126	79.1	79.9	80.8	81.6	82.5	83.3	84.2	85.0	85.9	86.7
127	78.9	79.8	80.6	81.5	82.3	83.2	84.0	84.9	85.7	86.6
128	78.7	79.6	80.5	81.3	82.2	83.0	83.9	84.7	85.5	86.4
129	78.6	79.5	80.3	81.2	82.0	82.9	83.7	84.5	85.4	86.2
130	78.4	79.2	80.1	80.9	81.8	82.7	83.5	84.4	85.2	86.1
131	78.3	79.1	80.0	80.8	81.7	82.5	83.4	84.2	85.0	85.9
132	78.2	79.0	79.8	80.7	81.5	82.4	83.2	84.1	84.9	85.7
133	78.0	78.8	79.7	80.5	81.4	82.2	83.1	83.9	84.7	85.6
134	77.9	78.7	79.5	80.4	81.2	82.1	82.9	83.7	84.6	85.4
135	77.7	78.5	79.4	80.2	81.1	81.9	82.7	83.6	84.4	85.2
136	77.6	78.4	79.2	80.1	80.9	81.7	82.6	83.4	84.2	85.1
137	77.4	78.2	79.1	79.9	80.8	81.6	82.4	83.3	84.1	84.9
138	77.3	78.1	78.9	79.8	80.6	81.4	82.3	83.1	83.9	84.7
139	77.1	78.0	78.8	79.6	80.4	81.3	82.1	82.9	83.8	84.6
140	77.0	77.8	78.6	79.5	80.3	81.1	81.9	82.8	83.6	84.4
141	76.8	77.7	78.5	79.3	80.1	81.0	81.8	82.6	83.4	84.3
142	76.7	77.5	78.3	79.2	80.0	80.8	81.6	82.5	83.3	84.1
143	76.5	77.4	78.2	79.0	79.8	80.7	81.5	82.3	83.1	83.9
144	76.4	77.2	78.0	78.9	79.7	80.5	81.3	82.1	83.0	83.8
145	76.2	77.1	77.9	78.7	79.5	80.4	81.2	82.0	82.8	83.6
146	76.1	76.9	77.7	78.6	79.4	80.2	81.0	81.8	82.6	83.5
147	76.0	76.8	77.6	78.4	79.2	80.0	80.9	81.7	82.5	83.3
148	75.8	76.6	77.5	78.3	79.1	79.9	80.7	81.5	82.3	83.1
149	75.7	76.5	77.3	78.1	78.9	79.7	80.6	81.4	82.2	83.0
150	75.5	76.3	77.2	78.0	78.8	79.6	80.4	81.2	82.0	82.8

Table 5 (*Continued*)

100° API   API Gravity Reduction to 60° F.   ASTM—IP

Observed Temperature, °F.	API Gravity at Observed Temperature 100 / Corresponding API Gravity at 60° F.	Observed Temperature, °F.	API Gravity at Observed Temperature 100 / Corresponding API Gravity at 60° F.	Observed Temperature, °F.	API Gravity at Observed Temperature 100 / Corresponding API Gravity at 60° F.	Observed Temperature, °F.	API Gravity at Observed Temperature 100 / Corresponding API Gravity at 60° F.
50	.....	75	96.9	100	92.1	125	87.7
51	.....	76	96.7	101	92.0	126	87.6
52	.....	77	96.5	102	91.8	127	87.4
53	.....	78	96.3	103	91.6	128	87.2
54	.....	79	96.1	104	91.4	129	87.1
55	.....	80	95.9	105	91.2	130	86.9
56	.....	81	95.7	106	91.1	131	86.7
57	.....	82	95.5	107	90.9	132	86.6
58	.....	83	95.3	108	90.7	133	86.4
59	.....	84	95.2	109	90.5	134	86.2
60	100.0	85	95.0	110	90.3	135	86.1
61	99.8	86	94.8	111	90.2	136	85.9
62	99.6	87	94.6	112	90.0	137	85.7
63	99.4	88	94.4	113	89.8	138	85.6
64	99.2	89	94.2	114	89.6	139	85.4
65	99.0	90	94.0	115	89.5	140	85.2
66	98.7	91	93.8	116	89.3	141	85.1
67	98.5	92	93.6	117	89.1	142	84.9
68	98.3	93	93.4	118	88.9	143	84.7
69	98.1	94	93.3	119	88.8	144	84.6
70	97.9	95	93.1	120	88.6	145	84.4
71	97.7	96	92.9	121	88.4	146	84.3
72	97.5	97	92.7	122	88.2	147	84.1
73	97.3	98	92.5	123	88.1	148	83.9
74	97.1	99	92.3	124	87.9	149	83.8
75	96.9	100	92.1	125	87.8	150	83.6

APPENDIX "C"

Table 7*

REDUCTION OF VOLUME TO 60° F
AGAINST API GRAVITY AT 60° F
(ABRIDGED TABLE)

This table gives the factors for converting oil volumes observed at temperatures other than 60° F to the corresponding volumes at 60° F for ranges of values of API gravity at 60° F.   This table is an abridged form of Table 6^a and is intended for use where accuracy lower than that given by Table 6^a can be tolerated.   For oils whose API gravity at 60° F is outside the range 0 to 100°, Table 24^a must be used.

Table 7 has been set up in eight ranges of API gravity as follows:

Group No.	Range of Group API Gravity 60 F	Coefficient of Expansion per °F at 60° F	Corresponding API Gravity 60° F
0..............	0 to 14.9	0.00035	6.0
1..............	15.0 to 34.9	0.00040	22.0
2..............	35.0 to 50.9	0.00050	44.0
3*.............	51.0 to 63.9	0.00060	58.0
4..............	64.0 to 78.9	0.00070	72.0
5..............	79.0 to 88.9	0.00080	86.0
6..............	89.0 to 93.9	0.00085	91.0
7..............	94.0 to 100.0	0.00090	97.0

* All blends of gasoline and benzene are considered to fall in Group 3; when the presence of benzene is uncertain, the oil shall be classified in Group 3 if the gravity is numerically less than 51.0° API and the 50 per cent distillation recovery point is less than 293° F.

It is very important to note that the Group classification of the oil is determined by its API gravity at 60° F.   Large errors (up to 0.5 per cent) may arise if the gravity at the observed temperature is used to determine the Group, because this error may place the oil in the wrong Group.

This table must be entered with API gravity at 60° F.   If the API gravity is known only at the observed temperature, the API gravity at 60° F must first be found from Table 5.

EXAMPLE

What is the volume of 60° F of the 8000 U.S. gallons of oil measured at 90° F when the gravity of the oil is 61.15° API at 60° F?

From the table above, note that an oil having an API gravity of 61.5 at
60° F falls in.. Group 3
Enter the table for the temperature range 50 to 100° F and in the column
for Group 3 note that factor opposite 90° F is..................... 0.9818
Then, the oil having a volume of 8000 U.S. gallons at 90° F has a volume
at 60° F of 8000×0.9818 or..................................... 7854 U.S. gallons

* Reproduced herein by permission of the copyright owner, The American Socy. for Testing Materials, 1916 Race St., Philadelphia 3, Pa.

Table 7

Volume Reduction to 60° F. 0–100° API

(Abridged Table)

Observed Temperature, °F.	Group Number and API Gravity Range at 60° F.							
	Group 0	Group 1	Group 2	Group 3	Group 4	Group 5	Group 6	Group 7
	0–14.9° API	15.0–34.9° API	35.0–50.9° API	51.0–63.9° API	64.0–78.9° API	79.0–88.9° API	89.0–93.9° API	94.0–100.0° API
	Factor for Reducing Volume to 60° F.							
0	1.0211	1.0241	1.0298	1.0362	1.0419	1.0478	1.0501	1.0532
1	1.0208	1.0237	1.0293	1.0356	1.0412	1.0470	1.0493	1.0523
2	1.0204	1.0233	1.0288	1.0350	1.0405	1.0462	1.0484	1.0514
3	1.0201	1.0229	1.0283	1.0344	1.0399	1.0454	1.0476	1.0506
4	1.0197	1.0225	1.0278	1.0338	1.0392	1.0446	1.0468	1.0497
5	1.0194	1.0221	1.0273	1.0332	1.0385	1.0438	1.0460	1.0488
6	1.0190	1.0217	1.0268	1.0326	1.0378	1.0430	1.0451	1.0479
7	1.0186	1.0213	1.0263	1.0320	1.0371	1.0423	1.0443	1.0470
8	1.0183	1.0209	1.0258	1.0314	1.0364	1.0415	1.0435	1.0462
9	1.0179	1.0205	1.0253	1.0308	1.0357	1.0407	1.0427	1.0453
10	1.0176	1.0201	1.0248	1.0302	1.0350	1.0399	1.0418	1.0444
11	1.0172	1.0197	1.0243	1.0296	1.0343	1.0391	1.0410	1.0435
12	1.0169	1.0193	1.0238	1.0290	1.0336	1.0383	1.0402	1.0427
13	1.0165	1.0189	1.0233	1.0284	1.0329	1.0375	1.0393	1.0418
14	1.0162	1.0185	1.0228	1.0278	1.0322	1.0367	1.0385	1.0409
15	1.0158	1.0181	1.0223	1.0272	1.0315	1.0359	1.0377	1.0400
16	1.0155	1.0177	1.0218	1.0266	1.0308	1.0351	1.0369	1.0391
17	1.0151	1.0173	1.0214	1.0260	1.0301	1.0343	1.0360	1.0383
18	1.0148	1.0168	1.0209	1.0253	1.0294	1.0036	1.0352	1.0374
19	1.0144	1.0164	1.0204	1.0247	1.0287	1.0328	1.0344	1.0365
20	1.0141	1.0160	1.0199	1.0241	1.0280	1.0320	1.0335	1.0356
21	1.0137	1.0156	1.0194	1.0235	1.0273	1.0312	1.0327	1.0347
22	1.0133	1.0152	1.0189	1.0229	1.0266	1.0304	1.0319	1.0338
23	1.0130	1.0148	1.0184	1.0223	1.0259	1.0296	1.0310	1.0330
24	1.0126	1.0144	1.0179	1.0217	1.0253	1.0288	1.0302	1.0321
25	1.0123	1.0140	1.0174	1.0211	1.0246	1.0280	1.0294	1.0312
26	1.0119	1.0136	1.0169	1.0205	1.0239	1.0272	1.0285	1.0303
27	1.0116	1.1032	1.0164	1.0199	1.0232	1.0264	1.0277	1.0294
28	1.0112	1.0128	1.0159	1.0193	1.0225	1.0256	1.0269	1.0285
29	1.0109	1.0124	1.0154	1.0187	1.0218	1.0248	1.0260	1.0276
30	1.0105	1.0120	1.0149	1.0181	1.0211	1.0240	1.0252	1.0268
31	1.0102	1.0116	1.0144	1.0175	1.0204	1.0232	1.0244	1.0259
32	1.0098	1.0112	1.0139	1.0169	1.0197	1.0224	1.0235	1.0250
33	1.0095	1.0108	1.0134	1.0163	1.0190	1.0216	1.0227	1.0241
34	1.0091	1.0104	1.0129	1.0157	1.0183	1.0208	1.0219	1.0232
35	1.0088	1.0100	1.0124	1.0151	1.0176	1.0200	1.0210	1.0223
36	1.0084	1.0096	1.0119	1.0145	1.0169	1.0192	1.0202	1.0214
37	1.0081	1.0092	1.0114	1.0139	1.0162	1.0181	1.0193	1.0205
38	1.0077	1.0088	1.0109	1.0133	1.0155	1.0176	1.0185	1.0197
39	1.0074	1.0084	1.0104	1.0127	1.0148	1.0168	1.0177	1.0188
40	1.0070	1.0080	1.0099	1.0121	1.0141	1.0160	1.0168	1.0179
41	1.0067	1.0076	1.0094	1.0115	1.0134	1.0152	1.0160	1.0170
42	1.0063	1.0072	1.0089	1.0109	1.0127	1.0144	1.0152	1.0161
43	1.0060	1.0068	1.0084	1.0103	1.0120	1.0136	1.0043	1.0152
44	1.0056	1.0064	1.0079	1.0097	1.0113	1.0128	1.0135	1.0143
45	1.0053	1.0060	1.0075	1.0091	1.0106	1.0120	1.0126	1.0134
46	1.0049	1.0056	1.0070	1.0085	1.0099	1.0112	1.0118	1.0125
47	1.0046	1.0052	1.0065	1.0079	1.0091	1.0104	1.0110	1.0116
48	1.0042	1.0048	1.0060	1.0073	1.0084	1.0096	1.0101	1.0107
49	1.0038	1.0044	1.0055	1.0067	1.0077	1.0088	1.0093	1.0099

Table 7 (*Continued*)

0–100° API

Volume Reduction to 60° F.

ASTM—IP

(Abridged Table)

Observed Temperature, °F.	Group Number and API Gravity Range at 60° F.							
	Group 0	Group 1	Group 2	Group 3	Group 4	Group 5	Group 6	Group 7
	0–14.9° API	15.0–34.9° API	35.0–50.9° API	51.0–63.9° API	64.0–78.9° API	79.0–88.9° API	89.0–93.9° API	94.0–100.0° API
	Factor for Reducing Volume to 60° F.							
50	1.0035	1.0040	1.0050	1.0061	1.0070	1.0080	1.0084	1.0090
51	1.0031	1.0036	1.0045	1.0054	1.0063	1.0072	1.0076	1.0081
52	1.0028	1.0032	1.0040	1.0048	1.0056	1.0064	1.0067	1.0072
53	1.0024	1.0028	1.0035	1.0042	1.0049	1.0056	1.0059	1.0063
54	1.0021	1.0024	1.0030	1.0036	1.0042	1.0048	1.0051	1.0054
55	1.0017	1.0020	1.0025	1.0030	1.0035	1.0040	1.0042	1.0045
56	1.0014	1.0016	1.0020	1.0024	1.0028	1.0032	1.0034	1.0036
57	1.0010	1.0012	1.0015	1.0018	1.0021	1.0024	1.0025	1.0027
58	1.0007	1.0008	1.0010	1.0012	1.0014	1.0016	1.0017	1.0018
59	1.0003	1.0004	1.0005	1.0006	1.0007	1.0008	1.0008	1.0009
60	1.0000	1.0000	1.0000	1.0000	1.0000	1.0000	1.0000	1.0000
61	0.9997	0.9996	0.9995	0.9994	0.9993	0.9992	0.9992	0.9991
62	0.9993	0.9992	0.9990	0.9988	0.9986	0.9984	0.9983	0.9982
63	0.9990	0.9988	0.9985	0.9982	0.9979	0.9976	0.9975	0.9973
64	0.9986	0.9984	0.9980	0.9976	0.9972	0.9968	0.9966	0.9964
65	0.9983	0.9980	0.9975	0.9970	0.9965	0.9960	0.9958	0.9955
66	0.9979	0.9976	0.9970	0.9964	0.9958	0.9952	0.9949	0.9946
67	0.9976	0.9972	0.9965	0.9958	0.9951	0.9944	0.9941	0.9937
68	0.9972	0.9968	0.9960	0.9951	0.9944	0.9935	0.9932	0.9928
69	0.9969	0.9964	0.9955	0.9945	0.9936	0.9927	0.9924	0.9919
70	0.9965	0.9960	0.9950	0.9939	0.9929	0.9919	0.9915	0.9910
71	0.9962	0.9956	0.9945	0.9933	0.9922	0.9911	0.9907	0.9901
72	0.9958	0.9952	0.9940	0.9927	0.9915	0.9903	0.9898	0.9892
73	0.9955	0.9948	0.9935	0.9921	0.9908	0.9895	0.9890	0.9883
74	0.9951	0.9944	0.9930	0.9915	0.9901	0.9887	0.9881	0.9874
75	0.9948	0.9940	0.9925	0.9909	0.9894	0.9879	0.9873	0.9865
76	0.9944	0.9936	0.9920	0.9903	0.9887	0.9871	0.9864	0.9856
77	0.9941	0.9932	0.9916	0.9897	0.9880	0.9863	0.9856	0.9847
78	0.9937	0.9929	0.9911	0.9891	0.9873	0.9855	0.9847	0.9938
79	0.9934	0.9925	0.9906	0.9885	0.9866	0.9846	0.9839	0.9829
80	0.9930	0.9921	0.9901	0.9879	0.9859	0.9838	0.9830	0.9820
81	0.9927	0.9917	0.9896	0.9873	0.9851	0.9830	0.9822	0.9811
82	0.9923	0.9913	0.9891	0.9866	0.9844	0.9822	0.9813	0.9802
83	0.9920	0.9909	0.9886	0.9860	0.9837	0.9814	0.9805	0.9792
84	0.9916	0.9905	0.9881	0.9554	0.9830	0.9806	0.9796	0.9783
85	0.9913	0.9901	0.9876	0.9848	0.9823	0.9798	0.9788	0.9774
86	0.9909	0.9897	0.9871	0.9842	0.9816	0.9790	0.9779	0.9765
87	0.9906	0.9893	0.9866	0.9836	0.9809	0.9781	0.9771	0.9756
88	0.9902	0.9889	0.9861	0.9830	0.9802	0.9773	0.9762	0.9747
89	0.9899	0.9885	0.9856	0.9824	0.9795	0.9765	0.9753	0.9738
90	0.9896	0.9881	0.9851	0.9818	0.9787	0.9757	0.9745	0.9729
91	0.9892	0.9877	0.9846	0.9812	0.9780	0.9749	0.9736	0.9720
92	0.9889	0.9873	0.9841	0.9806	0.9773	0.9741	0.9728	0.9711
93	0.9885	0.9869	0.9836	0.9799	0.9766	0.9733	0.9719	0.9702
94	0.9882	0.9865	0.9831	0.9793	0.9759	0.9724	0.9711	0.9693
95	0.9878	0.9861	0.9826	0.9787	0.9752	0.9716	0.9702	0.9683
96	0.9875	0.9857	0.9821	0.9781	0.9745	0.0708	0.9694	0.9674
97	0.9871	0.9854	0.9816	0.9775	0.9738	0.9700	0.9685	0.9665
98	0.9868	0.9850	0.9811	0.9769	0.9731	0.9692	0.9676	0.9656
99	0.9884	0.9846	0.9806	0.9763	0.9723	0.9681	0.9668	0.9647

Table 7 (*Continued*)

　　Volume Reduction to 60° F.　　　　0-100° API
(Abridged Table)

Observed Temper- ature, °F.	Group Number and API Gravity Range at 60° F.							
	Group 0	Group 1	Group 2	Group 3	Group 4	Group 5	Group 6	Group 7
	0-14.9° API	15.0-34.9° API	35.0-50.9° API	51.0-63.9° API	64.0-78.9° API	79.0-88.9° API	89.0-93.9° API	94.0-100.0° API
	Factor for Reducing Volume to 60° F.							
100	0.9861	0.9842	0.9801	0.9757	0.9716	0.9675	0.9659	0.9638
101	0.9857	0.9838	0.9796	0.9751	0.9709	0.9667	0.9651	0.9629
102	0.9854	0.9834	0.9791	0.9745	0.9702	0.9659	0.9642	0.9620
103	0.9851	0.9830	0.9786	0.9738	0.9695	0.9651	0.9633	0.9610
104	0.9847	0.9826	0.9781	0.9732	0.9688	0.9643	0.9625	0.9601
105	0.9844	0.9822	0.9776	0.9726	0.9681	0.9634	0.9616	0.9592
106	0.9840	0.9818	0.9771	0.9720	0.9673	0.9626	0.9608	0.9583
107	0.9837	0.9814	0.9766	0.9714	0.9666	0.9618	0.9509	0.9574
108	0.9833	0.9810	0.9761	0.9708	0.9659	0.9610	0.9590	0.9565
109	0.9830	0.9806	0.9756	0.9702	0.9652	0.9602	0.9582	0.9555
110	0.9826	0.9803	0.9751	0.9696	0.9645	0.9593	0.9573	0.9546
111	0.9823	0.9799	0.9746	0.9690	0.9638	0.9585	0.9565	0.9537
112	0.9819	0.9795	0.9741	0.9683	0.9630	0.9577	0.9556	0.9528
113	0.9816	0.9791	0.9736	0.9677	0.9623	0.9569	0.9547	0.9519
114	0.9813	0.9787	0.9731	0.9671	0.9616	0.9561	0.9539	0.9510
115	0.9809	0.9783	0.9726	0.9665	0.9609	0.9552	0.9530	0.9500
116	0.9806	0.9779	0.9721	0.9659	0.9602	0.9544	0.9521	0.9491
117	0.9802	0.9775	0.9717	0.9653	0.9595	0.9536	0.9513	0.9482
118	0.9799	0.9771	0.9712	0.9647	0.9587	0.9528	0.9504	0.9473
119	0.9795	0.9767	0.9707	0.9641	0.9580	0.9519	0.9495	0.9464
120	0.9792	0.9763	0.9702	0.9634	0.9573	0.9511	0.9487	0.9454
121	0.9788	0.9760	0.9697	0.9628	0.9566	0.9503	0.9478	0.9445
122	0.9785	0.9756	0.9692	0.9622	0.9559	0.9495	0.9469	0.9436
123	0.9782	0.9752	0.9687	0.9616	0.9552	0.9487	0.9461	0.9427
124	0.9778	0.9748	0.9682	0.9610	0.9544	0.9478	0.9452	0.9418
125	0.9775	0.9744	0.9677	0.9604	0.9537	0.9470	0.9443	0.9408
126	0.9771	0.9740	0.9672	0.9598	0.9530	0.9462	0.9435	0.9399
127	0.9768	0.9736	0.9667	0.9592	0.9523	0.9454	0.9426	0.9390
128	0.9764	0.9732	0.9662	0.9585	0.9516	0.9445	0.9417	0.9381
129	0.9761	0.9728	0.9657	0.9579	0.9508	0.9437	0.9409	0.9371
130	0.9758	0.9725	0.9652	0.9573	0.9501	0.9429	0.9400	0.9362
131	0.9754	0.9721	0.9647	0.9567	0.9494	0.9420	0.9391	0.9353
132	0.9751	0.9717	0.9642	0.9561	0.9487	0.9412	0.9383	0.9344
133	0.9747	0.9713	0.9637	0.9555	0.9480	0.9404	0.9374	0.9334
134	0.9744	0.9709	0.9632	0.9549	0.9472	0.9396	0.9365	0.9325
135	0.9740	0.9705	0.9627	0.9542	0.9465	0.9387	0.9357	0.9316
136	0.9737	0.9701	0.9622	0.9536	0.9458	0.9379	0.9348	0.9307
137	0.9734	0.9697	0.9617	0.9530	0.9451	0.9371	0.9339	0.9297
138	0.9730	0.9693	0.9612	0.9524	0.9444	0.9362	0.9330	0.9288
139	0.9727	0.9690	0.9607	0.9518	0.9436	0.9354	0.9322	0.9279
140	0.9723	0.9686	0.9602	0.9512	0.9429	0.9346	0.9313	0.9270
141	0.9720	0.9682	0.9597	0.9506	0.9422	0.9338	0.9304	0.9260
142	0.9716	0.9678	0.9592	0.9499	0.9415	0.9329	0.9296	0.9251
143	0.9713	0.9674	0.9587	0.9493	0.9407	0.9321	0.9287	0.9242
144	0.9710	0.9670	0.9582	0.9487	0.9400	0.9313	0.9278	0.9232
145	0.9706	0.9666	0.9577	0.9481	0.9393	0.9304	0.9269	0.9223
146	0.9703	0.9662	0.9572	0.9475	0.9386	0.9296	0.9261	0.9214
147	0.9699	0.9659	0.9567	0.9469	0.9379	0.9288	0.9252	0.9204
148	0.9696	0.9655	0.9562	0.9462	0.9371	0.9279	0.9243	0.9195
149	0.9693	0.9651	0.9557	0.9456	0.9364	0.9271	0.9234	0.9186
150	0.9689	0.9647	0.9552	0.9450	0.9357	0.9263	0.9226	0.9177

Table 7 (*Continued*)

0-63.9° API
150-250° F.

Volume Reduction to 60° F.
(Abridged Table)

ASTM—IP

Observed Temper- ature, °F.	Group Number and API Gravity Range at 60° F.				Observed Temper- ature, °F.	Group Number and API Gravity Range at 60° F.		
	Group 0	Group 1	Group 2	Group 3		Group 0	Group 1	Group 2
	0–14.9° API	15.0–34.9° API	35.0–50.9° API	51.0–63.9° API		0–14.9° API	15.0–34.9° API	35.0–50.9° API
	Factor for Reducing Volume to 60° F.					Factor for Reducing Volume to 60° F.		
150	0.9689	0.9647	0.9552	0.9450	200	0.9520	0.9456	0.9303
151	0.9686	0.9643	0.9547	0.9444	201	0.9516	0.9452	0.9298
152	0.9682	0.9639	0.9542	0.9438	202	0.9513	0.9448	0.9283
153	0.9679	0.9635	0.9537	0.9432	203	0.9509	0.9444	0.9288
154	0.9675	0.9632	0.9532	0.9426	204	0.9506	0.9441	0.9283
155	0.9672	0.9628	0.9527	0.9419	205	0.9503	0.9437	0.9278
156	0.9669	0.9624	0.9522	0.9413	206	0.9499	0.9433	0.9273
157	0.9665	0.9620	0.9517	0.9407	207	0.9496	0.9429	0.9268
158	0.9662	0.9616	0.6512	0.9401	208	0.9493	0.9425	0.9263
159	0.9658	0.9612	0.9507	0.9395	209	0.9489	0.9422	0.9258
160	0.9655	0.9609	0.9502	0.9389	210	0.9486	0.9418	0.9253
161	0.9652	0.9605	0.9497	0.9382	211	0.9483	0.9414	0.9248
162	0.9648	0.9601	0.9492	0.9376	212	0.9479	0.9410	0.9243
163	0.9645	0.9597	0.9487	0.9370	213	0.9476	0.9407	0.9238
164	0.9641	0.9593	0.9482	0.9364	214	0.9472	0.9403	0.9233
165	0.9638	0.9589	0.9477	0.9358	215	0.9469	0.9399	0.9228
166	0.9635	0.9585	0.9472	0.9351	216	0.9466	0.9395	0.9223
167	0.9631	0.9582	0.9467	0.9345	217	0.9462	0.9391	0.9218
168	0.9628	0.9578	0.9462	0.9339	218	0.9459	0.9388	0.9213
169	0.9624	0.9574	0.9457	0.9333	219	0.9456	0.9384	0.9208
170	0.9621	0.9570	0.9452	0.9327	220	0.9452	0.9380	0.9203
171	0.9618	0.9566	0.9447	0.9321	221	0.9449	0.9376	0.9198
172	0.9614	0.9562	0.9442	0.9314	222	0.9446	0.9373	0.9193
173	0.9611	0.9559	0.9437	0.9308	223	0.9442	0.9369	0.9188
174	0.9607	0.9555	0.9432	0.9302	224	0.9439	0.9365	0.9183
175	0.9604	0.9551	0.9428	0.9296	225	0.9436	0.9361	0.9178
176	0.9601	0.9547	0.9423	0.9290	226	0.9432	0.9358	0.9173
177	0.9597	0.9543	0.9418	0.9283	227	0.9429	0.9354	0.9168
178	0.9594	0.9539	0.9413	0.9277	228	0.9426	0.9350	0.9163
179	0.9590	0.9536	0.9408	0.9271	229	0.9422	0.9346	0.9158
180	0.9587	0.9532	0.9403	0.9265	230	0.9419	0.9343	0.9153
181	0.9584	0.9528	0.9398	0.9259	231	0.9416	0.9339	0.9148
182	0.9580	0.9524	0.9393	0.9252	232	0.9412	0.9335	0.9143
183	0.9577	0.9520	0.9388	0.9246	233	0.9409	0.9331	0.9138
184	0.9574	0.9517	0.9383	0.9240	234	0.9405	0.9328	0.9133
185	0.9570	0.9513	0.9378	0.9234	235	0.9402	0.9324	0.9128
186	0.9567	0.9509	0.9373	0.9228	236	0.9399	0.9320	0.9123
187	0.9563	0.9505	0.9368	0.9221	237	0.9395	0.9316	0.8118
188	0.9560	0.9501	0.9363	0.9215	238	0.9392	0.9313	0.9113
189	0.9557	0.9498	0.9358	0.9209	239	0.9389	0.9309	0.9108
190	0.9553	0.9494	0.9353	0.9203	240	0.9385	0.9305	0.9103
191	0.9550	0.9490	0.9348	0.9197	241	0.9382	0.9301	0.9098
192	0.9547	0.9486	0.9343	0.9190	242	0.9379	0.9298	0.9003
193	0.9543	0.9482	0.9338	0.9184	243	0.9375	0.9294	0.9088
194	0.9540	0.9478	0.9333	0.9178	244	0.9372	0.9290	0.9083
195	0.9536	0.9475	0.9328	0.9172	245	0.9369	0.9286	0.9078
196	0.9533	0.9471	0.9323	0.9166	246	0.9365	0.9283	0.9073
197	0.9530	0.9467	0.9318	0.9159	247	0.9362	0.9279	0.9068
198	0.9526	0.9463	0.9313	0.9153	248	0.9359	0.9275	0.9063
199	0.9523	0.9460	0.9308	0.9147	249	0.9356	0.9272	0.9058
200	0.9520	0.9456	0.9303	0.9141	250	0.9352	0.9268	0.9053

Table 7 (*Continued*)
Volume Reduction to 60° F.
(Abridged Table)

0–34.9° API
250–400° F.

ASTM–IP

Observed Temperature, °F.	Group Number and API Gravity Range at 60° F.		Observed Temperature, °F.	Group Number and API Gravity Range at 60° F.		Observed Temperature, °F.	Group Number and API Gravity Range at 60° F.	
	Group 0	Group 1		Group 0	Group 1		Group 0	Group 1
	0–14.9° API	15.0–34.9° API		0–14.9° API	15.0–34.9° API		0–14.9° API	15.0–34.9° API
	Factor for Reducing Volume to 60° F.			Factor for Reducing Volume to 60° F.			Factor for Reducing Volume to 60° F.	
250	0.9352	0.9268	300	0.9187	0.9083	350	0.9024	0.8902
251	0.9349	0.9264	301	0.9184	0.9080	351	0.9021	0.8899
252	0.9346	0.9260	302	0.9181	0.9076	352	0.9018	0.8895
253	0.9342	0.9257	303	0.9177	0.9072	353	0.9015	0.8891
254	0.9339	0.9253	304	0.9174	0.9069	354	0.9011	0.8888
255	0.9336	0.9249	305	0.9171	0.9065	355	0.9008	0.8884
256	0.9332	0.9245	306	0.9167	0.9061	356	0.9005	0.8881
257	0.9329	0.9242	307	0.9164	0.9058	357	0.9002	0.8877
258	0.9326	0.9238	308	0.9161	0.9054	358	0.8998	0.8873
259	0.9322	0.9234	309	0.9158	0.9050	359	0.8995	0.8870
260	0.9319	0.9231	310	0.0154	0.9047	360	0.8992	0.8866
261	0.9316	0.9227	311	0.9151	0.9043	361	0.8989	0.8863
262	0.9312	0.9223	312	0.9148	0.9039	362	0.8986	0.8859
263	0.9309	0.9219	313	0.9145	0.9036	363	0.8982	0.8856
264	0.9306	0.9216	314	0.9141	0.9032	364	0.8979	0.8852
265	0.9302	0.9212	315	0.9138	0.9029	365	0.8976	0.8848
266	0.9299	0.9208	316	0.9135	0.9025	366	0.8973	0.8845
267	0.9296	0.9205	317	0.9132	0.9021	367	0.8969	0.8841
268	0.9293	0.9201	318	0.9128	0.9018	368	0.8966	0.8838
269	0.9289	0.9197	319	0.9125	0.9014	369	0.8963	0.8834
270	0.9286	0.9194	320	0.9122	0.9010	370	0.8960	0.8831
271	0.9283	0.9190	321	0.9118	0.9007	371	0.8957	0.8827
272	0.9279	0.9186	322	0.9155	0.9003	372	0.8953	0.8823
273	0.9276	0.9182	323	0.9112	0.9000	373	0.8950	0.8820
274	0.9273	0.9179	324	0.9109	0.8996	374	0.8947	0.8816
275	0.9269	0.9175	325	0.9105	0.8992	375	0.8944	0.8813
276	0.9266	0.9171	326	0.9102	0.8989	376	0.8941	0.8809
277	0.9263	0.9168	327	0.9099	0.8985	377	0.8937	0.8806
278	0.9259	0.9164	328	0.9096	0.8981	378	0.8934	0.8802
279	0.9256	0.9160	329	0.9092	0.8978	379	0.8931	0.8799
280	0.9253	0.9157	330	0.9089	0.8974	380	0.8928	0.8795
281	0.9250	0.9153	331	0.9086	0.8971	381	0.8924	0.8792
282	0.9246	0.9149	332	0.9083	0.8967	382	0.8921	0.8788
283	0.9243	0.9146	333	0.9079	0.8963	383	0.8918	0.8784
284	0.9240	0.9142	334	0.9076	0.8960	384	0.8915	0.8781
285	0.9236	0.9138	335	0.9073	0.8956	385	0.8912	0.8777
286	0.9233	0.9135	336	0.9070	0.8952	386	0.8908	0.8774
287	0.9230	0.9131	337	0.9066	0.8949	387	0.8905	0.8770
268	0.9227	0.9127	338	0.9063	0.8945	388	0.8902	0.8767
289	0.9223	0.9124	339	0.9060	0.8942	389	0.8899	0.8763
290	0.9220	0.9120	340	0.9057	0.8938	390	0.8896	0.8760
291	0.9217	0.9116	341	0.9053	0.8934	391	0.8892	0.8756
292	0.9213	0.9113	342	0.9050	0.8931	392	0.8889	0.8753
293	0.9210	0.9109	343	0.9047	0.8927	393	0.8886	0.8749
294	0.9207	0.9105	344	0.9044	0.8924	394	0.8883	0.8746
295	0.9204	0.9102	345	0.9040	0.8920	395	0.8880	0.8742
296	0.9200	0.9098	346	0.9037	0.8916	396	0.8876	0.8738
297	0.9197	0.9094	347	0.9034	0.8913	397	0.8873	0.8735
298	0.9194	0.9091	348	0.9031	0.8909	398	0.8870	0.8731
299	0.9190	0.9087	349	0.9028	0.8906	399	0.8867	0.8728
300	0.9187	0.9083	350	0.9024	0.8902	400	0.8864	0.8724

Table 7 (*Continued*)

0-34.9° API
400-500° F.

Volume Reduction to 60° F.
(Abridged Table)

ASTM—IP

Observed Temperature, °F.	Group Number and API Gravity Range at 60° F.		Observed Temperature, °F.	Group Number and API Gravity Range at 60° F.		Observed Temperature, °F.	Group Number and API Gravity Range at 60° F.	
	Group 0	Group 1		Group 0	Group 1		Group 0	Group 1
	0–14.9° API	15.0–34.9° API		0–14.9° API	15.0–34.9° API		0–14.9° API	15.0–34.9° API
	Factor for Reducing Volume to 60° F.			Factor for Reducing Volume to 60° F.			Factor for Reducing Volume to 60° F.	
400	0.8864	0.8724	435	0.8753	0.8602	470	0.8643	0.8481
401	0.8861	0.8721	436	0.8749	0.8599	471	0.8640	0.8478
402	0.8857	0.8717	437	0.8746	0.8595	472	0.8636	0.8474
403	0.8854	0.8714	438	0.8743	0.8592	473	0.8633	0.8471
404	0.8851	0.8710	439	0.8740	0.8588	474	0.8630	0.8468
405	0.8848	0.8707	440	0.8737	0.8585	475	0.8627	0.8464
406	0.8845	0.8703	441	0.8734	0.8581	476	0.8624	0.8461
407	0.8841	0.8700	442	0.8731	0.8578	477	0.8621	0.8457
408	0.8838	0.8696	443	0.8727	0.8574	478	0.8618	0.8454
409	0.8835	0.8693	444	0.8724	0.8571	479	0.8615	0.8451
410	0.8832	0.8689	445	0.8721	0.8567	480	0.8611	0.8447
411	0.8829	0.8686	446	0.8718	0.8564	481	0.8608	0.8444
412	0.8826	0.8682	447	0.8715	0.8560	482	0.8605	0.8440
413	0.8822	0.8679	448	0.8712	0.8557	483	0.8602	0.8437
414	0.8819	0.8675	449	0.8709	0.8554	484	0.8599	0.8433
415	0.8816	0.8672	450	0.8705	0.8550	485	0.8596	0.8430
416	0.8813	0.8668	451	0.8702	0.8547	486	0.8593	0.8427
417	0.8810	0.8665	452	0.8699	0.8543	487	0.8590	0.8423
418	0.8806	0.8661	453	0.8696	0.8540	488	0.8587	0.8420
419	0.8803	0.8658	454	0.8693	0.8536	489	0.8583	0.8416
420	0.8800	0.8654	455	0.8690	0.8533	490	0.8580	0.8413
421	0.8797	0.8651	456	0.8687	0.8529	491	0.8577	0.8410
422	0.8794	0.8647	457	0.8683	0.8526	492	0.8574	0.8406
423	0.8791	0.8644	458	0.8680	0.8522	493	0.8571	0.8403
424	0.8787	0.8640	459	0.8677	0.8519	494	0.8568	0.8399
425	0.8784	0.8637	460	0.8674	0.8516	495	0.8565	0.8396
426	0.8781	0.8633	461	0.8671	0.8512	496	0.8562	0.8393
427	0.8778	0.8630	462	0.8668	0.8509	497	0.8559	0.8389
428	0.8775	0.8626	463	0.8665	0.8505	498	0.8556	0.8386
429	0.8772	0.8623	464	0.8661	0.8502	499	0.8552	0.8383
430	0.8768	0.8619	465	0.8658	0.8498	500	0.8549	0.8379
431	0.8765	0.8616	466	0.8655	0.8495			
432	0.8762	0.8612	467	0.8652	0.8492			
433	0.8759	0.8609	468	0.8649	0.8488			
434	0.8756	0.8605	469	0.8646	0.8485			
435	0.8753	0.8602	470	0.8643	0.8481			

PART V—AUTOMATIC LINE SAMPLERS

1400. INTRODUCTION

If mutually agreeable, automatic line sampling devices, which meet the standards set out hereinafter, may be used to withdraw line samples for the purpose of determining gravity, BS&W (basic sediment and water) and other characteristics required in custody transfer. The quantity of sample collected must be of sufficient size for analysis, and its composition should be identical with the composition of the batch flowing in the line while the sample is being taken. An automatic-sampler installation necessarily includes not only the automatic sampling device which extracts the samples from the line, but also a suitable probe, connecting lines, auxiliary equipment, and a container in which the sample is collected.

1401. TYPES OF AUTOMATIC SAMPLING DEVICES

Recognizing that acceptable automatic samplers may be designed and constructed in a variety of shapes and forms, this standard makes no attempt to limit the mechanical design or materials employed to accomplish a satisfactory result. All automatic samplers may be classified under the following headings:

1401.1. Time-cycle (Nonproportional) Type

a. A continuous sampler is defined as one which is designed and operated so as to transfer equal increments of liquid from a pipeline to the sample container at a uniform rate of one or more increments per minute.

b. An intermittent sampler is defined as one which is designed and operated so as to transfer equal increments of liquid from a pipeline to a sample container at a uniform rate of less than one increment per minute.

1401.2. Flow Responsive (Proportional) Type

The flow responsive (proportional) type of automatic sampler is designed and operated in such a manner that it can automatically adjust the quantity of sample in proportion to the rate of flow, either by varying the frequency of transfer of the incremental samples to the sample container, or by varying the volume of the incremental samples while maintaining a constant sampling frequency.

1401.3 General

The time-cycle type of sampler is recommended only where the rate of flow is reasonably constant during the entire sampling period. An automatic sampler of any type should be so designed that the volume of sample is not affected by variations in line pressure.

1402. SAMPLING PROBE

The function of the sampling probe is to permit withdrawal of a small quantity of liquid from a flowing stream that will be representative in all respects of the entire stream.

If representative samples are to be obtained, careful attention must be given to the design and location of the sampling probe and to the method used for the elimination of stratification.

1402.1. Design of Sampling Probe

Types of tubes which are commonly used for the withdrawal of liquid are as follows:

a. A tube extending to the center of the line and beveled at a 45-deg angle facing upstream.

b. A long radius-forged elbow or pipe bend extending to center of line facing upstream and reamed to a sharp entrance edge.

c. A tube extending across the pipeline with holes or slots facing upstream. The position and size of the sampling probe should be such that it will minimize stratification, or the dropping-out of heavier particles within the tube or the displacement of oil within the tube as a result of variation in gravity of the stream.

1402.2. Location of Sampling Probe

Since the pumped fluid may not in all cases be homogeneous, the tap should be located so as to counteract stratification effect; preferably located in a vertical run of pipe. In sampling horizontal lines, the tube should enter horizontally.

1402.3. Elimination of Stratification

A suitable method of mixing the fluid flow to insure a homogeneous mixture at all rates of flow should be installed upstream to the sampling tap.

Some effective devices for obtaining a homogeneous mixture are:
a. Reduction in pipe size,
b. A series of baffles,
c. An orifice or perforated plate, or
d. A combination of any of these methods.

The design or size of these devices is optional with the user, as long as the flow past the sampling point is homogeneous and stratification is eliminated.

1403. SAMPLE CONTAINER

A sample container is a suitable vessel to be used with an automatic-sampler installation for the purpose of retaining the sample.   The size of the container should be fixed by the quantity of sample needed and the period of time covered in the operation. The container may be of either the atmospheric or the closed type, depending upon service requirements.

1403.1. Atmospheric Container

The atmospheric container should be constructed so as to retard evaporation loss and to protect the contents from extraneous material such as rain, snow, dust, and trash.   It should be so constructed as to permit cleaning, interior inspection, and complete mixing of the sample prior to removal.   The receiver should be provided with a suitable vent.

1403.2. Closed Container

The purpose of closed containers is to prevent evaporation loss.   Such containers should be so constructed as to permit cleaning, interior inspection, and complete mixing of the sample prior to removal.   In most types a pressure-relief valve will be necessary.

1404. STANDARDS OF INSTALLATION

Automatic-sampler installations should meet all safety requirements in the plant or area where used, and should comply with the "American Standard Code for Pressure Piping" (*ASA B31.1-1955*) and other applicable codes. The sampler should be so installed as to provide ample access space for inspection and maintenance.

Small lines connecting various elements of the installation should be so arranged that complete purging of the automatic sampler and of all lines can be accomplished effectively.   All fluid remaining in the sampler and the lines from the preceding sampling cycle should be purged immediately before the start of any given sampling operation.

In those cases where the sampler design is such that complete purging of the sampling lines and the sampler is not possible, a small pump should be installed in order to circulate a continuous stream from the sampling tube past or through the sampler and back into the line.   The automatic sampler should then withdraw the sample from the sidestream through the shortest possible connection.

Under certain conditions, there may be a tendency for water and heavy particles to drop out in the discharge line from the sampling device and appear in the sample container during some subsequent sampling period.   To circumvent this possibility, the discharge pipe from the sampling device should be free of pockets or enlarged pipe areas, and preferably should be pitched downward to the sample container.

To insure clean, free-flowing lines, piping should be designed for periodic cleaning. When sampling waxy or high-viscosity oils, it may be necessary to heat the lines and sampler.

1405. FIELD TESTING

Automatic-sampler installations should be checked in a manner which meets with the approval of all parties concerned, at least once a month and more often if conditions warrant. In the case of time-cycle samplers, deviations in quantity of the sample taken should not exceed ±5 per cent for any given setting. In the case of flow responsive samplers, the deviation in quantity of sample taken per 1,000 barrels of flowing stream should not exceed ±5 per cent.

For the purpose of field-testing in installation, the composite sample obtained by the automatic sampler under test should be compared with a tank sample taken in strict compliance with Par. 1003.2.—A. of this standard. The sample should be taken under the following conditions:

a. The batch pumped during the test interval should be diverted into a clean tank, and a sample taken within one hour after cessation of pumping.

b. If the sampling of the delivery tank is to be delayed beyond one hour, then the tank selected must be equipped with an adequate mixing means. For valid comparison, the sampling of the delivery tank must be completed within eight hours after cessation of pumping, even though the tank is equipped with a motor-driven mixer.

c. When making a normal full-tank delivery from a tank, a sample taken in accordance with Par. 1003.2.—A. may be used to check the results of the sampler if the parties mutually agree to this procedure.